Hoover's Handbook of

Emerging Companies
2012

HOOVERS™

A D&B COMPANY

Austin, Texas

Hoover's Handbook of Emerging Companies 2012 is intended to provide readers with accurate and authoritative information about the enterprises covered in it. Hoover's researched all companies and organizations profiled, and in many cases contacted them directly so that companies represented could provide information. The information contained herein is as accurate as we could reasonably make it. In many cases we have relied on third-party material that we believe to be trustworthy, but were unable to independently verify. We do not warrant that the book is absolutely accurate or without error. Readers should not rely on any information contained herein in instances where such reliance might cause financial loss. The publisher, the editors, and their data suppliers specifically disclaim all warranties, including the implied warranties of merchantability and fitness for a specific purpose. This book is sold with the understanding that neither the publisher, the editors, nor any content contributors are engaged in providing investment, financial, accounting, legal, or other professional advice.

The financial data (Historical Financials sections) in this book are from a variety of sources. Morningstar, Inc., provided selected data for the Historical Financials sections of publicly traded companies. For private companies and for historical information on public companies prior to their becoming public, we obtained information directly from the companies or from trade sources deemed to be reliable. Hoover's, Inc., is solely responsible for the presentation of all data.

Many of the names of products and services mentioned in this book are the trademarks or service marks of the companies manufacturing or selling them and are subject to protection under US law. Space has not permitted us to indicate which names are subject to such protection, and readers are advised to consult with the owners of such marks regarding their use. Hoover's is a trademark of Hoover's, Inc.

A D&B COMPANY

10 9 8 7 6 5 4 3 2 1

Publishers Cataloging-in-Publication Data

Hoover's Handbook of Emerging Companies 2012

    Includes indexes.

    ISBN: 978-1-59274-964-5

    ISSN 1073-6433

    1. Business enterprises — Directories. 2. Corporations — Directories.

HF3010 338.7

U.S. AND WORLD BOOK SALES

Mergent Inc.

580 Kingsley Park Drive
Fort Mill, SC
29715
Phone: 800-342-5647
e-mail: orders@mergent.com
Web: www.mergents.com

MERGENT
BUSINESS PRESS

Mergent Inc.

Publisher: Jonathan Worrall

Executive Managing Director: John Pedernalis

Executive Vice President of Sales: Fred Jenkins

Managing Director of Relationship Management: Chris Henry

Senior Product Manager: Neel Gandhi

Managing Director of Print Products: Thomas Wecera

Director Print Products: Charlot Volny

Quality Assurance Editor: Wayne Arnold

Production Research Assistant: Erin Keane

Mergent Customer Service

Support and Fulfillment Manager: Melanie Horvat

ABOUT MERGENT INC.

Mergent, Inc. is a leading provider of business and financial data on global publicly listed companies. Based in the U.S, the company maintains a strong global presence, with offices in New York, Charlotte, San Diego, London, Tokyo and Melbourne.

Founded in 1900, Mergent operates one of the longest continuously collected databases of: descriptive and fundamental information on domestic and international companies; pricing and terms and conditions data on fixed income and equity securities; and corporate action data. In addition, Mergent's Indxis subsidiary develops and licenses equity and fixed income investment products based on its proprietary investment methodologies. Our licensed products have over $9 billion in assets under management and are offered by major investment management firms. The Indxis calculation platform is the chosen technology for some of the world's largest index companies. Its index calculation and pricing distribution protocols are used to administer index rules and distribute real-time pricing data.

Abbreviations

AFL-CIO – American Federation of Labor and Congress of Industrial Organizations

AMA – American Medical Association

AMEX – American Stock Exchange

ARM – adjustable-rate mortgage

ASP – application services provider

ATM – asynchronous transfer mode

ATM – automated teller machine

CAD/CAM – computer-aided design/computer-aided manufacturing

CD-ROM – compact disc – read-only memory

CD-R – CD-recordable

CEO – chief executive officer

CFO – chief financial officer

CMOS – complementary metal oxide silicon

COO – chief operating officer

DAT – digital audiotape

DOD – Department of Defense

DOE – Department of Energy

DOS – disk operating system

DOT – Department of Transportation

DRAM – dynamic random-access memory

DSL – digital subscriber line

DVD – digital versatile disc/digital video disc

DVD-R – DVD-recordable

EPA – Environmental Protection Agency

EPS – earnings per share

ESOP – employee stock ownership plan

EU – European Union

EVP – executive vice president

FCC – Federal Communications Commission

FDA – Food and Drug Administration

FDIC – Federal Deposit Insurance Corporation

FTC – Federal Trade Commission

GATT – General Agreement on Tariffs and Trade

GDP – gross domestic product

HMO – health maintenance organization

HR – human resources

HTML – hypertext markup language

ICC – Interstate Commerce Commission

IPO – initial public offering

IRS – Internal Revenue Service

ISP – Internet service provider

kWh – kilowatt-hour

LAN – local-area network

LBO – leveraged buyout

LCD – liquid crystal display

LNG – liquefied natural gas

LP – limited partnership

Ltd. – limited

mips – millions of instructions per second

MW – megawatt

NAFTA – North American Free Trade Agreement

NASA – National Aeronautics and Space Administration

NASDAQ – National Association of Securities Dealers Automated Quotations

NATO – North Atlantic Treaty Organization

NYSE – New York Stock Exchange

OCR – optical character recognition

OECD – Organization for Economic Cooperation and Development

OEM – original equipment manufacturer

OPEC – Organization of Petroleum Exporting Countries

OS – operating system

OSHA – Occupational Safety and Health Administration

OTC – over-the-counter

PBX – private branch exchange

PCMCIA – Personal Computer Memory Card International Association

P/E – price to earnings ratio

RAID – redundant array of independent disks

RAM – random-access memory

R&D – research and development

RBOC – regional Bell operating company

RISC – reduced instruction set computer

REIT – real estate investment trust

ROA – return on assets

ROE – return on equity

ROI – return on investment

ROM – read-only memory

S&L – savings and loan

SEC – Securities and Exchange Commission

SEVP – senior executive vice president

SIC – Standard Industrial Classification

SOC – system on a chip

SVP – senior vice president

USB – universal serial bus

VAR – value-added reseller

VAT – value-added tax

VC – venture capitalist

VoIP – Voice over Internet Protocol

VP – vice president

WAN – wide-area network

Contents

Companies Profiled

Companies Profiled (continued)

Companies Profiled (continued)

About Hoover's Handbook of Emerging Companies 2012

Hoover's Handbook of Emerging Companies enters its 19th year as one of America's premier sources of business information on younger, growth-oriented enterprises. Given our current economic realities, finding value in the marketplace becomes ever more difficult, and so we are particularly pleased to present this edition of Hoover's Handbook of Emerging Companies 2012 — the result of a search of our extensive database of business information for companies with demonstrated growth and the potential for future gains.

The 600 companies in this book were chosen from the universe of public US companies with sales between $10 million and $2.5 billion. Their selection was based primarily on sales growth and profitability, although in a few cases we made some rather subjective decisions about which companies we chose to include. They all have reported at least three years of sales and have sustained annualized sales growth of at least 7% during that time. Also, they are profitable (through year-end September 2011).

Hoover's Online for business needs

In addition to the 2,550 companies featured in our handbooks, comprehensive coverage of more than 40,000 business enterprises is available in electronic format on our website, Hoover's Online (www.hoovers.com). Our goal is to provide one site that offers authoritative, updated intelligence on US and global companies, industries, and the people who shape them. Hoover's has partnered with other prestigious business information and service providers to bring you all the right business information, services, and links in one place.

Hoover's Handbook of Emerging Companies is one of our four-title series of handbooks that covers, literally, the world of business. The series is available as an indexed set, and also includes Hoover's Handbook of American Business, Hoover's Handbook of World Business, and Hoover's Handbook of Private Companies. This series brings you information on the biggest, fastest-growing, and most influential enterprises in the world.

We believe that anyone who buys from, sells to, invests in, lends to, competes with, interviews with, or works for a company should know as much as possible about that enterprise. Taken together, Hoover's Handbook of Emerging Companies 2012 and the other Hoover's products represent the most complete source of basic corporate information readily available to the general public.

How to use this book

This book has four sections:

1. "Using Hoover's Handbooks" describes the contents of our profiles.

2. "A List-Lover's Compendium" contains lists of the fastest-growing and most profitable companies. The lists are based on the information in our profiles, or compiled from well-known sources.

3. The company profiles section makes up the largest and most important part of the book — 600 profiles arranged alphabetically. Each profile features an overview of the company; some larger and more visible companies have an additional History section. All companies have up to five years of financial information, product information where available, and a list of company executives and key competitors.

4. At the end of this volume are the combined indexes from our 2012 editions of all Hoover's Handbooks. The information is organized into three separate sections. The first sorts companies by industry groups, the second by headquarters location. The third index is a list of all the executives found in the Executives section of each company profile. For a more thorough description of our indexing style, see page xii.

Using Hoover's Handbooks

ORGANIZATION

The profiles in this volume are presented in alphabetical order. This alphabetization is generally word by word, which means that Bridge Bancorp precedes Bridgepoint Education. You will find the commonly used name of the enterprise at the beginning of the profile; the full, legal name is found in the Locations section. If a company name starts with initials, such as BJ's Restaurants or U.S. Physical Therapy, look for it under the combined initials (in the above example, BJ or US, respectively).

Basic financial data is listed under the heading Historical Financials; also included is the exchange on which the company's stock is traded, the ticker symbol used by the stock exchange, and the company's fiscal year-end. The annual financial information contained in the profiles is current through fiscal year-ends occurring as late as September 2010. We have included certain nonfinancial developments, such as officer changes, through January 2012.

OVERVIEW

In the first section of the profile, we have tried to give a thumbnail description of the company and what it does. The description will usually include information on the company's strategy, reputation, and ownership. We recommend that you read this section first.

HISTORY

This extended section, which is available for some of the larger and more well-known companies, reflects our belief that every enterprise is the sum of its history and that you have to know where you came from in order to know where you are going. While some companies have limited historical awareness, we think the vast majority of the enterprises in this book have colorful backgrounds. We have tried to focus on the people who made the enterprises what they are today. We have found these histories to be full of twists and ironies; they make fascinating reading.

EXECUTIVES

Here we list the names of the people who run the company, insofar as space allows. In the case of public companies, we have shown the ages and pay of key officers. The published data is for the previous fiscal year, although the company may have announced promotions or retirements since year-end. The pay represents cash compensation, including bonuses, but excludes stock option programs.

Although companies are free to structure their management titles any way they please, most modern corporations follow standard practices. The ultimate power in any corporation lies with the shareholders, who elect a board of directors, usually including officers or "insiders," as well as individuals from outside the company. The chief officer, the person on whose desk the buck stops, is usually called the chief executive officer (CEO). Often, he or she is also the chairman of the board.

As corporate management has become more complex, it is common for the CEO to have a "right-hand person" who oversees the day-to-day operations of the company, allowing the CEO plenty of time to focus on strategy and long-term issues. This right-hand person is usually designated the chief operating officer (COO) and is often the president of the company. In other cases one person is both chairman and president.

A multitude of other titles exists, including chief financial officer (CFO), chief administrative officer, and vice chairman. We have always tried to include the CFO, the chief legal officer, and the chief human resources or personnel officer. Our best advice is that officers' pay levels are clear indicators of who the board of directors thinks are the most important members of the management team.

The people named in the Executives section are indexed at the back of the book.

The Executives section also includes the name of the company's auditing (accounting) firm, where available.

LOCATIONS

Here we include the company's full legal name and its headquarters, street address, telephone and fax numbers, and website, as available. The back of the book includes an index of companies by headquarters locations.

In some cases we have also included information on the geographic distribution of the company's business, including sales and profit data. Note that these profit numbers, like those in the Products/Operations section below, are usually operating or pretax profits rather than net profits. Operating profits are generally those before financing costs (interest income and payments) and before taxes, which are considered costs attributable to the whole company rather than to one division or part of the world. For this reason the net income figures (in the Historical Financials section) are usually much lower, since they are after interest and taxes. Pretax profits are after interest but before taxes.

PRODUCTS/OPERATIONS

This section lists as many of the company's products, services, brand names, divisions, subsidiaries, and joint ventures as we could fit. We have tried to include all its major lines and all familiar brand names. The nature of this section varies by company and the amount of information available. If the company publishes sales and profit information by type of business, we have included it.

COMPETITORS

In this section we have listed companies that compete with the profiled company. This feature is included as a quick way to locate similar companies and compare them. The universe of competitors includes all public companies and all private companies with sales in excess of $500 million. In a few instances we have identified smaller private companies as key competitors.

HISTORICAL FINANCIALS

Here we have tried to present as much data about each enterprise's financial performance as we could compile in the allocated space. Although the information varies somewhat from industry to industry, the following is generally present.

A five-year table, with relevant annualized compound growth rates, covers:
- Sales — fiscal year sales (year-end assets for most financial companies)
- Net income — fiscal year net income (before accounting changes)
- Net profit margin — fiscal year net income as a percent of sales (as a percent of assets for most financial firms)
- Employees — fiscal year-end or average number of employees
- Stock price — the fiscal year closing price
- P/E — high and low price/earnings ratio
- Earnings per share — fiscal year earnings per share (EPS)
- Dividends per share — fiscal year dividends per share
- Book value per share — fiscal year-end book value (common shareholders' equity per share)

The information on the number of employees is intended to aid the reader interested in knowing whether a company has a long-term trend of increasing or decreasing employment. As far as we know, we are the only company that publishes this information in print format.

The numbers on the left in each row of the Historical Financials section give the month and the year in which the company's fiscal year actually ends. Thus, a company with a September 30, 2010, year-end is shown as 9/10.

In addition, we have provided in graph form a stock price history for each company. The graphs, covering up to five years, show the range of trading between the high and the low price, as well as the closing price for each fiscal year.

Key year-end statistics in this section generally show the financial strength of the enterprise, including:
- Debt ratio (long-term debt as a percent of shareholders' equity)
- Return on equity (net income divided by the average of beginning and ending common shareholders' equity)
- Cash and cash equivalents
- Current ratio (ratio of current assets to current liabilities)
- Total long-term debt (including capital lease obligations)
- Number of shares of common stock outstanding
- Dividend yield (fiscal year dividends per share divided by the fiscal year-end closing stock price)
- Dividend payout (fiscal year dividends divided by fiscal year EPS)
- Market value at fiscal year-end (fiscal year-end closing stock price multiplied by fiscal year-end number of shares outstanding)

Per-share data has been adjusted for stock splits. The data for public companies has been provided to us by Morningstar, Inc. Other public company information was compiled by Hoover's, which takes full responsibility for the content of this section.

Hoover's Handbook of

Emerging Companies

A List-Lover's Compendium

The 200 Largest Companies by Sales in
Hoover's Handbook of Emerging Companies 2012

Rank	Company	Sales ($ mil.)	Rank	Company	Sales ($ mil.)	Rank	Company	Sales ($ mil.)
1	Maxim Integrated Products	2472.3	61	Primoris	941.8	121	Advanced Energy Industries	459.4
2	MasTec	2308.0	62	Veeco Instruments	933.2	122	Regeneron Pharmaceuticals	459.1
3	NY Community Bancorp	2251.7	63	First Niagara Financial	932.2	123	Bio-Reference Labs	458.0
4	SunPower	2219.2	64	Och-Ziff Capital Management	924.5	124	Investors Bancorp	455.2
5	A. Schulman	2193.0	65	Dolby	922.7	125	Semtech	454.5
6	DeVry	2182.4	66	Red Hat	909.3	126	BioFuel Energy	453.4
7	Netflix	2162.6	67	Illumina	902.7	127	Syms	445.1
8	Green Plains	2133.0	68	GT Advanced Technologies	899.0	128	Ultra Clean Technology	443.1
9	Brocade Communications	2094.4	69	IMPAX Laboratories	879.5	129	Credit Acceptance	442.1
10	hhgregg	2077.7	70	TriQuint	878.7	130	ViroPharma	439.0
11	Skechers U.S.A.	2011.4	71	Digital Realty	865.4	131	Golden Star Resources	432.7
12	Altera	1954.4	72	Stream Global Services	800.2	132	Chesapeake Utilities	427.5
13	SXC	1948.4	73	DFC Global	788.4	133	Echo Global	426.4
14	Denbury Resources	1921.8	74	Kapstone Paper and Packaging	782.7	134	Capella Education	426.1
15	Corinthian Colleges	1868.8	75	Rackspace	780.6	135	KBW	425.9
16	JDS Uniphase	1804.5	76	Kulicke and Soffa	762.8	136	Hecla Mining	418.8
17	TPC Group	1781.5	77	Meadowbrook Insurance	750.1	137	MedQuist Holdings	417.3
18	Clean Harbors	1731.2	78	EZCORP	733.0	138	QuinStreet	403.0
19	salesforce.com	1657.1	79	Healthways, Inc.	720.3	139	UniTek Global Services	402.2
20	Alliance Resource	1610.1	80	Groupon	713.4	140	Evercore Partners	401.7
21	Alliance Holdings GP	1609.7	81	Bridgepoint Education	713.2	141	Cheniere Energy Partners	399.3
22	Teradyne	1608.7	82	MSCI	662.9	142	Aruba Networks	396.5
23	ITT Educational	1596.5	83	Informatica	650.1	143	InterDigital	394.5
24	Microchip Technology	1487.2	84	Trico Marine	642.2	144	MedAssets	391.3
25	Linear Technology	1484.0	85	Globe Specialty	641.9	145	TeleCommunication Systems	388.8
26	Tower Group	1458.7	86	Lincoln Educational Services	639.5	146	Grand Canyon Education	385.8
27	Coinstar	1436.4	87	Strayer Education	636.7	147	American Capital Agency Corp.	383.4
28	Intuitive Surgical	1413.0	88	Cubist Pharmaceuticals	636.5	148	NetLogic Microsystems	381.7
29	Stifel Financial	1395.2	89	Steven Madden	635.4	149	Encore Capital Group	381.3
30	Duke Realty	1393.6	90	LHC Group	635.0	150	Portfolio Recovery	372.7
31	Green Mountain Coffee	1356.8	91	rue21	634.7	151	Cirrus Logic	369.6
32	El Paso Pipeline Partners	1344.1	92	Silicon Graphics International	629.6	152	Vera Bradley	366.1
33	SunCoke Energy	1326.6	93	Atlantic Tele-Network	619.1	153	Green Dot	363.9
34	Materion	1302.3	94	Ameresco	618.2	154	IPC The Hospitalist Company	363.4
35	Am Eqty Invstmt Life Hldng	1285.6	95	JDA Software	617.2	155	Oxford Resource Partners	356.6
36	MWI Veterinary Supply	1229.3	96	Buffalo Wild Wings	613.3	156	Quality Systems	353.4
37	Equinix	1220.3	97	Diodes	612.9	157	Iridium	348.2
38	TTM Technologies	1179.7	98	Accretive Health	606.3	158	Amer Campus Communities	345.0
39	International Rectifier	1176.6	99	United Therapeutics	603.8	159	Industrial Services of America	343.0
40	Sykes Enterprises	1158.7	100	NCI	581.3	160	Senior Housing Properties	339.0
41	First Republic (CA)	1151.5	101	National Western	576.0	161	Evergreen Solar	338.8
42	IntercontinentalExchange	1149.9	102	Piper Jaffray	565.1	162	Mistras Group	338.6
43	East West Bancorp	1135.1	103	Trident Microsystems	557.2	163	Salix Pharmaceuticals	337.0
44	Boardwalk Pipeline	1116.8	104	Clearwire	556.8	164	Almost Family	336.9
45	FBL Financial	1108.6	105	Riverbed Technology	551.9	165	Pegasystems	336.6
46	Titan Machinery	1094.5	106	Rovi	541.5	166	Iconix Brand Group	332.6
47	Under Armour	1063.9	107	Alexion Pharmaceuticals	541.0	167	GeoEye	330.3
48	G-III Apparel	1063.4	108	WebMD Health	534.5	168	Fortinet	324.7
49	Vector Group	1063.3	109	IBERIABANK	530.3	169	Onyx Pharmaceuticals	324.5
50	Power-One	1047.1	110	TNS	527.1	170	Rambus	323.4
51	Par Pharmaceutical Comps	1008.9	111	K12	522.4	171	Cohu	322.7
52	AmTrust Financial	1002.5	112	Global Power Equipment	520.1	172	INX Inc.	312.0
53	Deckers Outdoor	1001.0	113	Coeur d'Alene Mines	515.5	173	Dolan Company	311.3
54	Imperial Sugar	992.7	114	Signature Bank	509.2	174	Shutterfly	307.7
55	Cree	987.6	115	Western Gas Partners	503.3	175	HMS Holdings	302.9
56	Concho	972.6	116	Winnebago	496.4	176	Ancestry.com	300.9
57	Diamond Foods	965.9	117	First Financial Bancorp	490.3	177	Power Integrations	299.8
58	OmniVision Technologies	956.5	118	Ares Capital	483.4	178	Volcano Corporation	294.1
59	Finisar	948.8	119	NuVasive	478.2	179	Datalink	293.7
60	Super Micro Computer	942.6	120	Oclaro	466.5	180	Redwood Trust	293.5

The 200 Largest Companies by Sales in
Hoover's Handbook of Emerging Companies 2012 (continued)

Rank	Company	Sales ($ mil.)	Rank	Company	Sales ($ mil.)	Rank	Company	Sales ($ mil.)
181	SCBT Financial	293.1	188	EnerNOC	280.2	195	Globecomm	274.2
182	ReachLocal	291.7	189	AutoInfo	279.7	196	DDi Corp.	267.8
183	Cheniere Energy	291.5	190	Active Network	279.6	197	KMG Chemicals	266.4
184	American Superconductor	286.6	191	Hatteras Financial	278.6	198	Multiband	265.6
185	Emergent BioSolutions	286.2	192	Ixia	276.8	199	Eagle Bulk Shipping	265.0
186	ICU Medical	284.6	193	Able Energy	276.4	200	DEI Holdings	262.9
187	Gleacher & Company	282.2	194	NetSpend	275.4			

The 200 Largest Employers in
Hoover's Handbook of Emerging Companies 2012

Rank	Company	Employees	Rank	Company	Employees	Rank	Company	Employees
1	Sykes Enterprises	43400	61	NCI	2600	121	OmniVision Technologies	1465
2	Stream Global Services	30000	62	Coinstar	2585	122	Steven Madden	1440
3	TTM Technologies	17448	63	STRATTEC	2556	123	Vera Bradley	1427
4	Corinthian Colleges	16600	64	K12	2500	124	AmTrust Financial	1400
5	Buffalo Wild Wings	15900	65	Syms	2500	125	Regeneron Pharmaceuticals	1395
6	EXL	12700	66	Active Network	2490	126	Nevada Gold & Casinos	1391
7	DeVry	12599	67	Golden Star Resources	2490	127	ReachLocal	1381
8	MedQuist Holdings	12000	68	Alliance Holdings GP	2487	128	Tower Group	1360
9	ITT Educational	11100	69	Materion	2484	129	Fortinet	1336
10	MasTec	9400	70	Portfolio Recovery	2473	130	Super Micro Computer	1272
11	Maxim Integrated Products	9370	71	Bio-Reference Labs	2424	131	Cavco	1250
12	Finisar	8065	72	Green Mountain Coffee	2380	132	Dolby	1244
13	LHC Group	7973	73	American Campus Communities	2334	133	Riverbed Technology	1244
14	rue21	7243	74	ICU Medical	2237	134	athenahealth	1242
15	Groupon	7107	75	Accretive Health	2222	135	Ultra Clean Technology	1241
16	Microchip Technology	6970	76	AdCare	2210	136	TNS	1237
17	Clean Harbors	6840	77	IBERIABANK	2193	137	SXC	1216
18	Almost Family	6400	78	American Public Education	2170	138	Globe Specialty	1213
19	Princeton Review	5866	79	G-III Apparel	2154	139	TeleCommunication Systems	1205
20	hhgregg	5600	80	East West Bancorp	2142	140	National American University	1200
21	Skechers U.S.A.	5440	81	Winnebago	2130	141	Rovi	1200
22	DFC Global	5375	82	Informatica	2126	142	Denbury Resources	1195
23	salesforce.com	5306	83	Illumina	2100	143	Energy Services of America	1190
24	SunPower	5150	84	Strayer Education	2099	144	Ebix	1179
25	JDS Uniphase	5000	85	MSCI	2077	145	MWI Veterinary Supply	1179
26	UniTek Global Services	5000	86	Full House Resorts	2069	146	Advanced Battery Technologies	1176
27	International Rectifier	4920	87	Dolan Company	2034	147	Taleo	1164
28	Stifel Financial	4906	88	A123 Systems	2032	148	Ruger	1160
29	EZCORP	4900	89	Equinix	1921	149	Heckmann Corporation	1148
30	Cree	4753	90	Encore Capital Group	1900	150	Volcano Corporation	1144
31	Brocade Communications	4651	91	Titan Machinery	1874	151	SunCoke Energy	1140
32	Linear Technology	4505	92	Teavana Holdings	1819	152	Boardwalk Pipeline	1100
33	Lincoln Educational Services	4500	93	Diamond Foods	1797	153	Cohu	1100
34	Netflix	4329	94	IPC The Hospitalist Company	1792	154	Human Genome Sciences	1100
35	Primoris	4034	95	Advanced Energy Industries	1788	155	Ixia	1100
36	Diodes	3986	96	Jaguar Mining	1788	156	Swisher Hygiene Inc.	1077
37	Under Armour	3900	97	Trico Marine	1780	157	Aruba Networks	1057
38	New York Community Bancorp	3883	98	Atlantic Tele-Network	1765	158	Piper Jaffray	1053
39	First Niagara Financial	3791	99	RealPage	1759	159	SuccessFactors	1047
40	Red Hat	3700	100	HMS Holdings	1736	160	TeleNav	1039
41	Clearwire	3600	101	FBL Financial	1679	161	Evergreen Solar	1034
42	Alliance Resource	3558	102	DDi Corp.	1676	162	Veeco Instruments	1023
43	Power-One	3470	103	First Financial Bancorp	1664	163	SCBT Financial	1015
44	Cavico Corp	3409	104	Intuitive Surgical	1660	164	Union First Market Bankshares	1005
45	Rackspace	3262	105	WebMD Health	1630	165	Duke Realty	1000
46	Multiband	3202	106	U.S. Auto Parts	1612	166	LinkedIn	990
47	MedAssets	3100	107	Kapstone Paper and Packaging	1600	167	Semtech	982
48	Oclaro	3085	108	L & L Energy	1600	168	Meadowbrook Insurance	967
49	A. Schulman	3000	109	NxStage	1600	169	Simclar	950
50	Bridgepoint Education	3000	110	Quality Systems	1579	170	IntercontinentalExchange	933
51	JDA Software	3000	111	Francesca¿s Holdings	1560	171	NeoStem	924
52	Teradyne	3000	112	ServiceSource	1536	172	comScore	920
53	Tri-S Security	3000	113	Trident Microsystems	1522	173	IMPAX Laboratories	918
54	Capella Education	2968	114	Pegasystems	1509	174	Tower Bancorp	912
55	Kulicke and Soffa	2950	115	First Republic (CA)	1502	175	Tesla Motors	899
56	Healthways, Inc.	2800	116	Deckers Outdoor	1500	176	DG FastChannel	897
57	TriQuint	2777	117	Silicon Graphics International	1500	177	Investors Bancorp	892
58	Mistras Group	2700	118	Dendreon	1497	178	Transcend Services	891
59	Altera	2666	119	ExamWorks	1485	179	Credit Acceptance	862
60	Grand Canyon Education	2600	120	Coeur d'Alene Mines	1471	180	KIT digital	842

The 200 Largest Employers in
Hoover's Handbook of Emerging Companies 2012 (continued)

Rank	Company	Employees	Rank	Company	Employees	Rank	Company	Employees
181	Oxford Resource Partners	836	188	Qlik	780	195	Merge Healthcare	750
182	Clarion Technologies	800	189	ICG Group	773	196	Ameresco	735
183	Eagle Bulk Shipping	800	190	Ener1	769	197	Chesapeake Utilities	734
184	Ancestry.com	795	191	Emergent BioSolutions	767	198	Constant Contact	734
185	Alexion Pharmaceuticals	792	192	Hampton Roads Bankshares	767	199	GeoEye	723
186	NuVasive	789	193	Synchronoss	758	200	KEYW	722
187	HomeAway	781	194	Tangoe	757			

The Top 200 Companies by Net Income in Hoover's Handbook of Emerging Companies 2012

Rank	Company	Net Income ($ mil.)	Rank	Company	Net Income ($ mil.)	Rank	Company	Sales ($ mil.)
1	Altera	782.9	61	United Therapeutics	105.9	121	Green Plains	48.0
2	Ares Capital	691.8	62	Cheniere Energy Partners	105.4	122	Healthways, Inc.	47.3
3	Linear Technology	580.8	63	Digital Realty	102.3	123	ICG Group	46.6
4	New York Community Bancorp	541.0	64	Signature Bank	102.1	124	Materion	46.4
5	Maxim Integrated Products	489.0	65	Iconix Brand Group	98.8	125	Rackspace	46.4
6	Microchip Technology	419.0	66	EZCORP	97.3	126	Vera Bradley	46.2
7	IntercontinentalExchange	398.3	67	Alexion Pharmaceuticals	97.0	127	SolarWinds	44.7
8	Intuitive Surgical	381.8	68	Cubist Pharmaceuticals	94.3	128	Grand Canyon Education	44.4
9	Teradyne	379.7	69	Par Pharmaceutical Companies	92.7	129	Acme Packet	43.0
10	El Paso Pipeline Partners	378.5	70	MSCI	92.2	130	Am Eqty Invstmt Life Hldng Co	42.9
11	ITT Educational	374.2	71	MasTec	90.5	131	DJSP Enterprises	42.9
12	Veeco Instruments	361.8	72	Finisar	88.1	132	TeleNav	42.6
13	DeVry	330.4	73	Informatica	86.3	133	Green Dot	42.2
14	Alliance Resource	321.0	74	ARIAD Pharmaceuticals	85.2	134	DG FastChannel	41.6
15	Boardwalk Pipeline	289.4	75	Green Mountain Coffee	79.5	135	Hi-Tech Pharmacal	41.5
16	American Capital Agency Corp.	288.1	76	NuVasive	78.3	136	Fortinet	41.2
17	Dolby	283.4	77	Diodes	76.7	137	A. Schulman	41.0
18	Denbury Resources	271.7	78	Steven Madden	75.7	138	Ellington Financial	40.6
19	First Republic (CA)	271.2	79	Portfolio Recovery	73.5	139	Global Power Equipment	40.6
20	IMPAX Laboratories	250.4	80	National Western	72.9	140	Super Micro Computer	40.2
21	Rovi	212.9	81	Semtech	72.6	141	HMS Holdings	40.1
22	Concho	204.4	82	JDS Uniphase	71.6	142	Main Street Capital	38.7
23	Cirrus Logic	203.5	83	TTM Technologies	71.5	143	Atlantic Tele-Network	38.5
24	TriQuint	190.8	84	Royal Gold	71.4	144	Buffalo Wild Wings	38.4
25	SunPower	178.7	85	Advanced Energy Industries	71.2	145	Rigel Pharmaceuticals	37.9
26	GT Advanced Technologies	174.8	86	Aruba Networks	70.7	146	Oiltanking Partners	37.8
27	Alliance Holdings GP	174.3	87	Lincoln Educational Services	69.7	147	Momenta Pharmaceuticals	37.3
28	Credit Acceptance	170.1	88	Under Armour	68.5	148	Cavium	37.1
29	Hatteras Financial	169.5	89	DFC Global	65.8	149	Walter Investment Management	37.1
30	International Rectifier	166.5	90	Duke Realty	65.8	150	Equinix	36.9
31	East West Bancorp	164.6	91	Kapstone Paper and Packaging	65.0	151	Ancestry.com	36.8
32	Netflix	160.9	92	Entropic Communications	64.7	152	L & L Energy	36.8
33	Deckers Outdoor	158.2	93	SXC	64.7	153	Advanced Battery Technologies	36.7
34	InterDigital	153.6	94	salesforce.com	64.5	154	Crestwood Midstream Partners	34.9
35	Rambus	150.9	95	Financial Engines	63.6	155	Riverbed Technology	34.2
36	Power-One	147.9	96	Investors Bancorp	62.0	156	Primoris	33.6
37	Cree	146.5	97	Quality Systems	61.6	157	MWI Veterinary Supply	33.4
38	AmTrust Financial	142.5	98	Capella Education	61.3	158	Jazz Pharmaceuticals	32.8
39	Kulicke and Soffa	142.1	99	Meadowbrook Insurance	59.7	159	Neutral Tandem	32.6
40	First Niagara Financial	140.4	100	First Financial Bancorp	59.3	160	Dolan Company	32.4
41	SunCoke Energy	139.2	101	Ebix	59.0	161	C&J Energy Services	32.3
42	Imperial Sugar	136.9	102	Holly Energy Partners	58.9	162	MV Oil Trust	31.7
43	Skechers U.S.A.	136.1	103	China North East Petroleum	58.4	163	MarketAxess	31.4
44	Strayer Education	131.3	104	Niska	57.5	164	ICU Medical	30.9
45	Clean Harbors	130.5	105	G-III Apparel	56.7	165	Almost Family	30.7
46	Bridgepoint Education	127.6	106	Nanometrics	55.9	166	DuPont Fabros	30.4
47	Spectra Energy Partners	126.7	107	Vector Group	54.1	167	rue21	30.2
48	Western Gas Partners	126.1	108	WebMD Health	54.1	168	American Public Education	29.9
49	ViroPharma	125.6	109	Globe Specialty	52.8	169	PAA Natural Gas Storage	29.8
50	Illumina	124.9	110	SCBT Financial	51.9	170	Life Partners Holdings	29.4
51	OmniVision Technologies	124.5	111	Emergent BioSolutions	51.7	171	Rubicon Technology	29.1
52	InterMune	122.4	112	Coinstar	51.0	172	Ameresco	28.7
53	FBL Financial	120.7	113	Diamond Foods	50.2	173	Volterra Semiconductor	28.4
54	Brocade Communications	118.9	114	Ubiquiti	49.7	174	Ruger	28.3
55	Prospect Capital	118.2	115	Power Integrations	49.5	175	Intevac	28.0
56	Tower Group	118.0	116	Encore Capital Group	49.1	176	Govt Properties Income Trust	27.8
57	Senior Housing Properties	116.5	117	Hecla Mining	49.0	177	QuinStreet	27.2
58	RAIT Financial Trust	111.8	118	IBERIABANK	48.8	178	Rudolph Technologies	27.0
59	Redwood Trust	110.1	119	LHC Group	48.8	179	Eagle Bulk Shipping	26.8
60	Red Hat	107.3	120	hhgregg	48.2	180	EXL	26.6

*Average annual sales growth measured over a three-year period.

The Top 200 Companies by Net Income in
Hoover's Handbook of Emerging Companies 2012 (continued)

Rank	Company	Net Income ($ mil.)	Rank	Company	Net Income ($ mil.)	Rank	Company	Sales ($ mil.)
181	KBW	26.6	189	Baldwin & Lyons	25.0	197	NetSpend	23.7
182	Bio-Reference Labs	26.4	190	EasyLink	24.7	198	TPC Group	23.7
183	Chesapeake Utilities	26.1	191	Cohu	24.6	199	Conrad Industries	23.0
184	Inphi	26.1	192	GeoEye	24.6	200	Union First Market Bankshares	22.9
185	OPTi	25.6	193	Piper Jaffray	24.4			
186	Washington Banking	25.6	194	IPC The Hospitalist Company	24.3			
187	Triangle Capital	25.4	195	NCI	23.9			
188	Higher One	25.1	196	Electro Rent	23.8			

The Top 200 Companies with the Highest P/E Ratios in Hoover's Handbook of Emerging Companies 2012

Rank	Company	P/E High	Rank	Company	P/E High	Rank	Company	Sales ($ mil.)
1	Taleo	3266	61	LogMeIn	56	121	American Public Education	31
2	Stifel Financial	1263	62	DTS	56	122	Mistras Group	30
3	Fusion-io	616	63	DuPont Fabros	55	123	Grand Canyon Education	30
4	salesforce.com	322	64	Informatica	55	124	DG FastChannel	29
5	Constant Contact	321	65	SRS Labs	55	125	Community Financial (VA)	29
6	Volcano Corporation	289	66	Sonabank	54	126	Aerosonic	29
7	Synchronoss	248	67	Cavium	52	127	Allied First Bancorp	29
8	Northern Oil and Gas	203	68	Higher One	50	128	Georgia Bancshares	29
9	Amexdrug	180	69	PAA Natural Gas Storage	49	129	LTX-Credence	29
10	Tower Bancorp	175	70	Royal Gold	48	130	Crestwood Midstream Partners LP	29
11	Riverbed Technology	172	71	MSCI	48	131	Dolby	29
12	Genomic Health	169	72	HMS Holdings	48	132	Promise Technology	28
13	Archipelago Learning	163	73	Sourcefire	48	133	Medifast	28
14	Outdoor Channel	146	74	Neogen	47	134	Rubicon Technology	28
15	Qlik	139	75	GeoEye	47	135	Vector Group	28
16	Equinix	135	76	Universal Manufacturing	46	136	Fifth Street Finance	28
17	athenahealth	133	77	Finisar	46	137	Datalink	28
18	OpenTable	132	78	QuinStreet	45	138	Denbury Resources	28
19	American Campus Communities	129	79	Under Armour	45	139	Senior Housing Properties	28
20	Green Dot	125	80	SXC	44	140	Power Integrations	28
21	Accretive Health	125	81	Coinstar	43	141	Radiant Logistics	28
22	Cavco	120	82	Piper Jaffray	43	142	National American University	28
23	Ixia 109		83	KBW	42	143	Transcend Services	27
24	K12	107	84	Echo Global	42	144	IPC The Hospitalist Company	27
25	1st United Bank	103	85	Intuitive Surgical	42	145	Volterra Semiconductor	27
26	EnerNOC	100	86	Concho	41	146	Amerigon	27
27	Craft Brewers Alliance	99	87	Blue River Bancshares	41	147	Strayer Education	27
28	Evercore Partners	98	88	Conmed Healthcare	41	148	Capella Education	27
29	Depomed	96	89	SolarWinds	41	149	MarketAxess	27
30	Digital Realty	94	90	interclick	41	150	Bio-Reference Labs	26
31	Acme Packet	94	91	Winnebago	40	151	hhgregg	26
32	JDS Uniphase	94	92	Ancestry.com	40	152	eHealth	26
33	Rackspace	93	93	EDAC Technologies	40	153	Medidata Solutions	26
34	Joe's Jeans	90	94	Quality Systems	39	154	Investors Bancorp	26
35	Red Hat	89	95	Globecomm	39	155	AMEN Properties	26
36	Hecla Mining	89	96	Simclar	38	156	Birner Dental	26
37	TNS	87	97	Brocade Communications	38	157	Holly Energy Partners	25
38	BroadSoft	85	98	TeleCommunication Systems	38	158	NuVasive	25
39	Alexion Pharmaceuticals	80	99	United Therapeutics	36	159	Buffalo Wild Wings	25
40	Targacept	77	100	Endologix	36	160	JMP Group	25
41	Illumina	77	101	Iridium	36	161	EXL	25
42	Roma Financial	76	102	Diamond Foods	36	162	Butler National	25
43	JDA Software	76	103	Local.com	35	163	Anika Therapeutics	25
44	LaPolla Industries	75	104	Govt Properties Income Trust	35	164	East West Bancorp	25
45	HomeFed	73	105	PSB Holdings, Inc.	35	165	Neutral Tandem	24
46	Netflix	71	106	NIC	35	166	Jazz Pharmaceuticals	24
47	First Bancorp of Indiana	69	107	Inphi	34	167	Peapack-Gladstone Financial	24
48	Fortinet	69	108	IBERIABANK	34	168	KMG Chemicals	24
49	LivePerson	69	109	Electromed	33	169	IntercontinentalExchange	24
50	Real Goods Solar	69	110	CPS Technologies	33	170	Atlantic Tele-Network	24
51	Green Mountain Coffee	65	111	Cheniere Energy Partners	33	171	STRATTEC	23
52	Electro Scientific Industries	65	112	InfoSpace	33	172	Boardwalk Pipeline	23
53	MaxLinear	65	113	Vera Bradley	33	173	InterMune	23
54	SPS Commerce	64	114	Momenta Pharmaceuticals	32	174	Osiris Therapeutics	23
55	Shutterfly	62	115	Rovi	32	175	ASB Financial	23
56	Aruba Networks	61	116	Patient Safety Technologies	32	176	South Street Financial	23
57	NetSpend	60	117	Cornerstone Therapeutics	32	177	ZAGG	22
58	WebMD Health	60	118	KEYW	31	178	Semtech	22
59	Digimarc	58	119	rue21	31	179	Summer Infant	22
60	Cree	57	120	Houston American Energy	31	180	Deckers Outdoor	22

The Top 200 Companies with the Highest P/E Ratios
in Hoover's Handbook of Emerging Companies 2012

Rank	Company	P/E High		Rank	Company	P/E High		Rank	Company	P/E High
181	MWI Veterinary Supply	22		188	LRAD Corporation	21		195	Meridian Interstate	20
182	Union First Market Bankshares	22		189	Super Micro Computer	21		196	Titan Machinery	20
183	First Financial Bancorp	22		190	Idaho Independent Bank	21		197	A. Schulman	20
184	Ameresco	22		191	US Global Investors	21		198	Rambus	20
185	Spectra Energy Partners	21		192	Dynasil	20		199	Cherokee Banking Company	20
186	First Niagara Financial	21		193	Kreisler Manufacturing	20		200	First South Bancorp (SC)	20
187	Signature Bank	21		194	United Financial Banking	20				

Hoover's Handbook of

Emerging
Companies

2012

1st United Bank

1st United Bancorp is the holding company for 1st United Bank, a community-based retail bank with 15 branches in the greater Miami area of Broward, Brevard, Indian River, Miami-Dade, and Palm Beach counties. 1st United Bank offers checking, savings, money market, and NOW accounts, as well as debit and credit cards. It caters mostly to professionals, entrepreneurs, and high-net-worth individuals. 1st United Bancorp has a mortgage-heavy loan portfolio; some 75% consists of commercial and residential real estate loans. 1st United Bancorp was founded in 2000 as Advantage Bancorp, the holding company for Advantage Bank.

When the bank began as Advantage Bancorp, it operated at a loss for its first three years until the current management took over, renamed it, and began buying smaller, failing banks. It acquired First Western Bank for $6.6 million in 2004, a one-branch bank that marked its entry into Broward Country. In 2007 and 2008 the company bought Equitable Financial Group and acquired Citrus Bank from Wisconsin-based CIB Marine. Since the bottom fell out of the banking industry in 2008 (Georgia and Florida have had the highest number of troubled banks), 1st United Bancorp has taken advantage of the state's failed banks. It took over three more banks in FDIC-assisted acquisitions from 2009 to 2011. The company arranged a more traditional transaction in 2011 when it agreed to buy Anderen Bank, which will add four locations in central Florida.

The acquisitions are paying off. 1st United Bancorp had its first record-earning year in 2009, when total revenue grew more than 65% with the addition of Republic Federal Bank. That year it also raised $70 million in a public offering.

EXECUTIVES

Chairman, Warren S. Orlando, age 67, $1,269,966 total compensation
President and Director; COO and CFO, 1st United Bank, John Marino, age 46, $1,477,949 total compensation
EVP and Chief Lending Officer, 1st United Bank, Wade E. Jacobson, age 41
EVP, 1st United Bank, H. William (Bill) Spute
VP, 1st United Bank, Beatrice Ferreiro
VP, 1st United Bank, Tammy Campbell
VP, 1st United Bank, William (Bill) Tamanini
VP, 1st United Bank, Joanna M. Brown
VP, 1st United Bank, Lorraine Lasek
VP, 1st United Bank, Jeff Klink
Director; CEO, 1st United Bank, Rudy E. Schupp, age 60, $1,504,151 total compensation
SVP, 1st United Bank, David Webb
SVP, 1st United Bank, Rene Webster
SVP, 1st United Bank, Gabriela Duran
SVP, 1st United Bank, Ivete Pinheiro
SVP, 1st United Bank, Julita Howard
SVP, 1st United Bank, Linda Casey
Senior Relationship Officer, Residential Lending, Jeffrey Toeniskoetter
Senior Relationship Officer, 1st United Bank, Pat Staunton
SVP Credit Administration, 1st United Bank, Lawrence Ostermayer, age 57
Auditors: Crowe Horwath LLP

LOCATIONS

HQ: 1st United Bancorp, Inc.
1 N. Federal Hwy., Boca Raton, FL 33432
Phone: 561-362-3400 **Fax:** 561-362-3436
Web: www.1stunitedbankfl.com

COMPETITORS

Bank of America	Interamerican Bank
BankAtlantic	JPMorgan Chase
BankUnited	Ocean Bankshares
BB&T	OptimumBank
Citibank	Regions Financial
Firstbank Florida	SunTrust
Great Florida Bank	Wells Fargo

HISTORICAL FINANCIALS

Company Type: Public

Income Statement

FYE: December 31

	ASSETS ($ mil.)	NET INCOME ($ mil.)	INCOME AS % OF ASSETS	EMPLOYEES
12/10	1,267.8	2.2	0.2%	301
12/09	1,015.6	4.7	0.5%	229
12/08	617.8	(1.4)	—	153
Annual Growth	43.3%	—	—	40.3%

2010 Year-End Financials

Equity as % of assets: 13.73% Dividends
Return on assets: 0.2%   Yield: —
Return on equity: 1.2%   Payout: —
Long-term debt ($ mil.): 9.8   Market value ($ mil.): 171.3
No. of shares (mil.): 24.8   Sales ($ mil.): 61.2

	STOCK PRICE ($) FY Close	P/E High/Low		PER SHARE ($) Earnings	Dividends	Book Value
12/10	6.91	104	63	0.09	0.00	7.02
12/09	7.14	27	5	0.30	0.00	6.95
12/08	6.00	—	—	(0.25)	0.00	11.55
Annual Growth	7.3%	—	—	—	—	(22.0%)

A. Schulman

A. Schulman adds color to plastic resins but keeps them from getting red hot. Schulman adds chemicals to basic plastics such as polypropylene, polyethylene, and PVC to give them color and desired characteristics like flexibility or the ability to retard flame. Its products include color and additive concentrates, engineered compounds (such as reinforced plastics), and value-added PVC. Customers include makers of plastics and auto parts, with more than a third of its sales to packaging manufacturers. In 2010 the company acquired ICO in a deal that valued the plastics maker at $190 million. The deal was designed to expand both Schulman's global presence and its masterbatch and molding businesses.

Schulman has spent much of the latter half of the decade dealing with investors who have questioned the direction of the company, sought to name directors to the board, and advocated for a merger or sale. The process began when investment firm the Barington Group demanded the right to name a director. Its success spurred another investor group, Ramius Capital, to offer up its own set of directors for A. Schulman's early-2008 elections. Ramius, like Barington, was eager to get Schulman to consider a sale or merger of the company, or, at the very least, a change in company strategy that had led to continually disappointing results. Ultimately, Ramius won the right to nominate candidates for the board.

Encouraged by the investors and their representative board members, the company idled one manufacturing facility and sold another in 2008; it also brought in UBS to explore possibilities of selling part or all of the company. (An offer from an unidentified buyer was turned down in mid-2008.)

After failing to find a manufacturing partner for its Invision line of plastic sheet products, it discontinued the line and shut down the operation in 2009. The next year, it moved several of its operations from its Crumlin, South Wales, operation to larger facilities and eliminated 30 jobs in a move to improve efficiency.

A. Schulman saw solid revenue gains in 2010, with sales jumping 24% over 2009. The increase was the result of higher tonnage, increased per-unit sales prices, and an jump in sales of those higher-priced products. Net income swung to a $44 million profit in 2010 from a $2.8 million loss the previous year.

In 2010 the company acquired McCann Color, an Ohio-based producer of color concentrates. The deal, for about $10 million in cash, will bolster A. Schulman's existing master batch manufacturing and product development facilities in Akron, Ohio, and San Luis Potosí, Mexico. It also acquired Brazilian plastics maker Mash Compostos Plásticos in 2010. Mash Compostos is a S o Paulo-based producer of additives and engineered plastics compounds.

HISTORY

Alex Schulman founded A. Schulman in 1928 as a rubber brokerage. In 1937 he hired William Zekan as an office boy after meeting the 18-year-old caddie on a golf course. With rubber in short supply during WWII, A. Schulman began using scrap plastic. Zekan was appointed head of the firm's New York sales office in 1947 and became #2 in the company in 1953.

A. Schulman abandoned the scrap market in the 1950s to focus on plastic compounds. Schulman died in 1962 and Zekan headed the company, taking it public in 1972. A. Schulman set up a joint venture in 1988 with Mitsubishi to supply plastic compounds to Honda, Nissan, and Toyota.

Zekan died in 1991 and was replaced by company veteran Terry Haines. He expanded A. Schulman through acquisitions that included Diffusion Plastique from Atochem (subsidiary of Elf Aquitaine, now called TOTAL) in 1991 and Exxon's ComAlloy International in 1994. The next year the company bought a polymer unit from J. M. Huber and polypropylene interests from Eastman Chemical.

A. Schulman opened its first plant in Asia in 1997. The next year it cut production to compensate for an industry slowdown. The company also bought an Italy-based distributor and agreed to supply all of the color concentrate for Procter & Gamble's molded white containers. In 1999 A. Schulman spent $35 million to renovate manufacturing facilities. It joined DuPont that year to make bumper fascias and other moldings for cars such as the Dodge Neon.

As pricing pressures continued in 2000, A. Schulman moved to cut its costs by closing a number of sales offices and its plant in Akron, Ohio. The company's 2001 sales were hurt by the weakening economy, especially in the US, where capacity utilization was down by 5%. Although A. Schulman's sales remained flat in 2002, the company managed to boost profits mostly through a workforce reduction and the closing of more costly facilities.

Haines and other members of management came under fire with investors' criticism that began in 2007, and Haines stepped down early in 2008. He was replaced by director Joseph Gingo, a former Goodyear executive.

EXECUTIVES

Chairman, President, and CEO; EVP and COO, North America, Joseph M. (Joe) Gingo, age 66, $2,966,022 total compensation

VP, CFO and Treasurer, Joseph J. (Joe) Levanduski, age 48

VP, Chief Legal Officer, and Secretary, David C. Minc, age 62

VP and CIO, John B. Broerman

VP Global Supply Chain and Chief Procurement Officer, Gary A. Miller, age 65

VP Global Human Resources, Kim L. Whiteman, age 54

SVP Marketing and Chief Marketing Officer, Paul R. Boulier, age 58

Managing Director, Mexico, Francisco Castillo

Business Unit Leader, Masterbatch, Americas, Roberto Lopez

Director Finance, Europe, Patrick Speek

Director Internal Audit, Stacy R. Walter

Chief Accounting Officer and Controller, Donald B. (Mickey) McMillan

Manager Corporate Marketing and Business Development, Sanja Valentic

Director Continuous Improvement Initiatives, Americas, Greg Agnew

Global Operations Specialist, Steve Barkmann

Director Corporate Communications and Investor Relations, Jennifer K. Beeman

Director New Business Applications, Dennis C. Smith

General Manager, ICO Australasia, Derek R. Bristow, age 50

General Manager and COO, Americas, Gustavo Pérez

Manager Financial Reporting, R. J. Schoger

General Manager and COO, EMEA, Bernard Rzepka, age 51, $1,104,482 total compensation

Assistant Corporate Controller, Malia Gelfo

Auditors: PricewaterhouseCoopers LLP

LOCATIONS

HQ: A. Schulman, Inc.
3550 W. Market St., Akron, OH 44333
Phone: 330-666-3751   **Fax:** 330-668-7204
Web: www.aschulman.com

2010 Sales

	$ mil.	% of total
Germany	496.0	31
US	231.9	15
Other countries	862.5	54
Total	**1,590.4**	**100**

PRODUCTS/OPERATIONS

2010 Sales

	$ mil.	% of total
Europe, Middle East, Africa	1,142.5	72
North American Masterbatch	132.3	8
North American Engineered Plastics	127.1	8
Asia Pacific	84.9	5
North American Rotomolding	77.5	5
Bayshore	26.1	2
Total	**1,590.4**	**100**

COMPETITORS

Albemarle	Georgia Gulf
Ampacet	PolyOne
Clariant	RTP Company
DuPont	Shintech International
Ferro	Spartech

HISTORICAL FINANCIALS

Company Type: Public

Income Statement

FYE: August 31

	REVENUE ($ mil.)	NET INCOME ($ mil.)	NET PROFIT MARGIN	EMPLOYEES
08/11	2,193.0	41.0	1.9%	3,000
08/10	1,590.4	43.9	2.8%	2,900
08/09	1,279.2	(2.8)	—	2,000
08/08	1,984.0	18.0	0.9%	2,200
08/07	1,787.1	22.6	1.3%	2,471
Annual Growth	**5.3%**	**16.1%**	**—**	**5.0%**

2011 Year-End Financials

Debt ratio: 33.7%	No. of shares (mil.): 30.6
Return on equity: 7.5%	Dividends
Cash ($ mil.): 155.8	Yield: 3.4%
Current ratio: 2.15	Payout: 47.0%
Long-term debt ($ mil.): 184.6	Market value ($ mil.): 558.3

	STOCK PRICE ($) FY Close	P/E High/Low		PER SHARE ($) Earnings	Dividends	Book Value
08/11	18.24	20	12	1.32	0.62	17.92
08/10	18.17	17	10	1.57	0.60	15.50
08/09	20.09	—	—	(0.11)	0.60	14.03
08/08	24.22	39	27	0.66	0.59	16.17
08/07	21.54	32	23	0.82	0.58	15.28
Annual Growth	**(4.1%)**	**—**	**—**	**12.6%**	**1.7%**	**4.1%**

A123 Systems

A123 Systems wants to get everyone all charged up over electric vehicles. And it plans to use rechargeable lithium-ion batteries to do it. The company develops and makes rechargeable batteries and battery systems for transportation, commercial, and electric grid applications. It targets the fast-growing hybrid and electric automotive and heavy-duty vehicle markets. In the electric grid sector, the company is working with AES to produce multi-megawatt battery systems that take the fluctuations out of the electricity grid and provide backup power during shortages. Its batteries are also used in home appliances, power tools, and other consumer products. Customers in the US make up nearly three-quarters of sales.

A123 has never been profitable, and continues to report losses — its net loss in 2010 was $80 million — as it invests in product development, sales, and marketing to support future growth. The company has incurred significant expenses in transitioning from prototype to volume production. It has more than doubled its worldwide manufacturing capacity, purchased capital equipment, and moved more of its production in-house. The company plans to increase hiring in the US as factories there take over more of the manufacturing chores. A123 also has manufacturing facilities in China and South Korea.

While most of its products are still manufactured at its plants in China, A123 is using federal and state funding initiatives to help build its US manufacturing base. In 2009 the company received a $249 million matching grant from the US Department of Energy and $100 million in refundable tax credits from Michigan Economic Development Corporation; the funding is being used to expand manufacturing facilities in Michigan. In addition, A123 was awarded a $10 million grant by the State of Michigan to establish a research and development institute that will collaborate with The University of Michigan and Michigan State University to further develop lithium-ion battery technology.

Much of A123's growth is tied to growth in the hybrid electric car and heavy-duty vehicle and electric grid storage markets. Overall sales were up just 7% in 2010 over 2009; a drop in product sales was offset by a 62% increase in services revenue related to higher revenues from government research contracts. In its products segment, sales in its electric grid storage product line were up 22%, while transportation products (which account for 45% of sales) sales were down nearly 4%. Cost of sales rose across the business, primarily due to a less profitable mix of products, low factory utilization, and higher than expected manufacturing costs.

The company has garnered several new customers in recent years, including Fisker Automotive and Navistar. Other significant customers with development or supply agreements include BAE Systems (propulsion systems for hybrid electric buses), BMW, Daimler, Delphi, Magna Steyr, Eaton, and General Electric.

A123 is also working with General Motors on a battery for its Volt car. In China, A123 has 49% stake in a joint venture with GM partner SAIC Motor. The venture, Shanghai Advanced Traction Battery Systems Co. (ATBS), will be the primary supplier of battery systems for hybrid and electric vehicles made by SAIC. A123 will supply the battery cells and license the technology for battery systems to ATBS.

In the commercial market, the company sells to Gillette (part of Proctor & Gamble) for use in its consumer products and to China-based Tianjin Lishen Battery. Lishen licenses the manufacturing process and cell design for consumer battery products, but must purchase the cathode materials from A123 and can only make batteries for certain consumer products. A123 also sells batteries to consumer through resellers and distributors. Sales of commercial products continued to fall in 2010, impacted by the economic downturn and lack of consumer demand. A123 is looking to lawn and garden equipment and vacuums as possible new consumer applications, but expects sales to the consumer market to continue to decline.

A123 was formed in 2001 and went public in 2009. The company is using the proceeds of its IPO to expand its manufacturing facilities and to fund additional research and development. The R&D side is a company stronghold, partly because its Nanophosphate technology comes from nanoscale materials developed at MIT.

EXECUTIVES

Chairman, Gururaj (Desh) Deshpande, age 60

President, CEO, and Director, David P. (Dave) Vieau, age 61, $710,312 total compensation

President, A123 China, Tao Zheng

VP Human Resources and Organizational Development, Andew Cole, age 45

VP Research and Development, CTO, and Director, Gilbert N. (Bart) Riley Jr., age 48, $431,506 total compensation

VP Cell Products Group, Christian M. (Chris) Tecca

VP and General Counsel, Eric J. Pyenson, age 54
VP Automotive Solutions Group, Jason M. Forcier, age 38
VP Marketing and Communications, Andy Chu
VP, Finance, Interm CFO, and Corporate Controller, John Granara, age 42
VP Operations, Louis M. Golato, age 56
VP Global Sales, Evan C. Sanders, age 52, $410,159 total compensation
VP And General Manager, Energy Solutions Group, Robert J. Johnson, age 44, $493,097 total compensation
Media Relations, Elizabeth Ames
Auditors: Deloitte & Touche LLP

LOCATIONS

HQ: A123 Systems, Inc.
 321 Arsenal St., Watertown, MA 02472
Phone: 617-778-5700   Fax: 617-924-8910
Web: www.a123systems.com

2010 Sales

	$ mil.	% of total
US	70.9	73
Germany	7.9	8
China	6.9	7
UK	1.7	2
Czech Republic	1.6	2
Mexico	1.0	1
South Korea, Malaysia & other countries	7.3	7
Total	**97.3**	**100**

PRODUCTS/OPERATIONS

2010 Sales

	$ mil.	% of total
Product		
Transportation	43.7	45
Commercial	16.6	17
Electric grid	13.5	14
Services	23.5	24
Total	**97.3**	**100**

COMPETITORS

Beacon Power	Mitsubishi Electric
BYD	NGK INSULATORS
China BAK	Panasonic Corp
China Shoto	Robert Bosch
Enerl	SAFT
GS Yuasa	Samsung Electronics
Hitachi	SANYO
Honda	Sony
Johnson Controls	Toshiba
LG Group	Valence Technology

HISTORICAL FINANCIALS

Company Type: Public

Income Statement

FYE: December 31

	REVENUE ($ mil.)	NET INCOME ($ mil.)	NET PROFIT MARGIN	EMPLOYEES
12/10	97.3	(152.6)	—	2,032
12/09	91.0	(85.8)	—	1,627
12/08	68.5	(80.4)	—	1,672
12/07	41.3	(31.0)	—	1,160
12/06	34.3	(15.7)	—	0
Annual Growth	**29.8%**	**—**	**—**	**20.5%**

2010 Year-End Financials

Debt ratio: 5.8%	No. of shares (mil.): 105.2
Return on equity: —	Dividends
Cash ($ mil.): 216.8	Yield: —
Current ratio: 2.61	Payout: —
Long-term debt ($ mil.): 23.3	Market value ($ mil.): 1,003.6

	STOCK PRICE ($) FY Close	P/E High/Low	Earnings	PER SHARE ($) Dividends	Book Value
12/10	9.54	— —	(1.46)	0.00	3.79
12/09	22.44	— —	(2.55)	0.00	5.15
Annual Growth	**(57.5%)**	**— —**	**—**	**—**	**(26.5%)**

Able Energy

Once an able consolidator in the fragmented heating-oil and motor fuels markets, Able Energy provided retail distribution of heating oil and other fuels to more than 30,000 residential and commercial customers in Florida, New Jersey, New York, and Pennsylvania. However, a downturn in the market and financial difficulty with its All American Plazas' business (which operated a network of travel plazas) forced the company to sell its assets. In 2010 Able Energy sold all but a couple of real estate holdings to high performance materials company Exousia Advanced Materials in return for a stake in that company.

Prior to the 2010 transaction the company was forced to exit its All American Plazas business in 2009 and sell a number of propane assets in order to meet its financial obligations.

The deal with Exousia required Able Energy to sell its asset to a third party, Evergreen Global Investments Ltd., which Exosuia then acquired. In addition to broadening Exosuia's portfolio by giving it access to the fuel distribution market in the Northeast US, the purchase gave Exousia the PriceEnergy internet platform for fuel distribution, and a biofuel plant in South Carolina.

EXECUTIVES

Chairman and CEO, Gregory D. Frost, age 63
President, Richard A. Mitstifer, age 54
President, Home Heating Oil Segment, Louis Aponte, age 38
EVP Business Development, Frank Nocito, age 63
VP Special Projects, Christopher P. (Chris) Westad, age 57
COO, William R. Roberts, age 58
Interim CFO, John F. O'Brien
COO, Price Energy Unit, John L. Vrabel, age 57
Director, Human Resources, Colleen Harrington
Auditors: Lazar Levine & Felix LLP

LOCATIONS

HQ: Able Energy, Inc.
 198 Green Pond Rd., Rockaway, NJ 07866
Phone: 973-625-1012   Fax: 973-586-9866
Web: www.ableenergy.com

HISTORICAL FINANCIALS

Company Type: Public

Income Statement

FYE: June 30

	REVENUE ($ mil.)	NET INCOME ($ mil.)	NET PROFIT MARGIN	EMPLOYEES
06/08	276.4	(12.9)	—	501
06/07	93.6	(6.6)	—	645
06/06	75.1	(6.2)	—	77
06/05	62.0	(2.1)	—	95
06/04	42.9	(0.1)	—	87
Annual Growth	**59.3%**	**—**	**—**	**54.9%**

2008 Year-End Financials

Debt ratio: 57.8%	No. of shares (mil.): —
Return on equity: —	Dividends
Cash ($ mil.): 3.0	Yield: —
Current ratio: 0.47	Payout: —
Long-term debt ($ mil.): 3.7	Market value ($ mil.): —

	STOCK PRICE ($) FY Close	P/E High/Low	Earnings	PER SHARE ($) Dividends	Book Value
06/08	0.38	— —	(0.86)	0.00	(0.00)
06/07	1.90	— —	(1.60)	0.00	(0.00)
06/06	5.69	— —	(2.23)	0.00	(0.00)
06/05	14.53	— —	(0.99)	0.00	0.84
06/04	2.45	— —	(0.04)	0.00	(0.00)
Annual Growth	**(37.2%)**	**— —**	**—**	**—**	**—**

ACADIA Pharmaceuticals

ACADIA Pharmaceuticals develops small molecule drugs for the treatment of central nervous system disorders. The biopharmaceutical company's most advanced compound, pimavanserin, is in clinical trials as a treatment for Parkinson's disease psychosis, which occurs in up to 40% of Parkinson's patients. Two other clinical-stage candidates are being developed in collaboration with Allergan to treat patients with chronic pain (AGN-XX/YY) and glaucoma (AC-262271). A preclinical candidate, AM-831, a compound that holds the potential for a new class of antipsychotic drugs, is being jointly developed with Japan's Meiji Seika Kaisha. All candidates are birthed from ACADIA's own R-SAT drug discovery platform.

Subsequent to drug discovery, ACADIA Pharmaceuticals' general strategy is to pursue strategic partnerships to lift some of the cost burdens of clinical development. However, it took a blow in late 2010 when key partner Biovail decided to terminate their collaborative agreement to develop pimavanserin. After Biovail was acquired by Valeant Pharmaceuticals, it was decided that the pimavanserin development program no longer fit in with the new Valeant's strategic focus. ACADIA regained North American commercialization rights to the product. But with substantial clinical development costs back on its shoulders, the company opted to scrap planned trials for pimavanserin as a treatment for Alzheimer's disease psychosis and schizophrenia. For now, it is focusing resources on its most advanced clinical trials testing pimavanserin for Parkinson's disease psychosis.

Parkinson's disease is a chronic and progressive neurological disorder. Psychosis develops in some patients with symptoms commonly consisting of hallucinations and delusions. There are no FDA-approved therapies for Parkinson's disease psychosis currently on the market. The only antipsychotic drug that has demonstrated efficacy in reducing psychosis in Parkinson's patients without further impairing motor function is a low-dose treatment of the generic drug clozapine. However, clozapine has been associated with the occurrence of a rare blood disorder. ACADIA is pursuing this indication for pimavanserin because of the unmet need for a treatment without such adverse side effects.

Oxford Bioscience Partners, a venture capital firm in which ACADIA director Dr. Alan Walton is a general partner, owns about 9% of the company.

EXECUTIVES

Chairman and Director, Leslie L. Iversen, age 73
CEO and Director, Uli Hacksell, age 60, $751,900 total compensation
EVP, CFO, Chief Business Officer, and Treasurer, Thomas H. Aasen, age 50, $315,373 total compensation
EVP Development, Roger G. Mills, age 53, $362,191 total compensation
VP Regulatory Affairs, David C. Furlano
VP Biosciences, Douglas W. Bonhaus
SVP Business Development, Brian Lundstrom, age 48
Director Investor Relations, Lisa Barthelemy
Director Human Resources, Natasha Bowman
Auditors: PricewaterhouseCoopers LLP

LOCATIONS

HQ: ACADIA Pharmaceuticals Inc.
3911 Sorrento Valley Blvd., San Diego, CA 92121-1402
Phone: 858-558-2871   **Fax:** 858-558-2872
Web: www.acadia-pharm.com

COMPETITORS

Akorn	Novartis
Allergan	Pharmaceuticals
AstraZeneca	Otsuka Pharmaceutical
Bristol-Myers Squibb	Pfizer
Eli Lilly	Shire
Johnson & Johnson	Titan Pharmaceuticals

HISTORICAL FINANCIALS

Company Type: Public

Income Statement				FYE: December 31
	REVENUE ($ mil.)	NET INCOME ($ mil.)	NET PROFIT MARGIN	EMPLOYEES
12/10	42.1	15.1	35.9%	27
12/09	6.4	(45.1)	—	27
12/08	1.6	(64.2)	—	63
12/07	7.6	(56.4)	—	143
12/06	8.1	(45.1)	—	138
Annual Growth	51.0%	—	—	(33.5%)

2010 Year-End Financials

Debt ratio: 0.1%
Return on equity: 51.0%
Cash ($ mil.): 6.8
Current ratio: 6.35
Long-term debt ($ mil.): 0.0
No. of shares (mil.): 39.4
Dividends
　Yield: —
　Payout: —
Market value ($ mil.): 47.2

	STOCK PRICE ($) FY Close	P/E High/Low		PER SHARE ($) Earnings	Dividends	Book Value
12/10	1.20	5	2	0.39	0.00	0.75
12/09	1.32	—	—	(1.20)	0.00	0.32
12/08	0.90	—	—	(1.73)	0.00	1.43
12/07	11.07	—	—	(1.60)	0.00	3.08
12/06	8.79	—	—	(1.61)	0.00	2.25
Annual Growth	(39.2%)	—	—	—	—	(23.9%)

Access Plans

Access Plans (formerly Alliance HealthCard) is an ally for people without health insurance. The company provides health care savings programs, serving individuals and families with limited health benefits or no insurance. Its membership programs offer access to hospitals, doctors, dentists, mental health services, pharmacies, physical therapy, and outpatient clinics at discounted rates for an annual fee. In addition, subsidiary Benefit Marketing Solutions (BMS) provides grocery, entertainment, auto, and rent-to-own membership programs, and BMS Insurance Agency provides leased property and other insurance coverage. Access Plans markets its service through retailers and financial services partners.

In late 2009 the company changed its name from Alliance HealthCard to Access Plans to reflect its broader operations. The firm had been growing rapidly through acquisitions. It also divided its operations into three divisions: retail plans, wholesale plans, and insurance marketing.

In 2009 the company expanded by purchasing discount health plan provider Access Plans USA. Through the stock transaction, Access Plans USA's shareholders received an approximate one-third stake in the merged entity. The acquisition strengthened the company's sales and marketing operations and bolstered its discount program and insurance marketing businesses. Access Plans USA now represents Access Plans' retail plans division.

Access Plans also significantly expanded its offerings into areas beyond health care with the acquisition of BMS in early 2007. BMS holds the company's wholesale operations. Following the transaction, BMS CEO Danny Wright took over the role of CEO at the parent company as well. Wright and COO Brett Wimberley, another BMS employee who has joined the company's executive ranks, each gained ownership stakes of around 25% in Access Plans through the deal.

The insurance marketing division is represented by the America's Health Care Plans subsidiary, which consists of an independent brokerage network for health insurance distribution.

EXECUTIVES

Chairman and CEO, Danny C. Wright, age 59
President, CFO, and Director, Brett Wimberley, age 47
President, USA, David Huguelet, age 51
President, Benefit Marketing Solutions (BMS), Susan Matthews, age 52
President, America's Health Care/Rx Plan Agency (AHCP), Charles (Charlie) Harris
Chief Accounting Officer, Rita W. McKeown, age 57
SVP General Counsel and Secretary, Bradley W. Denison, age 50
Auditors: Miller Ray & Houser LLP

LOCATIONS

HQ: Access Plans, Inc.
900 36th Ave. NW, Ste. 105, Norman, OK 73072
Phone: 405-579-8525
Web: www.accessplans.com

COMPETITORS

Aetna	Passport Unlimited
Affinion Group	Reader's Digest
American Automobile Association (AAA)	UnitedHealth Group
HealthSCOPE Benefits	Vertrue

HISTORICAL FINANCIALS

Company Type: Public

Income Statement				FYE: September 30
	ASSETS ($ mil.)	NET INCOME ($ mil.)	INCOME AS % OF ASSETS	EMPLOYEES
09/10	24.9	3.0	12.0%	78
09/09	26.0	3.4	13.1%	85
09/08	10.5	2.7	25.7%	0
09/07	10.2	1.4	13.7%	4
09/06	1.7	0.6	35.3%	17
Annual Growth	95.6%	49.5%	—	46.4%

2010 Year-End Financials

Equity as % of assets: —
Return on assets: 12.0%
Return on equity: 21.4%
Long-term debt ($ mil.): —
No. of shares (mil.): 19.9
Dividends
　Yield: —
　Payout: —
Market value ($ mil.): 17.9
Sales ($ mil.): 55.3

	STOCK PRICE ($) FY Close	P/E High/Low		PER SHARE ($) Earnings	Dividends	Book Value
09/10	0.90	9	5	0.15	0.00	0.72
09/09	1.00	6	2	0.19	0.00	0.53
09/08	0.70	11	3	0.18	0.00	0.22
09/07	1.90	—	—	(0.47)	0.00	0.03
09/06	0.55	8	4	0.13	0.00	(0.00)
Annual Growth	13.1%	—	—	3.6%	—	—

Accretive Health

You could say Accretive Health makes sure hospitals don't leave money on the *operations* table. The company provides its own employees and management systems to improve back-office operations for health care providers and specializes in maximizing profits while reducing costs. Services include benefit coordination, coding, billing, and collection management. Typical customers are hospital systems, independent medical centers and clinics, and physician practice groups such as Ascension Health, Dartmouth-Hitchcock Medical Center, and Henry Ford Health System. Accretive, founded in 2003 by chairman J. Michael Cline and CEO Mary Tolan, completed an initial public offering in 2010.

The company's IPO was completed in May 2010. Proceeds from the offering are being used to finance further growth and expansion by offering new services and, to a lesser extent, acquire related businesses. Accretive had filed to go public in September 2009 after a phenomenal rate of increase in revenue in the first few years of operation.

The company's revenue from contracts alone experienced a compound annual growth of about 40% from 2006 through 2010. Its rate of growth comes in part from the broad market opportunity to provide cost-control services to an industry under increasing financial pressure; an environment that has been enhanced by overall economic conditions and an increase in government health care reform proposals.

Accretive earns most of its revenue through managed service contract fees; the contracts typically also include additional incentive payments for increasing revenue for its clients. As the central part of a managed service agreement, a deployed team of Accretive employees (also called "infused management") take over the management of the entire revenue cycle, from pre-registration and admissions to patient and insurance billing. Once the contract expires, the hospital can either renew or transition to rely on its own employees, who have been trained by the infused management team (and are temporarily on Accretive's payroll).

In addition to its total revenue cycle management services, in 2010 the company started offering a quality and total cost-of-care package, which assists health care providers in managing defined patient groups. The solution helps hospitals identify high-risk individuals (those most likely to experience an adverse health event) and try to keep those patients healthy and well monitored.

Accretive aims to expand its customer base to include customers across the US, with a focus on large hospital systems. It also works to provide larger service packages to existing customers. As its customer base grows, the firm must also be able to attract and retain qualified personnel to serve on its management teams.

Chairman Michael Cline owns an approximate 20% stake in Accretive, down from about 25% prior to the IPO. CEO Mary Tolan's stake was reduced from 18% to about 15% through the offering. Investment firm Oak Hill Capital Partners owns about 15% of the company as well.

EXECUTIVES

Chairman, J. Michael Cline, age 51
CFO and Treasurer, John T. Staton, age 50, $800,140 total compensation
President, CEO, and Director, Mary A. Tolan, age 51, $1,123,760 total compensation
EVP, Etienne H. Deffarges, age 53, $899,015 total compensation
SVP, Gregory N. Kazarian, age 48, $483,500 total compensation
Corporate Controller, James M. Bolotin
Auditors: Ernst & Young LLP

LOCATIONS

HQ: Accretive Health, Inc.
401 N. Michigan Ave., Ste. 2700, Chicago, IL 60611
Phone: 312-324-7820
Web: www.accretivehealth.com

PRODUCTS/OPERATIONS

2010 Sales

	$ mil.	% of total
Net base fees for managed service contracts	518.2	86
Incentive payments for managed service contracts	74.7	12
Other services	13.4	2
Total	**606.3**	**100**

COMPETITORS

Advisory Board	Deloitte Consulting
athenahealth	Huron Consulting
CareMedic	MedAssets
CBIZ	Novation
Cerner	Perot Systems
Computer Sciences Corp.	QuadraMed

HISTORICAL FINANCIALS
Company Type: Public

Income Statement

FYE: December 31

	REVENUE ($ mil.)	NET INCOME ($ mil.)	NET PROFIT MARGIN	EMPLOYEES
12/10	606.3	12.6	2.1%	2,222
12/09	510.2	14.6	2.9%	1,623
12/08	398.5	1.2	0.3%	1,305
12/07	240.7	0.8	0.3%	0
12/06	160.7	(7.3)	—	0
Annual Growth	**39.4%**	**—**	**—**	**30.5%**

2010 Year-End Financials

Debt ratio: —	No. of shares (mil.): 94.8
Return on equity: 8.8%	Dividends
Cash ($ mil.): 155.6	Yield: —
Current ratio: 1.95	Payout: —
Long-term debt ($ mil.): —	Market value ($ mil.): 1,540.9

	STOCK PRICE ($) FY Close	P/E High/Low		PER SHARE ($) Earnings	Dividends	Book Value
12/10	16.25	125	64	0.13	0.00	1.51
Annual Growth	—	—	—	—	—	—

Acme Packet

Acme Packet brings networks together. The company makes equipment designed to ensure that advanced network services communicate with multiple Internet protocol-based networks. Acme's family of Net-Net session border controllers (SBCs) are used to connect networks operated by service providers and enterprise customers. SBCs handle interactive services, including VoIP. Acme Packet also provides multiservice security gateways and session routing proxies. The company markets directly and through distribution partnerships with vendors that include Alcatel-Lucent and Nokia Siemens. Acme Packet has sales offices in Japan, South Korea, Spain, the US, and the UK. About 40% of sales come from outside the US and Canada.

In spite of the prolonged global economic downturn, Acme Packet has continued to have solid sales and net income growth. In 2010 product revenues, which depend to some extent on the configuration of systems sold, rose by 74% over 2009. Its maintenance, support, and other services climbed by about 29%, primarily due to higher maintenance and support fees driven by a larger base of installed products. Service revenues come primarily from consulting, installation, network integration, and training. Net income rose more than 151% in 2010.

The company's strategy includes using distribution partnerships to expand its market presence, investing in product development, and maintaining a service and support organization aimed at retaining customers. Acme Packet also actively contributes to the development of standards for next-generation IP networks, which will be important as the market — and competition — grows.

The company acquired Covergence, a developer of software-based SBCs, for about $23 million in 2009. The purchase extends Acme's product line to address the enterprise market, as Covergence's offerings are targeted toward small offices and remote sites with as few as 20 employees.

SBCs are typically deployed at the borders between IP networks, such as where the networks of two service providers meet or at the intersection of a service provider's network and its business, residential, and mobile customers. SBCs integrate the control of signaling messages and media flows, complementing the functionality and effectiveness of routers, softswitches, and firewalls that reside within the network.

EXECUTIVES

CFO and Treasurer, Peter J. Minihane, age 62, $669,179 total compensation
President, CEO, and Director, Andrew D. (Andy) Ory, age 44, $1,111,556 total compensation
VP Product Management, Kevin Klett
VP Manufacturing Operations, John F. Shields, age 48
Chief Software Architect, Bob Penfield
SVP Sales and Business Development, Dino Di Palma, age 43, $697,028 total compensation
SVP Professional Services, Erin Medeiros, age 37
SVP Marketing and Product Management, James Seamus Hourihan, age 57, $514,126 total compensation
General Manager, Canada, Rob Saloman
Director Solutions Marketing, Kevin Mitchell
Corporate Secretary, Assistant Treasurer, and Director, Robert G. Ory, age 78
CTO and Director, Patrick J. MeLampy, age 52, $856,467 total compensation
Auditors: Ernst & Young LLP

LOCATIONS

HQ: Acme Packet, Inc.
71 3rd Ave., Burlington, MA 01803
Phone: 781-328-4400   **Fax:** 781-425-5077
Web: www.acmepacket.com

2010 Sales

	$ mil.	% of total
US & Canada	142.9	62
Other countries	88.3	38
Total	**231.2**	**100**

PRODUCTS/OPERATIONS

2010 Sales

	$ mil.	% of total
Product	186.8	80
Maintenance, support, & service	44.4	20
Total	**231.2**	**100**

COMPETITORS

AudioCodes	GENBAND
Cisco Systems	Huawei Technologies
Edgewater Networks	Juniper Networks
Ericsson	Sonus Networks

HISTORICAL FINANCIALS
Company Type: Public

Income Statement

FYE: December 31

	REVENUE ($ mil.)	NET INCOME ($ mil.)	NET PROFIT MARGIN	EMPLOYEES
12/10	231.2	43.0	18.6%	570
12/09	141.5	17.1	12.1%	450
12/08	116.4	11.6	10.0%	381
12/07	113.1	19.6	17.3%	322
12/06	84.1	28.9	34.4%	247
Annual Growth	**28.8%**	**10.4%**	**—**	**23.3%**

2010 Year-End Financials

Debt ratio: —
Return on equity: 13.4%
Cash ($ mil.): 91.7
Current ratio: 6.19
Long-term debt ($ mil.): —

No. of shares (mil.): 64.4
Dividends
  Yield: —
  Payout: —
Market value ($ mil.): 3,423.5

	STOCK PRICE ($) FY Close	P/E High/Low		PER SHARE ($) Earnings	Dividends	Book Value
12/10	53.16	94	16	0.63	0.00	4.98
12/09	11.00	44	13	0.28	0.00	3.41
12/08	5.26	61	16	0.18	0.00	2.40
12/07	12.59	67	34	0.30	0.00	2.71
12/06	20.64	44	26	0.50	0.00	2.24
Annual Growth	26.7%	—	—	5.9%	—	22.1%

Acorda Therapeutics

Acorda Therapeutics hopes its products really get on your nerves. The company is developing prescription drugs that aim to restore neurological function for patients with spinal cord injury and other central nervous system disorders. The company's marketed drugs include muscle spasm controller Zanaflex along with Ampyra, which enhances conduction in nerves damaged by blunt trauma or from multiple sclerosis (MS). It purchased the US rights to Zanaflex from Elan Corporation but developed Ampyra itself. Acorda is working with Biogen Idec to market Ampyra outside the US. Acorda's other drug candidates include potential therapies for MS and central nervous system, cardiac, and spinal cord injuries.

The company markets Zanaflex through a direct sales force that targets neurologists and and other specialists, as well as primary care physicians and managed care and drug distribution companies. The company uses Patheon and Elan as its third-party manufacturers for the Zanaflex products.

In 2010 Acorda gained FDA approval for Ampyra (formerly Fampridine) as a therapy to improve the ability to walk in people who suffer from MS. The drug is the first to improve the functionality of damaged nerve fibers. Other MS treatments generally treat symptoms or slow its progression. Acorda uses its own sales force to market the drug in the US; Elan and Patheon manufacture it.

Though the company has products on the market, it still invests heavily in marketing and R&D. In 2009 it received payments related to approval milestones but was required to pay Elan on a similar schedule. It also ramped up its sales and marketing teams and incurred additional administrative costs as the FDA approved Ampyra. Acorda expects to continued operating losses for the next several years as it continues to spend money.

Biogen Idec paid $110 million (plus potential future milestone payments of up to $400 million) in 2009 to obtain the rights to market Ampyra outside of the US. Biogen Idec already makes two of the best-known drugs to treat MS, but hopes to augment its pipeline with the new treatment. It plans to seek approval for Ampyra in Canada, the European Union, Australia, and other areas.

Acorda is exploring applications for its tissue repair technologies in areas such as cardiology, oncology, ophthalmology, and orthopedics. With Ampyra on the market, the company's next leading candidate is GGF2, purchased from CeNeS Pharmaceuticals. It may be able to protect and re-pair cells in the nervous system and heart as well as protect the heart and brain from toxic chemotherapy drugs.

EXECUTIVES

CFO, David Lawrence, age 53, $961,860 total compensation
President CEO, and Director, Ron Cohen, age 55, $1,577,881 total compensation
EVP, General Counsel and Corporate Secretary, Jane Wasman, age 54, $1,046,811 total compensation
EVP Commercial Development, Lauren M. Sabella, age 50
VP Research and Development, Anthony O. (Tony) Caggiano
VP Drug Safety, Douglas Kargman
VP Medical Affairs, Herbert Raymo (Herb) Henney III
VP Business Development, Ruhi Khan
Chief Scientific Officer, Andrew R. Blight, age 60, $1,085,097 total compensation
SVP Human Resources, Denise J. Duca
SVP Corporate Communications, Tierney Saccavino
SVP Medical Affairs, Adrian L. Rabinowicz
Chief Medical Officer, Thomas C. Wessel, age 55
Senior Director Corporate Communications, Jeff Macdonald
Auditors: KPMG LLP

LOCATIONS

HQ: Acorda Therapeutics, Inc.
15 Skyline Dr., Hawthorne, NY 10532
Phone: 914-347-4300   **Fax:** 914-347-4560
Web: www.acorda.com

PRODUCTS/OPERATIONS

2009 Sales

	$ mil.	% of total
Sales of Zanaflex	50.0	92
Licensing	4.7	8
Total	**54.7**	**100**

COMPETITORS

Alseres Pharmaceuticals	Cephalon
Apotex	Elan
Bayer HealthCare Pharmaceuticals	Merck Serono
Bayhill	Mylan
Biogen Idec	NovaDel Pharma
BioMarin Pharmaceutical	Sandoz
	Sanofi
	Shire
	Teva

HISTORICAL FINANCIALS

Company Type: Public

Income Statement   FYE: December 31

	REVENUE ($ mil.)	NET INCOME ($ mil.)	NET PROFIT MARGIN	EMPLOYEES
12/10	191.0	(11.8)	—	305
12/09	54.7	(83.9)	—	249
12/08	47.8	(74.3)	—	174
12/07	39.5	(38.0)	—	144
12/06	27.4	(24.5)	—	126
Annual Growth	62.5%	—	—	24.7%

2010 Year-End Financials

Debt ratio: 4.3%
Return on equity: —
Cash ($ mil.): 34.6
Current ratio: 3.30
Long-term debt ($ mil.): 6.6

No. of shares (mil.): 38.8
Dividends
  Yield: —
  Payout: —
Market value ($ mil.): 1,056.8

	STOCK PRICE ($) FY Close	P/E High/Low		PER SHARE ($) Earnings	Dividends	Book Value
12/10	27.26	—	—	(0.31)	0.00	3.90
12/09	25.20	—	—	(2.22)	0.00	3.62
12/08	20.51	—	—	(2.19)	0.00	5.49
12/07	21.96	—	—	(1.45)	0.00	2.22
12/06	15.84	—	—	(3.27)	0.00	0.81
Annual Growth	14.5%	—	—	—	—	48.1%

Acorn Energy

Holding company Acorn Energy is nuts about its seedlings. The company has controlling or equity positions in four energy infrastructure firms — CoaLogix, DSIT Solutions (Energy & Security Sonar Solutions), GridSense Systems, and US Sensor Systems (USSI). Its largest company, CoaLogix, helps coal and gas-fired power plants reduce pollution, while Israel-based DSIT Solutions offers underwater acoustic and sonar security systems for the military and offshore oil rigs. GridSense makes electronic monitoring systems for utility companies, and USSI designs fiber optic sensing systems for energy companies.

Acorn Energy bought the remaining 69% of shares in GridSense that it did not already own in late 2009. Acorn saw the acquisition as a way to tap into the emerging market for so-called "smart energy" systems designed to improve efficiency and reliability of electrical systems.

The company has pared down its portfolio to focus on investments that improve the efficiency of the energy grid, reduce the risk for owners of large energy assets, and reduce the environmental impact of the energy sector. Its strategy has been paying off.

CoaLogix saw its revenues grow 80% in 2009. CoaLogix offers selective catalytic reduction (SCR) services to coal and gas-fired power plants to reduce their emissions of nitrogen oxides. With the 2009 passage of the Clean Air Interstate Rule (CAIR), more companies are requiring CoaLogix's services to remain compliant. FLSmidth chose CoaLogix in 2010 to provide its mercury remediation services. The growth in ColaLogix and DSIT's Energy & Security Sonar Solutions sales helped to lift Acorn Energy's overall revenue and improve its net loss position in 2010.

In 2010 subsidiary Coreworx (which provides project management software to energy companies such as Chevron, Husky Energy, and USEC, bought Decision Dynamics Technology Ltd., a Canadian company that was registered on the Toronto Stock Exchange. Decision Dynamics' project cost management software, called Oncore, was re-branded Coreworx Oncore. However, that year Acorn Energy decide to exit this unprofitable business and sell it to the unit's management.

HISTORY

When software engineer George Morgenstern visited Israel in 1963, he was recruited to help develop radar and guidance software for the Israeli military. In 1979 he started Decision Systems Israel to provide software and systems analysis personnel to IAI, Israel's largest industrial company. By 1986 Morgenstern's company was providing computer consulting in both Israel and the US.

The company went public as Defense Software & Systems in 1992 and began providing remote meter reading equipment through its PowerCom division. In 1993 the company changed its name to Data Systems & Software Inc. (DSSI) to reflect its diversification beyond defense contracts. It acquired a majority stake in Tower Semiconductor (sold in 2000). In 1995 DSSI joined sports card marketer Topps to form CybrCard (multimedia software featuring sports stars).

Heavy investments in its help desk software and in CybrCard left the company in the red in 1996. Its acquisition of Topps' half of CybrCard in 1997 contributed to losses for that year. In 1998, after a battle with shareholders who criticized the losses, DSSI sold its help desk software operations and discontinued the activities of CybrCard. Reorganizing around new markets, DSSI that year merged automatic meter reading support technologies (acquired from Lucent) with PowerCom to form Comverge Technologies, and started a unit devoted to the Internet (sold in 2000). The refocus caused losses for 1998.

In 1999 Comverge bought Scientific-Atlanta's electric utility automation systems business. The next year DSSI sold its CinNetic systems integration subsidiary to Eclipse Networks as it continued to streamline operations.

In 2001, looking to bolster its consulting business (and counter declining revenues), DSSI acquired Endan IT Solutions, an Israel-based provider of information technology services and software for the billing and health-care markets. DSSI sold part of its Comverge subsidiary in 2003, keeping a 25% stake.

The company sold its dsIT Technologies outsourcing business, which operated primarily in Israel, in 2005, and the next year it sold its computer hardware sales subsidiary, Databit, to the unit's president, Schlomie Morgenstern.

In 2006 Acorn exited the computer hardware sales business when it sold its Databit subsidiary to Schlomie Morgenstern, Databit's president and a VP of the former DSSI. It used the proceeds to help fund its corporate activities in the US. In 2005 the company sold its dsIT Technologies outsourcing consulting business, which operated primarily in Israel.

Comverge went public in 2007 and Acorn sold its shares for more than $45 million.

In 2008 it sold its interest in Paketeria AG, a German company that offered "green" retail services such as bicycle mail delivery, recycling, and toner cartridge refills.

EXECUTIVES

Chairman Emeritus; Chairman, DSIT Technologies, George Morgenstern, age 77

Chairman, President, and CEO, John A. Moore, age 45, $632,417 total compensation

CFO, Acorn Energy and DSIT, Michael Barth, age 50

President and CEO, GridSense Systems, Lindon Shiao

Chairman, President, and CEO, Comverge, Robert M. (Bob) Chiste, age 63

President and CEO, DSIT Solutions, Benny Sela, age 63, $254,311 total compensation

President and CEO, Coreworx, Ray Simonson, age 62

CEO and President, CoaLogix, William J. McMahon, age 55, $575,654 total compensation

President and CEO, Comverge, Inc., R. Blake Young, age 52

EVP and VP Sales and Marketing, CoaLogix, Michael F. Mattes

VP and CTO, David T. Beatson

VP, Secretary, and General Counsel, Acorn and CoaLogix, Joe B. Cogdell Jr., age 58, $671,678 total compensation

Investor Relations, Jane Voisin

Senior Advisor, Edgar S. Woolard Jr., age 76

Auditors: Kesselman & Kesselman

LOCATIONS

HQ: Acorn Energy, Inc.
4 W. Rockland Rd., Montchanin, DE 19710
Phone: 302-656-1707   **Fax:** 302-994-3086
Web: www.acornfactor.com

PRODUCTS/OPERATIONS

2010 Sales

	$ in mil.	% of total
CoaLogix	21.4	60
Energy & Securtiy Sonar Solutions	10.2	28
GridSense	2.4	7
USSI	0.4	1
Other	1.3	4
Total	**35.7**	**100**

COMPETITORS

ABB	Invensys
Badger Meter	Itron
C-Tech	Kongsberg Power
ConneXt	Products
Electric & Gas	Pointer Telocation
Technology	PowerSecure
Enerfab	International
Equitrac	Schlumberger
Honeywell	Siemens AG
International	

HISTORICAL FINANCIALS

Company Type: Public

Income Statement

FYE: December 31

	REVENUE ($ mil.)	NET INCOME ($ mil.)	NET PROFIT MARGIN	EMPLOYEES
12/10	35.7	(25.1)	—	228
12/09	31.3	(5.8)	—	190
12/08	20.7	(7.9)	—	156
12/07	5.7	32.5	570.2%	86
12/06	4.1	(6.1)	—	70
Annual Growth	**71.8%**	**—**		**34.3%**

2010 Year-End Financials

Debt ratio: 1.2%   No. of shares (mil.): 17.3
Return on equity: —   Dividends
Cash ($ mil.): 7.4   Yield: —
Current ratio: 2.10   Payout: —
Long-term debt ($ mil.): 0.4   Market value ($ mil.): 67.0

	STOCK PRICE ($) FY Close	P/E High/Low		PER SHARE ($) Earnings	Dividends	Book Value
12/10	3.88	—	—	(1.68)	0.00	1.93
12/09	7.38	—	—	(0.50)	0.00	2.57
12/08	1.39	—	—	(0.69)	0.00	2.98
12/07	5.95	2	1	2.80	0.00	6.58
12/06	3.47	—	—	(0.71)	0.00	(0.05)
Annual Growth	**2.8%**	—	—	—	—	—

Active Network

Thinking about enrolling for a marathon or adventure race? The first step is to get fit, but the second one might involve The Active Network. The company makes software used to build websites that help participants find and register for sports events online. Using Active.com, organizers can administer online registration, promotion, and fundraising efforts. Other applications target parks, recreation agencies, and universities. The company's ActiveSports unit facilitates communication within teams, leagues, and camps. Virtually all sales come from North America. The Active Network went public in 2011.

The company intends to use proceeds from the sale of stock to repay debt and to fund potential acquisitions. The Active Network uses periodic acquisitions to build its product portfolio and expand into new markets. It moved into the faith market in 2011 with the purchase of Fellowship Technologies, a developer of software primarily for churches and other religious community organizations in North America.

It acquired Pleasanton, California-based online software and services provider Clubspace in 2010. The deal raised the company's profile in the youth and amateur sports markets. Clubspace's clients included organizations such as the American Youth Soccer Organization, the Amateur Softball Association, and American Youth Football, which used its online website creation, registration, and scheduling tools to manage their events. The Active Network integrated Clubspace's technology with its ActiveSports division. The company also bought a similar business, Channel:1 Corporation, that year to improve the functionality of its online tools, particularly in the areas of onsite event management and marketing.

The company acquired campground reservation services provider ReserveAmerica Holdings the previous year from IAC/InterActiveCorp (IAC). The stock swap deal gave IAC a 9% stake in The Active Network. In 2008 Active Network bought HY-TEK Sports Software, a provider of applications and services for use by track and field and swimming teams and organizations. It also purchased Automated License Systems, a maker of automated hunting and fishing license systems, that year.

The Active Network is extending its international reach by opening overseas sales offices. The company moved into the Asia/Pacific region in 2009 when it established operations in New Zealand and Singapore, and it expanded into the European market the previous year when it opened an office in London. It also has offices in Australia, Canada, China, and across the US.

ESPN and affiliates own about 16% of the the company. Director Stephen L. Green, through investment firm Canaan Partners, owns another 12%.

EXECUTIVES

Chairman and CEO, David (Dave) Alberga, age 48

CFO, Scott Mendel, age 44

President and Director, Matthew G. (Matt) Landa, age 46

EVP Sales, Alex Barnetson, age 49

EVP Human Resources, Sheryl Roland

VP Technology, Josh Schlesser

VP Technology, Andy George

VP Media and Marketing, Alan Cole

VP, Kristin Carroll

SVP Technology, Fredd Wall, age 41
SVP Business Development, Chief Legal Officer, General Counsel, and Secretary, Kourosh Vossoughi
Chief Strategy Officer, Matt Ehrlichman, age 31
General Manager, ActiveEndurance, Erin McCue
Media Contact, International, Events, and Camps, Dana McKeithen
Media Contact, Communities, Campgrounds, Education, Golf, and Government, Jake Gonzales
SVP Operations, Dennis Triplett, age 39
Media Contact, Corporate Communications, Web Properties, Active Marketing Group, Endurance Sprots, T, Tina Wilmott
Chief Media Officer, Jon Belmonte, age 42
General Manager, James Reyes
Development Manager, Jeremy Thomas
Auditors: Ernst & Young LLP

LOCATIONS

HQ: The Active Network, Inc.
10182 Telesis Ct., Ste. 100, San Diego, CA 92121
Phone: 858-964-3800
Web: www.theactivenetwork.com

2010 Sales

	$ mil.	% of total
North America	273.0	98
Europe & other regions	6.6	2
Total	**279.6**	**100**

PRODUCTS/OPERATIONS

2010 Sales

	$ mil.	% of total
Technology	237.7	85
Marketing services	41.9	15
Total	**279.6**	**100**

COMPETITORS

CA, Inc.	Microsoft
Epicor Software	Oracle
IBM	SAP
Lawson Software	

HISTORICAL FINANCIALS

Company Type: Public

Income Statement   FYE: December 31

	REVENUE ($ mil.)	NET INCOME ($ mil.)	NET PROFIT MARGIN	EMPLOYEES
12/10	279.6	(27.3)	—	2,490
12/09	242.9	(37.9)	—	2,490
12/08	173.2	(49.0)	—	0
12/07	101.9	(24.8)	—	0
12/06	62.7	—	—	0
Annual Growth	**45.3%**	**—**		**0.0%**

2010 Year-End Financials

Debt ratio: —
Return on equity: —
Cash ($ mil.): 31.4
Current ratio: 0.56
Long-term debt ($ mil.): 29.2

No. of shares (mil.): —
Dividends
Yield: —
Payout: —
Market value ($ mil.): —

	STOCK PRICE ($) FY Close	P/E High/Low	PER SHARE ($) Earnings	PER SHARE ($) Dividends	PER SHARE ($) Book Value
Annual Growth	—	— —	—	—	—

Active Power

Active Power keeps the juices flowing. The company's UPS (uninterruptible power system) products use a flywheel that stores kinetic energy by spinning, converting the kinetic energy into electricity when power quality problems are detected. It was developed in partnership with heavy equipment maker Caterpillar, which markets the product with its generator sets. Active Power also makes PowerHouse, a continuous power system that combines the company's flywheel UPS products with switchgear and a generator, which is sold primarily for military, utility, and data center applications. Customers in North America account for more than 70% of sales.

The company has yet to make a profit and has an accumulated deficit of more than $250 million. Active Power expects to continue to incur losses for the near term, though it recorded consecutive profitable quarters the latter half of 2010 and achieved its first ever positive cash flow on an annual basis that year. Overall sales increased by 61% in 2010 over 2009, primarily due to higher demand for data center infrastructure products and an improved global economic environment. Sales were up across all geographic regions, led by growth in North America. In Asia and Europe, sales improved as Active Power continued to build up its sales presence in the regions.

The company has expanded its direct sales and IT channel sales business, in order to offset a decline in sales through OEMs such as Caterpillar. Active Power works with such computer vendors as Hewlett-Packard and Oracle to market its products. Better profit margins through direct sales channels, along with higher product pricing, has helped improve the company's bottom line, in spite of fluctuations in operating expenses. Active Power trimmed its net loss to $4 million in 2010, from a loss of $11 million in 2009.

Though sales of flywheel-based UPS products have continued to make up nearly half of revenues, combined sales of continuous power systems (PowerHouse) and containerized data center infrastructure systems increased by more than 250% in 2010. PowerHouse was launched in 2009, and is expected to be a major contributor to sales in the future. The containerized power system, which can become a modular data center once customers add their IT racks and servers, was introduced in 2010 to complement the PowerHouse product line and to increase sales to the data center market. The company also sells to the health care, petrochemical, broadcasting, and telecommunications industries, among others.

The company has shipped more than 2,800 flywheels around the world. It manufactures its products in the US, and has international offices in China, Germany, Japan, and the UK.

Active Power is no longer actively marketing CleanSource DC, a stand-alone direct current (DC) product designed to replace conventional UPS products that use lead-acid batteries, due to limited demand from customers. It also no longer sells its CoolAir DC and CoolAir UPS products, backup power systems that incorporate the company's thermal and compressed air storage technology. CoolAir was targeted at uses in data centers, as well as applications in semiconductor and solar cell manufacturing.

EXECUTIVES

Chairman, Benjamin L. Scott, age 61
President, CEO, and Director, James A. (Jim) Clishem, age 54, $1,018,829 total compensation
VP Manufacturing, Jason P. Rubin, age 45
VP Engineering, Karl T. Schuetze, age 45
VP Sales, EMEA and Asia Pacific, Dietmar Papenfort, age 45
VP and General Manager, Global Sales and Business Development, Martin T. Olsen, age 49
VP Marketing and Sales Operations, Lisa M. Brown, age 45, $329,224 total compensation
VP Finance, CFO, and Secretary, John K. Penver, age 48, $473,641 total compensation
Manager Public Relations, Lee Higgins
Manager Investor Relations, Debbie Laudermilk
CTO and VP Engineering, Uwe Schrader-Hausmann, age 56
Auditors: Grant Thornton LLP

LOCATIONS

HQ: Active Power, Inc.
2128 W. Braker Ln., Bldg. 12, Austin, TX 78758
Phone: 512-836-6464   **Fax:** 512-836-4511
Web: www.activepower.com

2010 Sales

	$ mil.	% of total
North America	47.5	73
Europe, Middle East & Africa	13.0	20
Asia/Pacific	4.4	7
Total	**64.9**	**100**

PRODUCTS/OPERATIONS

2010 Sales

	$ mil.	% of total
Product revenue		
UPS product	31.1	48
Continuous power systems	13.1	20
Data center infrastructure systems	11.4	18
Service & other	9.3	14
Total	**64.9**	**100**

Selected Products

CleanSource DC (250-2,000 kilowatt systems)
CleanSource UPS (130-3,600 kilovolt-ampere systems)
Continuous Power Systems (CPS, used in modular data center infrastructure applications)
GenSTART (battery-free modular system for starting diesel generators)
PowerHouse (integrated power system with CleanSource UPS, GenSTART, diesel generator, and switchgear)

COMPETITORS

Beacon Power	SL Industries
Chloride Group	Technology Research
Liebert Corporation	Corp.
Piller	Trippe Manufacturing
Power-One	UNIPOWER
Schneider Electric	ZBB Energy

HISTORICAL FINANCIALS

Company Type: Public

Income Statement   FYE: December 31

	REVENUE ($ mil.)	NET INCOME ($ mil.)	NET PROFIT MARGIN	EMPLOYEES
12/10	65.0	(3.9)	—	181
12/09	40.3	(11.0)	—	149
12/08	43.0	(13.4)	—	149
12/07	33.6	(20.5)	—	155
12/06	25.0	(21.1)	—	145
Annual Growth	**27.0%**	**—**	**—**	**5.7%**

2010 Year-End Financials

Debt ratio: —   No. of shares (mil.): 79.7
Return on equity: —   Dividends
Cash ($ mil.): 15.4   Yield: —
Current ratio: 2.05   Payout: —
Long-term debt ($ mil.): —   Market value ($ mil.): 196.2

	STOCK PRICE ($) FY Close	P/E High/Low		PER SHARE ($) Earnings	Dividends	Book Value
12/10	2.46	—	—	(0.05)	0.00	0.26
12/09	1.06	—	—	(0.17)	0.00	0.22
12/08	0.32	—	—	(0.22)	0.00	0.34
12/07	2.20	—	—	(0.38)	0.00	0.55
12/06	2.62	—	—	(0.43)	0.00	0.77
Annual Growth	(1.6%)	—	—	—	—	(23.8%)

AdCare

Retirement keeps AdCare Health Systems working. The company manages about 45 nursing homes, assisted-living facilities, and independent retirement communities in Alabama, Arkansas, Georgia, North Carolina, and Ohio with a total of about 2,500 residences. It owns all or part of about half of its facilities, including the Hearth & Home assisted living facilities. Services include Alzheimer's and subacute care. AdCare also operates a home health care business, Assured Health Care, which offers nursing, therapy, and living assistance services, as well as administrative services for insurance coordination and caregiver hiring.

Adcare has committed itself to growing by offering more residential and home health senior living services, both through acquisitions and by achieving higher occupancy rates and employing more home health field workers. It is targeting facilities that have gone into foreclosure, which it can purchase below regular market prices, then improve with its operational efficiencies.

The company began an aggressive acquisition push in late 2009 to extend its operations into new territories. AdCare made its first expansion outside Ohio in 2010 with the acquisition of two privately-held nursing homes (totaling 315 beds) and one assisted living facility (with 105 units) in Alabama for $18 million and $5 million, respectively. That same year it also leased eight nursing homes in Georgia, and acquired a 100-bed nursing home in North Carolina for about $6 million.

Continuing its strategy, during 2011 the company acquired or leased several more skilled nursing facilities in Alabama, Arkansas, Georgia, and North Carolina, and moved into Oklahoma with the purchase of five facilities (totaling 357 beds). The company also laid out plans to enter the new markets of Missouri, South Carolina, Tennessee, and Virginia.

Chairman David Tenwick owns about 10% of AdCare Health, while vice chairman (and chief acquisitions officer) Christopher Brogdon owns a 20% stake.

EXECUTIVES

Chairman, David A. (Dave) Tenwick, age 73, $563,655 total compensation
President, Co-CEO, and Director, Gary L. Wade, age 74, $397,030 total compensation
CFO, Scott Cunningham, age 43, $174,152 total compensation

VP Human Resources and Information Systems and Secretary, Carol Groeber, age 54
VP Business Development, Andy Wade
VP Assisted Living Operations, Kim Henry
Vice Chairman and Chief Acquisitions Officer, Chris Brogdon, age 62, $290,754 total compensation
Co-CEO and Director, Boyd P. Gentry
Administrator, Legacy Village, Rene Pandsian
Administrator, Community's Hearth & Home, Urbana, Crystal Wright
Administrator, Adkins Care Centers, Steve Zkinak
Administrator, SpringMeade Residence, Kathy Davidson
Administrator, The Pavilion, Marianne Wildermuth
Administrator, SpringMeade HealthCenter, Phil Crawford
Administrator, Koester Pavilion, Kari DeBanto
Administrator, Lincoln Lodge Retirement Residence, Lana Rodgers
Administrator, Covington Care Center, Brenda Lewis
SVP Nursing Home Operations, Sharon L. Reynolds, age 65, $184,184 total compensation
Administrator, Assured Health Care, Holly Hall
Administrator, Community's Hearth and Home, El Camino, Harding, and Urbana, Debbie Cordle
Administrator, Hearth and Home at Vandalia, Rose Siddle
Administrator, Hearth and Care at Greenfield, India Chrisman
Administrator, Hearth and Home at Van Wert, Lisa Stemen
Auditors: Battelle & Battelle LLP

LOCATIONS

HQ: AdCare Health Systems, Inc.
5057 Troy Rd., Springfield, OH 45502
Phone: 937-964-8974   **Fax:** 937-964-8961
Web: www.adcarehealth.com

PRODUCTS/OPERATIONS

2008 Sales

	$ mil.	% of total
Facility care	23.8	89
Home care	2.8	11
Adjustments	(1.8)	-
Total	**24.8**	**100**

COMPETITORS

Amedisys
Brookdale Senior Living
Catholic Health Initiatives
Catholic Health Partners
Clinical Specialties
Consulate Health Care
Deaconess Associations
Gentiva
Greene Memorial Hospital
Kettering Health Network
Kindred Healthcare
Manor Care
Ohio Presbyteri

HISTORICAL FINANCIALS

Company Type: Public

Income Statement   FYE: December 31

	REVENUE ($ mil.)	NET INCOME ($ mil.)	NET PROFIT MARGIN	EMPLOYEES
12/10	53.2	(2.7)	—	2,210
12/09	26.7	0.4	1.5%	846
12/08	24.8	(1.1)	—	906
12/07	23.7	(0.2)	—	898
12/06	22.5	(2.4)	—	934
Annual Growth	24.0%	—	—	24.0%

2010 Year-End Financials

Debt ratio: 335.7%   No. of shares (mil.): 8.8
Return on equity: —   Dividends
Cash ($ mil.): 3.9   Yield: —
Current ratio: 1.04   Payout: —
Long-term debt ($ mil.): 47.2 Market value ($ mil.): 32.6

	STOCK PRICE ($) FY Close	P/E High/Low		PER SHARE ($) Earnings	Dividends	Book Value
12/10	3.71	—	—	(0.38)	0.00	1.60
12/09	3.57	45	5	0.09	0.00	1.31
12/08	0.96	—	—	(0.25)	0.00	1.08
12/07	0.73	—	—	(0.05)	0.00	1.17
12/06	2.54	—	—	(0.99)	0.00	(0.00)
Annual Growth	9.9%	—	—	—	—	—

Advanced Battery Technologies

Advanced Battery Technologies hopes to ride the rising wave of electric and hybrid-electric vehicles all the way to the bank. Its Wuxi ZQ subsidiary makes electric and hybrid-electric scooters, electric bicycles, motors, and accessories. Subsidiary ZQ Power-Tech makes rechargeable polymer lithium-ion batteries for use in cars, buses, cell phones, and other gear. Its batteries can be as thin as one-tenth of an inch or as large as 500 pounds (for commuter buses). ZQ Power-Tech also makes lamps used on miners' helmets, but most of its products are sold to OEMs for use in their finished goods. Customers for vehicle battery components have included Aiyingsi, ZAP, and Beijing Guoqiang Global Technology Development.

Sales are roughly split between electric vehicles and battery operations. Advanced Battery reported sales that were more than 50% higher in 2010 than 2009, primarily due to the inclusion of a full year of electric vehicles sales. A 10% increase in battery sales was attributable almost exclusively to sales of medium capacity batteries, which more than doubled between 2009 and 2010. The medium capacity batteries — used in electric scooters and bicycles, along with power tools, miner's lamps, and searchlights — are also sold to Advanced Battery's Wuxi ZQ subsidiary, though that amount is not included in 2010 sales. The company's sales of miner's lamps fell by around 40%, since the contract with its primary customer expired and those sales have not been replaced.

Net income increased by 68% in 2010, boosted by increased efficiencies in its vehicle manufacturing operations, which were thought to have a slimmer profit margin than its battery operations. Advanced Battery managed to boost the profit margins for electric vehicles to more than 40% in 2010, compared to 33% in 2009, by controlling production costs as Wuxi ZQ.

In 2009 Advanced Battery Technologies acquired fellow Chinese firm Wuxi Angell Autocycle, a maker of electric and hybrid-electric vehicles that use ZQ Power-Tech batteries. Wuxi Angell was renamed Wuxi Zhongqiang Autocycle (Wuxi ZQ). Wuxi Angell was a major customer of ZQ Power-Tech prior to the acquisition.

Other customers of Wuxi ZQ include Ampere (an India-based distributor of motorcycles), Floretti (a distributor of battery-powered motorcycles in Europe), and All-Power America (a US distributor). In addition, the company has orders to provide electric vehicles to customers in Brazil, Chile, Denmark, Indonesia, Israel, Italy, and Turkey, among other countries. Wuxi ZQ has expanded quickly to produce 20 types of vehicles. The company can also increase production at its Wuxi-based manufacturing facility to meet demand.

Chairman and CEO Zhiguo Fu formed the company in 2002. Fu, who pays for the company's New York office out of his own pocket, owns about 12% of Advanced Battery Technologies, a holding company consisting solely of Cashtech Investment, which is itself a holding company.

EXECUTIVES

Chairman and CEO, Zhiguo Fu, age 60
CFO, Sharon Tang, age 51
Media Contact, Rita Lai
Sales Manager, Renkun Shao
Auditors: EFP Rotenberg, LLP

LOCATIONS

HQ: Advanced Battery Technologies, Inc.
  15 W. 39th St., 14th Fl., New York, NY 10018
Phone: 212-391-2752   **Fax:** 212-391-2751
Web: www.abat.com.cn

PRODUCTS/OPERATIONS

2010 Sales

	$ mil.	% of total
Electric vehicles	49.2	51
Batteries		
Medium capacity	19.7	20
Large capacity	15.7	16
Miner's lamp	7.9	8
Small capacity	4.6	5
Total	**97.1**	**100**

COMPETITORS

China BAK	SAFT
Ener1	SION Power
Honda	Suzuki Motor
Johnson Controls Power	Ultralife
Solutions	Unitech Battery
Kandi Technologies	Valence Technology
Maxell	Yamaha Motor

HISTORICAL FINANCIALS

Company Type: Public

Income Statement

FYE: December 31

	REVENUE ($ mil.)	NET INCOME ($ mil.)	NET PROFIT MARGIN	EMPLOYEES
12/10	97.1	36.7	37.8%	1,176
12/09	63.6	21.4	33.6%	854
12/08	45.2	16.1	35.6%	909
12/07	31.9	10.2	32.0%	1,262
12/06	16.3	6.0	36.8%	1,264
Annual Growth	**56.2%**	**57.3%**	**—**	**(1.8%)**

2010 Year-End Financials

Debt ratio: —	No. of shares (mil.): 76.4
Return on equity: 17.9%	Dividends
Cash ($ mil.): 111.1	Yield: —
Current ratio: 18.21	Payout: —
Long-term debt ($ mil.): —	Market value ($ mil.): 294.2

	STOCK PRICE ($) FY Close	P/E High/Low		PER SHARE ($) Earnings	Dividends	Book Value
12/10	3.85	10	6	0.48	0.00	2.69
12/09	4.00	14	5	0.35	0.00	1.92
12/08	2.66	28	4	0.31	0.00	1.40
12/07	4.70	44	3	0.22	0.00	0.73
12/06	0.63	9	3	0.13	0.00	0.43
Annual Growth	**57.2%**	**—**	**—**	**38.6%**	**—**	**58.4%**

Advanced Energy Industries

Advanced Energy Industries advances ordinary electrical power to the head of the high-tech class. The company's power conversion products transform raw electricity, making it uniform enough to ensure consistent production in high-precision manufacturing. Top clients have included semiconductor equipment makers Applied Materials, Axcelis, Lam Research, Novellus, and ULVAC. Advanced Energy's gear also is used in the production of flat-panel displays, solar panels, data storage devices (including hard disks, CD-ROMs, and DVDs), architectural glass, and other thin-film products. The company gets nearly 60% of its sales from the US.

Advanced Energy has diversified its customer base beyond the highly cyclical semiconductor industry by focusing on products for the flat-panel display and thin-film renewables markets. It has also expanded the range of its product offerings for chip equipment makers in anticipation of an industry shift from DRAM to NAND flash memory, commonly used in tablet products such as Apple's iPad. Advanced Energy expects to continue to see growth in products for etch tools as OEMs and foundries add capacity for next-generation display panels over the next year or so, especially in South Korea.

A recovery in all of the markets that Advanced Energy serves drove an overall 184% increase in 2010 sales. The company posted net income of $71 million that year, compared to a net loss of $102 million in 2009, on higher sales and slightly lower operating expenses. Sales of products to non-semiconductor equipment markets rose a whopping 284% over 2009, as flat-panel display and solar panel makers invested in capital equipment needed to expand capacity. Another factor contributing to higher sales was continued international expansion, primarily in China, Europe, and South Korea.

In the semiconductor equipment market, sales were up about 177% in 2010 over the prior period, as foundries increased capacity to meet a resurgence in demand for consumer electronics. Though Advanced Energy expects that 2011 sales will be about the same as 2010 sales in this market, over the long term the transition to NAND flash memory will require that manufacturers invest in new products.

The company also expanded its presence in the market for photovoltaic (PV) power conversion equipment in a big way. Sales to the solar inverter market rose by more than 1,200% in 2010 over 2009. Advanced Energy stands to become one of the top manufacturers of solar inverters in North

America with its 2010 purchase of PV Powered, which makes solar inverters for the commercial, residential, and utility-scale markets. Advanced Energy paid $50 million in cash and stock for PV Powered, offering an additional earnout payment of up to $40 million that depends on 2010 results. Outside of higher sales of solar inverters in China and Europe, the company expects demand for solar inverters in the North American market to increase as the number of solar power plants in the US and Canada continues to grow.

As part of its strategy to focus on its core power conversion products, late in 2010 Advanced Energy sold its Aera mass flow control and related product lines to Hitachi Metals for about $44 million.

Advanced Energy has operations in China, Germany, Japan, South Korea, Taiwan, and the US. Chairman and founder Douglas Schatz owns about 10% of the company.

HISTORY

Douglas Schatz (chairman), a veteran of Applied Materials, and Brent Backman, who had worked for Hughes Aircraft (sold to General Motors in 1986), founded Advanced Energy Industries in 1981. The company's first product replaced a refrigerator-sized power source with one the size of a bread box. Also during the 1980s the company introduced its first direct-current system for use in semiconductor deposition processes.

The company went public in 1995. The following year, sales growth slowed as the chip industry went through one of its periodic slumps. To cushion its dependence on the volatile semiconductor market, in 1997 and 1998 Advanced Energy acquired power supply firms Tower Electronics (products used in the telecommunications, medical, and non-impact printing industries) and MIK Physics (power supplies used in industrial vacuum coating), among others. Advanced Energy also bought one of its main rivals, RF Power Products. In 2000 Advanced Energy bought Noah Holding, a privately held maker of temperature control systems.

In 2001 the company acquired Engineering Measurements Company (EMCO), a maker of flow meters and other precision measurement equipment. During 2001 the company twice cut its workforce — by a total of one-fourth — in response to a sharp decline in the worldwide electronics industry.

In 2002 Advanced Energy acquired Aera Japan (mass flow controllers) for about $80 million in cash and debt assumption. Later that year it acquired Germany-based Dressler HF Technik (power systems for plasma-based production equipment), and the e-diagnostics applications of privately held Symphony Systems (Web-based software used to control wafer manufacturing processes).

In 2005 Doug Schatz said he would retire as president and CEO once a successor could be found. Hans-Georg Betz, CEO of West STEAG Partners (a German venture capital firm) and a director of Advanced Energy since 2004, was named president and CEO later that year. Schatz remained as nonexecutive chairman of the company.

Later that year, Advanced Energy raised around $92 million in a secondary stock offering. The company marked its 25th anniversary in business during 2006.

The company closed its plant in Stolberg, Germany, in 2007. Manufacturing was shifted to Advanced Energy's high-volume plant in Shenzhen, China, and to its advanced manufacturing facility in Fort Collins, Colorado. The company said the decision came down to deciding whether to expand the plants in Stolberg and Shenzhen, with the Chinese facility getting the nod. Advanced Energy acquired the Stolberg location through the acquisition of Dressler HF Technik in 2002. The German plant employed about 65 people.

Bolstering its power conversion products for the solar market, in 2010 Advanced Energy acquired PV Powered, a maker solar inverters for the commercial, residential, and utility-scale markets. Later the same year, the company sold its Aera mass flow control and related product lines to Hitachi Metals for about $44 million, in order to focus on its core power product lines.

EXECUTIVES

Chairman, Douglas S. (Doug) Schatz, age 65
President and COO, Yuval Wasserman, age 56, $639,108 total compensation
CEO and Director, Hans-Georg Betz, age 64, $1,264,030 total compensation
EVP and CFO, Danny C. Herron, age 56
Principal Financial Officer; VP and Corporate Controller, John McMahon
Auditors: Grant Thornton LLP

LOCATIONS

HQ: Advanced Energy Industries, Inc.
1625 Sharp Point Dr., Fort Collins, CO 80525
Phone: 970-221-0108   **Fax:** 970-407-6550
Web: www.advanced-energy.com

2010 Sales

	$ mil.	% of total
US	270.6	59
Asia/Pacific		
China	48.0	11
Other countries	88.9	19
Europe		
Germany	47.3	10
Other countries	4.6	1
Total	**459.4**	**100**

PRODUCTS/OPERATIONS

2010 Sales

	$ mil.	% of total
Non-semiconductor equipment	236.9	52
Semiconductor capital equipment	174.4	38
Global support	48.1	10
Total	**459.4**	**100**

Selected Products

Inductively coupled plasma sources
Ion sources
Optical fiber thermometers
Photovoltaic (PV) power inverters
  Bipolar, transformerless inverters (Solaron)
  Grid-tie PV inverters (PV Powered)
Power control and conversion systems (used with wafer etching and vapor deposition equipment)
  AC power supply
  Direct-current (DC) products
  High-power products
  Low-frequency products
  Mid-frequency power supplies
  Radio-frequency generators
Radio-frequency power systems (cables, generators, instrumentation, power supplies, power delivery systems, and variable frequency generators)

COMPETITORS

Acme Electric	Satcon Technology
BASF SE	Schneider Electric
MKS Instruments	Siemens AG
Power-One	SMA Solar Technology

HISTORICAL FINANCIALS

Company Type: Public

Income Statement

FYE: December 31

	REVENUE ($ mil.)	NET INCOME ($ mil.)	NET PROFIT MARGIN	EMPLOYEES
12/10	459.4	71.2	15.5%	1,788
12/09	186.4	(102.7)	—	1,316
12/08	328.9	(1.8)	—	1,679
12/07	384.7	34.4	8.9%	1,611
12/06	410.7	88.3	21.5%	1,583
Annual Growth	**2.8%**	**(5.2%)**	**—**	**3.1%**

2010 Year-End Financials

Debt ratio: —
Return on equity: 19.0%
Cash ($ mil.): 130.9
Current ratio: 3.54
Long-term debt ($ mil.): —
No. of shares (mil.): 43.3
Dividends
  Yield: —
  Payout: —
Market value ($ mil.): 591.0

	STOCK PRICE ($) FY Close	P/E High/Low		PER SHARE ($) Earnings	Dividends	Book Value
12/10	13.64	11	7	1.64	0.00	8.63
12/09	15.08	—	—	(2.45)	0.00	6.62
12/08	9.95	—	—	(0.04)	0.00	9.00
12/07	13.08	35	16	0.75	0.00	8.99
12/06	18.87	10	6	1.95	0.00	7.94
Annual Growth	**(7.8%)**	**—**	**—**	**(4.2%)**	**—**	**2.1%**

Aerosonic

Aerosonic helps pilots straighten up and fly right. The company makes a broad range of mechanical aircraft instruments, including altimeters, airspeed indicators, vertical speed indicators, mach airspeed gauges, artificial horizon indicators, cabin differential indicators, cabin altimeters, maximum allowable airspeed indicators, and stall warning systems. To ensure that everything's working before the wheels leave the ground, Aerosonic also makes aircraft instrument testing equipment. Korea Aerospace Industries accounts for 14% of sales and US government agencies 10%.

Aerosonic is working to maintain its share of the niche markets it serves. To that end, Aerosonic will continue to develop its digital instrumentation product line as replacements for older mechanical designs such as air data measurement systems, airspeed indicators, altimeters, angle of attack indicators, flight display systems, and stall warning systems.

Net sales for fiscal 2011 were down nearly 5% compared to the previous year. Gross profits for 2011 were also down by about 16% as the company's product mix favored mechanical products, which have a lower gross margin than its digital products. As trends in the aerospace industry have evolved, the company has shifted to one-year fixed-price contracts with options for one to five year pricing targets.

EXECUTIVES

President, CEO, and Director, Douglas J. Hillman, age 55, $403,477 total compensation
EVP and CFO, Kevin J. Purcell, age 53
EVP Sales and Marketing and Director, P. Mark Perkins, age 54, $260,037 total compensation

EVP and COO, Thomas W. Cason, age 56, $110,864 total compensation
Director Sales and Marketing, Jack Rafferty
Controller, Douglas (Doug) Morris
Director Human Resources, Sheryl Vaughn
Auditors: Kirkland, Russ, Murphy & Tapp

LOCATIONS

HQ: Aerosonic Corporation
1212 N. Hercules Ave., Clearwater, FL 33765
Phone: 727-461-3000   **Fax:** 727-447-5926
Web: www.aerosonic.com

2011 Sales

	% of total
US	75
Other countries	25
Total	**100**

PRODUCTS/OPERATIONS

2011 Sales

	% of total
Private sector	66
US military	34
Total	**100**

Selected Products

Digital and mechanical standby displays
Integrated cockpit displays
Probes
Sensors

COMPETITORS

AAI Corporation	Kollsman
BAE Systems Inc.	L-3 Avionics
Herley Industries	Meggitt
Hickok	Rockwell Automation
Honeywell	Smiths Group
International	Universal Avionics
Innovative Solutions	

HISTORICAL FINANCIALS

Company Type: Public

Income Statement

FYE: January 31

	REVENUE ($ mil.)	NET INCOME ($ mil.)	NET PROFIT MARGIN	EMPLOYEES
01/11	29.6	0.6	2.0%	218
01/10	31.1	4.3	13.8%	206
01/09	20.5	(5.3)	—	195
01/08	25.4	(3.4)	—	216
01/07	31.3	0.6	1.9%	240
Annual Growth	**(1.4%)**	**0.0%**	**—**	**(2.4%)**

2011 Year-End Financials

Debt ratio: 56.4%
Return on equity: 7.1%
Cash ($ mil.): 0.2
Current ratio: 1.87
Long-term debt ($ mil.): 5.0
No. of shares (mil.): 3.7
Dividends
  Yield: —
  Payout: —
Market value ($ mil.): 13.4

	STOCK PRICE ($) FY Close	P/E High/Low		PER SHARE ($) Earnings	Dividends	Book Value
01/11	3.57	29	17	0.15	0.00	2.36
01/10	3.94	7	0	1.09	0.00	2.07
01/09	0.85	—	—	(1.48)	0.00	0.77
01/08	5.00	—	—	(0.95)	0.00	2.18
01/07	7.28	71	33	0.16	0.00	3.15
Annual Growth	**(16.3%)**	**—**	**—**	**(1.6%)**	**—**	**(7.0%)**

Alexion Pharmaceuticals

Alexion Pharmaceuticals can't suppress its enthusiasm for treating immune functions gone awry. The firm develops drugs that inhibit certain immune system functions that cause autoimmune, hematology, kidney, and neurology disorders, as well as cancers and other diseases. The company's first marketed antibody product, Soliris, has won approval in the US, Canada, and some European and Asia/Pacific countries for the treatment of a rare genetic blood disorder known as paroxysmal nocturnal hemoglobinuria (PNH). Alexion is also developing Soliris as a potential treatment for other autoimmune and inflammatory conditions. The company has additional development programs for cancer-fighting antibodies.

Soliris is the first drug approved for the treatment of PNH, a rare disorder in which the death of red blood cells can bring on bouts of severe anemia, as well as blood clotting and organ damage. The drug is taken by relatively few and at a hefty cost: more than $400,000 per patient per year. Alexion markets the drug through a specialized direct sales force.

Soliris originally received approval in the EU and the US in 2007, and revenues for the company have since skyrocketed. Alexion is working to expand Soliris' sales into new markets: The drug gained approvals in Australia, Canada, South Korea, and Switzerland in 2009 and 2010, and the company is pursuing regulatory approval in Japan as well. The company is researching the drug as a treatment for additional conditions, including other rare blood disorders, transplant rejection, and severe asthma.

To date, Soliris is the only drug of its kind on the market to treat PNH. However, Taligen Therapeutics has a lead candidate that would have competed with Soliris, if not for the fact that Alexion agreed to acquire Taligen Therapeutics (and with it TT30 for the treatment of PNH) in early 2011 for about $111 million. Taligen Therapeutic's pipeline also includes a potential treatment for age-related macular degeneration and other eye diseases.

Alexion has historically relied only on contract manufacturers (such as Lonza) to make Soliris, but in 2009 it began making its own biopharmaceuticals at a facility in Rhode Island.

EXECUTIVES

Chairman, Max E. Link, age 70
CEO, Treasurer, and Director, Leonard Bell, age 53, $3,939,351 total compensation
EVP and Head, Research and Development, Stephen P. Squinto, age 54, $1,516,625 total compensation
VP Site Operations and Engineering, Daniel N. (Dan) Caron, age 47
VP Human Resources, Glenn R. Melrose, age 55
VP Global Hematology Franchise, Margaret M. Olinger
VP Corporate Strategy and Business Development, Jeremy P. Springhorn
VP Global Nephrology Franchise, Sarah Boyce
VP Global Government Affairs, Heidi L. Wagner
VP and CIO, James P. Bilotta
Chief Accounting Officer and Controller, Scott Phillips, age 34
SVP and CFO, Vikas Sinha, age 47, $2,072,933 total compensation
SVP Global Medical Affairs, Thomas Bock

SVP and President, Alexion Pharma International, S rl, Patrice Coissac, age 62
Senior Director Corporate Communications and Public Policy, Irving Adler
SVP Strategic Product Development and Global Regulatory Affairs, Claude Nicaise
SVP Global Commercial Operations, David L. Hallal, age 45
SVP Technical Operations, M. Stacy Hooks, age 43
SVP and Chief Legal Officer, Thomas Dubin, age 48, $1,427,293 total compensation
SVP Translational Medicine, Abbie Celniker
SVP and Chief Medical Officer, Camille L. Bedrosian, age 57
Auditors: PricewaterhouseCoopers LLP

LOCATIONS

HQ: Alexion Pharmaceuticals, Inc.
352 Knotter Dr., Cheshire, CT 06410
Phone: 203-272-2596   **Fax:** 203-271-8198
Web: www.alexionpharm.com

2009 Sales

	$ mil.	% of total
Europe	215.8	56
US	159.8	41
Other regions & countries	11.2	3
Total	**386.8**	**100**

PRODUCTS/OPERATIONS

Selected Products
Approved
Soliris (eculizumab, paroxysmal nocturnal hemoglobinuria)
In development
Samalizumab (CD200 monoclonal antibody; chronic lymphocytic leukemia, multiple myeloma)
Soliris (atypical hemolytic uremic syndrome, dense deposit disease, myasthenia gravis, neuromyelitis optica, multifocal motor neuropathy, age-related macular degeneration, transplant rejection)

COMPETITORS

Abbott Labs	GlaxoSmithKline
Amgen	Millennium: The Takeda
Archemix	Oncology Company
AstraZeneca	MorphoSys
Baxter International	Novo Nordisk
Celldex Therapeutics	Pfizer
ChemoCentryx	Pharming
CSL Behring	Sanofi-Aventis U.S
Dyax	XOMA
Genentech	

HISTORICAL FINANCIALS
Company Type: Public

Income Statement
FYE: December 31

	REVENUE ($ mil.)	NET INCOME ($ mil.)	NET PROFIT MARGIN	EMPLOYEES
12/10	541.0	97.0	17.9%	792
12/09	386.8	295.2	76.3%	673
12/08	259.1	33.1	12.8%	504
12/07	72.0	(92.3)	—	434
12/06	1.6	(131.5)	—	296
Annual Growth	**328.8%**	**—**	**—**	**27.9%**

2010 Year-End Financials
Debt ratio: 0.5%
Return on equity: 11.3%
Cash ($ mil.): 267.1
Current ratio: 4.67
Long-term debt ($ mil.): 4.5
No. of shares (mil.): 183.0
Dividends
  Yield: —
  Payout: —
Market value ($ mil.): 7,369.8

	STOCK PRICE ($) FY Close	P/E High/Low		PER SHARE ($) Earnings	Dividends	Book Value
12/10	40.28	80	43	0.52	0.00	4.70
12/09	24.41	15	9	1.63	0.00	3.87
12/08	18.09	123	63	0.19	0.00	1.58
12/07	18.76	—	—	(0.63)	0.00	0.68
12/06	10.10	—	—	(1.04)	0.00	0.98
Annual Growth	**41.3%**	**—**	**—**	**—**	**—**	**48.0%**

Alexza

Alexza Pharmaceuticals has found that its inhalation technologies can lead to swifter drug absorption. That is the basis for the company's primary product, Staccato inhalers, which it is developing to treat central nervous system (CNS) disorders. The inhalers contain a heating element coated with a thin layer of medicine. Before use, the patient triggers the heating element, which vaporizes the medicine, allowing the patient to inhale it. The medicine is then rapidly absorbed through the lungs at a rate typically faster than oral and intravenous applications. Alexza Pharmaceuticals targets neurological disorders including addiction and anxiety.

The company's lead drug candidates include Staccato loxapine, which is in FDA review stages to treat acute agitation in schizophrenia or bipolar patients, and Staccato nicotine, which aims to help smokers quit. Another product, Staccato zaleplon, works to treat insomnia. Other candidates in earlier or inactive stages of development include Staccato alprazolam for panic attacks and a low-dose version of Staccato loxapine for migraines.

The company had formerly been developing Staccato loxapine with Valeant Pharmaceuticals (formerly Biovail), but that partnership ended in 2010 when Valeant decided the program no longer fit with its strategic direction. Alexza is going forward with seeking FDA approval for Staccato loxapine, but it is also on the hunt for a new partner to help it commercialize the drug worldwide.

Alexza formed a new partnership with Cypress Bioscience in 2010 to work together on the development of Staccato nicotine. Cypress licensed development and commercialization rights to the drug for some $5 million and will market the drug if it receives regulatory approval.

In 2009 Alexza acquired former development partner Symphony Allegro from investment group Symphony Capital to gain full rights to certain development candidates. Symphony Capital gained a minority stake in Alexza through the deal.

As with most other development-stage drug firms, Alexza has yet to record a profit. The company expects to continue to incur losses until it is able to usher at least one of its products through clinical trials, FDA approval, and commercialization processes.

As such, the company relies on funding from its partners to support its R&D programs and to help it expand its development pipeline. As such, the loss of a partner can have a harsh impact on the firm's operations; for instance, in 2007 when its partnership to develop a pain drug with Endo Pharmaceuticals ended, Alexza had to cut about one-third of its workforce and narrow its R&D pipeline to focus on core product candidates.

Alexza also completed an initial public offering in 2006 to raise additional funds to support its clinical studies. The firm was originally founded in 2000 as FaxMed.

EXECUTIVES

President, CEO, and Director, Thomas B. King, age 56, $987,637 total compensation
VP Commercial Manufacturing, Joseph L. Baker, age 56
VP Global Supply Chain and Sustainment Engineering, Christopher Kurtz, age 44
VP Product Research and Development, Peter D. Noymer, age 44
VP Finance, Controller, and Principal Accounting Officer, Mark K. Oki
VP Human Resources, Emily Lee Kelley, age 53
VP Technology Outlicensing, Jeffrey S. (Jeff) Williams, age 46
VP Clinical Operations, Robert S. Fishman, age 49
VP Quality, Carlos A. Parra, age 58
VP International Development Operations, Anthony (Tony) Clarke, age 55
VP Quality, Darl S. Moreland
SVP Research and Development, James V. (Jim) Cassella, age 56, $691,559 total compensation
SVP Operations and Manufacturing, Michael J. Simms, age 49, $514,499 total compensation
Director Business Development, Tatjana Naranda
SVP, CFO, and General Counsel, August J. Moretti, age 60, $629,028 total compensation
Auditors: Ernst & Young LLP

LOCATIONS

HQ: Alexza Pharmaceuticals, Inc.
2091 Stierlin Ct., Mountain View, CA 94043
Phone: 650-944-7000   **Fax:** 650-944-7999
Web: www.alexza.com

COMPETITORS

A.P. Pharma	Cedarburg Hauser
Abbott Labs	Cephalon
Alkermes plc	Consort Medical
Altea Therapeutics	DURECT
Aradigm	Eli Lilly
AstraZeneca	Janssen
Pharmaceuticals	Pharmaceuticals
BioDelivery Sciences	MannKind
International	Par Pharmaceuti
Bristol-Myers Squibb	

HISTORICAL FINANCIALS

Company Type: Public

Income Statement   FYE: December 31

	REVENUE ($ mil.)	NET INCOME ($ mil.)	NET PROFIT MARGIN	EMPLOYEES
12/10	42.9	(1.5)	—	97
12/09	9.5	(103.6)	—	90
12/08	0.5	(58.5)	—	111
12/06	1.0	(41.8)	—	141
12/05	2.2	(32.4)	—	120
Annual Growth	**81.1%**	—	—	**(4.2%)**

2010 Year-End Financials

Debt ratio: —
Return on equity: —
Cash ($ mil.): 13.7
Current ratio: 1.23
Long-term debt ($ mil.): —
No. of shares (mil.): 59.8
Dividends
  Yield: —
  Payout: —
Market value ($ mil.): 74.7

	STOCK PRICE ($) FY Close	P/E High/Low	Earnings	PER SHARE ($) Dividends	Book Value
12/10	1.25	— —	(0.03)	0.00	0.21
12/09	2.40	— —	(2.68)	0.00	(0.14)
12/08	3.17	— —	(1.81)	0.00	1.03
12/06	8.09	— —	(1.58)	0.00	2.45
12/05	11.39	— —	(2.13)	0.00	2.09
Annual Growth	**(42.4%)**	— —	—	—	**(44.0%)**

ALJ Regional Holdings

ALJ Regional Holdings owns a steel mini-mill in Kentucky, which it acquired in 2005. The mill is operated by Kentucky Electric Steel, which produces bar flat products that it sells to service centers as well as makers of truck trailers, steel springs, and cold drawn bars. Kentucky Electric Steel produces steel in both Merchant Bar Quality and Special Bar Quality. The company also recycles steel from scrap to produce steel. Kentucky Electric Steel operates mainly in the US, Canada, and Mexico.

EXECUTIVES

President and CEO, John Scheel, age 55
CFO and Secretary, Rob Christ
Auditors: Mountjoy & Bressler, LLP

LOCATIONS

HQ: ALJ Regional Holdings, Inc.
244 Madison Ave., PMB #358, New York, NY 10016
Phone: 212-883-0083   **Fax:** 212-622-7301

HISTORICAL FINANCIALS

Company Type: Public

Income Statement   FYE: September 30

	REVENUE ($ mil.)	NET INCOME ($ mil.)	NET PROFIT MARGIN	EMPLOYEES
09/07	150.9	6.6	4.4%	149
09/06	139.8	2.4	1.7%	146
09/05	69.2	(3.4)	—	143
09/03*	9.2	(3.1)	—	153
06/02	33.1	(20.5)	—	245
Annual Growth	**35.4%**	—	—	**(9.5%)**

*Fiscal year change

Debt ratio: —
Return on equity: —
Cash ($ mil.): 13.7
Current ratio: 1.23
Long-term debt ($ mil.): —
No. of shares (mil.): 59.8
Dividends
  Yield: —
  Payout: —
Market value ($ mil.): 74.7

Alliance Holdings GP

When it comes to coal mining, it takes more than one company to make an Alliance. Alliance Holdings GP owns Alliance Resource Management GP, which is the managing general partner of coal mining company Alliance Resource Partners, L.P.

That company has eight coal mining complexes in Illinois, Indiana, Kentucky, and Maryland, plus other coal interests in West Virginia. Alliance Holdings GP generates revenue from its general partnership interest and its 42% ownership stake in Alliance Resource Partners, L.P. The Alliance companies have been assembled by Joseph Craft III, who is chairman, president, CEO, and majority owner of Alliance Holdings GP.

EXECUTIVES

Chairman, President, and CEO, Joseph W. Craft III, age 60, $516,287 total compensation
EVP and Director, Charles R. Wesley, age 56, $644,316 total compensation
EVP Marketing, Alliance Resources Management, Robert G. Sachse, age 62, $767,017 total compensation
SVP and COO, Thomas M. Wynne, age 54
SVP and CFO, Brian L. Cantrell, age 51, $676,041 total compensation
SVP, General Counsel, and Secretary, R. Eberley Davis, age 54, $716,555 total compensation
Auditors: Deloitte & Touche LLP

LOCATIONS

HQ: Alliance Holdings GP, L.P.
1717 S. Boulder Ave., Ste. 400, Tulsa, OK 74119
Phone: 918-295-1415   **Fax:** 918-295-7361
Web: www.ahgp.com

2009 Sales

	$ mil.	% of total
Illinois Basin	883.8	71
Central Appalachia	181.0	14
Northern Appalachia	148.3	12
Corporate, other	40.0	3
Adjustments	(22.5)	-
Total	**1,230.6**	**100**

PRODUCTS/OPERATIONS

2009 Sales

	$ mil.	% of total
Coal	1,163.9	94
Transportation	45.7	4
Other	21.0	2
Total	**1,230.6**	**100**

COMPETITORS

Alpha Natural Resources	International Coal Group
Arch Coal	James River Coal
CONSOL Energy	Peabody Energy
Drummond Company	

HISTORICAL FINANCIALS

Company Type: Public

Income Statement   FYE: December 31

	REVENUE ($ mil.)	NET INCOME ($ mil.)	NET PROFIT MARGIN	EMPLOYEES
12/10	1,609.7	174.3	10.8%	2,487
12/09	1,230.6	114.2	9.3%	2,230
12/08	1,156.1	81.2	7.0%	2,955
12/07	1,033.0	87.9	8.5%	2,600
12/06	967.2	85.7	8.9%	2,500
Annual Growth	**13.6%**	**19.4%**	—	**(0.1%)**

2010 Year-End Financials

Debt ratio: —
Return on equity: —
Cash ($ mil.): 342.2
Current ratio: 3.26
Long-term debt ($ mil.): 704.2
No. of shares (mil.): 59.9
Dividends
  Yield: 3.9%
  Payout: 65.3%
Market value ($ mil.): 2,881.4

	STOCK PRICE ($) FY Close	P/E High/Low		PER SHARE ($) Earnings	Dividends	Book Value
12/10	48.13	17	9	2.91	1.90	(0.00)
12/09	27.41	15	7	1.91	1.68	(0.00)
12/08	14.80	23	7	1.36	1.32	(0.00)
12/07	23.73	23	14	1.47	1.03	4.39
12/06	19.76	17	12	1.55	0.34	3.80
Annual Growth	24.9%	—	—	17.1%	53.8%	—

Alliance Resource

Coal is the main resource of Alliance Resource Partners. The company has nine underground coal mining complexes in Illinois, Indiana, Kentucky, Maryland, Pennsylvania, and West Virginia. Another mine is under construction in West Virginia. Alliance controls about 650 million tons of reserves. The company produces about 25 million tons of coal annually, nearly all of which is sold to electric utilities. President and CEO Joseph Craft III controls a more than 40% stake in Alliance Resource Partners. Craft, a coal industry veteran, owns his stake in Alliance Resource Partners through Alliance Holdings GP, a company he controls that went public in 2006.

Despite a decrease in sales and production volume in 2009, Alliance Resource Partners showed a significant gain in both revenues and net income over the previous year. Higher average sales prices and significantly lower operating costs kept the bottom line in good shape.

EXECUTIVES

Chairman, John P. Neafsey, age 70
President, CEO, and Director, Joseph W. Craft III, age 60, $516,287 total compensation
EVP Marketing, Robert G. Sachse, age 62, $767,017 total compensation
EVP and Director, Charles R. Wesley, age 56, $644,316 total compensation
SVP and COO, Thomas M. Wynne, age 54
SVP and CFO, Brian L. Cantrell, age 51, $676,041 total compensation
SVP, General Counsel, and Secretary, R. Eberley Davis, age 54, $716,555 total compensation
Auditors: Deloitte & Touche LLP

LOCATIONS

HQ: Alliance Resource Partners, L.P.
1717 S. Boulder Ave., Ste. 400, Tulsa, OK 74119
Phone: 918-295-7600   **Fax:** 918-295-7358
Web: www.arlp.com

PRODUCTS/OPERATIONS

2009 Sales

	$ mil.	% of total
Coal sales	1,163.9	94
Transportation	45.7	4
Other	21.4	2
Total	1,231.0	100

2009 Sales

	$ mil.	% of total
Illinois Basin	848.1	69
Central Appalachia	179.6	15
Northern Appalachia	139.7	11
Other & corporate	40.4	3
Adjustments	23.2	2
Total	1,231.0	100

COMPETITORS

Alpha Natural Resources	International Coal Group
Arch Coal	James River Coal
CONSOL Energy	Peabody Energy
Drummond Company	

HISTORICAL FINANCIALS

Company Type: Public

Income Statement

FYE: December 31

	REVENUE ($ mil.)	NET INCOME ($ mil.)	NET PROFIT MARGIN	EMPLOYEES
12/10	1,610.1	321.0	19.9%	3,558
12/09	1,231.0	192.2	15.6%	3,090
12/08	1,156.5	134.2	11.6%	2,955
12/07	1,033.3	170.4	16.5%	2,600
12/06	967.6	172.9	17.9%	2,500
Annual Growth	13.6%	16.7%	—	9.2%

2010 Year-End Financials

Debt ratio: —
Return on equity: —
Cash ($ mil.): 339.6
Current ratio: 3.26
Long-term debt ($ mil.): 706.1

No. of shares (mil.): 36.7
Dividends
  Yield: 4.9%
  Payout: 48.0%
Market value ($ mil.): 2,414.5

	STOCK PRICE ($) FY Close	P/E High/Low		PER SHARE ($) Earnings	Dividends	Book Value
12/10	65.76	10	6	6.68	3.20	(0.00)
12/09	43.37	15	8	3.00	2.95	(0.00)
12/08	26.88	24	7	2.41	2.53	(0.00)
12/07	36.27	15	10	3.05	2.20	8.68
12/06	34.52	14	11	3.03	1.92	6.82
Annual Growth	17.5%	—	—	21.9%	13.6%	—

Allied First Bancorp

Allied First Bancorp is the holding company for Allied First Bank, which has a single suburban Chicago location in Oswego, Illinois. The bank offers standard deposit products such as checking and savings accounts, money market accounts, and CDs, in addition to credit and debit cards. One- to four-family residential mortgages account for more than 60% of its loan portfolio; commercial and industrial loans, consumer loans, and commercial mortgages round out its lending activities. The bank offers insurance and investments through an agreement with Smith Barney, a unit of Citigroup.

EXECUTIVES

Chairman, John G. Maxwell Jr., age 66
President, CEO, and Director, Kenneth L. Bertrand, age 49
VP, Operations, Allied First Bank, Eugene M. O'Sullivan, age 53
VP and CFO, Brian K. Weiss, age 39
VP, Lending, Allied First Bank, Mitchell D. Trier, age 45
Auditors:

LOCATIONS

HQ: Allied First Bancorp, Inc.
3201 Orchard Rd., Oswego, IL 60543
Phone: 630-554-8899   **Fax:** 630-554-3311
Web: www.alliedfirst.com

COMPETITORS

Fifth Third	Old Second Bancorp
Harris	TCF Financial
JPMorgan Chase	U.S. Bancorp

HISTORICAL FINANCIALS

Company Type: Public

Income Statement

FYE: June 30

	ASSETS ($ mil.)	NET INCOME ($ mil.)	INCOME AS % OF ASSETS	EMPLOYEES
06/07	160.6	0.3	0.2%	38
06/06	165.2	0.4	0.2%	33
06/05	143.6	0.2	0.1%	33
06/04	132.8	1.1	0.8%	26
06/03	101.6	0.4	0.4%	23
Annual Growth	12.1%	(6.9%)	—	13.4%

2007 Year-End Financials

Equity as % of assets: 6.69%
Return on assets: 0.2%
Return on equity: 3.0%
Long-term debt ($ mil.): 36.0
No. of shares (mil.): —

Dividends
  Yield: —
  Payout: —
Market value ($ mil.): —
Sales ($ mil.): 11.5

	STOCK PRICE ($) FY Close	P/E High/Low		PER SHARE ($) Earnings	Dividends	Book Value
06/07	16.10	29	25	0.63	0.00	(0.00)
06/06	16.40	27	23	0.69	0.00	(0.00)
06/05	18.00	48	31	0.45	0.00	(0.00)
06/04	14.75	9	7	2.01	0.00	(0.00)
06/03	13.25	21	17	0.64	0.00	(0.00)
Annual Growth	5.0%	—	—	(0.4%)	—	—

Allin

Allin wants to be an all-in-one information technology (IT) provider on the high seas and dry land. The company (pronounced "all in") offers interactive media development and integration for cruise lines, technology infrastructure services, and systems integration. The company uses video equipment and services provided by On Command for its interactive TV operations. Formerly a provider of Microsoft-focused services, the company sold that business to PC maker Dell in 2009. With warrants, Pittsburgh investor Henry Posner controls just over 50% of Allin.

Dell paid $12 million to acquire Allin's business units in Philadelphia, Pittsburgh, San Jose, and Walnut Creek, California.

EXECUTIVES

President and CEO, Richard W. (Rich) Talarico, age 53
VP Finance, CFO, Treasurer, and Secretary, Dean C. Praskach, age 51
Managing Director, Boston, Brian Carpenter
Managing Director, Florida, Brian Blair
Auditors:

LOCATIONS

HQ: Allin Corporation
381 Mansfield Ave., Ste. 400, Pittsburgh, PA 15220
Phone: 412-928-8800   **Fax:** 412-928-0887
Web: www.allin.com

2007 Sales

	$ mil.	% of total
US		
Northeastern	11.5	46
Western	5.7	22
Southern	1.7	7
Midwestern	0.5	2
Europe	5.1	21
Other regions	0.3	1
At sea	0.3	1
Total	**25.1**	**100**

PRODUCTS/OPERATIONS

2007 Sales

	$ mil.	% of total
Collaborative solutions	9.6	38
Systems integration	4.8	19
Business process	2.9	12
Technology infrastructure	2.4	10
Interactive media	2.4	10
Information system product sales	1.1	4
Other	1.9	7
Total	**25.1**	**100**

COMPETITORS

Accenture	Deloitte
Capgemini North	ePartners
America	Hewlett-Packard
Computer Sciences	IBM
Corp.	

HISTORICAL FINANCIALS

Company Type: Public

Income Statement

FYE: December 31

	REVENUE ($ mil.)	NET INCOME ($ mil.)	NET PROFIT MARGIN	EMPLOYEES
12/07	25.1	3.3	13.1%	167
12/06	19.0	1.9	10.0%	153
12/05	14.3	(1.0)	—	135
12/04	12.6	0.3	2.4%	101
12/03	12.9	0.8	6.2%	84
Annual Growth	**18.1%**	**42.5%**	**—**	**18.7%**

2007 Year-End Financials

Debt ratio: —
Return on equity: (241.4)%
Cash ($ mil.): 0.9
Current ratio: 1.20
Long-term debt ($ mil.): —

No. of shares (mil.): —
Dividends
  Yield: —
  Payout: —
Market value ($ mil.): —

	STOCK PRICE ($) FY Close	P/E High/Low		PER SHARE ($) Earnings	Dividends	Book Value
12/07	0.98	6	3	0.17	0.00	(0.00)
12/06	0.48	16	4	0.06	0.00	(0.00)
12/05	0.53	—	—	(0.26)	0.00	(0.00)
12/04	0.26	—	—	(0.07)	0.00	(0.00)
12/03	0.38	58	14	0.01	0.00	(0.00)
Annual Growth	**26.7%**	—	—	**103.1%**	**—**	**—**

Allos Therapeutics

Drug developer Allos Therapeutics is looking for the next big breakthrough in the fight against cancer. The company's first FDA-approved drug, Folotyn (pralatrexate), was launched commercially in the US in 2010 to treat a relatively rare blood cancer called peripheral T-cell lymphoma (PTCL).

Allos Therapeutics is also investigating the compound as a potential treatment in other oncology applications, including additional forms of lymphoma; Folotyn is also in clinical trial and research studies for non-small cell lung cancer (NSCLC) and bladder and breast cancers.

Allos Therapeutics had agreed to be acquired by AMAG Pharmaceuticals in mid-2011 in a $686 million deal; however, the companies terminated the merger agreement later in the year after AMAG's shareholders failed to approve the transaction. AMAG focuses on treatments for iron deficiency anemia, and the acquisition would have created a company with a more diversified product base and development pipeline.

Shrugging off the failed merger, Allos Therapeutics has stated its intention to focus on growing sales of Folotyn in the US, pursuing further development of the product for additional indications, and gaining EU approval for Folotyn.

Allos Therapeutics received FDA approval for Folotyn in 2009 and began selling the product through wholesale distributors the following year. The company has hired on a force of internal sales representatives to market the drug to oncologists across the US. In early 2011, the company formed a collaboration with Mundipharma International to market Folotyn in markets outside North America.

The company is also on the lookout for other oncology compounds to in-license or acquire. It discontinued its development of its RH1 candidate, a potential chemotherapy agent for treatment of non-Hodgkin's lymphoma, in 2009 to focus on its more promising Folotyn program.

Private equity firm Warburg Pincus owns about one-fourth of Allos Therapeutics.

EXECUTIVES

Chairman, Stephen J. Hoffman, age 57
President, CEO, and Director, Paul L. Berns, age 44, $2,091,600 total compensation
EVP and Chief Medical Officer, Charles Morris
VP Pharmaceutical Operations, Bruce K. Bennett Jr., age 59
VP Sales and Marketing, Michael Schick
VP Corporate Development, Jeremy Bender
VP Finance, Treasurer, and Assistant Secretary, David C. Clark, age 42, $466,600 total compensation
VP Corporate Communications and Investor Relations, Monique M. Greer, age 52
SVP Corporate Development, Bruce A. Goldsmith
SVP, General Counsel, and Secretary, Marc H. Graboyes, age 41, $719,000 total compensation
Senior Manager Human Resources, Vicki Baca
Auditors: PricewaterhouseCoopers LLP

LOCATIONS

HQ: Allos Therapeutics, Inc.
  11080 CirclePoint Rd., Ste. 200, Westminster, CO 80020
Phone: 303-426-6262   **Fax:** 303-426-4731
Web: www.allos.com

COMPETITORS

Amgen	GlaxoSmithKline
BioCryst	ImmunoGe
Pharmaceuticals	Johnson & Johnson
Biogen Idec	Millennium: The Takeda
Bristol-Myers Squibb	Oncology Company
Cell Therapeutics	Novartis
Cephalon	Pfizer
Eli Lilly	Poniard
Genentech	Pharmaceuticals
Genmab	Sanofi
Genzyme	

HISTORICAL FINANCIALS

Company Type: Public

Income Statement

FYE: December 31

	REVENUE ($ mil.)	NET INCOME ($ mil.)	NET PROFIT MARGIN	EMPLOYEES
12/10	35.2	(77.4)	—	156
12/09	3.6	(73.6)	—	170
12/99	0.1	(11.3)	—	27
12/97	0.0	(6.5)	—	0
Annual Growth	**—**	**—**		**17.3%**

2010 Year-End Financials

Debt ratio: —
Return on equity: —
Cash ($ mil.): 48.2
Current ratio: 5.02
Long-term debt ($ mil.): —

No. of shares (mil.): 105.5
Dividends
  Yield: —
  Payout: —
Market value ($ mil.): 486.3

	STOCK PRICE ($) FY Close	P/E High/Low		PER SHARE ($) Earnings	Dividends	Book Value
12/10	4.61	—	—	(0.74)	0.00	0.93
12/09	6.58	—	—	(0.81)	0.00	1.53
12/99	6.12	—	—	(0.69)	0.00	0.98
12/97	6.29	—	—	(0.60)	0.00	0.79
00/00	5.85	—	—	(0.55)	0.00	0.53
Annual Growth	**(5.8%)**	—	—	**—**	**—**	**15.2%**

Almost Family

If you live in California and you're worried about Mom's failing health back in Florida, you could call Almost Family. With its home health nursing services, Almost Family offers senior citizens in 11 states (including Florida) an alternative to institutional care. Its Visiting Nurse unit provides skilled nursing care at home under a variety of names, including Apex, Caretenders, Community Home Health, and Mederi-Caretenders. Its Personal Care Services segment, operating under the Almost Family banner, offers custodial care, such as housekeeping, meal preparation, and medication management. Almost Family operates 90 Visiting Nurse agencies and more than 20 Personal Care Services locations.

The company's services are carried out by nurses, speech and occupational therapists, medical social workers, and home health aides. The services provided to a patient are determined by physician's prescribed plan of care — generally issued upon the patient's discharge from a hospital.

Payments from Medicare account for 90% of revenue in the Visiting Nurse segment, making Almost Family sensitive to any changes in Medicare reimbursement policies. The Personal Care segment, only receives 70% of its revenues from Medicare payments, with the balance coming from private insurance, private pay, and Medicaid. This diversification of reimbursement risk is intentional, but the company is also confident that its home-based services will always be lower in cost than institutional care.

Whereas the Visiting Nurse segment brings in most of the money for the company, Almost Family's strategy has been to grow that part of the business through a steady stream of acquisitions. During 2008 the company acquired nearly a dozen visiting nurse branch locations, adding to its market presence in Florida, Connecticut, and Ohio, as well as marking its entry into the New Jersey and Pennsylvania skilled nursing markets. Acquisitions in 2009 and 2010 brought in the home health agencies affiliated with Florida-based Central Florida Health Alliance, and a small home health agency in Ohio. In 2011 it paid some $32.5 million to acquire Cambridge Home Health Care, deepening its coverage in Ohio and Pennsylvania.

To continue with its strategy of growing by buying (which it maintains it does), Almost Family intends to seek additional capital investments.

HISTORY

Almost Family was founded in 1976 as National Health Industries, a Louisville, Kentucky-based home health care company. After William Yarmuth became president in 1981, he expanded the company into such service areas as home infusion and home medical equipment.

The company became Caretenders Health in 1985, and in 1991 the company merged with Senior Service Corporation, a small, public adult day care services company. The company further expanded the range of services it offered to the elderly through its home health care operations. It established beachheads in new geographic markets by opening home health offices (or buying them), and then adding day care centers. It also bought some existing care centers.

The company grew energetically following its decision to specialize in elder care. It made three acquisitions in 1997 and surpassed that feat by closing on four acquisitions in little over a month in early 1998. The company lost one of its revenue streams that year: Two home health agencies in the Louisville area that had been managed by Caretenders were sold by their owner, Columbia/HCA (now HCA). Caretenders sued Columbia/HCA for breach of contract and in 1999 won a $1.5 million settlement.

That year the company also sharpened its focus by selling its product operations (including infusion therapy, respiratory, and medical equipment) to Lincare Holdings, but decided not to discontinue its visiting nurses services.

In 2000 the company changed its name to Almost Family to underscore its focus on adult day care. The following year it bought back the 23% stake that rehabilitation titan HEALTHSOUTH had maintained in the company.

Almost Family acquired one adult day care center per year during 1999, 2000, and 2001. In July 2002 the company announced it had completed the acquisition of Medlink of Ohio, a provider of home health care services that operated in Cleveland and Akron, Ohio.

To expand its visiting nurse segment, Almost Family acquired two home health agencies in 2005: Florida Palliative Home Care and Bradenton Florida Home Health. Also in 2005 the company sold its adult day care division to Active Services for $15 million.

In 2006 it acquired several home health agencies in Florida, including 21 locations owned by Mederi in Florida, Missouri, and Illinois for some $20 million.

EXECUTIVES

Chairman, President, and CEO, William B. Yarmuth, age 58, $1,083,295 total compensation
VP and General Counsel, Jerry Perchik
VP and CIO, Michael Spurlock
VP Reimbursement, Cathy Pedigo
VP Operations, VN Northeast Region, Ray Rasa

VP Operations, VN North Central Florida Region, Nancy Ralston, age 51
VP Personal Care Operations, Carla J. Hengst, age 55
VP Operations, VN Florida Region, Vicki Suplizio
VP Human Resources, Mark Sutton
VP and Chief Accounting Officer, John Walker, age 52
VP Operations, VN North Region, Susan Long
VP Operations, PC Operations, David Pruitt, age 47
VP Sales and Marketing, James Spriggs
VP Group Living Facilities, Michael Moses
SVP Administration, Patrick Todd Lyles, age 49, $447,216 total compensation
SVP Operations, Phillis D. Montville, age 62
SVP Operations, VN North Region, Anne T. Liechty, age 58, $357,459 total compensation
SVP, CFO, Secretary, and Treasurer, C. Steven (Steve) Guenthner, age 50, $554,928 total compensation
SVP Sales and Clinical Programs, Cathy S. Newhouse, $307,493 total compensation
Auditors: Ernst & Young LLP

LOCATIONS

HQ: Almost Family, Inc.
9510 Ormsby Station Rd., Ste. 300, Louisville, KY 40223
Phone: 502-891-1000   **Fax:** 502-891-8067
Web: www.almostfamily.com

2010 Branch Locations

care	Visiting nurses	Personal care
Florida	42	7
Kentucky	17	4
Ohio	7	4
Connecticut	4	7
Illinois	4	-
Missouri	4	-
New Jersey	4	-
Massachusetts	3	1
Alabama	2	-
Indiana	2	-
Pennsylvania	1	-
Total	**90**	**23**

PRODUCTS/OPERATIONS

2010 Revenue

	$ mil.	% of total
Visiting Nurses	294.9	87
Personal Care	42.0	13
Total	**336.9**	**100**

2010 Revenue

	% of total
Medicare	80
Medicaid & other government programs	15
Insurance & private pay	5
Total	**100**

Selected Agencies

Almost Family Medlink
Apex Home Healthcare Services
Better@Home
Cambridge Home Health Care
Caretenders
Community Home Health
Florida Home Health
Mederi Caretenders
Patient Care
Quality of Life

COMPETITORS

Amedisys	LHC Group
Apria Healthcare	Manor Care
Gentiva	National Home Health
Girling Health Care	NHC
Home Instead	

HISTORICAL FINANCIALS

Company Type: Public

Income Statement

FYE: December 31

	REVENUE ($ mil.)	NET INCOME ($ mil.)	NET PROFIT MARGIN	EMPLOYEES
12/10	336.9	30.7	9.1%	6,400
12/09	297.8	24.6	8.3%	6,123
12/08	212.6	16.3	7.7%	5,700
12/07	132.1	7.6	5.8%	4,800
12/06	91.8	4.2	4.6%	4,000
Annual Growth	**38.4%**	**64.4%**	**—**	**12.5%**

2010 Year-End Financials

Debt ratio: 0.7%	No. of shares (mil.): 9.2
Return on equity: 16.9%	Dividends
Cash ($ mil.): 47.9	Yield: —
Current ratio: 3.61	Payout: —
Long-term debt ($ mil.): 1.3	Market value ($ mil.): 355.0

	STOCK PRICE ($) FY Close	P/E High/Low		PER SHARE ($) Earnings	Dividends	Book Value
12/10	38.42	13	7	3.28	0.00	19.72
12/09	39.53	17	5	2.86	0.00	16.28
12/08	44.98	25	8	2.16	0.00	11.65
12/07	19.43	20	10	1.36	0.00	6.41
12/06	21.91	27	9	0.80	0.00	5.74
Annual Growth	**15.1%**	**—**	**—**	**42.3%**	**—**	**36.1%**

Alphatec Spine

Alphatec Holdings aims to help people stand up straight and keep moving. The company develops and manufactures products used to treat spinal disorders including stenosis and degenerating disks. Through its Alphatec Spine subsidiary, the company makes a variety of FDA-approved products primarily for the spine fusion market in the US. Its product line includes grafting materials, spinal implant systems, and surgical instruments. Alphatec markets its products to surgeons through a network of independent but exclusive distributors, as well as a direct sales force. The company develops its products through its manufacturing facilities in California and France.

In addition to the titanium, ceramic, and plastic products it manufactures, the company sells allograft (from human tissue) spacers and bone grafting materials. Other products include bone cement and wound barriers. Moving beyond its traditional screws and plates, the company's new product development also includes stem cell-based products to speed up fusion and healing.

Alphatec Spine is concentrating its manufacturing efforts on creating products designed to treat spinal problems related to aging. As the Baby Boomers age and more Americans grapple with obesity, their backs are more likely to seize up, compress, or crumble, giving Alphatec a growing population to serve. The company also intends to continue developing new products that are less invasive than existing therapies and to gain access to new products through licensing agreements with other developers.

Alphatec Spine already had a presence in Europe, but in late 2009 increased its global presence considerably with the buy of Scient'x Groupe SAS, a spinal implant manufacturer based in France.

Scient'x distributes its products through sales forces in France, Italy, and the UK and uses independent distributors in 45 other countries. Beyond Europe, the company is also planning to expand into Asia and South America as its products receive regulatory clearance in each country. The company's Alphatec Pacific subsidiary sells spine fusion and orthopedic trauma devices in Japan.

The Scient'x acquisition was paid for with stock traded to private equity investment company HealthpointCapital Partners. HealthpointCapital now owns some 38% of the company and holds two seats on its board of directors.

EXECUTIVES

Chairman, Mortimer Berkowitz III, age 57
President, Alphatec Pacific, Mitsuo Asai, age 55, $412,830 total compensation
President, CEO, and Director, Dirk Kuyper, age 54, $871,444 total compensation
VP Operations, Kermit P. Stott, age 58
VP and General Manager, Europe, Peter Kohlbecher
VP Sales, Stephen A. Lubischer, age 48, $504,927 total compensation
VP Human Resources, Susan L. Johnson
VP Research and Development, Jens P. (J. P.) Timm, age 36, $543,620 total compensation
VP Accounting and Corporate Controller, Brandi Roberts
VP Clinical, Quality, and Regulatory, Michael J. Sarrasin
VP and General Manager, Latin America, Armin Weichert
VP, CFO, and Treasurer, Michael O Neill
VP Product Marketing, Kristine M. (Kris) Jacques
VP, General Counsel, and Secretary, Ebun S. Garner, age 39, $342,348 total compensation
VP Corporate Accounts, Gary Fredericks
SVP Global Human Resources, Heather Rider
SVP Strategic Initiatives, Peter C. Wulff, age 52, $454,530 total compensation
Auditors: Ernst & Young LLP

LOCATIONS

HQ: Alphatec Holdings, Inc.
5818 El Camino Real, Carlsbad, CA 92008
Phone: 760-431-9286   **Fax:** 760-431-9823
Web: www.alphatecspine.com

2009 Sales

	$ mil.	% of total
US	104.5	79
Asia	23.5	18
Europe	4.1	3
Total	**132.1**	**100**

PRODUCTS/OPERATIONS

Selected Products

CervicoThoracic
  DeltaLoc Reveal
  Solanas
  Trestle
ThoracoLumbar
  Anterior Lumbar Plate
  ILLICO MIS
  OsseoScrew
  Zodiac
  CORE
Interbody/VBR
  Cervical Novel XS & Novel CIS
  Novel Corpectomy
  ALIF Novel ALS
  PLIF Novel SD & LCC
  TLIF Novel TL & SD
Biologics
  AlphaGRAFT Demineralized
  Bone Matrix

AlphaGRAFT Profuse
AlphaGRAFT Structural
Allografts
Minimally Invasive Solutions
  ILLICO Retractor
  ILLICO Posterior Fusion
  GLIF
Vertebral Compression Fractures
  OsseoFix

COMPETITORS

Biomet	Orthofix
DePuy Spine	Stryker
Medtronic Sofamor	Synthes
Danek	Zimmer Holdings
NuVasive	

HISTORICAL FINANCIALS

Company Type: Public

Income Statement

FYE: December 31

	REVENUE ($ mil.)	NET INCOME ($ mil.)	NET PROFIT MARGIN	EMPLOYEES
12/10	171.6	(14.4)	—	460
12/09	132.2	(13.3)	—	300
12/08	101.3	(29.3)	—	290
12/07	80.0	(20.2)	—	263
12/06	74.0	(25.8)	—	295
Annual Growth	**23.4%**	**—**	**—**	**11.7%**

2010 Year-End Financials

Debt ratio: 12.2%	No. of shares (mil.): 89.0
Return on equity: —	Dividends
Cash ($ mil.): 23.2	Yield: —
Current ratio: 2.82	Payout: —
Long-term debt ($ mil.): 32.5	Market value ($ mil.): 240.4

	STOCK PRICE ($) FY Close	P/E High/Low	PER SHARE ($) Earnings	Dividends	Book Value
12/10	2.70	— —	(0.18)	0.00	2.99
12/09	5.34	— —	(0.27)	0.00	1.42
12/08	2.35	— —	(0.63)	0.00	1.51
12/07	5.04	— —	(0.54)	0.00	2.01
12/06	3.73	— —	(1.07)	0.00	2.16
Annual Growth	**(7.8%)**	**— —**	**—**	**—**	**8.5%**

Altera

Altera is programmed to give you the gate — hundreds of thousands of logic gates per device. The fabless semiconductor company specializes in R&D of high-density programmable logic devices (PLDs) — integrated circuits (ICs) that OEMs program to perform logic functions in electronic systems. PLDs are an alternative to custom-designed ICs, and offer a quick, reduced-cost chip. Altera outsources fabrication of the devices to top silicon foundry TSMC. Altera PLDs are used in communications network gear, consumer electronics, and industrial equipment. PLD sales rely heavily on a network of distributors; Arrow accounts for more than 45% of sales. Customers outside the US represent more than 80% of Altera's sales.

Altera saw its nets sales rise in 2010, by about 64%. The company attributes its healthy bottom line indirectly to cost-cutting and improvements in productivity during the global financial crisis of 2009 and 2009. These measures have allowed the

company to invest in product development that it expects will bring more sales growth. The company believes that its gross margin percentage rose by 4.2 points in 2010 compared to 2009 mainly because of cuts in manufacturing expenses.

Altera has more than 13,000 customers in a variety of industries. Distributors handle +80% of the company's sales.

Altera classifies its products by life-cycle stage into New, Mainstream, and Mature and Other products. New products, which are the company's most advanced products, provide more than 40% the company's net sales. Mainstream products are of older vintage and account for about 30% of sales. Mature products, accounting for about 30% of sales, serve older systems that have endured in use.

Among the PLD types made by Altera, field-programmable gate arrays (FPGAs) are the most popular device of choice, representing more than 80% of sales in the PLD category. Complex PLDs, or CPLDs, account for more than 10% of sales in the PLD category, with other logic devices and software tools making up about 6% of the PLD category.

Offerings frequently compete with chief rival Xilinx (the two companies dominate the market for PLDs), and makers of application-specific integrated circuits (ASICs), a type of customized chip used for many of the same functions as PLDs. Altera PLDs' competitive position claims greater functionality and reduced power consumption at a lower price.

Altera made its first acquisition in more than a decade when it bought Avalon Microelectronics in late 2010 for an undisclosed amount. Avalon, based in Canada, provides wireline equipment manufacturers with optical transport network (OTN) intellectual property (IP); it is the sole supplier of Altera's 100G OTN in its FPGAs. With the acquisition, Altera will expand its portfolio of custom IP products for OTN applications.

HISTORY

Altera (short for "alterable") was formed in 1983 by a group of former Fairchild Semiconductor managers. The company introduced the world's first erasable programmable logic device (PLD) in 1984 and the first high-density PLD the following year. In 1988 Altera went public and bought a stake in Cypress Semiconductor. Altera trotted out new generations of chips in 1988, 1991, and 1992 (the company's first electrically erasable read-only memory). In 1994 it acquired Intel's PLD business, increasing its market share to 20% and adding 15 devices to its product line.

The company joined Taiwan Semiconductor Manufacturing (TSMC), Integrated Silicon Solution, and Analog Devices in 1996 to form a wafer fabrication joint venture called WaferTech. New chips in Altera's FLEX family, unveiled in 1997, expanded the company's product range into the higher-end PLD market (dominated by rival Xilinx).

In 1999 the company acquired software maker Boulder Creek Engineering, as well as Hammercores, a Canadian developer of programmable chip cores. That year the company sold its stake in Cypress. Late in 1999 longtime chairman and CEO Rodney Smith announced the search for his successor.

The next year Altera bought DesignPRO (chip cores and other technologies for optical networking) and Right Track CAD (PLD design software). Later that year the company tapped LSI Logic (now LSI Corp.) executive John Daane as CEO; Smith remained chairman. Also in 2000 the company sold its interest in WaferTech to joint-venture partner TSMC.

Smith retired as chairman in 2003; Daane succeeded him in that role as well. In 2004 Altera opened an office at the Cork Airport Business Park in Ireland to support its European customer base. The company also consolidated its product marketing and applications business groups that year.

In 2005 the Securities and Exchange Commission asked Altera to voluntarily provide information on the company's communications with stock analysts and investment firms. The request came after an equity analyst for Wells Fargo Securities reported he would stop covering the company after Altera cut off all communications to him and wouldn't let him ask questions on quarterly conference calls. Altera's CFO publicly apologized for the gaffe.

The following year the company's board set up a special committee to review Altera's practices in granting stock options from 1996 through 2000. Soon after the company received a subpoena from federal prosecutors in Northern California regarding information on stock options, and the SEC opened an informal inquiry into the same topic.

Like many other high-tech firms, Altera's special committee found there were discrepancies between the recorded dates of stock-option grants and the actual dates those options were granted. As a result, the company restated financial results from 1996 to 2005. The SEC investigation into stock-option practices ended in 2007, with the commission not taking any enforcement actions.

Rodney Smith, the company's CEO for its first 17 years of existence and its chairman for 20 years, was killed in 2007 while he was riding a bicycle on Sand Hill Road in Menlo Park, California, and was struck by an automobile. He was 67 years old.

Altera managed to increase its market share in PLDs, field-programmable gate arrays, and complex PLDs between 2004 and 2009.

EXECUTIVES

Chairman, President, and CEO, John P. Daane, age 47, $4,737,527 total compensation
VP Human Resources, Kevin H. Lyman, age 56
VP, General Counsel, and Corporate Secretary, Katherine E. Schuelke, age 48
VP Finance and Corporate Controller, James W. Callas, $462,505 total compensation
VP Investor Relations, Scott Wylie
SVP Research and Development, Misha R. Burich, age 63, $1,675,614 total compensation
SVP Worldwide Sales, George A. Papa, age 62, $1,620,613 total compensation
SVP Worldwide Operations and Engineering, William Y. Hata, age 51
SVP and CFO, Ronald J. (Ron) Pasek, age 50, $2,445,424 total compensation
SVP Business Development, Lance M. Lissner, age 61
Senior Manager Public Relations, Mark Plungy
SVP Marketing, Danny K. Biran, age 54
Senior Director Component Product Marketing, Luanne M. Schirrmeister
SVP and General Manager, Altera Penang, Jordan S. Plofsky, age 50, $1,766,300 total compensation
Auditors: PricewaterhouseCoopers LLP

LOCATIONS

HQ: Altera Corporation
101 Innovation Dr., San Jose, CA 95134-2020
Phone: 408-544-7000 **Fax:** 408-544-6408
Web: www.altera.com

2010 Sales

	$ mil.	% of total
China	635.4	32
US	327.5	17
Japan	315.8	16
Other countries	675.7	35
Total	**1,954.4**	**100**

PRODUCTS/OPERATIONS

2010 Net Sales By Vertical Market

	% of total
Telecom & wireless	44
Industrial automation, military, & automotive	21
Networking, computer, & storage	14
Other	21
Total	**100**

Selected Products

Development Tools
  Software used to design for and program programmable logic devices (PLDs; MAX+PLUS II and Quartus II lines)
Intellectual Property
  Proprietary chip core designs
Semiconductors
  Complex programmable logic devices (CPLDs; MAX 7000 series)
  Field-programmable gate arrays (FPGAs)
    Embedded intellectual property-based products
      Embedded processors (Excalibur line)
      Programmable application-specific standard products (ASSPs; Mercury line)
    General-purpose FPGAs (ACEX, APEX, Cyclone, FLEX, and Stratix lines)
  Masked devices (HardCopy; converts PLD designs into application-specific integrated circuit — or ASIC — format to reduce development time and manufacturing complexity)

COMPETITORS

Altium	Microchip Technology
Atmel	Microsemi SoC
Cypress Semiconductor	PLX Technology
eSilicon	QuickLo
Fujitsu Semiconductor	Sajan
IBM Microelectronics	Texas Instruments
Lattice Semiconductor	Toshiba Semiconductor
LSI Corp.	Xilinx
Maxim Integrated Products	

HISTORICAL FINANCIALS

Company Type: Public

Income Statement

FYE: December 31

	REVENUE ($ mil.)	NET INCOME ($ mil.)	NET PROFIT MARGIN	EMPLOYEES
12/10	1,954.4	782.9	40.1%	2,666
12/09	1,195.4	251.1	21.0%	2,551
12/08	1,367.2	359.7	26.3%	2,760
12/07	1,263.5	290.0	23.0%	2,651
12/06	1,285.5	323.2	25.1%	2,654
Annual Growth	**11.0%**	**24.8%**	**—**	**0.1%**

2010 Year-End Financials

Debt ratio: 21.5%
Return on equity: 33.7%
Cash ($ mil.): 2,765.2
Current ratio: 5.07
Long-term debt ($ mil.): 500.0
No. of shares (mil.): 319.5
Dividends
  Yield: 0.6%
  Payout: 8.8%
Market value ($ mil.): 11,367.6

	STOCK PRICE ($) FY Close	P/E High/Low		PER SHARE ($) Earnings	Dividends	Book Value
12/10	35.58	15	8	2.49	0.22	7.27
12/09	22.63	28	17	0.84	0.20	3.66
12/08	16.71	21	11	1.18	0.19	2.69
12/07	19.32	32	22	0.82	0.12	2.80
12/06	19.68	25	18	0.88	0.00	4.44
Annual Growth	**16.0%**	**—**	**—**	**29.7%**	**—**	**13.1%**

Amacore

The Amacore Group wants you to be able to see a smaller optometry bill. Amacore is a provider of non-insurance based discount plans for eyewear and eyecare services, including surgery. Amacore Group's products are marketed to individuals, families, and businesses, as well as through the company's affiliations with insurance companies and other membership groups. The company has expanded its discount program offerings to include dental, hearing, chiropractic, and other health services. It also offers traditional health plans through partnerships with insurance providers.

Amacore has made grand efforts to expand its service offerings outside of the eye care arena in recent years. It has partnered with life and health insurance companies to expand its market base, and it has upgraded its marketing and payment processing systems. The company has also made acquisitions and formed new subsidiaries to offer administrative services to other health care companies.

EXECUTIVES

CEO and Director, Jay Shafer, age 52, $381,257 total compensation
President and Director, Guy Norberg, age 51, $381,527 total compensation
President, US Health Benefits Group, Howard Knaster
VP Finance and Principal Accounting Officer, Jason Post, age 36
COO and Interim CFO, G. Scott Smith, age 59, $250,000 total compensation
Chief Marketing Officer, Bill Heneghan III
SVP Sales and Marketing, Mark Cairo
SVP, Mark Jarvis, age 51
Co-President, JRM Benefits Consultants, Jim Mignogna
Co-President, JRM Benefits Consultants, Jim Read
Auditors: Brimmer, Burek & Keelan LLP

LOCATIONS

HQ: The Amacore Group, Inc.
485 N. Keller Rd., Ste. 450, Maitland, FL 32751
Phone: 407-805-8900 **Fax:** 407-805-0045
Web: www.amacoregroup.com

COMPETITORS

Access Plans USA	HealthSCOPE Benefits
Aetna	Spectera
Assurant Health	Vertrue
Davis Vision	Vision Service Plan
EyeMed Vision Care	

HISTORICAL FINANCIALS

Company Type: Public

Income Statement
FYE: December 31

	ASSETS ($ mil.)	NET INCOME ($ mil.)	INCOME AS % OF ASSETS	EMPLOYEES
12/09	12.0	(10.7)	—	99
12/08	17.2	(33.9)	—	103
12/07	19.3	(21.2)	—	76
12/06	0.3	(1.7)	—	9
12/05	0.2	(4.4)	—	8
Annual Growth	178.3%	—	—	87.6%

2009 Year-End Financials

Equity as % of assets: (-84.32)%	Dividends
Return on assets: 10.7	Yield: —
Return on equity: —	Payout: —
Long-term debt ($ mil.): 1.8	Market value ($ mil.): 30.4
No. of shares (mil.): 1,047.9	Sales ($ mil.): 28.8

	STOCK PRICE ($) FY Close	P/E High/Low	PER SHARE ($) Earnings	Dividends	Book Value
12/09	0.03	— —	(0.02)	0.00	(0.01)
12/08	0.12	— —	(0.28)	0.00	(0.00)
12/07	0.45	— —	(0.18)	0.00	(0.00)
12/06	0.04	— —	(0.03)	0.00	(0.00)
12/05	0.05	— —	(0.13)	0.00	(0.00)
Annual Growth	(12.0%)	— —	—	—	—

AMAG Pharmaceuticals

It's rare when the illness and cure are one in the same; but in AMAG Pharmaceuticals' case, iron is the problem and the solution. The biopharmaceutical company is focused on the development and commercialization of an iron compound to treat iron deficiency anemia (IDA). Its primary money maker is its Feraheme Injection to treat IDA in patients with chronic kidney disease (CKD). AMAG sells Feraheme in the US through its own sales force; in Europe, some Asian countries, Canada, India, and Turkey through an exclusive licensing agreement with Takeda. AMAG's other product, GastroMARK, is marketed in the US, Europe, and other countries, and is used for delineating the bowel in abdominal imaging.

In a move to try to diversify its product base, AMAG agreed to buy Allos Therapeutics (maker of cancer drug Folotyn) in mid-2011 in a deal worth about $686 million; however, the deal was terminated later that year. In the midst of its negotiations with Allos Therapeutics, AMAG received a proposal from one of its minority investors, MSMB Capital Management, which sought to acquire AMAG for some $378 million. MSMB opposed the Allos transaction, believing that the company's current strategy was not beneficial to its stockholders. AMAG's board disagreed and rejected MSMB's bid, choosing instead to continue with plans to acquire Allos. Ultimately though, the Allos transaction was voted down by AMAG's shareholders.

Following the failure of the Allos deal, AMAG returned to its previous growth strategy, which hinges upon gaining approval for additional uses of Feraheme in more countries and regions. The drug is currently approved for use as an IV iron

replacement therapy in both the dialysis and non-dialysis CKD markets.

The company pours nearly all of its research and development funds into growing applications and markets for Feraheme, since the drug has seen a decline in sales in the US due to changes in the way dialysis services are reimbursed by programs such as Medicare and Medicaid. The changes make it less likely that dialysis providers would choose to use Feraheme, so AMAG expects the majority of demand for Feraheme in the US to come from the non-dialysis CKD market.

To diversify its uses, Feraheme is being tested to treat iron deficiency in a broad range of patients for whom oral iron treatments don't work including women with abnormal uterine bleeding, patients with cancer or gastrointestinal diseases, and post-partum women.

Sales of GastroMARK, on the other hand, have been stable for many years and AMAG does not expect that trend to change any time soon.

Along with Takeda, AMAG has licensing agreements with Covidien (for GastroMARK in the US), Guerbet (to sell GastroMARK in western Europe and Brazil), and 3SBio (for the sale of Feraheme in China).

EXECUTIVES

Chairman, Michael A. Narachi, age 51
President, CEO, and Director, Brian J. G. Pereira, age 53
EVP and Chief Medical Officer, Lee F. Allen, age 59, $1,097,043 total compensation
EVP and Chief Commercial Officer, Gary J. Zieziula, age 57
EVP, CFO, and Chief Business Officer, David A. Arkowitz, age 49, $1,118,713 total compensation
SVP Business Development and Corporate Planning, Christopher G. (Chris) White, age 49
SVP Legal Affairs and General Counsel, Joseph L. Farmer, age 39
Senior Director Corporate Communications and Investor Relations, Kristen Galfetti
SVP Commercial Operations, Timothy G. Healey, age 45, $1,262,376 total compensation
Auditors: PricewaterhouseCoopers LLP

LOCATIONS

HQ: AMAG Pharmaceuticals, Inc.
100 Hayden Ave., Lexington, MA 02421
Phone: 617-498-3300   **Fax:** 617-499-3361
Web: www.amagpharma.com

PRODUCTS/OPERATIONS

Selected Products
Approved
  Feraheme (ferumoxytol, iron replacement therapy)
  GastroMARK (marking of the bowel in abdominal imaging)

COMPETITORS

Bayer HealthCare Pharmaceuticals	Luitpold Pharmaceuticals
Daiichi Sankyo	Luna Innovations
FMCNA	Regent Medical
Guerbet	Watson Pharmaceuticals

HISTORICAL FINANCIALS

Company Type: Public

Income Statement
FYE: September 30

	REVENUE ($ mil.)	NET INCOME ($ mil.)	NET PROFIT MARGIN	EMPLOYEES
12/10	66.2	(81.2)	—	226
12/09	17.2	(93.4)	—	283
12/08	1.9	(71.6)	—	259
12/07*	2.6	(33.9)	—	88
09/06	2.7	(25.4)	—	44
Annual Growth	122.5%	—	—	50.5%

*Fiscal year change

2010 Year-End Financials

Debt ratio: —	No. of shares (mil.): 21.1
Return on equity: —	Dividends
Cash ($ mil.): 112.6	Yield: —
Current ratio: 7.92	Payout: —
Long-term debt ($ mil.): —	Market value ($ mil.): 382.6

	STOCK PRICE ($) FY Close	P/E High/Low	PER SHARE ($) Earnings	Dividends	Book Value
12/10	18.10	— —	(3.90)	0.00	11.60
12/09	38.03	— —	(5.46)	0.00	8.23
12/08	35.85	— —	(4.22)	0.00	12.55
12/07*	60.13	— —	(2.15)	0.00	16.92
09/06	34.30	— —	(2.31)	0.00	3.02
Annual Growth	(14.8%)	— —	—	—	40.0%

*Fiscal year change

Ambient Corp.

Ambient wants to put real power behind communications. The company develops technology that allows power lines to serve as high-speed data communications networks. Ambient's products — including nodes, couplers, and network management software - utilize Broadband over Power Line (BPL) and other technologies to create advanced power grids (also known as smart grids) with two-way communication capabilities. Its systems are designed to be used by utility companies for such applications as demand management, direct load control, meter reading, and real-time pricing. Ambient has partnerships with utilities such as Con Ed and Duke Energy to develop and deploy its technology.

The company saw its sales jump to $20.4 million in 2010 from $2.2 million the previous year. The dramatic increase was driven by sales of the its communications nodes to Duke Energy, which is incorporating them into a smart grid project in Ohio. Sales of software licenses for the company's AmbientNMS application also improved for the year. While expenses were up across the board, Ambient's losses for the year were significantly less in 2010 than in 2009.

This much-improved performance marks a shift in the company's fortunes from previous years in which Ambient's auditors expressed doubts about the its ability to continue as a going concern due to ongoing losses.

In addition to Con Edison and Duke Energy, Ambient has pilot BPL network deployments with Entergy and FirstEnergy.

EXECUTIVES

Chairman, President, CEO, and Treasurer, John J. Joyce, age 59, $388,760 total compensation
VP Operations, Michael (Mike) Quarella
VP Services, John C. Burruss
VP Business Development, Douglas T. McMurray
CTO, Ramdas (Ram) Rao, age 46, $263,000 total compensation
Manager Business Development and Environmental Affairs, Jay Ganson
Director Software Engineering, David Holland
Director Systems Architecture and Design, David (Dave) Goldblatt
Director Corporate Communications, Anna E. Croop
Chief Engineer, Yehuda Cern
Director Compliance and Standardization, Aron Viner
Auditors: Rotenberg Meril Solomon Bertiger & Guttilla, P.C.

LOCATIONS

HQ: Ambient Corporation
7 Wells Ave., Newton, MA 02459
Phone: 617-332-0004   **Fax:** 617-332-7260
Web: www.ambientcorp.com

COMPETITORS

Amperion	Main.net - PLC
Comverge	MainNet
EnerNOC	SmartSynch
GridPoint	Telkonet

HISTORICAL FINANCIALS

Company Type: Public

Income Statement

FYE: December 31

	REVENUE ($ mil.)	NET INCOME ($ mil.)	NET PROFIT MARGIN	EMPLOYEES
12/10	20.4	(3.2)	—	59
12/09	2.2	(14.2)	—	44
12/08	12.6	(11.3)	—	38
12/07	2.3	(15.8)	—	28
12/06	2.3	(12.7)	—	34
Annual Growth	72.6%	—	—	14.8%

2010 Year-End Financials

Debt ratio: —
Return on equity: —
Cash ($ mil.): 7.0
Current ratio: 2.31
Long-term debt ($ mil.): —
No. of shares (mil.): 16.5
Dividends
  Yield: —
  Payout: —
Market value ($ mil.): 168.1

	STOCK PRICE ($) FY Close	P/E High/Low	PER SHARE ($) Earnings	Dividends	Book Value
12/10	10.20	— —	(0.00)	0.00	0.37
12/09	14.90	— —	(2.00)	0.00	(1.06)
12/08	1.80	— —	(4.00)	0.00	2.93
12/07	2.90	— —	(7.00)	0.00	(0.58)
12/06	8.50	— —	(7.00)	0.00	1.50
Annual Growth	4.7%	— —	—	—	(29.4%)

AMEN Properties

AMEN Properties is hoping that the answer to its prayers are power and energy, and a little property thrown in for good measure. The company's Priority Power subsidiary provides energy management and consulting services. This unit has current or previous business activities in Texas and 21 other states, and serves more than 1,200 clients (including a large number of oil and gas companies.) These activities include electricity load aggregation, natural gas and electricity procurement, energy risk management, and energy consulting. AMEN Properties also invests in commercial real estate in secondary markets and in oil and gas royalties.

EXECUTIVES

Chairman, Eric L. Oliver, age 52
CEO and Director, Jon M. Morgan, age 52
CFO and Secretary, Kris Oliver, age 45
VP Priority Power, Padraig (Pat) Ennis, age 51
COO, Kevin Yung, age 47
Auditors: Johnson, Miller & Co.

LOCATIONS

HQ: AMEN Properties, Inc.
303 W. Wall St., Ste. 2300, Midland, TX 79701
Phone: 972-664-1610
Web: amenproperties.com

PRODUCTS/OPERATIONS

Selected Subsidiaries
Amen Delaware, L.P.
Amen Minerals, L.P. (gas and oil royalty interests)
NEMA Properties, LLC
Priority Power Management, Ltd.

COMPETITORS

Constellation	Equity Office
NewEnergy	Highwoods Properties
Direct Energy	Sabine Royalty Trust

HISTORICAL FINANCIALS

Company Type: Public

Income Statement

FYE: December 31

	REVENUE ($ mil.)	NET INCOME ($ mil.)	NET PROFIT MARGIN	EMPLOYEES
12/07	14.3	1.3	9.1%	27
12/06	15.1	2.2	14.6%	11
12/05	10.2	(0.7)	—	11
12/04	4.3	0.8	18.6%	0
12/03	4.3	0.4	9.3%	0
Annual Growth	35.0%	34.3%	—	56.7%

2007 Year-End Financials

Debt ratio: 17.9%
Return on equity: 8.8%
Cash ($ mil.): 1.5
Current ratio: 0.88
Long-term debt ($ mil.): 2.6
No. of shares (mil.): —
Dividends
  Yield: —
  Payout: —
Market value ($ mil.): —

	STOCK PRICE ($) FY Close	P/E High/Low	PER SHARE ($) Earnings	Dividends	Book Value
12/07	704.00	26 14	35.00	0.00	(0.00)
12/06	571.00	15 7	56.00	0.00	(0.00)
12/05	575.00	— —	(32.00)	0.00	(0.00)
12/04	430.00	19 6	26.00	0.00	(0.00)
12/03	150.00	27 8	13.00	0.00	(0.00)
Annual Growth	47.2%	— —	28.1%	—	—

Ameresco

Ameresco gives its customers alternative ways to cut their energy bills. Serving the commercial, industrial, government, and other sectors, Ameresco provides development, engineering, and installation services to customers seeking to upgrade and improve the efficiency of their heating and air conditioning, ventilation, lighting, and other building systems. Other services include developing and constructing small-scale, on-site (or near-site) renewable energy plants for customers, as well as installing solar panels, wind turbines, and other alternative energy sources. The company operates throughout the US through more than 55 locations. Ameresco went public via an initial public offering (IPO) in 2010.

Ameresco is using the $87 million raised in the offering — somewhat less than the $125 million it hoped to — to repay debt and to fund general corporate activities including opening new offices, expanding sales and marketing efforts, and increasing renewable energy plant activities. It is also making investments such as 2010 acquisition of Quantum Engineering (since renamed Ameresco Quantum), an energy firm serving the Pacific Northwest. In 2011 the company acquired APS Energy Services, which help clients in the Southwest reduce their energy usage.

The company wasn't alone in experiencing lukewarm response to its IPO, as the broader markets have struggled with lackluster pricings in the wake of the financial crisis. It does stand to benefit from the widespread need to cut operating costs and has secured lucrative new contracts with clients including the city of Portland, Maine, and school districts in New York and Virginia.

Although system design and development services account for most of Ameresco's sales, the company also earns recurring, contract-based revenue by selling electricity and other energy it produces. Its plants, often built near landfills, convert biomass (fermented plant and other matter) or methane gas released by landfill waste into energy. The company has been growing its renewable energy plants business and plans to continue to do so in the future.

Founded in 2000, Ameresco became profitable early and has been growing year over year. It has grown mainly by broadening its service offerings and expanding its geographical reach. Its ongoing growth strategy includes the pursuit of additional acquisitions, as well as organic growth opportunities, into new markets in the US, Canada, and Europe. The company will also bolster its sales personnel and focus on increasing its customer base.

Prior to Ameresco's IPO filing, founder and CEO George P. Sakellaris owned nearly a quarter of the company. He now owns some 15% of the firm's

Class A and all of its Class B common stock, which gives him more than 80% total voting power.

EXECUTIVES

Chairman, President, and CEO, George P. Sakellaris, age 64
President, Ameresco Canada, Mario P. Iusi
EVP Business Development and Director, David J. Anderson, age 50
EVP Engineering and Operations, Joseph P. DeManche, age 54
EVP and General Manager, Federal Operations, Keith A. Derrington, age 50
EVP and General Manager, Central Region, Louis P. Maltezos, age 44
EVP, General Counsel, and Director, David J. Corrsin, age 52
VP and CFO, Andrew B. Spence, age 54
VP Citizens Conservation Services, Janice S. DeBarros
VP and Assistant General Counsel, Paul M. Dello Iacono
VP Corporate Services, David W. Maksymuik
VP, John L. Bosch
VP, William (Bill) Skosky
VP Energy Supply and Risk Management, Bruce McLeish
VP Utility Information Management and Analytics, Mark Feichtner
VP Canadian Operations, Anthony A. DaSilva
VP Strategic Development, Peter W. Wallis
VP Planning, Michael R. Castonguay
VP Sales and Marketing, Eric Longbottom
VP, B. N. Tripathi
SVP Corporate Government Relations, William J. (Bill) Cunningham, age 51
SVP Renewable Energy, Michael T. Bakas, age 42
Auditors: McGladrey & Pullen, LLP

LOCATIONS

HQ: Ameresco, Inc.
111 Speen St., Ste. 410, Framingham, MA 01701
Phone: 508-661-2200
Web: www.ameresco.com

2010 Sales

	$ mil.	% of total
US	514.4	83
Canada	101.8	17
Other countries	2.0	-
Total	**618.2**	**100**

PRODUCTS/OPERATIONS

2010 Sales

	$ mil.	% of total
Energy efficiency services	455.3	74
Renewable energy	162.9	26
Total	**618.2**	**100**

Selected Subsidiaries

Ameresco Canada Inc.
Ameresco CEPRO Solar Inc.
Ameresco Chicopee Energy LLC
Ameresco Enertech, Inc.
Ameresco Evansville LLC
Ameresco Federal Solutions, Inc.
Ameresco Huntington Beach, L.L.C.
Ameresco Mt. Olive LLC
Ameresco Planergy Housing, Inc.
Ameresco Quantum, Inc.
Ameresco Select, Inc.
Ameresco Solar - Technologies LLC
Ameresco Vasco Road LLC
AmerescoSolutions, Inc.
EI Fund, One

COMPETITORS

Building Technologies	Johnson Controls
Constellation Energy Group	Lime Energy
	NORESCO
EPS	Onsite Energy
Honeywell ACS	

HISTORICAL FINANCIALS

Company Type: Public

Income Statement

FYE: December 31

	REVENUE ($ mil.)	NET INCOME ($ mil.)	NET PROFIT MARGIN	EMPLOYEES
12/10	618.2	28.7	4.6%	735
12/09	428.5	19.9	4.6%	639
12/08	395.9	18.3	4.6%	0
12/07	378.5	13.9	3.7%	0
Annual Growth	**17.8%**	**27.3%**	**—**	**15.0%**

2010 Year-End Financials

Debt ratio: 103.8%
Return on equity: 14.7%
Cash ($ mil.): 44.7
Current ratio: 1.51
Long-term debt ($ mil.): 202.4

No. of shares (mil.): 41.1
Dividends
  Yield: —
  Payout: —
Market value ($ mil.): 590.1

	STOCK PRICE ($) FY Close	P/E High/Low		PER SHARE ($) Earnings	Dividends	Book Value
12/10	14.36	22	14	0.69	0.00	4.75
Annual Growth	**—**	**—**	**—**	**—**	**—**	**—**

American Bank Holdings

American Bank Holdings owns American Bank, which has about five branches in Maryland and Washington, DC. The bank offers traditional deposit services such as checking, savings, and money market accounts and certificates of deposit. Its loan portfolio consists largely of one- to four-family residential mortgages and loans for construction and land development. The bank also offers commercial mortgages, business loans, auto loans, and lease financing, and a lower number of unsecured consumer loans. American Bank terminated an agreement to buy four Baltimore-area branches from BCSB Bancorp in 2010.

EXECUTIVES

Chairman, American Bank Holdings and American Bank, J. R. Schuble Jr., age 44
President and CEO; COO, American Bank, James E. Plack, age 39
SVP Lending, Dennis N. Argerson, age 47
SVP, Leasing, Charles I. (Chuck) Ledford, age 63
SVP, Mortgage, American Bank Holdings and American Bank, Robert N. Kemp Jr., age 60
SVP and CFO, American Bank Holdings and American Bank, John M. Wright, age 44
Auditors: Beard Miller Company LLP

LOCATIONS

HQ: American Bank Holdings, Inc.
4800 Montgomery Ln., 10th Fl., Bethesda, MD 20814
Phone: 301-572-3740   **Fax:** 301-572-1601
Web: www.americanfsb.com

COMPETITORS

Bank of America	Sandy Spring Bancorp
BB&T	SunTrust
Capital One	Tri-County Financial
M&T Bank	WSB Holdings
OBA Financial Services	

HISTORICAL FINANCIALS

Company Type: Public

Income Statement

FYE: December 31

	ASSETS ($ mil.)	NET INCOME ($ mil.)	INCOME AS % OF ASSETS	EMPLOYEES
12/05	306.5	3.0	1.0%	72
12/04	251.0	2.5	1.0%	78
12/03	236.9	1.1	0.5%	57
12/02	179.7	1.0	0.6%	0
12/01	154.3	0.9	0.6%	0
Annual Growth	**18.7%**	**35.1%**	**—**	**12.4%**

2005 Year-End Financials

Equity as % of assets: 9.77%
Return on assets: 1.0%
Return on equity: 10.2%
Long-term debt ($ mil.): 3.1
No. of shares (mil.): —

Dividends
  Yield: —
  Payout: —
Market value ($ mil.): —
Sales ($ mil.): 23.0

	STOCK PRICE ($) FY Close	P/E High/Low		PER SHARE ($) Earnings	Dividends	Book Value
12/05	24,800.00	9	6	2,860.00	0.00	(0.00)
12/04	18,800.00	8	6	2,500.00	0.00	(0.00)
12/03	16,000.00	15	13	1,040.00	0.00	(0.00)
12/02	13,800.00	14	13	960.00	0.00	(0.00)
12/01	12,762.00	17	10	820.00	0.00	(0.00)
Annual Growth	**18.1%**	**—**	**—**	**36.7%**	**—**	**—**

American Business Bank

What's a middle-market, closely held, owner-managed business gotta do to get *FORTUNE* 500 treatment from a bank? American Business Bank caters to private companies in Southern California with annual sales between $5 million and $200 million, with an emphasis on wholesalers, manufacturers, service businesses, not-for-profit organizations, and professionals. It has offices in Irvine, Los Angeles, Ontario, Torrance, and Woodland Hills. The bank's commercial lending services include commercial real estate loans (more than half of its portfolio), asset-based lending, equipment finance, construction loans, and revolving lines of credit. Its deposit products consist of checking, savings, and money market accounts, and CDs.

American Business Bank facilitates international trade by offering import letters of credit, export financing, foreign exchange, and international money transfers. The bank also offers its business clients cash management services, including automated clearing house disbursement and collection, and investment management services, such as placing orders for government securities, municipal bonds, short-term commercial paper, and other financial instruments.

EXECUTIVES

Chairman, Robert F. Schack
President, CEO, and Director, Donald P. (Don) Johnson
EVP and Chief Credit Officer, Robin C. Paterson
EVP and Manager Corporate Banking, Leon I. Blankstein
VP Bank Operations and Customer Service, Lori Sandborn
VP and Relationship Manager, San Fernando Valley, Jonathan Hersholt
VP and Relationship Manager, Dennis Johnson
VP and Relationship Manager, South Bay, Thomas Buescher
VP and Relationship Manager, Orange County, Morgan Lanchantin
VP and Asset Based Loan Manager, Mark Martinez
VP Branch Operations, Larry Meyer
VP and International Department Manager, Tony Mastrangelo
VP and Manager, Cash Management, Jackie T. Nixon
VP and Relationship Manager, Jagdith Jaganath
VP and Controller, Hugo Fiorentini
VP and Manager Cash Management, Pamela Van Dueck- Patterson
VP and Relationship Manager, South Bay, Brian Ishida
Vice Chairman, EVP, CFO, and COO, Wesley E. (Wes) Schaefer
First VP Note Department, Debbie Williams
Personnel Officer, Renee Moore
Regional VP and Relationship Manager, Inland Empire, Phil Feghali
First VP and Relationship Manager, Ken Bettencourt
SVP, Cashier, and Department Manager, Debbie Dair
Regional VP and Realtionship Manager, San Fernando Valley, Gary Coleman
Regional VP and Relationship Manager, Orange County, David Wolf
First VP, Relationship Manager, and Senior Loan and Credit Officer, Orange County, Erik Dickerson
Regional VP and Relationship Manager, South Bay, Patti A. Vollmer
Regional VP, Relationship Manager, and Senior Loan and Credit Manager, Silvia Marjoram
Auditors:

LOCATIONS

HQ: American Business Bank
523 W. 6th St., Ste. 900, Los Angeles, CA 90014
Phone: 213-430-4000   **Fax:** 213-627-2784
Web: www.americanbusinessbank.com

COMPETITORS

Bank of America	First California
Broadway Financial	Financial
Cathay General Bancorp	JPMorgan Chase
Center Financial	Nara Bancorp
Citigroup	NCAL Bancorp
Comerica	Wells Fargo
East West Bancorp	Wilshire Bancorp

HISTORICAL FINANCIALS
Company Type: Public

Income Statement
FYE: December 31

	ASSETS ($ mil.)	NET INCOME ($ mil.)	INCOME AS % OF ASSETS	EMPLOYEES
12/07	608.3	5.2	0.9%	72
12/06	537.2	5.0	0.9%	69
12/05	508.5	5.3	1.0%	57
12/04	458.0	3.4	0.7%	52
12/03	361.4	2.1	0.6%	45
Annual Growth	13.9%	25.4%	—	12.5%

2007 Year-End Financials

Equity as % of assets: 7.17%	Dividends
Return on assets: 0.9%	Yield: —
Return on equity: 11.9%	Payout: —
Long-term debt ($ mil.): 8.0	Market value ($ mil.): —
No. of shares (mil.): —	Sales ($ mil.): 33.8

	STOCK PRICE ($) FY Close	P/E High/Low		PER SHARE ($) Earnings	Dividends	Book Value
12/07	18.18	17	14	1.22	0.00	(0.00)
12/06	21.49	19	17	1.19	0.00	(0.00)
12/05	22.04	21	15	1.24	0.00	(0.00)
12/04	18.89	24	15	0.79	0.00	(0.00)
12/03	12.72	31	16	0.51	0.00	(0.00)
Annual Growth	9.3%	—	—	24.4%	—	—

American Campus Communities

American Campus Communities (ACC) actually does most of its business *off* campus. The self-managed real estate investment trust (REIT) owns and operates student housing properties located at or near colleges and universities in more than 25 states. The company leases the ground for on-campus properties from the schools, which in turn receive half of the net cash flow from these properties. ACC also works with schools to develop new properties and renovate existing housing, and provides third-party leasing and management services for other student housing owners. In all, the REIT manages about 140 properties (with some 94,000 beds) at more than 85 schools in the US and Canada.

The company has expanded its portfolio by both buying existing properties and developing new ones. It regularly buys properties in bulk, adding thousands of beds at a time. In 2010 it acquired the rest of 11 properties it previously only held a minority stake in. Two years earlier, ACC entered 40 new markets when it bought the student housing business of former rival GMH Communities Trust. That transaction included more than 70 off-campus properties.

Many of ACC's properties feature resort-style amenities, making them more desirable than your typical dorm facility. The company has been successful in establishing strong relationships with school systems, which pays off in earning repeat business as various campuses seek to add new housing options. Among the REIT's most recent developments are new sites in Texas and New Mexico, which opened for business in 2011. ACC

also provides third-party development services for other property investors.

EXECUTIVES

President, CEO, and Director, William C. Bayless Jr., age 47, $1,136,192 total compensation
EVP Project Management and Construction, James C. Hopke Jr., age 49, $402,924 total compensation
EVP Public and Private Partnerships, Jamie E. Wilhelm III, age 47
EVP, CFO, and Treasurer, Jonathan A. Graf, age 46, $498,967 total compensation
SEVP and COO, Greg A. Dowell, age 47, $677,430 total compensation
SVP Project Management and Construction, Victor Young, age 38
SVP Capital Markets, Daniel Perry, age 37
SVP Leasing Administration, Jennifer Beese, age 37
SVP Construction Management, Clint Braun, age 38
SVP Investments, William Talbot, age 36
SVP Management Services, James R. (Jim) Sholders, age 41
SVP Transactions, Brian N. Winger, age 43
SVP On-Campus Development, Jason R. Wills, age 39
SVP Information Technologies, Jorge de Cárdenas, age 47
SVP Management Services, Steve Crawford, age 41
Investor Relations, Gina Cowart
SVP and Controller, Kim K. Voss, age 36
Auditors: Ernst & Young LLP

LOCATIONS

HQ: American Campus Communities, Inc.
12700 Hill Country Blvd., Ste. T-200, Austin, TX 78738
Phone: 512-732-1000   **Fax:** 512-732-2450
Web: www.americancampus.com

Selected Property Locations
Alabama
    Shelton State College
    Stillman College
    University of Alabama - Birmingham
    University of Alabama - Tuscaloosa
Alberta
    Southern Alberta Institute of Technology
Arizona
    Arizona State University
    Pima Community College
    University of Arizona
California
    American River Community College
    California State University - Fresno
    Fresno Pacific University
    San Diego State University
    Sierra College
Colorado
    Community College of Denver
    Front Range Community College
    Regis University
    University of Denver
Florida
    Santa Fe Community College
    Seminole State College of Florida
    University of Florida - Gainesville
    Valencia Comunity College
Georgia
    Athens Technical College
    East Georgia College
    Georgia Gwinnett College
    Piedmont College - Athens Campus
    Wiregrass Georgia Technical College
Hawaii
    University of Hawaii - Manoa
Illinois
    Parkland College, University of Illinois
Indiana
    Indiana/Purdue University
    Indiana University
Iowa
    Des Moines University

Drake University
Kaplin University
Kentucky
  Blue Grass Technical College
  Bowling Green Community College
  Western Kentucky University
Louisiana
  Baton Rouge Community College
  Louisiana State University
  Southern University
  University of New Orleans
Maryland
  Morgan State University
  University of Maryland
Michigan
  Central Michigan University
  Eastern Michigan University
  Kalamazoo Valley Community College
  Michigan State University
  University of Michigan
  Western Michigan University
Minnesota
  Art Institute International
  Minnesota State University
  University of Minnesota
Mississippi
  East Mississippi Community College
  Mississippi State University
Nebraska
  Nebraska Wesleyan University
  Southeast Community College
  University of Nebraska
Nevada
  University of Nevada at Reno
New Jersey
  Bloomfield College
  Essex County College
  Seton Hall University
New Mexico
  University of New Mexico
New York
  Buffalo State College
  Canisius College
  Medaille College
  State University of New York at Buffalo
North Carolina
  Central Piedmont Community College
  Durham Tech
  Johnson & Wales
  UNC Chapel Hill
Ohio
  Cleveland State University
  Owens Community College
  University of Toledo
Oklahoma
  Oklahoma City Community College
  Rose State College
  University of Oklahoma
Ontario
  Fanshawe College
  London College
  University of Western Ontario
Pennsylvania
  Drexel
  Penn State University
  Temple University
South Carolina
  Columbia College
  Midlands Tech
Tennessee
  Daymar Institute
  East Tennessee State University
  Milligan College
  Pellissippi State Community College
  University of Tennessee
Texas
  Blinn College
  Lubbock Christian University
  Sam Houston State University
  Texas A&M University
  University of Houston - Victoria
Virginia
  Blue Ridge Community College
  Eastern Mennonite University
  New River Community College
  University of Virginia
  Virginia Tech

West Virginia
  Fairmont State College
  Marshall University
  Potomac State
  West Virginia University

PRODUCTS/OPERATIONS

2010 Sales

	$ mil.	% of total
Wholly owned properties	301.7	87
On-campus participating properties	24.0	7
Third-party development services	9.3	3
Third-party management services	8.7	3
Resident services	1.3	-
Total	**345.0**	**100**

COMPETITORS

Allen & O'Hara	Campus Apartments
Alliance Residential	Campus Crest
AMLI Residential	Education Realty
Apartment Investment	Fairfield Residential
and Management	JPI
Camden Property	Place Properties

HISTORICAL FINANCIALS
Company Type: Public

Income Statement
FYE: December 31

	REVENUE ($ mil.)	NET INCOME ($ mil.)	NET PROFIT MARGIN	EMPLOYEES
12/10	345.0	16.2	4.7%	2,334
12/09	309.6	(12.8)	—	2,183
12/08	235.4	(13.1)	—	2,301
12/07	147.1	(1.7)	—	1,084
12/06	119.0	22.6	19.0%	897
Annual Growth	**30.5%**	**(8.0%)**	**—**	**27.0%**

2010 Year-End Financials

Debt ratio: 110.8%
Return on equity: 1.3%
Cash ($ mil.): 113.5
Current ratio: 2.06
Long-term debt ($ mil.): 1,345.1

No. of shares (mil.): 66.9
Dividends
  Yield: 4.3%
  Payout: 337.5%
Market value ($ mil.): 2,124.0

	STOCK PRICE ($) FY Close	P/E High/Low		PER SHARE ($) Earnings	Dividends	Book Value
12/10	31.76	129	91	0.26	1.35	18.15
12/09	28.10	—	—	(0.28)	1.35	17.22
12/08	20.48	—	—	(0.34)	1.35	18.63
12/07	26.85	—	—	(0.07)	1.35	16.29
12/06	28.47	26	19	1.17	1.35	16.13
Annual Growth	**2.8%**	**—**	**—**	**(31.3%)**	**(0.0%)**	**3.0%**

American Capital Agency Corp.

American Capital Agency is taking on the rocky real estate market. The real estate investment trust (REIT) was created in 2008 to invest in securities backed by single-family residential mortgages and collateralized mortgage obligations guaranteed by government agencies Fannie Mae, Freddie Mac, and Ginnie Mae. The company is externally managed and advised by American Capital Agency Management, a subsidiary of US publicly traded alternative asset manager American Capital, which spun off American Capital Agency in 2008, but retained about a 33% stake in the REIT.

American Capital Agency raised some $300 million from its 2008 IPO. The REIT used the proceeds from the offering to build and develop its investment portfolio.

EXECUTIVES

Chairman, President, and CEO; President, American Capital Agency Management, Malon Wilkus, age 59
EVP and Secretary; VP and Secretary, American Capital Agency Management, Samuel A. Flax, age 54
EVP and CFO; VP and Treasurer, American Capital Agency Management, John R. Erickson, age 51
VP, American Capital Agency Management, Thomas A. (Tom) McHale
SVP and Chief Investment Officer; SVP and Managing Director, American Capital, Gary D. Kain, age 46
Auditors: Ernst & Young LLP

LOCATIONS

HQ: American Capital Agency Corp.
2 Bethesda Metro Center, 14th Fl., Bethesda, MD 20814
Phone: 301-968-9300
Web: www.agnc.com

PRODUCTS/OPERATIONS

2009 Sales

	$ mil	% of total
Interest income	127.9	72
Gain on sale of agency securities	49.9	28
Adjustments	(4.2)	-
Total	**173.6**	**100**

COMPETITORS

Annaly Capital	Capstead Mortgage
Management	Chimera
Anworth Mortgage Asset	CIFC
ARMOUR Residential	Hatteras Financial
REIT	MFA Financial
Bimini Capital	Redwood Trust
Management	

HISTORICAL FINANCIALS
Company Type: Public

Income Statement
FYE: December 31

	REVENUE ($ mil.)	NET INCOME ($ mil.)	NET PROFIT MARGIN	EMPLOYEES
12/10	383.4	288.1	75.1%	0
12/09	173.6	118.6	68.3%	0
12/08	66.0	35.4	53.6%	0
Annual Growth	**141.0%**	**185.3%**	**—**	**—**

2010 Year-End Financials

Debt ratio: —
Return on equity: 18.3%
Cash ($ mil.): 173.3
Current ratio: —
Long-term debt ($ mil.): —

No. of shares (mil.): 64.9
Dividends
  Yield: 19.5%
  Payout: 71.0%
Market value ($ mil.): 1,864.0

	STOCK PRICE ($) FY Close	P/E High/Low		PER SHARE ($) Earnings	Dividends	Book Value
12/10	28.74	4	3	7.89	5.60	24.24
12/09	26.54	5	2	6.78	5.15	22.48
12/08	21.36	10	5	2.36	2.51	17.20
Annual Growth	**16.0%**	**—**	**—**	**82.8%**	**49.4%**	**18.7%**

American Equity Investment Life Holding Company

Seeking to save? American Equity Investment Life Holding Company issues and administers fixed-rate and indexed annuities through subsidiaries American Equity Investment Life Insurance and American Equity Investment Life Insurance Company of New York. Licensed in 50 states and the District of Columbia, the company sells its products through more than 40,000 independent agents and 50 national marketing associations. American Equity Investment Life targets individuals between the ages of 45 to 75. The company also offers a variety of whole, term, and universal life insurance products.

The top five states bringing income to American Equity Investment Life's business together account for more than 40% of premiums: California, Florida, Illinois, Ohio, and Texas. The company is working to increase sales in core service territories by enhancing its relationships with regional independent agents. It is also looking to expand by creating new competitive product offerings. For instance, the firm formed its Eagle Life subsidiary in 2008 to develop a network of brokers to sell its fixed annuity products, which are growing in popularity with consumers.

However, American Equity Investment Life experienced a significant dip in revenues and net income in 2008 as economic conditions impacted its overall annuity sales. The company also suffered due to investments in commercial mortgages following the collapse of the US real estate market. American Equity Investment Life made a substantial turnaround effort in 2009 to bring its operating results back up to par.

Earlier that year American Equity Investment Life Insurance had settled a class-action suit brought by the Minnesota State Attorney General. The suit alleged that the subsidiary had engaged in improper sales techniques, particularly with regard to senior citizens, including violation of a law requiring insurance companies to ensure that an annuity is appropriate for the person to whom it is sold. Without admitting any wrongdoing, American Equity agreed to accept and review refund claims for persons 65 and older who were sold annuities that were either unsuitable for their needs or about which they were misinformed.

EXECUTIVES

Chairman, American Equity Investment and American Equity Life, David J. (D.J.) Noble, age 79, $719,794 total compensation
President, American Equity Life Insurance Co., Ronald J. (Ron) Grensteiner
President, CEO, and Director, Wendy C. Waugaman, age 50, $697,021 total compensation
EVP, Chief Administrative Officer, Secretary, and Director, Debra J. Richardson, age 54, $644,537 total compensation
EVP; EVP, COO, Treasurer, and Director, American Equity Life, Terry A. Reimer, age 65
EVP and Director, James M. Gerlach, age 68, $405,003 total compensation
VP and Controller, Ted M. Johnson
SVP Investments, Jeffrey D. (Jeff) Lorenzen, age 45

Vice Chairman, CFO, and Treasurer, John M. Matovina, age 56, $604,109 total compensation
Director Investor Relations, Julie L. LaFollette
Auditors: KPMG LLP

LOCATIONS

HQ: American Equity Investment Life Holding Company
5000 Westown Pkwy., Ste. 440, West Des Moines, IA 50266
Phone: 515-221-0002   **Fax:** 515-221-9947
Web: www.american-equity.com

COMPETITORS

AEGON USA	Lincoln Financial
AIG	Group
Allianz Life	MetLife
Aviva	Nationwide
FBL Financial	Northwestern Mutual
Fidelity & Guaranty	Presidential Life
Life	Prudential
ING	Sammons Financial
Integrity Life	The Hartford
Kansas City Life	Union Central

HISTORICAL FINANCIALS

Company Type: Public

Income Statement

FYE: December 31

	ASSETS ($ mil.)	NET INCOME ($ mil.)	INCOME AS % OF ASSETS	EMPLOYEES
12/10	26,426.8	42.9	0.2%	360
12/09	21,312.0	68.5	0.3%	360
12/08	17,087.8	20.8	0.1%	330
12/07	16,394.4	29.0	0.2%	290
12/06	14,990.1	75.5	0.5%	280
Annual Growth	15.2%	(13.2%)	—	6.5%

2010 Year-End Financials

Equity as % of assets: 3.55%	Dividends
Return on assets: 0.2%	Yield: 0.8%
Return on equity: 4.6%	Payout: 14.7%
Long-term debt ($ mil.): 268.4	Market value ($ mil.): 715.0
No. of shares (mil.): 57.0	Sales ($ mil.): 1,285.6

	STOCK PRICE ($) FY Close	P/E High/Low		PER SHARE ($) Earnings	Dividends	Book Value
12/10	12.55	19	10	0.68	0.10	16.47
12/09	7.44	8	3	1.18	0.08	13.43
12/08	7.00	30	9	0.39	0.07	9.26
12/07	8.29	28	16	0.50	0.06	10.75
12/06	13.03	11	8	1.34	0.05	10.65
Annual Growth	(0.9%)	—	—	(15.6%)	18.9%	11.5%

American Public Education

American Public Education (APE) promotes military intelligence. The company offers online postsecondary education to those in the military and other public servants such as police and firefighters. Its American Military University and American Public University make up the American Public University System, which offers roughly 80 degree programs and nearly as many certificate programs in such disciplines as business administration, criminal justice, intelligence, technology, liberal arts, and homeland security. Enrollment in the online university consists of more than 83,000 students from all 50 states and about 100 foreign countries. More than 60% of APE's students serve in the US military on active duty.

APE's nationally and regionally accredited online education system offers associate's, bachelor's, and master's degrees. It is specifically geared toward adult students who are on call for rapid-response missions or extended deployment. APE has an open enrollment system, accepting all applicants with a high school diploma or equivalent. For those with limited financial resources, tuition assistance programs offered by the US Department of Defense constitute about half of the company's annual revenues.

APE is ramping up its outreach efforts, focusing on retention of students in its core military market (which represents more than 2 million potential students), while marketing the availability of federal student aid grants and low-cost loans to the public service and civilian markets. It is also expanding the number and type of degrees offered based on demographic trends. In 2010 APE received approval from the Higher Learning Commission to offer degree programs in Information Technology, Psychology, and Nursing.

Its efforts have paid off, with the company experiencing a more than 35% increase in its revenue between 2008 and 2010. Its course registration rate increased about 40% in 2009 and 30% in 2010. APE attributes the increases to high student satisfaction and referral rates, accreditation (such as the three new programs accredited in 2010), the increasing acceptance of online learning as a viable alternative to bricks and mortar schooling, and the variety and affordability of APE's programs.

APE was founded in 1991 as American Military University by a retired Marine Corps major. It went public in 2007 and used the proceeds to pay stockholders more than $93 million.

EXECUTIVES

President, CEO, and Director, Wallace E. (Wally) Boston Jr., age 56, $1,229,940 total compensation
EVP and CFO, Harry T. Wilkins, age 54, $810,475 total compensation
EVP and COO, Sharon van Wyk, age 51
EVP Programs and Marketing, Carol S. Gilbert, age 52, $388,688 total compensation
VP Military Programs, James M. (Jim) Sweizer
VP Student Services, Lyn M. Geer
VP Academic Systems, Thomas E. Downey
VP Academic Services, Phillip A. McNair
Vice Chairman, J. Christopher Everett, age 63
SVP and Chief Administrative Officer, Peter W. (Pete) Gibbons, age 58
SVP and CIO, W. Dale Young, age 61
SVP Finance, Lisa Kessler
SVP and Academic Dean, Karan H. Powell
Auditors: McGladrey & Pullen, LLP

LOCATIONS

HQ: American Public Education, Inc.
111 W. Congress St., Charles Town, WV 25414
Phone: 304-724-3700   **Fax:** 304-724-3780
Web: www.apus.edu

PRODUCTS/OPERATIONS

2010 Selected Programs

Programs@1col Table head A:	Number
Master of Arts	16
Master of Business Administration	1
Master of Education	3
Master of Public Administration	1
Master of Public Health	1
Master of Science	4
Bachelor of Arts	22
Bachelor of Business Administration	1
Bachelor of Science	11
Associate of Arts	12
Associate of Science	7
Certificates	
Graduate	32
Undergraduate	33
Total	**144**

Selected Degree Programs

Accounting
Business Administration
Communication
Computer Applications
Counter Terrorism
Criminal Justice
Database Application
Early Childhood Development
Emergency and Disaster Management
English
Environmental Services
Explosive Ordnance Disposal
Fire Science
General Studies
History
Homeland Security
Hospitality
Information Technology
Intelligence Studies
Legal Studies
Management
Marketing
Middle Eastern Studies
Military History
Paralegal Studies
Personnel Administration
Philosophy
Psychology
Public Health
Real Estate Studies
Religion
Space Studies
Transportation and Logistics Management
Weapons of Mass Destruction Preparedness
Web Publishing

COMPETITORS

Apollo Group
Capella Education
Career Education
Corinthian Colleges
DeVry
Embry-Riddle Aeronautical University
Heald College
ITT Educational
Kaplan
Strayer Education
Touro College
University of Maryland

HISTORICAL FINANCIALS

Company Type: Public

Income Statement

FYE: December 31

	REVENUE ($ mil.)	NET INCOME ($ mil.)	NET PROFIT MARGIN	EMPLOYEES
12/10	198.2	29.9	15.1%	2,170
12/09	149.0	23.9	16.0%	1,480
12/08	107.1	16.2	15.1%	1,180
12/07	69.1	8.8	12.7%	910
12/06	40.0	1.8	4.5%	798
Annual Growth	49.2%	101.9%	—	28.4%

2010 Year-End Financials

Debt ratio: —
Return on equity: 30.7%
Cash ($ mil.): 81.4
Current ratio: 2.61
Long-term debt ($ mil.): —

No. of shares (mil.): 17.9
Dividends
  Yield: —
  Payout: —
Market value ($ mil.): 667.0

	STOCK PRICE ($) FY Close	P/E High/Low		PER SHARE ($) Earnings	Dividends	Book Value
12/10	37.24	31	15	1.59	0.00	5.43
12/09	34.36	37	24	1.27	0.00	4.49
12/08	37.19	62	32	0.86	0.00	2.98
12/07	41.78	73	46	0.64	0.00	1.90
Annual Growth	(3.8%)	—	—	35.4%	—	42.0%

American Spectrum Realty

American Spectrum Realty invests in and manages commercial real estate, primarily multitenant office and industrial space. The company and its subsidiaries own, manage, or lease 90 properties valued at more than $1 billion. Most properties are located in Texas, but it also owns assets in California and 20 other states. In 2010 subsidiary American Spectrum Realty Management acquired the property and asset management assets from Evergreen Realty Group. The deal, which included contracts for 80 properties ranging from storage units to student housing, helped American Spectrum expand its third-party management and leasing capabilities across the US. CEO William Carden controls about 40% of the company.

EXECUTIVES

Chairman, President, and CEO, William J. Carden, age 66, $569,500 total compensation
President, American Spectrum Realty Management, Jonathan T. Brohard
VP Investments; VP Asset Management, Commercial, American Spectrum Realty Management, Richard M. (Ric) Holland, age 57, $230,000 total compensation
VP Property Management, American Spectrum Management Group, G. Wayne Reyes
VP, CFO, Controller, Treasurer, and Secretary, G. Anthony Eppolito, age 43, $183,750 total compensation
VP American Spectrum Realty Management, Bill McGrath
Managing Director, American Spectrum Realty Advisors, Paul E. Perkins, age 41
Auditors:

LOCATIONS

HQ: American Spectrum Realty, Inc.
  2401 Fountain View, Ste. 510, Houston, TX 77057
Phone: 713-706-6200   **Fax:** 713-706-6201
Web: www.americanspectrum.com

PRODUCTS/OPERATIONS

COMPETITORS

Brookfield Office
  Properties
Crescent Real Estate
Equity Office

Kimco Realty
Parkway Properties
ProLogis
PS Business Parks

HISTORICAL FINANCIALS

Company Type: Public

Income Statement

FYE: December 31

	REVENUE ($ mil.)	NET INCOME ($ mil.)	NET PROFIT MARGIN	EMPLOYEES
12/10	55.6	(8.0)	—	219
12/09	33.3	(8.3)	—	283
12/08	35.1	(6.6)	—	40
12/07	30.5	(10.1)	—	44
12/06	26.0	6.5	25.0%	34
Annual Growth	20.9%	—	—	59.3%

2010 Year-End Financials

Debt ratio: —
Return on equity: —
Cash ($ mil.): 2.0
Current ratio: 0.10
Long-term debt ($ mil.): —

No. of shares (mil.): 3.0
Dividends
  Yield: 0.0%
  Payout: —
Market value ($ mil.): 51.7

	STOCK PRICE ($) FY Close	P/E High/Low		PER SHARE ($) Earnings	Dividends	Book Value
12/10	17.52	—	—	(2.76)	0.00	(4.91)
12/09	11.14	—	—	(2.94)	0.00	(2.48)
12/08	12.35	—	—	(2.41)	0.00	0.40
12/07	11.26	—	—	(3.19)	0.00	2.20
12/06	11.83	5	3	2.36	0.00	5.56
Annual Growth	10.3%	—	—	—	—	—

American Superconductor

American Superconductor (AMSC) gets a charge out of carrying a heavy load. The company has two units — AMSC Power Systems and AMSC Superconductors. AMSC Power Systems makes electronic converters for wind turbines and electrical transmitters that modulate power faster than electromechanical switches. AMSC Superconductors makes high-temperature superconductor (HTS) wire used in the electrical control systems for wind turbines; it accounts for less than 5% of sales. Austrian subsidiary AMSC Windtec designs wind turbines and supports wind turbine manufacturers. Customers in the Asia/Pacific region account for more than 85% of sales. MIT professors Gregory Yurek and John Vander Sande formed AMSC in 1987.

The AMSC Power Systems segment, which accounts for about 95% of sales, saw its revenues shoot up more than 80% in fiscal 2010; (the company's overall revenues grew by more than 70%). AMSC Power Systems sold plenty of wind turbine electrical systems and core components to its top customer in China, Sinovel Wind Group, which accounted for about 70% of sales in 2009, and is the world's third-largest wind turbine manufacturer.

In 2011, however, trouble blew in when Sinovel stopped accepting shipments to combat an inventory pileup. As uncertainty lingered, AMSC's losses mounted and its share price dropped (more than 70% in the months following the news), contributing to its decision to cut its global team by 30% as it worked to solidify its relationship with Sinovel. Most departments at AMSC were affected by the layoffs, but the company made a particular effort to preserve its customer-facing and R&D personnel.

In order to expand its growing wind turbine business, in 2011 AMSC agreed to buy Finland-based The Switch Engineering Oy for about E190 million (around $265 million) in cash and stock. The Switch sells power converter systems and permanent magnet generators to wind turbine makers in China, Europe, South Korea, and the US. The purchase would add complementary products to AMSC Windtec's offerings, expand AMSC's customer base in Asia, and strengthen the company's presence in the US and Europe. Customers of The Switch include Sinovel, Goldwind, and Dongfang in China, and GE in the US. The deal was called off late in the year due to economic conditions. The two companies announced plans to maintian their close collaboration working to increasing wind turbine reliability and lower cost of energy production.

AMSC Superconductors' HTS wire is used by electric utilities for high-capacity power cables and as a component in such products as motors, generators, and specialty magnets. The company is also developing stand-alone fault-current limiters (FCLs) with Siemens and Nexans. AMSC Superconductors distributes wire to LS Cable, Southwire, TECO-Westinghouse, and Vestas. AMSC considers its superconductor products to be in the early stages of commercialization, while others, such as FCLs, are still under development.

AMSC has one major institutional investor; BlackRock owns 17% of the company's stock. Investor Kevin Douglas, who owns California-based Douglas Telecommunications, owns 12%.

HISTORY

Superconductors were first identified in 1911, but until the 1980s were mostly materials that required cooling with costly liquid helium to maintain their conductivity. In 1986 IBM researchers discovered materials that could be cooled more cheaply and easily using liquid nitrogen. MIT professors Gregory Yurek (AMSC's chairman, president, and CEO) and John Vander Sande (a director) began using them to create HTS products, and in 1987 they formed AMSC to commercialize patents resulting from their research. AMSC went public in 1991. In 1994 the company produced its first HTS wire both flexible and strong enough for commercial use. Its first commercial products — heat-reducing current leads — were unveiled in 1996.

In 1997 AMSC's commercialization efforts got a boost when it bought Superconductivity, Inc., a maker of low-temperature superconducting magnetic energy storage (LT-SMES) devices; the next year AMSC introduced two commercial SMES products (one year ahead of schedule) and its first SMES unit went on line in a North Carolina plas-

tics factory. Also in 1998 Electricité de France, AMSC, and electrical power transformer maker ABB began a $15 million program to develop HTS wire for power transformers. In 1999 AMSC won a US Department of Energy contract to develop and install the first HTS transformer in the US's electric utility network.

In 2003 AMSC received funding from Oak Ridge National Laboratory to develop advanced manufacturing processes for making second-generation HTS wire. That same year, the company raised more than $44 million through a secondary stock offering.

In 2007 AMSC acquired a company that previously was a customer, Windtec Consulting, to expand into the alternative energy market. The Austrian firm develops and licenses wind turbine system designs, and sells wind turbine electrical systems. Windtec became part of AMSC Power Systems. Later that year AMSC bought Power Quality Systems (PQS) for nearly $4 million in stock. PQS made reactive compensation products based on its proprietary thyristor switch technology that enhance the reliability of power transmission and distribution grids and improve the quality of power for manufacturing operations. The products complement what AMSC previously offered electrical utilities in the area of reactive compensation. PQS also became part of AMSC Power Systems.

Sales hovered around $50 million until 2008, a year after the company reorganized. The previous year AMSC closed the SuperMachines plant in Westborough, Massachusetts, and transferred production to its facility in nearby Devens. AMSC also cut its Massachusetts workforce by 37 employees, or about 13% of its headcount. It also decided to close its headquarters building in Westborough and to relocate the remaining personnel to its facility in Devens.

In 2011 president and COO Daniel McGahn was appointed CEO, replacing company founder Gregory Yurek who retired as CEO, but remained chairman. McGahn joined AMSC in 2006.

EXECUTIVES

President, CEO, and Director, Daniel P. (Dan) McGahn, age 39, $911,402 total compensation
EVP and General Manager AMSC Power Systems, Charles W. (Chuck) Stankiewicz, age 52, $1,314,508 total compensation
VP Government Programs, John M. Ulliman
VP Corporate Administration, Susan DiCecco
VP Superconductor Projects, James F. Maguire
SVP Global Manufacturing, Angelo R. Santamaria, age 48, $967,441 total compensation
Director Corporate Communications, Jason Fredette
SVP, CFO, and Treasurer, and Secretary, David A. (Dave) Henry, age 49, $1,511,182 total compensation
SVP Global Sales and Business Development, Timothy D. (Tim) Poor, age 44
SVP and Chief Strategy Officer, John R. Collett
Auditors: PricewaterhouseCoopers LLP

LOCATIONS

HQ: American Superconductor Corporation
68 Jackson Rd., Devens, MA 01434-4020
Phone: 978-842-3000   **Fax:** 978-842-3024
Web: www.amsuper.com

2010 Sales

	$ mil.	% of total
Asia/Pacific	256.0	81
US	40.8	13
Europe	14.8	5
Canada	4.4	1
Total	**316.0**	**100**

PRODUCTS/OPERATIONS

2010 Sales

	$ mil.	% of total
AMSC Power Systems	304.3	96
AMSC Superconductors	11.7	4
Total	**316.0**	**100**

COMPETITORS

ABB	Nexans Hellas
ALSTOM	REpower Systems
AREVA	S&C Electric
Bruker Energy	Satcon Technology
Converteam	Schneider Electric
Fuhrländer AG	Siemens AG
Gamesa	Sumitomo Electric
GE Energy	Toshiba
Hitachi	Vestas Wind Systems
HYPRES	Woodward G
Mitsubishi Electric	

HISTORICAL FINANCIALS

Company Type: Public

Income Statement

FYE: March 31

	REVENUE ($ mil.)	NET INCOME ($ mil.)	NET PROFIT MARGIN	EMPLOYEES
03/11	286.6	(186.3)	—	599
03/10	316.0	16.2	5.1%	714
03/09	182.8	(16.6)	—	519
03/08	112.4	(25.4)	—	382
03/07	52.2	(34.7)	—	263
Annual Growth	**53.1%**	**—**	**—**	**22.8%**

2011 Year-End Financials

Debt ratio: —	No. of shares (mil.): 50.7
Return on equity: —	Dividends
Cash ($ mil.): 123.8	Yield: —
Current ratio: 2.20	Payout: —
Long-term debt ($ mil.): —	Market value ($ mil.): 1,261.4

	STOCK PRICE ($) FY Close	P/E High/Low		PER SHARE ($) Earnings	Dividends	Book Value
03/11	24.87	—	—	(3.95)	0.00	5.77
03/10	28.90	122	48	0.36	0.00	6.27
03/09	17.31	—	—	(0.39)	0.00	5.13
03/08	23.19	—	—	(0.65)	0.00	5.02
03/07	13.47	—	—	(1.04)	0.00	2.85
Annual Growth	**16.6%**	**—**	**—**	**—**	**—**	**19.3%**

Amerigon

If Bob, Carol, TED, and Alice are in your bed, chances are TED is keeping the mattress cool . . . or warm. Amerigon developed thermoelectric device (TED) technology and has incorporated it into the company's branded Climate-Control Seat (CCS), which allows year-round temperature control and ventilation of car seats on more than 40 vehicle models available in North America and Asia that are made by Ford, General Motors, and Nissan; the three customers collectively account for more than 70% of the company's sales. Amerigon provides the CCS under contracts with auto industry suppliers such as Lear, Bridgewater, and NHK Spring. Amerigon makes about 60% of its sales outside the US.

To support its non-US customers, the company formed Amerigon Europe in fall 2010 to support design, development and engineering in Europe. The company opened a technical support office in Germany to spur sales in that region.

Expanding even further into the European market, Amerigon purchased about 76% of stockholder voting rights for W.E.T. Automotive Systems, a German-based firm that manufactures thermal systems for automotive seat applications. The company plans to pick up the remaining voting shares by launching a tender offer. The transaction is valued at approximately $168 million. In this case, acquisitions make strange bedfellows, just like politics, since Amerigon and W.E.T. are presently embroiled in lawsuits over intellectual property. In 2008 W.E.T. launched a thermal seat system to be installed in GM vehicles, and Amerigon filed a patent infringement lawsuit against W.E.T. the following year. The two companies, however, are willing to put the lawsuit on hold pending the successful completion of the acquisition.

Amerigon acquired its research and development subsidiary BSST in 2010. Preceding the acquisition, BSST formed a 50/50 partnership in 2009 with 5N Plus, a Canadian manufacturer of high-purity metals and compounds for electronic applications, to create a joint venture known as ZT Plus. The business was formed to develop and make thermoelectric materials, but the venture was short-lived. Its development progress was not as speedy as 5N Plus expected, spurring the company to sell its entire stake in ZT Plus to Amerigon just a year later.

BSST heads a development team comprising Visteon, BMW, Ford, Marlow Industries, and the Department of Energy's National Renewable Energy Laboratory and Jet Propulsion Laboratory at the California Institute of Technology. The group is developing a heat recovery and power generation system that will improve the efficiency of vehicles with internal combustion engines, with the DOE supplying more than $7 million in program funding.

Not just automotive seats, cups, and mattresses are warming up — so are Amerigon's revenues. The company reported a hot sales increase of 84% for 2010 over 2009. The company was slammed a couple of years prior when automotive production was at an all-time low, but since North American manufacturers increased vehicle output by almost 40% in 2010, and Amerigon's sales have been on the rise.

Amerigon's bottom line was also helped with the launch of a couple of new products. In late 2010 it debuted its heated and cooled dual cup holder for vehicles, with Chrysler's Dodge Charger being the first recipient. Also in 2010 the company premiered its heated and cooled suite of mattresses using Amerigon's thermoelectric technologies. The branded YuMe mattresses are sold through retailer Mattress Firm, the retail subsidiary of Mattress Holding.

Another non-automotive product is Amerigon's C2 climate control device — a personal heating/cooling system, standing only 10 inches tall, for use in regulating the temperature in personal workspaces, such as offices or cubicles. The C2 is offered exclusively through office furniture maker Herman Miller.

EXECUTIVES

Chairman, Oscar B. (Bud) Marx III, age 72
President, CEO, and Director, Daniel R. Coker, age 58, $877,866 total compensation

VP Finance, CFO, Secretary, and Treasurer, Barry G. Steele, age 40, $385,278 total compensation
VP Sales and Marketing, Daniel J. Pace, age 59, $337,463 total compensation
VP Quality and Operations, James L. Mertes, age 58, $359,105 total compensation
CIO; CFO, BSST, Sandra L. Grouf, age 51
Auditors: Grant Thornton LLP

LOCATIONS

HQ: Amerigon Incorporated
  21680 Haggerty Rd., Ste. 101, Northville, MI 48167
Phone: 248-504-0500   **Fax:** 248-348-9735
Web: amerigon.com

2010 Sales

	$ mil.	% of total
US	41.9	37
Japan	21.1	19
South Korea	18.7	16
Mexico	16.0	14
UK	8.6	8
Canada	4.3	4
China	1.1	1
Germany	0.7	1
Taiwan	-	-
Total	**112.4**	**100**

PRODUCTS/OPERATIONS

2010 Sales by Customer

	% of total
Ford Motor Company	32
General Motors	22
Nissan	17
Hyundai	16
Jaguar/Land Rover	8
Toyota	5
Total	**100**

Selected Capabilities

Advancing core technology
Noise, vibration, and airflow management
Program management
Testing
Thermoelectric applications

COMPETITORS

Delphi Automotive	Robert Bosch
Leggett & Platt	Toyota Boshoku
Magna International	Visteon

HISTORICAL FINANCIALS

Company Type: Public

Income Statement

FYE: December 31

	REVENUE ($ mil.)	NET INCOME ($ mil.)	NET PROFIT MARGIN	EMPLOYEES
12/10	112.4	9.9	8.8%	93
12/09	60.9	0.7	1.1%	68
12/08	63.6	3.6	5.7%	78
12/07	63.6	7.4	11.6%	71
12/06	50.6	3.5	6.9%	59
Annual Growth	**22.1%**	**29.7%**	**—**	**12.0%**

2010 Year-End Financials

Debt ratio: —	No. of shares (mil.): 22.0
Return on equity: 17.3%	Dividends
Cash ($ mil.): 26.6	Yield: —
Current ratio: 3.23	Payout: —
Long-term debt ($ mil.): —	Market value ($ mil.): 239.8

	STOCK PRICE ($) FY Close	P/E High/Low		PER SHARE ($) Earnings	Dividends	Book Value
12/10	10.88	27	16	0.44	0.00	2.61
12/09	7.94	328	71	0.03	0.00	2.24
12/08	3.26	127	15	0.16	0.00	2.03
12/07	21.14	68	28	0.33	0.00	1.96
12/06	9.66	66	29	0.16	0.00	1.56
Annual Growth	**3.0%**	**—**	**—**	**28.8%**	**—**	**13.8%**

Amexdrug

Amexdrug, through subsidiaries Allied Med and Dermagen, is a wholesale distributor of pharmaceuticals, nutritional supplements, and beauty products to pharmacies and other retailers. The company allows small pharmacies to get the lower prices that large pharmaceutical chains such as Walgreen and CVS enjoy. Its customers are primarily located in California. Part of Allied Med's growth strategy includes increasing its online traffic, so it is increasing its name recognition and branding efforts. Top executive Jack Amin and his wife own more than 90% of the company.

Amexdrug expanded in the western US by acquiring health care distribution company Dermagen in 2005, which also has health and beauty product manufacturing operations. The company plans to further expand its service area.

The company has formed two new subsidiaries to increase its manufacturing operations. BioRx repackages and sells generic and branded pharmaceutical products. Royal Health Care was formed to manufacture health and beauty products but is not yet active.

EXECUTIVES

President, Secretary, Treasurer, and Director, Jack Amin, age 52
Auditors: HJ Associates & Consultants, LLP

LOCATIONS

HQ: Amexdrug Corporation
  8909 W. Olympic Blvd., Ste. 208, Beverly Hills, CA 90211
Phone: 310-855-0475   **Fax:** 888-325-2499
Web: www.amexdrug.com

PRODUCTS/OPERATIONS

2007 Sales

	$ mil.	% of total
Distribution	5.9	97
Health & beauty products	0.2	3
Total	**6.1**	**100**

COMPETITORS

AmerisourceBergen	Purity Wholesale
Apothecary Products	Grocers
Cardinal Health	The Harvard Drug Group
Diamond Drugs Inc.	Watson Pharmaceuticals
McKesson	

Income Statement				FYE: December 31
	REVENUE ($ mil.)	NET INCOME ($ mil.)	NET PROFIT MARGIN	EMPLOYEES
12/10	11.5	0.2	1.7%	11
12/09	9.8	—	—	14
12/08	5.7	—	—	15
12/07	6.1	—	—	6
12/06	4.6	—	—	6
Annual Growth	25.7%	—	—	16.4%

2010 Year-End Financials

Debt ratio: —	No. of shares (mil.): 8.5
Return on equity: 75.5%	Dividends
Cash ($ mil.): 0.4	Yield: —
Current ratio: 1.19	Payout: —
Long-term debt ($ mil.): —	Market value ($ mil.): 12.9

	STOCK PRICE ($) FY Close	P/E High/Low		PER SHARE ($) Earnings	Dividends	Book Value
12/10	1.52	180	5	0.02	0.00	0.03
12/09	2.20	—	—	(0.00)	0.00	0.01
12/08	1.02	—	—	(0.00)	0.00	0.01
12/07	1.20	—	—	(0.00)	0.00	0.00
12/06	2.05	—	—	(0.00)	0.00	0.00
Annual Growth	(7.2%)	—	—	—	—	68.9%

Amtech Systems

Amtech Systems furnishes fabs with furnaces and more. The company operates through four subsidiaries — Tempress Systems makes diffusion furnaces for semiconductor and solar cell fabrication, as well as for precision thermal processing (annealing, brazing, silvering, sealing, and soldering) of electronic devices, including optical components and photovoltaic (PV) solar cells. P.R. Hoffman Machine Products makes equipment used to polish items such as silicon wafers, precision optics, ceramic components, and disk media. Bruce Technologies makes horizontal diffusion furnace systems, and R2D Automation is in France. Most of its revenues come from customers in the Asia/Pacific region, primarily from China and Taiwan.

R2D Automation supplies automation equipment used to make semiconductors and solar cells. Acquired late in 2007, the purchase expanded Amtech's automation product line and gave the company the ability to offer an integrated system for solar cell manufacturing.

Amtech manufactures most of its products in the Netherlands; facilities in France and the US account for about a quarter of production. The company also markets plasma-enhanced chemical vapor deposition systems, antireflective coating systems, and dry etch systems for solar cells produced by PST Co., Ltd., a South Korea-based maker of vertical thermal processing systems.

Amtech was one of the first suppliers of semiconductor production equipment to provide equipment for making photovoltaic solar cells, which are made in a process similar to semiconductor manufacturing on silicon wafers. The company started supplying Tempress diffusion furnaces for solar cell manufacturing in the early 21st century, a

move since emulated by Applied Materials and other big vendors of semiconductor equipment.

After several years of growth, business in this market dropped off in 2009 due to oversupply in the global solar industry along with reductions in spending on capital equipment by manufacturers. Amtech responded to reduced demand for its products by managing its costs, including cutting its workforce by 28% that year.

The company returned to profitability in 2010, however, reporting record revenues of 127% growth. That year it also stopped offering semiconductor manufacturing support services.

The company continues to see future growth in the solar cell manufacturing sector, specifically in China, home to hundreds of manufacturers in the solar cell supply chain. (China accounted for almost two-thirds of sales in 2010). In 2011 it bought a 55% stake in Kingstone Technology, the Hong Kong owner of Kingstone Semiconductor, a Shanghai-based company that makes ion implantation technology for the solar and semiconductor industries. Amtech paid $4 million for the Kingstone stake, which will be used to develop a next-generation solar ion implant machine.

EXECUTIVES

Chairman amd CEO, Jong S. Whang, age 65, $631,293 total compensation
President, Fokko Pentinga
VP Finance, CFO, Treasurer, and Secretary, Bradley C. Anderson, age 49, $403,180 total compensation
Chief Accounting Officer, Robert T. Hass, age 60, $189,315 total compensation
Auditors: Mayer Hoffman McCann P.C.

LOCATIONS

HQ: Amtech Systems, Inc.
131 S. Clark Dr., Tempe, AZ 85281-3008
Phone: 480-967-5146 **Fax:** 480-968-3763
Web: www.amtechsystems.com

2010 Sales

	$ mil.	% of total
The Netherlands	93.4	78
US	15.0	12
France	11.6	10
Total	**120.0**	**100**

PRODUCTS/OPERATIONS

Products
Atmoscan (controlled-environment wafer processing systems)
Diffusion furnaces (horizontal and conveyor diffusion furnace systems)
Double-sided precision lapping and polishing machines
Carriers
Plates, gears, and other parts
Polishing templates
Individual boats with automated loading (IBAL) systems and modules
IBAL Butler (wafer transferring device)
IBAL Queue (staging area and automated boat loading)
IBAL Trolley (automatic boat placement, used with Atmoscan)
Load stations (mounting for IBAL systems or diffusion furnaces)

COMPETITORS

Applied Materials	Mattson Technology
Brooks Automation	MRL Industries
CVD Equipment	Novellus
Esec	OTB Group
GT Advanced Technologies	Tokyo Electron

Income Statement				FYE: September 30
	REVENUE ($ mil.)	NET INCOME ($ mil.)	NET PROFIT MARGIN	EMPLOYEES
09/10	120.0	9.6	8.0%	360
09/09	53.0	(1.6)	—	190
09/08	80.3	2.9	3.6%	210
09/07	46.0	2.4	5.2%	165
09/06	40.4	1.3	3.2%	153
Annual Growth	31.3%	64.8%	—	23.9%

2010 Year-End Financials

Debt ratio: —	No. of shares (mil.): 9.2
Return on equity: 11.4%	Dividends
Cash ($ mil.): 56.8	Yield: —
Current ratio: 2.29	Payout: —
Long-term debt ($ mil.): —	Market value ($ mil.): 165.4

	STOCK PRICE ($) FY Close	P/E High/Low		PER SHARE ($) Earnings	Dividends	Book Value
09/10	17.96	18	5	1.04	0.00	9.15
09/09	5.30	—	—	(0.18)	0.00	8.24
09/08	9.31	55	27	0.32	0.00	8.19
09/07	12.82	32	14	0.44	0.00	5.86
09/06	6.65	27	14	0.38	0.00	4.49
Annual Growth	28.2%	—	—	28.6%	—	19.5%

AmTrust Financial

Insurance holding company AmTrust Financial Services likes a mix of businesses on its plate. Its subsidiaries offer a range of commercial property/casualty insurance products for small and midsized customers, including workers' compensation products, auto and general liability, and extended service and warranty coverage of consumer and commercial goods. It also provides a small amount of personal auto reinsurance. It operates in Bermuda, Ireland, the UK, and the US and distributes is products through brokers, agents, and claims administrators. The company's customers include restaurants, retail stores, physicians' offices, auto and consumer electronics manufacturers, and trucking operations.

Historically, AmTrust's premium revenue was fairly evenly split among three segments: Small Commercial Business, Specialty Risk and Extended Warranty, and Specialty Middle Market Business. In 2010 it gained a minority stake in GMAC Insurance Personal Lines, the former US consumer property/casualty insurance business of GMAC (now known as Ally Financial). That stake gave the company access to writing 10% of the reinsurance on GMAC's US personal auto insurance. While that business only accounts for a small portion of AmTrust's premiums, it gave it access to a distribution network of more than 10,000 independent agents and helped to diversify the company's revenue streams.

AmTrust's small commercial business is limited to the US. However the EU accounts for more than 70% of its specialty risk and extended warranty coverage. Key to AmTrust's overall business strategy is keeping its portfolio diversified by both business line and geography.

The company has been able to expand its product offerings and geographic reach through acquisitions of smaller competitors, though it approaches its purchases with a conservative eye, avoiding huge financial investments. Past buys include Princeton Insurance in the Northeast; The Covenant Group, Inc. in the South; Associated Industries Insurance in Florida; Muirfield Underwriters in the Midwest; and IGI Group in the UK. In other instances, the company simply acquires the renewal rights to blocks of policies issued by other companies. It acquired the renewal rights to Unitrin's Business Insurance unit in 2008, and picked up a block of workers' compensation policies from Majestic Insurance Company in 2011.

To diversify into new areas, the company has made small investments in a range of businesses including one that acquires life settlement contracts and another that provides risk services.

The company took a larger bite out of the warranty business through the purchase of Warrantech in 2010. AmTrust previously held a minority stake in Warrantech; it made the third-party warranty administration company a wholly owned subsidiary by purchasing the 73% interest held by H.I.G. Capital through a $35 million cash and debt transaction.

AmTrust was established in 1998, when it was acquired from Wang Laboratories. Chairman Michael Karfunkel holds 25% of AmTrust, his brother George Karfunkel holds 25%, and his son-in-law CEO Barry Zyskind holds 10%. The same men formed Bermuda-based Maiden Holdings which enjoys reinsurance agreements with AmTrust.

The company had been in a struggle with unrelated AmTrust Bank over the use of the name "AmTrust" until the bank went out of business in 2009. AmTrust Financial Services is also unrelated to AmTrust Financial Corp., the former parent of AmTrust Bank.

EXECUTIVES

Chairman, Michael Karfunkel, age 68
President, CEO, and Director, Barry D. Zyskind, age 39, $2,233,649 total compensation
CFO, Ronald E. Pipoly Jr., age 44, $1,108,823 total compensation
CEO, AmTrust Europe; President, AmTrust International Insurance, Max G. Caviet, age 58, $1,115,063 total compensation
VP Investor Relations, Hilly Gross
COO, Michael J. Saxon, age 52, $1,235,476 total compensation
CIO, Christopher M. Longo, age 37, $987,560 total compensation
Investor Relations, Ellen Taylor
General Counsel and Secretary, Stephen B. Ungar
Auditors: BDO Seidman, LLP

LOCATIONS

HQ: AmTrust Financial Services, Inc.
59 Maiden Ln., 6th Fl., New York, NY 10038
Phone: 212-220-7120   **Fax:** 212-220-7130
Web: www.amtrustgroup.com

PRODUCTS/OPERATIONS

2010 Earned Premiums

	% of total
Specialty risk & extended warranty	41
Small commercial business	34
Specialty	19
Personal lines reinsurance	6
Total	**100**

Selected Subsidiaries

AmTrust Europe, Ltd. (specialty risk and extended warranty coverage, EU)
AmTrust International Insurance Ltd. (reinsurance, Bermuda)
AmTrust International Underwriters Limited (specialty risk and extended warranty coverage, EU)
Associated Industries Insurance Company, Inc. (workers' compensation)
Milwaukee Casualty Insurance Company (small commercial business)
Rochdale Insurance Company (specialty property/casualty, specialty risk and extended warranty, workers' compensation)
Security National Insurance Company (small commercial business)
Technology Insurance Company, Inc. (specialty property/casualty, specialty risk and extended warranty, workers' compensation)
Wesco Insurance Company (specialty property/casualty, specialty risk and extended warranty, workers' compensation)

COMPETITORS

AIG	Liberty Mutual
Allianz Insurance	National Indemnity
Amica Mutual	Company
Bankers Financial	The Hartford
Berkshire Hathaway	Travelers Companies
FCCI	

HISTORICAL FINANCIALS

Company Type: Public

Income Statement

FYE: December 31

	ASSETS ($ mil.)	NET INCOME ($ mil.)	INCOME AS % OF ASSETS	EMPLOYEES
12/10	4,182.5	142.5	3.4%	1,400
12/09	3,400.4	103.2	3.0%	1,000
12/08	3,143.9	82.9	2.6%	900
12/07	2,322.8	90.1	3.9%	625
12/06	1,185.4	48.9	4.1%	325
Annual Growth	37.1%	30.7%	—	44.1%

2010 Year-End Financials

Equity as % of assets: —	Dividends
Return on assets: 3.4%	Yield: 1.7%
Return on equity: 19.9%	Payout: 12.3%
Long-term debt ($ mil.): 130.4	Market value ($ mil.): 1,042.4
No. of shares (mil.): 59.6	Sales ($ mil.): 1,002.5

	STOCK PRICE ($) FY Close	P/E High	P/E Low	PER SHARE ($) Earnings	Dividends	Book Value
12/10	17.50	8	5	2.36	0.29	12.03
12/09	11.82	8	4	1.72	0.23	9.60
12/08	11.60	13	4	1.37	0.18	6.54
12/07	13.77	15	6	1.49	0.11	6.51
12/06	8.55	11	9	0.87	0.02	5.68
Annual Growth	19.6%	—	—	28.3%	95.1%	20.6%

Amyris

Amyris Biotechnologies is engineering yeast to rise over the world's dependence on petroleum. The company developed a process that uses genetically modified molecules from yeast to create biofuels and other renewable chemicals as an alternative to petroleum products. Amyris uses fermented yeast from Brazilian sugarcane to produce Biofene, a chemical that can replace petroleum as the basis for such products as detergent, cosmetics, perfume, industrial lubricants, and fuel. The company, which has operations in the US and Brazil through a joint venture with sugar giant Grupo S o Martinho called SMA Industria Quimica S.A. Amyris, went public in 2010 and expects to have its products ready for market by 2012.

Amyris began trading shares in September 2010, raising $86 million. It plans to use proceeds from its IPO to convert an ethanol plants in Brazil into a production plant. Net income was a loss in 2010, as the company is still in development and has yet to generate a profit.

Its strategy is to commercialize in select specialty chemical markets in order to generate revenues with current production process efficiencies; leverage its technology platforms to improve efficiencies; focus on Brazilian sugar cane as its primary raw material; and keep its production facilities simple and scalable. Amyris' focus is commercialization and production of a single molecule, Biofene and its derivatives, for use in a range of specialty chemical applications within the cosmetics, lubricants, flavors and fragrances, polymers, consumer products, and transportation fuels markets.In 2010, Amyris entered into an agreement with Usina S o Martinho, one of the largest sugar and ethanol producers in Brazil, to establish a joint venture to construct and operate the first commercial plant dedicated to the production of Amyris renewable products. The plant is expected to be operational in 2012.

Amyris also has agreements with Brazilian sugar and ethanol producers Bunge Limited, Cosan, and Açúcar Guarani (a subsidiary of Tereos) to explore producing plant-based fuels and specialty chemicals. Producing Biofene instead of ethanol from fermented sugarcane won't require a major overhaul to the companies' production process. Amyris plans to utilize the companies' already-established production plants and ethanol producers to expand its product base and adapt to demand (or lack thereof) in the ethanol market.

Amyris also has a fuel distribution arm, Amyris Fuels, LLC, which imports biofuels from Brazil into the US. Amyris Fuels imports ethanol from other manufacturers in order to establish relationships with US trading partners. Once Amyris's own biofuel is ready for market, the company plans to integrate it into the distribution network.The company has also negotiated development and commercialization agreements with an affiliate of Total SA, initially focusing on renewable lubricants and jet fuel, and with Firmenich and Givaudan, global flavors and fragrances companies firms, focusing on a key ingredients for the flavors and fragrances market.

Amyris was initially created to develop strains of yeast into a new treatment for malaria. CTO Dr. Neil Renninger was earning his Ph.D. from the University of California Berkeley when his work was funded by a grant from the Bill & Melinda Gates Foundation and Amyris was born. The malarial technology was licensed to Sanofi in 2008, after Amyris' research grew into biofuel.

EXECUTIVES

CFO, Jeryl L. Hilleman, age 53, $468,198 total compensation
President, CEO, and Director, John G. Melo, age 45, $829,950 total compensation
COO, Mario Portela, age 49
CTO, Neil Renninger, age 36
Chief Commercial Officer, Peter (Pete) Boynton, age 56

SVP Research Programs and Operations, Joel Cherry, age 50, $1,094,420 total compensation
SVP Process Development and Manufacturing, Jefferson Lievense, age 56, $589,843 total compensation
Sales and Marketing, Amyris Fuels, Mike Montalvo
Supply and Risk Management, Amyris Fuels, Andrew Meyer
SVP Vertical Markets and Sales Operations, Jim Richardson
Investor and Media Relations, Erin Kinsella
SVP Research, Jack D. Newman, age 44
SVP, General Counsel, and Secretary, Tamara Tompkins, age 46, $362,748 total compensation
SVP Corporate Development and Director, Keith Kinkead Reiling, age 37
Auditors: PricewaterhouseCoopers LLP

LOCATIONS

HQ: Amyris, Inc.
5885 Hollis St., Ste. 100, Emeryville, CA 94608
Phone: 510-450-0761   Fax: 510-225-2646
Web: www.amyris.com

PRODUCTS/OPERATIONS

2010 Sales

	$ mil	% of total
Product sales	68.7	86
Collaborative research	11.7	14
Total	**80.3**	**100**

COMPETITORS

Abengoa Bioenergy	Global Environmental
Aventine	Infinity Bio-Energy
BioFuel Energy	Mascoma Corp
Codexis	Novozymes
Copersucar	Shell Renewables
FutureFuel	

HISTORICAL FINANCIALS

Company Type: Public

Income Statement

FYE: December 31

	REVENUE ($ mil.)	NET INCOME ($ mil.)	NET PROFIT MARGIN	EMPLOYEES
12/10	80.3	(81.9)	—	371
12/09	64.6	(64.5)	—	248
12/08	13.9	(41.9)	—	0
12/07	6.2	(11.8)	—	0
Annual Growth	134.8%	—	—	49.6%

2010 Year-End Financials

Debt ratio: 2.5%	No. of shares (mil.): 43.8
Return on equity: —	Dividends
Cash ($ mil.): 143.1	Yield: —
Current ratio: 9.91	Payout: —
Long-term debt ($ mil.): 7.8	Market value ($ mil.): 1,169.8

	STOCK PRICE ($) FY Close	P/E High/Low		PER SHARE ($) Earnings	Dividends	Book Value
12/10	26.68	—	—	(8.35)	0.00	7.01
Annual Growth	—	—	—	—	—	—

Ancestry.com

Got the urge to know your roots? Ancestry.com helps people discover, research, and share family histories, and create family trees. Users can search through a variety of documents, photographs, maps, and newspapers on the company's website. In addition to this data, Ancestry.com relies on user-generated content and social networking activities — including uploading and sharing family trees, photographs, and documents, and writing stories — to encourage collaboration among users. The company also provides family-history desktop software Family Tree Maker and offers research services. Most of its revenue comes from subscription fees — about 1.4 million paying subscribers access Ancestry.com's offerings.

Ancestry.com subscribers have created more than 20 million family trees containing about 2 billion profiles. They have also uploaded more than 50 million photographs, scanned documents, and written stories. The company focuses on growing its subscriber base by adding new content and tools, improving marketing efforts to increase brand awareness, and expanding internationally. Such efforts have lead to growth in revenues and net income for two consecutive years (2008 to 2010).

Content sources include digitized archives of publicly available US and UK census records and other government documents, historical societies, religious institutions, and private collectors of historical content. The company continues to add new content through acquisitions. It purchased professional genealogical research firm ProGenealogists in 2010. ProGenealogists specializes in genealogical, forensic, and family history research. Later that year it purchased iArchives for approximately $27 million in a mix of stock, cash, and assumption of liabilities. iArchives digitizes images of American historical records of individuals involved in the Revolutionary War, Continental Congress, Civil War, and other US historical events. The deal also added iArchives' American-history website Footnote.com to its holdings.

Boosting its marketing efforts to increase brand awareness, the company has a branding partnership with NBC in the TV show *Who Do You Think You Are?*. The US version of the BBC television series began airing on NBC in 2010, tracing the family histories of celebrities such as Sarah Jessica Parker, Lisa Kudrow, and Spike Lee. Part of the product integration includes a co-branded Ancestry.com website developed in cooperation with NBC. The high-profile nature of Ancestry.com's marketing efforts reveal its competitive advantage as the dominant player in the online market for family history.

Ancestry.com's international growth is the result of the 2010 acquisition of Genline AB, the Swedish market leader in genealogy and local heritage research. The year before, Ancestry.com launched Mundia.com, a global, multilanguage family-history networking product. And in 2008 the company launched Chinese family history website Jiapu.com.

Ancestry.com was founded in 1983 and went public in 2009. In addition to paying down debt, the company used proceeds from its IPO to expand through acquisitions and investments. Private-equity firm Spectrum Equity Investors controls some 40% of Ancestry.com's voting power.

EXECUTIVES

CFO, Howard Hochhauser, age 40
President, CEO, and Director, Timothy P. (Tim) Sullivan, age 48
EVP and General Manager, Ancestry.com, Joshua (Josh) Hanna, age 39
VP International Finance, Jonathan R. H. Wales
VP Community Relations, Loretto Denni (Lou) Szucs
VP International Legal, Ruth Daniels
VP International, Olivier Van Calster
VP Engineering, Scott Sorenson
VP Acquisition, Debra Chesterton
VP People, Jeff Weber
SVP Technology Operations, Jonathan Young
SVP Product, Eric Shoup, age 38
Director Public Relations, Sean Pate
Media Contact, Heather Erickson
SVP and General Manager, DNA, Ken Chahine
Investor Relations, Ryan Ostler
Global VP Customer Relationship Management, Rob Singer
SVP Strategy and Corporate Development, David H. Rinn, age 47
Director International Public Relations, Simon Ziviani
SVP New Business Initiatives, Christopher Tracy, age 43
General Counsel and Corporate Secretary, William C. Stern, age 47
Auditors: Ernst & Young LLP

LOCATIONS

HQ: Ancestry.com Inc.
360 W. 4800 North, Provo, UT 84604
Phone: 801-705-7000   Fax: 801-705-7001
Web: corporate.ancestry.com

2010 Subscription Sales

	% of total
US	75
UK	15
Other countries	10
Total	**100**

PRODUCTS/OPERATIONS

2010 Sales

	$ mil.	% of total
Subscriptions	281.7	94
Product & other	19.2	6
Total	**300.9**	**100**

Selected Products

Ancestry.com DNA (DNA testing kit)
Family Tree Maker (family history desktop software)
Jiapu.com (Chinese website)
Mundia.com (global website)
MyCanvas.com (digital publishing platform)
myfamily.com (family networking service for content sharing)
ProGenealogists (genealogical research)

Selected Sources

Birth, marriage, and death records
Census records
Court, land, and probate records
Immigration records
Military records
Newspapers

HISTORICAL FINANCIALS
Company Type: Public

Income Statement
FYE: December 31

	REVENUE ($ mil.)	NET INCOME ($ mil.)	NET PROFIT MARGIN	EMPLOYEES
12/10	300.9	36.8	12.2%	795
12/09	224.9	21.3	9.5%	720
12/08	197.6	2.4	1.2%	670
12/07	166.4	6.5	3.9%	0
12/06	150.6	8.1	5.4%	0
Annual Growth	18.9%	46.0%	—	8.9%

2010 Year-End Financials
Debt ratio: —	No. of shares (mil.): 45.2
Return on equity: 10.1%	Dividends
Cash ($ mil.): 65.5	Yield: —
Current ratio: 0.71	Payout: —
Long-term debt ($ mil.): —	Market value ($ mil.): 1,279.5

	STOCK PRICE ($) FY Close	P/E High/Low		PER SHARE ($) Earnings	Dividends	Book Value
12/10	28.32	40	18	0.76	0.00	8.05
12/09	14.01	32	25	0.51	0.00	6.95
Annual Growth	102.1%	—	—	49.0%	—	15.8%

Anika Therapeutics

Anika Therapeutics thinks tissue repair is rooster-errific. The company uses hyaluronic acid (HA), a natural polymer extracted from rooster combs and other sources, to make products that treat bone, cartilage, and soft tissue. Anika's Orthovisc treats osteoarthritis of the knee and other joints and is available in the US and overseas. (DePuy Mitek sells the product in the US.) The company also makes and sells products that maintain eye shape and protect tissue during eye surgery, some of which are marketed by Bausch & Lomb. Other items include surgical anti-adhesive products, veterinary osteoarthritis therapies, and dermatology products.

Orthopedic products make up more than half of the company's annual revenues. In addition to Orthovisc, Anika markets two newer osteoarthritis drugs in international markets: Orthovisc mini (for treatment in small joints) and Monovisc, a next-generation, single-injection therapy. Anika is looking to move these products into new markets. For instance, it received Canadian approval for Monovisc in 2009, and it hopes to gain FDA approval to market Monovisc in the US. It has additional osteoarthritis and joint health treatments under development.

The company expanded its orthobiologic offerings in 2009 when it acquired Fidia Farmaceutici Biopolymers (FAB), an Italian producer of HA-based products in a number of therapeutic areas including the regeneration of connective and structural tissues damaged by injuries, aging, or degenerative diseases. FAB's products, which are primarily marketed in Europe, include Hyalograft C for cartilage regeneration and Hyalofast for bone marrow support. The purchase of FAB also added commercialized products in a range of wound care and surgical areas, which were added to Anika's existing dermatology and surgical product lines.

As the exclusive marketer of eye surgery viscoelastic agent Amvisc, Bausch & Lomb has historically accounted for the bulk of Anika's ophthalmic revenues. However, an agreement restricting Anika from marketing its own viscoelastic products expired at the end of 2010, after which the firm moved to commercialize its own competing product, AnikaVisc. The companies also plan to transition the manufacturing of Amvisc to a third-party supplier.

While Anika markets some products on its own, a number of items are sold through additional partnering firms and distribution representatives. A unit of Boehringer Ingelheim sells Anika's osteoarthritis treatment for racehorses, Hyvisc.

Depuy Mitek and Bausch & Lomb are Anika's largest customers, accounting for 40% and 20% of product sales, respectively.

Italian drugmaker Fidia Farmaceutici, former parent of FAB, owns a 15% stake in Anika.

EXECUTIVES
President, CEO, and Director, Charles H. Sherwood, age 64, $882,865 total compensation
CFO, Treasurer and Secretary, Kevin W. Quinlan, age 61, $401,636 total compensation
VP Human Resources, William J. Mrachek, age 67, $318,610 total compensation
VP Regulatory and Clinical Affairs, Irina B. Kulinets, age 56, $348,098 total compensation
VP Operations, Randall W. (Randy) Wilhoite, age 46
COO, Frank J. Luppino, age 42, $480,545 total compensation
CTO, Andrew J. Carter, age 55, $492,012 total compensation
Auditors: PricewaterhouseCoopers LLP

LOCATIONS
HQ: Anika Therapeutics, Inc.
32 Wiggins Ave., Bedford, MA 01730
Phone: 781-457-9000   **Fax:** 781-305-9720
Web: www.anikatherapeutics.com

PRODUCTS/OPERATIONS

2010 Sales

	$ mil.	% of total
Product sales		
Orthobiologics	30.7	55
Opthalmic surgery	12.0	22
Surgical	3.9	7
Dermal	3.6	6
Veterinary	2.6	5
Licensing, milestone & contract revenue	2.8	5
Total	**55.6**	**100**

Selected Products
Orthobiologics
  Hyalofast (bone marrow support)
  Hyaloglide (tenolysis)
  Hyalograft C (autograft for cartilage regeneration)
  Hyalonect (graft gauze wrap)
  Hyaloss (bone regeneration)
  Monovisc (osteoarthritis)
  OrthoVisc (osteoarthritis, marketed by DePuy Mitek)
  OrthoVisc mini (osteoarthritis in small joints)
Dermal
  Elevess/Hydrelle (aesthetic dermatology products)
  Hyalograft 3D (skin regeneration)
  Hyalomatrix (burn and ulcer treatment)
Ophthalmic
  Amvisc (eye surgery product, sold by Bausch & Lomb)
  Amvisc Plus (eye surgery product, sold by Bausch & Lomb)
  AnikaVisc (eye surgery product)
  Optivisc (formerly ShellGel, ophthalmic product)
  STAARVISC II (ophthalmic product, sold by STAAR Surgical)
Surgical
  Hyalobarrier (post-operative adhesion barrier)
  Incert (post-surgical adhesion prevention product)
Veterinary
  Hyvisc (equine osteoarthritis treatment, distributed by Boehringer Ingelheim)

COMPETITORS
Allergan	Pfizer
Fibrocell Science	Smith & Nephew
Genzyme Biosurgery	Solta Medical
Integra LifeSciences	Stellar Pharmaceuticals
Lifecore Biomedical	
Medicis Pharmaceutical	Stryker
Merz Aesthetics	Zimmer Holdings
OrthoLogic	
Pathfinder Cell Therapy	

HISTORICAL FINANCIALS
Company Type: Public

Income Statement
FYE: December 31

	REVENUE ($ mil.)	NET INCOME ($ mil.)	NET PROFIT MARGIN	EMPLOYEES
12/10	55.6	4.3	7.7%	114
12/09	40.1	3.7	9.2%	133
12/08	35.8	3.6	10.1%	84
12/07	30.8	6.0	19.5%	82
12/06	26.8	4.6	17.2%	64
Annual Growth	20.0%	(1.7%)	—	15.5%

2010 Year-End Financials
Debt ratio: 13.1%	No. of shares (mil.): 13.5
Return on equity: 5.1%	Dividends
Cash ($ mil.): 28.2	Yield: —
Current ratio: 2.91	Payout: —
Long-term debt ($ mil.): 11.2	Market value ($ mil.): 89.9

	STOCK PRICE ($) FY Close	P/E High/Low		PER SHARE ($) Earnings	Dividends	Book Value
12/10	6.67	25	15	0.32	0.00	6.32
12/09	7.63	29	9	0.32	0.00	6.12
12/08	3.04	46	9	0.32	0.00	5.34
12/07	14.55	42	23	0.53	0.00	4.92
12/06	13.27	37	23	0.41	0.00	4.24
Annual Growth	(15.8%)	—	—	(6.0%)	—	10.5%

Antares Pharma

Antares Pharma understands antagonism towards needles. The company develops needle-free systems for administering injectable drugs. Its Medi-Jector Vision system, for instance, injects a thin, high-pressure stream of liquid, eliminating the need for a needle. The Vision system is used primarily for the delivery of insulin and of human growth hormones; it is available over-the-counter and by prescription in the US and is also sold overseas. In addition to its needle-free systems, the company develops other drug-delivery platforms, including topical gels, orally administered disintegrating tablets, and mini-needle injection systems.

Much of the company's revenue, particularly for its injection devices, comes via agreements with pharmaceutical partners, which sell its needle-free injectors along with their drugs. Dutch drug firm Ferring, which distributes Antares' needle-free device for use with its human growth hormone, is the company's largest customer, accounting for about 40% of sales. In 2009 partner Teva Pharmaceutical launched a human growth hormone product using the Antares technology.

Antares is working on two second-generation versions of its Medi-Jector Vision system. The Vibex pressure-assisted auto injector is a disposable device that uses similar technology to the Vision system, but is designed to work faster and more effectively. The company is also working on a disposable pen injector system that uses multiple small needles.

The company won FDA approval for its first topical gel product, the Elestrin treatment for menopausal symptoms, with BioSante in 2006. It is working on a number of other gel-based drugs, including one for the treatment of overactive bladder. The company expanded its relationship with Ferring to include development of some gel products in 2009.

Antares was formed in 2001 when Medi-Ject (the company's former name) completed a reverse acquisition of Permatec, a Swiss company with expertise in topical and oral drug delivery technologies. Director Jacques Gonella, the founder of Permatec, owns about 15% of Antares Pharma.

EXECUTIVES

Chairman, Leonard S. Jacob, age 62
President, CEO, and Director, Paul K. Wotton, age 50, $288,687 total compensation
EVP, CFO, Corporate Secretary; President, Parenteral Products, Robert F. (Bob) Apple, age 44, $489,020 total compensation
VP Clinical and Regulatory Affairs, Kaushik J. Dave
SVP Business Development, Pavan Handa
SVP and Managing Director, Parenteral Products, Peter L. Sadowski, age 63, $332,198 total compensation
Auditors: KPMG LLP

LOCATIONS

HQ: Antares Pharma, Inc.
250 Phillips Blvd., Ste. 290, Ewing, NJ 08618
Phone: 609-359-3020   **Fax:** 609-359-3015
Web: www.antarespharma.com

2009 Sales

	$ mil.	% of total
US	4.4	53
Europe	3.7	45
Other	0.2	2
Total	**8.3**	**100**

PRODUCTS/OPERATIONS

2009 Sales

	$ mil.	% of total
Product sales	3.5	42
Development revenue	2.6	32
Licensing fees	1.6	19
Royalties	0.6	7
Total	**8.3**	**100**

COMPETITORS

Abbott Labs	Columbia Laboratories
Apricus	Elan
Aradigm	Novavax
Auxilium	Owen Mumford
Pharmaceuticals	SkyePharma
Becton, Dickinson	Watson Pharmaceuticals
Bioject Medical	Zogenix

HISTORICAL FINANCIALS

Company Type: Public

Income Statement

FYE: December 31

	REVENUE ($ mil.)	NET INCOME ($ mil.)	NET PROFIT MARGIN	EMPLOYEES
12/10	12.8	(6.1)	—	21
12/09	8.3	(10.3)	—	19
12/08	5.7	(12.7)	—	24
12/07	7.9	(8.6)	—	33
12/06	4.3	(8.1)	—	30
Annual Growth	**31.4%**	**—**	**—**	**(8.5%)**

2010 Year-End Financials

Debt ratio: —
Return on equity: —
Cash ($ mil.): 9.8
Current ratio: 1.87
Long-term debt ($ mil.): —

No. of shares (mil.): 84.2
Dividends
Yield: —
Payout: —
Market value ($ mil.): 143.1

	STOCK PRICE ($) FY Close	P/E High/Low		PER SHARE ($) Earnings	Dividends	Book Value
12/10	1.70	—	—	(0.07)	0.00	0.08
12/09	1.14	—	—	(0.14)	0.00	0.11
12/08	0.37	—	—	(0.19)	0.00	0.11
12/07	0.98	—	—	(0.14)	0.00	0.27
12/06	1.20	—	—	(0.16)	0.00	0.10
Annual Growth	**9.1%**	**—**	**—**	**—**	**—**	**(4.8%)**

API Technologies

API Technologies is good at defense. Through various operating subsidiaries, the company designs and manufactures highly-engineered electronic components and robotics, as well as secure communications systems for military and aerospace applications. It develops products for missile, electronic warfare, flight control, and range finder systems, as well as devices that remotely manage critical IT and communications systems. With manufacturing facilities in North America and the UK, API maintains a direct sales and marketing team and primarily sells to defense prime contractors and contract manufacturers. Roughly half of its revenues are generated by US Department of Defense subcontractors.

Other customers include the governments of Canada and the UK, NATO, the European Union, and a number of Fortune 500 companies.

Furthering its access to the US defense industry, API Technologies and the Defense Department have established a corporate structure through proxy agreement that allows the company to compete for classified programs and contracts through its subsidiary, API Defense USA. As part of the agreement, all of API Technologies' operating subsidiaries will become subsidiaries of security-cleared API Defense USA, which will be governed by a Proxy Board with the required security clearances. By creating this new structure, the company enters the classified projects market, the fastest-growing segment of defense contracting.

API Technologies took its current name in 2009 following a major acquisition of Cryptek Technologies, now API Cryptek, a provider of secure network and hardware systems. The deal about doubled API's size and gave it a portfolio of security products that help shield sensitive IT systems and data. API Cryptek's products, including TEMPEST emanation security and Netgard MFD smartcard authentication devices, are used by governments and other international organizations that require an extremely high level of security.

After changing its name to API Technologies, the company made a second significant acquisition of the Kuchera Group of Companies (KGC) in early 2010. The purchase gave API new product lines in engineered components and robotics for the defense, aerospace, and communications markets. Shortly after that acquisition, API closed and sold its former business, a historically unprofitable nanotechnology research and development subsidiary.

In its third acquisition in as many years, API Technologies bought electronics manufacturing services company SenDEC in 2011. The purchase adds new manufacturing capabilities and more than doubles the size of API in terms of sales; it also provides API with $30 million in cash, which it will use to pay down debt. The acquisition was paid for with stock issued to private equity firm Vintage Capital Management, which becomes API's majority shareholder.

API followed the SenDEC acquisition with the 2011 purchase of Spectrum Control, a maker of custom electronic products for the defense, aerospace, medical, and industrial industries. API paid about $270 million in cash for the company, which became a subsidiary. By combining its own products with those of Spectrum Control, API saw an opportunity to provide its defense and aerospace customers with a wider range of products and services.

EXECUTIVES

Chairman and CEO, Brian R. Kahn, age 37
President and COO, Bel Lazar, age 50
CEO, Defense USA, Stephen B. (Steve) Pudles, age 52, $985,217 total compensation
EVP; General Manager, API Defense and API Systems, Carl Sax
EVP, Jonathan Pollack, age 40
VP Finance and Chief Accounting Officer, Andrew Laurence
VP Finance and CFO, Claudio A. Mannarino, age 41, $173,393 total compensation
VP; General Manager Components and Subsystems, Defense USA, Arnold (Arnie) Markowitz, age 53
VP Sales and Marketing, Defense USA, Brian Throneberry
Director; CEO, SenDEC, Kenton W. Fiske
Director Marketing, Tara Flynn Condon
Auditors: WithumSmith+Brown, PC

LOCATIONS

HQ: API Technologies Corp.
2200 Smithtown Ave., Ronkonkoma, NY 11779
Phone: 631-981-2400   **Fax:** 631-981-2445
Web: www.apitech.com

PRODUCTS/OPERATIONS

2010 Sales

	$ mil.	% of total
Engineered systems & components	46.3	68
Secure communications	22.2	32
Total	**68.5**	**100**

Selected Products & Services

Components & Subsystems
Controllers
Filters
Hybrid circuits & transformers
Optical components
Transistors

Defense & Aerospace
 Cable & wire harness manufacturing
 Circuit card manufacturing assembly
 Electronics manufacturing services (EMS) & systems
  integration
Emanation Security
 Computing systems
 Network & communications systems
 Office systems
 Ruggedized systems
Secure Communication & Networking
 Network access & authentication
 Remote device administration
Systems & Engineering
 Payloads & accessories
 Robot-assisted inspection, diffusion & detonation
  technology
 Unmanned air vehicles & electric vehicles
 Tactical equipment

COMPETITORS

Aeroflex	Microsemi
Anaren	Pulse Electronics
Bel Fuse	Sanmina-SCI
Celestica	Semtech
Flextronics	
International	
Rectifier	

HISTORICAL FINANCIALS

Company Type: Public

Income Statement

FYE: May 31

	REVENUE ($ mil.)	NET INCOME ($ mil.)	NET PROFIT MARGIN	EMPLOYEES
05/11	108.3	(26.2)	—	630
05/10	68.6	(9.0)	—	597
05/09	25.7	(6.4)	—	250
05/08	31.0	(6.6)	—	336
05/07	20.5	(1.0)	—	320
Annual Growth	**51.6%**	**—**	**—**	**18.5%**

2011 Year-End Financials

Debt ratio: 0.8%	No. of shares (mil.): 49.1
Return on equity: —	Dividends
Cash ($ mil.): 108.4	Yield: —
Current ratio: 5.35	Payout: —
Long-term debt ($ mil.): 1.9	Market value ($ mil.): 337.6

	STOCK PRICE ($) FY Close	P/E High/Low	PER SHARE ($) Earnings	Dividends	Book Value
05/11	6.87	— —	(1.27)	0.00	4.92
05/10	5.24	— —	(1.04)	0.00	2.31
05/09	2.80	— —	(0.76)	0.00	2.39
05/08	5.88	— —	(1.20)	0.00	3.86
05/07	32.52	— —	(0.24)	0.00	3.64
Annual Growth	**(32.2%)**	**— —**	**—**	**—**	**7.8%**

Archipelago Learning

Archipelago Learning is a subscription-based online education company that provides instruction, assessment, and productivity tools to improve student and teacher performance. Its products, *Study Island* and *EducationCity* are used by more than 37,000 elementary and secondary schools in the US, Canada, and the UK to improve student performance on standardized tests. The company's *Northstar Learning* products offer adult education study and exam prep services. It also distributes *Reading Eggs*, an online reading program for younger children. Providence Equity Partners owns nearly half of the company's stock.

Following its 2009 initial public offering, the company used the proceeds (about $75 million) to pay for general business expenses and to fund acquisitions of complementary businesses and in-house product development. Such new development included its 2009 entry into the adult education market through the introduction of its Northstar Learning line. The product provides GED test preparation, college transition courses, and health career and teacher certification exam preparation products.

In its first geographic leap, the company expanded into the UK online education market with the 2010 purchase of EducationCity. The *EducationCity* online product is geared to serve pre-school through sixth grade, neatly overlapping parts of the Study Island product, and is available to schools in the UK and US. Later in 2010 the company inked an agreement with Australia's Blake Publishing to distribute the *Reading Eggs* online reading program in the US, and then extended a royalty agreement to expand the *EducationCity* products into China through a third party.

To deepen its offerings in the US and enter the English language learning market, in 2011 the company paid some $2 million cash to acquire Alloy Multimedia, the publisher of ESL ReadingSmart. The online program offers English as a second language instruction geared for grades 4-12.

Despite recession-triggered budget cuts, the company is sanguine that school districts will start to make the move from print to digital educational content products and test preparation. And, because education standards vary from state to state, the *Study Island* products have been tailored to fit each state. The US Department of Education introduced Common Core Standards for elementary and secondary programs in 2010, and tied some federal funding of local education programming to adoption of the standards. Archipelago Learning immediately invested in products to support the Common Core standards.

CEO Tim McEwen joined on the company in 2007. Archipelago Learning acquired education portal company TeacherWeb in 2008, only to turn around and sell the business the very next year to competitor Edline Holdings for $13 million, 11% of Edline's shares, and three seats on its board. In 2011 it chose to sell the Edline shares to Blackboard, Inc. for some $12.2 million.

EXECUTIVES

Chairman, Peter O. Wilde, age 42
Chairman, President and CEO, Tim McEwen, age 57, $1,504,091 total compensation
EVP and CTO, Ray Lowrey, age 53, $1,309,454 total compensation
EVP Global Sales, Julie Huston, age 44, $618,953 total compensation
EVP, CFO, and Secretary, James B. Walburg, age 57, $1,263,292 total compensation
VP, David (Dave) Muzzo, age 36, $321,821 total compensation
VP, Cameron (Cam) Chalmers, age 35, $318,133 total compensation
VP Product Development, Cathy Caldwell
VP and General Manager, Northstar Learning, Becky Wofford
VP Customer Retention, Greg Smith
VP Publishing, Language Arts and Social Studies, Heather Harper
SVP and COO, Martijn Tel, age 41, $835,966 total compensation

SVP and Chief Marketing Officer, Allison L. Duquette, age 51
Controller, James Creech
Auditors: Deloitte & Touche LLP

LOCATIONS

HQ: Archipelago Learning, Inc.
3232 McKinney Ave., Ste. 400, Dallas, TX 75204
Phone: 800-419-3191   **Fax:** 877-592-1357
Web: www.archipelagolearning.com

2010 Sales

	$ mil.	% of total
US	55.6	95
UK	3.0	5
Total	**58.6**	**100**

PRODUCTS/OPERATIONS

Selected Products

EducationCity (Pre-K-6, assessment program)
Northstar Learning (postsecondary test preparation)
Reading Eggs (preschool-2, literacy program)
Study Island (K-12 standardized test preparation)

COMPETITORS

Cengage Learning	PLATO Learning
Houghton Mifflin	Reed Elsevier Group
Harcourt	Renaissance Learning
McGraw-Hill	Tom Snyder Productions
Pearson Digital	
Learning	

HISTORICAL FINANCIALS

Company Type: Public

Income Statement

FYE: December 31

	REVENUE ($ mil.)	NET INCOME ($ mil.)	NET PROFIT MARGIN	EMPLOYEES
12/10	58.7	3.5	6.0%	402
12/09	42.8	6.7	15.7%	221
12/08	32.1	0.3	0.9%	206
12/07	18.3	2.9	15.8%	0
12/06	10.1	3.7	36.6%	0
Annual Growth	**55.3%**	**(1.4%)**	**—**	**39.7%**

2010 Year-End Financials

Debt ratio: 69.8%	No. of shares (mil.): 26.4
Return on equity: 3.2%	Dividends
Cash ($ mil.): 32.4	Yield: —
Current ratio: 0.92	Payout: —
Long-term debt ($ mil.): 74.9	Market value ($ mil.): 258.5

	STOCK PRICE ($) FY Close	P/E High/Low	PER SHARE ($) Earnings	Dividends	Book Value
12/10	9.81	163 63	0.13	0.00	4.07
12/09	20.70	63 50	0.33	0.00	3.31
Annual Growth	**(52.6%)**	**— —**	**(60.6%)**	**—**	**23.2%**

Ardea Biosciences

Ardea Biosciences is on a quest to cure the incurable disease. The biotechnology company discovers and develops therapies for the treatment of ailments such as HIV, cancer, gout, and inflammatory diseases. The company, which focuses on the development of small-molecule therapies (named as such because the molecular compounds weigh less than 1,000 Daltons), has drug candidates in clinical and preclinical stages of development. In addition to internal programs, Ardea Biosciences is pursuing new therapies through partnerships and licensing efforts.

EXECUTIVES

President, CEO, and Director, Barry D. Quart, age 54, $1,239,327 total compensation
EVP and COO, Stephen R. Davis
SVP Pharmaceutical Sciences, Colin E. Rowlings, age 47
General Counsel, Christian Waage
SVP Regulatory Affairs and Development Operations, Kimberly J. Manhard, age 51, $568,057 total compensation
SVP Finance and Operations and CFO, John W. Beck, age 51, $505,963 total compensation
Auditors: Stonefield Josephson, Inc.

LOCATIONS

HQ: Ardea Biosciences, Inc.
4939 Directors Place, San Diego, CA 92121
Phone: 858-652-6500 **Fax:** 858-625-0760
Web: www.ardeabiosciences.com

COMPETITORS

Amgen	Merck
Eli Lilly	Novartis
Genentech	Pfizer
Hoffmann-La Roche	Sanofi
Incyte	Savient
Locus Pharmaceuticals	

HISTORICAL FINANCIALS

Company Type: Public

Income Statement

FYE: December 31

	REVENUE ($ mil.)	NET INCOME ($ mil.)	NET PROFIT MARGIN	EMPLOYEES
12/10	27.4	(41.6)	—	77
12/09	22.9	(30.9)	—	62
12/08	0.3	(55.0)	—	81
12/07	3.1	(25.1)	—	73
12/00	0.0	(45.6)	—	141
Annual Growth	—	—	—	(5.9%)

2010 Year-End Financials

Debt ratio: 0.3%	No. of shares (mil.): 23.4
Return on equity: —	Dividends
Cash ($ mil.): 15.9	Yield: —
Current ratio: 4.73	Payout: —
Long-term debt ($ mil.): 0.3	Market value ($ mil.): 607.5

	STOCK PRICE ($) FY Close	P/E High/Low	Earnings	PER SHARE ($) Dividends	Book Value
12/10	26.00	— —	(1.91)	0.00	3.30
12/09	14.00	— —	(1.70)	0.00	1.34
12/08	11.97	— —	(3.79)	0.00	3.05
12/07	15.30	— —	(2.55)	0.00	6.26
12/00	4.36	— —	(0.07)	0.00	5.25
Annual Growth	56.3%	— —	—	—	(11.0%)

Arena Pharmaceuticals

Arena Pharmaceuticals is working to put weight loss in the spotlight. The company is focused on developing biopharmaceutical treatments for cardiovascular, central nervous system, inflammatory, and metabolic diseases. Its lead drug candidate lorcaserin could help assist in weight loss and maintenance in obese patients and patients with type 2 diabetes; however, the drug has had trouble gaining FDA approval. From its manufacturing facility in Switzerland, Arena earns a portion of its revenues as a contract manufacturer for another pharmaceutical company. It also supports its operations with income from R&D partnerships and licensing agreements.

The FDA denied approval of lorcaserin in 2010 and requested more clinical trial data before Arena could submit another approval request. As a result, Arena announced plans to control internal expenses through restructuring measures, including a 25% workforce reduction, and focus on core R&D programs. At the same time, the company continues to work with partner Eisai Inc. (the US division of Japanese drugmaker Eisai), to further advance the development of lorcaserin. Eisai and Arena hope to resubmit lorcaserin for FDA approval by the end of 2011; if successful, Eisai will have exclusive rights to market the drug in the US market.

Other candidates in clinical and preclinical research stages include potential treatments for arterial thrombosis, narcolepsy, insomnia, multiple sclerosis, and arthritis. The company also has an early stage candidate for the treatment of type 2 diabetes; this program was conducted through a partnership with Ortho-McNeil until late 2010 when Ortho-McNeil terminated the collaboration. All of the company's candidates are oral drug formulations that target responses in certain protein receptors that mediate cell-to-cell communications.

Arena was entirely dependent upon market support and collaboration agreements to fund its research until 2008, when it purchased a drug manufacturing facility from Siegfried Ltd. Through a long-term supply agreement, it took over the manufacture of certain products for Siegfried, which now accounts for over 40% of its revenues. The company also manufactures its clinical trial supply of lorcaserin at this facility, and it plans to manufacture any commercial products there as well.

EXECUTIVES

Chairman, President, CEO, and Principal Financial Officer, Jack Lief, age 65, $1,563,992 total compensation
VP Marketing and Business Development, Louis J. Scotti, age 55
SVP and Chief Medical Officer, William R. Shanahan, age 62, $620,054 total compensation
SVP, General Counsel, and Secretary, Steven W. Spector, age 46, $700,338 total compensation
SVP, Chief Scientific Officer, and Director, Dominic P. Behan, age 47, $715,327 total compensation
Manager Investor Relations and Corporate Communications, Cindy McGee
Senior Director Corporate Communications, David A. Walsey
SVP Quality and Regulatory Compliance, K. A. Ajit-Simh, age 58
Auditors: Ernst & Young LLP

LOCATIONS

HQ: Arena Pharmaceuticals, Inc.
6166 Nancy Ridge Dr., San Diego, CA 92121
Phone: 858-453-7200 **Fax:** 858-453-7210
Web: www.arenapharm.com

PRODUCTS/OPERATIONS

2010 Sales

	$ mil.	% of total
Collaborative agreements	9.5	57
Manufacturing services	7.1	43
Total	**16.6**	**100**

Selected Drug Candidates

ADP125 (insomnia)
ADP334 (multiple sclerosis)
APD597 (type 2 diabetes)
APD791 (arterial thrombosis)
ADP811 (pulmonary arterial hypertension)
ADP916 (narcolepsy and cataplexy)
CB2 (osteoarthritis and pain)
GPR119 (type 2 diabetes)
Lorcaserin (weight management)

COMPETITORS

Array BioPharma	Pfizer
Cephalon	Roche Holding
GlaxoSmithKline	Sanofi
Johnson & Johnson	Somaxon
Merck	Takeda Pharmaceutical
Orexigen Therapeutics	VIVUS
Palatin Technologies	

HISTORICAL FINANCIALS

Company Type: Public

Income Statement

FYE: December 31

	REVENUE ($ mil.)	NET INCOME ($ mil.)	NET PROFIT MARGIN	EMPLOYEES
12/10	16.6	(124.5)	—	351
12/09	10.4	(153.2)	—	358
12/08	9.8	(237.6)	—	499
12/07	19.3	(143.2)	—	491
12/06	30.6	(86.2)	—	371
Annual Growth	(14.2%)	—	—	(1.4%)

2010 Year-End Financials

Debt ratio: 128.9%	No. of shares (mil.): 121.5
Return on equity: —	Dividends
Cash ($ mil.): 150.7	Yield: —
Current ratio: 4.25	Payout: —
Long-term debt ($ mil.): 103.2	Market value ($ mil.): 209.0

	STOCK PRICE ($) FY Close	P/E High/Low	Earnings	PER SHARE ($) Dividends	Book Value
12/10	1.72	— —	(1.14)	0.00	0.66
12/09	3.55	— —	(1.82)	0.00	0.80
12/08	4.17	— —	(3.24)	0.00	1.59
12/07	7.83	— —	(2.31)	0.00	4.66
12/06	12.91	— —	(1.89)	0.00	7.71
Annual Growth	(39.6%)	— —	—	—	(45.9%)

Ares Capital

Targeting US middle-market companies, Ares Capital invests in senior debt loans (secured loans that receive repayment priority over other types of debt) and mezzanine debt; it also makes equity investments. The firm, which typically invests between $20 and $200 million per transaction, manages a portfolio of more than 90 companies representing the health care, education, food service, beverage, financial services industries, among others. Founded in 2004, Ares Capital is externally managed by Ares Capital Management, a subsidiary of Ares Management LLC. It acquired Allied Capital in 2010, making it one of the largest business development companies in the US, with some $13 billion of capital under management.

The all stock merger was valued at more than $900 million. Ares Capital is looking to sell off some non-core assets that were acquired as part of the Allied deal. However, the Allied deal helped increase Ares Capital's market coverage, scale, and gave it a stronger capital base.

The added strength will help the firm take advantage of an attractive investment environment. Ares Capital sees new opportunities to invest in middle-market companies. The dislocation in the credit markets, as a result of the the recession, has reduced competition and created more favorable conditions for deals.

Ares Capital keeps close tabs on its portfolio companies. It maintains a regular dialogue with the companies and sometimes Ares investment professionals take board seats. The firm targets market-leading companies with growth potential. Key investment sectors include manufacturing, business services, consumer products, health care services, and education. Some of its current investments include INC Research, Campus Management, Savers, and Wastequip.

In addition to its own direct investments Ares Capital also has made investments in subsidiary Ivy Hill Asset Management, which manages 10 unconsolidated senior debt funds. Ares Capital also co-manages an unconsolidated senior debut fund along with GE Commercial Finance Advisory Services.

EXECUTIVES

Chairman, Bennett Rosenthal, age 47
President and Director, Michael J. Arougheti, age 38
CFO, Penni F. Roll, age 45
VP and Chief Compliance Officer, Michael D. Weiner, age 58
VP, Daniel F. Nguyen, age 39
Chief Compliance Officer, Karen A. Tallman, age 53
Managing Director, Ares Capital Management, Mark R. Affolter
Assistant Treasurer; Chief Accounting Officer, Ares Capital Management, Scott C. Lem
Secretary and Assistant Treasurer, Merritt S. Hooper
Auditors: KPMG LLP

LOCATIONS

HQ: Ares Capital Corporation
  280 Park Ave., 44th Fl., New York, NY 10167
Phone: 212-750-7300
Web: www.arescapitalcorp.com

PRODUCTS/OPERATIONS

2010 Sales

	$ in mil.	% of total
Interest from investments	393.5	81
Capital structuring service fees	54.7	11
Management fees	14.4	3
Dividend income	14.4	3
Other	6.4	2
Total	**483.4**	**100**

COMPETITORS

American Capital   Fortress Investment

Apollo Investment   Group
Barclays   Full Circle Capital
BlackRock   Gladstone Investment
Buxbaum Group   MCG Capital
Calamos Asset   Newtek Business
  Management   Services
Cohen & Steers

HISTORICAL FINANCIALS
Company Type: Public

Income Statement
FYE: December 31

	REVENUE ($ mil.)	NET INCOME ($ mil.)	NET PROFIT MARGIN	EMPLOYEES
12/10	483.4	691.8	143.1%	360
12/09	245.3	202.7	82.6%	250
12/08	240.5	(139.5)	—	250
12/07	188.9	94.9	50.2%	0
12/06	120.0	69.7	58.1%	0
Annual Growth	**41.7%**	**77.5%**	**—**	**20.0%**

2010 Year-End Financials

Debt ratio: 45.2%	No. of shares (mil.): 204.4
Return on equity: 22.7%	Dividends
Cash ($ mil.): 100.8	Yield: 8.5%
Current ratio: 1.36	Payout: 35.8%
Long-term debt ($ mil.): 1,378.5	Market value ($ mil.): 3,368.8

	STOCK PRICE ($) FY Close	P/E High/Low		PER SHARE ($) Earnings	Dividends	Book Value
12/10	16.48	4	3	3.91	1.40	14.92
12/09	12.45	6	2	1.99	1.47	11.44
12/08	6.33	—	—	(1.56)	1.68	11.27
12/07	14.63	15	10	1.37	1.66	15.47
12/06	19.11	12	10	1.61	1.54	16.08
Annual Growth	**(3.6%)**	**—**	**—**	**24.8%**	**(2.4%)**	**(1.9%)**

ARIAD Pharmaceuticals

ARIAD Pharmaceuticals is exploring the myriad possibilities for new cancer treatments. The firm has three lead drug candidates: ridaforolimus, ponatinib, and AP26113, each being studied for the treatment of various types of cancer. ARIAD is developing ridaforolimus with Merck and is seeking a development partner for ponatinib, which is being investigated as a possible treatment for chronic myeloid leukemia and other malignancies. AP26113 is in preclinical studies for lung cancer and lymphoma. ARIAD's drug candidates are in varying stages of clinical trials; ridaforolimus is closest to market launch for the treatment of soft tissue and bone sarcomas (aka cancers).

Ridaforolimus works by blocking the cellular functions essential to the disease process by basically starving cancerous cells. It has also shown promise in preventing blockage in blood vessels, so the company has partnered with medical device firms Icon Medical and Medinol to develop drug-eluting stents.

The company's most lucrative development deal by far is the one it has with Merck. ARIAD first landed Merck as a development and marketing partner for ridaforolimus in 2007. The original deal gave ARIAD up-front funding, plus the promise of payments for reaching sales and development milestones, and the understanding that if the drug is approved by the FDA, the two companies

would co-promote it in the US, and Merck would handle marketing and sales internationally. The amended 2010 deal gave Merck responsibility for all ridaforolimus activities related to the development, manufacturing, and commercialization of ridaforolimus. Probably most importantly for ARIAD, the deal gave the company a cash infusion of about $50 million. In addition, ARIAD has the potential to earn another $514 million in milestone payments plus royalties.

Like most drug development companies, ARIAD counts on revenue from such collaborations to remain afloat. Most of the money the company has brought in over the past few years has been from its partnership with Merck and it's anticipating milestone payments for making certain regulatory filings will help keep it afloat once its cash reserves run out. It also expects that its 2011 earnings will drop significantly as compared to 2010 unless it's able to nail down lucrative partnership deals for ponatinib and AP26113.

ARIAD's name refers to the mythical Ariadne, who gave her lover Theseus a spool of thread that guided him safely out of a dangerous labyrinth. Similarly, the firm's drug development efforts focus on the labyrinthine molecular pathways that regulate disease.

EXECUTIVES

Chairman, President, and CEO, Harvey J. Berger, age 60, $1,694,701 total compensation
President, Research and Development and Chief Scientific Officer, Timothy P. (Tim) Clackson, age 45, $740,402 total compensation
EVP, CFO, and Treasurer, Edward M. (Ed) Fitzgerald, age 56, $736,973 total compensation
VP Information Technology and Operations, Kelly M. Schmitz
VP and Chief Medical Officer, Frank G. Haluska
VP Human Resources, Virginia Dean
VP Clinical Operations, Ross D. Pettit
VP Corporate Communications and Investor Relations, Maria E. Cantor
VP Finance and Controller, Joseph Bratica, age 47
VP Research Technologies, David C. Dalgarno, age 52
VP Biostatistics and Outcomes Research, John W. Loewy
VP Manufacturing Operations, Andreas Woppmann
VP Program and Alliance Management, Shirish Hirani
SVP and Chief Intellectual Property Officer, David L. Berstein, age 58
SVP, General Counsel, Secretary, and Chief Compliance Officer, Raymond T. Keane, age 52
SVP Regulatory Affairs and Quality, Daniel M. Bollag, age 50
Investor Relations, Sondra Newman
SVP Development, John D. Iuliucci, age 68, $792,657 total compensation
Auditors: Deloitte & Touche LLP

LOCATIONS

HQ: ARIAD Pharmaceuticals, Inc.
  26 Landsdowne St., Cambridge, MA 02139-4234
Phone: 617-494-0400   **Fax:** 617-494-8144
Web: www.ariad.com

PRODUCTS/OPERATIONS

Selected Drug Candidates
AP26113 (lung cancer, lymphoma)
Ponatinib (leukemia, solid tumors)
Ridaforolimus (solid tumors, blood cancers)

COMPETITORS

Amgen	Merck KGaA
AstraZeneca	Novartis
Biogen Idec	Onyx Pharmaceuticals
Bristol-Myers Squibb	OSI Pharmaceuticals
Eli Lilly	Pfizer
Genzyme	Roche Holding
GlaxoSmithKline	Telik, Inc.
Johnson & Johnson	Zeltia
Merck	

HISTORICAL FINANCIALS

Company Type: Public

Income Statement

FYE: December 31

	REVENUE ($ mil.)	NET INCOME ($ mil.)	NET PROFIT MARGIN	EMPLOYEES
12/10	179.0	85.2	47.6%	122
12/09	8.3	(80.0)	—	149
12/08	7.1	(71.1)	—	150
12/07	3.6	(58.5)	—	116
12/06	0.9	(61.9)	—	103
Annual Growth	275.5%	—	—	4.3%

2010 Year-End Financials

Debt ratio: 12.9%	No. of shares (mil.): 126.9
Return on equity: 133.0%	Dividends
Cash ($ mil.): 103.6	Yield: —
Current ratio: 6.41	Payout: —
Long-term debt ($ mil.): 8.3	Market value ($ mil.): 647.4

	STOCK PRICE ($) FY Close	P/E High/Low		PER SHARE ($) Earnings	Dividends	Book Value
12/10	5.10	7	3	0.74	0.00	0.50
12/09	2.28	—	—	(0.86)	0.00	(0.82)
12/08	0.85	—	—	(1.02)	0.00	(0.99)
12/07	4.25	—	—	(0.86)	0.00	(0.11)
12/06	5.14	—	—	(0.99)	0.00	0.46
Annual Growth	(0.2%)	—	—	—	—	2.2%

ArQule

ArQule is pursuing a drug research major in molecular biology, with a focus on cancer cell termination. The biotechnology firm works independently and with other drugmakers to discover new potential drug compounds based on its cancer-inhibiting technology platform. ArQule is developing a portfolio of oncology drugs, with a handful of anti-cancer compounds undergoing clinical trials. It is testing its most advanced candidate, ARQ 197, as a treatment for a variety of tumor types such as non-small cell lung cancer and colorectal cancer through a partnership with Daiichi Sankyo.

Under terms of ArQule's partnership deal with Daiichi Sankyo the two firms collaborate on the development of Tivantinib (also known as ARQ 197) in the US, Europe, and several other international markets. Kyowa Hakko has development rights to the compound in Japan, China, South Korea, and Taiwan. Tivantinib is in late stage clinical testing and is the closest to being marketed of all ArQule's candidates.

ArQule is hoping that its proprietary oncology technologies will help it advance effective new drugs to market. In addition to its own internal development efforts and its existing collaborations, it intends to look for other strategic alliances, in the form of licensing agreements, acquisitions, or collaborations.

The company also has agreements with Wyeth (now Pfizer) to discover and develop Alzheimer's disease treatments and with Solvay now part of Abbott Laboratories for irritable bowel syndrome. In fact, ArQule partnering with other, larger pharmaceutical companies for its development efforts is a key component of ArQule's strategy. Past and present partners include Daiichi, Kyowa, Roche, Sankyo, Solvay, Novartis, and others.

EXECUTIVES

Chairman, Patrick J. (Pat) Zenner, age 63
CEO and Director, Paolo Pucci, age 50, $1,433,253 total compensation
President, COO, General Counsel, and Secretary, Peter S. Lawrence, age 47, $1,137,075 total compensation
VP Finance, Robert Weiskopf
VP Oncology Lead Discovery, Dennis France
VP Human Development, Anthony S. (Tony) Messina
VP Investor Relations and Corporate Communications, William B. (Bill) Boni
VP Finance, Corporate Controller, Treasurer, and Principal Accounting Officer, Robert J. (Rob) Weiskopf, age 57
SVP and Chief Medical Officer, Brian Schwartz, age 49, $248,000 total compensation
SVP and Chief Scientific Officer, Thomas C. K. Chan, age 55, $498,693 total compensation
Auditors: PricewaterhouseCoopers LLP

LOCATIONS

HQ: ArQule, Inc.
19 Presidential Way, Woburn, MA 01801-5140
Phone: 781-994-0300   **Fax:** 781-376-6019
Web: www.arqule.com

PRODUCTS/OPERATIONS

Selected Pipeline

Tivantinib (cancer, Daiichi Sankyo/Kyowa Hakko)
ARQ 621 (oncology)
ARQ 736 (oncology)
FGFR Inhibitor (oncology)
Non-ATP Competitive Kinase Inhibitors (Daiichi Sankyo)

COMPETITORS

Amgen	Cytokinetics
ARIAD Pharmaceuticals	Exelixis
Array BioPharma	GlaxoSmithKline
Astex Pharmaceuticals	Idera
AVEO	Infinity
Bristol-Myers Squibb	Pharmaceuticals
Cell Therapeutics	MethylGene
Cephalon	Onyx Pharmaceuticals
Compugen	OSI Pharmaceuticals
Curis	

HISTORICAL FINANCIALS

Company Type: Public

Income Statement

FYE: December 31

	REVENUE ($ mil.)	NET INCOME ($ mil.)	NET PROFIT MARGIN	EMPLOYEES
12/10	29.2	(30.1)	—	115
12/09	25.2	(36.1)	—	111
12/08	14.1	(50.9)	—	107
12/07	9.2	(53.4)	—	113
12/06	6.6	(31.4)	—	98
Annual Growth	45.0%	—	—	4.1%

2010 Year-End Financials

Debt ratio: —	No. of shares (mil.): 45.0
Return on equity: —	Dividends
Cash ($ mil.): 20.5	Yield: —
Current ratio: 1.74	Payout: —
Long-term debt ($ mil.): —	Market value ($ mil.): 264.0

	STOCK PRICE ($) FY Close	P/E High/Low		PER SHARE ($) Earnings	Dividends	Book Value
12/10	5.87	—	—	(0.68)	0.00	(0.32)
12/09	3.69	—	—	(0.82)	0.00	0.26
12/08	4.22	—	—	(1.16)	0.00	0.98
12/07	5.80	—	—	(1.33)	0.00	2.01
12/06	5.92	—	—	(0.88)	0.00	2.24
Annual Growth	(0.2%)	—	—	—	—	—

Array BioPharma

Array BioPharma wants to offer sufferers of cancer, inflammatory, and metabolic diseases a multitude of treatment options. The development-stage company has seven wholly-owned programs in its development pipeline. Candidates include therapies for solid tumors (ARRY-543), arthritis (ARRY-162), breast cancer (ARRY-380), and type 2 diabetes (ARRY-403). Array also out-licenses some drug programs to AstraZeneca and Genentech; ARRY-886, developed with AstraZeneca, is in clinical trials for melanoma. Array's agreement with Genetech includes five candidates in various stages of development for the treatment of cancer. The company also has R&D agreements with Amgen, InterMune, Celgene, and others.

Array's drug discovery efforts on behalf of other biotechs cover a broad range of therapeutic areas including diabetes, infectious diseases, and diseases of the central nervous system.

Over the past few years, the company has undergone a transformation from a strictly R&D services provider to full-fledged drug development firm. Array now spends its energy and money on developing its own pipeline of potential therapies. Though it out-licenses some of its internally developed candidates to other firms, it intends to retain a greater financial stake in those licensed candidates than it has in the past.

A deal with privately held VentiRx Pharmaceuticals serves as the company's template for future collaborations. Under the deal, Array received an up-front payment for its toll-like receptor program (a research program that works on therapies that stimulate the immune system); and Array obtained an equity stake in VentiRx, as well as the option to buy 50% ownership in any cancer drugs the program produces.

Down the road, Array intends to develop a specialty sales force for any drugs it gets approved. To speed up its transformation, it is keeping an eye out for late-stage candidates or already approved drugs that it could in-license or acquire.

Collaborative partnerships bring in almost all of the company's revenue, with its Genentech partnership alone accounting for more than half of revenue in 2009.

EXECUTIVES

Chairman, Kyle A. Lefkoff, age 52
CFO, R. Michael Carruthers, age 52, $518,433 total compensation
President, Chief Scientific Officer, and Director, Kevin Koch, age 50, $1,007,649 total compensation
CEO and Director, Robert E. (Bob) Conway, age 56, $1,312,180 total compensation
VP, General Counsel, and Secretary, John R. Moore, age 46, $551,897 total compensation
VP Discovery and Translational Biology, James D. (Jim) Winkler, age 56
VP Business Development, COO, and Director, David L. Snitman, age 58, $739,236 total compensation
VP Biostatistics and Data Management, Gary M. Clark
VP Clinical Development, Bengt Bergstrom
VP Discovery Chemistry, John A. Josey, age 50
Chief Medical Officer, John Yates
Auditors: KPMG LLP

LOCATIONS

HQ: Array BioPharma Inc.
3200 Walnut St., Boulder, CO 80301
Phone: 303-381-6600   **Fax:** 303-386-1390
Web: www.arraybiopharma.com

2009 Sales

	$ mil.	% of total
North America	24.5	98
Europe	0.4	2
Total	**24.9**	**100**

PRODUCTS/OPERATIONS

2009 Sales

	$ mil.	% of total
Collaborations	17.2	69
Licensing & milestone payments	7.7	31
Total	**24.9**	**100**

Selected Proprietary Drug Candidates

ARRY-162 (rheumatoid arthritis)
ARRY-300 (meant to back-up ARRY-162 for rheumatoid arthritis)
ARRY-380 (cancer)
ARRY-403 (type 2 diabetes)
ARRY-520 (acute myelogenous leukemia)
ARRY-543 (metastatic breast cancer)
ARRY-614 (cancer and/or inflammation)
ARRY-797 (subacute pain/cancer)

Selected Collaborations

AstraZeneca (cancer)
Amgen (type 2 diabetes)
Celgene (cancer and inflammation)
Genentech (cancer)
InterMune (hepatitis C)
Novartis (cancer)
VentiRx (cancer and allergy)

COMPETITORS

Albany Molecular Research	Exelixis
Amgen	Genentech
Arena Pharmaceuticals	Genzyme Oncology
ARIAD Pharmaceuticals	GlaxoSmithKline
ArQule	ImClone
AstraZeneca	Incyte
Bristol-Myers Squibb	Janssen Biotech
Cytokinetics	Novartis
EntreMed	Pfizer
Evotec	Seattle Gen

HISTORICAL FINANCIALS

Company Type: Public

Income Statement

FYE: June 30

	REVENUE ($ mil.)	NET INCOME ($ mil.)	NET PROFIT MARGIN	EMPLOYEES
06/11	71.9	(56.3)	—	259
06/10	53.9	(77.6)	—	340
06/09	25.0	(127.8)	—	355
06/08	28.8	(96.3)	—	386
06/07	37.0	(55.4)	—	311
Annual Growth	**18.1%**	**—**	**—**	**(4.5%)**

2011 Year-End Financials

Debt ratio: —
Return on equity: —
Cash ($ mil.): 48.1
Current ratio: 1.01
Long-term debt ($ mil.): 91.4
No. of shares (mil.): 57.0
Dividends
Yield: —
Payout: —
Market value ($ mil.): 127.7

	STOCK PRICE ($) FY Close	P/E High/Low		PER SHARE ($) Earnings	Dividends	Book Value
06/11	2.24	—	—	(1.02)	0.00	(2.29)
06/10	3.05	—	—	(1.55)	0.00	(2.19)
06/09	3.14	—	—	(2.67)	0.00	(1.53)
06/08	4.70	—	—	(2.04)	0.00	0.80
06/07	11.67	—	—	(1.36)	0.00	2.29
Annual Growth	**(33.8%)**	**—**	**—**	**—**	**—**	**—**

Aruba Networks

Aruba Networks wants to turn your business into a wireless paradise. The company designs equipment for enterprise wireless LANs. Its products include controllers, access points, and concentrators, as well as operating system and management software. Aruba also provides professional and support services. The company targets the corporate, education, and government sectors, selling directly and through distributors, resellers, and OEMs. Customers include California State University, Microsoft, BAA, Saudi Aramco, LAWSON, and the US Air Force. Aruba outsources most manufacturing to partners such as Flextronics, Sercomm, Accton, and Wistron. About two-thirds of sales comes from the US.

The company gets nearly 95% of sales through indirect channels, particularly with ScanSource (nearly 20% of sales), Avnet (17%), and Alcatel-Lucent (14%).

While the rest of the world has been weathering a stormy economy, Aruba revenue has had a relative day at the beach, increasing each year since 2006. Its bottom line, however, hasn't been able to keep its head above water. At last, in 2011, the company got some air, ending the year in the black, but that was thanks to an income tax benefit of $71.6 million. That said, its operating loss of $4.7 million was a marked improvement over years of double digit million dollar losses, and its accumulated deficit improved from about $175 million to around $100 million.

Aruba's nearly 50% increase in sales for 2011 was due to increased demand in all regions and verticals. It expanded its customer base by nearly 5,000 as Wi-Fi mobility popularity continued, along with a rise in demand for multimedia mobility and server and desktop virtualization.

The company's key strategic pillars include a focus on a bring-your-own-device landscape, unified communications, and enterprise-wide penetration. Its software is powered by the ArubaOS, which houses its encryption, authentication, and network access technology. Aruba introduced its Mobile Virtual Enterprise (MOVE) architecture in 2011. It unifies access between wired and wireless network infrastructures for enterprise employees both at and away from the office.

As part of its unified communications endeavors, Aruba maintains a partnership with Microsoft that includes a vendor agreement and a technology development collaboration; Microsoft has installed Aruba products in various sites, and Aruba supports Microsoft's network security and communications products such as Microsoft Lync.

In 2010 Aruba acquired Azalea Networks, a supplier of outdoor mesh networks, for about $40 million in stock and cash. The company bought Azalea for its expertise in industrial enterprise networking, which can be more challenging than in offices and other indoor venues. Azalea serves customers in the energy, logistics, manufacturing, mining, petrochemical, public safety, smart grid, and transportation sectors. At the end of the year, Aruba bought Sydney-based network authentication products maker Amigopod.

EXECUTIVES

Chairman, President, and CEO, Dominic P. Orr, age 59, $2,552,312 total compensation
CFO, Michael Galvin
VP Engineering, Sriram Ramachandran, age 46, $570,652 total compensation
VP Human Resources, Aaron Bean
VP Legal and General Counsel, Alexa King
VP Worldwide Sales, Michael Kirby, age 56
VP Worldwide Channel Sales, Bob Bruce
COO, Hitesh Sheth, age 44
CTO and Director, Keerti Melkote, age 40, $562,328 total compensation
Chief Marketing Officer, Ben Gibson
Head Education Marketing, Robert Fenstermacher
Head Global Channel Operations, Peter Cellarius
Head of Strategic Marketing, Analyst and Press Relations, Michael Tennefoss
US Federal Sales Contact, Harry McLarnon
General Manager US Federal Markets, Dave Logan
Auditors: PricewaterhouseCoopers LLP

LOCATIONS

HQ: Aruba Networks, Inc.
1344 Crossman Ave., Sunnyvale, CA 94089-1113
Phone: 408-227-4500   **Fax:** 408-227-4550
Web: www.arubanetworks.com

2011 Sales

	$ mil.	% of total
US	251.0	63
Asia/Pacific	70.2	18
Europe, Middle East & Africa	62.6	16
Other regions	12.7	3
Total	**396.5**	**100**

PRODUCTS/OPERATIONS

2011 Sales

	$ mil.	% of total
Products	334.9	84
Professional services & support	61.0	16
Ratable products and related services & support	0.6	-
Total	**396.5**	**100**

2011 Sales by Channel

	$ mil.	% of total
Indirect	368.9	93
Direct	27.6	7
Total	**396.5**	**100**

Selected products

Hardware
  Access points
  Controllers
Software
  Management
  Mobility and security modules
  Operating system

COMPETITORS

AirMagnet	Hewlett-Packard
Belkin	Meru Networks
Cisco Systems	Motorola Solutions
D-Link	NETGEAR
EF Johnson	Proxim Wireless
Technologies	Red-M

HISTORICAL FINANCIALS

Company Type: Public

Income Statement   FYE: July 31

	REVENUE ($ mil.)	NET INCOME ($ mil.)	NET PROFIT MARGIN	EMPLOYEES
07/11	396.5	70.7	17.8%	1,057
07/10	266.5	(34.0)	—	681
07/09	199.3	(23.4)	—	545
07/08	178.3	(17.1)	—	541
07/07	127.5	(24.4)	—	441
Annual Growth	**32.8%**	**—**	**—**	**24.4%**

2011 Year-End Financials

Debt ratio: —
Return on equity: 20.5%
Cash ($ mil.): 80.8
Current ratio: 3.11
Long-term debt ($ mil.): —
No. of shares (mil.): 104.9
Dividends
  Yield: —
  Payout: —
Market value ($ mil.): 2,407.6

	STOCK PRICE ($) FY Close	P/E High/Low		PER SHARE ($) Earnings	Dividends	Book Value
07/11	22.95	61	27	0.60	0.00	3.29
07/10	16.98	—	—	(0.38)	0.00	1.61
07/09	8.88	—	—	(0.28)	0.00	1.59
07/08	5.83	—	—	(0.22)	0.00	1.58
07/07	20.08	—	—	(0.70)	0.00	1.42
Annual Growth	**3.4%**	**—**	**—**	**—**	**—**	**23.3%**

ASB Financial

ASB Financial is the holding company for American Savings Bank. Operating since 1892, the bank serves Scioto and Pike counties in southern Ohio, as well as communities across the Ohio River in northern Kentucky. From about five offices, the thrift originates a variety of loans, more than half of which are one- to four-family mortgages. Other loan products include commercial real estate, construction, business, consumer, and land loans. American Savings' deposit products include traditional checking and savings accounts, NOW and money market accounts, CDs, IRAs, and health savings accounts. The thrift also provides access to financial planning services.

EXECUTIVES

President and Director; President, CEO, and Director, American Savings Bank, Robert M. Smith, age 61
VP, ASB Financial and American Savings Bank, Jack A. Stephenson, age 56
VP and CFO, ASB Financial and American Savings Bank, Michael L. Gampp, age 39
VP Operations and Secretary, ASB Financial and American Savings Bank, Carlisa R. Baker, age 45
Auditors: Grant Thornton LLP

LOCATIONS

HQ: ASB Financial Corp.
503 Chillicothe St., Portsmouth, OH 45662
Phone: 740-354-3177   **Fax:** 740-355-1142
Web: www.asbfinancialcorp.com

HISTORICAL FINANCIALS

Company Type: Public

Income Statement   FYE: June 30

	ASSETS ($ mil.)	NET INCOME ($ mil.)	INCOME AS % OF ASSETS	EMPLOYEES
06/07	211.7	1.5	0.7%	0
06/06	198.5	1.7	0.9%	0
06/05	184.8	2.2	1.2%	0
06/04	166.4	2.0	1.2%	42
06/03	152.8	2.1	1.4%	42
Annual Growth	**8.5%**	**(8.1%)**	**—**	**0.0%**

2007 Year-End Financials

Equity as % of assets: —
Return on assets: 0.7%
Return on equity: 8.7%
Long-term debt ($ mil.): 21.6
No. of shares (mil.): 1.9
Dividends
  Yield: 3.4%
  Payout: 70.8%
Market value ($ mil.): 37.5
Sales ($ mil.): 14.1

	STOCK PRICE ($) FY Close	P/E High/Low		PER SHARE ($) Earnings	Dividends	Book Value
06/07	20.22	23	20	0.96	0.68	9.39
06/06	20.22	24	18	1.05	0.64	10.63
06/05	0.00	—	—	(0.00)	0.00	(0.00)
06/04	22.93	25	15	1.18	0.56	10.45
Annual Growth	**(4.1%)**	**—**	**—**	**(6.6%)**	**6.7%**	**(3.5%)**

athenahealth

athenahealth knows that managing physician practices can result in a splitting headache, especially when patients are late paying bills. The company provides health care organizations with Web-based software (athenaCollector) and services that streamline practice management, workflow routing, revenue management, patient information management, billing and collection, and other health care management tasks. athenahealth also offers a clinical cycle management service (athenaClinicals) that automates and manages medical record-related functions for physician practices.

More than 23,000 medical providers (including about 16,000 physicians) use the company's services, with clients spanning more than 40 states and 60 medical specialties. In 2009 athenahealth's offerings were used by its clients to post nearly $5 billion in physicians' collections and to process about 40 million medical claims.

athenahealth's strategy includes expanding its athenaClinicals client base and maintaining and expanding its payer rules database, which increases the likelihood that client transactions are successfully executed and take the least amount of time possible to resolve.

The company completed its first major acquisition in 2008, purchasing Crest Line Technologies, a provider of automated appointment reminder technology. In 2009 athenahealth bought Anodyne Health Partners, a provider of on-demand business intelligence software for health care providers. athenahealth will incorporate Anodyne's reporting and business intelligence capabilities into its broader product lines.

EXECUTIVES

Chairman, President, and CEO, Jonathan S. Bush, age 41, $1,094,075 total compensation
President, Enterprise Services, Stephen N. Kahane, age 53
EVP and COO, Ed Park
SVP, CFO, and Treasurer, Timothy M. (Tim) Adams, age 51
SVP and CTO, Jeremy Delinsky
SVP, General Counsel, and Secretary, Daniel H. Orenstein
SVP People and Process, Leslie Locke, age 39
SVP Sales, Robert M. Hueber, age 56, $617,134 total compensation
SVP Business Development and Product Strategy, Derek Hedges
SVP and Chief Marketing Officer, Robert L. (Rob) Cosinuke, age 50, $1,229,211 total compensation
Chief Accounting Officer, Treasurer, and Principal Accounting Officer, Dawn Griffiths, age 44
Auditors: Deloitte & Touche LLP

LOCATIONS

HQ: athenahealth, Inc.
311 Arsenal St., Watertown, MA 02472
Phone: 617-402-1000   **Fax:** 617-402-1099
Web: www.athenahealth.com

PRODUCTS/OPERATIONS

2009 Sales

	$ mil.	% of total
Business services	183.2	97
Implementation & other	5.3	3
Total	**188.5**	**100**

Selected Software
athenaClinicals (medical record management)
athenaCollector (claims management)

COMPETITORS

Allscripts	Quality Systems
CBIZ	Sage Group
eClinicalWorks	Sage Software
GE Healthcare	Siemens Healthcare
McKesson	

HISTORICAL FINANCIALS

Company Type: Public

Income Statement

FYE: December 31

	REVENUE ($ mil.)	NET INCOME ($ mil.)	NET PROFIT MARGIN	EMPLOYEES
12/10	245.5	12.7	5.2%	1,242
12/09	188.5	9.3	4.9%	1,035
12/08	139.6	28.9	20.7%	824
12/07	100.8	(3.5)	—	380
12/06	75.8	(9.2)	—	564
Annual Growth	34.2%	—	—	21.8%

2010 Year-End Financials

Debt ratio: 3.7%	No. of shares (mil.): 34.5
Return on equity: 7.4%	Dividends
Cash ($ mil.): 35.9	Yield: —
Current ratio: 4.03	Payout: —
Long-term debt ($ mil.): 6.3	Market value ($ mil.): 1,415.0

	STOCK PRICE ($) FY Close	P/E High/Low	PER SHARE ($) Earnings	Dividends	Book Value
12/10	40.98	133 60	0.36	0.00	4.95
12/09	45.24	177 86	0.27	0.00	3.76
12/08	37.62	46 23	0.83	0.00	3.50
12/07	36.00	— —	(0.28)	0.00	2.34
Annual Growth	4.4%	— —	—	—	28.3%

Atlantic Tele-Network

Atlantic Tele-Network (ATN) makes connections from the rain forests of Guyana to the maple groves of Vermont. ATN owns 80% of mobile phone carrier Guyana Telephone & Telegraph (GT&T), which has about 150,000 fixed-access telephone lines and about 290,000 cellular subscribers. In the US, ATN provides wholesale wireless voice and data roaming services to local and national communications carriers through subsidiary Commnet. The company provides voice and broadband Internet communcations services in New England, particularly in Vermont, through its SoVerNet subsidiary. SoVerNet subsidiary ION offers fiber-optic transport services in New York State on a wholesale basis.

ATN also provides communications services in the Caribbean through its subsidiaries, including Choice Communications, which provides Internet access service in the US Virgin Islands under the ClearChoice brand. It serves mobile customers in Bermuda through Bermuda Digital Communications (BDC); in 2008 BDC began to offer mobile services in the Turks and Caicos islands through Islandcom Telecommunications.

ATN acquired wireless assets in six states (Georgia, Idaho, Illinois, North Carolina, Ohio, and South Carolina) from Verizon Wireless in 2010. The deal was part of a broader disposal by Verizon of certain overlapping operations acquired in its 2009 purchase of Alltel; the sale was required to satisfy anti-trust conditions laid out by federal regulators. The $200 million purchase, which expanded ATN's subscriber base by about 800,000 in mostly rural areas, was part of the company's ongoing plan to build its service area through acquisitions, as well as through partnerships with other carriers.

The company is reacting to the declining international long distance business of its GT&T sub-sidiary (nearly one quarter of ATN sales) by investing in its infrastructure. To boost network capacity and reduce its reliance on a small number of foreign operators for sales, GT&T began improving its fiber-optic links to Guyana in 2009 in partnership with Caracas-based network operator and broadcaster TeleSUR. Top customers for long-distance calls into and out of Guyana have historically been US carriers like AT&T and IDT.

Chairman Cornelius Prior owns about 37% of the company.

EXECUTIVES

President, CEO, and Director, Michael T. Prior, age 46, $1,097,097 total compensation
CEO, Guyana Telephone and Telegraph, Sonita Jagan, age 44
CEO, Atlantic Wireless Communications, Frank A. O'Mara, age 44
President, International Operations, Paul R. Bowersock
Chairman; Chairman, Guyana Telephone and Telegraph, Cornelius B. Prior Jr., age 77
CFO and Treasurer, Justin D. Benincasa, age 49, $568,497 total compensation
VP Financial Analysis and Planning, John P. Audet, age 53, $260,812 total compensation
VP, General Counsel, and Secretary, Douglas J. Minster, age 50
Chief Accounting Officer, Andrew S. Fienberg, age 43, $255,881 total compensation
SVP Corporate Development, William F. (Bill) Kreisher, age 48, $471,909 total compensation
SVP and Corporate Controller, Karl D. Noone, age 42
Auditors: PricewaterhouseCoopers LLP

LOCATIONS

HQ: Atlantic Tele-Network, Inc.
10 Derby Sq., Salem, MA 01970
Phone: 978-619-1300   **Fax:** 978-744-3951
Web: www.atni.com

2009 Sales

	% of total
US	54
Guyana	38
Other countries	8
Total	**100**

PRODUCTS/OPERATIONS

2009 Sales

	$ mil.	% of total
Wireless	147.0	61
Local telephone & data	55.3	23
International long distance	38.2	15
Other	1.2	1
Total	**241.7**	**100**

Selected Subsidiaries

Bermuda Digital Communications, Ltd. (BDC, 58%, cellular services)
Choice Communications, LLC (ISP and wireless TV provider, US Virgin Islands)
Commnet Wireless, LLC (wireless roaming provider)
Guyana Telephone and Telegraph Company Limited (GT&T, 80%, local and long distance phone services)
SoVerNet, Inc. (96%, facilities-based voice and data services)

COMPETITORS

AT&T Mobility	Sprint Nextel
FairPoint Communications, Inc.	Verizon

HISTORICAL FINANCIALS

Company Type: Public

Income Statement

FYE: December 31

	REVENUE ($ mil.)	NET INCOME ($ mil.)	NET PROFIT MARGIN	EMPLOYEES
12/10	619.1	38.5	6.2%	1,765
12/09	241.7	35.5	14.7%	889
12/08	207.3	34.8	16.8%	864
12/07	186.7	37.9	20.3%	823
12/06	155.4	23.5	15.1%	852
Annual Growth	41.3%	13.1%	—	20.0%

2010 Year-End Financials

Debt ratio: 95.9%	No. of shares (mil.): 15.4
Return on equity: 13.6%	Dividends
Cash ($ mil.): 37.3	Yield: 2.2%
Current ratio: 1.12	Payout: 33.9%
Long-term debt ($ mil.): 272.0	Market value ($ mil.): 590.3

	STOCK PRICE ($) FY Close	P/E High/Low	PER SHARE ($) Earnings	Dividends	Book Value
12/10	38.37	24 13	2.48	0.84	18.45
12/09	54.95	25 6	2.32	0.76	16.79
12/08	26.55	16 7	2.28	0.68	15.06
12/07	33.78	16 10	2.48	0.60	13.73
12/06	29.30	17 9	1.72	0.52	11.82
Annual Growth	7.0%	— —	9.6%	12.7%	11.8%

Atna Resources

Atna Resources is a mineral exploration company that purchases, explores, and develops mineral resource properties. The company concentrates on precious metals and operates in Canada, the United States, and Chile. While it does operate internationally, Atna's focus is developing its properties in the western US. The company's greatest geographic concentration is in Nevada, home to seven gold projects. In 2008 it paid $26 million in stock to buy gold miner Canyon Resources, whose properties were already in production and close to Atna's. In 2011 the company expanded its gold resources by acquiring the Pinson Gold Mine in the Getchell gold belt of northern Nevada from a subsidiary of Barrick Gold Corporation.

EXECUTIVES

Chairman, David H. Watkins, age 66
President and CEO, James K. B. Hesketh
VP Exploration, William R. (Bill) Stanley
VP and CFO, David P. Suleski
Investor Relations Manager, Geologist, Kendra Johnston
Corporate Secretary, Bonnie L. Whelan
Manager, Corporate Communications, Deanna McDonald
Auditors: De Visser Gray

LOCATIONS

HQ: Atna Resources Ltd.
14142 Denver West Pkwy, Ste. 250, Golden, CO 80401
Phone: 303-278-8464   **Fax:** 303-279-3772
Web: www.atna.com

HISTORICAL FINANCIALS

Company Type: Public

Income Statement

FYE: December 31

	REVENUE ($ mil.)	NET INCOME ($ mil.)	NET PROFIT MARGIN	EMPLOYEES
12/10	30.6	(8.8)	—	127
12/09	8.7	(6.0)	—	129
12/08	0.1	16.5	16500.0%	41
12/00	0.0	(1.8)	—	0
12/99	0.1	(1.2)	—	0
Annual Growth	68.3%	—	—	76.0%

2010 Year-End Financials

Debt ratio: 5.7%
Return on equity: —
Cash ($ mil.): 9.6
Current ratio: 1.94
Long-term debt ($ mil.): 3.1

No. of shares (mil.): 99.0
Dividends
 Yield: —
 Payout: —
Market value ($ mil.): 62.4

	STOCK PRICE ($) FY Close	P/E High/Low		PER SHARE ($) Earnings	Dividends	Book Value
12/10	0.63	—	—	(0.10)	0.00	0.55
12/09	0.71	—	—	(0.07)	0.00	0.65
12/08	0.59	8	1	0.21	0.00	0.70
12/00	1.52	—	—	(0.08)	0.00	0.44
12/99	1.35	—	—	(0.01)	0.00	0.44
Annual Growth	(17.3%)	—	—	—	—	5.4%

AutoInfo

Once an automobile financing company, AutoInfo is still focused on transportation — but of goods, not people. Through its Sunteck Transport and Fleets Logistics subsidiaries the company acts as a freight broker, arranging the transportation of freight for customers in the US and Canada through alliances with both truckload and less-than-truckload carriers, along with air, rail, and ocean transportation providers. The company acts as a contract carrier, generating business through a network of sales agents and contracting with truck owner-operators to haul customers' freight. AutoInfo doesn't own any transportation equipment of its own. Its agent support services include loans for training and expansion.

AutoInfo will continue to grow both organically as well as through affiliations with independent sales agents in the US and Canada. Although currently only a small portion of the company's revenue stream, AutoInfo is looking to expand its agent support services. AutoInfo also hopes to capitalize on the current trend of smaller businesses outsourcing delivery and transportation needs to third-party freight brokers.

President and CEO Harry Wachtel owns about 19% of AutoInfo.

EXECUTIVES

CFO, William I. (Bill) Wunderlich, age 62, $505,000 total compensation
President, CEO, and Director; President, Sunteck Transport, Harry M. Wachtel, age 51, $595,000 total compensation
COO and General Counsel, Michael P. Williams, age 43, $203,000 total compensation
Auditors: Dworken, Hillman, LaMorte & Sterczala, P.C.

LOCATIONS

HQ: AutoInfo, Inc.
 6413 Congress Ave., Ste. 260, Boca Raton, FL 33487
Phone: 561-988-9456   **Fax:** 561-994-8033
Web: www.suntecktransport.com

PRODUCTS/OPERATIONS

2009 Sales

	$ mil.	% of total
Transportation services	182.4	99
Agent support services	1.5	1
Total	**183.9**	**100**

COMPETITORS

APL Logistics
C.H. Robinson Worldwide
Expeditors
Hub Group
J.B. Hunt
Landstar System
Mainfreight USA
Menlo Worldwide
Pacer International

Schneider National
Swift Transportation
Transplace
TTS
U.S. Xp
Universal Truckload Services
UPS Supply Chain Solutions

HISTORICAL FINANCIALS

Company Type: Public

Income Statement

FYE: December 31

	REVENUE ($ mil.)	NET INCOME ($ mil.)	NET PROFIT MARGIN	EMPLOYEES
12/10	279.7	3.1	1.1%	61
12/09	183.9	1.4	0.8%	62
12/08	180.2	2.2	1.2%	52
12/07	110.3	1.6	1.5%	52
12/06	84.1	3.6	4.3%	45
Annual Growth	35.0%	(3.7%)		7.9%

2010 Year-End Financials

Debt ratio: 106.3%
Return on equity: 14.5%
Cash ($ mil.): 0.3
Current ratio: 2.30
Long-term debt ($ mil.): 22.4

No. of shares (mil.): 33.5
Dividends
 Yield: —
 Payout: —
Market value ($ mil.): 21.1

	STOCK PRICE ($) FY Close	P/E High/Low		PER SHARE ($) Earnings	Dividends	Book Value
12/10	0.63	8	2	0.09	0.00	0.63
12/09	0.40	14	6	0.04	0.00	0.54
12/08	0.34	11	3	0.07	0.00	0.50
12/07	0.68	21	12	0.05	0.00	0.42
12/06	1.03	20	5	0.10	0.00	0.37
Annual Growth	(11.6%)	—	—	(2.6%)	—	13.9%

Auxilium Pharmaceuticals

Auxilium Pharmaceuticals wants to be firm on some things and flexible on others. The biopharmaceutical developer's marketed products are Testim, a topical testosterone gel used to treat hypogonadism (low testosterone production) and XIAFLEX, an injectable enzyme approved to treat Dupuytren's condition (a progressive disease which causes a person's fingers to contract permanently). While third parties manufacture its finished products, Auxilium manufactures the active ingredient for XIAFLEX at its own facility. The company's pipeline of candidates includes potential treatments for unusual soft tissue conditions and pain.

While Testim holds a quarter of the US market of testosterone gels, it faces stiff competition from other testosterone and erectile dysfunction treatments. To increase Testim's market penetration, Auxilium has entered into partnerships to disseminate its product abroad. Paladin Labs sells Testim in Canada, while Ferring International markets it in Europe where it is approved for sale in some 15 countries.

XIAFLEX received FDA approval to treat Dupuytren's in 2010, but is also being investigated as a therapy for Frozen Shoulder and Peyronie's disease, which leads to penile scar tissue that can interfere with sexual intercourse. Auxilium received the license to develop the injectable form of the drug from BioSpecifics Technologies. To prepare for commercialization of the drug, during 2009 the company sank money into readying its manufacturing facility. Following the drug's US approval, Auxilium built up its sales force and established a network of specialty pharmaceutical distributors to supply health care providers with XIAFLEX. Pfizer has signed on to market it in about 50 European and Asian countries.

Auxilium has obtained a license to develop drug candidates using an oral transmucosal drug delivery system. Its candidates include a compound to treat overactive bladder and a version of cancer drug Fentanyl.

EXECUTIVES

Chairman, Rolf A. Classon, age 65
President, CEO, and Director, Armando Anido, age 53, $2,854,826 total compensation
CFO, James E. (Jim) Fickenscher, age 47, $1,286,549 total compensation
EVP Corporate Development, Alan J. Wills, age 47
EVP, Secretary, General Counsel, and Human Resources, Jennifer Evans-Stacey, age 46, $944,333 total compensation
EVP Regulatory Affairs and Project Management, Benjamin J. Del Tito Jr., age 55
EVP Sales and Marketing, Roger D. Graham Jr., age 48, $1,262,430 total compensation
VP Investor Relations and Corporate Communications, William Q. (Will) Sargent Jr.
SVP Sales, Edward F. (Ed) Kessig, age 50
Auditors: PricewaterhouseCoopers LLP

LOCATIONS

HQ: Auxilium Pharmaceuticals, Inc.
 40 Valley Stream Pkwy., Malvern, PA 19355
Phone: 484-321-5900   **Fax:** 484-321-5999
Web: www.auxilium.com

COMPETITORS

Abbott Labs
BioSante
Clarus Therapeutics
Halozyme
Par Pharmaceutical Companies

ProStrakan
Repros Therapeutics
Watson Pharmaceuticals

HISTORICAL FINANCIALS
Company Type: Public

Income Statement
FYE: December 31

	REVENUE ($ mil.)	NET INCOME ($ mil.)	NET PROFIT MARGIN	EMPLOYEES
12/10	211.4	(51.2)	—	565
12/09	164.0	(53.5)	—	540
12/08	125.4	(46.3)	—	340
12/07	95.7	(40.7)	—	300
12/06	68.5	(45.9)	—	278
Annual Growth	32.5%	—	—	19.4%

2010 Year-End Financials

Debt ratio: —	No. of shares (mil.): 47.8
Return on equity: —	Dividends
Cash ($ mil.): 128.2	Yield: —
Current ratio: 3.16	Payout: —
Long-term debt ($ mil.): —	Market value ($ mil.): 1,008.2

	STOCK PRICE ($) FY Close	P/E High/Low	Earnings	PER SHARE ($) Dividends	Book Value
12/10	21.10	— —	(1.08)	0.00	1.98
12/09	29.98	— —	(1.22)	0.00	2.55
12/08	28.44	— —	(1.12)	0.00	0.83
12/07	29.99	— —	(1.07)	0.00	1.59
12/06	14.69	— —	(1.48)	0.00	1.20
Annual Growth	9.5%	— —	—	—	13.3%

AVEO

AVEO Pharmaceuticals' models don't pout, strut, or even turn heads — unless you're a cancer drug researcher. The biotech firm develops cancer models to uncover how genes mutate into tumors and how tumors progress through additional mutations. AVEO then builds genetic profiles of such tumors and applies them to antibody (protein) drug candidates in preclinical and clinical development to help predict actual human responses. In addition to its own pipeline of potential drugs, AVEO has partnered with other pharmaceutical developers to apply its Human Response Platform to their drug candidates. The company completed an IPO in 2010.

AVEO first filed an IPO in late 2009 and began trading the following March. The company conducted the public offering to further its goals of developing and commercializing proprietary drug compounds, including lead candidate tivozanib, as well as pharmaceutical candidates developed through collaborations with other drug companies. Proceeds from the IPO (totaling about $80 million) are being used to fund such research and development programs, as well as to finance general corporate and operational expenses.

AVEO also depends on financing from strategic development partners and licensees to fund clinical trials on its drug candidates, which are in various stages of development. Tivozanib is in late-stage clinical trials for the treatment of kidney cancer and other types of tumorous cancers. In 2011 the company teamed up with Astellas Pharma to conduct further development and commercialization efforts for tivozanib; Astellas paid AVEO $125 million, and the firm could be eligible for up to $1.3 billion in milestone payments through the deal.

An agreement with Biogen Idec was established in 2009 to develop and commercialize AVEO's AV-203 candidate, which is in preclinical development for the treatment of advanced solid tumors. Another key candidate, AVEO's ficlatuzumab (AV-299) for multiple cancer targets, was being co-developed through a partnership with Merck. However, Merck terminated the partnership in 2010 to focus on other projects. AVEO continues to develop the candidate on its own.

The company formed a partnership with Johnson & Johnson subsidiary Janssen Biotech (formerly Centocor Ortho Biotech) in 2011 to develop other anti-tumor candidates. The program could be worth up to $555 million and will focus on one of AVEO's proprietary lines of antibodies currently in preclinical development stages.

The company also has a collaborative alliance with OSI Pharmaceuticals (a subsidiary of Astellas) to develop tumor models for OSI's oncological drug discovery process. AVEO and OSI expanded their partnership in 2009 to include cancer target validation and increased access to AVEO's technologies.

The company plans to widen its portfolio of candidates through internal development efforts and by forming new partnerships. It also intends to further license its Human Response Platform technology to other companies for their own research programs; licensees have thus far included Merck and OSI.

Partner Biogen Idec owns an 8% stake in AVEO, which was founded in 2002 under the name Gen-Path Pharmaceuticals.

EXECUTIVES
Chairman, Anthony B. (Tony) Evnin, age 69
CFO, David B. Johnston, age 55, $614,376 total compensation
President, CEO, and Director, Tuan Ha-Ngoc, age 59, $876,345 total compensation
EVP and Chief Business Officer, Elan Ezickson, age 47, $469,209 total compensation
VP Clinical Research, Pankaj Bhargava
VP Translational Research, M. Isabel Chiu
VP Intellectual Property, Gary Creason
VP Program and Alliance Management, David Graham
VP Finance, Suzanne Fleming
VP Technical Operations, Donna Radzik
VP and Corporate Counsel, Joseph Vittiglio
Chief Commercial Officer, Michael P. Bailey, age 45
SVP Translational Medicine, Murray Robinson
Chief Medical Officer, William J. Slichenmyer, age 53
SVP and Head Research, Jeno Gyuris, age 50, $394,141 total compensation
Auditors: Ernst & Young LLP

LOCATIONS
HQ: AVEO Pharmaceuticals, Inc.
75 Sidney St., Cambridge, MA 02139
Phone: 617-299-5000   **Fax:** 617-995-4995
Web: aveopharma.com

PRODUCTS/OPERATIONS

2010 Sales

	$ mil.	% of total
Merck partnership	22.6	51
OSI partnership	16.2	36
Biogen Idec partnership	5.7	13
Other	0.2	-
Total	**44.7**	**100**

Selected Candidates
AV-203 (solid tumors, with Biogen)
ficlatuzumab (non-small cell lung cancer)
tivozanib (kidney cancer and other cancers, with Astellas)

COMPETITORS

Abbott Labs	Exelixis
Affymetrix	Genzyme Oncology
Amgen	GlaxoSmithKline
ArQule	Incyte
AstraZeneca	MethylGene
Bayer HealthCare	Novartis
Boehringer Ingelheim	Onyx Pharmaceuticals
Bristol-Myers Squibb	Pfizer
Daiichi Sankyo	Reg
Eli Lilly	Roche Holding
EntreMed	

HISTORICAL FINANCIALS
Company Type: Public

Income Statement
FYE: December 31

	REVENUE ($ mil.)	NET INCOME ($ mil.)	NET PROFIT MARGIN	EMPLOYEES
12/10	44.7	(58.8)	—	147
12/09	20.7	(44.1)	—	133
12/08	19.7	(32.5)	—	134
12/07	11.0	(25.0)	—	0
12/06	7.8	(24.9)	—	0
Annual Growth	54.7%	—	—	4.7%

2010 Year-End Financials

Debt ratio: 24.6%	No. of shares (mil.): 35.6
Return on equity: —	Dividends
Cash ($ mil.): 45.8	Yield: —
Current ratio: 3.46	Payout: —
Long-term debt ($ mil.): 17.6	Market value ($ mil.): 520.5

	STOCK PRICE ($) FY Close	P/E High/Low	Earnings	PER SHARE ($) Dividends	Book Value
12/10	14.62	— —	(2.30)	0.00	2.02
Annual Growth	—	— —	—	—	—

Avistar Communications

If geography prevents you from concluding business with a firm handshake, Avistar Communications is ready to furnish the next-best thing. The company provides communication software and hardware used to equip communications networks with video capabilities. Its systems enable video-conferencing, content creation, video broadcasting, and data sharing between users over telephony networks and the Internet. Avistar markets its products primarily to corporations in the financial services industry, including UBS Investment Bank, Deutsche Bank, and JPMorgan Chase. Chairman Gerald Burnett owns about 42% of the company.

Patent licensing had been one of the company's largest sources of revenue but in 2010 it sold the bulk of its patent portfolio to Intellectual Ventures for $11 million.

EXECUTIVES

Chairman, Gerald J. Burnett, age 68, $299,083 total compensation
President, CEO and Director, Robert F. (Bob) Kirk
CFO, Elias MurrayMetzger, age 40
President, Intellectual Property, Anton F. Rodde, age 67, $331,417 total compensation
VP Intellectual Property Division, Lester F. Ludwig
VP Operations and Customer Support, Michael (Mike) Horn, age 37
CTO, J. Chris Lauwers, age 51, $377,092 total compensation
SVP Sales, Michael (Mike) Dignen
Manager Marketing, Angela Smith
Chief Marketing Officer, Stephen Epstein, age 46, $482,022 total compensation
Director Contracts and Assistant Corporate Secretary, Rima Vanhill
Communications Corporation, Lisa Farley
Auditors: Burr, Pilger & Mayer LLP

LOCATIONS

HQ: Avistar Communications Corporation
1875 S. Grant St., 10th Fl., San Mateo, CA 94402
Phone: 650-525-3300 **Fax:** 650-525-1360
Web: www.avistar.com

PRODUCTS/OPERATIONS

2009 Sales

	% of total
Product	45
Services	45
Licensing	10
Total	**100**

Selected Products

Cameras
Gateways and switches
Servers
Software (call reporting, collaboration, directory)
Speakers
Video systems

COMPETITORS

Avaya	Microsoft
Cisco Systems	NEC
Cisco WebEx	Nortel Networks
ClearOne	Polycom
Emblaze-VCON	RADVISION
Ezenia!	TANDBERG
IBM	ViewCast.com

HISTORICAL FINANCIALS

Company Type: Public

Income Statement

FYE: December 31

	REVENUE ($ mil.)	NET INCOME ($ mil.)	NET PROFIT MARGIN	EMPLOYEES
12/10	19.7	4.4	22.3%	51
12/09	8.8	(4.0)	—	49
12/08	8.8	(6.4)	—	50
12/07	12.0	(2.9)	—	74
12/06	13.2	(8.1)	—	88
Annual Growth	**10.5%**	**—**	**—**	**(12.7%)**

2010 Year-End Financials

Debt ratio: —
Return on equity: (56.7)%
Cash ($ mil.): 1.8
Current ratio: 0.27
Long-term debt ($ mil.): —
No. of shares (mil.): 39.1
Dividends
  Yield: —
  Payout: —
Market value ($ mil.): 23.9

	STOCK PRICE ($) FY Close	P/E High/Low		PER SHARE ($) Earnings	Dividends	Book Value
12/10	0.61	10	3	0.11	0.00	(0.20)
12/09	0.45	—	—	(0.11)	0.00	(0.35)
12/08	0.88	—	—	(0.18)	0.00	(0.42)
12/07	0.36	—	—	(0.09)	0.00	(0.29)
12/06	1.77	—	—	(0.24)	0.00	(0.28)
Annual Growth	**(23.4%)**	**—**	**—**	**—**	**—**	**—**

Azure Dynamics

Azure Dynamics (AZD) has a blue-sky vision for how to make heavy vehicles run in an ecologically friendly way. The development-stage company designs energy management systems for use in commercial vehicles. AZD's hybrid electric vehicle (HEV) control systems include both vehicle management software and controllers used with a variety of drive components. Customers and partners include Canada Post, the US Postal Service, Federal Express, and Purolator Courier. As part of efforts to build a US battery supply base and infrastructure support for hybrid electric vehicles, AZD signed a five-year agreement with lithium-ion suppliers Johnson Controls-SAFT (a joint venture) in early 2009.

AZD operates from three primary product groups: full hybrid electric, mild hybrid electric, and pure electric solutions. AZD works to align its product development with complementary industry players such as battery and vehicle manufacturers. The partnerships give AZD access to product development as well as distribution outlets. To that end, AZD has partnered with Ford to produce hybrid vehicles.

AZD will purchase up to 20,000 battery systems for use in its Balance Hybrid Electric vehicles used by fleet customers AT&T, Con Edison, and Federal Express.

The company restructured in early 2009, cutting its workforce by about 25% and reducing discretionary expenses. AZD cited the pressures of the economic downturn and its resulting effects on the automotive industry for the cost reductions. The company said it would seek low-cost loans from the Canadian and US governments to support development of more fuel-efficient vehicles.

EXECUTIVES

Chairman, D. Campbell (Cam) Deacon, age 62
CEO and Director, Scott T. Harrison, age 45
CFO, Ryan Carr
VP Sales, Jay A. Sandler
VP Marketing, Michael L. Elwood
VP Engineering, Ricardo Espinosa
COO, Curt A. Huston
CTO, Ronald V. Iacobelli
Auditors: BDO Dunwoody LLP

LOCATIONS

HQ: Azure Dynamics Corporation
14925 W. Eleven Mile Rd., Oak Park, MI 48237-2103
Phone: 248-298-2403 **Fax:** 248-298-2410
Web: www.azuredynamics.com

2009 Sales

	% of total
US	77
Canada	19
Other countries	4
Total	**100**

PRODUCTS/OPERATIONS

Selected Products

Balance Hybrid Electric E450 (hybrid electric drive system for Ford's E450 cutaway and strip chassis trucks)
CitiBus Hybrid Electric StarTrans (hybrid drives for commercial vehicles)
Force Drive Electric Solutions (hybrid drives for passenger cars and electric delivery vehicles)
LEEP Systems (low emission electric power for auxiliary applications)

COMPETITORS

Ballard Power	Hydrogenics
Enova Systems	Palcan Fuel Cells
FuelCell Energy	Plug Power
General Motors	Quantum Fuel Systems

HISTORICAL FINANCIALS

Company Type: Public

Income Statement

FYE: December 31

	REVENUE ($ mil.)	NET INCOME ($ mil.)	NET PROFIT MARGIN	EMPLOYEES
12/10	21.9	(28.1)	—	119
12/09	9.0	(26.5)	—	119
12/08	6.3	(31.8)	—	148
12/07	2.9	(30.8)	—	112
12/06	4.9	(20.1)	—	112
Annual Growth	**45.4%**	**—**	**—**	**1.5%**

2010 Year-End Financials

Debt ratio: 0.4%
Return on equity: —
Cash ($ mil.): 11.8
Current ratio: 1.51
Long-term debt ($ mil.): 0.1
No. of shares (mil.): 626.9
Dividends
  Yield: —
  Payout: —
Market value ($ mil.): 191.2

	STOCK PRICE ($) FY Close	P/E High/Low		PER SHARE ($) Earnings	Dividends	Book Value
12/10	0.30	—	—	(0.05)	0.00	0.04
12/09	0.18	—	—	(0.07)	0.00	0.07
12/08	0.03	—	—	(0.10)	0.00	0.07
12/07	0.39	—	—	(0.14)	0.00	0.18
12/06	0.68	—	—	(0.12)	0.00	0.21
Annual Growth	**(18.5%)**	**—**	**—**	**—**	**—**	**(34.8%)**

Bacterin

Bacterin International has your back(bone). The company develops, manufactures, and markets biomedical devices, including orthopedic biomaterials used for bone grafts, joint surgery, and other skeletal reconstructive procedures. Its biologics products include OsteoSponge, a bone void filler made of 100% human bone; OsteoLock, a stabilization dowel for spinal procedures; and BacFast, a dowel with demineralization technology to aid in bone grafting. It also sells sports allografts for ligament repairs and the hMatrix dermal scaffold. Bacterin International was founded in 1998.

In recent years, Bacterin International has shifted from its development roots to focus on marketing and distribution of its products, and in 2009 the company started creating a direct sales network. It is expecting its internal sales force to eventually represent 50% of its revenue.

The Brook Army Medical Hospital reported that it will be using Bacterin International's wound drain product, the ViaTM, system wide, and Bacterin International hopes this will open the doors to other VA hospital systems. The company's second generation product, called Elutia wound drains, are covered with anti-microbial coating designed to reduce post-surgical infections.

EXECUTIVES

Chairman, President, CEO, and Chief Scientific Officer, Guy Cook, age 46
Auditors: Child, Van Wagoner & Bradshaw, PLLC

LOCATIONS

HQ: Bacterin International Holdings, Inc.
 600 Cruiser Ln., Belgrade, MT 59714
Phone: 406-388-0480   **Fax:** 406-388-1354
Web: www.bacterin.com

2010 Sales

	$ mil.	% of total
US	14.9	97
Other countries	0.5	3
Total	**15.4**	**100**

COMPETITORS

Arthrex	Medtronic
ArthroCare	Orthofix
Biomet	Orthovita
CONMED Corporation	Smith & Nephew
DePuy	Stryker
Exactech	Synthes
Integra LifeSciences	

HISTORICAL FINANCIALS

Company Type: Public

Income Statement FYE: December 31

	REVENUE ($ mil.)	NET INCOME ($ mil.)	NET PROFIT MARGIN	EMPLOYEES
12/10	15.4	(19.5)	—	117
12/09	7.4	(4.1)	—	0
12/08	0.5	—	—	0
Annual Growth	**455.0%**	**—**	**—**	**—**

Debt ratio: 0.4%	No. of shares (mil.): 626.9
Return on equity: —	Dividends
Cash ($ mil.): 11.8	Yield: —
Current ratio: 1.51	Payout: —
Long-term debt ($ mil.): 0.1	Market value ($ mil.): 191.2

Baldwin & Lyons

Baldwin & Lyons (B&L) insures truckers and the bad motorists who terrorize them. The company's Protective Insurance subsidiary, licensed in the US and Canada, writes property/casualty insurance for large to midsized trucking fleets and public transportation fleets. It also covers independent contractors in the trucking industry.

B&L's Sagamore Insurance subsidiary provides insurance to high-risk private auto drivers throughout most of the US through a network of independent agents. It also markets physical-damage insurance and liability insurance for small trucking fleets and for large and midsized bus fleets. Founded in 1930, B&L also provides property/casualty reinsurance and brokerage services.

B&L markets its policies through its brokerage services division, which offers insurance placement, claims handling, loss prevention, and Department of Transportation compliance services. The brokerage unit caters to transportation fleet clients. B&L sells other types of insurance coverage through a network of independent agents and managing general agents.

Through its Protective Specialty Insurance subsidiary, B&L formed a new professional liability unit in 2009. The unit began underwriting policies, providing errors and omissions coverage for professionals in most states, in 2010.

Besides its services, products, and experienced management, the company counts among its competitive advantages its willingness to custom build policies for its customers and its extensive use of technology with regard to its insureds and independent agents.

The Shapiro family owns nearly half of Baldwin & Lyons.

EXECUTIVES

President, CEO, COO, and Director; President and Director, Protective Insurance and Sagamore Insuran, Joseph J. DeVito, age 59
Chairman; Chairman and CEO, Protective, Sagamore, and B & L Insurance, Gary W. Miller, age 70
EVP and CFO, G. Patrick (Pat) Corydon, age 62
EVP Sales, Marketing and Underwriting, Mark L. Bonini, age 52
VP Reinsurance and Actuarial Services, Jennie L. LaReau
VP Reinsurance and Actuarial Services, John E. Mitchell
VP Administration, James D. Isham
SVP Claims, Legal and Corporate Secretary, Craig C. Morfas, age 52
Director Human Resources, Hugh Cameron
Treasurer; VP, Protective, Walter D. (Daryl) Osborne
Auditors: Ernst & Young LLP

LOCATIONS

HQ: Baldwin & Lyons, Inc.
 1099 N. Meridian St., Ste. 700, Indianapolis, IN 46204
Phone: 317-636-9800   **Fax:** 317-632-9444
Web: www.baldwinandlyons.com

PRODUCTS/OPERATIONS

2010 Sales

	$ mil.	% of total
Premiums		
Property & casualty insurance	174.0	70
Property reinsurance	40.7	16
Investment income	11.3	5
Commissions & other	6.9	3
Gains/losses on investments	16.5	6
Adjustments	0.1	-
Total	**249.5**	**100**

Selected Subsidiaries

B&L Brokerage Services, Inc. - insurance broker licensed in the US
B&L Insurance, Ltd. - domiciled and licensed in Bermuda
Protective Insurance Company

Protective Specialty Insurance - approved for excess and surplus lines business in 40 states
Sagamore Insurance Company - licensed in 47 states and approved for excess and surplus lines business in Florida

COMPETITORS

AMERISAFE	Kingsway America
Canal Insurance	McM Corporation
Carolina Casualty	Nationwide
EMC Insurance	Philadelphia Insurance
Essex Insurance	Companies
Fairfax Financial	Progr
Holdings	State Farm
GAINSCO	Transport Insurance
GEICO	Agency
Great West Casualty	

HISTORICAL FINANCIALS

Company Type: Public

Income Statement FYE: December 31

	ASSETS ($ mil.)	NET INCOME ($ mil.)	INCOME AS % OF ASSETS	EMPLOYEES
12/10	837.9	25.0	3.0%	299
12/09	851.3	44.8	5.3%	293
12/08	777.7	(7.7)	—	312
12/07	842.8	55.1	6.5%	284
12/06	853.7	38.2	4.5%	279
Annual Growth	**(0.5%)**	**(10.1%)**	**—**	**1.7%**

2010 Year-End Financials

Equity as % of assets: 44.01%	Dividends
Return on assets: 3.0%	Yield: 4.3%
Return on equity: 6.8%	Payout: 59.2%
Long-term debt ($ mil.): —	Market value ($ mil.): 348.5
No. of shares (mil.): 14.8	Sales ($ mil.): 249.5

	STOCK PRICE ($) FY Close	P/E High/Low		PER SHARE ($) Earnings	Dividends	Book Value
12/10	23.53	16	12	1.69	1.00	24.90
12/09	24.62	8	5	3.04	1.00	25.31
12/08	18.19	—	—	(0.51)	1.00	22.08
12/07	27.46	8	6	3.63	1.00	25.01
12/06	25.54	11	9	2.54	0.85	23.67
Annual Growth	**(2.0%)**	**—**	**—**	**(9.7%)**	**4.1%**	**1.3%**

Ballantyne Strong

Ballantyne Strong projects a lot of images. The company is an international supplier of motion picture theater equipment used by major theater chains such as AMC Entertainment and Regal Entertainment. Primary offerings include its Strong brand of film and digital projectors and accessories. Major international customers include Regal Entertainment and China Film Jingdian Cinema Investment Company. While its theater products account for most of the company's revenues, Ballantyne Strong also has a lighting division. Its spotlights and searchlights have been used by clients such as Walt Disney World and Universal Studios. The company has international operations in Canada, Hong Kong, Beijing, and China.

Ballantyne is active in the digital cinema marketplace as a distributor of digital equipment through an agreement with NEC Solutions. In 2010 overall revenues and profits grew due to an increased sale of digital products, a result of the industry's continued transition from analog to digital projection. Specifically, that year Ballantyne's profits grew by more than $6 million, and digital products sales rose to $87 from about $28 million in 2009.

Also in 2010, sales outside the US increased to about $60 million vs some $33 million in 2009, mostly due to increased demand in China and South America. The company plans to expand its presence in the digital cinema marketplace by distributing digital equipment to additional geographic territories. It is looking for international growth in areas beyond North and South America, Hong Kong, China, and other areas of Asia.

Ballantyne is also looking to grow its lighting division, which currently only accounts for less than 5% of sales. Part of these efforts include the distribution of a new line of LED products marketed under the Litetude brand. Ballantyne's Technobeam light projects logos and images for the entertainment lighting industry. The company's lights have been used at live performances such as Super Bowl half-time shows and the opening and closing ceremonies of various Olympic games. They also illuminate such venues as the Luxor Hotel and Casino and the Stratosphere Hotel and Casino in Las Vegas.

In 2010 the company appointed Gary Cavey as its President and CEO. Cavey replaced the retiring John Wilmers, who had led the business since 1997.

HISTORY

Robert Ballantyne began supplying movie theater equipment in 1932, and after WWII his company, Ballantyne of Omaha, began making equipment for drive-in theaters. Ballantyne retired in 1960 and sold his firm to ABC Vending. Under its new parent, the company entered the foodservice business, making pressure fryers for theater snack stands. Lightbulb maker Canrad-Hanovia bought Ballantyne in 1976, later merging it with its Strong Electric unit (spotlights and projector lamphouses). After Canrad acquired Simplex Projector in 1983, ARC International purchased Canrad in 1989 and merged Ballantyne, Strong, and Simplex. Ballantyne went public in 1995.

In 1996 the company was buoyed by the rapid growth of IMAX theaters and Iwerks motion simulator rides. Ballantyne acquired Xenotech and Sky-Tracker of America in 1997, makers of high-intensity searchlights. John Wilmers took over as CEO, and the following year Ballantyne acquired Design and Manufacturing (film platter systems), teamed with MegaSystems to develop a 3-D projection system, and increased its overseas sales force.

Ballantyne struck a $45 million agreement with Regal Cinemas (now part of Regal Entertainment Group) in 1999 to provide at least 2,000 projection systems over the next two years, marking the company's largest-ever purchase agreement. But a nationwide slowdown in theater construction hurt the company's bottom line in 2000, forcing it to lay off 18% of its employees. To add insult to injury, Ballantyne's stock was delisted from the New York Stock Exchange and its parent company, ARC International, went into receivership. ARC's stake in Ballantyne was acquired by Omaha merchant bank The McCarthy Group the next year. Also in 2001 the company was contracted to supply searchlights for the Kennedy Space Center in Florida.

The company discontinued its restaurant equipment product line in 2007. That year the company moved further into the digital realm with the for-

mation of a venture between Ballantyne and digital technology firm RealD. The venture is researching 3D technology and ways to fund the outfitting of digital projectors to movie exhibitors. Also that year the company acquired Marcel Desrochers, a Canadian manufacturer of screen systems for North America. In addition, its lighting division purchased the Technobeam lighting product line from High End Systems in 2007.

The company in 2009 began distribution of digital equipment through an agreement with NEC Solutions. Allso that year it changed its name from Ballantyne of Omaha, as the majority of customers associate the business with the Strong brand. The following year Gary Cavey replaced the retiring John Wilmers as CEO.

EXECUTIVES

Chairman, William F. Welsh II, age 69
CFO, Secretary, and Treasurer, Kevin S. Herrmann, age 45, $229,690 total compensation
President, CEO, and Director, Gary L. Cavey, age 62
VP Manufacturing, Gerhard Marburg
VP Technical Services, John Biegel
VP Projection & Display, Pat Moore
VP Engineering, Rick Sanjurjo
VP Lighting, Paul Rabinovitz
SVP, Ray F. Boegner, age 61, $276,845 total compensation
SVP and COO, Christopher D. (Chris) Stark, age 50, $237,545 total compensation
Managing Director, Strong Westrex, P. L. Wong
General Manager, Strong Screen System (MDI), Benoit Mailloux
Auditors: KPMG LLP

LOCATIONS

HQ: Ballantyne Strong, Inc.
4350 McKinley St., Omaha, NE 68112
Phone: 402-453-4444   **Fax:** 402-453-7238
Web: www.ballantyne-omaha.com

2010 Sales

	$ mil.	% of total
US	76.2	56
China	34.9	26
South America	10.1	7
Mexico	5.7	4
Canada	4.4	3
Europe	2.8	2
Other regions	2.2	2
Total	**136.3**	**100**

PRODUCTS/OPERATIONS

2010 Sales

	$ mil.	% of total
Theater		
Products	125.0	92
Services	7.9	6
Lighting & other	3.4	2
Total	**136.3**	**100**

Subsidiaries

American West Beijing Trading Company (sales and services in China)
Strong Technical Services (film and digital operations)
Strong Westrex (Hong Kong sales and service)
Strong/MDI Screen Systems (cinema screen and related accessories manufacturing)

COMPETITORS

Barco	Panavision
Chapman/Leonard	Production Resource
Christie Digital	Group
Cinemeccanica	Sony
High End Systems	

HISTORICAL FINANCIALS

Company Type: Public

Income Statement

FYE: December 31

	REVENUE ($ mil.)	NET INCOME ($ mil.)	NET PROFIT MARGIN	EMPLOYEES
12/10	136.3	8.4	6.2%	289
12/09	72.1	2.1	2.9%	181
12/08	54.8	(2.7)	—	173
12/07	51.5	0.2	0.4%	187
12/06	49.7	1.6	3.2%	197
Annual Growth	**28.7%**	**51.4%**	**—**	**10.1%**

2010 Year-End Financials

Debt ratio: —	No. of shares (mil.): 14.3
Return on equity: 16.1%	Dividends
Cash ($ mil.): 22.3	Yield: —
Current ratio: 2.04	Payout: —
Long-term debt ($ mil.): —	Market value ($ mil.): 111.2

	STOCK PRICE ($) FY Close	P/E High/Low		PER SHARE ($) Earnings	Dividends	Book Value
12/10	7.77	17	5	0.59	0.00	3.66
12/09	3.73	27	6	0.15	0.00	3.01
12/08	1.23	—	—	(0.19)	0.00	2.78
12/07	5.85	340	241	0.02	0.00	3.11
12/06	5.29	48	32	0.11	0.00	3.09
Annual Growth	**10.1%**	**—**	**—**	**52.2%**	**—**	**4.3%**

Bank of Commerce

Bank of Commerce Holdings provides traditional banking services through subsidiary Redding Bank of Commerce and its Roseville Bank of Commerce and Sutter Bank of Commerce divisions. It targets small to midsized businesses and medium-to high-net-worth individuals in the northern California communities of Redding, Roseville, and Yuba City. Through more than five branches, the banks offer checking and savings accounts, CDs, IRAs, and money market accounts. Commercial mortgages and business and industrial loans account for more than two-thirds of the company's loan portfolio.

EXECUTIVES

Chairman, Kenneth R. Gifford Jr., age 66
President, CEO, and Director, Patrick J. (Pat) Moty, age 53, $323,189 total compensation
EVP and COO, Linda J. Miles, age 58, $311,243 total compensation
VP, Commercial Banking, Roseville Bank of Commerce, Allan Bernhard
VP and Controller, David J. Gonzales
VP, Regional Operations Manager, Roseville Bank of Commerce, Pamela Halperin
VP, Business Development, Redding Bank of Commerce, Cheryl Whitmer
VP and Information Services Officer, Redding Bank of Commerce, Karen Perry
VP and Loan Review Officer, Redding Bank of Commerce, Larry E. Sterk
VP and Loan Officer, Redding Bank of Commerce, Allen K. Felsenthal
VP Business Development and Group Manager, Redding Bank of Commerce, Tammy S. Parker
VP and Commercial Loan Officer, Redding Bank of Commerce, Dale Orchard

VP Human Resources, Redding Bank of Commerce, Donna J. Moore

Vice Chairman, Lyle L. Tullis, age 61

SVP and CFO, Samuel D. Jimenez, age 47

SVP and Chief Administrative Officer, Debra A. Sylvester, age 53

SVP and Lending Group Manager, Dennis E. Lee

SVP and Regional Credit Manager, Roseville Bank of Commerce, Robert J. O'Neil, age 56, $162,480 total compensation

SVP and Senior Loan Officer, John C. Rainey

SVP and CIO, Redding Bank of Commerce, Caryn A. Blais, age 60, $191,205 total compensation

SVP and Chief Credit Officer, Theodore M. (Ted) Cumming, age 54, $147,800 total compensation

Assistant VP and Loan Officer, Redding Bank of Commerce, Leona S. McCoach

Assistant VP and Loan Services Administration Manager, Redding Bank of Commerce, Deni Jauch

Assistant VP, Administrative Operations, Redding Bank of Commerce, Jacquie Arends

Assistant VP, Commercial Banking, Roseville Bank of Commerce, Robert Lim

Assistant VP and Information Systems Supervisor, Redding Bank of Commerce, Brenda Truett

Regional President, Roseville Bank of Commerce, Randall S. (Randy) Eslick, age 54, $208,328 total compensation

Assistant VP and Loan Admistrator II, Bank of Commerce Roseville, Deborah Mortimeyer

Assistant VP Business Development, Bank of Commerce Roseville, Diane Pleines

Payroll and Benefit Services, Redding Bank of Commerce, Becky Looper

Assistant VP & Operations, Bank of Commerce Roseville, Cathy Smallhouse

SVP and Lending Group Manager, Redding Bank of Commerce - Churn Creek Division, Robert A. Matranga, age 58

Corporate Secretary and Director, David H. Scott, age 67

Auditors: Moss Adams, LLP

LOCATIONS

HQ: Bank of Commerce Holdings
1901 Churn Creek Rd., Redding, CA 96002
Phone: 530-224-3333   **Fax:** 530-224-3337
Web: www.bankofcommerceholdings.com

PRODUCTS/OPERATIONS

2007 Sales

	$ mil.	% of total
Interest		
Loans, including fees	36.1	79
Securities	4.4	10
Other	0.7	1
Noninterest		
Life insurance policy benefits	2.4	5
Merchant credit card service income	0.4	1
Payroll & benefit processing fees	0.4	1
Other	1.4	3
Total	**45.8**	**100**

COMPETITORS

American River Bankshares
Bank of America
North Valley Bancorp
Plumas Bancorp
PremierWest
U.S. Bancorp
Wells Fargo

HISTORICAL FINANCIALS

Company Type: Public

Income Statement

FYE: December 31

	ASSETS ($ mil.)	NET INCOME ($ mil.)	INCOME AS % OF ASSETS	EMPLOYEES
12/10	939.1	6.2	0.7%	313
12/09	813.4	6.0	0.7%	259
12/08	774.2	2.2	0.3%	120
12/07	618.3	6.1	1.0%	114
12/06	583.4	6.6	1.1%	115
Annual Growth	**12.6%**	**(1.6%)**	**—**	**28.4%**

2010 Year-End Financials

Equity as % of assets: 10.77%
Return on assets: 0.7%
Return on equity: 7.4%
Long-term debt ($ mil.): 156.5
No. of shares (mil.): 17.0
Dividends
Yield: 4.2%
Payout: 51.4%
Market value ($ mil): 72.2
Sales ($ mil.): 62.2

	STOCK PRICE ($) FY Close	P/E High/Low		PER SHARE ($) Earnings	Dividends	Book Value
12/10	4.25	16	10	0.35	0.18	5.95
12/09	5.28	11	7	0.58	0.24	7.63
12/08	4.23	34	16	0.25	0.32	7.18
12/07	8.75	18	12	0.68	0.32	5.26
12/06	11.99	17	12	0.74	0.30	4.92
Annual Growth	**(22.8%)**	**—**	**—**	**(17.1%)**	**(12.0%)**	**4.9%**

BCB Bancorp

BCB Bancorp *be* the holding company for BCB Community Bank, which opened its doors in late 2000. The independent bank serves Hudson County and the surrounding area from about 15 offices in New Jersey's Bayonne, Hoboken, Jersey City, and Monroe. The bank offers traditional deposit products and services, including savings accounts, money market accounts, CDs, and IRAs. Funds from deposits are used to originate mortgages and loans, primarily commercial real estate and multi-family property loans (which together account for more than half of the bank's loan portfolio). BCB Bancorp's branch network tripled in size when it added 10 locations through its 2010 acquisition of Pamrapo Bancorp.

EXECUTIVES

Chairman, Mark D. Hogan, age 45

President, CEO, CFO, and Director; President and CEO, BCB Community Bank, Donald Mindiak, age 52, $244,107 total compensation

VP Commercial Lending, BCB Community Bank, Amer Saleem, age 56

Director; Senior Lending Officer, BCB Community Bank, James E. Collins, age 62, $193,471 total compensation

COO and Director; COO and CFO, BCB Community Bank, Thomas M. Coughlin, age 51, $215,685 total compensation

Auditors: Beard Miller Company LLP

LOCATIONS

HQ: BCB Bancorp, Inc.
104-110 Ave. C, Bayonne, NJ 07002
Phone: 201-823-0700   **Fax:** 201-339-0403
Web: bayonnecommunitybank.com

COMPETITORS

Bank of America
City National Bancshares
Hudson City Bancorp
Meridian Capital Group
New York Community Bancorp
PNC Financial
Provident Financial Services
Provident New York Bancorp
Stewardship Financial

HISTORICAL FINANCIALS

Company Type: Public

Income Statement

FYE: December 31

	ASSETS ($ mil.)	NET INCOME ($ mil.)	INCOME AS % OF ASSETS	EMPLOYEES
12/10	1,106.9	14.3	1.3%	174
12/09	631.5	3.7	0.6%	91
12/08	578.6	3.5	0.6%	93
12/07	563.5	4.4	0.8%	104
12/06	510.8	5.6	1.1%	99
Annual Growth	**21.3%**	**26.4%**	**—**	**15.1%**

2010 Year-End Financials

Equity as % of assets: —
Return on assets: 1.3%
Return on equity: 14.5%
Long-term debt ($ mil.): 114.1
No. of shares (mil.): 9.4
Dividends
Yield: 4.9%
Payout: 23.4%
Market value ($ mil.): 92.0
Sales ($ mil.): 54.0

	STOCK PRICE ($) FY Close	P/E High/Low		PER SHARE ($) Earnings	Dividends	Book Value
12/10	9.80	6	3	2.05	0.48	10.55
12/09	9.01	14	9	0.80	0.48	11.03
12/08	10.40	21	13	0.74	0.41	10.84
12/07	15.55	20	16	0.90	0.32	10.39
12/06	16.76	16	13	1.08	0.00	10.38
Annual Growth	**(12.6%)**	**—**	**—**	**17.4%**	**—**	**0.4%**

Berkshire Income Realty

If you enjoy attractive landscaping and swimming pools, but can't stand the upkeep and maintenance, Berkshire Income Realty might have just the spot for you. The real estate investment trust (REIT) invests and operates apartment communities. It owns more than 25 properties in major cities in Texas, Georgia, Florida, California, Oregon, North Carolina, and Pennsylvania, as well as the Washington D.C., metropolitan area. The company (which is controlled by chairman Donald Krupp and his family) often acquires neglected properties and then rehabilitates them. Affiliate Berkshire Property Advisors provides day-to-day management and business operations services to the company.

EXECUTIVES

President, CFO, and Director, David C. Quade, age 67

VP and Secretary, Mary Beth Bloom, age 37

VP and Treasurer, Frank Apeseche, age 53

VP, Jack Dent

VP, Controller and Assistant Secretary, Christopher M. Nichols, age 46

Auditors: PricewaterhouseCoopers LLP

LOCATIONS

HQ: Berkshire Income Realty, Inc.
1 Beacon St., Ste. 1500, Boston, MA 02108
Phone: 617-523-7722   **Fax:** 617-646-2375
Web: www.berkshireincomerealty.com

COMPETITORS

Apartment Investment and Management	Camden Property
	Equity Residential
Archstone	Home Properties
AvalonBay	UDR

HISTORICAL FINANCIALS

Company Type: Public

Income Statement

FYE: December 31

	REVENUE ($ mil.)	NET INCOME ($ mil.)	NET PROFIT MARGIN	EMPLOYEES
12/07	85.3	2.9	3.4%	0
12/06	72.4	(20.0)	—	0
12/05	59.7	6.4	10.7%	0
12/04	40.5	(7.8)	—	0
12/03	30.2	3.6	11.9%	0
Annual Growth	**29.6%**	**(5.3%)**	**—**	**—**

Debt ratio: 115.3%   No. of shares (mil.): 9.4
Return on equity: 14.5%   Dividends
Cash ($ mil.): 121.1   Yield: 4.9%
Current ratio: —   Payout: 23.4%
Long-term debt ($ mil.): 114.1   Market value ($ mil.): 92.0

Bio-Reference Labs

Bio-Reference Laboratories tests positive as the lab of choice for many in the Northeast. Primarily serving the greater New York Metropolitan Area, the company offers routine clinical tests, including Pap smears, pregnancy tests, cholesterol checks, and blood cell counts. Through its GenPath business unit, it also performs more sophisticated esoteric testing such as cancer pathology and molecular diagnostics. It gets most of its orders (close to 5 million per year) from doctors' offices, collecting specimens at draw stations scattered throughout its primary service area in the New York area. Bio-Reference Laboratories also provides services in Connecticut, Delaware, Maryland, New Jersey, and Pennsylvania.

The company's laboratory service in the New York Metro area is its core business, but it is growing steadily and now offers some of its testing services nationwide. Bio-Reference's primary client base is composed of doctors, employers, clinics, and governmental units.

The company offers focused expertise in specialty areas through its various subsidiaries. It operates as a national oncology laboratory through its GenPath subsidiary. GenPath also houses Bio-Reference's women's health testing unit. GeneDX, another wholly owned subsidiary, performs testing of rare and ultra-rare genetic diseases nationally. Bio-Reference intends to build a marketing team to cross-sell its genetic testing and women's health testing capabilities to doctors who specialize in prenatal care.

Bio-Reference grows its services by tapping into emerging laboratory markets. The company is focused on developing its cardiology, histology, and women's health diagnostic testing capabilities to

complement its existing hemostasis (process by which blood changes from fluid to a solid state), hematopathology (tests for congenital disorders), and correctional health care initiatives.

Part of Bio-Reference's strategy for expanding in those testing areas is to partner with medical providers whose expertise can help expedite the development process. In 2010 Bio-Reference entered into one such agreement with Massachusetts General Hospital to develop a line of clinical diagnostic tests designed to identify and help treat solid tumors. The test will make use of the emerging field of personalized medicine, in which a patient's unique genetic make-up is used to help tailor testing and treatment to best address that patient's individual needs.

Bio-Reference's specialty testing operations (both esoteric and for emerging markets) have been growing at a faster clip than its core routine testing business, and now routine lab tests account for less than half of the company's sales.

Still, demand for the both its routine and esoteric lab testing is expected to increase, thanks to a growing US trend of shorter inpatient stays at hospitals. With patients being discharged earlier, some of the business that would typically go straight to the hospital-based lab is instead being sent to labs like Bio-Reference by the patients' after-care physicians.

Doctors can place orders for lab tests and get test results using the company's proprietary CareEvolve online portal. Outside of its customer relationships with doctors' offices, Bio-Reference serves government agencies, large employers (for substance abuse testing, for instance) and prison systems in the northeastern US.

Another Bio-Reference unit, PSIMedica, makes health informatics software that combines information from health care claims, lab results, and other sources and markets it to managed care organizations. The CareEvolve subsidiary markets the company's online connectivity software to other laboratories. Revenues from PSIMedica and CareEvolve contribute a negligible percentage of the company's overall sales.

Founder, chairman, and CEO Marc Grodman owns 10% of the company.

HISTORY

Marc Grodman founded Med-Mobile in 1981, offering mobile medical examination services. In 1987 it opened a clinical laboratory in New Jersey. The purchase of Cytology and Pathology Associates, a small, specialized lab, followed in 1988. Demand for tests rose, leading the company to relocate all operations to a modern lab near New York City. It renamed itself Bio-Reference Laboratories in 1989 and went public in 1993.

The company moved into specialty testing to compensate for the industrywide drop in reimbursement rates that hit its general labs, acquiring GenCare Biomedical Research (cancer testing, 1995), Oncodec Labs (gene mutations, 1995), and SmithKline Beecham's renal dialysis testing business (1996). Late in 1996 the firm sued SmithKline Beecham, accusing it of fraud regarding the purchase.

In 1997 the company sold part of its GenCare oncology laboratory services division to IMPATH. To build its regional presence, the company acquired Medilabs from Long Term Care in 1998. The next year it ventured into new frontiers, opening and acquiring websites for online ventures and buying the Right Body Foods health foods business.

In 2000 Bio-Reference Laboratories expanded its Internet presence (including a business-to-business Web portal for health care professionals, CareEvolve.com) and re-entered the oncology market, resuming full-service testing to physicians and institutions.

In the following years the company was intent on expanding its geographic reach and adding services to its roster to make push itself into a leading position in the testing industry. Some of its key acquisitions include the 2006 purchases of Diagnostic Pathology Services, a Maryland-based anatomic pathology lab serving the mid-Atlantic states, and GeneDx, which specializes in diagnosing rare genetic disorders using DNA sequencing technology. That buy fit with GeneDx' strategy to develop and its expand its genetic diagnostic testing capabilities.

EXECUTIVES

Chairman, President, and CEO, Marc D. Grodman, age 59, $1,172,788 total compensation
President, CareEvolve, Cory Fishkin
CEO and Scientific Director, GeneDx, John Compton, age 62
President and Clinical Director, GeneDx, Sherri Bale
EVP, COO, and Director, Howard Dubinett, age 59, $459,638 total compensation
VP, Genpath, Maryanne Amato
VP Accounts Receivable, Sally Howlett
VP and Director Logistics, Ron Rayot
VP and Director Phlebotomy, Chris Smith
VP Marketing, Amar Kamath
VP Technical Operations and Laboratory Director, Nick Cetani
SVP, Chief Medical Officer and Laboratory Director, James Weisberger, age 55
SVP Financial Operations, Nicholas Papazicos
SVP, Azmy Awad
SVP, Scott Fein
SVP and Director Operations, Warren Erdmann
SVP Sales and Marketing, Charles T. Todd Jr., age 59, $603,247 total compensation
SVP, CFO, Chief Accounting Officer, and Director, Sam Singer Sr., age 67, $459,808 total compensation
CIO; President, PsiMedica, Richard L. Faherty, age 64, $685,820 total compensation
Manager Laboratory and Operations, Patricia Neybold
Director Quality Systems, Kathleen (Kathy) Phillips
Manager Client Service, Marisol Aviles
Manager Technical Services, Estrella Moran
Director Investor Relations, Tara Mackay
Manager Operations, Ada Gazzillo
Director Technical Sales and Marketing, Edward Clayton
Auditors: Moore Stephens, P.C.

LOCATIONS

HQ: Bio-Reference Laboratories, Inc.
481 Edward H. Ross Dr., Elmwood Park, NJ 07407
Phone: 201-791-2600   **Fax:** 201-791-1941
Web: www.bioreference.com

2010 Sales by Payor

	% of total
Commercial insurance	53
Medicare	22
Professional billing	20
Direct patient billing	3
Medicaid	2
Total	**100**

PRODUCTS/OPERATIONS

2010 Sales

	% of total
Esoteric testing	56
Routine testing	44
Total	**100**

Selected Products and Services

Routine testing (Performed in Elmwood Park, New Jersey)
  Blood cell counts
  Cholesterol levels
  HIV tests
  Pap smears
  Pregnancy tests
  Substance abuse tests
  Urinalysis
Esoteric testing (Performed in Elmwood Park, Milford, Massachusetts, and Gaithersburg, Maryland)
  Endocrinology
  Genetics
  Immunology
  Microbiology
  Oncology
  Serology
  Toxicology
Other
  CareEvolve (physician-based connectivity portal for clinical laboratories)
  PSIMedica Clinical Knowledge Management System (health informatics software)

COMPETITORS

American Bio Medica	Kroll Background
Athena Diagnostics	America
Carilion-Spectrum	LabCorp
eScreen	MEDTOX Laboratories
Genzyme Genetics	Orchid Cellmark
IDENTIGENE	Quest Diagnostics

HISTORICAL FINANCIALS

Company Type: Public

Income Statement
FYE: October 31

	REVENUE ($ mil.)	NET INCOME ($ mil.)	NET PROFIT MARGIN	EMPLOYEES
10/10	458.0	26.4	5.8%	2,424
10/09	362.7	21.9	6.0%	2,174
10/08	301.1	15.6	5.2%	1,907
10/07	250.4	14.0	5.6%	1,648
10/06	193.1	11.3	5.9%	1,551
Annual Growth	**24.1%**	**23.6%**	**—**	**11.8%**

2010 Year-End Financials

Debt ratio: 5.0%
Return on equity: 17.3%
Cash ($ mil.): 17.8
Current ratio: 2.07
Long-term debt ($ mil.): 7.7

No. of shares (mil.): 27.8
Dividends
  Yield: —
  Payout: —
Market value ($ mil.): 600.4

	STOCK PRICE ($) FY Close	P/E High/Low		PER SHARE ($) Earnings	Dividends	Book Value
10/10	21.56	26	16	0.94	0.00	5.47
10/09	16.17	23	12	0.79	0.00	4.50
10/08	12.30	32	18	0.56	0.00	3.69
10/07	16.04	35	22	0.50	0.00	3.11
10/06	11.81	29	19	0.43	0.00	2.63
Annual Growth	**16.2%**	**—**	**—**	**21.6%**	**—**	**20.1%**

BioFuel Energy

BioFuel Energy has climbed aboard the ethanol bandwagon. Now that bandwagon seems to be on an uncertain course. The company's two plants have the combined capacity to produce 220 million gallons of ethanol annually, as well as 720,000 tons of distillers grains. The company sells all of its production to agribusiness giant Cargill, which in turn gives it reliable corn supplies, an established logistics/transportation network, and marketing expertise. BioFuel Energy went public in 2007, using the proceeds to repay outstanding debts, as well as to fund construction of its ethanol facilities. Hedge fund firms Greenlight Capital and Third Point control more than 50% of the company. Cargill owns another 10%.

Cargill, which had owned 5% of the company's stock since 2007, gained another 5% from BioFuel Energy's rights offering in February 2011, which satisfied the company's debt to Cargill.

Despite favorable tax credits for renewable fuels, BioFuel Energy has been struggling since a slump in the ethanol market began in 2009. Several ethanol plants were shuttered after the economic downturn and high gasoline prices caused people to drive less. The prices of corn, the company's main ingredient, had increased in June 2008. BioFuel Energy experienced hedging losses on corn, and subsequently restructured its debt with Cargill.

Cargill supplies all of the corn that is needed by BioFuel Energy, about 41 million bushels per year at each of its two plants. BioFuel believes that its plants' proximity to corn supplies, natural gas, and rail transportation position it to compete favorably in the ethanol industry. Its strategy is to focus on cost control and production efficiency, as well as to rely on Cargill's marketing expertise in feed merchandising.

BioFuel Energy had net sales of $453.4 million in fiscal 2010, a 9% increase over net sales of $415.5 million in fiscal 2009. The increase was caused by higher ethanol revenues, although sales of distillers grains decreased. Higher ethanol sales resulted from more production in 2010 compared to 2009, as well as higher per unit prices ($1.77 in 2010, compared to $1.64 in 2009).

BioFuel Energy is subject to "crush spread," due to the fluctuations in commodity prices, primarily the price of its main commodity input - corn - relative to the price of its main commodity product - ethanol. The prices of the commodities can be volatile. The company attributed its net losses of $25.2 million in 2010 and $19.7 million in 2009 to the fluctuation of the crush spreads in each of these years. In addition, its experience with hedging has limited its financial resources and therefore put it at more commodity price risk. Rising prices for both corn and natural gas have resulted in lowered profit margins.

EXECUTIVES

Chairman, Mark W. Wong, age 62
President, CEO and Director, Scott H. Pearce, age 45, $419,582 total compensation
EVP and COO, Daniel J. Simon, age 42, $369,176 total compensation
VP, General Counsel, and Corporate Secretary, Mark L. Zoeller
VP Finance and CFO, Kelly G. Maguire, age 47, $370,386 total compensation
VP Operations, Douglas M. Anderson, age 55
Auditors: Deloitte & Touche LLP

LOCATIONS

HQ: BioFuel Energy Corp.
1600 Broadway, Ste. 2200, Denver, CO 80202
Phone: 303-640-6500   **Fax:** 303-592-8117
Web: www.bfenergy.com

COMPETITORS

Abengoa Bioenergy	Hawkeye Energy
ADM	Holdings
Cargill	Valero Energy
Encore Energy Systems	

HISTORICAL FINANCIALS

Company Type: Public

Income Statement
FYE: December 31

	REVENUE ($ mil.)	NET INCOME ($ mil.)	NET PROFIT MARGIN	EMPLOYEES
12/10	453.4	(20.0)	—	151
12/09	415.5	(13.6)	—	150
12/08	179.9	(40.9)	—	151
12/05	1.0	0.4	40.0%	12
Annual Growth	**239.9%**	**—**	**—**	**65.9%**

2010 Year-End Financials

Debt ratio: 407.5%
Return on equity: —
Cash ($ mil.): 7.4
Current ratio: 1.22
Long-term debt ($ mil.): 220.7

No. of shares (mil.): 33.4
Dividends
  Yield: —
  Payout: —
Market value ($ mil.): 58.1

	STOCK PRICE ($) FY Close	P/E High/Low		PER SHARE ($) Earnings	Dividends	Book Value
12/10	1.74	—	—	(0.79)	0.00	1.62
12/09	2.71	—	—	(0.57)	0.00	2.16
12/08	0.35	—	—	(2.65)	0.00	2.48
12/05	7.03	—	—	(0.35)	0.00	3.66
Annual Growth	**(37.2%)**	**—**	**—**	**—**	**—**	**(23.7%)**

Birner Dental

Birner Dental Management Services hopes to leave its customers smiling. The company acquires, develops, and manages dental practice networks, freeing dentists of their administrative duties by providing management services such as billing, accounting, and marketing. Birner Dental manages about 60 offices under the Perfect Teeth brand name; more than 40 of the practices are located in Colorado, and the rest are in Arizona and New Mexico. Some locations offer special services such as orthodontics, oral surgery, and periodontics. Brothers and co-founders Frederic (chairman and CEO) and Mark Birner (president) together own more than one-quarter of the company.

Birner Dental Management Services has grown by acquiring individual and group dental practices, as well as opening new practices of its own. In recent years the firm has opened new offices in Albuquerque, New Mexico; Phoenix and Tucson, Arizona; and Denver. At its existing practices, it plans to grow by expanding its specialty service offerings and by aggressively recruiting new dentists.

Dennis Genty, CFO and co-founder along with the Birners, owns 11% of the company.

EXECUTIVES

Chairman and CEO, Frederic W. J. Birner, age 53, $517,394 total compensation
President and Director, Mark A. Birner, age 51, $367,095 total compensation
CFO, Secretary, and Treasurer, Dennis N. Genty, age 53, $369,620 total compensation
Auditors:

LOCATIONS

HQ: Birner Dental Management Services, Inc.
3801 E. Florida Ave., Ste. 508, Denver, CO 80210
Phone: 303-691-0680　　**Fax:** 303-691-0889
Web: www.bdms-perfectteeth.com

COMPETITORS

American Dental Partners	Pacific Dental Services, Inc.
InterDent	Smile Brands
OrthoSynetics	

HISTORICAL FINANCIALS

Company Type: Public

Income Statement

FYE: December 31

	REVENUE ($ mil.)	NET INCOME ($ mil.)	NET PROFIT MARGIN	EMPLOYEES
12/10	64.0	1.4	2.2%	708
12/09	59.6	1.9	3.2%	565
12/08	34.5	1.8	5.2%	546
12/07	40.8	2.4	5.9%	565
12/06	39.4	2.3	5.8%	566
Annual Growth	12.9%	(11.7%)	—	5.8%

2010 Year-End Financials

Debt ratio: 47.3%	No. of shares (mil.): 1.9
Return on equity: 18.2%	Dividends
Cash ($ mil.): 0.4	Yield: 4.2%
Current ratio: 0.70	Payout: 106.7%
Long-term debt ($ mil.): 3.7	Market value ($ mil.): 35.3

	STOCK PRICE ($) FY Close	P/E High/Low	PER SHARE ($) Earnings	Dividends	Book Value
12/10	19.00	26 20	0.75	0.80	4.26
12/09	16.75	18 10	1.02	0.68	4.10
12/08	11.30	26 12	0.86	0.68	3.44
12/07	21.44	25 17	1.08	0.60	4.71
12/06	19.05	23 16	0.94	0.52	4.54
Annual Growth	(0.1%)	— —	(5.5%)	11.4%	(1.6%)

Blue River Bancshares

Linda Ronstadt took "Blue Bayou" to the bank, but the folks in the Hoosier State take their green to Blue River Bancshares. The firm is the holding company for SBC Bank (also known as Shelby County Bank), which has a handful of branches in Shelby County, Indiana. The bank offers a variety of deposit products such as checking, savings, NOW, and money market accounts; CDs; and IRAs. With funds raised from deposits, it primarily originates one- to four-family residential mortgage loans, commercial mortgages, home equity and other consumer loans, and business loans. Blue River sold the Paramount Bank division of SBC Bank in Lexington, Kentucky, to Porter Bancorp in 2008.

EXECUTIVES

Chairman, President, and CEO; Chairman, Paramount Bank, Russell Breeden III, age 57
EVP and Secretary; President and CEO, Shelby County Bank, Randy J. Collier, age 49
VP and Controller; SVP and CFO, Shelby County Bank, Patrice M. Lima, age 54
Vice Chairman; Chairman and Chief Credit Officer, Shelby County Bank, Steven R. Abel, age 57
SVP and Director Internal Audit and Compliance, Richard E. Walke
Auditors:

LOCATIONS

HQ: Blue River Bancshares, Inc.
29 E. Washington St., Shelbyville, IN 46176
Phone: 317-398-9721　　**Fax:** 317-392-6208
Web: www.shelbycountybank.com

COMPETITORS

Ameriana Bancorp	KeyCorp
Fifth Third	National Bank of Indianapolis
First Financial (IN)	
JPMorgan Chase	PNC Financial

HISTORICAL FINANCIALS

Company Type: Public

Income Statement

FYE: December 31

	ASSETS ($ mil.)	NET INCOME ($ mil.)	INCOME AS % OF ASSETS	EMPLOYEES
12/06	226.5	0.6	0.3%	70
12/05	221.2	1.6	0.7%	64
12/04	206.6	(0.3)	—	68
12/03	198.8	0.1	0.1%	63
12/02	95.1	(2.1)	—	43
Annual Growth	24.2%	—		13.0%

2006 Year-End Financials

Equity as % of assets: —	Dividends
Return on assets: 0.3%	Yield: 0.5%
Return on equity: 3.4%	Payout: 19.1%
Long-term debt ($ mil.): 23.3	Market value ($ mil.): 21.4
No. of shares (mil.): 3.5	Sales ($ mil.): 15.7

	STOCK PRICE ($) FY Close	P/E High/Low	PER SHARE ($) Earnings	Dividends	Book Value
12/06	6.10	41 30	0.17	0.03	5.08
12/05	5.20	13 10	0.45	0.00	(0.00)
12/04	5.18	— —	(0.08)	0.00	4.63
12/03	6.24	175 106	0.04	0.00	(0.00)
12/02	4.30	— —	(2.71)	0.00	(0.00)
Annual Growth	9.1%	— —	—	—	—

BNC Bancorp

BNC Bancorp knows the ABCs of the financial world. The firm is the holding company for Bank of North Carolina, which has about 20 locations in both North and South Carolina. The bank offers community-oriented services to local business and retail customers, providing checking, savings, and money market accounts, credit cards, and certificates of deposit. Its loan portfolio is mainly composed of residential and commercial mortgages and construction loans. Bank of North Carolina

also offers insurance, retirement planning, and other investment products and services.

In 2010 BNC Bancorp acquired the failed Beach First National Bank in an FDIC-assisted transaction, expanding Bank of North Carolina's branch network into South Carolina. The acquisition of Regent Bank, which is pending, will further extend the bank's reach in the state.

Also in 2010 Aquiline Capital Partners, a private equity firm specializing in the financial services industry, invested nearly $35 million in BNC Bancorp. The transaction netted the investor approximately 10% of the bank holding company, as well as convertible shares that could equate to an additional 15% stake.

EXECUTIVES

Chairman of the Board, Thomas R. Sloan, age 66
Chairman Emeritus, W. Groome Fulton Jr., age 72
President, CEO, and Director; President and CEO, Bank of North Carolina, W. Swope Montgomery Jr., age 62, $617,000 total compensation
EVP and CFO BNC and Bank of North Carolina, David B. Spencer, age 48, $413,523 total compensation
EVP, COO, and Director; EVP and COO, Bank of North Carolina, Richard D. Callicutt II, age 51, $400,927 total compensation
SVP and City Executive, Lexington, Bank of North Carolina, William H. McMurray III, $267,655 total compensation
Secretary and Director, Richard F. Wood, age 66
SVP, Bank of North Carolina, Thomas N. Nelson, $235,571 total compensation
Auditors: Cherry, Bekaert & Holland, LLP

LOCATIONS

HQ: BNC Bancorp
831 Julian Ave., Thomasville, NC 27360
Phone: 336-476-9200　　**Fax:** 336-476-5818
Web: www.bankofnc.com

PRODUCTS/OPERATIONS

2008 Sales

	$ mil.	% of total
Interest		
Loans, including fees	64.8	85
Debt securities	5.7	7
Other	0.5	1
Noninterest		
Service charges	3.0	4
Mortgage fees	0.8	1
Other	1.8	2
Total	**76.6**	**100**

COMPETITORS

Bank of America	FNB United
Bank of the Carolinas	NewBridge Bancorp
BB&T	Piedmont Federal
Carolina Bank	RBC Bank
First Bancorp (NC)	Southern Community Financial
First Citizens BancShares	Wells Fargo

HISTORICAL FINANCIALS

Company Type: Public

Income Statement

FYE: December 31

	ASSETS ($ mil.)	NET INCOME ($ mil.)	INCOME AS % OF ASSETS	EMPLOYEES
12/10	2,149.9	7.7	0.4%	372
12/09	1,634.2	6.5	0.4%	262
12/08	1,572.9	4.0	0.3%	222
12/07	1,130.1	7.4	0.7%	223
12/06	951.7	6.2	0.7%	193
Annual Growth	22.6%	5.6%	—	17.8%

2010 Year-End Financials

Equity as % of assets: 7.08% Dividends
Return on assets: 0.4%   Yield: 2.2%
Return on equity: 7.3%   Payout: 32.8%
Long-term debt ($ mil.): 97.7 Market value ($ mil.): 81.5
No. of shares (mil.): 9.1   Sales ($ mil.): 123.8

	STOCK PRICE ($) FY Close	P/E High/Low		PER SHARE ($) Earnings	Dividends	Book Value
12/10	9.00	18	11	0.61	0.20	16.81
12/09	7.59	13	6	0.62	0.20	17.19
12/08	7.51	33	13	0.52	0.20	16.40
12/07	16.91	20	15	1.05	0.18	12.50
12/06	18.58	20	16	0.95	0.15	10.82
Annual Growth	(16.6%)	—	—	(10.5%)	7.5%	11.7%

Boardwalk Pipeline

Boardwalk Pipeline Partners is in the business of interstate transportation, gathering, and storage of natural gas, and it operates three subsidiaries — Texas Gas Transmission, Gulf South Pipeline Company, and Gulf Crossing Pipeline Company — with a combined 14,200 miles of pipeline in 12 states. Texas Gas operates in Arkansas, Illinois, Indiana, Kentucky, Louisiana, Mississippi, Ohio, Tennessee, and Texas. Gulf South operates in Alabama, Florida, Louisiana, Mississippi, and Texas. Customers include local gas distribution companies, local governments, other interstate and intrastate pipeline companies, industrial users, and electric power generators. Boardwalk Pipeline Partners is owned by Loews Corporation.

In 2010 the company's pipeline systems shipped about 2.5 trillion cu. ft. of natural gas. Its eleven natural gas storage facilities in four states reported an aggregate gas capacity of 167 billion cu. ft.

Boardwalk Pipeline Partners' strategy is to expand its pipeline and storage assets organically and by making acquisitions that complement its existing portfolio.

Expanding its interstate pipeline operations, in 2009 the company opened the Gulf Crossing Pipeline (350 miles of 42-inch pipeline) which originates near Sherman, Texas, and supplies gas from the Barnett Shale and Caney Woodford Shale plays to end users in the Midwest, Northeast, and Southeast. All told, the company added more than 1,000 miles of pipeline in 2009 and 2010 to keep pace with shell gas discoveries.

Despite the down economy and lower commodity prices, Boardwalk Pipeline Partners posted increased revenues in 2009, driven by its pipeline expansion. However, the increase in depreciation and property taxes associated with its expansion projects caused the company's net income to drop sharply that year.

Higher transportation revenues from pipeline expansion projects and gains on gas sales associated with its Western Kentucky Storage Expansion project (which went into service in 2009) lifted Boardwalk Pipeline Partners' revenues in 2010. The increase in revenues outpaced the jump in expenses for the year, lifting its net income.

Further growing its natural gas storage assets, in 2011 a company joint venture agreed to acquire Petal Gas Storage and Hattiesburg Gas Storage from Enterprise Products Partners for $550 million. Petal and Hattiesburg operate seven salt dome natural gas storage caverns in Forrest County, Mississippi, with 29 billion cu. ft. of total storage capacity.

EXECUTIVES

Chairman, Boardwalk GP, LLC, Arthur L. Rebell, age 70
COO, Boardwalk GP LLC, Brian A. Cody, age 53
Director Investor Relations, Allison McLean
SVP, General Counsel, and Secretary, Michael E. McMahon, age 55
SVP, Controller, and Chief Accounting Officer, Steven Barkauskas
SVP, CFO, and Treasurer, Jamie L. Buskill, age 46
Auditors: Deloitte & Touche LLP

LOCATIONS

HQ: Boardwalk Pipeline Partners, LP
9 Greenway Plaza, Ste. 2800, Houston, TX 77046
Phone: 713-479-8000
Web: www.boardwalkpipelines.com

PRODUCTS/OPERATIONS

2010 Sales

	$ mil.	% of total
Gas transportation	1,015.4	91
Gas storage	55.4	5
Parking & lending	28.1	2
Other	17.9	2
Total	**1,116.8**	**100**

2010 Sales

	% of total
Producers	44
Local distribution companies	22
Marketers	19
Pipelines	11
Power generators	3
Industrial end users & other customers	1
Total	**100**

COMPETITORS

Columbia Gulf Transmission	Florida Gas Transmission
El Paso Corporation	Southwest Gas
Energy Future	Williams Gas Pipeline

HISTORICAL FINANCIALS

Company Type: Public

Income Statement

FYE: December 31

	REVENUE ($ mil.)	NET INCOME ($ mil.)	NET PROFIT MARGIN	EMPLOYEES
12/10	1,116.8	289.4	25.9%	1,100
12/09	909.2	162.7	17.9%	1,110
12/08	784.8	294.0	37.5%	1,128
12/07	643.3	220.7	34.3%	1,084
12/06	607.6	197.6	32.5%	1,150
Annual Growth	16.4%	10.0%	—	(1.1%)

2010 Year-End Financials

Debt ratio: —   No. of shares (mil.): 192.6
Return on equity: —   Dividends
Cash ($ mil.): 55.0   Yield: 6.5%
Current ratio: 0.95   Payout: 138.1%
Long-term debt ($ mil.): 3,252.3   Market value ($ mil.): 5,995.6

	STOCK PRICE ($) FY Close	P/E High/Low		PER SHARE ($) Earnings	Dividends	Book Value
12/10	31.13	23	11	1.47	2.03	(0.00)
12/09	30.03	35	22	0.88	1.95	(0.00)
12/08	17.78	18	8	1.80	1.87	(0.00)
12/07	31.10	21	15	1.91	1.74	14.57
12/06	30.82	17	10	1.85	1.32	12.56
Annual Growth	0.3%	—	—	(5.6%)	11.4%	—

Bofl

Bofl Holding owns Bank of Internet USA, a savings bank that operates online in all 50 states. The bank offers checking, savings, and money market accounts, CDs, and ATM and check cards. Multi-family real estate loans account for nearly two-thirds of the company's loan portfolio, although the bank only offers them in selected states; it also acquires them on the secondary market. Offered nationwide, single-family residential mortgages make up nearly 30% of its loan portfolio. Bank of Internet USA also issues home equity, automobile, and recreational vehicle loans. Officers and directors own more than 30% of Bofl Holding's stock.

EXECUTIVES

Chairman, Theodore C. (Ted) Allrich, age 65
President and CEO, Gregory Garrabrants, age 39
VP and CTO, Bank of Internet USA, Michael J. (Mike) Berengolts, age 38
VP Internet Development, Barbara Fronek
Vice Chairman, Nicholas A. Mosich
SVP and Chief Risk Officer, Thomas Williams
SVP and CFO, Andrew J. Micheletti, age 51
Auditors: Crowe Horwath LLP

LOCATIONS

HQ: Bofl Holding, Inc.
12777 High Bluff Dr., Ste. 100, San Diego, CA 92130
Phone: 858-350-6200   **Fax:** 858-350-0443
Web: www.bofiholding.com

COMPETITORS

Allstate Bank	ING DIRECT USA
Bank of America	ISN Bank
Citigroup	Steel Partners
E*TRADE Bank	Holdings
First IB	UnionBanCal

HISTORICAL FINANCIALS

Company Type: Public

Income Statement

FYE: June 30

	ASSETS ($ mil.)	NET INCOME ($ mil.)	INCOME AS % OF ASSETS	EMPLOYEES
06/11	1,940.1	20.6	1.1%	173
06/10	1,421.1	21.1	1.5%	90
06/09	1,302.2	6.5	0.5%	57
06/08	1,194.2	4.2	0.4%	44
06/07	947.2	3.3	0.3%	40
Annual Growth	19.6%	58.1%	—	44.2%

2011 Year-End Financials

Equity as % of assets: 7.62%   Dividends
Return on assets: 1.1%   Yield: —
Return on equity: 14.4%   Payout: —
Long-term debt ($ mil.): 312.7 Market value ($ mil.): 150.4
No. of shares (mil.): 10.4   Sales ($ mil.): 100.9

	STOCK PRICE ($) FY Close	P/E High/Low		PER SHARE ($) Earnings	Dividends	Book Value
06/11	14.41	9	6	1.87	0.00	14.16
06/10	14.12	9	2	2.22	0.00	12.75
06/09	6.09	10	4	0.78	0.00	11.00
06/08	7.39	18	12	0.46	0.00	10.02
06/07	7.24	22	17	0.36	0.00	8.80
Annual Growth	18.8%	—	—	51.0%		12.6%

Boingo

Boingo tries to keep travellers with laptops and smartphones connected as they bounce around unfamiliar locales. The company sells access to a global Wi-Fi network of about 200,000 public hot spots to nearly as many subscribers through wholesale agreements with wireless network and hot spot operators. Access is offered mainly in such venues as hotels, convention centers, airports, and restaurants, including McDonalds and Krispy Kreme. Additionally, Boingo offers its roaming network and software to ISPs and managed network service providers. Fiberlink and Verizon Business are among the company's corporate customers. Established in 2001 by chairman and Earthlink founder Sky Dayton, the company completed an IPO in 2011.

Boingo slated the proceeds from the public offering of stock to support future investments in its software development, customer acquisition, and the expansion of its network. The IPO came following a fiscal year in which the company's sales and profits rose significantly due to its efforts to boost the profile of its brand and add subscribers both in the US and abroad.

To extend its reach in 2010 the company added three sports stadiums and four shopping malls to its network in the US. Boingo is also looking overseas for growth, particularly in the Europe and Asia. To that end the company signed an agreement with BAA Airports to operate hotspots at seven UK airports, and it forged deals with Asian telecommunications service providers China Telecom, KT Corporation, and NTT in 2010. Other international deals that year included agreements with Madrid-based Gowex and Winnipeg-based MTS Allstream.

Boingo has increased its sales significantly in recent years, to the point that it turned a profit in 2009 after years of losses by keeping its costs from growing too much over 2008. Notably, its revenue in 2009 was eight times higher than in 2005. The company achieved this by steadily building its retail subscriber base; it had more than 54,000 retail subscribers in 2007, 74,000 in 2008, and 140 in 2009. Sales to both retail and wholesale customers grew substantially in 2009.

The company's wholesale network usage partnerships include an extensive list of global carriers and ISP's which includes BT, China Telecom, Livedoor, T-Mobile. Boingo also operates neutral host Wi-Fi and DAS networks in more than 20 major North American airports through its Concourse Communications subsidiary.

Boingo is backed by such investors as New Enterprise Associates, Mitsui & Co., Red Rock Ventures, and Sprint Nextel.

EXECUTIVES

Chairman, Sky D. Dayton, age 39
President, CEO, and Director, David (Dave) Hagan, age 50
CFO, Edward K. (Ed) Zinser, age 53
VP Marketing, Dawn Callahan
VP Network Strategy, Luis A. Serrano
CTO, Niels Jonker, age 38
SVP Finance, Peter Hovenier, age 43
General Manager, Mobile and Product Management, Johnathan Mendelson
SVP Strategy and Business Development, Colby Goff
Director of Asia Pacific, Allen J. Pan
Media Relations, Christian Gunning
Auditors: PricewaterhouseCoopers LLP

LOCATIONS

HQ: Boingo Wireless, Inc.
10960 Wilshire Blvd., Ste. 800, Los Angeles, CA 90024
Phone: 310-586-5180   **Fax:** 310-586-4060
Web: www.boingo.com

COMPETITORS

AT&T Mobility	iPass
BT	LodgeNet
Cable & Wireless	Orange Business
Cellco	Services
China Mobile	Sprint Nextel
EarthLink	T-Mobile HotSpot
iBAHN	Vodafone
ICOA	

HISTORICAL FINANCIALS

Company Type: Public

Income Statement

FYE: December 31

	REVENUE ($ mil.)	NET INCOME ($ mil.)	NET PROFIT MARGIN	EMPLOYEES
12/10	80.4	15.7	19.5%	91
12/09	65.7	1.0	1.5%	135
12/08	56.7	(5.9)	—	0
12/07	41.2	(2.6)	—	0
Annual Growth	25.0%	—	—	(32.6%)

2010 Year-End Financials

Debt ratio: —	No. of shares (mil.): —
Return on equity: 21.5%	Dividends
Cash ($ mil.): 25.7	Yield: —
Current ratio: 1.67	Payout: —
Long-term debt ($ mil.): —	Market value ($ mil.): —

BPZ Resources

BPZ Resources is committed to exploring for oil and gas resources in South America. The company is focusing on oil and gas exploration and production in recent years. It operates through its BPZ Energy subsidiary and that unit's BPZ Energy International Holdings subsidiary. BPZ Resources owns 2.4 million acres of oil and gas properties in northwest Peru. It also holds acreage in Ecuador, where it holds a 10% stake in producing block. In 2009 the company reported proved reserves of 37.5 million barrels of oil equivalent (of which 27.5 million barrels is located in the Corvina field, and 10 million barrels in the Albacora field, both of which are located offshore of northwest Peru.

BPZ Resources' primary strategy is to develop mature, long-lived properties in northwest Peru that have been previously explored or partially developed by other oil and gas companies. In 2009 the company had operations in four exploration blocks in Peru. To date, all of its oil sales have been made to Peruvian national oil company, Petroleos del Peru.

In addition to exploration and production activities, BPZ Resources is also looking to use natural gas from its Corvina field to fuel a (to-be-developed) gas-fired power generation plant, as a separate revenue stream.

The global recession, with its lower commodity prices and weakened demand for oil and gas, hurt the company's revenues and income in 2009. Increased lease operating costs and higher depreciation, depletion, and amortization expenses outstripped lower revenues, leading to deeper operating loss that year.

Originally a computer services concern, in 2002 the company discontinued reselling operations that had previously offered customers third-party computer hardware and networking equipment systems. In 2004 the company acquired BPZ Energy, and moved into the oil and gas business.

EXECUTIVES

Chairman Emeritus, Fernando Zúñiga y Rivero, age 84, $419,500 total compensation
Chairman, James B. Taylor, age 73
President, CEO, and Director, Manuel Pablo Zúñiga-Pflücker, age 70, $952,600 total compensation
CFO, Edward G. (Ed) Caminos, age 48, $559,100 total compensation
VP Geosciences, Tomás E. Vargas, age 66
VP Operations, Cesar Ortega
VP Business Development, Xavier A. Súñiga, age 53
COO, Richard J. Spies
Chief Strategy and Technology, Frederic J.L. Briens, age 51, $777,400 total compensation
Chief Legal, Commercial and Administrative Officer, J. Durkin Ledgard, age 50
Director Investor Relations and Corporate Communications, Greg Smith
General Manager, Peru, Rafael Zoeger, age 61
Auditors: BDO USA, LLP

LOCATIONS

HQ: BPZ Resources, Inc.
580 Westlake Park Blvd., Ste. 525, Houston, TX 77079
Phone: 281-556-6200   **Fax:** 281-556-6377
Web: www.bpzenergy.com

COMPETITORS

Exxon Mobil	Occidental Petroleum
HKN	Perupetro S.A.
Hunt Oil	Petroecuador

HISTORICAL FINANCIALS

Company Type: Public

Income Statement

FYE: December 31

	REVENUE ($ mil.)	NET INCOME ($ mil.)	NET PROFIT MARGIN	EMPLOYEES
12/10	110.5	(59.8)	—	262
12/09	52.5	(35.8)	—	180
12/08	63.0	(9.6)	—	172
12/07	2.4	(20.5)	—	67
12/03	1.0	(4.1)	—	25
Annual Growth	95.8%	—	—	39.9%

2010 Year-End Financials

Debt ratio: 62.4%	No. of shares (mil.): 115.5
Return on equity: —	Dividends
Cash ($ mil.): 11.8	Yield: —
Current ratio: 1.37	Payout: —
Long-term debt ($ mil.): 156.8	Market value ($ mil.): 549.7

	STOCK PRICE ($) FY Close	P/E High/Low		PER SHARE ($) Earnings	Dividends	Book Value
12/10	4.76	— —		(0.52)	0.00	2.18
12/09	9.50	— —		(0.35)	0.00	2.36
12/08	6.40	— —		(0.12)	0.00	2.02
12/07	11.18	— —		(0.30)	0.00	1.42
12/03	4.10	— —		(0.35)	0.00	1.34
Annual Growth	3.8%	— —		—	—	12.8%

Bridgepoint Education

Bridgepoint Education invites students from all walks of life to cross on over to the higher-education side. The for-profit company offers more than 70 graduate and undergraduate programs online and at its bricks-and-mortar campuses: Ashford University in Iowa and University of the Rockies in Colorado. Academic disciplines include education, business, psychology, and health and social sciences. Most of the company's campus-based revenues are derived from federal financial aid. About 99% of Bridgepoint Education's nearly 80,000 students are enrolled exclusively online. Hoping to take advantage of the growing market for online and nontraditional schools, the company went public in 2009.

The IPO filing came on the heels of the public offerings of other education companies China Distance Education Holdings and Grand Canyon Education. Bridgepoint raised roughly $141 million in its IPO and plans to use the funds to pay investors and for general corporate purposes. Principal investor Warburg Pincus retained ownership of more than 60% of Bridgepoint's shares after the IPO.

Much like a community college, Bridgepoint appeals to students who might find tuition costs, credit transfer, or work schedules to be barriers to attending traditional universities. Bridgepoint tries to remove those barriers by accepting up to 99 prior credits to ease transferability, by continuously expanding its online course offerings to increase accessibility, and by structuring the price of its tuition to fall below Title IV loan limits so most students can afford to attend the school without having to take out substantial private loans or make cash tuition payments. Title IV loans are generally easier to obtain than private loans and carry lower, fixed interest rates. Some examples include the Unsubsidized Federal Stafford loan, Federal Pell Grants, and Federal Perkins Loans. In 2010 about 85% of Ashford University's revenue and 86% of the University of the Rockies' revenue came from Title IV programs.

Bridgepoint bases its growth strategy on expanding its academic offerings to attract more students. It identifies new programs by listening to student and faculty feedback, as well as by researching macro market trends to identify which job areas will experience demand in coming years and introducing programs to educate students in those fields (such as health care and education).

The company also seeks to increase its student base by offering special programs for corporate employees and military personnel. Both of Bridgepoint's universities work with employers offering education reimbursement programs, and Ashford University has a grant program offering tuition discounts to FedEx, Nationwide, and Verizon employees (among others) seeking degrees.

Ashford University offers educational opportunities to active-duty personnel and veterans of US armed forces branches (US Army, Marine Corps, Navy, Air Force, and Coast Guard) with special tuition rates, waived fees, and free books and shipping costs. Nearly 20% of its students are with the military.

Ashford University was founded in 1918 as Mount St. Clare College by the Sisters of St. Francis. It became The Franciscan University in 2002 and was purchased in 2005 by Bridgepoint, which changed the university's name. In 2007 Bridgepoint acquired University of the Rockies (formerly Colorado School of Professional Psychology), which focuses on offering graduate degrees in psychology.

CEO and president Andrew Clark founded Bridgepoint Education in 2004. Clark was assisted by other executives of the company, and the formation of Bridgepoint Education was backed by investor Warburg Pincus.

EXECUTIVES

Chairman, Patrick T. (Pat) Hackett, age 49
President, CEO, and Director, Andrew S. Clark, age 45, $1,249,901 total compensation
President, Ashford University, Elizabeth T. Tice
EVP and CFO, Daniel J. (Dan) Devine, age 46, $562,466 total compensation
EVP and Chief Academic Officer, Jane McAuliffe, age 43
EVP and Chief Administrative Officer, Rodney T. (Rocky) Sheng, age 44, $570,088 total compensation
VP, Chief Accounting Officer, and Controller, Brandon Pope, age 46
VP Corporate Communications, Diane Salucci
VP and Senior Corporate Attorney, Robert Wernli Jr.
VP Learning Resources, Elizabeth Aguiar
VP; President, University of the Rockies, Charlita Shelton
VP Finance, T. R. Irwin
VP Compliance, Steve Isbister
VP Government Affairs, Sheryl Wright
VP Software Development, Ravi Rajaratnam
VP Real Estate, Kenny Lin
VP IT, Dan Stoneman
VP Administrative Services, Sheri Jones
VP Risk Management, Mike Stansbury
SVP and General Counsel, Diane L. Thompson, age 54
SVP and CIO, Thomas (Tom) Ashbrook, age 45
SVP Human Resources, Charlene Dackerman, age 50
Provost, University of the Rockies, Ernest Price
Director Public Relations, Shari Rodriguez
SVP Strategy and Corporate Development, Douglas C. Abts
SVP and Chief Marketing Officer, Ross L. Woodard, age 44, $546,096 total compensation
SVP Corporate Development, Wayne Clugston
Auditors: PricewaterhouseCoopers LLP

LOCATIONS

HQ: Bridgepoint Education, Inc.
13500 Evening Creek Dr. North, Ste. 600, San Diego, CA 92128
Phone: 858-668-2586 **Fax:** 858-408-2903
Web: www.bridgepointeducation.com

PRODUCTS/OPERATIONS

2010 Student Enrollment

	No.	% of total
Online	77,033	99
Ground	859	1
Total	**77,892**	**100**

2010 Enrollment by Degree Type

	No.	% of total
Bachelor's	57,905	74
Associate's	10,720	14
Master's	8,414	11
Doctoral	618	1
Other	235	-
Total	**77,892**	**100**

Selected Programs

Associate of Arts
  Business
Bachelor of Applied Science
  Accounting
  Computer
  Computer Graphic Design Core
Bachelor of Arts
  Accounting
  Business Administration
  Communication Studies
  Education
  Health Care Administration
  Liberal Arts
  Political Science and Government
  Psychology
  Social and Criminal Justice
  Social Science
  Sociology
  Visual Arts
Bachelor of Science
  Biology
  Clinical Cytotechnology
  Health Science Administration
  Natural Science
Doctorate
  Psychology
Master of Arts
  Education
  Organizational Management
  Psychology
  Teaching and Learning with Technology
Master of Business Administration
Master of Public Administration

COMPETITORS

American Public Education
Apollo Group
Capella Education
Career Education
Corinthian Colleges
DeVry
Education Management
Grand Canyon Education
International Scholarship and Tuition Services
ITT Educational
Laureate Education
Lincoln Educational Services

HISTORICAL FINANCIALS

Company Type: Public

Income Statement

FYE: December 31

	REVENUE ($ mil.)	NET INCOME ($ mil.)	NET PROFIT MARGIN	EMPLOYEES
12/10	713.2	127.6	17.9%	3,000
12/09	454.3	47.1	10.4%	2,495
12/08	218.3	26.4	12.1%	1,200
12/07	85.7	3.3	3.9%	2,800
12/06	28.6	(5.2)	—	0
Annual Growth	**123.5%**	**—**	**—**	**2.3%**

2010 Year-End Financials

Debt ratio: —	No. of shares (mil.): 52.8
Return on equity: 53.6%	Dividends
Cash ($ mil.): 188.5	Yield: —
Current ratio: 1.67	Payout: —
Long-term debt ($ mil.): —	Market value ($ mil.): 1,003.2

	STOCK PRICE ($) FY Close	P/E High/Low		PER SHARE ($) Earnings	Dividends	Book Value
12/10	19.00	13	6	2.14	0.00	4.51
12/09	15.02	30	13	0.74	0.00	2.48
Annual Growth	**26.5%**	**—**	**—**	**189.2%**	**—**	**81.9%**

BroadSoft

BroadSoft hopes to remove some of hard work from the process of supplying voice and data services. The company designs software that fixed-line, mobile, and cable service providers use to provide voice and data services over Internet protocol-based networks. Clients use its BroadWorks software to offer their own clients services such as video calling, hosted multimedia communications, PBX exchanges, and collaboration tools. Customers include phone and cable companies and ISP's such as Korea Telecom, SingTel, Telefónica de Espana, Telstra, and Verizon.

In 2011, it acquired Phoenix-based web conferencing provider iLinc Communications in an all-cash deal. iLinc's Software-as-a-Service products serve public and private sector entities including educational institutions, adding enterprise collaboration capabilities to BroadSoft's BroadCloud offerings.

The company completed an IPO in 2010. The company will use the proceeds of about $45 million from its IPO for funding acquisitions, general corporate purposes, developing new products, and paying down debt. BroadSoft relies heavily on its BroadWorks software product, which accounts for more than 80% of its overall sales. It has failed to reach profitability in any of the last three years and had an accumulated deficit of about $97 million when it filed for its IPO in 2010.

Also that year BroadSoft bought California-based content and messaging management software developer Casabi for about $1.95 million. The deal served to expand the company's hosted software product line and bolstered its partnership with cable provider Comcast which has partnerships with both companies.

In 2009 the company purchased Packet Island, a provider of on-demand software for quality of service assessment and monitoring of VoIP and video networks and services. The deal expands BroadSoft's offerings to include tools to not just implement and deploy VoIP services but to monitor and perform quality assurance functions as well. The previous year the company acquired GENBAND's M6 application server business and purchased Sylantro; the deals expanded Broad-Soft's technology assets and grew its customer base.

While many service providers originally developed Internet protocol (IP) networks for the sole purpose of transmitting high speed data, they're turning to software providers such as BroadSoft to leverage their IP networks for other purposes. BroadSoft's products are installed on servers typically located in clients' data centers, enabling the use of existing IP networks for broader tasks such as delivering video calls, providing hosted PBX exchanges, and enabling collaboration and conferencing.

BroadSoft was founded in 1998 and received funding from investors including Charles River Ventures and Grotech Partners.

EXECUTIVES

Chairman, Robert P. (Bob) Goodman, age 50
CFO, Assistant Secretary, and Assistant Treasurer, James A. (Jim) Tholen, age 51, $527,046 total compensation
President, CEO, and Director, Michael (Mike) Tessler, age 50, $960,356 total compensation
VP Engineering, Robert (Bob) Weidenfeller
VP Sales, EMEA, Craig Decker
VP Products, David Bukovsky
VP and General Counsel, Mary Ellen Seravalli, age 50
VP Operations, Geoffrey K. (Geoff) Hicks
VP Cloud Research and Development, Greg E. Pounds
VP Business Development, Ken Rokoff
VP Marketing, Leslie Ferry
VP Asia/Pacific, Jonathan Reid
VP Sales, Greg Callanan
Auditors: PricewaterhouseCoopers LLP

LOCATIONS

HQ: BroadSoft, Inc.
220 Perry Pkwy., Gaithersburg, MD 20877
Phone: 301-977-9440
Web: www.broadsoft.com

2009 Sales

	% of total
US	48
Other countries	52
Total	**100**

PRODUCTS/OPERATIONS

2009 Sales

	$ mil.	% of total
Licenses	37.9	55
Maintenance & professional services	31.0	45
Total	**68.9**	**100**

Selected Products

Communications software and servers to support provisioning of telephony services (BroadWorks).

COMPETITORS

Alcatel-Lucent	Huawei Technologies
Amdocs	Metaswitch
Avaya	Nokia Siemens Networks
Cisco Systems	Sonus Networks
Comverse Technology	Telcordia
Ericsson	

HISTORICAL FINANCIALS

Company Type: Public

Income Statement

FYE: December 31

	REVENUE ($ mil.)	NET INCOME ($ mil.)	NET PROFIT MARGIN	EMPLOYEES
12/10	95.6	8.0	8.4%	372
12/09	68.9	(7.8)	—	318
12/08	61.8	(11.2)	—	0
12/07	61.6	(1.8)	—	0
Annual Growth	**15.8%**	**—**	**—**	**17.0%**

2010 Year-End Financials

Debt ratio: 1.5%
Return on equity: 15.2%
Cash ($ mil.): 47.3
Current ratio: 1.50
Long-term debt ($ mil.): 0.8
No. of shares (mil.): 25.5
Dividends
  Yield: —
  Payout: —
Market value ($ mil.): 607.8

	STOCK PRICE ($) FY Close	P/E High/Low		PER SHARE ($) Earnings	Dividends	Book Value
12/10	23.88	85	23	0.32	0.00	2.06
Annual Growth	**—**	**—**		**—**	**—**	**—**

Broadview Institute

Broadview Institute isn't narrow-minded about education. The company owns and operates C Square Educational Enterprises, dba Utah Career College or UCC, which offers career vocational training programs in the Salt Lake City area to about 1,000 students. Its degree programs span four growing industries: business and accounting, health sciences (including veterinary studies), information technology, and legal science. Classes are offered at three campuses in Utah and through online and accelerated programs. Chairman Terry Myhre owns about 65% of Broadview. Additionally, Myhre has controlling interest in two other post-secondary career colleges, Globe University and Minnesota School of Business.

The college's newest branch opened in Orem in Fall 2008. Plans for future growth include opening new campuses around Utah and rebranding the Utah Career College with a name that will open up markets in other states. It also plans to introduce its first graduate degree, a Master's in Managment, though a timetable for this has not been announced.

In 2006 the company changed its name from Broadview Media to Broadview Institute to reflect its transition toward post-secondary education. The company formerly created and produced television shows, communication, and educational products. It discontinued its Media Production segment at the end of 2008 in order to focus solely on UCC.

Terry Myhre stepped down as CEO in early 2008 (he remained chairman) and was replaced by Larry Zipkin. Later that year, Zipkin was succeeded by Jeffrey Myhre, Terry's son.

EXECUTIVES

Chairman, Terry L. Myhre, age 66
CEO, Jeffrey D. Myhre, age 37
CFO, Kenneth J. (Ken) McCarthy, age 37
Auditors:

LOCATIONS

HQ: Broadview Institute, Inc.
8089 Globe Dr., Woodbury, MN 55125
Phone: 651-332-8000   **Fax:** 651-332-8001
Web: www.BroadviewMedia.com

COMPETITORS

Salt Lake Community College	University of Utah
	Westminster College

HISTORICAL FINANCIALS

Company Type: Public

Income Statement

FYE: March 31

	REVENUE ($ mil.)	NET INCOME ($ mil.)	NET PROFIT MARGIN	EMPLOYEES
03/11	20.5	(0.1)	—	246
03/10	19.0	2.0	10.5%	233
03/09	12.4	0.3	2.4%	200
03/08	10.3	2.3	22.3%	154
03/07	9.2	0.2	2.2%	124
Annual Growth	**22.2%**	**—**	**—**	**18.7%**

2011 Year-End Financials

Debt ratio: —
Return on equity: —
Cash ($ mil.): 4.5
Current ratio: 4.75
Long-term debt ($ mil.): —

No. of shares (mil.): 8.2
Dividends
  Yield: —
  Payout: —
Market value ($ mil.): 8.2

	STOCK PRICE ($) FY Close	P/E High/Low		PER SHARE ($) Earnings	Dividends	Book Value
03/11	1.00	—	—	(0.02)	0.00	0.92
03/10	2.90	22	4	0.23	0.00	0.92
03/09	0.98	88	32	0.03	0.00	0.66
03/08	2.06	13	6	0.25	0.00	0.62
03/07	1.70	135	58	0.02	0.00	0.32
Annual Growth	(12.4%)	—	—	—	—	30.0%

Brocade Communications

Brocade Communications Systems maintains silky smooth computer network operations. A leading supplier of data center networking products, Brocade makes Fibre Channel switches and related software for connecting corporate storage systems and servers. Its products are used in storage area networks (SANs), which pool storage resources across enterprises for easier management and more efficient utilization of assets. The company's SilkWorm switches automatically reroute data upon path failure and reconfigure the SAN when new devices are added. Brocade sells its products primarily through equipment manufacturers, including EMC, Hewlett-Packard, and IBM, which together generate nearly half of the company's revenues.

The storage networking market has seen widespread consolidation in recent years, with both startups and industry leaders being targeted. Brocade acquired rival McDATA in 2007. The stock swap was valued at approximately $973 million. Brocade has a history of using acquisitions to widen its product and technology portfolio. It also purchased network acceleration specialist Silverback Systems in 2007.

The following year it acquired network switch maker Foundry Networks for $2.6 billion. The purchase of Foundry added a number of new products to Brocade's lineup, including network edge and core switches, network management software, and Web switches and accelerators. It also moved the company into more direct competition with such companies as Cisco Systems and Juniper Networks.

Enterprises continue to migrate away from older storage technologies — namely direct-attached storage, or DAS — toward networked storage architectures, fueling the market for Fibre Channel specialists such as Brocade. (Fibre Channel is currently the most popular transport technology for SANs.) Brocade leads the Fibre Channel switch market, but its competition is not limited to similarly positioned companies. Cisco Systems (one of the storage industry's newer entrants) hopes to leverage its Internet protocol (IP) networking expertise in the storage arena; a host of startups, many of which champion competing technologies, have also entered the fray.

Brocade is in an intensely competitive market, and industry consolidation continues to narrow the number of leading players. The company must keep up with new products and services to remain competitive among its industry peers. Brocade took on about $1.1 billion of debt through its acquisition of Foundry Networks, and the increased indebtedness may make it difficult for the company to obtain credit or financing, reducing its financial flexibility.

Brocade's products are made by contract electronics manufacturers Celestica, Flextronics International, Hon Hai Precision (Foxconn Electronics), Quanta Computer, and Sanmina-SCI, among others.

Gregory Reyes, who resigned as Brocade's CEO in 2005 in the wake of allegations over the company's past practices in granting stock options, was convicted in 2007 on 10 federal criminal charges for backdating stock options and later sentenced to 21 months in prison and a fine of $15 million. His conviction was overturned in 2009, and he was retried in 2010. The second trial ended in conviction on nine of the 10 charges.

Another executive, former HR VP Stephanie Jensen, was separately tried and convicted on backdating charges in 2007. On appeal, her conviction was upheld, but the appeals court ordered the trial court to resentence Jensen, who originally was sentenced to serve four months in prison and to pay a fine of $1.25 million. The trial judge then cut her prison term in half, to two months, and retained the fine.

EXECUTIVES

Chairman, David L. (Dave) House, age 67
CEO and Director, Michael (Mike) Klayko, age 56, $10,707,452 total compensation
VP Finance and CFO, Daniel W. (Dan) Fairfax, age 55
VP, General Counsel, Chief Compliance Officer, and Corporate Secretary, Tyler Wall, age 45, $3,085,278 total compensation
VP Data Center and Enterprise Networking, Jason Nolet
VP Human Resources, Lisa D. McGill
VP and Chief Marketing Officer, John McHugh, age 49
VP Information Technology and CIO, Tim Graumann
VP Engineering, Parviz Ghalambor
VP Operations and Information Technology, Raymond Lee
VP Corporate Development, Tejinder (TJ) Grewal, age 43, $3,164,157 total compensation
VP Service Provider Products, Ken K. Cheng, age 55
CTO, Dave Stevens
SVP Worldwide Sales, Ian Whiting, age 46, $3,703,016 total compensation
Director Corporate Communications, Elizabeth Walther
Manager Corporate Communications, Jennifer Miu
Senior Director Corporate Communications, John Noh
Manager Corporate Communications, Pavel Radda
Corporate Communications Specialist, Ashton Bothman
Manager Corporate Communications, APJ, Wendy Lang
Manager Corporate Communications, Emory Epperson
Manager Corporate Communications, EMEA, Stuart Marks
Manager Corporate Communications, Ron Schmidt
Manager Corporate Communications, Michelle Lindeman
Corporate Communications Specialist, Kelly Maxwell
Auditors: KPMG LLP

LOCATIONS

HQ: Brocade Communications Systems, Inc.
  1745 Technology Dr., San Jose, CA 95110
Phone: 408-333-8000   **Fax:** 408-333-8101
Web: www.brocade.com

2009 Sales

	$ mil.	% of total
North America	1,300.6	67
Europe, Middle East & Africa	451.0	23
Asia/Pacific		
Japan	59.8	3
Other countries	141.5	7
Total	**1,952.9**	**100**

PRODUCTS/OPERATIONS

2009 Sales

	$ mil.	% of total
Data Storage	1,191.1	61
Ethernet Products	424.4	22
Global Services	337.4	17
Total	**1,952.9**	**100**

COMPETITORS

Alcatel-Lucent	Force10
Cisco Systems	Hewlett-Packard
Crossroads Systems	Huawei Technologies
Emulex	Juniper Networks
Enterasys	Nortel Networks
Extreme Networks	QLogic
F5 Networks	Voltaire
Finisar	

HISTORICAL FINANCIALS

Company Type: Public

Income Statement

FYE: Saturday nearest 10/31

	REVENUE ($ mil.)	NET INCOME ($ mil.)	NET PROFIT MARGIN	EMPLOYEES
10/10	2,094.4	118.9	5.7%	4,651
10/09	1,952.9	(76.6)	—	4,070
10/08	1,466.9	167.1	11.4%	2,834
10/07	1,236.9	76.9	6.2%	2,368
10/06	750.6	67.6	9.0%	1,440
Annual Growth	29.2%	15.2%	—	34.1%

2010 Year-End Financials

Debt ratio: 44.1%
Return on equity: 5.8%
Cash ($ mil.): 334.0
Current ratio: 1.54
Long-term debt ($ mil.): 903.3

No. of shares (mil.): 461.3
Dividends
  Yield: —
  Payout: —
Market value ($ mil.): 2,929.2

	STOCK PRICE ($) FY Close	P/E High/Low		PER SHARE ($) Earnings	Dividends	Book Value
10/10	6.35	38	19	0.25	0.00	4.44
10/09	8.60	—	—	(0.19)	0.00	4.07
10/08	3.77	22	6	0.43	0.00	3.45
10/07	9.51	50	23	0.21	0.00	3.25
10/06	8.11	36	14	0.25	0.00	2.28
Annual Growth	(5.9%)	—	—	(0.0%)	—	18.1%

Bsquare

Bsquare hips its clients on how to integrate Microsoft applications with their own products. The company primarily resells software from Microsoft.

Domestically, its sales center around the Microsoft General Embedded operating system (OS), while international customers look to Bsquare for Microsoft's Windows Mobile OS. Makers of consumer electronics (cell phones) and automobiles in particular power portions of their goods with Microsoft's applications. Bsquare sells software from such other vendors as Adobe and McAfee. Additionally, it provides engineering and development services to clients who require help integrating Windows products. The company also sells its own electronics testing software.

Bsquare's top client is Ford; other key customers have included Micros Systems and Qualcomm. Sales to Ford represented 13% of Bsquare's total revenue in 2010, down from 23% the previous year. Spending by the company's largest customer has declined due to the completion by Bsquare of its main project for the automaker, MyFord Touch, an in-car communications and entertainment system. While Ford remains a client, the company expects its spending to decline further in the future.

Overall, Bsquare's sales rose by 50% in 2010, driven by increased sales of third-party products. The company also turned a profit for the year after losing money in 2009. International sales rose by 16% in 2010, due largely to greater demand for the Microsoft Windows Mobile OS.

As the company continues to look overseas for growth, it is targeting Asia by adding a direct sales force in South Korea and expanding its sales presence in China; investments in sales operations in Japan and Taiwan are pending. Bsquare has also built up its development activities in Taiwan, and it plans to add another development facility in China. The company also has a sales presence in India, Japan, and the UK. In 2011 it added sales and support staff in the UK and Germany to better serve its manufacturing clients in Europe.

While the company's offerings are largely centered around the Windows operating systems, Bsquare is also developing products based on other operating systems such as Google's Android mobile comunications platform. Additionally, in 2010 the company formed a partnership with Qualcomm to sell its Snapdragon mobile development platform.

EXECUTIVES

Chairman, Elliott H. (Ren) Jurgensen Jr., age 66
President, CEO, and Director, Brian T. Crowley, age 50, $272,735 total compensation
VP Finance and Operations, CFO, Secretary, and Treasurer, Scott C. Mahan, age 46, $211,000 total compensation
VP Products, John Traynor
VP Business Development, Michael Tidwell
VP Professional Engineering Services, Carey E. Butler, age 56
VP Worldwide Sales and Marketing, Mark E. McMillan, age 48
VP Products, Rajesh (Raj) Khera, age 41
Senior Software Architect, Larry Schiefer
Manager Wireless Products, Stephen Wampler
Solution Architect, Mike Cannon
Auditors: Moss Adams, LLP

LOCATIONS

HQ: Bsquare Corporation
110 110th Ave. NE, Ste. 200, Bellevue, WA 98004-5840
Phone: 425-519-5900 **Fax:** 425-519-5999
Web: www.bsquare.com

2010 Sales

	$ mil.	% of total
North America	80.8	83
Asia	14.2	14
Other regions	1.8	3
Total	**96.8**	**100**

PRODUCTS/OPERATIONS

2010 Sales

	$ mil.	% of total
Software		
Third-party	63.9	66
Proprietary	5.2	5
Services	72.7	29
Total	**96.8**	**100**

COMPETITORS

Arrow Electronics	Motorola Mobility
Avnet	Smith Micro
Intrinsyc Software	Wind River Systems
Keynote Systems	Wipro Technologies

HISTORICAL FINANCIALS

Company Type: Public

Income Statement

FYE: December 31

	REVENUE ($ mil.)	NET INCOME ($ mil.)	NET PROFIT MARGIN	EMPLOYEES
12/10	96.8	6.2	6.4%	279
12/09	64.4	(2.7)	—	275
12/08	65.8	2.0	3.0%	232
12/07	59.4	2.8	4.7%	175
12/06	49.8	(0.5)	—	170
Annual Growth	**18.1%**	**—**	**—**	**13.2%**

2010 Year-End Financials

Debt ratio: —
Return on equity: 24.6%
Cash ($ mil.): 10.8
Current ratio: 2.20
Long-term debt ($ mil.): —

No. of shares (mil.): 10.4
Dividends
  Yield: —
  Payout: —
Market value ($ mil.): 91.1

	STOCK PRICE ($) FY Close	P/E High/Low		PER SHARE ($) Earnings	Dividends	Book Value
12/10	8.75	17	4	0.56	0.00	2.41
12/09	2.50	—	—	(0.27)	0.00	1.72
12/08	2.36	36	11	0.19	0.00	1.88
12/07	6.79	28	10	0.27	0.00	1.66
12/06	2.85	—	—	(0.05)	0.00	1.26
Annual Growth	**32.4%**			**—**	**—**	**17.6%**

Buffalo Wild Wings

Hot sauce fuels the flight of this restaurateur. Buffalo Wild Wings (BWW) operates a chain of more than 700 Buffalo Wild Wings Grill & Bar quick-casual dining spots that specialize in serving Buffalo-style chicken wings. The eateries, found in about 40 states, offer more than a dozen unique dipping sauces to go with the spicy wings, as well as a complement of other items such as chicken tenders and legs. BWW's menu also features appetizers, burgers, tacos, salads, and desserts, along with beer, wine, and other beverages. The company owns and operates about 250 of the restaurants, while the rest are operated by franchisees.

Typical in the casual dining industry, the BWW chain comprises a mix of corporate-run and franchised locations. Its large estate of owned and operated eateries accounts for the greatest share of the company's sales (about 90%) and allows it to maintain control over the Buffalo Wild Wings dining experience, while its franchising efforts help expand the chain with fewer construction and operating costs. Local franchise operators such as Michigan-based Diversified Restaurant Holdings typically pay the company royalties and other fees in order to use the Buffalo Wild Wings brand and marketing.

Many BWW locations are found in suburban areas, typically near established retail and entertainment developments. The concept is designed to appeal to a broad mix of customers, but the chain promotes itself as a place for groups and families to gather and watch sporting events. (Some locations have as many as 50 TV screens to give everyone a good view of the big game.) BWW competes broadly against other casual dining chains, such as Applebee's and T.G.I. Friday's (owned by Carlson Restaurants Worldwide), but within its target audience the chain faces competition from Dave & Buster's, the Fox & Hound chain of sports bars, and of course Hooters.

The company has been expanding rapidly since its 2003 IPO, when it had about 220 locations. During 2010 BWW opened more than 80 new restaurants after about 90 openings in 2009. The company is working toward the goal of eventually reaching about 1,400 locations, with plans calling for corporate-owned restaurants to make up about 40% of the chain. BWW will open its first international location in Toronto, Canada in 2011 with plans to have 50 Canadian outposts of the restaurant up and running by 2016.

Jim Disbrow and Scott Lowery opened the first Buffalo Wild Wings restaurant on the campus of Ohio State University in Columbus in 1982. (Legend has it that they started the eatery because they craved the style of chicken wings they had eaten in Buffalo, New York.) Originally called Buffalo Wild Wings & Weck (a reference to the Kimmelweck brand rolls used for sandwiches), the chain became known as BW3 for short. Rapid expansion and financial mismanagement pushed Buffalo Wild Wings to the brink of bankruptcy by the mid-1990s. Sally Smith became CEO in 1996 and helped retool the chain's branding strategy to appeal more to families and non-students.

EXECUTIVES

Chairman, James M. Damian, age 60
President, CEO, and Director, Sally J. Smith, age 53, $2,413,355 total compensation
EVP and COO, James M. Schmidt, age 51, $1,045,674 total compensation
EVP, CFO, and Treasurer, Mary J. Twinem, age 50, $1,257,136 total compensation
EVP Global Marketing and Brand Development, Kathleen M. (Kathy) Benning, age 48, $756,947 total compensation
EVP Global Operations and Human Resources, Judith A. (Judy) Shoulak, age 51, $887,497 total compensation
Regional Manager, Canada, Robert Stewart
Managing Director, International, Mounir N. (Mo) Sawda, age 53
General Manager, Oshawa, Canada, Carol Law
Auditors: KPMG LLP

LOCATIONS

HQ: Buffalo Wild Wings, Inc.
5500 Wayzata Blvd., Ste. 1600, Minneapolis, MN 55416
Phone: 952-593-9943   **Fax:** 952-593-9787
Web: www.buffalowildwings.com

2010 Locations

	No.
Texas	86
Ohio	85
Illinois	57
Indiana	48
Michigan	41
Virginia	30
Minnesota	27
Florida	24
Wisconsin	24
Missouri	23
California	22
New York	19
North Carolina	18
Arizona	17
Kentucky	17
Tennessee	17
Colorado	16
Iowa	13
Oklahoma	13
Alabama	10
Georgia	10
Nevada	10
Kansas	9
Louisiana	9
Maryland	9
Nebraska	8
South Carolina	8
West Virginia	8
Mississippi	7
Arkansas	5
Connecticut	5
Delaware	5
North Dakota	5
Oregon	5
Pennsylvania	5
Idaho	3
Montana	3
New Mexico	3
New Jersey	2
South Dakota	2
Hawaii	1
Massachusetts	1
Vermont	1
Washington	1
Total	**732**

PRODUCTS/OPERATIONS

2010 Sales

	$ mil.	% of total
Restaurants	555.1	91
Franchising	58.1	9
Total	**613.2**	**100**

2010 Locations

	No.
Franchised	473
Company-owned	259
Total	**732**

COMPETITORS

Applebee's Services	Hooters
Brinker	Houlihan's
Carlson Restaurants	Johnny Rockets
Damon's	OSI Restaurant
Darden	Partners
Dave & Buster's	Rock Bottom
Famous Dave's	Restaurants
Fox & Hound Restaurant	Ruby Tuesday

HISTORICAL FINANCIALS

Company Type: Public

Income Statement

FYE: Last Sunday in December

	REVENUE ($ mil.)	NET INCOME ($ mil.)	NET PROFIT MARGIN	EMPLOYEES
12/10	613.3	38.4	6.3%	15,900
12/09	538.9	30.7	5.7%	14,000
12/08	422.4	24.4	5.8%	12,000
12/07	329.7	19.7	6.0%	9,564
12/06	278.2	16.3	5.9%	7,482
Annual Growth	**21.9%**	**23.9%**	**—**	**20.7%**

2010 Year-End Financials

Debt ratio: —
Return on equity: 15.0%
Cash ($ mil.): 15.3
Current ratio: 1.70
Long-term debt ($ mil.): —

No. of shares (mil.): 18.2
Dividends
  Yield: —
  Payout: —
Market value ($ mil.): 798.7

	STOCK PRICE ($) FY Close	P/E High/Low		PER SHARE ($) Earnings	Dividends	Book Value
12/10	43.85	25	16	2.10	0.00	14.10
12/09	40.27	27	13	1.69	0.00	11.62
12/08	25.65	33	11	1.36	0.00	9.63
12/07	23.22	43	21	1.10	0.00	8.01
12/06	26.60	32	16	0.93	0.00	6.75
Annual Growth	**13.3%**	**—**	**—**	**22.6%**	**—**	**20.2%**

Burke & Herbert Bank

Founded in 1852, Burke & Herbert Bank & Trust is one of the oldest banks in Virginia. Placing an emphasis on personal service, it operates about 20 branches in the northern part of the state, including part of the Washington, DC, metropolitan area. The bank offers standard products such as checking and savings accounts, money market accounts, CDs, IRAs, and debit cards. It is primarily a real estate lender, with residential and commercial mortgages making up almost all of its loan portfolio. Construction, business, and consumer loans round out the bank's lending activities. Burke & Herbert Bank & Trust also offers trust and financial planning services.

EXECUTIVES

Chairman Emeritus, David M Burke
Chairman, Charles K. Collum Jr.
CEO, E. Hunt Burke
President and COO, W. Scott McSween
EVP and Cashier, Jeffrey L. Stryker
VP, Criscella J. Ford
VP, Thomas A. DeMik
VP, Carl Ford
VP, Elizabeth V. Ellis
VP, Harvey R. Boltwood
VP and Trust Officer, Judith A. Cagnon
VP and Trust Officer, M. Patricia Barron
VP and General Auditor, Mary Ann Michniak
VP and Security Officer, Kenneth R. Benarick
VP, Anthony B. Riolo
Comptroller, Kathy J. Younger
SEVP and Director, C. S. Taylo Burke III
SVP and Trust Officer, Charles B. Lanman Jr.
SVP, Donna Udvari
SVP, Carl E. Pollard Jr.
Marketing Officer and Director Public Relations, Toni M. Andrews
Auditors:

LOCATIONS

HQ: Burke & Herbert Bank & Trust Company
100 S. Fairfax St., Alexandria, VA 22314
Phone: 703-549-6600   **Fax:** 703-548-5759
Web: www.burkeandherbertbank.com

COMPETITORS

Bank of America	United Bankshares
BB&T	Virginia Commerce
Cardinal Financial	Bancorp
SunTrust	

HISTORICAL FINANCIALS

Company Type: Public

Income Statement

FYE: June 30

	ASSETS ($ mil.)	NET INCOME ($ mil.)	INCOME AS % OF ASSETS	EMPLOYEES
12/06	1,477.4	20.6	1.4%	328
12/05	1,434.2	22.2	1.5%	337
12/04	1,265.6	20.8	1.6%	317
12/03	1,167.1	20.5	1.8%	308
12/02	1,078.4	19.6	1.8%	0
Annual Growth	**8.2%**	**1.3%**	**—**	**2.1%**

2006 Year-End Financials

Equity as % of assets: 9.97%
Return on assets: 1.4%
Return on equity: 14.0%
Long-term debt ($ mil.): 70.0
No. of shares (mil.): 0.2

Dividends
  Yield: —
  Payout: —
Market value ($ mil.): 333.9
Sales ($ mil.): 87.4

	STOCK PRICE ($) FY Close	P/E High/Low		PER SHARE ($) Earnings	Dividends	Book Value
12/06	1,700.00	19	16	104.68	0.00	750.09
12/05	2,000.00	19	16	112.75	0.00	701.35
12/04	2,000.00	24	19	105.67	0.00	657.57
12/03	2,125.00	20	12	103.95	0.00	604.87
12/02	1,172.00	13	8	98.99	0.00	570.64
Annual Growth	**9.7%**	**—**	**—**	**1.4%**	**—**	**7.1%**

Butler National

This Butler is at the service of aircraft operators. Butler National's Avcon subsidiary (over half of sales) provides aircraft modification services, including the conversion of passenger planes to freighters. The company works mainly on Learjet models; it also modifies Beechcraft, Cessna, and Dassault Falcon aircraft. It adds aerial photography capability to aircraft and offers stability enhancements. The company's avionics unit makes airborne electronic switching components. Other Butler National businesses provide remote water and wastewater monitoring (SCADA Systems) and architectural services (BCS Design), as well as gaming management services to Indian tribes (Butler National Service Corporation; BNSC).

Butler National's aerospace segment, which also buys, modifies, and sells Learjets, acquired the JET Autopilot product line from L-3 Avionics Systems in 2008. The product line enhances Butler National's Learjet refurbishment capabilities. The company focuses on providing support systems to commercial and military aircraft, including the Boeing 737 and 747, and switching equipment for

Boeing McDonnell Douglas aircraft, as well as weapon control systems for Boeing helicopters.

Subsidiary BNSC opened the Boot Hill Casino and Resort in Dodge City, Kansas, in December 2010. Butler will operate the casino-hotel under a contract with the Kansas Lottery and the Kansas Racing and Gaming Commission. Phase II of the project, which includes a hotel expansion, salon and spa, and conference and entertainment facility, is scheduled for completion in 2012.

Chairman R. Warren Wagoner owns more than 6% of Butler National. President and CEO since 1989, Clark Stewart holds a stake in excess of 5%.

EXECUTIVES

Chairman, R. Warren Wagoner, age 59, $249,686 total compensation
President, CEO, and Director, Clark D. Stewart, age 71, $402,215 total compensation
CFO, Angela D. Shinabargar, age 47, $153,969 total compensation
President, Butler National Services, Curtis Beadle, age 46
President, BCS Design, Jeffrey H. Shinkle
President, Avcon Industries, Larry W. Franke, age 66
VP and Secretary, Christopher J. Reedy, age 45, $199,623 total compensation
Treasurer, Kathy L. Gorrell, age 50
General Manager, Boot Hill Casino and Resort, Mark Kashuda
Investor Relations, Craig D. Stewart
Auditors: Weaver & Martin, LLC

LOCATIONS

HQ: Butler National Corporation
19920 W. 161st St., Olathe, KS 66062
Phone: 913-780-9595   **Fax:** 913-780-5088
Web: butlernational.com

PRODUCTS/OPERATIONS

2010 Sales

	$ mil.	% of total
Aircraft modifications	13.5	41
Gaming	8.3	26
Avionics	5.5	17
Management & professional services	5.3	16
Total	**32.6**	**100**

Selected Products and Services
Aircraft modifications
Architecture and engineering
Avionics (manufacturing of airborne electronic switching units)
Monitoring services (electronic monitoring of water and wastewater remote monitoring stations, related repair services)
Gaming (business management services for Indian casinos)

Selected Subsidiaries
Avcon Industries, Inc. (aircraft modifications)
BCS Design, Inc. (architecture and engineering)
Butler National Corporation (classic aviation products, and management services)
Butler National Corp-Tempe (avionics, and defense contracting and electronics)
Butler National Services, Inc. (environmental monitoring)

COMPETITORS

AAR Corp.	First Aviation
Alabama Aircraft	Goodrich Corp.
American Innovations	Pure Technologies
Aristocrat Leisure	
Danze & Davis Architects	

HISTORICAL FINANCIALS
Company Type: Public

Income Statement
FYE: April 30

	REVENUE ($ mil.)	NET INCOME ($ mil.)	NET PROFIT MARGIN	EMPLOYEES
04/11	46.3	1.3	2.8%	110
04/10	32.6	2.9	8.9%	92
04/09	18.1	0.8	4.4%	100
04/08	17.6	1.3	7.4%	89
04/07	14.7	0.6	4.1%	88
Annual Growth	**33.2%**	**21.3%**	**—**	**5.7%**

2011 Year-End Financials
Debt ratio: 27.4%
Return on equity: 7.0%
Cash ($ mil.): 8.5
Current ratio: 2.02
Long-term debt ($ mil.): 4.9
No. of shares (mil.): 57.2
Dividends
  Yield: —
  Payout: —
Market value ($ mil.): 24.6

	STOCK PRICE ($) FY Close	P/E High/Low		PER SHARE ($) Earnings	Dividends	Book Value
04/11	0.43	25	16	0.02	0.00	0.32
04/10	0.44	10	4	0.05	0.00	0.29
04/09	0.22	29	6	0.02	0.00	0.24
04/08	0.38	24	11	0.02	0.00	0.23
04/07	0.47	61	25	0.01	0.00	0.20
Annual Growth	**(2.2%)**	**—**	**—**	**18.9%**	**—**	**12.3%**

C&J Energy Services

"Fracturing" normally carries negative implications, unless of course you're in the oil and gas industry. Serving oil and gas companies, C&J Energy Services provides hydraulic fracturing services in geologically challenging areas in Texas, Louisiana, and Oklahoma. (Hydraulic fracturing enhances well production by using high-pressure fluids to create fractures in wells.) The company also provides coiled tubing and pressure pumping services, which are used during well completion, maintenance, and other projects. Major customers have included EOG Resources, EXCO Resources, Anadarko Petroleum, Penn Virginia, Apache, Plains Exploration, and Chesapeake. Formed in 2006, C&J Energy went public in 2011.

The company intends to use a portion of the proceeds of $113 million from its IPO to repay debt. The company will also use some of the proceeds to fund future capital expenditures and for general corporate purposes. Prior to the filing, Energy Spectrum Partners owned a 16% stake in C&J Energy.

As part of its future growth strategy, the company plans to bolster its fleet of hydraulic fracturing units and expand its presence into other US regions. C&J Energy has, in recent years, been working to grow its fleet and has experienced an increase in demand for its services. The increase in business has also led to a dramatic rise in revenues and profits for the company.

EXECUTIVES

Chairman, President, and CEO, Joshua E. Comstock, age 41
EVP, CFO, Treasurer, and Director, Randall C. McMullen Jr., age 35
VP Coiled Tubing, John D. Foret

VP Coiled Tubing, Brandon D. Simmons, age 42
VP Sales and Marketing, J. P. (Pat) Winstead, age 53
VP Hydraulic Fracturing, William D. Driver, age 44
VP, General Counsel, and Secretary, Theodore R. Moore, age 33
COO, Bretton W. Barrier, age 45
Director, H. H. Wommack III, age 55
Auditors: UHY LLP

LOCATIONS

HQ: C&J Energy Services, Inc.
10375 Richmond Ave., Ste. 2000, Houston, TX 77042
Phone: 713-260-9900
Web: www.cjenergy.com

PRODUCTS/OPERATIONS

2010 Sales

	$ mil.	% of total
Hydraulic fracturing	182.7	75
Coiled tubing services	50.6	21
Pressure pumping services	10.9	4
Total	**244.2**	**100**

COMPETITORS

Baker Hughes	RPC
Complete Production Services	Schlumberger
FTS International	Weatherford International
Halliburton	

HISTORICAL FINANCIALS
Company Type: Public

Income Statement
FYE: December 31

	REVENUE ($ mil.)	NET INCOME ($ mil.)	NET PROFIT MARGIN	EMPLOYEES
12/10	244.2	32.3	13.2%	580
12/09	67.0	(2.4)	—	0
12/08	62.4	1.1	1.8%	0
Annual Growth	**97.8%**	**441.9%**	**—**	**—**

Debt ratio: 27.4%
Return on equity: 7.0%
Cash ($ mil.): 8.5
Current ratio: 2.02
Long-term debt ($ mil.): 4.9
No. of shares (mil.): 57.2
Dividends
  Yield: —
  Payout: —
Market value ($ mil.): 24.6

CalWest Bancorp

CalWest Bancorp is the holding company for South County Bank. Serving Southern California, the bank has branches in Irvine and Rancho Santa Margarita; its Surf City Bank and Inland Valley Bank divisions operate in Huntington Beach and Redlands and Moreno Valley, respectively. The banks target consumers, businesses, and professionals, offering standard deposit products and lending services. Commercial loans account for more than half of the company's loan portfolio; mortgages are about a third. Consumer and construction loans round out the banks' lending activities. To cut costs, CalWest Bancorp reduced its workforce by more than a quarter in 2008.

EXECUTIVES

Chairman, CalWest Bancorp and South County Bank, Bruce Williams
President and CEO, CalWest Bancorp and South County Bank, Thomas E. Yott
EVP and CFO, CalWest Bancorp and South County Bank, Najam Saiduddin
EVP and Chief Credit Officer, South County Bank, Robert Cole
Vice Chairman, CalWest Bancorp and South County Bank, Walter Storch
Auditors: Vavrinek, Trine, Day & Co., LLP

LOCATIONS

HQ: CalWest Bancorp
22342 Avenida Empresa, Rancho Santa Margarita, CA 92688
Phone: 949-766-3000 **Fax:** 949-766-3098
Web: www.southcountybank.com

HISTORICAL FINANCIALS

Company Type: Public

Income Statement

FYE: December 31

	ASSETS ($ mil.)	NET INCOME ($ mil.)	INCOME AS % OF ASSETS	EMPLOYEES
12/07	193.8	(0.3)	—	74
12/06	171.0	0.8	0.5%	42
12/05	172.7	0.7	0.4%	42
12/04	137.4	0.8	0.6%	43
12/03	110.4	0.1	0.1%	38
Annual Growth	15.1%	—	—	18.1%

2007 Year-End Financials

Equity as % of assets: 11.48%
Return on assets: 0.3
Return on equity: —
Long-term debt ($ mil.): 5.0
No. of shares (mil.): —
Dividends
Yield: —
Payout: —
Market value ($ mil.): —
Sales ($ mil.): 14.8

	STOCK PRICE ($) FY Close	P/E High/Low		PER SHARE ($) Earnings	Dividends	Book Value
12/07	8.15	—	—	(0.14)	0.00	(0.00)
12/06	14.95	49	36	0.37	0.00	(0.00)
12/05	14.88	46	28	0.41	0.00	(0.00)
12/04	13.07	29	20	0.49	0.00	(0.00)
12/03	10.14	303	196	0.05	0.00	4.35
Annual Growth	(5.3%)	—	—	—	—	—

Cambium Learning Group

Sometimes struggling students need help making the voyage from straight Ds to straight As; that's where Cambium Learning Group comes in. Through its Voyager and Sopris business units the company provides comprehensive reading and math programs, as well as academic support services for pre-K through 12th grade students, particularly those who are at risk or have special learning needs. It also offers instructional software and interactive Web tools through its Cambium Learning Technologies unit. Cambium Learning Group offers these products and services to school districts across the US. The company was formed in late 2009 by the merger of Cambium Learning, Inc. and Voyager Learning Company.

With an expanded range of products and services, Cambium Learning Group is now a leading US provider of educational tools aimed at underperforming students. The company touts its instructional materials and technology platforms as research based and culturally responsive, intended to supplement existing teaching methods and school curricula.

The company is poised for growth since the market for educational tools is one that is pretty much always in demand. Even during the toughest of economic times, parents still want their children to excel in school, and will request services such as those Cambium Learning Group offers be available at their schools. Additionally, federal funding for educational programs has remained strong (a primary source of funding for Cambium Learning Group's programs), despite budget cuts at the state level. Enrollment for pre-K through 12th grade is in the tens of millions and of those millions of students, Cambium Learning Group estimates nearly half could benefit from its interventional services.

Cambium Learning Group is increasing the amount of services it offers online in line with the growing trend of teaching students via electronic platforms. Each of its divisions: Voyager, Sopris, and Cambium Learning Technologies administer classes and services online and via electronic supplemental materials. Voyager and Sopris also provide printed materials to classrooms nationwide.

To accelerate its growth, the company has announced it will spend $4.5 million to acquire the assets of Class.com which includes online courses for at-risk high school and adult learners.

The company is majority owned by private equity firm Veronis Suhler Stevenson.

EXECUTIVES

EVP; President, Sopris, George A. Logue, age 57
Director and CEO, Ronald D. (Ron) Klausner, age 58
Director and President; President, Voyager, David F. Cappellucci
SVP and CFO, Bradley C. (Brad) Almond, age 44
SVP; President, Cambium Learning Technologies, John Campbell
Controller and Principal Accounting Officer, Barbara Benson, age 40
SVP, General Counsel, and Secretary, Todd W. Buchardt, age 51
Head Investor Relations, Shannan Overbeck
Auditors:

LOCATIONS

HQ: Cambium Learning Group, Inc.
17855 North Dallas Parkway, Suite 400, Dallas, TX 75287
Phone: 214-932-9500
Web: www.cambiumlearning.com

PRODUCTS/OPERATIONS

2010 Sales

	$ mil.	% of total
Product revenue		
Voyager	100.4	56
Cambium Learning Technologies	38.1	21
Sopris	22.2	12
Service revenue		
Voyager	17.5	10
Sopris	2.5	1
Cambium Learning Technologies	0.5	-
Total	181.2	100

COMPETITORS

American Education Corp.	Pearson Digital Learning
Archipelago Learning	PLATO Learning
Houghton Mifflin Harcourt	Renaissance Learning
McGraw-Hill Education	Scientific Learning
	Tom Snyder Productions

HISTORICAL FINANCIALS

Company Type: Public

Income Statement

FYE: December 31

	REVENUE ($ mil.)	NET INCOME ($ mil.)	NET PROFIT MARGIN	EMPLOYEES
12/10	181.3	(15.9)	—	564
12/09	101.0	(35.8)	—	622
12/08	99.7	(69.6)	—	0
Annual Growth	34.9%	—	—	(9.3%)

2010 Year-End Financials

Debt ratio: 131.6%
Return on equity: —
Cash ($ mil.): 11.8
Current ratio: 1.14
Long-term debt ($ mil.): 163.2
No. of shares (mil.): 43.9
Dividends
Yield: —
Payout: —
Market value ($ mil.): 150.9

	STOCK PRICE ($) FY Close	P/E High/Low		PER SHARE ($) Earnings	Dividends	Book Value
12/10	3.44	—	—	(0.36)	0.00	2.83
12/09	3.92	—	—	(1.63)	0.00	3.19
Annual Growth	(12.2%)	—	—	—	—	(11.3%)

Campus Crest

College dorms have moved beyond cinder block walls and Murphy beds, thanks to Campus Crest Communities. The company develops, builds, and manages on- and off-campus student housing apartment communities at medium-sized colleges and universities. Campus Crest owns interests in more than 25 communities, which are branded as The Grove, located mostly in the South. Its properties feature furnished apartments with such amenities as a pool, library, volleyball and basketball courts, fitness center, tanning beds, and gated entry with keyed bedroom locks. The student-friendly rents include utilities. Campus Crest, which went public via a 2010 IPO, has converted to a real estate investment trust (REIT).

The stock offering raised approximately $325 million for the company, a rather hefty sum during a real estate slump. Campus Crest is one of only a few residential real estate development companies to attempt to go public since the start of 2009 (commercial property investor Younan filed a $575 million IPO and hotel REIT Clearview Hotel Trust filed a $375 million offering around the same time as Campus Crest). The company plans to use the majority of its IPO proceeds to acquire additional properties, pay down debt on its mortgages and construction loans, and to buy out Harrison Street Real Estate, a private equity firm that it has a joint venture with for six of its properties.

Altogether, Campus Crest oversees more than 5,000 apartment units and 13,500 beds. Student housing is considered multifamily housing, but the apartments are leased by the bed, not the unit, with rent generally under $500 per person. (Each bedroom has its own lock and private bathroom.) With properties located on or near campuses, Campus Crest has an approximately 90% occupancy rate.

The REIT aims to build between five to seven new student housing properties per year. It targets college campuses that have at least 8,000 students, the majority of whom live off-campus, and where land isn't too expensive. Campus Crest has identified more than 200 markets and about 80 sites as potential development opportunities.

The company was founded in 2004 as Campus Crest Group. It opened its first property, The Grove at Asheville, near the University of North Carolina in 2005.

EXECUTIVES

President, COO, and Director, Earl C. Howell, $372,000 total compensation

EVP and CFO, Donald L. Bobbitt Jr., age 42, $487,000 total compensation

EVP and Division President, Development, Construction, and Facilities, Brian L. Sharpe, age 52

Co-Chairman and CEO, Ted W. Rollins, age 48, $372,000 total compensation

SVP and Corporate Controller, Howard J. Weissman, age 42

Co-Chairman and Chief Investment Officer, Michael S. Hartnett, age 52, $372,000 total compensation

Auditors: KPMG LLP

LOCATIONS

HQ: Campus Crest Communities, Inc.
2100 Rexford Rd., Ste. 414, Charlotte, NC 28211
Phone: 704-496-2500
Web: www.campuscrest.com

PRODUCTS/OPERATIONS

Selected Properties

The Grove at Abilene (Abilene Christian University)
The Grove at Asheville (University of North Carolina at Asheville)
The Grove at Carrollton (The State University of West Georgia)
The Grove at Cheney (Eastern Washington University)
The Grove at Clarksville (Austin Peay State University)
The Grove at Conway (University of Central Arkansas)
The Grove at Ellensburg (Central Washington University)
The Grove at Greenley (University of Northern Colorado)
The Grove at Huntsville (Sam Houston State University)
The Grove at Jacksonville (Jacksonville State University)
The Grove at Jonesboro (Arkansas State University)
The Grove at Las Cruces (New Mexico State University)
The Grove at Lawrence (University of Kansas)
The Grove at Mobile (University of South Alabama)
The Grove at Milledgeville (Georgia College and State University)
The Grove at Moscow (University of Idaho)
The Grove at Nagodoches (Stephen F. Austin State University)
The Grove at Reno (University of Nevada)
The Grove at San Angelo (Angelo State University)
The Grove at San Marcos (Texas State University)
The Grove at Troy (Troy University)
The Grove at Statesboro (Georgia Southern University)
The Grove at Stephenville (Tarleton State University)
The Grove at Waco (Baylor University)
The Grove at Wichita (Wichita State University)

COMPETITORS

Alliance Residential
Ambling Companies
JPI
Lane Company

American Campus Communities
Education Realty
Place Properties
Riverstone Residential

HISTORICAL FINANCIALS

Company Type: Public

Income Statement				FYE: December 31
	REVENUE ($ mil.)	NET INCOME ($ mil.)	NET PROFIT MARGIN	EMPLOYEES
12/10	87.5	(14.8)	—	525
12/09	106.7	(6.7)	—	424
12/08	34.1	(25.2)	—	0
12/07	15.7	(9.6)	—	0
Annual Growth	77.3%	—	—	23.8%

2010 Year-End Financials

Debt ratio: 42.5%
Return on equity: —
Cash ($ mil.): 2.3
Current ratio: 0.85
Long-term debt ($ mil.): 103.3

No. of shares (mil.): 30.7
Dividends
 Yield: 0.9%
 Payout: —
Market value ($ mil.): 430.2

	STOCK PRICE ($)	P/E		PER SHARE ($)		
	FY Close	High/Low	Earnings	Dividends	Book Value
12/10	14.02	— —	(0.00)	0.13	7.93
Annual Growth	—	— —	—	—	—

Capella Education

Capella Education is all about the digital age. The fast-growing company operates Capella University, an online school that offers more than 40 undergraduate and graduate degree programs with nearly 140 specializations. Its 39,000 students are primarily composed of working adults, 80% of which are pursuing master's or doctoral degrees. They come from all 50 states and about 50 countries, primarily from urban settings. Capella's 1,200 faculty members are mostly part-time employees, typically teaching one to three courses per semester. More than three-quarters of the company's revenues are derived from federal student financial aid programs.

Founded in 1991, Capella Education has grown its revenue and enrollment through the expansion of its program offerings. It also boosts enrollment by establishing working relationships with corporations, the military, and other entities, offering rebates on programs and professional development for those organizations' workforces. It attributes those measures, among others, for a 17% increase in enrollment (and nearly 30% increase in revenue) in 2010 compared to the previous year. The growing acceptance of online education has undoubtedly helped business as well, as working adults seek to take advantage of the flexibility of online learning.

The company grew its offerings in 2010 by forming a joint venture with Sophia Learning. Sophia offers users tutorials — called learning packets — focused on helping to teach a specific learning objective. Learning packets are technology based and can be created using virtually any type of media including text, images, slide shows, video, and audio.

Then in 2011 Capella agreed to buy UK distance learning provider Resource Development

International (RDI) for 9.3 million ($14.9 million). RDI is awaiting a decision from the Quality Assurance Agency's decision to be given degree awarding powers (TDAP). Historically, RDI taught degree courses designed by UK universities. If its application for TDAP is successful it will no longer need to seek external validation for its courses. Capella will pay an additional 4 million if the application is successful.

Capella Education's sales consist principally of tuition, application and graduation fees as well as commissions it earns from bookstore and publication sales. Factors affecting Capella Education's revenue include the number of students enrolled, the number of courses each student takes, the number of programs and specializations it offers, annual tuition adjustments, and the number of symposium events Capella University offers and how many students attend each event.

Capella University considers itself to be in a strong competitive position even in the highly-fragmented, highly-competitive postsecondary education market because all of its academic programs are designed specifically for online delivery. In contrast to institutions that try to convert traditional classes into online classes, each of Capella University's classes was conceived and developed to promote flexibility and interactivity. Along that same line, its classes are also designed to appeal to working adults, taking advantage of a growing market of people looking to advance further in their current careers or switch careers altogether.

Capella Education's founder, Stephen Shank, stepped down as CEO in 2009. Kevin Gilligan, the former CEO of United Subcontractors, filled the executive post. Shank owns some 8% of Capella Education; institutional investors hold about another 35%.

EXECUTIVES

Chairman and CEO, J. Kevin Gilligan, age 56, $2,347,197 total compensation

President, Capella University, Christopher (Chris) Cassirer, age 46

VP Marketing and Portfolio Strategies, Jason Van de Loo, age 33

VP Government Affairs, General Counsel, and Secretary, Gregory W. (Greg) Thom, age 54, $564,332 total compensation

SVP and CFO, Steven L. (Steve) Polacek, age 51

SVP Operations and CIO, Scott M. Henkel, age 56

SVP Capella Experience, Sally B. Chial, age 50, $644,665 total compensation

Chancellor, Capella University, Michael J. (Mike) Offerman, age 63, $605,422 total compensation

SVP Strategy and Business Development, Kyle M. Carpenter, age 57

Director Investor Relations, Heide Erickson

Manager Public Relations, Michael Walsh

Auditors: Ernst & Young LLP

LOCATIONS

HQ: Capella Education Company
Capella Tower, 225 S. 6th St., 9th Fl., Minneapolis, MN 55402
Phone: 612-977-5060   **Fax:** 612-977-5060
Web: www.capellaeducation.com

PRODUCTS/OPERATIONS

2010 Students by Program

	No.	% of total
Master's	18,740	47
Doctoral	12,058	31
Bachelor's	8,435	21
Other	244	1
Total	**39,477**	**100**

Selected Academic Programs

Bachelor of Science in Business
Bachelor of Science in Information Technology
Bachelor of Science in Public Safety
Bachelor of Science in Psychology
Doctor of Philosophy in Business
Doctor of Philosophy in Counselor Education and
 Supervision
Doctor of Philosophy in Education
Doctor of Philosophy in Human Services
Doctor of Philosophy in Information Technology
Doctor of Philosophy in Organization and Management
Doctor of Philosophy in Public Safety
Doctor of Philosophy in Psychology
Doctor of Psychology
Master of Business Administration
Master of Science in Education
Master of Science in Human Resource Management
Master of Science in Human Services
Master of Science in Information Technology
Master of Science in Nursing
Master of Science in Organizational Development
Master of Science in Psychology
Master of Science in Public Health
Master of Science in Public Safety

COMPETITORS

American Public Education	Education Management
Apollo Group	Grand Canyon Education
Argosy Education	Jones Knowledge
Cardean Learning Group	Kaplan
Corinthian Colleges	Laureate Education
DeVry	Strayer Education
eCollege.com	The College Network

HISTORICAL FINANCIALS

Company Type: Public

Income Statement

FYE: December 31

	REVENUE ($ mil.)	NET INCOME ($ mil.)	NET PROFIT MARGIN	EMPLOYEES
12/10	426.1	61.3	14.4%	2,968
12/09	334.6	42.7	12.8%	2,635
12/08	272.3	28.8	10.6%	1,140
12/07	226.2	22.8	10.1%	2,207
12/06	179.9	13.4	7.4%	1,787
Annual Growth	**24.1%**	**46.2%**	**—**	**13.5%**

2010 Year-End Financials

Debt ratio: —
Return on equity: 29.4%
Cash ($ mil.): 77.4
Current ratio: 5.34
Long-term debt ($ mil.): —

No. of shares (mil.): 16.3
Dividends
 Yield: —
 Payout: —
Market value ($ mil.): 1,085.7

	STOCK PRICE ($) FY Close	P/E High/Low		PER SHARE ($) Earnings	Dividends	Book Value
12/10	66.58	27	14	3.64	0.00	12.79
12/09	75.30	31	18	2.51	0.00	10.99
12/08	58.76	42	21	1.66	0.00	8.45
12/07	65.46	57	18	1.33	0.00	9.11
12/06	24.25	25	22	1.06	0.00	6.10
Annual Growth	**28.7%**	**—**	**—**	**36.1%**	**—**	**20.3%**

Capstone Turbine

Capstone Turbine's theme song could be "My Generation." The company makes the Capstone MicroTurbine, a power-generating system that produces environmentally friendly electricity and heat. The microturbines, which can operate on a standalone basis or be connected to the utility grid, run on a variety of liquid and gaseous fuels, such as natural gas, diesel, kerosene, propane, and flare gases from landfills and sewage plants. In the event of a power outage, customers can use microturbines to produce their own secure power for extended periods of time; microturbines can also be used as onboard battery chargers for hybrid electric vehicles. Customers located outside the US make up about 80% of sales.

Capstone has never been profitable, and expects the trend to continue until unit sales volumes increase enough to cover manufacturing costs. Sales for fiscal 2010 rose by around 40% over 2009. Even though the number of units sold was only slightly higher, the revenue mix for 2010 included a full year of sales for its higher-priced C200 and C1000 series products, which were launched in 2009. Average revenue per unit rose from $66,000 per unit in 2009 to $98,000 per unit in 2010. Sales for 2010 also included the company's new TA100 series model, a product line acquired from Calnetix Power Solutions in early 2010.

The company's net loss was $67 million in fiscal 2010, compared to $42 million in 2009. Capstone had higher warranty and inventory costs in 2010, as well as a non-cash warrant liability charge related to an accounting change. In addition, the company had lower profit margins because of introductory pricing and higher than expected production costs for its new products.

Capstone continues to look for ways to reduce its costs, such as outsourcing manufacturing chores and finding lower cost sources of supply for components. It has announced plans to provide direct sales and service, rather than relying exclusively on third-party distributors and authorized service agents. Another way Capstone has reduced its operating costs is through layoffs. In early 2010, the company laid off 28 employees, about 13% of its workforce. The most recent job cuts were in addition to cutting 42 employees in two rounds of job cuts during 2009, resulting in a 17% reduction in headcount.

Due to the nature of the company's products, it sells to a limited number of customers, with a limited amount of repeat business. In order to increase sales, the company is focusing on vertical markets that have high short-term growth potential. The oil and gas market continues to be a major focus for the company, but Capstone is also targeting sales to biogas facilities, high-rise buildings, and hybrid electric vehicles for new opportunities.

Capstone has traditionally marketed its microturbines for use in cogeneration (using both electricity and heat), resource recovery (burning oil and gas and waste by-products), backup power supply, and remote power applications. Capstone also does a small business in onboard power generation for hybrid electric buses and railcars.

Customers include its Russian distributor, Banking Production Centre; an Australian distributor, Aquatec-Maxcon; and UTC Power, an affiliate of United Technologies.

EXECUTIVES

Chairman, Eliot G. Protsch, age 57
President, CEO, and Director, Darren R. Jamison, age 45, $1,102,716 total compensation
EVP and CFO, Edward I. (Ed) Reich, age 48, $541,684 total compensation
EVP and CTO, Mark G. Gilbreth, age 39, $644,440 total compensation
EVP Sales and Marketing, James D. (Jim) Crouse, age 47, $523,841 total compensation
VP Finance and Chief Accounting Officer, Jayme L. Brooks, age 40, $273,239 total compensation
VP Marketing and Business Development, Steve Gillette
VP Customer Service, Freddie Sarhan
SVP Operations, Leigh L. Estus, age 61
SVP Human Resources, Larry N. Colson
SVP Customer Service, Shelby Ahmann
Director Investor and Public Relations, Alice Barsoomian
Auditors: Deloitte & Touche LLP

LOCATIONS

HQ: Capstone Turbine Corporation
 21211 Nordhoff St., Chatsworth, CA 91311
Phone: 818-734-5300   **Fax:** 818-734-5320
Web: www.microturbine.com

2010 Sales

	$ mil.	% of total
Europe		
Russia	9.6	16
Other countries	14.3	23
North America		
US	13.0	21
Mexico	4.2	7
Other countries	1.2	2
Australia	8.9	14
Asia/Pacific	5.3	9
Other regions	5.1	8
Total	**61.6**	**100**

PRODUCTS/OPERATIONS

2010 Sales

	$ mil.	% of total
Microturbine products	48.7	79
Accessories, parts & service	12.9	21
Total	**61.6**	**100**

Selected Products

MicroTurbine Engines
 C30 (30kW)
 C65 (65kW)
 C200 (200kW)
 C1000 (1000kW)

COMPETITORS

Ballard Power	Ingersoll-Rand
BP Solar	Kohler
Caterpillar	Plug Power
Cummins	ReliOn
DEUTZ	SCHOTT Solar
Dresser, Inc.	Suntech Power
Ebara	Toyota
FuelCell Energy	Turbo Power Systems
GE Energy	UTC Power
GE Oil	Waukesha-Pearce

HISTORICAL FINANCIALS

Company Type: Public

Income Statement

FYE: March 31

	REVENUE ($ mil.)	NET INCOME ($ mil.)	NET PROFIT MARGIN	EMPLOYEES
03/11	81.9	(38.5)	—	195
03/10	61.6	(67.2)	—	182
03/09	43.9	(41.7)	—	212
03/08	31.3	(36.1)	—	216
03/07	21.0	(36.7)	—	195
Annual Growth	40.5%	—	—	0.0%

2011 Year-End Financials

Debt ratio: 0.2%
Return on equity: —
Cash ($ mil.): 33.5
Current ratio: 1.43
Long-term debt ($ mil.): 0.1

No. of shares (mil.): 258.6
Dividends
Yield: —
Payout: —
Market value ($ mil.): 468.1

	STOCK PRICE ($) FY Close	P/E High/Low		PER SHARE ($) Earnings	Dividends	Book Value
03/11	1.81	—	—	(0.16)	0.00	0.13
03/10	1.27	—	—	(0.34)	0.00	0.19
03/09	0.72	—	—	(0.25)	0.00	0.29
03/08	2.12	—	—	(0.25)	0.00	0.36
03/07	1.06	—	—	(0.32)	0.00	0.57
Annual Growth	14.3%	—	—	—	—	(30.3%)

Carbiz

CarBiz operates one-stop shops for car buyers with poor credit. The company owns and operates a chain of "buy-here pay-here" used automobile dealerships. Catering primarily to buyers with poor credit histories, such dealerships finance vehicles with their own money. CarBiz's group of auto finance credit centers includes more than 25 locations in eight states. The company in 2009 acquired about $10 million in consumer loans from Star Financial Services, a California-based indirect lender.

EXECUTIVES

Chairman and CEO, Carl Ritter, age 51, $802,551 total compensation
President, Secretary, and Director, Ross R. (Rick) Lye, age 65, $506,974 total compensation
CFO and Director, Stanton Heintz, age 61, $507,542 total compensation
VP Finance, Jennifer Halloran
COO, Paul R. Whitley
Quality Control Manager, Virginia Witter
Business Development Manager, Mike Downey
Software Operations Manager, Jennifer Downey
Regional Manager, Carbiz Auto Credit, Mark Dubois
Auditors: Christopher, Smith, Leonard, Bristow, Stanell & Wells, PA

LOCATIONS

HQ: CarBiz Inc.
7115 16th St. East, Sarasota, FL 34243
Phone: 941-952-9255   **Fax:** 941-953-3580
Web: www.carbiz.com

COMPETITORS

America's Car-Mart	Group 1 Automotive
Asbury Automotive	Penske Automotive
AutoNation	Group
CarMax	

HISTORICAL FINANCIALS

Company Type: Public

Income Statement

FYE: January 31

	REVENUE ($ mil.)	NET INCOME ($ mil.)	NET PROFIT MARGIN	EMPLOYEES
01/09	35.6	(19.4)	—	160
01/08	8.2	(14.2)	—	165
01/07	3.2	(4.8)	—	37
01/05	3.4	(2.0)	—	0
01/04	3.2	(1.2)	—	0
Annual Growth	61.9%	—	—	108.0%

2009 Year-End Financials

Debt ratio: —
Return on equity: —
Cash ($ mil.): 0.7
Current ratio: 0.17
Long-term debt ($ mil.): 1.9

No. of shares (mil.): 104.6
Dividends
Yield: —
Payout: —
Market value ($ mil.): 8.4

	STOCK PRICE ($) FY Close	P/E High/Low		PER SHARE ($) Earnings	Dividends	Book Value
01/09	0.08	—	—	(0.28)	0.00	(0.33)
01/08	0.21	—	—	(0.23)	0.00	(0.17)
01/07	0.18	—	—	(0.10)	0.00	(0.05)
Annual Growth	(33.3%)	—	—	—	—	—

Carbonite

Carbonite's online backup software preserves your files just like it did Han Solo. The company's Web-based software backs up documents, emails, music, photos, and settings on PCs (Windows and Mac) and mobile devices, such as the iPhone, BlackBerry, and Android phones. Carbonite's software is used by more than 1 million consumers and small businesses customers in 100 countries; it charges a flat rate for one year of unlimited online backup. Its backup software saves customers' files on servers at the company's two data centers in Boston, so customers with crashed hard drives or stolen laptops need not fear that anything is permanently lost. Carbonite filed a $100 million initial public offering in May 2011.

The company launched its Carbonite product in 2006 and has experienced significant growth for a startup, with its revenues doubling from 2009 to 2010. Believing the market for online backup is in the early stages of development, Carbonite spends some two-thirds of its revenue on advertising, including print, radio and TV, online display, paid search, and direct marketing. It generally spends more on ads in the first and third quarters of each year based on the seasonality of customer purchases and fluctuations in advertising rates.

Carbonite has yet to be profitable as it grows its business. It has recorded a net loss every year and has an accumulated deficit of $83.2 million. The company expects to continue making significant investments for advertising, customer acquisition, technology infrastructure, storage capacity, and product development in order to expand and become profitable. Carbonite opened a development office in China and is looking to establish an international presence there. It is also moving its customer service operations from India back to the US; known as reverse outsourcing, the move is sure to satisfy customers calling its help desk lines and reaching someone in Portland, Maine. In addition, the company plans to open a third data center and relocate some existing servers. Carbonite plans to use the proceeds from its initial public offering to accomplish these goals.

While most established security and storage software firms cater to the corporate market, Carbonite, a small company compared to giants like McAfee and Symantec, is focused on individual consumers. It only began offering a version of its online backup software for small and midsized businesses designed for multiple computers and users in 2010. Out of the other, smaller companies geared toward the consumer market, including CrashPlan, Mozy (owned by EMC), Prosoftnet, SOS Online Backup, and SugarSync, Carbonite is the first venture-backed firm to go public. Prior to the offering, venture capital firm Menlo Ventures owned almost a third of Carbonite's stock.

EXECUTIVES

Chairman, President, and CEO, David Friend, age 63
CFO, Andrew Keenan, age 49
VP Marketing, Thomas (Tom) Murray, age 42
VP Product, William (Bill) Phelan, age 46
VP Customer Service, Richard (Rich) Surace, age 44
CTO, Eric J. Golin, age 51
General Counsel and Secretary, Danielle Sheer, age 30
Chief Architect and Director, Jeffry (Jeff) Flowers, age 57
SVP and General Manager Small Business Group, Peter T. (Pete) Lamson, age 48
SVP and General Manager Consumer Group, Swami Kumaresan, age 32
Director, William G. (Bill) Nelson, age 76
Auditors: Ernst & Young LLP

LOCATIONS

HQ: Carbonite, Inc.
177 Huntington Ave., Boston, MA 02115
Phone: 617-587-1100
Web: www.carbonite.com

COMPETITORS

Acronis	Kaspersky Lab
BMC Software	McAfee
CA, Inc.	NovaStor
CyberDefender	Symantec
Corporation	Trend Micro
IBM Software	

HISTORICAL FINANCIALS

Company Type: Public

Income Statement

FYE: December 31

	REVENUE ($ mil.)	NET INCOME ($ mil.)	NET PROFIT MARGIN	EMPLOYEES
12/10	38.6	(25.8)	—	163
12/09	19.1	(19.2)	—	0
12/08	8.2	(17.4)	—	0
Annual Growth	117.0%	—	—	—

Debt ratio: — No. of shares (mil.): 104.6
Return on equity: — Dividends
Cash ($ mil.): 0.7 Yield: —
Current ratio: 0.17 Payout: —
Long-term debt ($ mil.): 1.9 Market value ($ mil.): 8.4

Cardiovascular Systems

While Cardiovascular Systems, Inc. (CSI) deals with blood, there's no crime scene investigation here. The company's Diamondback 360° and Predator 360° products are minimally invasive catheter systems that help restore blood flow to the legs of patients with peripheral arterial disease (PAD), a condition that occurs when plaque builds up on limb arteries. The device is also being developed for use in coronary artery disease (CAD) patients. Complementary products for the devices include guidewires and lubricants. CSI sells directly to physicians and hospitals in the US. The company, formerly Replidyne, changed its name in 2009 after completing a reverse merger with its predecessor Cardiovascular Systems Inc.

The former Cardiovascular Systems had filed a planned IPO in 2008 to fund its operations, but then in 2009 it decided to enter the public market faster by completing a reverse merger transaction with Replidyne. The deal gave Replidyne's former shareholders 17% of the combined company, while Cardiovascular Systems shareholders received 83%. Replidyne CEO Kenneth Collins was replaced by existing Cardiovascular Systems CEO David Martin.

CSI plans to advance the commercialization of its products, including the expansion of sales and marketing operations, with proceeds gained through the merger. Marketing efforts are directed towards primary care and specialty physicians (including cardiologists and radiologists) and aim to educate doctors on the usefulness of its catheters as a precursor to more severe surgical procedures, especially when compared to other angioplasty devices, such as balloons or stents. CSI is focused on the US market.

The now defunct Replidyne was a biopharmaceutical firm seeking to market lead drug candidate faropenem medoxomil, an oral antibiotic developed to treat respiratory tract infections. The company sought FDA approval for use of the drug in adults and kids but was told it would have to go through further clinical trials before it could get the regulatory green light and be commercialized. After that disappointment, plus the loss of funding from development and marketing partner Forest Laboratories, the company systematically laid off most of its workers, halted its development programs, and began seeking strategic options.

EXECUTIVES

Chairman, Glen D. Nelson, age 73
President, CEO, and Director, David L. (Dave) Martin, age 47, $1,514,333 total compensation
CFO, Laurence L. (Larry) Betterley, age 55, $658,774 total compensation
EVP, Robert J. (Bob) Thatcher
VP Commercial Operations, Brian Doughty
VP Manufacturing, Paul Koehn
VP Sales, Scott Kraus, $589,703 total compensation

VP Business Development, Paul Tyska
Chief Administrative Officer, James E. (Jim) Flaherty
Chief Scientific Officer and Director, Michael J. (Mike) Kallok
Auditors: PricewaterhouseCoopers LLP

LOCATIONS

HQ: Cardiovascular Systems, Inc.
651 Campus Dr., St. Paul, MN 55112-3495
Phone: 651-259-1600 **Fax:** 651-259-1696
Web: www.csi360.com

COMPETITORS

Abbott Labs ev3
Boston Scientific Johnson & Johnson
Cook Incorporated Medtronic
Cordis CardioVascular
Covidien Spectranetics

HISTORICAL FINANCIALS

Company Type: Public

Income Statement

FYE: December 31

	REVENUE ($ mil.)	NET INCOME ($ mil.)	NET PROFIT MARGIN	EMPLOYEES
06/11	78.8	(11.1)	—	286
06/10	64.8	(23.9)	—	287
06/09*	56.5	(9.1)	—	239
12/08	0.0	(41.1)	—	3
12/07	58.6	7.7	13.1%	53
Annual Growth	7.7%	—	—	52.4%

*Fiscal year change

2011 Year-End Financials

Debt ratio: 38.5% No. of shares (mil.): 17.0
Return on equity: — Dividends
Cash ($ mil.): 21.2 Yield: —
Current ratio: 2.70 Payout: —
Long-term debt ($ mil.): 8.3 Market value ($ mil.): 247.3

	STOCK PRICE ($) FY Close	P/E High/Low		PER SHARE ($) Earnings	Dividends	Book Value
06/11	14.56	—	—	(0.70)	0.00	1.27
06/10	4.48	—	—	(1.62)	0.00	1.17
06/09*	7.71	—	—	(1.13)	0.00	2.15
12/08	9.30	—	—	(15.20)	0.00	15.54
12/07	31.00	27	11	2.80	0.00	30.39
Annual Growth	(17.2%)	—	—	—	—	(54.8%)

*Fiscal year change

EXECUTIVES

President, CEO, and Director, J. Michael Cline, age 56
SVP and Chief Credit Officer, Richard M. Rager
SVP and Senior Lender, Mort M. Wadsworth
SVP and Director Human Resources, Treva J. Carey, age 57
SVP and CFO, Donald J. Boyer, age 55
Auditors: Dixon Hughes PLLC

LOCATIONS

HQ: Carolina Trust Bank
901 E. Main St., Lincolnton, NC 28092
Phone: 704-735-1104 **Fax:** 704-735-1258
Web: www.carolinatrust.com

COMPETITORS

Bank of Granite Peoples Bancorp (NC)
BB&T
First Citizens
BancShares

HISTORICAL FINANCIALS

Company Type: Public

Income Statement

FYE: December 31

	ASSETS ($ mil.)	NET INCOME ($ mil.)	INCOME AS % OF ASSETS	EMPLOYEES
12/10	267.9	0.2	0.1%	52
12/09	269.0	(2.4)	—	52
12/08	160.4	(0.6)	—	44
12/07	136.9	1.0	0.7%	40
12/06	116.7	1.6	1.4%	40
Annual Growth	23.1%	(40.5%)	—	6.8%

2010 Year-End Financials

Equity as % of assets: 8.55% Dividends
Return on assets: 0.1% Yield: —
Return on equity: 1.2% Payout: —
Long-term debt ($ mil.): 15.0 Market value ($ mil.): 9.8
No. of shares (mil.): 2.8 Sales ($ mil.): 15.5

	STOCK PRICE ($) FY Close	P/E High/Low		PER SHARE ($) Earnings	Dividends	Book Value
12/10	3.45	—	—	(0.02)	0.00	8.04
12/09	5.00	—	—	(1.39)	0.00	8.67
12/08	6.15	—	—	(0.33)	0.00	9.19
12/07	14.50	31	22	0.57	0.00	9.48
12/06	16.45	20	15	0.87	0.00	15.84
Annual Growth	(32.3%)	—	—	—	—	(15.6%)

Carolina Trust Bank

Carolina Trust Bank serves southwestern North Carolina through about a half-dozen locations. It provides a variety of commercial and personal financial services including checking and savings accounts, IRAs, CDs, and credit cards. The bank is mainly a real estate lender, with one- to four-family residential mortgage, commercial real estate, construction, and land development loans comprising most of its portfolio. The company acquired the single-branch Carolina Commerce Bank in 2009. Carolina Trust was founded in 2000.

Cavco

Cavco's constructions keep customers covered, whether they're at home, work, or vacation. Cavco Industries produces some 4,700 manufactured homes a year (retail prices range from $26,000 to more than $190,000) under brands including Cavco, Palm Harbor, and Fleetwood. Its products include full-sized homes (about 500 sq. ft. to 3,300 sq. ft.); park model homes (less than 400 sq. ft.) for use as recreational and retirement units; camping cabins; and commercial structures for use as portable classrooms, showrooms, and offices. Cavco operates about 20 factories in the West and Midwest; its homes are available from some 1,000 independent retailers and company-owned outlets in the US, Canada, Mexico, and Japan.

In 2009 acquired nine plants from failed competitor Fleetwood for $22 billion. The deal included mothballed facilities in California and Texas, as well as operations in new states for Cavco: Idaho, Georgia, Oregon, Tennessee, and Virginia. Two years later, Cavco went shopping for another ailing competitor. It formed a new subsidiary, Fleetwood Homes, which bought the assets of bankrupt Palm Harbor Homes for more than $83 million. The deal included Palm Harbor's construction, retail, and finance units.

Fleetwood and Palm Harbor fell victim to the economic downturn, which has also impacted Cavco. The company's earnings had been dropping for years, as the manufactured housing industry declined overall. The overall housing and credit crisis didn't help, either, as lenders tightened credit restrictions on subprime borrowers or even exited the subprime business. By acquiring assets of its former rivals, Cavco has added production capacity, especially for niche market opportunities. In fiscal 2011, it sold nearly 4,800 homes — nearly double what it sold in 2009. It also reported the highest revenues earned in five years. To help its bottom line, the company has also cut costs through plant consolidations and is considering selling certain operations.

Cavco primarily targets the manufactured housing industry's mainstream market — high-value homes for entry-level and move-up buyers. It also targets specialty markets such as vacation homebuyers and developers of residential subdivisions and senior living communities. Cavco is one of the nation's largest producers of HUD-code manufactured homes, which account for some 80% of the manufacturer's homes.

HISTORY

Alfred Ghelfi and partner Bob Curtis began a part-time business in 1965 making pickup truck camper shells. The business, Roadrunner Manufacturing, became Cavalier Manufacturing in 1966, incorporated in 1968, and went public in 1969. The Cavalier name was already in use, so in 1974 the company's name was changed to Cavco. After the 1970s oil crisis nearly wiped out the firm, Ghelfi bought out Curtis' share and began making mobile homes. In time Cavco began leasing movable storage buildings, but the only successful part of that business was the security container segment (the rest was sold in 1994). A mid-1980s housing market crash in Arizona spurred Cavco to enter a totally new field — health care utilization management — in 1987.

In 1995 Cavco partnered with Japan's Auto Berg Enterprises to begin selling modular housing in Japan. The next year Cavco teamed up with Arizona Public Service to develop solar-powered manufactured housing, and it also sold its health care business. Centex acquired nearly 80% of Cavco for $75 million in 1997. The next year Cavco moved into Texas (one of the biggest markets for factory-built homes), acquiring Texas retailer Boerne Homes.

With demand shrinking and surplus inventory building up, the company closed its Belen, New Mexico, factory in 2000 and moved its production to plants in Phoenix and Seguin, Texas. That fall Centex tapped manufactured housing veteran Joseph Stegmayer as chairman of its manufactured housing segment.

In 2001 the company launched Factory Liquidators, a new retail concept focusing on repossessed homes.

Centex's board of directors approved the tax-free distribution to its shareholders of all of Cavco's outstanding common stock in 2003. The spin-off was completed in June of that year. Continued weakness within the industry forced Cavco to close eight of its company-owned retail outlets in fiscal 2004 and seven more in 2005.

EXECUTIVES

Chairman, President, and CEO, Joseph H. (Joe) Stegmayer, age 60, $1,056,670 total compensation
VP and General Manager, Cavco Park Homes and Cabins, Timothy M. Gage
VP and General Manager, Durango, Paul A. Deroo
VP, CFO, and Treasurer, Daniel L. Urness, age 42, $481,020 total compensation
General Counsel and Secretary, James P. Glew
Auditors: Ernst & Young LLP

LOCATIONS

HQ: Cavco Industries, Inc.
1001 N. Central Ave., 8th Fl., Phoenix, AZ 85004
Phone: 602-256-6263   **Fax:** 602-256-6189
Web: www.cavco.com

PRODUCTS/OPERATIONS

2011 Sales

	$ mil.	% of total
Manufacturing	166.9	94
Retail	10.2	6
Adjustments	(5.3)	-
Total	**171.8**	**100**

2011 Homes Sold

	No. of homes
Multi-section	2,503
Single-section	2,268
Total	**4,771**

2011 Sales Channels

	No. of homes sold
Independent retail outlets	4,648
Company-owned retail centers	123
Total	**4,771**

Selected Operations

Camping cabins
Commercial structures
Manufactured homes
Model homes and vacation homes
Park model homes

Selected Trademarks

AAA Homes
Catalina
Cavco
Cavco Cabins
Cavco Gold Key Guarantee
Cavco Home Center
Cavco Homes
Cedar Court
Desert Rose
Elite
Litchfield Limited
Nationwide Homes
Palm Harbor Homes
Saguaro
SmartBuilt
Sun Villa
Sunbuilt
Sunburst
Vantage
Villager
Westcourt
Winrock

COMPETITORS

All American Group	Fairmont Homes
American Homestar	Liberty Homes
Cavalier Homes	PulteGroup
Champion Enterprises	Skyline
Clayton Homes	Sunshine Homes

HISTORICAL FINANCIALS

Company Type: Public

Income Statement

FYE: March 31

	REVENUE ($ mil.)	NET INCOME ($ mil.)	NET PROFIT MARGIN	EMPLOYEES
03/11	171.8	2.8	1.6%	1,250
03/10	115.6	(3.4)	—	1,300
03/09	105.4	0.5	0.5%	660
03/08	141.9	6.3	4.4%	1,005
03/07	169.1	11.5	6.8%	1,075
Annual Growth	0.4%	(29.8%)	—	3.8%

2011 Year-End Financials

Debt ratio: —	No. of shares (mil.): 6.8
Return on equity: 1.9%	Dividends
Cash ($ mil.): 76.5	Yield: —
Current ratio: 2.23	Payout: —
Long-term debt ($ mil.): —	Market value ($ mil.): 307.9

	STOCK PRICE ($) FY Close	P/E High/Low		PER SHARE ($) Earnings	Dividends	Book Value
03/11	45.16	120	77	0.41	0.00	22.10
03/10	34.14	—	—	(0.52)	0.00	22.28
03/09	23.60	594	269	0.07	0.00	22.75
03/08	35.04	45	29	0.95	0.00	22.68
03/07	34.95	29	17	1.74	0.00	21.58
Annual Growth	6.6%	—	—	(30.3%)	—	0.6%

Cavico Corp

Cavico is a US headquartered company that conducts its construction business in Vietnam. Wholly-owned subsidiary Cavico Vietnam and its numerous operating subsidiaries make the company the largest non-state-owned heavy civil contractor in the country. It primarily serves public sector clients on large infrastructure projects, such as bridges, dams, mines, roads, tunnels, urban buildings, and water power facilities. Additionally, the company invests in hydropower electric and cement production plants, mining operations, and urban real estate developments in Laos and Vietnam. Cavico has offices throughout Vietnam, as well as a satellite location in Australia.

Hydroelectric tunnel and dam construction accounts for a big slice of Cavico's revenues. However, the company is attempting to diversify its business in several ways. First, it's taking work as a subcontractor for several large Japanese construction companies, including Kumagai Gumi, Kajima, and Maeda. This increases its involvement in large projects overseas, also thereby boosting its profile on the global construction market. Its subcontract work includes building highway tunnels in Algeria and hydropower tunnels in Laos. Secondly, Cavico is expanding beyond its core civil work into other construction fields, undertaking steel fabrication and mechanical services for clients in Australia and elsewhere. It believes adding capabilities, services, and even products will allow it to compete more effectively for contracts.

The company's expansion efforts are being bolstered by Vietnam's strong, growing economy. The government has set aside significant funds to invest in building, improving, and repairing the country's infrastructure, especially in the areas of transporation and water. Cavico anticipates demand for more construction of tunnels for roads and highways in the large metropolitan areas of Hanoi, Ho Chi Minh, Haiphong, and Danang. Vietnam is also recognized in Southeast Asia as a prime market for alternative energy. Cavico is thus taking on more hydroelectric and wind energy projects. One of its subsidiaries is working with German renewable energy company Altus to study and evaluate areas for possible wind farms.

EXECUTIVES

Chairman and CEO, Ha Quang Bui, age 46
CFO, Philip C. (Phil) Bolles, age 66
EVP and Director, Hung Manh Tran, age 47
VP, Giang Linh Bui, age 38
VP, Hai Thanh Tran, age 47
VP and Director, Timothy Dac Pham, age 43
VP, Hieu Van Phan, age 45
Principal Accounting Officer, Bao Quoc Tran
Auditors: PMB Helin Donovan, LLP

LOCATIONS

HQ: Cavico Corp.
  17011 Beach Blvd., Ste. 1230, Huntington Beach, CA 92647
Phone: 714-843-5456   **Fax:** 714-843-5451
Web: www.cavicocorp.com

PRODUCTS/OPERATIONS

2009 Sales

	$ mil.	% of total
Civil construction	52.58	86
Commercial activities	8.51	14
Total	**61.09**	**100**

COMPETITORS

GS Engineering	Maeda Corp
Kajima	Obayashi
Kumagai Gumi	

HISTORICAL FINANCIALS

Company Type: Public

Income Statement

FYE: December 31

	REVENUE ($ mil.)	NET INCOME ($ mil.)	NET PROFIT MARGIN	EMPLOYEES
12/09	61.1	(4.8)	—	3,409
12/08	58.0	0.6	1.0%	0
12/07	37.9	6.8	17.9%	3,000
12/06	24.1	0.7	2.9%	0
Annual Growth	**36.4%**	**—**	**—**	**6.6%**

2009 Year-End Financials

Debt ratio: 2049.2%	No. of shares (mil.): 3.3
Return on equity: —	Dividends
Cash ($ mil.): 2.4	Yield: —
Current ratio: 0.74	Payout: —
Long-term debt ($ mil.): 17.1	Market value ($ mil.): 15.5

	STOCK PRICE ($) FY Close	P/E High/Low		PER SHARE ($) Earnings	Dividends	Book Value
12/09	4.73	—	—	(1.56)	0.00	0.25
Annual Growth	**—**	—	—	**—**	**—**	**—**

Cavium

Cavium (formerly Cavium Networks) can help keep networks secure without hiding them in a cave somewhere. The company designs specialized microprocessors used in secure network transmissions, based on processor technology developed by ARM and MIPS Technologies. Cavium's customers have included Cisco Systems, Fujitsu, Nokia, Samsung Electronics, Sumitomo, and ZTE. Manufacturing is contracted out to Fujitsu Semiconductor, Taiwan Semiconductor Manufacturing, and United Microelectronics. Distributors handle around one-third of sales. Customers in the US account for more than a third of Cavium's sales.

Revenue for 2010 more than doubled from 2009 thanks in part to strong sales of wireless infrastructure equipment and the 2009 acquisition of MontaVista Software, which makes Linux-based operating systems.

Cavium in 2011 paid about $55 million in cash and stock to buy Beijing-based fabless semiconductor company Celestial Semiconductor. The deal gave the company a leg up in the market for chips designed to process data for multimedia purposes as the global demand for high-quality digital video increases. Celestial specializes in ARM-based system-on-chip (SoC) processors for a variety of digital media applications such as HD video processing and multi-format video playback in televisions, portable media players, and digital cable boxes among other consumer electronics products.

EXECUTIVES

Chairman, President, and CEO, Syed B. Ali, age 52, $678,191 total compensation
VP Software Engineering and CTO, Muhammad R. Hussain, age 38
VP Corporate and Business Development, Amer Haider
VP Operations, Syed A. Zaheer, age 42
VP and General Manager, Broadband and Consumer, Manoj Gujral
VP Sales, Andrew J. (Andy) Rava, age 52
VP Finance and Administration, CFO, and Secretary, Arthur D. (Art) Chadwick, age 54, $324,228 total compensation
COO, Rajiv Khemani, age 43, $547,503 total compensation
Corporate VP IC Engineering, Anil K. Jain, age 54, $357,891 total compensation
SVP and General Counsel, Vincent P. Pangrazio
Marketing Communications Manager, Angel Atondo
Auditors: PricewaterhouseCoopers LLP

LOCATIONS

HQ: Cavium, Inc.
  805 E. Middlefield Rd., Mountain View, CA 94043
Phone: 650-623-7000   **Fax:** 650-625-9751
Web: www.cavium.com

2010 Sales

	$ mil.	% of total
US	70.2	34
China	58.0	28
Taiwan	28.4	14
Japan	19.3	9
Malaysia	12.7	6
Other countries	17.9	9
Total	**206.5**	**100**

PRODUCTS/OPERATIONS

2010 Sales

	$ mil.	% of total
Semiconductor products	175.2	85
Software & services	31.3	15
Total	**206.5100Selected**	

Products

Accelerator boards
ECONA ARM-based processors
Embedded processors
Intelligent network adapters
NITROX security macro processors
OCTEON MIPS64 processors
PureVu video processors

COMPETITORS

Applied Micro Circuits	Ikanos
Broadcom	Intel
Certicom	Marvell Technology
Elliptic Technologies	Mindspeed
Exar	NetLogic Microsystems
Freescale	PMC-Sierra
Semiconductor	SafeNet

HISTORICAL FINANCIALS

Company Type: Public

Income Statement

FYE: December 31

	REVENUE ($ mil.)	NET INCOME ($ mil.)	NET PROFIT MARGIN	EMPLOYEES
12/10	206.5	37.1	18.0%	633
12/09	101.2	(21.4)	—	467
12/08	86.6	1.5	1.7%	347
12/07	54.2	2.2	4.1%	202
12/06	34.2	(9.0)	—	157
Annual Growth	**56.8%**	**—**		**41.7%**

2010 Year-End Financials

Debt ratio: 1.3%	No. of shares (mil.): 46.3
Return on equity: 15.8%	Dividends
Cash ($ mil.): 90.7	Yield: —
Current ratio: 3.58	Payout: —
Long-term debt ($ mil.): 3.0	Market value ($ mil.): 1,746.0

	STOCK PRICE ($) FY Close	P/E High/Low		PER SHARE ($) Earnings	Dividends	Book Value
12/10	37.68	52	28	0.77	0.00	5.06
12/09	23.83	—	—	(0.52)	0.00	3.59
12/08	10.51	665	205	0.04	0.00	3.15
12/07	23.02	509	235	0.07	0.00	2.94
Annual Growth	**17.9%**	—	—	**122.4%**	**—**	**19.8%**

CCF Holding

CCF Holding Company sees green in the Peach State. The institution is the parent of Heritage Bank, which operates about a half-dozen branches in Clayton, Fayette, and Henry counties in greater metropolitan Atlanta. Centered in the fast-growing Hartsfield International Airport region, the bank targets individuals and local businesses, offering such standard services as checking and savings accounts, money market accounts, CDs, IRAs, and credit cards. Real estate loans, including construction and land development loan, commercial and residential mortgages, and farmland loans, account for about 95% of the bank's lending portfolio. Heritage Bank also writes consumer and business loans.

Celldex Therapeutics

Celldex Therapeutics develops immunotherapies to treat specific forms of cancer, autoimmune diseases, and infections. The biopharmaceutical company's Precision Targeted Immunotherapeutics platform uses monoclonal antibodies, antibody-targeted vaccines, and immune system modulator to create disease-specific drugs. Two of its lead candidates are in clinical development for the treatment of brain cancer (CDX-110) and melanoma and breast cancer (CDX-011). Celldex takes candidates through earlier stages of development, then typically seeks partners to usher them through late stages. Formerly AVANT Immunotherapeutics, the company merged with Celldex Therapeutics in 2008 and took its name.

AVANT brought its infectious disease vaccines into the marriage, while Celldex brought in programs using monoclonal antibodies and tumor-targeting technologies to develop therapeutic vaccines for cancers and inflammatory disorders. As part of a deal struck with pre-merger Celldex, Pfizer agreed to fund the research and development of CDX-110 in exchange for worldwide marketing rights to the drug. In 2010, however, Pfizer terminated the agreement, saying that its development was no longer a strategic priority, and Celldex regained worldwide rights to it.

CDX-110 is a peptide-based immunotherapy that targets a tumor-specific molecule called EGFRvIII, a variant of a protein that is commonly present in an aggressive form of brain cancer called glioblastoma multiforme. It also has been observed in other forms of cancer, including breast, colorectal, ovarian, and prostate. Celldex's second lead candidate CDX-011 is an antibody-drug conjugate that combines a human monoclonal antibody with a cell-killing drug that specifically targets a protein that is expressed in breast cancer and melanoma. Celldex acquired rights to CDX-011 (formerly CR011) when it bought biotech firm CuraGen for about $96 million in 2009.

A previous drug that Celldex developed, Rotarix, is now an FDA-approved vaccine that combats rotavirus infection, which causes diarrhea and vomiting in infants. Partner GlaxoSmithKline sells the product worldwide. Royalties related to GlaxoSmithKline's worldwide sales of Rotarix are the Celldex's largest source of revenue. Rotarix got first approval in Mexico in 2004 and since gained approval in Europe in 2006 and the US in 2008.

The rest of Celldex's portfolio consists of clinical and preclinical candidates that are being studied for their efficacy in treating solid tumors, kidney disease, and acute and chronic inflammatory conditions, such as organ transplantation, multiple sclerosis, and rheumatoid arthritis. Celldex is building its development program based on the belief that certain immunotherapy products are not effective enough to be commercialized as a single therapy but may be more effective when used in combination with other therapeutic agents.

EXECUTIVES

Chairman, Larry Ellberger, age 63
President, CEO, and Director, Anthony S. Marucci, age 48, $1,170,867 total compensation
SVP and Chief Scientific Officer, Tibor Keler, age 52, $1,076,306 total compensation
SVP and Chief Medical Officer, Thomas A. (Tom) Davis, age 46, $717,412 total compensation
SVP, CFO, and Secretary, Avery W. (Chip) Catlin, age 62, $529,923 total compensation
SVP and Chief Business Officer, Ronald A. Pepin, age 56
Auditors: PricewaterhouseCoopers LLP

LOCATIONS

HQ: Celldex Therapeutics, Inc.
119 4th Ave., Needham, MA 02494-2725
Phone: 781-433-0771   **Fax:** 781-433-0262
Web: www.celldextherapeutics.com

PRODUCTS/OPERATIONS

2009 Sales

	$ mil.	% of total
Product royalties	7.72	51
Product development & licensing agreements	5.66	37
Contracts & grants	1.80	12
Total	**15.18**	**100**

Selected Products

Marketed
  Rotarix (rotavirus, with GlaxoSmithKline)
In development
  CDX-110 (brain cancer)
  CDX-1135 (organ tranplantation)
  CholeraGarde (cholera)
  ETEC (*E. coli* infection)
  Ty800 (typhoid fever)

COMPETITORS

Agenus	GlaxoSmithKline
Alexion	Hoffmann-La Roche
Pharmaceuticals	Idera
Anadys Pharmaceuticals	ImClone
AstraZeneca	ImmunoGen
Baxter International	Intercell
BioSante	Maxygen
Crucell	Merck
Dendreon	No
Eli Lilly	Northwest
Emergent BioSolutions	Biotherapeutics

HISTORICAL FINANCIALS

Company Type: Public

Income Statement   FYE: December 31

	REVENUE ($ mil.)	NET INCOME ($ mil.)	NET PROFIT MARGIN	EMPLOYEES
12/10	46.8	(2.5)	—	100
12/09	15.2	(36.5)	—	93
12/08	7.5	(47.5)	—	81
12/07	5.1	(21.6)	—	53
12/06	4.9	(20.4)	—	99
Annual Growth	**75.8%**	**—**	**—**	**0.3%**

2010 Year-End Financials

Debt ratio: 11.8%	No. of shares (mil.): 32.1
Return on equity: —	Dividends
Cash ($ mil.): 21.3	Yield: —
Current ratio: 3.11	Payout: —
Long-term debt ($ mil.): 8.9	Market value ($ mil.): 132.1

	STOCK PRICE ($) FY Close	P/E High/Low	PER SHARE ($) Earnings	Dividends	Book Value
12/10	4.12	— —	(0.08)	0.00	2.35
12/09	4.67	— —	(1.84)	0.00	2.33
12/08	7.92	— —	(3.34)	0.00	1.15
12/07	6.00	— —	(41.40)	0.00	(3.08)
12/06	16.11	— —	(3.24)	0.00	0.35
Annual Growth	**(28.9%)**	**— —**	**—**	**—**	**61.0%**

CenterState Banks

CenterState Banks (formerly CenterState Banks of Florida) is a multibank holding company serving the Sunshine State from more than 40 branch locations. It owns CenterState Bank, CenterState Bank of Florida, CenterState Bank Central Florida, and Valrico State Bank. The banks offer standard retail products and services such as checking and savings accounts, money market accounts, and CDs. They focus on real estate lending, primarily mortgages, construction loans, and land development loans. The banks also sell mutual funds, annuities, and other investment products. Each bank is managed by its own team of executives and board members. CenterState Banks also provides correspondent banking and bond sales services.

CenterState began offering correspondent banking services in 2008. The business rapidly became one of the company's largest revenue-earners. The division provides bond securities, accounting, and loans to small and midsized banks in the Southeast.

In 2010 the company acquired the failed four-branch Olde Cypress Community Bank in an FDIC-assisted transaction. Olde Cypress now operates as a division of CenterState Bank. In 2011 the company agreed to buy Federal Trust Corporation, parent company of the 11-branch Federal Trust Bank in Central Florida, from insurance group The Hartford.

EXECUTIVES

Chairman, President, and CEO; Chairman, CenterState Bank Central Florida, CenterState Bank West Florida, and CenterState Bank, Ernest S. (Ernie) Pinner, age 63, $631,661 total compensation
Chairman Emeritus, James H. White, age 85
President and CEO, CenterState Bank, Timothy A. Pierson, age 51
President and CEO, Valrico State Bank, Jerry L. Ball, age 55
President and CEO, CenterState Bank Central Florida, Thomas E. White, age 56, $241,524 total compensation
CFO, CenterState Bank of Florida, Steve Young
EVP and Director Lending, Valrico State Bank, Donald M. Weaver
EVP and Chief Credit Officer, CenterState Bank, Joseph D. Cioppa
EVP and Director; President and CEO, Centerstate Bank of Florida, John Corbett, age 42, $295,840 total compensation
VP Operations, Valrico State Bank, Beth A. Bravis
VP and Operations Officer, CenterState Bank, Synthia L. Bohannon
VP and Business Development Officer, CenterState Bank Central Florida, Charles A. Rogers
SVP and Corporate Auditor, J. Wayne Stewart
SVP, CFO, and Corporate Secretary, James J. Antal, age 60, $249,564 total compensation
SVP and COO, Rodney A. Anthony
Area Executive, Ocala, CenterState Bank of Florida, George T. Durkan
Area Executive, Winter Haven, CenterState Bank of Florida, J. Brett Barnhardt
Area Executive, Ridge, Centerstate Bank of Florida, Paul W. Gerrard Jr.
SVP and Chief Credit Oficer, CenterState Bank Central Florida, Mark W. Thompson
SVP and COO, CenterState Bank Central Florida, D. Charles Anderson
Assistant VP and Controller, Valrico State Bank, Thomas K. Snider
SVP and CFO, CenterState Bank Central Florida, Christa Murphy
SVP and COO, Valrico State Bank, Susan L. Radford-Butler
SVP and CFO, CenterState Bank, John L. Rust
Chief Credit Officer, CenterState Bank of Florida, Robert Dodd
SVP and COO, CenterState Bank, Elizabeth J. Bowen
COO, CenterState Bank of Florida, Jennifer Ison
Auditors: Crowe Horwath LLP

LOCATIONS

HQ: CenterState Banks, Inc.
42745 US Hwy. 27, Davenport, FL 33837
Phone: 863-419-7750
Web: www.centerstatebanks.com

PRODUCTS/OPERATIONS

2009 Sales

	$ mil.	% of total
Interest		
Loans	53.4	51
Investment securities available for sale	19.9	19
Other	0.6	1
Noninterest		
Correspondent banking & bond sales	17.9	17
Service charges on deposit accounts	5.5	5
Net gain on sale of securities	2.5	3
Other	4.2	4
Total	**104.0**	**100**

COMPETITORS

Bank of America	BB&T
BankAtlantic	SunTrust

HISTORICAL FINANCIALS

Company Type: Public

Income Statement

FYE: December 31

	ASSETS ($ mil.)	NET INCOME ($ mil.)	INCOME AS % OF ASSETS	EMPLOYEES
12/10	2,063.3	(5.5)	—	600
12/09	1,751.3	(6.2)	—	478
12/08	1,333.1	3.4	0.3%	399
12/07	1,217.4	7.8	0.6%	371
12/06	1,077.1	8.5	0.8%	320
Annual Growth	**17.6%**	**—**	**—**	**17.0%**

2010 Year-End Financials

Equity as % of assets: 12.24%	Dividends
Return on assets: 5.5	Yield: 0.5%
Return on equity: —	Payout: —
Long-term debt ($ mil.): 15.0	Market value ($ mil.): 237.6
No. of shares (mil.): 30.0	Sales ($ mil.): 130.1

	STOCK PRICE ($) FY Close	P/E High/Low		PER SHARE ($) Earnings	Dividends	Book Value
12/10	7.92	—	—	(0.20)	0.04	8.42
12/09	10.09	—	—	(0.47)	0.07	8.90
12/08	16.99	69	37	0.26	0.16	14.37
12/07	12.10	33	19	0.63	0.15	11.93
12/06	20.90	30	23	0.75	0.14	10.55
Annual Growth	**(21.5%)**	**—**	**—**	**—**	**(26.9%)**	**(5.5%)**

Cerus

Cerus is no religious organization, but it does preach the power of purity. The firm develops blood purification systems under the name INTERCEPT that kill bacteria, viruses, and other pathogens in donated blood to improve the safety of blood transfusions. Its INTERCEPT Blood Systems for platelets and plasma are approved for sale in some European and Middle Eastern countries, where they are marketed directly to customers through subsidiary Cerus Europe. The company is pursuing regulatory approval for its INTERCEPT plasma and platelets products to sell them in the US market, as well as in other foreign countries. Cerus also has a system for red blood cell purification in clinical development.

The INTERCEPT system is designed to target and inactivate blood-borne pathogens, such as viruses (for example, HIV, West Nile, SARS, and hepatitis B and C), bacteria and parasites, as well as potentially harmful white blood cells, while preserving the therapeutic properties of platelet, plasma, and red blood cell transfusion products.

Cerus operates in a very concentrated market dominated by a few blood collection agencies and without a lot of customers to go around (just three customers account for about half of all of the company's income) which means Cerus has to stay on its toes with regard to getting its products approved to be sold in more markets. It also has to have an aggressive marketing strategy and competitive pricing. Cerus' strategy of being nearly solely focused on getting additional approvals seems to have paid off, as Cerus has seen its product revenue increase each year over the past few years. That increase has led to a decrease in its net losses, which, though still present, have dropped a little each year. Cerus expects to continue to incur financial losses until INTERCEPT gains more market acceptance.

Along with product revenue, Cerus receives a small amount of income from grants and contracts with the federal government, specifically the Department of Defense for use in the armed forces.

The company's product line used to include a range of immunotherapy including Listeria and KBMA vaccine platforms until a few years ago when Cerus decided to spin-off the immunotherapy division to a newly formed company named Anza Therapeutics. The spinoff was funded by venture capital firms; Cerus retained a 15% stake in Anza.

A lack of funding caused Anza to cease operations in 2009. Later that year, Cerus entered into a three-way license agreement with Anza and Aduro BioTech, through which Anza transferred all of its intellectual property to Aduro. Cerus received a 10% stake in Aduro, a 1% royalty on all future product sales related to the transferred technology, and about $500,000 in cash from Aduro.

EXECUTIVES

Chairman, B. J. Cassin, age 77
President, CEO, and Director, Claes Glassell, age 60, $750,652 total compensation
President, CEO, and Director, William M. (Obi) Greenman, age 44, $489,023 total compensation
VP Legal Affairs and Chief Legal Officer, Howard G. Ervin, age 63, $432,448 total compensation
VP Finance and Chief Accounting Officer, Kevin D. Green, age 39
VP Development and Manufacturing, Suzanne C. Margerum

VP Administration and Corporate Secretary, Lori L. Roll
VP Regulatory Affairs and Quality and Clinical, Carol M. Moore
SVP, Chief Medical Officer, and Director, Laurence M. Corash, age 67, $412,594 total compensation
General Manager, Cerus Europe, Caspar Hogeboom
Director Global Communications and Marketing, Lainie Corten
Auditors: Ernst & Young LLP

LOCATIONS

HQ: Cerus Corporation
2550 Stanwell Dr., Concord, CA 94520
Phone: 925-288-6000   **Fax:** 925-288-6001
Web: www.cerus.com

2010 Sales by Customer

	% of total
Movaco SA (Spain and other EU countries)	19
Delrus Inc. (Russia)	16
Etablissement Francais du Sang (France)	13
Service Francophone du Sang (Belgium)	12
Other	40
Total	**100**

PRODUCTS/OPERATIONS

2010 Sales

	$ mil.	% of total
Product sales	21.7	94
Government grant & cooperative agreements	1.4	6
Total	**23.1**	**100**

COMPETITORS

Baxter International	Gen-Probe
EMD Millipore	Haemonetics
Fresenius Kabi	Novartis
Gambro AB	Pall Corporation

HISTORICAL FINANCIALS

Company Type: Public

Income Statement

FYE: December 31

	REVENUE ($ mil.)	NET INCOME ($ mil.)	NET PROFIT MARGIN	EMPLOYEES
12/10	23.1	(16.9)	—	79
12/09	18.0	(24.1)	—	73
12/08	16.5	(29.2)	—	107
12/07	11.0	(45.3)	—	111
12/06	35.6	(4.8)	—	124
Annual Growth	**(10.2%)**	**—**	**—**	**(10.7%)**

2010 Year-End Financials

Debt ratio: 22.0%
Return on equity: —
Cash ($ mil.): 28.9
Current ratio: 2.12
Long-term debt ($ mil.): 3.1
No. of shares (mil.): 47.3
Dividends
  Yield: —
  Payout: —
Market value ($ mil.): 116.4

	STOCK PRICE ($) FY Close	P/E High/Low		PER SHARE ($) Earnings	Dividends	Book Value
12/10	2.46	—	—	(0.42)	0.00	0.50
12/09	1.99	—	—	(0.69)	0.00	0.55
12/08	0.70	—	—	(0.90)	0.00	1.05
12/07	6.51	—	—	(1.42)	0.00	1.86
12/06	6.14	—	—	(0.18)	0.00	3.63
Annual Growth	**(20.4%)**	**—**	**—**	**—**	**—**	**(39.0%)**

Cheniere Energy

Gaseous form or liquid state are both OK with Cheniere Energy, which is engaged in the development of a liquefied natural gas (LNG) receiving-terminal business. It owns and operates Sabine Pass LNG terminal in Louisiana (with an LNG storage capacity of 16.9 billion cu. ft.) and the Creole Trail Pipeline, which interconnects the Sabine Pass LNG terminal with North American natural gas markets. Cheniere Energy also operates an LNG and natural gas marketing business and has minor exploration and production assets. The company plans to build three onshore US Gulf Coast LNG receiving terminals: Sabine Pass, Corpus Christi, and Creole Trail. Its Cheniere Energy Partners unit operates Sabine Pass LNG terminal.

Cheniere Energy's primary strategy is to leverage the 4 billion cu. ft. of natural gas per day regasification capacity at the Sabine Pass LNG facility in Louisiana, and to build additional LNG receiving terminals and natural gas pipelines and related infrastructure as market and financial conditions allow.

(In 2004 the company formed Creole Trail LNG to develop the Creole Trail LNG terminal in Louisiana. In 2005 Cheniere Energy acquired BPU LNG, which held the rights to build and LNG terminal in Corpus Christi. That year Cheniere Energy began construction on the Sabine Pass LNG receiving terminal, which commenced operating in 2008).

In 2010 the company sold its 30% stake in a Texas-based LNG terminal project, Freeport LNG Development, in order to raise $104 million to help pay down debt. Higher output from its Sabine LNG terminal, coupled with higher commodity prices helped the debt-heavy company to report an improvement in revenues and operating income in 2010.

Looking to grow its capital investment, in 2011 the company signed deals to expand its processing capacity at the Sabine Pass terminal with Endesa, Enel and Sumitomo.

The company was founded in 1996 as Cheniere Energy Operating Co., and oil and gas exploration business focused on the Louisiana Gulf Coast. That year it reorganized, and went public as Cheniere Energy, Inc. In 1999, it began developing its LNG receiving terminal business.

EXECUTIVES

Chairman, President, and CEO, Charif Souki, age 58, $7,305,171 total compensation
VP Human Resources and Administration, Ann Raden
VP and Chief Accounting Officer, Jerry D. Smith, age 36
VP and CIO, Scott Abshire
VP and Treasurer, Graham A. McArthur, age 46
VP Finance and Investor Relations, Katie Pipkin
VP and General Counsel, Timothy J. Neumann
VP Governmental and Regulatory Affairs, Patricia Outtrim
VP Engineering and Construction, E. Darron Granger
SVP and CFO, Meg A. Gentle, age 36, $1,881,225 total compensation
SVP Asset Group; President, Pipeline; and President and COO, Cheniere Energy Partners GP, LLC, R. Keith Teague, age 46, $1,881,225 total compensation
SVP International, Jean Abiteboul, age 59, $2,022,671 total compensation
Media Relations, Diane Haggard

Assistant General Counsel and Corporate Secretary, Anne V. Vaughan
SVP Marketing and President, Cheniere Marketing, H. Davis Thames, age 43, $1,881,225 total compensation
Investor Relations, Christina Cavarretta
Auditors: UHY LLP

LOCATIONS

HQ: Cheniere Energy, Inc.
700 Milam St., Ste. 800, Houston, TX 77002
Phone: 713-375-5000   **Fax:** 713-375-6000
Web: www.cheniere.com

PRODUCTS/OPERATIONS

2010 Sales

	$ mil.	% of total
LNG terminals	269.5	92
Marketing & trading	19.0	7
Oil & gas	2.9	1
Other	0.1	-
Total	**291.5**	**100**

Selected Subsidiaries

Cheniere Energy Partners, L.P. (90%)
Cheniere LNG Financial Services, Inc.
Cheniere LNG, Inc.
Cheniere LNG Terminals, Inc.
Sabine Pass LNG-LP, LLC

COMPETITORS

BG Group	McMoRan Exploration
BP	Newfield Exploration
Chevron	Nexen
ConocoPhillips	Occidental Petroleum
Dow Chemical	Panhandle Energy
Exxon Mobil	Stone Energy
Hunt Oil	
Kinder Morgan Energy Partners	

HISTORICAL FINANCIALS

Company Type: Public

Income Statement

FYE: December 31

	REVENUE ($ mil.)	NET INCOME ($ mil.)	NET PROFIT MARGIN	EMPLOYEES
12/10	291.5	(76.2)	—	196
12/09	181.1	(161.5)	—	196
12/08	7.1	(356.5)	—	208
12/07	0.6	(181.8)	—	378
12/06	2.4	(145.9)	—	256
Annual Growth	**232.0%**	**—**	**—**	**(6.5%)**

2010 Year-End Financials

Debt ratio: —
Return on equity: —
Cash ($ mil.): 74.2
Current ratio: 2.50
Long-term debt ($ mil.): 2,927.5
No. of shares (mil.): 67.8
Dividends
  Yield: —
  Payout: —
Market value ($ mil.): 374.3

	STOCK PRICE ($) FY Close	P/E High/Low		PER SHARE ($) Earnings	Dividends	Book Value
12/10	5.52	—	—	(1.37)	0.00	(9.76)
12/09	2.42	—	—	(3.13)	0.00	(11.47)
12/08	2.85	—	—	(7.53)	0.00	(11.93)
12/07	32.64	—	—	(3.60)	0.00	(6.36)
12/06	28.87	—	—	(2.68)	0.00	2.60
Annual Growth	**(33.9%)**	**—**	**—**	**—**	**—**	**—**

Cheniere Energy Partners

Cheniere Energy Partners, a subsidiary of Cheniere Energy, Inc., plans to be North America's biggest gas station — natural gas, that is. Construction began on the Sabine Pass LNG (liquefied natural gas) receiving terminal in 2005, and was completed in 2008. The terminal is the largest of its kind in North America. The terminal boasts 4 billion cu. ft. per day of regasification capacity as well as 16.9 billion cu. ft. of LNG storage capacity. All of the Sabine Pass LNG receiving terminal's capacity has already been contracted to Total Gas and Power North America (an affiliate of TOTAL S.A.), Chevron U.S.A., and Cheniere Energy Inc. subsidiary Cheniere Marketing.

EXECUTIVES

President, COO, and Director, R. Keith Teague, age 46
CFO and Director, Meg A. Gentle, age 36
Chairman, CEO, and Director, Charif Souki, age 58
Communications Coordinator, Diane Haggard
Corporate Secretary, Anne V. Vaughan
Chief Accounting Officer, Jerry D. Smith, age 36
Treasurer, Graham A. McArthur, age 46
Manager Investor Relations, Christina Cavarretta
Auditors:

LOCATIONS

HQ: Cheniere Energy Partners, L.P.
700 Milam St., Ste. 800, Houston, TX 77002
Phone: 713-375-5000   **Fax:** 713-375-6000
Web: www.cheniereenergypartners.com

COMPETITORS

AES	McMoRan Exploration
Chevron	Royal Dutch Shell
ConocoPhillips	Sempra Energy
Exxon Mobil	

HISTORICAL FINANCIALS

Company Type: Public

Income Statement				FYE: December 31
	REVENUE ($ mil.)	NET INCOME ($ mil.)	NET PROFIT MARGIN	EMPLOYEES
12/10	399.3	105.4	26.4%	196
12/09	416.8	186.9	44.8%	0
12/08	15.0	(78.3)	—	0
Annual Growth	415.9%	—	—	—

2010 Year-End Financials

Debt ratio: —
Return on equity: —
Cash ($ mil.): 53.3
Current ratio: 1.51
Long-term debt ($ mil.): 2,187.7

No. of shares (mil.): 161.8
Dividends
  Yield: 8.0%
  Payout: 261.5%
Market value ($ mil.): 3,448.0

	STOCK PRICE ($) FY Close	P/E High/Low		Earnings	PER SHARE ($) Dividends	Book Value
12/10	21.31	33	20	0.65	1.70	(0.00)
12/09	12.91	12	4	1.13	1.70	(0.00)
12/08	3.71	—	—	(0.48)	1.70	(0.00)
00/00	16.06	—	—	(0.23)	0.88	(1.41)
Annual Growth	9.9%	—	—	—	24.5%	—

Cherokee Banking Company

Cherokee Banking Company is the holding company for Cherokee Bank, an independent institution serving individuals and local businesses in Georgia's Cherokee County. It has a handful of branches in Canton City and Woodstock, just north of metropolitan Atlanta. The bank offers standard retail products and services, including checking and savings accounts, IRAs, and CDs. Cherokee Bank also offers business loans and business credit services.

EXECUTIVES

Chairman, Donald F. Stevens
President, CEO, and Director, Dennis W. Burnette
SVP, CFO, and Director, A. R. (Rick) Roberts III
Auditors: Porter Keadle Moore, LLP

LOCATIONS

HQ: Cherokee Banking Company
1275 Riverstone Pkwy., Canton, GA 30114
Phone: 770-479-3400   **Fax:** 770-720-6923
Web: www.cherokeebank.com

HISTORICAL FINANCIALS

Company Type: Public

Income Statement				FYE: December 31
	ASSETS ($ mil.)	NET INCOME ($ mil.)	INCOME AS % OF ASSETS	EMPLOYEES
12/06	206.0	1.7	0.8%	51
12/05	170.1	1.1	0.6%	48
12/04	147.5	0.6	0.4%	41
12/03	117.9	0.5	0.4%	37
12/02	96.9	0.4	0.4%	33
Annual Growth	20.7%	43.6%	—	11.5%

2006 Year-End Financials

Equity as % of assets: —
Return on assets: 0.8%
Return on equity: 11.1%
Long-term debt ($ mil.): —
No. of shares (mil.): —

Dividends
  Yield: —
  Payout: —
Market value ($ mil.): —
Sales ($ mil.): 14.0

	STOCK PRICE ($) FY Close	P/E High/Low		Earnings	PER SHARE ($) Dividends	Book Value
12/06	27.00	20	12	1.35	0.00	(0.00)
12/05	17.00	21	17	0.87	0.00	(0.00)
12/04	15.20	43	32	0.44	0.00	(0.00)
12/03	17.00	42	24	0.50	0.00	(0.00)
12/02	13.41	28	18	0.50	0.00	(0.00)
Annual Growth	19.1%	—	—	28.2%	—	—

Chesapeake Utilities

Chesapeake Utilities gasses up the Chesapeake Bay, and then some. Chesapeake's regulated natural gas distribution divisions serve 120,200 customers in the Northeast and Florida. Another unit distributes power to 31,000 power in Florida. On the unregulated side, the company also serves about 48,100 retail propane customers in Delaware, Florida, Maryland, and Virginia. Another subsidiary, Xeron, sells propane at wholesale to distributors, industrial users, and resellers throughout the US. In addition, Chesapeake has interstate gas pipeline and gas marketing operations. Through BravePoint, the company also offers data services, consulting, and software development.

Chesapeake Utilities' business strategy is to grow its core energy businesses while exploring strategic acquisitions to diversify its portfolio. In 2009 the company acquired Florida Public Utilities Company in a move that raised its profile in that state and boosted its customer base to about 200,000. It added 51,500 natural gas, 31,000 electric (and a new business line), and 14,000 propane customers.

The growth and expansion of the company's regulated businesses, coupled with rate increases and favorable weather conditions (which spiked demand) helped to lift the company's revenues and net income in 2010, despite a drag from weak propane prices.

In 2011 Chesapeake Utilities president and COO Michael McMasters was appointed as CEO, replacing John Schimkaitis, who retained his role as vice chairman.

The company was founded in 1859 as the Dover Gas Light Company. It became Chesapeake Utilities Corporation in 1947. During 2003 Chesapeake began to exit the water services business, selling six of its seven dealerships. The company sold the remaining water dealership in 2004.

EXECUTIVES

Chairman, Ralph J. Adkins, age 68
President, CEO and Director, Michael P. (Mike) McMasters, age 53, $604,713 total compensation
President, Florida Public Utilities, Jeffry M. Householder
President, Florida Public Utilities, Jeff Householder
President and COO, Sharp Energy, S. Robert (Bob) Zola, age 59, $258,965 total compensation
President and COO, BravePoint, John R. Harlow, age 55
President and COO, Xeron, David E. (Dave) Snyder, age 63
VP, Jeffrey R. (Jeff) Tietbohl
VP; President, PESCO, Joseph (Joe) Cummiskey, age 39
VP Strategic Development, Elaine B. Bittner, age 41
Vice Chairman, John R. Schimkaitis, age 63, $978,931 total compensation
SVP; President, Eastern Shore Natural Gas, Stephen C. (Steve) Thompson, age 50, $518,205 total compensation
Communications Manager, Sydney H. Davis
Assistant VP and Controller, Matthew M. Kim
Investor Relations Administrator, Heidi W. Watkins
SVP, CFO, Corporate Secretary, and Treasurer, Beth W. Cooper, age 44, $338,186 total compensation
Auditors:

LOCATIONS

HQ: Chesapeake Utilities Corporation
909 Silver Lake Blvd., Dover, DE 19904
Phone: 302-734-6799   **Fax:** 302-734-6750
Web: www.chpk.com

PRODUCTS/OPERATIONS

2010 Sales

	$ mil.	% of total
Regulated energy	269.9	63
Unregulated energy	146.8	34
Other	10.8	3
Total	**427.5**	**100**

Selected Subsidiaries

Chesapeake Service Company
  BravePoint, Inc. (formerly United Systems, Inc.,
    information technology)
  Chesapeake Investment Company (real estate
    investments)
  Eastern Shore Real Estate, Inc. (office building
    leases)
  Skipjack, Inc. (office building leases)
Eastern Shore Natural Gas Company (transmission)
Florida Public Utilities Company (gas, power, and
  propane distribution)
Flo-Gas Corporation
Peninsula Energy Services Company, Inc
Peninsula Pipeline Company, Inc.
Sharp Energy, Inc. (propane distribution)
  Sharpgas, Inc.
Xeron, Inc. (propane marketing)

COMPETITORS

Allegheny Energy	JEA
Constellation Energy	New Jersey Resources
Group	NextEra Energy
Delmarva Power	Suburban Propane
Energy Transfer	UGI
Ferrellgas Partners	

HISTORICAL FINANCIALS

Company Type: Public

Income Statement

FYE: December 31

	REVENUE ($ mil.)	NET INCOME ($ mil.)	NET PROFIT MARGIN	EMPLOYEES
12/10	427.5	26.1	6.1%	734
12/09	268.8	15.9	5.9%	757
12/08	291.4	13.6	4.7%	448
12/07	258.3	13.2	5.1%	445
12/06	231.2	10.5	4.5%	437
Annual Growth	**16.6%**	**25.6%**	**—**	**13.8%**

2010 Year-End Financials

Debt ratio: 39.6%	No. of shares (mil.): 9.5
Return on equity: 11.5%	Dividends
Cash ($ mil.): 1.6	Yield: 3.1%
Current ratio: 0.69	Payout: 47.8%
Long-term debt ($ mil.): 89.6	Market value ($ mil.): 395.4

	STOCK PRICE ($) FY Close	P/E High/Low		PER SHARE ($) Earnings	Dividends	Book Value
12/10	41.52	15	10	2.73	1.30	23.75
12/09	32.05	16	10	2.15	1.25	22.33
12/08	31.48	18	11	1.98	1.21	18.05
12/07	31.85	19	14	1.94	1.17	17.66
12/06	30.65	21	16	1.72	1.15	18.55
Annual Growth	**7.9%**	**—**	**—**	**12.2%**	**3.1%**	**6.4%**

China North East Petroleum

China North East Petroleum Holdings is engaged in the extraction and production of crude oil in a region of Northern China. Its current operations are focused on four oilfields located in China's Jilin province, where it operates about 250 producing wells. It operates in tandem with oil giant PetroChina to exploit a number of 20-year leases held by PetroChina. China North East Petroleum Holdings has proved reserves of approximately 5.5 million barrels of crude oil equivalent. Large-scale commercial drilling at the Jilin Quinan Oil Field started in 1986. The company also has exclusive exploration and drilling rights to the Durimu oilfield in Inner Mongolia.

EXECUTIVES

Chairman and President, Hong Jun Wang, age 40,
  $160,894 total compensation
EVP Finance and Secretary, Chao Jiang, age 32
Acting CFO, Shaohui (Steven) Chen
Acting CEO and Director, Jingfu Li
Auditors: Jimmy C. H. Cheung & Co., CPA

LOCATIONS

HQ: China North East Petroleum Holdings Limited
  445 Park Ave., 10th Fl., New York, NY 10022
Phone: 212-307-3568   **Fax:** 718-685-2650
Web: www.cnepetroleum.com/

HISTORICAL FINANCIALS

Company Type: Public

Income Statement

FYE: December 31

	REVENUE ($ mil.)	NET INCOME ($ mil.)	NET PROFIT MARGIN	EMPLOYEES
12/10	99.5	58.4	58.7%	715
12/09	64.7	(22.1)	—	464
12/08	58.6	19.6	33.4%	257
12/07	19.5	5.1	26.2%	312
12/06	2.7	0.9	33.3%	78
Annual Growth	**146.4%**	**183.8%**	**—**	**74.0%**

2010 Year-End Financials

Debt ratio: —	No. of shares (mil.): 29.6
Return on equity: 52.8%	Dividends
Cash ($ mil.): 61.0	Yield: —
Current ratio: 6.11	Payout: —
Long-term debt ($ mil.): —	Market value ($ mil.): 170.5

	STOCK PRICE ($) FY Close	P/E High/Low		PER SHARE ($) Earnings	Dividends	Book Value
12/10	5.76	6	2	1.86	0.00	3.74
12/09	9.25	—	—	(0.99)	0.00	1.44
12/08	1.68	6	1	0.98	0.00	2.37
12/07	2.36	22	1	0.21	0.00	(0.00)
12/06	0.40	17	3	0.05	0.00	(0.00)
Annual Growth	**94.8%**	**—**	**—**	**147.0%**	**—**	**—**

Cirrus Logic

Cirrus Logic's approach to the chip business is hardly cloudy. The fabless semiconductor company, long a leader in audio chips of all kinds, develops integrated circuits (ICs) for specialized applications in consumer electronics, energy, and industrial equipment. Its more than 700 products include audio encoder/decoders (codecs), digital amplifiers, digital audio converters, energy management devices, and power amplifiers. Cirrus Logic also develops system-on-a-chip products, which unite processors, controllers, memory, and other components on a single chip. The company gets about three-quarters of its sales outside the US, primarily from customers in China and other Asian countries.

The company's 3,000-plus customers include Apple (36% of sales, mostly through multiple contract manufacturers), distributor Avnet (about one-quarter of sales), Bose, Cisco Systems, LG Electronics, Philips, Samsung, Sony, and Technicolor.

The global financial crisis of 2008, which restricted the worldwide availability of credit, destabilized the general economy and triggered a significant slowdown in orders for Cirrus Logic. While the recession and credit crisis continued into 2009, severely hampering sales of most consumer electronics, Apple was a good customer to have in the economic downturn, as it generally defied the trend, dramatically increasing sales of iPhones. As a result, Cirrus Logic was able to boost its sales by more than one-quarter during fiscal 2010. With the recession easing and Apple bringing out more new products, such as the iPad and more advanced iPhone models, Cirrus Logic stands to benefit from the upturn in sales of electronics.

Although Cirrus Logic ran counter to the 2009 trend of lower sales for chip makers, the company has a spotty record on profitability in the past decade, due to the notorious cyclicality of the semiconductor industry and other factors. It carries an accumulated deficit of more than $733 million.

Once the top maker of graphics chips for PCs, Cirrus Logic exited that extremely volatile market and moved into a variety of other niches — such as precision data acquisition chips for industrial applications. Its biggest focus remains on audio; the company now rivals Texas Instruments, for example, as the market leader for Internet audio chips. While it continues to make some industrial chips, Cirrus Logic paired its leadership in audio with an aggressive acquisition strategy to support its overall focus on chips for consumer entertainment applications, such as DVD recorders and components for DVD game consoles. The company teamed with legendary guitar maker Gibson to develop digital networking products for audio and video transport. Cirrus is also developing processors for DVD-based entertainment products that will incorporate MPEG-4 technology, but is not developing products for stand-alone DVD players.

The company has its own device assembly and test facility in Tucson, Arizona. Other than this plant, Cirrus Logic outsources its manufacturing functions to various contractors, which make the company's chips, package them, and test the finished products.

Cirrus Logic has offices in China, Hong Kong, Japan, Singapore, South Korea, Taiwan, the UK, and the US.

HISTORY

Suhas Patil, a professor who had developed a chip-level software system for controlling disk drives while at MIT, founded Patil Systems in 1981. When his firm failed to find buyers for its advanced products, Patil sought advice from semiconductor executive Michael Hackworth. Impressed with the products' possibilities, Hackworth joined Patil Systems as CEO. In 1984 the company was renamed Cirrus Logic, after the high-flying clouds.

The company initially focused on chips for computer peripherals, but during the 1980s it also began making chips for PCs. It debuted the first controller chips small enough to be built directly into a disk drive unit, an advance that prompted the PC industry's shift to smaller-profile disk drives. When IBM introduced its Video Graphics Array (VGA) graphics display standard in 1987, Cirrus Logic quickly followed with the market's first VGA controller chip.

Cirrus Logic went public in 1989. Its 1991 acquisitions of Crystal Semiconductor and Pixel Semiconductor provided it with access to audio and video technology for the multimedia and fax/modem markets. It bought PC graphics chip maker Acumos in 1992 and Pacific Communication Sciences (products for cellular communications) in 1993. The next year it bought PicoPower Technology, a maker of system controller chips.

In 1996 Cirrus Logic sold its wireless infrastructure equipment unit to ADC Telecommunications. That year the company formed wafer fabrication joint venture Cirent with Lucent's microelectronics unit (which became Agere Systems, later acquired by LSI Corp.).

An industry downturn led Cirrus Logic to cut its workforce by 13% in 1996, and by another 15% in 1997. That year Patil stepped away from the company's day-to-day operations (he continued to serve as chairman emeritus and a director) and Hackworth became chairman.

In 1998, continuing to expand its offerings, Cirrus Logic debuted products for DVDs. In response to a prolonged slump in the semiconductor industry, it eliminated its PC graphics and video accelerator product lines and sold voice compression technology subsidiary Nuera Communications to management. Also that year Cirrus Logic spun off its PC modem business as Ambient Technologies. Analog Devices VP/GM David French was named president and COO in 1998.

In 1999 about 500 more employees were laid off. In an effort to phase out more of its wafer fabrication operations, the company that year handed over control of its MiCRUS joint venture (founded in 1994) to partner IBM and transferred its ownership of Cirent to Lucent (now Alcatel-Lucent). Also that year French became CEO; Hackworth remained chairman.

In 2000 Cirrus Logic moved its headquarters from Fremont, California, to Austin, Texas. The next year the company announced that it would focus growth efforts on semiconductors used in consumer entertainment devices. Despite historically dismal conditions in the chip industry, Cirrus Logic took steps to pursue this strategy in 2001, when it acquired private chip makers Peak Audio (digital audio hardware and software), LuxSonor ($65 million, DVD video processors), ShareWave ($92 million, wireless home networking chips and software), and Stream Machine ($110 million, digital video encoding chips).

Later in 2001 the company announced that it would lay off about 300 workers — 30% of its staff — in the face of continued poor conditions in the global chip market. The next year Cirrus exited the magnetic storage chip business in order to focus on products for the consumer entertainment market. In 2003 the company announced more job cuts and discontinued the wireless product line acquired as part of the ShareWave acquisition. It also sold its chip testing facilities to ChipPAC (now part of STATS ChipPAC), which in turn supplied Cirrus Logic with assembly, test, and packaging services.

As conditions in the worldwide semiconductor market turned choppy again in 2004, Cirrus Logic had a 7% reduction in force, more than 50 workers, mostly affecting employees in California and Texas.

In 2005 the company received $25 million from a legal settlement with Amkor Technology, Fujitsu, and Sumitomo Bakelite. The litigation was over faulty semiconductors sold by Cirrus to Fujitsu. Cirrus and Fujitsu first sued each other in 2001; Amkor and Sumitomo were added as parties to the litigation (which shifted from federal court to state court) in 2003. The insurance carriers for the four vendors reached a settlement through arbitration in 2005.

That same year Cirrus Logic sold its digital video IC product line to Magnum Semiconductor, an entity formed by investors led by Investcorp and August Capital Management. The company received a minority equity stake in Magnum Semi for the assets of the digital video line.

In 2006 Cirrus acquired Shanghai-based Caretta Integrated Circuits for about $10 million in cash. Caretta designed power management ICs for the large, single-cell lithium-ion battery market.

David French resigned as president and CEO in 2007 after a special committee of the board investigated the company's past practices in granting stock options and found that French was significantly involved in backdating certain option grants. Chairman Michael Hackworth stepped in as acting president and CEO. VP/GM Jason Rhode, a Cirrus Logic employee since 1995, was named to succeed French as president and CEO.

In 2007 the SEC's Division of Enforcement informed Cirrus Logic that its informal investigation of the company's historical stock option practices, initiated a year earlier, was elevated to a formal inquiry. The SEC later notified the company that the inquiry was concluded and the commission's staff was not recommending any enforcement action against the company.

Cirrus acquired Apex Microtechnology for $42 million in cash in 2007. Apex Micro developed precision high-power analog amplifiers for aerospace and industrial applications, used in motors, piezoelectrics, programmable power supplies, and other devices. Founded in 1980, the company (also known as Apex Precision Products) had some 1,200 customers, with about $20 million in annual sales, and employed around 90 people.

In 2008 the company decided that things weren't working out with Caretta Integrated Circuits, in terms of its long-term strategic plan. It shut down the subsidiary and laid off about 30 employees in China as a result.

EXECUTIVES

Chairman, Michael L. (Mike) Hackworth, age 70
President, CEO, and Board Member, Jason P. Rhode, age 41, $1,700,784 total compensation
VP, General Counsel, and Secretary, Gregory S. (Scott) Thomas, age 45, $653,884 total compensation
VP and General Manager, Apex Precision Power, Gregory L. (Greg) Brennan
VP Supply Chain Management, Randy Carlson
VP Coporate Marketing Communications and Human Resources, Jo-Dee M. Benson, age 51
VP Worldwide Sales, Tim Turk, age 54, $643,528 total compensation
VP and General Manager, EXL, Thomas (Tom) Stein, age 39
VP Corporate Quality, Lewis Venters
VP Finance, CFO, and Treasurer, Thurman K. Case, age 54, $538,984 total compensation
SVP; General Manager, Mixed-Signal Audio Division, Scott A. Anderson, age 57, $632,055 total compensation
Senior Marcom Manager, Asia, Regina Shum
Manager Public Relations, North America and Europe, Bill Schnell
Auditors: Ernst & Young LLP

LOCATIONS

HQ: Cirrus Logic, Inc.
2901 Via Fortuna, Austin, TX 78746
Phone: 512-851-4000   **Fax:** 512-851-4977
Web: www.cirrus.com

2010 Sales

	$ mil.	% of total
Asia/Pacific		
China	104.0	47
Japan	12.3	5
Taiwan	10.6	5
South Korea	10.1	5
Hong Kong	5.6	2
Other countries	12.4	6
US	47.9	22
Europe		
UK	1.4	1
Other countries	15.8	7
Other regions	0.9	–
Total	**221.0**	**100**

PRODUCTS/OPERATIONS

2010 Sales

	$ mil.	% of total
Audio products	153.7	70
Energy products	67.3	30
Total	**221.0**	**100**

Selected Products

Analog-to-digital (A/D) and digital-to-analog (D/A) converters (audio, industrial, and power metering applications)
Audio
   Amplifiers
   Digital audio transmitters and receivers
   Digital signal processors (DSPs)
   Encoder/decoders (codecs)
   Music synthesizers
   Peripheral component interconnect (PCI) audio accelerators and controllers
   Volume control devices
Embedded processors (used in portable electronic devices)
Infrared transceivers
Line interface units (LIUs)

COMPETITORS

Actions Semiconductor	LSI Corp.
Analogic	Macronix International
Asahi Kasei	Marvell Technology
austriamicrosystems	Maxim Integrated
Dialog Semiconductor	Products
Freescale	O2M
Semiconductor	STMicroelectronics
Integrated Device	Texas Instruments
Technology	

HISTORICAL FINANCIALS

Company Type: Public

Income Statement

FYE: Saturday nearest March 31

	REVENUE ($ mil.)	NET INCOME ($ mil.)	NET PROFIT MARGIN	EMPLOYEES
03/11	369.6	203.5	55.1%	570
03/10	221.0	38.4	17.4%	505
03/09	174.6	3.5	2.0%	479
03/08	181.9	(5.8)	—	473
03/07	182.3	27.9	15.3%	456
Annual Growth	19.3%	64.3%	—	5.7%

2011 Year-End Financials

Debt ratio: —	No. of shares (mil.): 68.7
Return on equity: 46.4%	Dividends
Cash ($ mil.): 37.0	Yield: —
Current ratio: 6.14	Payout: —
Long-term debt ($ mil.): —	Market value ($ mil.): 1,444.0

	STOCK PRICE ($) FY Close	P/E High/Low		PER SHARE ($) Earnings	Dividends	Book Value
03/11	21.03	9	3	2.82	0.00	6.38
03/10	8.39	15	6	0.59	0.00	3.33
03/09	3.76	153	43	0.05	0.00	2.65
03/08	6.72	—	—	(0.07)	0.00	2.70
03/07	7.66	34	19	0.31	0.00	3.44
Annual Growth	28.7%	—	—	73.7%	—	16.8%

Citizens South

Citizens South Banking Corporation is a holding company that owns Citizens South Bank, which has more than 20 branches in North Carolina and Georgia. The bank offers standard deposit products, such as checking, savings, and money market accounts; CDs; and IRAs. It also issues credit cards, provides retirement planning, and writes business and consumer loans (primarily real estate loans). Its Citizens South Financial Services subsidiary (dba Citizens South Investment Services) sells financial products. Two acquisitions of failed banks helped Citizens South move into the Georgia market. It first bought Bank of Hiawassee in 2010. The following year Citizens South acquired New Horizons Bank.

EXECUTIVES

Chairman, David W. Hoyle, age 72
President, CEO, and Director; President and CEO, Citizens South Bank, Kim S. Price, age 55, $393,874 total compensation
EVP, Chief Administrative Officer, and Secretary; EVP, Chief Administrative Officer, and Secretary,, Paul L. Teem Jr., age 63
EVP, CFO, and Treasurer; EVP, CFO, and Treasurer, Citizens South Bank, Gary F. Hoskins, age 48, $198,196 total compensation
EVP and Chief Risk Officer, Kenneth A. (Ken) Icenhour
EVP and COO, Citizens South Bank, Daniel M. (Dan) Boyd IV, age 49, $229,767 total compensation
VP and Branch Manager, Citizens South Bank, Thomas C. (Cliff) Hunnicutt III
VP and Assistant Secretary, Wanda W. Spencer
VP and Assistant Secretary, Pamela Kay P. Sanders
VP and Controller, Citizens South Bank, Kelly A. W. Byrd

VP and Financial Consultant, Citizens South Bank, Chris B. Leazer
VP and Assistant Secretary, Citizens South Bank, Angie M. Painter
VP Human Resources, Citizens South Bank, Betty B. Gaddis
VP Information Systems and Operations, Citizens South Bank, Dennis S. Cox
VP, Citizens South Bank, Mark A. Porch
VP, Citizens South Bank, Marilyn L. Reime Robertson
VP, Citizens South Bank, Lori H. Patrick
VP, Citizens South Bank, William K. (Chuck) Raburn
VP, Citizens South Bank, Rebecca Jane S. Berolatti
VP, Citizens South Bank, Michelle M. Blair
VP, Citizens South Bank, Terry L. Gladden
VP, Citizens South Bank, Jesse F. Milliken
Vice Chairman, Ben R. Rudisill II, age 67
SVP and CIO, Citizens South Bank, Kimberly G. Cooke, age 42
SVP and Chief Credit Officer, Citizens South Bank, Michael R. Maguire, age 53
SVP and Market Executive Gaston County, Citizens South Bank, W. Gordon Quarles Jr.
SVP and Dallas Area Executive, Citizens South Bank, Mark A. Carswell II
SVP and President, Retail Banking, Citizens South Bank, Patricia T. (Pat) Kahle, age 51
SVP and President, North Georgia, Citizens South Bank, Anthony N. (Tony) Stancil, age 47
SVP and Manager Commercial Banking, Citizens South Bank, Ira M. (Don) Flowe Jr., age 46
SVP and Senior Commercial Lending Officer, Citizens South Bank, Robert E. (Ed) Robinson Jr.
SVP, Citizens South Client, Timothy J. P. Ignasher
SVP, Citizens South Bank, Alfred R. Singleton Jr.
SVP, Citizens South Bank, James L. (Jim) Brewer
SVP, Citizens South Bank, J. Stephen (Steve) Huffstetler, age 55
Auditors: Cherry, Bekaert & Holland, LLP

LOCATIONS

HQ: Citizens South Banking Corporation
519 S. New Hope Rd., Gastonia, NC 28054-4040
Phone: 704-868-5200   **Fax:** 704-868-5226
Web: www.citizenssouth.com

COMPETITORS

Bank of America	First Trust Bank
BB&T	NewBridge Bancorp
Carolina Trust Bank	Peoples Bancorp (NC)
Clover Community Bankshares	RBC Bank
First Citizens BancShares	

HISTORICAL FINANCIALS

Company Type: Public

Income Statement

FYE: December 31

	ASSETS ($ mil.)	NET INCOME ($ mil.)	INCOME AS % OF ASSETS	EMPLOYEES
12/10	1,064.5	8.6	0.8%	243
12/09	791.5	(30.0)	—	153
12/08	817.2	3.1	0.4%	164
12/07	779.1	5.7	0.7%	160
12/06	743.4	5.5	0.7%	151
Annual Growth	9.4%	11.8%	—	12.6%

2010 Year-End Financials

Equity as % of assets: 8.78%	Dividends
Return on assets: 0.8%	Yield: 2.9%
Return on equity: 11.9%	Payout: 15.9%
Long-term debt ($ mil.): 101.2	Market value ($ mil.): 49.9
No. of shares (mil.): 11.5	Sales ($ mil.): 71.1

	STOCK PRICE ($) FY Close	P/E High/Low		PER SHARE ($) Earnings	Dividends	Book Value
12/10	4.34	9	5	0.78	0.12	8.12
12/09	4.36	—	—	(3.99)	0.20	9.15
12/08	5.70	26	14	0.40	0.32	13.27
12/07	9.65	18	13	0.70	0.30	10.36
12/06	12.32	21	18	0.64	0.28	10.02
Annual Growth	(23.0%)	—	—	5.1%	(19.1%)	(5.1%)

Clarion Technologies

Clarion Technologies has answered the clarion call for injection-molded products. The company is a custom manufacturer of injection-molded plastic parts used in the automotive and consumer goods industries. Auto products include interior and seating components, appliqué molding, and overhead consoles. In consumer markets, Clarion produces parts for refrigerators and clothes washers, as well as drawer and lighting assemblies. In 2010 the company partnered with Commemorative Casket USA to make thermoplastic caskets. Clarion's customers include Electrolux Home Products, Ford, and Lear. The company operates facilities in Michigan and South Carolina, and Mexico (Juarez). Chairman Craig Wierda is a majority owner.

EXECUTIVES

Chairman, Craig A. Wierda
President, CEO, and Director, Steven W. (Steve) Olmstead
COO and Acting CFO, John Brownlow
Auditors: BDO Seidman, LLP

LOCATIONS

HQ: Clarion Technologies, Inc.
501 S. Cedar St., Greenville, MI 48838
Phone: 616-698-7277   **Fax:** 616-698-1296
Web: www.clariontechnologies.com

PRODUCTS/OPERATIONS

Selected Products

Auto parts
    Colored Class A interior components and assemblies
        Appliqué molding
        Dome lamps and assemblies
        Grab handles
        HVAC vents
        Overhead consoles
    Lens grade polycarbonate
    Seating components
Consumer products
    Caskets
    Class A surface precolored trim
    Decorative in-mold decorating solutions
    Drawer/storage solutions
    Lenses/lighting assemblies
Home appliance parts
    Appliqué molding
    Control box assemblies
    Dairy doors
    Detergent dispenser assemblies
    Gas assist grab handles
    Ice dispenser components
    Ice/water housing assemblies
    Laundry door assemblies
    Lighting assemblies
    SAN/PC crisper bins with graphics
    Shelf supports/glass inserts
    Two-shot knobs/handles

COMPETITORS

Blue Star Plastics	Jordan Industries
Continental Plastics	Key Plastics
Core Molding	Klöckner Pentaplast
Technologies	M-Tek
Crane Composites	Milacron
Deswell	Nicolet
Hoffer Plastics	Rotonics Manufacturing
Indoff	Soligen 2006

HISTORICAL FINANCIALS

Company Type: Public

Income Statement
FYE: Saturday nearest December 31

	REVENUE ($ mil.)	NET INCOME ($ mil.)	NET PROFIT MARGIN	EMPLOYEES
12/05	145.5	(5.7)	—	800
12/04	117.7	(1.7)	—	675
12/03	97.7	0.8	0.8%	700
12/02	80.6	(7.2)	—	575
12/01	105.6	(35.1)	—	600
Annual Growth	8.3%	—	—	7.5%

2005 Year-End Financials

Debt ratio: —	No. of shares (mil.): —
Return on equity: —	Dividends
Cash ($ mil.): 0.1	Yield: —
Current ratio: 0.33	Payout: —
Long-term debt ($ mil.): 0.4	Market value ($ mil.): —

	STOCK PRICE ($) FY Close	P/E High/Low		PER SHARE ($) Earnings	Dividends	Book Value
12/05	0.05	—	—	(0.40)	0.00	(0.00)
12/04	0.29	—	—	(0.26)	0.00	(0.00)
12/03	0.66	—	—	(0.17)	0.00	(0.00)
12/02	0.46	—	—	(0.28)	0.00	(0.00)
12/01	0.33	—	—	(1.65)	0.00	(0.00)
Annual Growth	(37.6%)	—	—	—	—	—

Clarkston Financial

Clarkston Financial, the holding company for Clarkston State Bank, threw its hat into the ring of retail banking in 1998. The community bank serves area consumers and small to midsized businesses from about five locations in Oakland County, Michigan, north of Detroit. The bank offers standard deposit services, including checking, savings, and money market accounts, certificates of deposit, and IRAs. Clarkston Savings Bank uses these funds primarily to originate real estate loans; commercial mortgages account for the largest portion of its portfolio, followed by residential mortgages and construction and land development loans.

EXECUTIVES

Chairman, Edwin L. Adler, age 73
CFO, James W. Distelrath
CEO and Director; President and CEO, Clarkston State Bank, J. Grant Smith, age 41
President and CEO, Huron Valley State Bank, Jack J. Shubitowski, age 48
EVP Retail Banking, Clarkston State Bank, Dawn M. Horner, age 50
SVP, Commercial Lending, Clarkston State Bank, Donald M. Bolton

Secretary, Treasurer, and Director, Mark A. Murvay, age 71
Auditors: Plante & Moran, PLLC

LOCATIONS

HQ: Clarkston Financial Corporation
6600 Highland Rd., Ste. 24, Waterford, MI 48327
Phone: 248-922-0086   **Fax:** 248-886-1432
Web: www.clarkstonstatebank.com

COMPETITORS

Bank of America	Flagstar Bancorp
Citizens Republic	Huntington Bancshares
Bancorp	JPMorgan Chase
Fifth Third	Oxford Bank

HISTORICAL FINANCIALS

Company Type: Public

Income Statement
FYE: December 31

	ASSETS ($ mil.)	NET INCOME ($ mil.)	INCOME AS % OF ASSETS	EMPLOYEES
12/06	220.4	(0.7)	—	60
12/05	195.6	—	—	59
12/04	163.4	1.3	0.8%	51
12/03	142.6	1.5	1.1%	39
12/02	115.3	0.8	0.7%	23
Annual Growth	17.6%	—	—	27.1%

2006 Year-End Financials

Equity as % of assets: 6.70%	Dividends
Return on assets: 0.7	Yield: —
Return on equity: —	Payout: —
Long-term debt ($ mil.): 19.2	Market value ($ mil.): —
No. of shares (mil.): —	Sales ($ mil.): 14.3

	STOCK PRICE ($) FY Close	P/E High/Low		PER SHARE ($) Earnings	Dividends	Book Value
12/06	13.75	—	—	(0.57)	0.00	(0.00)
12/05	15.25	—	—	(0.02)	0.00	(0.00)
12/04	20.62	18	14	1.20	0.00	(0.00)
12/03	16.45	12	6	1.41	0.00	(0.00)
12/02	8.60	12	10	0.78	0.00	(0.00)
Annual Growth	12.4%	—	—	—	—	—

Clean Diesel

Clean Diesel Technologies has developed a few cool technologies to counteract global warming. The company is starting to commercialize its chemical fuel additives and other products for reducing diesel engine emissions and improving fuel economy. These include its platinum fuel catalysts, which are marketed in Europe and the US under the Platinum Plus brand. Clean Diesel Technologies also manufactures and licenses nitrogen oxide reduction systems (under the brand name ARIS) and chemical fuel additives to help control diesel engine emissions. The company has a licensing deal with Mitsui to use the ARIS technology.

Clean Diesel's strategy is to target segments of the diesel emission reduction market where regulatory requirements create a customer need for the company's product and technology. The company sell its products through license agreements, direct sales or distribution arrangements, targeting

original equipment manufacturers, Tier One suppliers, retrofit system integrators, and others.

In a move to expand its product offerings, Clean Diesel acquired Catalytic Solutions, a manufacturer and distributor of emissions control systems and products, in a 2010 stock swap. Catalytic Solutions will operate as a subsidiary of Clean Diesel. With the deal, Clean Diesel expands both its customer base and its operational scale.

Relaxed emission requirements for motor vehicles in London led to a slump in sales of the company's diesel particulate filter product, a big seller in 2008, resulting in an 85% drop in year-over-year product revenues.

Timothy Rogers was named Clean Diesel's CEO in 2010. He replaced Michael Asmussen, who resigned.

EXECUTIVES

CEO and Director, Charles F. Call Jr., age 63
CFO, Nikhil A. Mehta
VP Sales and Marketing, Daniel K. Skelton, age 37, $289,095 total compensation
COO, Christopher J. Harris
CTO, Stephen J. Golden
SVP Product Development and Director, Timothy (Tim) Rogers, age 49, $439,832 total compensation
Auditors:

LOCATIONS

HQ: Clean Diesel Technologies, Inc.
4567 Telephone Rd., Ste. 206, Ventura, CA 93003
Phone: 805-639-9458   **Fax:** 805-639-9466
Web: www.cdti.com

2009 Sales

	$ mil.	% of total
US	0.6	50
Europe	0.4	33
Asia	0.2	17
Total	1.2	100

PRODUCTS/OPERATIONS

2009 Sales

	$ mil.	% of total
Products	1.0	84
Licensing & royalties	0.2	16
Total	1.2	100

COMPETITORS

BASF Catalysts	Lubrizol
Cummins Filtration	Migami
Donaldson Company	Rhodia
Innospec	Robert Bosch
Johnson Matthey	

HISTORICAL FINANCIALS

Company Type: Public

Income Statement
FYE: December 31

	REVENUE ($ mil.)	NET INCOME ($ mil.)	NET PROFIT MARGIN	EMPLOYEES
12/10	48.1	(8.4)	—	156
12/09	1.2	(6.7)	—	14
12/08	7.5	(9.4)	—	21
12/07	4.9	(4.5)	—	17
12/06	1.1	(5.4)	—	15
Annual Growth	157.2%	—	—	79.6%

2010 Year-End Financials

Debt ratio: 9.5%
Return on equity: —
Cash ($ mil.): 5.0
Current ratio: 1.20
Long-term debt ($ mil.): 1.5

No. of shares (mil.): 4.0
Dividends
  Yield: —
  Payout: —
Market value ($ mil.): 37.6

	STOCK PRICE ($) FY Close	P/E High/Low	PER SHARE ($) Earnings	Dividends	Book Value
12/10	9.49	— —	(6.77)	0.00	3.88
12/09	8.64	— —	(4.98)	0.00	6.40
12/08	15.58	— —	(6.90)	0.00	10.83
12/07	138.00	— —	(3.96)	0.00	18.66
12/06	54.00	— —	(6.30)	0.00	9.11
Annual Growth	(35.3%)	— —	—	—	(19.2%)

Clean Energy Fuels

Forget cooking with gas — Clean Energy Fuels is driving with gas. Natural gas, that is. The company owns and/or supplies more than 220 natural gas fueling stations across the US and Canada. These enable Clean Energy's 480 fleet customers to tank up their more than 21,270 fleet vehicles with compressed natural gas (CNG) or liquefied natural gas (LNG). Clean Energy also helps customers buy natural gas vehicles and obtain government incentives. The company buys CNG from local utilities and produces LNG at its two plants (in California and Texas) with a combined capacity of 60 million gallons a year.

The company also helps with the design, building, and maintaining of CNG and LNG stations.

Pickens puts his money where his mouth is. Clean Energy is hoping to parlay the interest shown in the Pickens Plan (which advocates, in part, using natural gas to power motor vehicles as a cheaper alternative to gasoline and diesel) to harness the untapped potential in the US. In 2009 there were 10 million vehicles worldwide that were powered by natural gas, compared to only 100,000 in the US. Clean Energy is planning to increase that number by focusing on high-volume fleet customers (bus lines, utilities and regional trucking forms) as its core market.

In 2010 Clean Energy acquired IMW Industries for $125 million in a cash and stock deal. IMW manufactures and services natural gas fueling compressors and related equipment that is sold to station operators and commercial fleets. With plants in the US and China, the acquisition expands both Clean Energy's capabilities and its geographic reach in the CNG market. In 2011 it bought CNG fueling system technologies company Wyoming NorthStar for $10.9 million.

The company's strategy includes expanding internationally (through a joint venture in Peru, and a Canadian project to process hydrogen waste for use in vehicles); developing hydrogen projects (hydrogen fuel cell vehicles, including a hydrogen fueling station at Los Angeles International Airport); and capitalizing on cost savings of using CNG and LNG.

Clean Energy is also acquiring fleet vehicles it will later sell to customers and buying complementary companies to expand its portfolio of assets and services. In this context, in 2009 the company acquired Dallas-based BAF Technologies, a leading provider of natural gas vehicle systems

and conversions. The deal enables Clean Energy to increase the supply of light-duty vehicles.

Acquisitions and organic growth saw the company's revenues grow in 2009, in spite of the global recession, while lower fuel costs related to the downturn helped to ease its net loss that year. Increased production and sales volumes in 2010 boosted revenues and further improved the company's net loss.

Founder and billionaire oilman T. Boone Pickens and wife Madeleine own about 41% of Clean Energy.

EXECUTIVES

Chairman, Warren I. Mitchell, age 73
President, CEO, and Director, Andrew J. Littlefair, age 50, $1,939,850 total compensation
CFO, Richard R. Wheeler, age 46, $1,388,069 total compensation
VP Federal Government Relations, James L. Hooley
VP (Transit), John A. Somers
VP Operations, Brian Powers
VP Business Development (Refuse), Raymond P. Burke
VP National Accounts & Infrastructure, Greg Roche
VP Engineering and Construction, Dennis C.K. Ding
COO, Mitchell W. Pratt, age 51, $1,243,407 total compensation
Assistant VP Technology Advancement, Michael Eaves
Chief Marketing Officer, James N. Harger, age 52, $1,475,400 total compensation
SVP Sales and Finance, Peter Grace
SVP Strategic Development, Barclay F. (Clay) Corbus, age 44, $1,149,735 total compensation
Media Relations, Bruce Russell
Director Public Policy, Todd Campbell
Investor Relations, Ina McGuinness
Auditors: KPMG LLP

LOCATIONS

HQ: Clean Energy Fuels Corp.
3020 Old Ranch Pkwy, Ste. 200, Seal Beach, CA 90740
Phone: 562-493-2804   **Fax:** 562-493-4532
Web: www.cleanenergyfuels.com

2010 Sales

	$ mil.	% of total
US	194.5	92
Canada	6.1	3
Other countries	11.2	5
Total	**211.8**	**100**

PRODUCTS/OPERATIONS

2010 Sales

	$ mil.	% of total
Product	189.8	90
Services	22.0	10
Total	**211.8**	**100**

COMPETITORS

Atlas Copco
BP
Enerflex
Exterran
Exxon Mobil
Production Operators

HISTORICAL FINANCIALS

Company Type: Public

Income Statement

FYE: December 31

	REVENUE ($ mil.)	NET INCOME ($ mil.)	NET PROFIT MARGIN	EMPLOYEES
12/10	211.8	(2.5)	—	710
12/09	131.5	(33.2)	—	229
12/08	129.5	(40.9)	—	140
12/07	117.7	(8.9)	—	121
12/06	91.5	(77.5)	—	84
Annual Growth	23.3%	—	—	70.5%

2010 Year-End Financials

Debt ratio: 10.1%
Return on equity: —
Cash ($ mil.): 55.2
Current ratio: 1.67
Long-term debt ($ mil.): 41.7

No. of shares (mil.): 69.6
Dividends
  Yield: —
  Payout: —
Market value ($ mil.): 963.4

	STOCK PRICE ($) FY Close	P/E High/Low	PER SHARE ($) Earnings	Dividends	Book Value
12/10	13.84	— —	(0.04)	0.00	5.94
12/09	15.41	— —	(0.60)	0.00	4.63
12/08	6.04	— —	(0.90)	0.00	5.36
12/07	15.14	— —	(0.22)	0.00	5.22
Annual Growth	(2.9%)	— —	—	—	4.4%

Clean Harbors

Hazardous-waste management company Clean Harbors does more than its name suggests. Its major business lines are its technical services and industrial services units. Its technical services group, which accounts for more than 40% of sales, provides for the collection, transportation, treatment, and disposal of hazardous waste, including chemical and laboratory waste (but not nuclear waste). Its industrial services unit provides high-pressure and chemical cleaning, catalyst handling, decoking, material processing, and industrial lodging services. The company also has a field services segment and an exploration services unit. Alan McKim, the company's chairman and CEO, controls about 10% of Clean Harbors.

Its field services segment provides a wide variety of environmental cleanup services on customer sites or other locations on a scheduled or emergency response basis, while its exploration services group provides exploration and directional boring services to the energy sector serving oil and gas exploration, production, and power generation.

The company's 175 service locations include some 50 waste management facilities located throughout North America in 36 US states, seven Canadian provinces, Mexico, and Puerto Rico. The company also operates locations in Bulgaria, China, Singapore, Sweden, Thailand, and the UK.

Clean Harbors boosted its revenues to record levels in 2010, up 61% over the previous year, due to an overall resurgence in demand for environmental services and its participation in the oil spill response to disasters in the Gulf of Mexico and Michigan. The company saw revenue increases across all of its main lines of business. Accordingly, net income was up more than 255% on the strength of its oil spill containment activities and income from the sale of a discontinued business line.

The company's strategy for business growth involves both expanding its service offerings and the geographic regions in which it operates; cross-selling its services among its four business segments; pursuing large-scale projects; and grow its business through both organic growth and acquisitions.

In a deal to allow Clean Harbors to expand into key markets in western Canada, the company in 2011 acquired Peak Energy Services Ltd., an oil and gas services firm, for $167 million.

That same year, however, Clean Harbors failed in a bid to acquire Calgary-based Badger Daylighting, a provider of hydrovac services, for $248 million. Badger shareholders rejected the deal.

Clean Harbors acquired Eveready Inc., a Canadian firm that provides industrial maintenance and production, and exploration services to the oil and gas industries, for $387 million in 2009. The deals helped Clean Harbors expand its presence in the industrial services market.

In 2008 the company acquired two solvent recycling facilities in Hebron, Ohio, and Chicago from Safety-Kleen. It also purchased Universal Environmental, an environmental services company based near San Francisco in Benicia, California.

EXECUTIVES

Chairman, President, and CEO, Alan S. McKim, age 56, $720,552 total compensation
President, Clean Harbors Development, William J. (Bill) Geary, age 63
EVP Energy and Industrial Services, Clean Harbors Environmental Services, David M. Parry, age 45, $405,237 total compensation
EVP Environmental Services, Clean Harbors Environmental Services, Eric W. Gerstenberg, age 42, $391,703 total compensation
EVP Corporate Planning and Development, Clean Harbors Environmental Services, Brian P. Weber, age 43, $446,627 total compensation
EVP Pricing and Proposals, Clean Harbors Environmental Services, George L. Curtis, age 52
EVP and Chief Administration Officer, Clean Harbors Environmental Services, Michael J. Twohig, age 48
EVP Corporate Sales and Marketing, Clean Harbors Environmental Services, Deirdre J. Evens, age 47
EVP Exploration Services, Marvin Lefebvre, age 53
VP, Corporate Controller, and Chief Accounting Officer, John R. Beals, age 56
VP Marketing, Clean Harbors Environmental Services, David N. Proud
Vice Chairman, EVP, CFO and Treasurer, James M. Rutledge, age 58, $578,822 total compensation
SVP Regulatory Affairs, Clean Harbors Environmental Services, Phillip G. Retallick, age 58
SVP Internal Audit and Compliance, Clean Harbors Environmental Services, Simon R. Gerlin, age 53
Secretary, C. Michael Malm
SVP and General Counsel, Clean Harbors Environmental Services, Michael R. McDonald, age 46
SVP Risk Management, Clean Harbors Environmental Services, William F. O'Connor, age 61
SVP Environmental Sales, Clean Harbors Environmental Services, Jerry E. Correll, age 61
Auditors: Deloitte & Touche LLP

LOCATIONS

HQ: Clean Harbors, Inc.
42 Longwater Dr., Norwell, MA 02061-9149
Phone: 781-792-5000   **Fax:** 781-792-5900
Web: www.cleanharbors.com

PRODUCTS/OPERATIONS

2010 Sales

	$ mil.	% of total
Technical Services	720.6	42
Industrial Services	504.8	29
Field Services	460.8	26
Exploration Services	46.8	3
Adjustments	(1.8)	-
Total	**1,074.2**	**100**

COMPETITORS

Heritage Environmental Services	SUEZ Environnement
Philip Services	Veolia ES Technical Solutions
Siemens Water Technologies	Waste Management

HISTORICAL FINANCIALS

Company Type: Public

Income Statement

FYE: December 31

	REVENUE ($ mil.)	NET INCOME ($ mil.)	NET PROFIT MARGIN	EMPLOYEES
12/10	1,731.2	130.5	7.5%	6,840
12/09	1,074.2	36.7	3.4%	6,399
12/08	1,030.7	57.5	5.6%	4,804
12/07	946.9	44.2	4.7%	4,769
12/06	829.8	46.7	5.6%	4,574
Annual Growth	**20.2%**	**29.3%**	**—**	**10.6%**

2010 Year-End Financials

Debt ratio: 34.7%	No. of shares (mil.): 52.8
Return on equity: 16.7%	Dividends
Cash ($ mil.): 302.2	Yield: —
Current ratio: 2.46	Payout: —
Long-term debt ($ mil.): 270.8	Market value ($ mil.): 2,218.6

	STOCK PRICE ($) FY Close	P/E High/Low		PER SHARE ($) Earnings	Dividends	Book Value
12/10	42.04	17	11	2.46	0.00	14.80
12/09	29.81	44	28	0.74	0.00	11.70
12/08	31.72	33	18	1.25	0.00	9.04
12/07	25.85	26	20	1.07	0.00	5.10
12/06	24.20	22	11	1.13	0.00	4.40
Annual Growth	**14.8%**	**—**	**—**	**21.5%**	**—**	**35.4%**

Clearwire

This ISP wants to give mobile Web users their moments of clarity. Clearwire provides high-speed Internet access and computer telephony services to some 4 million subscribers in the US under the CLEAR brand via its 4G wireless broadband network. The company's service area covers about 70 markets located mainly along the East and West Coasts, the Midwest, and in Florida, Texas, and the Carolinas. Wholesale partners such as Comcast and Time Warner resell Clearwire's services to supplement their own, accounting for about three-quarters of the company's customer base. Clearwire also serves about 40,000 international subscribers mainly in Europe. Sprint Nextel controls about 54% of Clearwire's voting power.

Rapidly growing Clearwire has never been profitable, and it expects to continuing losing money in the immediate future as it builds out its network to expand business. Sales more than doubled in 2010, after an increase of more than 1,000% the previous year. The company's net loss also grew in 2010, more than doubling due to additional expenses incurred from its push into new markets. Clearwire has seen sales, marketing, customer service, and advertising costs rise as its wholesale and retail subscriber numbers swell. Costs related to its growing employee ranks are taking their toll on the bottom line as well; the company's headcount rose by half in 2010, after more than doubling in 2009. The company is seeking new sources of funding in order to continue to grow.

Clearwire continued to add subscribers in 2010, increasing its total by nearly 3.7 million during the year; most of these were wholesale customers contributed by Sprint. That year Clearwire also added new wholesale partners including Best Buy and Cbeyond. The company's roll out of its network in large metro areas, including New York, San Francisco, Boston, and Los Angeles, helped to fuel its expansion in 2010 and 2011.

Established in 2007, Clearwire combined its network with Sprint's 4G business the following year, giving Sprint a controlling stake in the company. Other investors include Intel, Google, Comcast, FMR, and Time Warner Cable, which collectively control more than a third of Clearwire, and tap its wireless network through wholesale agreements. In 2011 Sprint Nextel firmed up its wholesale relationship with Clearwire by agreeing to spend as much as $1 billion with Clearwire during 2011 and 2012 to enable 4G wireless data services across additional parts of its service area.

Clearwire founder, wireless pioneer Craig McCaw (who also ran the one-time leading cellular service McCaw Cellular), resigned as company chairman in 2011 amid financial woes that led Clearwire to lay off 15% of staff, cut back on its use of contractors, and curtail some marketing and business development activities. McCaw continues to hold about 4% of voting control in the company through Eagle River Holdings.

As part of its effort to cut operational costs, Clearwire outsourced the day-to-day management of its network to top tier global wireless equipment and infrastructure services provider Ericsson in 2011. Clearwire still owns its networks and oversees interactions with its customers. The outsourcing deal was part of a broader agreement that saw Ericsson take over the operation of Sprint Nextel's network.

EXECUTIVES

Chairman and Interim CEO, John W. Stanton, age 55
CFO, Hope F. Cochran, age 37
President, International, Barry J. West, age 64
President, Strategic Partnerships and Wholesale, Teresa Elder
Chief Accounting Officer, Robert DeLucia, age 45
SVP and Chief Strategy Officer, David Maquera
SVP, General Counsel, and Secretary, Broady R. Hodder, age 38
SVP and CTO, John Saw
Media Contact, East and Central Regions, Chris Comes
General Manager Washington, D.C., Clearwire Communications, Jeff Fugate
Media Contact, Corporate and Financial, Susan Johnston
Media Contact, West Region, Debra Havins
General Manager, Houston, John Smith
General Manager Baltimore, Clearwire Communications, Dean Young
General Manager Kansas City, Clearwire Communications, John O'Donnellas
General Manager, Philadelphia, Andrew Kupiec

COO, Erik E. Prusch, age 44
SVP Corporate Development, Scott Hopper
Chief People Officer, Laurent J. Bentitou
General Manager, Puget Sound Market, Clear Water
 Communications, Brian Carter
SVP Sales and Distribution, Jim Ryder
Auditors: Deloitte & Touche LLP

LOCATIONS

HQ: Clearwire Corporation
 4400 Carillon Point, Kirkland, WA 98033
Phone: 425-216-7600
Web: www.clearwire.com

2010 Sales

	$ mil	% of total
US	535.1	96
Other countries	21.7	4
Total	**556.8**	**100**

PRODUCTS/OPERATIONS

2010 Sales

	$ mil.	% of total
Retail	502.3	90
Wholesale	50.6	9
Other	3.9	1
Total	**556.8**	**100**

COMPETITORS

AT&T	EchoStar
CenturyLink	LightSquared
Charter Communications	Sprint Nextel
Comcast Cable	Time Warner Cable
Cox Communications	Verizon
DIRECTV	WildBlue
DISH Network	

HISTORICAL FINANCIALS

Company Type: Public

Income Statement

FYE: December 31

	REVENUE ($ mil.)	NET INCOME ($ mil.)	NET PROFIT MARGIN	EMPLOYEES
12/10	556.8	(487.4)	—	3,600
12/09	274.5	(325.6)	—	3,440
12/08	20.5	(432.6)	—	1,635
12/07	151.4	(727.5)	—	1,990
12/06	100.2	(284.2)	—	1,245
Annual Growth	**53.5%**	**—**	**—**	**30.4%**

2010 Year-End Financials

Debt ratio: 303.6%
Return on equity: —
Cash ($ mil.): 1,233.6
Current ratio: 2.72
Long-term debt ($ mil.): 4,017.0

No. of shares (mil.): 987.0
Dividends
 Yield: —
 Payout: —
Market value ($ mil.): 5,083.2

	STOCK PRICE ($) FY Close	P/E High/Low	PER SHARE ($) Earnings	Dividends	Book Value
12/10	5.15	— —	(2.46)	0.00	1.34
12/09	6.76	— —	(1.74)	0.00	1.71
12/08	4.93	— —	(0.28)	0.00	2.85
12/07	13.71	— —	(4.58)	0.00	7.09
Annual Growth	**(27.8%)**	**— —**	**—**	**—**	**(42.6%)**

Cleveland BioLabs

Cleveland BioLabs' scientists are working hard to develop drugs that help healthy cells stay that way, as well as drugs that promote cell death in cancerous tumors. The company has based its research on the suppression and stimulation of the process known as apoptosis, a form of cell-death that occurs after exposure to radiation, toxic chemicals, or internal stresses. In development are two product lines: protectans (suppressing apoptosis in healthy cells after radiation exposure) and curaxins (stimulating apoptosis in some forms of cancer). Protectans have applications in reducing side effects from cancer treatment and terrorist or nuclear events, while curaxins are being developed as anticancer therapies.

Cleveland BioLabs is pursuing commercialization of its potential anti-radiation and cancer therapy candidates both independently and through collaborative efforts. It has research partnerships with the Cleveland Clinic Foundation and ChemBridge, two of the company's founders and minority shareholders. The company also receives funding from the Department of Defense to develop a protectan candidate to treat radiation injuries.

In early 2010, the company formed a joint venture with a Russian venture capital fund to help develop its curaxin compounds. The new entity, Incuron, will help move the potential drugs through early stage trials and into human trials.

EXECUTIVES

Chairman, Bernard L. Kasten
President, CEO, and Director, Michael Fonstein, age 51, $246,179 total compensation
CFO, John A. Marhofer Jr., age 48, $165,856 total compensation
VP Pharmaceutical Development, Ed Venkat
Chief Medical Officer, Michael R. Kurman, age 59
Chief Scientific Officer and Director, Andrei Gudkov, age 54
SVP Drug Development, Farrel Fort
Director Clinical Operations, Michael Paterno
Director Corporate Development and
 Communications, Rachel Levine
COO, Secretary, and Director, Yakov Kogan, age 38, $217,686 total compensation
Auditors: Meaden & Moore, Ltd.

LOCATIONS

HQ: Cleveland BioLabs, Inc.
 73 High St., Buffalo, NY 14203
Phone: 716-849-6810
Web: www.cbiolabs.com

PRODUCTS/OPERATIONS

2009 Sales

	$ mil.	% of total
Government contract or grant	12.7	88
Commercial	1.7	12
Total	**14.4**	**100**

COMPETITORS

Aeolus	Genzyme
Amgen	Geron
AstraZeneca	Harbor BioSciences
Bayer HealthCare	ImmunoGen
Pharmaceuticals Inc.	Osiris Therapeutics
Cangene	

HISTORICAL FINANCIALS

Company Type: Public

Income Statement

FYE: December 31

	REVENUE ($ mil.)	NET INCOME ($ mil.)	NET PROFIT MARGIN	EMPLOYEES
12/10	15.3	(26.4)	—	55
12/09	14.3	(12.8)	—	38
12/08	4.7	(14.0)	—	33
12/07	2.0	(27.0)	—	48
12/06	1.7	(7.2)	—	35
Annual Growth	**73.2%**	**—**	**—**	**12.0%**

2010 Year-End Financials

Debt ratio: —
Return on equity: —
Cash ($ mil.): 10.9
Current ratio: 0.58
Long-term debt ($ mil.): —

No. of shares (mil.): 29.0
Dividends
 Yield: —
 Payout: —
Market value ($ mil.): 209.1

	STOCK PRICE ($) FY Close	P/E High/Low	PER SHARE ($) Earnings	Dividends	Book Value
12/10	7.22	— —	(1.01)	0.00	(0.54)
12/09	3.31	— —	(0.82)	0.00	(0.34)
12/08	2.13	— —	(1.13)	0.00	0.04
12/07	8.80	— —	(2.34)	0.00	1.17
12/06	5.04	— —	(0.84)	0.00	0.47
Annual Growth	**9.4%**	**— —**	**—**	**—**	**—**

Coast Bancorp

Dude, where's my car loan? Maybe with Coast Bancorp, holding company for Coast National Bank. Founded in 1997, the bank operates about five branches along California's central coastal region. It offers traditional products and services including checking, savings, money market, and individual retirement accounts; certificates of deposit; and Internet banking. Commercial real estate loans constitute the largest portion of the bank's loan portfolio, followed by construction and land development loans, commercial and industrial loans, and one- to four-family residential mortgages.

EXECUTIVES

Chairman, President, and CEO, Coast Bancorp and
 Coast National Bank, Jack C. Wauchope, age 75
EVP and Chief Credit Officer, Coast National Bank,
 Leah M. Pauly, age 48
EVP and Manager, Small Business Loan Center,
 Coast National Bank, Davina Palazzo, age 40
Vice Chairman, Jack W. Robasciotti, age 83
SVP and Branch Manager, Coast National Bank, Julie
 A. Joslin, age 51
SVP and CFO, Coast National Bank, Karan C. Pohl,
 age 39
Secretary and Director, Marilyn M. Britton, age 71
Auditors: Vavrinek, Trine, Day & Co., LLP

LOCATIONS

HQ: Coast Bancorp
 500 Marsh St., San Luis Obispo, CA 93401
Phone: 805-541-0400   Fax: 805-541-5758
Web: www.coastnationalbank.com

COMPETITORS

Bank of America
Community West
  Bancshares
Heritage Oaks Bancorp
Mission Community
  Bancorp

Pacific Capital
  Bancorp
Rabobank America
Santa Lucia Bancorp

HISTORICAL FINANCIALS

Company Type: Public

Income Statement
FYE: December 31

	ASSETS ($ mil.)	NET INCOME ($ mil.)	INCOME AS % OF ASSETS	EMPLOYEES
12/06	180.7	1.4	0.8%	70
12/05	185.7	1.1	0.6%	58
12/04	159.9	1.1	0.7%	66
12/03	142.1	1.0	0.7%	63
12/02	122.0	0.8	0.7%	54
Annual Growth	10.3%	15.0%	—	6.7%

2006 Year-End Financials

Equity as % of assets: 7.03%
Return on assets: 0.8%
Return on equity: 10.8%
Long-term debt ($ mil.): 5.2
No. of shares (mil.): —

Dividends
  Yield: 0.6%
  Payout: 10.4%
Market value ($ mil.): —
Sales ($ mil.): 14.7

	STOCK PRICE ($) FY Close	P/E High/Low		PER SHARE ($) Earnings	Dividends	Book Value
12/06	33.75	19	14	1.93	0.20	(0.00)
12/05	30.00	19	17	1.56	0.17	(0.00)
12/04	28.00	18	15	1.58	0.15	(0.00)
12/03	23.50	16	11	1.46	0.10	(0.00)
12/02	17.60	16	12	1.17	0.08	(0.00)
Annual Growth	17.7%	—	—	13.3%	25.7%	—

Codexis

The pharmaceutical and the biodiesel industries don't seem like they have much in common, but they both use the chemicals produced by Codexis. The company develops biocatalysts — chemicals used to manufacture other chemicals in a way that's easy on the environment. Its technology is used to make the active ingredients in pharmaceuticals and produce biofuel from plant material. Codexis has a research agreement with Shell to develop new ways of converting biomass to biofuel; Shell accounts for more than half of Codexis's sales. The company is also working within other markets to use its technology to manage carbon emissions from coal-fired power plants and treat wastewater. Codexis went public in 2010.

The company earned about $78 million in initial sales of its shares on the NASDAQ exchange. Codexis plans to use the proceeds to drive organic, internal growth as well as for possible acquisitions.

The company's revenues increased more than 29% in 2010, due primarily to increased product sales to Merck & Co. and to generic pharmaceutical customers. The company's Collaborative Research and Development unit also saw a significant jump in revenues. The company's net income also increased in 2010 though it remained a loss.

Shell not only is the company's largest customer, but it also retained its 20% stake in Codexis following the IPO. Maxygen, the biotech company

that originally spun off Codexis, distributed the 17% of Codexis shares it had retained in the IPO to its shareholders later that year.

In the pharmaceuticals market, Codexis has partnerships with Merck, Pfizer, and Teva. Codexis' custom biocatalysts aid in the manufacturing process for the cholesterol-fighting drug Lipitor, as well as for the generic equivalents of allergy drug Singulair and antidepressant Cymbalta.

EXECUTIVES

Chairman, Thomas R. (Tom) Baruch, age 72
President, CEO, and Director, Alan Shaw, age 48, $950,636 total compensation
President, Pharmaceuticals, Nicholas Green, age 46
VP and Managing Director, Codexis Laboratories Singapore, Thomas Daussmann
VP and General Manager, Bioindustrials, Michael J. Knauf, age 51
VP Intellectual Property, Lynn Marcus-Wyner
VP and General Manager, Pharma Services, Peter Seufer-Wasserthal, $395,701 total compensation
VP Human Resources, Andrea Danforth
VP and General Manager, Generics, Gregory Rocklin
VP Systems Biology, Lori Giver
VP Operations, David Walshaw, age 50
VP Strategic Planning, Technology, Vonnie Estes
VP Corporate Development and Strategy, Jacques Beaudry-Losique
SVP Process Development and Manufacturing and CTO, David L. (Dave) Anton, age 57, $487,368 total compensation
SVP Science and Innovation and Chief Science Officer, John H. Grate, age 58
SVP and CFO, Robert J. (Bob) Lawson, age 46
Chief Business Officer; President, Pharmaceutical Services and Enzyme Products, Joseph J. Sarret, age 43
SVP, General Counsel and Secretary, Douglas T. Sheehy, age 43, $395,781 total compensation
SVP Commercial Operations, Peter M. Strumph, age 45
Media Relations, Lyn Christenson
Auditors: Ernst & Young LLP

LOCATIONS

HQ: Codexis, Inc.
  200 Penobscot Dr., Redwood City, CA 94063
Phone: 650-421-8100   **Fax:** 650-421-8102
Web: www.codexis.com

2010 Sales

	$ mil.	% of total
Americas	72.9	68
Asia	24.3	23
Europe	9.9	9
Total	**107.1**	**100**

PRODUCTS/OPERATIONS

2010 Sales

	$ mil.	% of total
Related Party R&D	66.1	62
Product	32.8	30
Collaborative R&D	4.1	4
Government grants	4.1	4
Total	**107.1**	**100**

COMPETITORS

ABITEC
ADM
BASF SE
BioFuel Energy
DSM

Lonza
Novozymes
Renewable Energy Group
Solvay

HISTORICAL FINANCIALS

Company Type: Public

Income Statement
FYE: December 31

	REVENUE ($ mil.)	NET INCOME ($ mil.)	NET PROFIT MARGIN	EMPLOYEES
12/10	107.1	(8.5)	—	291
12/09	82.9	(20.3)	—	290
12/08	50.5	(45.1)	—	300
12/07	25.3	(39.0)	—	230
12/06	12.1	(18.7)	—	0
Annual Growth	72.5%	—	—	8.2%

2010 Year-End Financials

Debt ratio: —
Return on equity: —
Cash ($ mil.): 72.4
Current ratio: 3.35
Long-term debt ($ mil.): —

No. of shares (mil.): 34.8
Dividends
  Yield: —
  Payout: —
Market value ($ mil.): 369.2

	STOCK PRICE ($) FY Close	P/E High/Low	PER SHARE ($) Earnings	Dividends	Book Value
12/10	10.60	— —	(0.35)	0.00	3.08
Annual Growth	—	— —	—	—	—

Coeur d'Alene Mines

Coeur d'Alene Mines gets to the heart of the matter when it comes to precious metals. A leading primary silver producer, the company holds interests in silver and gold properties in Africa, Australia, North America, and South America. It produces about 17 million ounces of silver and 170,000 ounces of gold annually. Coeur d'Alene has proved and probable reserves of about 270 million ounces of silver and 3 million ounces of gold. Coeur d'Alene produces most of its revenue from the San Bartolomé mine in Bolivia and Palmarejo mine in Mexico. Sales of silver account for about three-fourths of the company's revenue. Most of the minerals are sold to bullion-trading banks and to smelters.

Coeur d' Alene sales from silver and gold increased by almost 76% in 2009, due mainly to increased silver production from its newest mine, San Bartolomé, and its Palmarejo operation. The added production led to an increase of $129.7 million in revenues for 2009. However, a 79% increase in production costs combined with significant losses on derivatives took a bite out of the 2009 bottom line, leaving the company with a net loss of about $32 million.

Coeur d'Alene sold its Minera Cerro Bayo subsidiary in Patagonia, Chile to Mandalay Resources for cash and stock in 2010. The main asset is the Cerro Bayo silver-gold mine. In 2009 it sold its Broken Hill Mine in New South Walks, UK, for about $55 million in cash.

In 2007 it bought Australian miner Bolnisi Gold and the Canadian Palmarejo in a deal valued at $1.1 billion. Besides its primary operations in the US and Chile, Coeur d'Alene has interests in exploration-stage properties in Argentina, Bolivia, Chile, Tanzania, and the US. The combination with Bolnisi and Palmarejo created the world's largest primary silver producer. Those two companies had already been linked in that Bolnisi owned almost three-quarters of Palmarejo, whose biggest asset was the Palmarejo silver and gold project in the Mexican state of Chihuahua.

Chairman, President, and CEO, Dennis E. Wheeler, age 68, $2,245,157 total compensation
President, Coeur South America, Huberto Rada, age 58
VP and Managing Director, Coeur Tanzania, Godfrey B. Mramba
VP and General Manager, Kensington Project, Coeur Alaska, Thomas C. (Tom) Henderson
VP Human Resources, Larry A. Nelson, age 58
VP Environmental Services, Luther J. Russell, age 55
SVP Operations, K. Leon Hardy, age 57
SVP and CFO, Mitchell J. Krebs, age 39, $646,635 total compensation
SVP Exploration, CDE Chilean Mining, Alfredo Cruzat
SVP and Chief Accounting Officer, Thomas T. (Tom) Angelos, age 55
SVP Exploration, Donald J. Birak, age 57, $620,087 total compensation
General Manager, Technical Support Services, Bernie O'Leary
Corporate Mine Engineering Manager, Al Tattersall
Treasurer, Elizabeth M. (Beth) Druffel
General Manager, Martha Mine, Gordon Babcock
Director Investor Relations Australia and Asia, John Blue
Director Investor Relations, North America, Karli Anderson
Controller, Kenneth L. (Ken) Koski, age 42
SVP, Chief Administrative Officer, General Counsel, and Corporate Secretary, Kelli C. Kast, age 44
Director Corporate Communications, Tony Ebersole
General Manager, San Bartolomé, Stuart O'Brien
Auditors: KPMG LLP

LOCATIONS

HQ: Coeur d'Alene Mines Corporation
400 Coeur d'Alene Mines Bldg., 505 Front Ave., Coeur d'Alene, ID 83816-0316
Phone: 208-667-3511   **Fax:** 208-667-2213
Web: www.coeur.com

2009 Sales

	$ mil.	% of total
Bolivia	113.7	38
Mexico	89.1	30
US	45.5	15
Argentina	44.8	14
Australia	5.8	2
Chile	1.7	1
Total	**300.6**	**100**

PRODUCTS/OPERATIONS

2009 Sales

	% of total
Silver	81
Gold	19
Total	**100**

COMPETITORS

Agnico-Eagle	Kinross Gold
Barrick Gold	Newmont Mining
BHP Billiton	Pan American Silver
Hecla Mining	Pe oles

HISTORICAL FINANCIALS

Company Type: Public

Income Statement

FYE: December 31

	REVENUE ($ mil.)	NET INCOME ($ mil.)	NET PROFIT MARGIN	EMPLOYEES
12/10	515.5	(91.3)	—	1,471
12/09	300.6	(31.9)	—	1,294
12/08	189.5	—	—	1,034
12/07	215.3	43.9	20.4%	1,047
12/06	216.6	88.5	40.9%	931
Annual Growth	**24.2%**	**—**	**—**	**12.1%**

2010 Year-End Financials

Debt ratio: 17.1%   No. of shares (mil.): 89.3
Return on equity: —   Dividends
Cash ($ mil.): 66.1   Yield: 0.0%
Current ratio: 0.98   Payout: —
Long-term debt ($ mil.): 348.2   Market value ($ mil.): 2,440.1

	STOCK PRICE ($) FY Close	P/E High/Low		PER SHARE ($) Earnings	Dividends	Book Value
12/10	27.32	—	—	(1.05)	0.00	22.85
12/09	18.06	—	—	(0.45)	0.00	24.82
12/08	8.80	—	—	(0.00)	0.00	31.50
12/07	49.40	36	21	1.40	0.00	61.96
12/06	49.50	25	13	3.00	0.00	20.90
Annual Growth	**(13.8%)**	**—**	**—**	**—**	**—**	**2.3%**

Cohu

Cohu tries to blend various technologies into one coherent business. Of the company's three segments, the largest is semiconductor equipment (Delta Design and Rasco), which makes handling equipment used to protect semiconductors during testing procedures. Top customers include Advanced Micro Devices, Intel, and Texas Instruments. The other segments are video cameras (closed-circuit television systems for surveillance, medical, and industrial applications) and Broadcast Microwave Services (microwave radios, antenna systems, and support equipment). Cohu gets about 80% of sales from customers outside the US.

Cohu's sales increased 88% in 2010 over 2009, ending a four year slump. The company also reported profits after two consecutive years in the red. Sales of semiconductor equipment, which account for around 80% of Cohu's sales, were up 128%, on higher demand from chip makers for the capital equipment needed to handle the high rates of capacity utilization. The company expanded its equipment offerings with the acquisition of Rasco from Dover in 2008. The combination of Delta Design's IC test handlers and thermal technology, and Rasco's gravity-feed and test-on-strip systems, offers customers a broad line of products.

The company's other operations help cushion its dependence on the notoriously volatile semiconductor industry. Cohu Electronics has sold closed-circuit television (CCTV) equipment for more than 50 years. The customer base for these products includes traffic control, scientific imaging, and security/surveillance markets. The current product line consists of indoor/outdoor CCTV cameras and camera control equipment, which are used by government agencies, OEMs, and contractors. Addi-

tional accessories, such as monitors and lenses, are offered.

Broadcast Microwave Services (BMS) produces antenna systems and associated equipment used for the transmission of video, audio, and telemetry. Applications include electronic newsgathering, unmanned aerial vehicles, law enforcement, and security/surveillance. Customers for BMS' products include television broadcasters, entertainment companies, professional sports teams, government agencies, law enforcement, public safety organizations, and unmanned air vehicle program contractors.

To remain competitive the company offers a broad range of products, maintains customer support and service centers worldwide, and invests in research and development of new products (Cohu spent $36 million on R&D in 2010). The company supports manufacturing operations in the US, Germany, Mexico, and the Philippines. It is contracting out more of its manufacturing in a bid to cut costs.

HISTORY

Kalbfell Laboratories was incorporated in 1947, an outgrowth of a research and development partnership founded in 1945. The company originally made electronic devices for government agencies. It shifted its emphasis to power supply units in 1952 and a year later expanded into closed-circuit television (CCTV) equipment. The company was renamed Kay Lab in 1954 and Cohu Electronics (after chairman La Motte Cohu) in 1957. It became Cohu, Inc. in 1972.

During the 1980s CEO James Barnes directed Cohu's entry into semiconductor test handling equipment. The company acquired microwave equipment maker Broadcast Microwave Services in 1984.

Chip handling gear became Cohu's primary business during the chip boom of the early 1990s. The company established its Singapore subsidiary in 1993. The next year it acquired Daymarc, a maker of gravity-feed semiconductor handling equipment, to complement its Delta Design pick-and-place machines.

Company insider Charles Schwan replaced the retiring Barnes in 1996. Sales fell in 1998, the result of a prolonged downturn in the semiconductor industry, but then surged in 1999 as the chip industry entered a record boom.

In 2000 Cohu merged Delta Design and Daymarc to create its Delta Design test handler subsidiary. Later that spring Schwan announced that he would retire as CEO (he remained chairman); president and COO James Donahue became CEO.

In 2001 Cohu acquired the automated systems business of Schlumberger's Semiconductor Solutions division to shore up its own chip testing capabilities. During a brutal chip industry slump that lasted from 2001 to 2003, Cohu consolidated some facilities to control its costs. After consolidating facilities in the US, Delta Design in 2004 opened a facility for equipment assembly and spare-parts supply in the Philippines, near Manila.

In 2005 Delta Design received a supplier award from Intel, a rare distinction from the world's largest chip maker, which generally doesn't reveal its suppliers of semiconductor equipment and materials. It was the second time Delta Design received Intel's highest award for suppliers.

In 2006 Cohu sold the assets of its Fisher Research Laboratory (metal and leak detectors for industry and hobbyists) subsidiary, also known as FRL, to First Texas Products (maker of the Bounty Hunter line of metal detectors) for about $3 million in cash. The unprofitable business accounted for around 3% of Cohu's sales.

In 2006 Cohu acquired the patents, intellectual property, certain semiconductor burn-in products, and other assets from the Unigen operations of Unisys for $8 million. The company also acquired a Unigen facility in Chandler, Arizona, measuring 10,000 sq. ft., and hired about 40 engineers and other employees from Unigen.

Cohu acquired Rasco from Dover in 2008 for about $80 million in cash. The combination of Delta Design's IC test handlers and thermal technology, and Rasco's gravity-feed and test-on-strip systems, bolstered the company's broad line of products.

EXECUTIVES

Chairman, President, and CEO, James A. Donahue, age 62, $1,161,833 total compensation
President, Cohu Electronics Division, Brian Leedy, age 44
President, Broadcast Microwave Services, Graham Bunney, age 55
President, Semiconductor Equipment, Luis A. Muller
VP Sales and Service Delta, Rasco, Roger J. Hopkins, age 61, $295,851 total compensation
VP Finance and CFO, Jeffrey D. Jones, age 50, $399,217 total compensation
VP Operations, Delta Design, Thomas G. Lightner, age 66
VP Manufacturing, Delta Design, James P. Walsh, age 42, $342,839 total compensation
SVP Delta Design, James G. McFarlane, age 55, $480,817 total compensation
Auditors: Ernst & Young LLP

LOCATIONS

HQ: Cohu, Inc.
12367 Crosthwaite Circle, Poway, CA 92064-6817
Phone: 858-848-8100   **Fax:** 858-848-8185
Web: www.cohu.com

2010 Sales

	$ mil.	% of total
US	65.0	20
Malaysia	52.5	16
Philippines	51.7	16
China	50.5	16
Singapore	21.2	7
Other countries	81.8	25
Total	**322.7**	**100**

PRODUCTS/OPERATIONS

2010 Sales

	$ mil.	% of total
Semiconductor equipment	273.6	85
Microwave communications	31.7	10
Video cameras	17.4	5
Total	**322.7**	**100**

Operations and Selected Products

Semiconductor Equipment
  Delta Design (semiconductor test handling equipment and thermal technology)
    Automated test handlers
    Burn-in board loaders and unloaders
    Device kits
    Docking interfaces
    Environmental chambers
  Rasco (semiconductor test handling)
    Gravity-feed and test-on-strip systems
Cohu Electronics (closed-circuit television systems)
  Cameras and control equipment
  Control systems
  Design services
  Lenses
  Software

Broadcast Microwave Services (microwave communications equipment)
Antenna systems
Microwave radio equipment

COMPETITORS

Advantest	Data I/O
Aetrium	EG Systems
Anaren	Honeywell
Bosch	International
Brooks Automation	inTEST
CalAmp	Mirae
Checkpoint Systems	Vicon Industries
Comtech	
Telecommunications	

HISTORICAL FINANCIALS
Company Type: Public

Income Statement
FYE: December 31

	REVENUE ($ mil.)	NET INCOME ($ mil.)	NET PROFIT MARGIN	EMPLOYEES
12/10	322.7	24.6	7.6%	1,100
12/09	171.3	(28.2)	—	1,000
12/08	199.7	(5.4)	—	1,100
12/07	241.4	8.0	3.3%	1,000
12/06	270.1	17.7	6.6%	1,100
Annual Growth	**4.5%**	**8.6%**	**—**	**0.0%**

2010 Year-End Financials

Debt ratio: —
Return on equity: 9.0%
Cash ($ mil.): 45.9
Current ratio: 3.36
Long-term debt ($ mil.): —

No. of shares (mil.): 24.0
Dividends
  Yield: 1.4%
  Payout: 23.5%
Market value ($ mil.): 397.7

	STOCK PRICE ($) FY Close	P/E High/Low		PER SHARE ($) Earnings	Dividends	Book Value
12/10	16.58	17	11	1.02	0.24	11.45
12/09	13.95	—	—	(1.20)	0.18	10.92
12/08	12.15	—	—	(0.23)	0.24	12.28
12/07	15.30	70	42	0.34	0.24	12.33
12/06	20.16	38	18	0.77	0.24	12.01
Annual Growth	**(4.8%)**	—	—	**7.3%**	**(0.0%)**	**(1.2%)**

Coinstar

There's big money in spare change, and Coinstar has turned the previously underutilized "fourth wall" area between the cash registers and the door in retail stores into a potential profit center. Perhaps best-known for its eponymous coin-counting machines, the company underwent a major transformation in 2008 when it acquired Redbox, which, along with Coinstar's DVDXpress subsidiary, operates some 33,000 DVD rental kiosks at supermarkets, big-box retailers, drug and convenience stores, and restaurants nationwide. Coinstar operates about 19,000 coin counting and cashing machines in the US, Canada, Ireland, and the UK that process approximately $3 billion in coins annually.

One of the company's added services allows customers to change their coins for retailer gift cards or eCertificates, or use them to donate to charity. Partners include Starbucks, Amazon.com, Apple's iTunes, the World Wildlife Fund, and the American Red Cross. Coinstar's coin-counting machines

are located mainly in supermarkets, including Kroger and SUPERVALU; its DVD rental kiosks can be found at stores such as Wal-Mart (its largest client), Walgreen, and McDonald's (from which it bought Redbox).

Over the past several years, Coinstar has transitioned from a one-product company — offering just coin-counting services — to a business that offers a variety of products and services. The company has grown primarily through acquisitions and is said to be exploring the sale of beauty products and coffee in vending machines. Still, its acquisitions have not been nearly as successful as Redbox, which now accounts for approximately two-thirds of Coinstar's revenues.

Focusing on its top-earning divisions, the company has been exiting less profitable enterprises amid tough economic conditions worldwide. In mid-2011 Coinstar sold its money-transfer business, which served the US and Latin America, to California-based financial serves firm Sigue. The deal, valued at about $40 million, strengthens Sigue's coverage as it provides money-transfer services in more than 135 countries and allows Coinstar to concentrate on its automated retail strategy (i.e., coin counting and video rental).

Coinstar has dived headlong into the DVD rental business. Since 2009, it has inked licensing and revenue-sharing agreements with movie producers and distributors such as Sony Pictures, Warner Bros., Lions Gate, and Universal Studios that should keep its movie kiosks humming for the next several years, at least. It's also extending its reach into video game rentals through its Redbox business, which has competitor GameFly adjusting its playbook to jockey for position.

Five unaffiliated institutional investors own more than 40% of Coinstar's stock, including FMR and Guardian Life, which each hold more than 10%.

EXECUTIVES

Chairman, Deborah L. Bevier, age 59
President and COO, Gregg A. Kaplan, age 41, $2,167,870 total compensation
CFO, J. Scott Di Valerio, age 48
President, Coin, Michael J. (Mike) Skinner, age 57
President, RedBox, J. Mitchell (Mitch) Lowe, age 58
President and CEO, Coinstar Entertainment Services, Kevin Wall
CEO and Director, Paul D. Davis, age 54, $2,274,523 total compensation
VP Engineering, Alex A. Doumani, age 51
VP New Ventures, Peter D. Rowan, age 44
Chief People Officer, Raquel Karls
Chief Legal Officer, General Counsel and Corporate Secretary, Donald R. (Don) Rench, age 44, $589,997 total compensation
Chief Customer Officer, Maria D. Stipp
Corporate VP Manufacturing and Supply Chain, Carl Poteete
Chief Accounting Officer, Saul M. Gates, age 44
Chief Performance Officer, Mary A. Leonard
Auditors: KPMG LLP

LOCATIONS

HQ: Coinstar, Inc.
1800 114th Ave. SE, Bellevue, WA 98004
Phone: 425-943-8000   **Fax:** 425-637-0045
Web: www.coinstar.com

2009 Sales

	$ mil.	% of total
North America	1,071.7	94
International	73.1	6
Total	**1,144.8**	**100**

PRODUCTS/OPERATIONS

2009 Sales

	$ mil.	% of total
DVD services	773.5	67
Coin services	258.8	23
Money transfer services	87.7	8
E-payment services	24.8	2
Total	**1,144.8**	**100**

Selected Subsidiaries

CellCards LLC
Coin-Op Factory Inc.
Coinstar E-Payment Services Inc.
Coinstar E-Payment Services Limited (UK)
Coinstar International, Inc.
Coinstar Ireland Limited
Coinstar Limited (UK)
Coinstar UK Holdings Limited
DVDXpress UK Limited
GroupEx Financial Corporation
GroupEx Financial, S.A. (Guatemala)
GroupEx LLC
Redbox Automated Retail, LLC
Sesame Holdings, Inc.

COMPETITORS

Amazon.com	Global Payment
Blockbuster	Technologies
Cash Technologies	Hulu
Cummins-American	Netflix
GameFly	Safeway

HISTORICAL FINANCIALS

Company Type: Public

Income Statement
FYE: December 31

	REVENUE ($ mil.)	NET INCOME ($ mil.)	NET PROFIT MARGIN	EMPLOYEES
12/10	1,436.4	51.0	3.6%	2,585
12/09	1,144.8	53.6	4.7%	2,600
12/08	911.9	14.1	1.5%	0
12/07	546.3	(22.3)	—	1,900
12/06	534.4	18.6	3.5%	1,900
Annual Growth	**28.0%**	**28.7%**	**—**	**8.0%**

2010 Year-End Financials

Debt ratio: 40.5%   No. of shares (mil.): 31.8
Return on equity: 11.5%   Dividends
Cash ($ mil.): 183.4   Yield: —
Current ratio: 0.77   Payout: —
Long-term debt ($ mil.): 179.4   Market value ($ mil.): 1,795.6

	STOCK PRICE ($) FY Close	P/E High/Low		PER SHARE ($) Earnings	Dividends	Book Value
12/10	56.44	43	16	1.57	0.00	13.93
12/09	27.78	22	11	1.76	0.00	13.27
12/08	19.51	78	31	0.50	0.00	11.33
12/07	28.15	—	—	(0.80)	0.00	10.91
12/06	30.57	52	33	0.66	0.00	11.62
Annual Growth	**16.6%**	**—**	**—**	**24.2%**	**—**	**4.6%**

Comarco

Comarco is charging ahead with renewed focus. The company markets a line of battery chargers, called ChargeSource, designed for mobile phones, notebook computers, and a variety of other portable devices. It markets ChargeSource products through its retail partner, Kensington Com-

puter Products (a division of ACCO Brands), which sells the products under its own label. Comarco previously operated two other businesses — emergency call box installation and maintenance and wireless network monitoring products — but it divested those operations between 2008 and 2009.

Comarco sold its call box business to CASE Systems in 2008. Looking to focus exclusively on its ChargeSource division, the company sold its wireless test solutions business to Ascom Holding for about $13 million in cash in 2009.

In fiscal 2008 Comarco's call box segment accounted for roughly half of its revenues; its remaining sales were roughly split between its wireless and ChargeSource divisions.

EXECUTIVES

Chairman, Michael R. Levin, age 49
President, CEO, and Director, Samuel M. Inman III, age 59, $459,270 total compensation
VP Manufacturing and Operations, Donald L. McKeefery, age 48
VP and CFO, Winston E. Hickman, age 68, $331,889 total compensation
VP Sales and Marketing, Fredrik L. Torstensson, age 40
VP and CTO, Comarco Wireless Technologies, Thomas W. Lanni, age 57, $281,655 total compensation
VP, Corporate Controller, and Secretary, Alisha Charlton, age 41
Auditors: BDO Seidman, LLP

LOCATIONS

HQ: Comarco, Inc.
25541 Commercentre Dr., Lake Forest, CA 92630-8870
Phone: 949-599-7400   **Fax:** 949-599-1415
Web: www.comarco.com

2008 Sales

	$ mil.	% of total
North America	19.0	82
Europe	2.3	10
Latin America	1.0	4
Asia/Pacific	0.9	4
Total	**23.2**	**100**

PRODUCTS/OPERATIONS

2008 Sales

	$ mil.	% of total
Call Box	11.1	48
Wireless Test Solutions	6.7	29
ChargeSource	5.4	23
Total	**23.2**	**100**

COMPETITORS

Belkin	iGo Inc.
Delta Electronics	

HISTORICAL FINANCIALS

Company Type: Public

Income Statement
FYE: January 31

	REVENUE ($ mil.)	NET INCOME ($ mil.)	NET PROFIT MARGIN	EMPLOYEES
01/11	28.9	(6.0)	—	24
01/10	26.4	(7.4)	—	36
01/09	13.5	(4.5)	—	30
01/08	23.2	(10.0)	—	119
01/07	47.8	1.8	3.8%	120
Annual Growth	**(11.8%)**	**—**	**—**	**(33.1%)**

2011 Year-End Financials

Debt ratio: —   No. of shares (mil.): 7.3
Return on equity: —   Dividends
Cash ($ mil.): 6.4   Yield: 0.0%
Current ratio: 1.38   Payout: —
Long-term debt ($ mil.): —   Market value ($ mil.): 2.5

	STOCK PRICE ($) FY Close	P/E High/Low		PER SHARE ($) Earnings	Dividends	Book Value
01/11	0.34	—	—	(0.81)	0.00	0.52
01/10	2.65	—	—	(1.01)	0.00	1.29
01/09	0.95	—	—	(0.61)	0.00	2.27
01/08	5.42	—	—	(1.36)	0.00	2.84
01/07	7.65	55	30	0.24	0.00	5.15
Annual Growth	**(54.1%)**	**—**	**—**	**—**	**—**	**(43.6%)**

Community Bankers Trust

Community Bankers Trust Corporation, formerly Community Bankers Acquisition, is the holding company for the Bank of Essex and TransCommunity Bank. Additional divisions of TransCommunity operate as Bank of Goochland, Bank of Powhatan, Bank of Louisa, and Bank of Rockbridge. The company grew in 2008 when it merged with former bank holding companies TransCommunity Financial and BOE Financial Services of Virginia. The company now includes about a dozen bank branches west and north of Richmond, Virginia. Subsidiaries offer securities and insurance products. Community Bankers Trust expanded into Georgia when it acquired the branches and deposits of The Community Bank, which was the 20th bank to fail in 2008.

EXECUTIVES

President and CEO, Bank of Goochland, Gregory C. Tripp
President and CEO, Bank of Rockbridge, Dennis Traubert
President, Bank of Essex, M. Andrew McLean, age 56
President and CEO, Bank of Louisa, George D. Yancey, age 60
EVP and Chief Banking Officer, Essex Bank, Rex L. Smith III, age 53
SVP and CFO, Bruce E. Thomas, age 47, $221,513 total compensation
President and CEO, Bank of Powhatan, James F. Keller, age 55
General Counsel and Secretary, Thomas M. Oakey III
Chief Accounting Officer, Patrick J. Tewell, age 46, $161,738 total compensation
Auditors: Elliott Davis LLC

LOCATIONS

HQ: Community Bankers Trust Corporation
4235 Innslake Dr., Ste. 200, Glen Allen, VA 23060
Phone: 804-934-9999   **Fax:** 804-934-9299
Web: www.cbtrustcorp.com

PRODUCTS/OPERATIONS

2008 Sales

	$ mil.	% of total
Interest income		
Fees & loans	19.7	78
Other	3.6	15
Non-interest income		
Service charges	1.2	5
Other	0.6	2
Total	**25.1**	**100**

COMPETITORS

Bank of America	Eastern Virginia
Bank of McKenney	Bankshares
Bank of Virginia	First Capital Bancorp
BB&T	Union First Market
Central Virginia	Bankshares
Bankshares	Village Bank & Trust

HISTORICAL FINANCIALS

Company Type: Public

Income Statement

FYE: December 31

	ASSETS ($ mil.)	NET INCOME ($ mil.)	INCOME AS % OF ASSETS	EMPLOYEES
12/10	1,115.6	(21.0)	—	287
12/09	1,226.7	(29.3)	—	290
12/08*	1,029.1	1.2	0.1%	220
03/07	58.8	1.1	1.9%	0
03/06	0.4	—	—	0
Annual Growth	**626.7%**	**—**	**—**	**14.2%**

*Fiscal year change

2010 Year-End Financials

Equity as % of assets: 9.60%	Dividends
Return on assets: 21.0	Yield: 3.8%
Return on equity: —	Payout: —
Long-term debt ($ mil.): 41.1	Market value ($ mil.): 22.5
No. of shares (mil.): 21.5	Sales ($ mil.): 60.6

	STOCK PRICE ($) FY Close	P/E High/Low		Earnings	PER SHARE ($) Dividends	Book Value
12/10	1.05	—	—	(1.03)	0.04	4.99
12/09	3.26	—	—	(1.41)	0.16	6.13
12/08*	3.00	109	27	0.07	0.08	7.62
03/07	7.26	69	64	0.11	0.00	4.72
Annual Growth	**(47.5%)**	—	—	—	—	**1.8%**

*Fiscal year change

Community Financial (VA)

Community Financial is the holding company for Community Bank, originally organized as a Virginia building and loan association in 1928. The institution has a number of branches in the central portion of the state and two offices near the coast in Virginia Beach. Deposit options include checking, savings, NOW, and money market accounts; IRAs; and CDs. The bank also issues credit cards. Its loan portfolio is chiefly composed of real estate loans: Residential and commercial mortgages and construction loans account for some 70% of all loans. Consumer and business loans round out the loan portfolio.

EXECUTIVES

Chairman, James R. Cooke Jr., age 72
CEO and Director, Norman C. (Butch) Smiley III, age 49
SVP Retail Banking, John J. Howerton, age 54
SVP Lending, Lyle A. Moffett, age 43
SVP Retail Banking, Community Financial and Community Bank, Benny N. Werner, age 62
SVP and CFO, Community Financial and Community Bank, R. Jerry Giles, age 62
Auditors: Yount, Hyde & Barbour, P.C.

LOCATIONS

HQ: Community Financial Corporation
38 N. Central Ave., Staunton, VA 24401
Phone: 540-886-0796   **Fax:** 540-885-0643
Web: www.cbnk.com

PRODUCTS/OPERATIONS

COMPETITORS

Bank of America	SunTrust
BB&T	United Bankshares
First Citizens	
BancShares	

HISTORICAL FINANCIALS

Company Type: Public

Income Statement

FYE: March 31

	ASSETS ($ mil.)	NET INCOME ($ mil.)	INCOME AS % OF ASSETS	EMPLOYEES
03/11	530.1	1.5	0.3%	162
03/10	547.2	3.6	0.7%	156
03/09	512.7	(5.8)	—	155
03/08	491.2	3.8	0.8%	134
03/07	463.1	4.1	0.9%	135
Annual Growth	**3.4%**	**(22.2%)**	**—**	**4.7%**

2011 Year-End Financials

Equity as % of assets: 9.39%	Dividends
Return on assets: 0.3%	Yield: 0.0%
Return on equity: 4.1%	Payout: —
Long-term debt ($ mil.): 97.0	Market value ($ mil.): 13.7
No. of shares (mil.): 4.4	Sales ($ mil.): 31.7

	STOCK PRICE ($) FY Close	P/E High/Low		Earnings	PER SHARE ($) Dividends	Book Value
03/11	3.14	29	15	0.18	0.00	11.41
03/10	4.16	9	5	0.65	0.00	11.24
03/09	4.00	—	—	(1.39)	0.13	10.62
03/08	8.00	14	8	0.87	0.26	8.98
03/07	11.75	14	11	0.93	0.25	8.98
Annual Growth	**(28.1%)**	—	—	**(33.7%)**	**—**	**6.2%**

comScore

comScore knows the score when it comes to measuring online audience behavior. The company provides data, analysis, and consultancy to some 1,200 clients looking to fortify their marketing, sales, and trading initiatives. Its global panel of more than 2 million Internet users measures and tracks consumer behaviors, demographics, and advertising responsiveness for clients in such industries as travel, pharmaceuticals, finance, and telecommunications. Branded products include comScore's Media Metrix suite of website and online advertising network measurement tools and comScore's Marketing Solutions products, which provide custom research and analysis from its panel. The company was established in 1999.

From 2009 to 2010, comScore saw its revenue jump 37% from $128 million to $175 million. It attributed organic growth and acquisitions as main reasons for the revenue climb. However, the company suffered a rare net loss of $1.6 million for 2010, due to higher marketing, research and development, and administrative expenses. The majority of the company's revenue (85% in 2010) comes from the fees it charges for its subscription-based services. The remaining percentage comes from its custom research services. In 2010 Microsoft alone accounted for 11% of its revenue.

comScore's plan for growth involves broadening its international scope. Its European panel's presence is mostly in the UK, and the company plans to expand its consumer research and analysis to additional European clients as well as other global clients looking to conduct audience research in Europe. In 2010 it improved its technology for measuring the European market when it acquired Netherlands-based Nedstat, a provider of Web analytics and video measurement services, for about $37 million. In late 2009 comScore snatched up Certifica, Inc., a Web measurement firm based in Latin America. Certifica has a presence in six Latin American countries.

comScore is also focused on strengthening its position in measuring cell phone usage. In early 2010, it bought ARSGroup, which specialized in measuring advertising effectiveness of multimedia and TV campaigns. ARSGroup was subsequently renamed comScore ARS. A few months later, comScore obtained the products division of Nexius, Inc, and the deal enhanced comScore's ability to analyze operational efficiencies and capital expenditures within the mobile phone market.

EXECUTIVES

Chairman, Gian M. Fulgoni, age 63, $1,378,964 total compensation
President, CEO, and Director, Magid M. Abraham, age 53, $1,865,129 total compensation
CFO, Kenneth (Ken) Tarpey, $1,616,766 total compensation
President Media Metrix, comScore Canada, Brent Bernie
EVP Analytics, Cameron Meierhoefer
EVP, comScore ARS, Jeff Cox
EVP Asia-Pacific Region, Will Hodgman
EVP, Serge Matta
EVP Advertising Solutions, Lynn Bolger
EVP International Markets, Wolf Allisat
VP Research International Operations, Pat Pellegrini
VP Advertising Effectiveness Products, Anne Hunter
VP Media, Leslie Litton
VP, Kevin Levitt
VP Television Sales and Business Development, Joan FitzGerald
VP Sales, comScore Canada, Bryan Segal
VP Sales, Southeast Asia, Joe Nguyen
VP Product Management, Steve Dennen
COO, Gregory T. (Greg) Dale, age 41, $1,065,402 total compensation
CTO, Chris Nicotra
Chief Marketing Officer, Linda Bolan Abraham
SVP, Jeff Hackett
SVP, Mike Hurt
SVP, Brian Jurutka
SVP Mobile Products, Mark Donovan

SVP and Managing Director, comScore Europe, Mike Read
SVP U.S. Ad Agency Sales, Hugh McGoran
Chief Scientist, Mike Brown
General Counsel and Chief Privacy Officer, Christiana L. Lin, age 41, $751,780 total compensation
Chief Research Officer, Josh Chasin
Senior Director Marketing Communications, Andrew Lipsman
Senior Director, Video and Cross-Media products, Tania Yuki
Search Evangelist and Product Management, Eli Goodman
Auditors: Ernst & Young LLP

LOCATIONS

HQ: comScore, Inc.
11950 Democracy Dr., Ste. 600, Reston, VA 20190
Phone: 703-438-2000   Fax: 703-438-2051
Web: www.comscore.com

2010 Sales

	$ mil.	% of total
US	142.3	81
Europe	17.3	10
Canada	8.0	5
Latin America	5.4	3
Asia	2.0	1
Total	**175.0**	**100**

COMPETITORS

Arbitron	Kantar Group
Coremetrics	Nielsen Holdings
Dynamic Logic	Nielsen Media Research
GfK	Nielsen Mobile
Google	Synovate
Harris Interactive	TNS Custom
Hitwise	ValueClick
IMS Health	Webtrends
Ipsos	WPP

HISTORICAL FINANCIALS

Company Type: Public

Income Statement

FYE: December 31

	REVENUE ($ mil.)	NET INCOME ($ mil.)	NET PROFIT MARGIN	EMPLOYEES
12/10	175.0	(1.6)	—	920
12/09	127.7	4.0	3.1%	593
12/08	117.4	25.2	21.5%	581
12/07	87.2	19.3	22.1%	452
12/06	66.3	5.7	8.6%	377
Annual Growth	**27.5%**	**—**	**—**	**25.0%**

2010 Year-End Financials

Debt ratio: 4.8%
Return on equity: —
Cash ($ mil.): 33.7
Current ratio: 1.06
Long-term debt ($ mil.): 8.0
No. of shares (mil.): 31.5
Dividends
  Yield: —
  Payout: —
Market value ($ mil.): 704.2

	STOCK PRICE ($) FY Close	P/E High/Low		PER SHARE ($) Earnings	Dividends	Book Value
12/10	22.34	—	—	(0.05)	0.00	5.26
12/09	17.55	151	57	0.13	0.00	4.87
12/08	12.75	38	8	0.83	0.00	4.64
12/07	32.63	48	22	0.88	0.00	3.68
Annual Growth	**(11.9%)**	**—**	**—**	**—**	**—**	**12.7%**

Comverge

Comverge seeks a convergence of communications enabling the lights to stay on. The company provides demand management software and systems to electric utilities and other energy suppliers and sells automated meters and related equipment with communications links. The company's products are used by more than 500 utilities and energy providers, including PEPCO, as well as some 2,100 commercial and industrial customers, such as Barnes and Noble and Foot Locker. Its products include software and hardware that help control energy load, read meters remotely, manage billing, and detect theft and outages. The company has installed about 5 million meters in residences.

Comverge not only sells its demand management products to utilities and grid operators, but also provides capacity itself where it signs long-term contracts to actively manage electrical demand for clients. By using products and services such as Comverge's, customers can avoid building costly new power generation facilities by instead maximizing the efficiency of their existing infrastructure.

The company's Residential Business segment, which provides utilities with energy management networks for use by residential and commercial end users, accounts for 57% of sales. The Commercial and Industrial segment, which provides energy management products for utilities and independent systems operators that serve large enterprise customers, accounts for 43% of sales.

Revenue for the company as a whole was up 21% year-over-year in 2010, though it struggled with an annual net loss that year and the previous two years. Comverge has an accumulated deficit of more than $215 million.

An increase in turnkey programs — when the customers own the intelligent energy management networks they use — was an important factor in the company's higher revenue in 2010. The Commercial and Industrial segment contributed to the year's revenue uptick with stronger sales in the open market — when capacity is sold to independent system operators — as well as virtual peaking capacity (VPC) programs, through which Comverge provides energy capacity to its customers during peak periods by remotely managing high-energy consuming devices.

To build more business Comverge is pursuing an investment strategy that has spent more than $20 million from 2001 to 2010 solely on research and development and an acquisition strategy that focuses on companies that serve specific niches and customer segments of the industry. The company has partnerships with Digi International, Elster, Itron, and others.

EXECUTIVES

Chairman, Alec G. Dreyer, age 53
President, CEO, and Director, R. Blake Young, age 52
EVP Sales and Chief Marketing Officer, Chris Camino
EVP and COO, Steve Moffitt
EVP Program Delivery, Edward J. (Ed) Myszka, age 48, $509,942 total compensation
EVP, CFO, and Director, Michael D. (Mike) Picchi, age 44, $518,274 total compensation
VP Regulatory Affairs, Eric C. Woychik
VP Regulatory, Markets, and Government Affairs, Jeff Bladen
VP Engineering, Chris Quire

VP and Corporate Controller, John Waterworth, age 33
VP Business Development, Alternative Energy Resources Group, John Rossi
VP Risk Management and Administration, Mark Schaefer, age 43
CTO and SVP Utility, Arthur (Bud) Vos IV, age 36
SVP, General Counsel, and Secretary, Matthew H. Smith, age 36, $273,721 total compensation
Executive Director Sales Northeastern US and Canadian Provinces (New Brunswick, Newfoundland, Nova S, Bill Mayer
Executive Director Sales Southeastern US, Blake Morrison
Senior Director, Product Management, Howard Ng
SVP Utility Sales, D. John Gagnon
Manager Communications, Kristin Mastrandrea
Director Marketing, Chris Neff
Executive Director Sales Western US and Canadian Provinces (Alberta and British Columbia) and Centra, David (Dave) Lentsch
Executive Director Sales Midwest and Canadian Provinces, Dave Hyland
SVP Business Development, Information and Engineering Department, Enerwise Group, David Ellis
SVP Major Accounts, George Hunt
Manager Corporate Communications, Christina Kelly
Auditors: PricewaterhouseCoopers LLP

LOCATIONS

HQ: Comverge, Inc.
120 Eagle Rock Rd., Ste. 190, East Hanover, NJ 07936
Phone: 973-884-5970   Fax: 973-884-3504
Web: www.comverge.com

PRODUCTS/OPERATIONS

2010 Sales

	$ mil.	% of total
Residential business	67.6	57
Commercial & industrial business	51.8	43
Total	**119.4**	**100**

COMPETITORS

Cooper Industries	Itron
EnerNOC	SmartSynch
ESCO Technologies	
Honeywell International	

HISTORICAL FINANCIALS

Company Type: Public

Income Statement

FYE: December 31

	REVENUE ($ mil.)	NET INCOME ($ mil.)	NET PROFIT MARGIN	EMPLOYEES
12/10	119.4	(31.4)	—	562
12/09	98.8	(31.7)	—	440
12/08	77.2	(94.1)	—	385
12/07	55.2	(6.6)	—	381
12/06	33.9	(6.2)	—	117
Annual Growth	**37.0%**	**—**	**—**	**48.0%**

2010 Year-End Financials

Debt ratio: 47.2%
Return on equity: —
Cash ($ mil.): 7.8
Current ratio: 1.94
Long-term debt ($ mil.): 21.8
No. of shares (mil.): 25.3
Dividends
  Yield: —
  Payout: —
Market value ($ mil.): 175.0

	STOCK PRICE ($) FY Close	P/E High/Low	PER SHARE ($) Earnings	Dividends	Book Value
12/10	6.91	— —	(1.27)	0.00	1.82
12/09	11.24	— —	(1.45)	0.00	2.95
12/08	4.90	— —	(4.45)	0.00	3.09
12/07	31.49	— —	(0.46)	0.00	7.82
Annual Growth	(39.7%)	— —	—	—	(38.5%)

Concho

Concho Resources has more than a hunch that a lucrative resource lies under its feet in Southeastern New Mexico and West Texas. The company explores and develops properties (about 375,000 net acres), located primarily in the Permian Basin region, in which it produces oil and natural gas. It also owns properties in North Dakota and Arkansas. About two-thirds of the company's 323.4 million barrels of proved reserves is crude oil, while the rest is natural gas. Concho Resources gets the bulk of its sales from crude oil. Regional refiner Navajo Refining Company accounted for 32% of the company's total sales in 2010.

The company has been focused on expanding its holdings through medium- and large-sized acquisitions. To boost its Permian Basin holdings, in 2008 Concho Resources spent $585 million to buy Henry Petroleum and in late 2009 it acquired two plays in the Wolfberry play in the Permian Basin for $260 million. In a major move, in 2010 the company also acquired Marbob Energy (which had operations located in the Permian Basin) for about $1.2 billion. The purchase added 76 million barrels of oil equivalent and a net daily production of 14,000 barrels of oil equivalent.

To free up cash to help pay for its expansion, in 2010 the company sold non-core Permian Basin oil and natural gas properties to Legacy Reserves for $103 million. In 2011 it also sold Bakken assets to Linn Energy for $196 million.

The acquisitions, and a 46% increase in production, coupled with high oil prices, helped to lift Concho Resources' revenues and income dramatically in 2010.

EXECUTIVES

Chairman, CEO, and President, Timothy A. Leach, age 51, $2,635,465 total compensation

VP Exploration and Land, Matthew G. Hyde, age 55, $1,141,352 total compensation

VP and Chief Accounting Officer, Don O. McCormack, age 50

VP, CFO, and Treasurer, Darin G. Holderness, age 47, $1,002,033 total compensation

SVP, General Counsel, and Secretary, C. William Giraud

SVP and COO, E. Joseph Wright, age 51, $1,145,155 total compensation

SVP and Chief of Staff, Jack F. Harper, age 39, $1,171,896 total compensation

Manager Investor Relations, Toffee McAlister

Auditors: Grant Thornton LLP

LOCATIONS

HQ: Concho Resources Inc.
550 W. Texas Ave., Ste. 100, Midland, TX 79701
Phone: 432-683-7443   **Fax:** 432-683-7441
Web: www.conchoresources.com/index.html

PRODUCTS/OPERATIONS

2010 Sales

	% of total
Navajo Refining	32
ConocoPhillips	14
DCP Midstream	12
Plains Marketing and Transportation	11
Other customers	31
Total	**100**

2010 Sales

	$ mil.	$ of total
Oil	767.2	79
Natural gas	205.4	21
Total	**972.6**	**100**

COMPETITORS

Apache
Brigham Exploration
Chevron
ConocoPhillips
Encore Energy
Exxon Mobil
Legacy Reserves
Marathon Petroleum
Occidental Petroleum
SandRidge Energy
Vanguard Natural Resources
Whiting Petroleum

HISTORICAL FINANCIALS

Company Type: Public

Income Statement

FYE: December 31

	REVENUE ($ mil.)	NET INCOME ($ mil.)	NET PROFIT MARGIN	EMPLOYEES
12/10	972.6	204.4	21.0%	443
12/09	544.4	(9.8)	—	284
12/08	533.8	278.7	52.2%	245
12/07	294.3	25.4	8.6%	113
12/06	198.3	19.7	9.9%	80
Annual Growth	48.8%	79.5%	—	53.4%

2010 Year-End Financials

Debt ratio: 70.0%
Return on equity: 8.6%
Cash ($ mil.): 0.4
Current ratio: 0.65
Long-term debt ($ mil.): 1,668.5
No. of shares (mil.): 102.8
Dividends
Yield: —
Payout: —
Market value ($ mil.): 9,013.4

	STOCK PRICE ($) FY Close	P/E High/Low	PER SHARE ($) Earnings	Dividends	Book Value
12/10	87.67	41 20	2.18	0.00	23.19
12/09	44.90	— —	(0.12)	0.00	15.56
12/08	22.82	12 4	3.46	0.00	15.64
12/07	20.61	59 31	0.38	0.00	10.24
Annual Growth	62.0%	— —	79.0%	—	31.3%

Conmed Healthcare

Because convicts need medical care too! Conmed Healthcare Management provides contract health care services to county jails. The company has contracts to provide cost-effective basic and ancillary services to almost 40 adult county jails in seven states — Arizona, Kansas, Maryland, Oklahoma, Oregon, Virginia, and Washington. Subsidiary Correctional Mental Health Services (CMHS), bought in 2008, provides behavioral health services and evaluations. Conmed staffs doctors, nurses, dentists, psychiatrists, pharmacists, social workers, and technicians to work at its contracted facilities. The company was founded in 1984, went public in 2007, and agreed to be taken private by Ayelet Investments in 2011.

The $57 million transaction by Ayelet Investments, an investment firm controlled by Dr. James Desnick, is supported by another equity firm, Levine Leichtman Capital Partners. Desnick already owns a 9% stake in the company through his Medical Management of America entity.

Conmed provides health care services such as acute and general care, dentistry, dialysis, IV therapy, laboratory services, pharmacy services, physical therapy and X-rays. It arranges and contracts with outside hospitals when surgery is necessary. The company either performs its services within the jails or subcontracts them to be performed outside the facility, such as emergency room visits. However, due to security and cost considerations, it tries to provide most services within the jails.

The market for contracted health care services at correctional centers is relatively small, with fewer than 10 major players, and, unlike most, is publicly traded. While some competitors serve state and federal prison systems, Conmed is focused on the smaller operations at county jails. However, most counties provide and staff their own health services at county-run facilities.

The company's contracts are primarily multi-year, fixed-cost contracts with annual escalations, caps on out-of-facility health care and catastrophic expenses to limit exposure, and often contain adjustments on a per diem basis for changes as inmate population fluctuates. In contrast, the majority of rival America Service Group's contracts are population-based, making it dependent on overcrowded jails. Conmed's top two contracts are with the Baltimore County Detention Center in its home state of Maryland and at the Pima County Detention Center in Arizona. These two contracts accounted for a quarter of revenues and more than 20% of profit in 2010. It landed four new contracts since 2009 that boosted sales almost 15% in 2010 and helped it to get out of the red and record a profit for the year.

The company's growth strategy calls for winning new contracts in its existing states and expanding to new states, primarily across the south, where there are about 300 jails with more than 250 beds each, a metric that matches Conmed's service capabilities. It would also like to sign more of its existing facilities up for behavioral health care services through CMHS.

Conmed's largest shareholder is venture capitalist and company director John Pappajohn, with a 20% stake. The bankrupt investment firm Lehman Brothers owns another 20%. The company is not related to medical equipment firm CONMED Corporation.

EXECUTIVES

Chairman and CEO, Richard W. Turner, age 63
EVP and President, Correctional Mental Health Services, LLC, Stephen B. Goldberg
VP Human Resources, McKinley G. Littlejohn
VP Quality Assurance and Standards, Lawrence E. Delbridge
VP Strategic Development, Larry F. Doll
Chief Medical Officer, Robert Younes
SVP, CFO, and Secretary, Thomas W. Fry, age 65
SVP, Site Administration, Ronald H. (Ron) Grubman
Quality Assurance Director and Operations Manager, Correctional Mental Health Services, Scott Kesson
Medical Director, Correctional Mental Health Services, Johannes Dalmasy
Auditors: McGladrey & Pullen, LLP

LOCATIONS

HQ: Conmed Healthcare Management, Inc.
7250 Parkway Dr., Ste. 400, Hanover, MD 21076
Phone: 410-567-5520   **Fax:** 410-712-4760
Web: www.conmedinc.com

COMPETITORS

Corizon
Correctional Medical Services
Corrections Corporation of America
GEO Group
MHM Services
PHS Correctional Healthcare
Wexford Health

HISTORICAL FINANCIALS

Company Type: Public

Income Statement   FYE: December 31

	REVENUE ($ mil.)	NET INCOME ($ mil.)	NET PROFIT MARGIN	EMPLOYEES
12/10	60.7	1.5	2.5%	570
12/09	52.8	—	—	922
12/08	40.6	(0.9)	—	444
12/07	24.6	(1.8)	—	499
Annual Growth	35.1%	—	—	4.5%

2010 Year-End Financials

Debt ratio: —   No. of shares (mil.): 12.8
Return on equity: 8.5%   Dividends
Cash ($ mil.): 13.3   Yield: —
Current ratio: 2.33   Payout: —
Long-term debt ($ mil.): —   Market value ($ mil.): 39.2

	STOCK PRICE ($) FY Close	P/E High/Low		PER SHARE ($) Earnings	Dividends	Book Value
12/10	3.05	41	30	0.09	0.00	1.42
12/09	3.07	—	—	(0.00)	0.00	1.23
12/08	2.10	—	—	(0.08)	0.00	1.20
12/07	2.90	—	—	(0.17)	0.00	1.24
00/00	3.30	—	—	(2.40)	0.00	4.74
Annual Growth	(2.0%)	—	—	—	—	(26.1%)

Conrad Industries

Like the story of Noah's Ark, Conrad Industries starts anew by rescuing the things its likes. Conrad Industries builds, converts, and repairs small to midsized vessels for commercial and government customers. More than half of the company's work is in constructing barges, liftboats, towboats, and tugboats. Its boat-conversion projects mainly involve lengthening vessel mid-bodies or modifying vessels to perform different functions. Conrad Industries operates shipyards along the Gulf Coast, in Louisiana and Texas. Conrad also offers fabrication of modular components, used on offshore drilling rigs, as well as storage and offloading of vessels. Established in 1948, the company is led by the founding Conrad family.

EXECUTIVES

VP and COO, Terry T. Frickey
VP, CFO, and Director, Cecil A. Hernandez, age 51
Co-Chairman, J. Parker Conrad, age 92
Co-Chairman, President and CEO, John P. (Johnny) Conrad Jr., age 65
Director, Marketing and Sales, Gary Lipely
General Manager, Repair, Jim McElroy
General Manager, New Construction, Brian Barbier
Safety and Personnel Director, Shane Alfred
General Manager, Orange Shipbuilding, Brett Wolbrink
Auditors: Darnall, Sikes, Gardes & Frederick

LOCATIONS

HQ: Conrad Industries, Inc.
1100 Brashear Ave., Ste. 200, Morgan City, LA 70381-1501
Phone: 985-702-0195   **Fax:** 985-702-1126
Web: www.conradindustries.com

PRODUCTS/OPERATIONS

Selected Services

Vessel construction
  Large and small deck cargo barges
  Lift boats
  Offshore supply vessels
  Offshore tug boats
  Push boats and towboats
  Single and double hull tank barges
Repair and conversion
  Conversions
  Dry dock repairs
  Underwater and topside repairs

COMPETITORS

Bollinger Shipyards   Quality Shipyards
General Dynamics   RPC
Northrop Grumman   Vigor Shipyards

HISTORICAL FINANCIALS

Company Type: Public

Income Statement   FYE: December 31

	REVENUE ($ mil.)	NET INCOME ($ mil.)	NET PROFIT MARGIN	EMPLOYEES
12/08	191.1	23.0	12.0%	539
12/07	168.5	19.2	11.4%	498
12/06	121.8	5.9	4.8%	520
12/05	64.6	0.1	0.2%	384
12/04	37.1	(7.1)	—	275
Annual Growth	50.7%	—	—	18.3%

2008 Year-End Financials

Debt ratio: 8.5%   No. of shares (mil.): 6.4
Return on equity: 40.3%   Dividends
Cash ($ mil.): 17.5   Yield: —
Current ratio: 2.09   Payout: —
Long-term debt ($ mil.): 4.8   Market value ($ mil.): 33.8

	STOCK PRICE ($) FY Close	P/E High/Low		PER SHARE ($) Earnings	Dividends	Book Value
12/08	5.25	4	2	3.29	0.00	8.86
12/07	15.00	7	2	2.63	0.00	6.75
12/06	6.10	8	2	0.81	0.00	3.77
12/05	1.80	126	57	0.02	0.00	2.85
Annual Growth	42.9%	—	—	447.9%	—	45.9%

Constant Contact

Constant Contact makes sure businesses never lose touch with their most important customers. The company provides small businesses with Web-based marketing software and services for managing e-mail campaigns and online surveys. Its offerings include easy-to-use tools for creating, implementing, tracking, managing, and analyzing marketing materials. The company's customers include retailers, restaurants, and other businesses, as well as non-profit organizations, alumni associations, and churches; two-thirds of its clients have fewer than 10 employees. Constant Contact claims more than 350,000 customers for its e-mail marketing products.

The company focuses its own marketing efforts on small businesses and organizations, most of which pay a fixed, monthly subscription fee based on the number of e-mail addresses in their account. Though the majority of its customers tailor their own campaigns using Constant Contact's tools, the company also provides professional marketing and survey creation services. Towards the end of 2009, the company released an event-marketing product that lets customers promote and manage events, track registrations, and collect payments online. The following year the company added social media marketing and notification tools

Subscriptions to its e-mail marketing tools typically cost between $15-$150/month, which allows Constant Contact to serve a market that is typically ignored by larger CRM and marketing software competitors such as Oracle, SAP, salesforce.com, and others. The company has seen rapid organic growth in recent years, with its customer base growing from 25,000 in 2004 to some 400,000 in 2010.

Because of its rapid growth, Constant Contact's sales have risen quickly. In 2009 its sales were up by 48% over 2008. Expenses have gone up equally fast, as the company has had to invest in additional hosting capacity and customer support personnel. In addition, the company had higher credit card fees due to more billing transactions. It trimmed its net loss to $1.3 million in 2009, from $2.1 million in 2008 and $8.2 million in 2007.

The company relies on its more than 5,000 strategic partners (which include service providers, software firms, and financial services companies) to generate leads and sales, as well as through its own marketing efforts. Partners include Network Solutions and American Express.

In 2011 Constant Contact added social CRM capabilities with the acquisition of Bantam Networks LLC for $15 million in cash. Its Bantam Live application gives small businesses a place to launch and monitor customer engagement campaigns across social media platforms. In 2010 the company acquired NutshellMail, giving its customers a tool for engaging social media networks from their e-mail inbox. With the acquisition of Menlo Park, California-based NutshellMail, Constant Contact reported it would open an office in the San Francisco Bay area.

EXECUTIVES

Chairman, President, and CEO, Gail F. Goodman, age 50, $887,549 total compensation
EVP, CFO, and Treasurer, Harpreet S. Grewal, age 44
VP and Chief Marketing Officer, Nancie G. Freitas, age 49, $523,833 total compensation

VP; General Manager, Event Marketing, Christopher M. Litster, age 41

VP and Chief Human Resources Officer, Robert D. (Bob) Nicoson, age 60

VP Constant Contact Labs, Daniel A. (Dan) Richards, age 51

VP and General Counsel, Robert P. (Bob) Nault, age 47, $551,887 total compensation

CTO, Stefan Piesche

SVP Customer Operations, Thomas C. (Tom) Howd, age 51

SVP Product Strategy, Ellen M. Brezniak, age 52, $508,266 total compensation

SVP Engineering and Operations, John J. Walsh Jr., age 46

SVP Corporate Strategy, Development, and Innovation, Eric S. Groves, age 47

Auditors: PricewaterhouseCoopers LLP

LOCATIONS

HQ: Constant Contact, Inc.
1601 Trapelo Rd., Ste. 329, Waltham, MA 02451
Phone: 781-472-8100   **Fax:** 781-472-8101
Web: www.constantcontact.com

PRODUCTS/OPERATIONS

Selected Products

Contact list management tools
E-mail campaign creation interface (Campaign Creation Wizard)
E-mail delivery management
E-mail message templates
E-mail tracking and reporting tools
Event marketing
Image hosting services
Security and privacy compliance services
Social media marketing platform (Flowtown)
Social media notification tool (NutshellMail)
Survey tools

COMPETITORS

Active Network	Microsoft
Alterian	Responsys
Evite	Silverpop
ExactTarget	Topica
Experian CheetahMail	VerticalResponse
Google	Vistaprint
Lyris	Yahoo!
MarketTools	yesmail

HISTORICAL FINANCIALS

Company Type: Public

Income Statement

FYE: December 31

	REVENUE ($ mil.)	NET INCOME ($ mil.)	NET PROFIT MARGIN	EMPLOYEES
12/10	174.2	2.9	1.7%	734
12/09	129.1	(1.3)	—	625
12/08	87.3	(2.1)	—	456
12/07	50.5	(8.3)	—	318
12/06	27.6	(7.8)	—	275
Annual Growth	58.5%	—	—	27.8%

2010 Year-End Financials

Debt ratio: —
Return on equity: 2.3%
Cash ($ mil.): 32.9
Current ratio: 3.31
Long-term debt ($ mil.): —
No. of shares (mil.): 29.3
Dividends
  Yield: —
  Payout: —
Market value ($ mil.): 909.2

	STOCK PRICE ($) FY Close	P/E High/Low	PER SHARE ($) Earnings	Dividends	Book Value
12/10	30.99	321 164	0.10	0.00	4.30
12/09	16.00	— —	(0.04)	0.00	3.70
12/08	13.25	— —	(0.07)	0.00	3.56
12/07	21.50	— —	(0.97)	0.00	3.42
Annual Growth	13.0%	— —	—	—	8.0%

CoreSite

CoreSite Realty leases data center space to those with data center needs. The real estate investment trust (REIT) owns, develops, and operates these specialized facilities, which require enough power, security, and network interconnection to handle often complex IT operations. Its portfolio includes about 10 operating data center facilities, as well as one under construction and one under development. These properties comprise more than 2 million rentable sq. ft. and are located in major US tech hubs. Tenants include enterprise organizations, communications service providers, media and content companies, government agencies, and schools. CoreSite Realty went public via a 2010 IPO.

The US GSA is one of the company's largest tenants. Other major customers based on rent include Facebook, Intermap Network Services, NBCUniversal, and Verizon Communications.

The properties in CoreSite's portfolio are strategically located in major metropolitan cities known for being high-tech hotbeds, such as Boston, Chicago, Los Angeles, New York City, and the San Francisco Bay and Northern Virginia areas. Data centers, especially outsourced ones (which are cheaper than in-house ones) are growing in these cities and others because they meet specific technology needs with specialized infrastructures that supply multiple network connectivity, uninterruptible power, backup generators, cooling equipment, fire suppression systems, and physical security.

CoreSite plans to use the proceeds of its IPO to develop and redevelop additional data centers and to pay down debt. The company hopes to capitalize on demand that is outpacing supply for outsourced data centers in these markets. Supply of new data center facilities has been hampered in part by industry consolidation and lack of capital to develop additional space. CoreSite intends to market its existing portfolio — coupled with its development capabilities and the network interconnection services it offers — to attract more quality tenants.

The company's first data center was purchased in 2000. Acquisitions of these properties throughout its history have been funded and held through real estate funds affiliated with global private equity firm The Carlyle Group.

EXECUTIVES

President, CEO, and Director, Thomas M. (Tom) Ray, age 48, $540,000 total compensation

CFO, Jeffrey S. Finnin, age 47

SVP Information Technology, Charles D. (Chuck) Price, age 44

SVP Operations, CoreSite Services, Dominic M. Tobin, age 57

SVP Sales, Christopher M. (Chris) Bair, age 42

SVP Marketing and Business Development, David W. Dunn, age 31, $429,310 total compensation

SVP Capital Markets, Robert M. (Rob) Sistek, age 34

SVP, Acquisitions, Robert K. (Rob) Rockwood, age 50, $490,028 total compensation

General Counsel, Derek McCandless, age 39

SVP Data Centers, Billie R. Haggard, age 45

Auditors: KPMG LLP

LOCATIONS

HQ: CoreSite Realty Corporation
1050 17th St., Ste. 800, Denver, CO 80265
Phone: 866-777-2673   **Fax:** 303-405-1011
Web: www.coresite.com

COMPETITORS

Brandywine Realty	Mission West
Digital Realty	Properties
DuPont Fabros	SAVVIS
Equinix	Telx Group
Equity Office	Terremark Worldwide

HISTORICAL FINANCIALS

Company Type: Public

Income Statement

FYE: December 31

	REVENUE ($ mil.)	NET INCOME ($ mil.)	NET PROFIT MARGIN	EMPLOYEES
12/10	73.9	(4.9)	—	179
12/09	28.8	(7.0)	—	155
12/08	15.6	(13.9)	—	0
12/07	10.3	(1.9)	—	0
Annual Growth	92.9%	—	—	15.5%

2010 Year-End Financials

Debt ratio: 53.8%
Return on equity: —
Cash ($ mil.): 86.2
Current ratio: 3.72
Long-term debt ($ mil.): 124.9
No. of shares (mil.): 19.6
Dividends
  Yield: 1.0%
  Payout: —
Market value ($ mil.): 267.9

	STOCK PRICE ($) FY Close	P/E High/Low	PER SHARE ($) Earnings	Dividends	Book Value
12/10	13.64	— —	(0.17)	0.13	11.82
Annual Growth	—	— —	—	—	—

Corinthian Colleges

Corinthian Colleges believes more in marketable skills than in ivory towers. One of the largest for-profit, post-secondary education companies in North America, Corinthian focuses educating on career-oriented students. It has more than 110,000 students enrolled in about 100 schools in the US and nearly 20 schools in Ontario. Corinthian's institutions operate under the Everest College, WyoTech (for automotive training), and Heald College brand names. The majority of Corinthian's students are enrolled in associate's degree or diploma programs, but the schools also offer bachelor's and master's degrees. Additionally, Corinthian offers some 20 online degrees through Everest College.

The company offers degrees and diplomas in health care, business, technology, hospitality management, criminal justice, medical assisting, and court reporting. Corinthian also operates several training centers that provide ongoing professional education and short-term certificate programs.

Corinthian has been significantly increasing its online course offerings; in 2010 online learning at the company grew by approximately 45% from the previous year to some 24,000 students and about 325 courses. Along with increasing its online presence, Corinthian grows by acquisition (it has bought about 85 campuses since it was founded in 1995) and by establishing new campuses.

The company acquired Heald College in early 2010 for $395 million, adding approximately 13,000 new students. The regional institution operates about a dozen campuses in Northern California, Hawaii, and Oregon.

Unlike most other businesses, the tumultuous economy has helped Corinthian's bottom line. People who have been laid off for an extended period of time often head back to school in an effort to sharpen their marketable skills or to switch careers entirely. Corinthian actually began losing money when the economy was still in good shape and unemployment was low in 2007. That, combined with an aggressive growth strategy and subsequent outlay of millions of dollars, spelled financial trouble for the for-profit educator. It wasn't until the economy tanked, the company closed some underperforming campuses, and enrollment began to climb concurrent with unemployment rates, that Corinthian's income also began its ascent back to profitability.

Federally funded student financial aid programs account for the majority of the company's revenues. Newly proposed regulations by the Department of Education requiring that for-profit schools pass certain educational thresholds have the potential to affect Corinthian's financial results if its campuses fail to meet the new, proposed standards. In response (and because they are more likely to default on loans) the company dropped enrollment of non-high school graduates who can demonstrate an ability to benefit (ATB) at its Everest and WyoTech institutions in late 2010. ATB students (who have to pass an admission test to enter the school, hence the "ability to benefit" moniker) accounted for about 15% of Corinthian Colleges' admissions in 2010.

Peter Waller, who had served as Corinthian's president and COO since 2006, was named CEO in 2009. He replaced Jack Massimino, who assumed the chairman position.

EXECUTIVES

Chairman and CEO, Jack D. Massimino, age 62, $3,032,703 total compensation
President, Heald College, Eeva Deshon
President and COO, Everest Florida Division, Janis Y. Schoonmaker, age 54
EVP Legislative and Regulatory Affairs, Mark L. Pelesh, age 57, $1,289,635 total compensation
EVP and Chief Business Development Officer, David A. Poldoian, age 58
EVP Marketing, William B. (Bill) Buchanan, age 45
EVP and CFO, Robert C. (Bob) Owen, age 50
EVP, General Counsel, and Secretary, Stan A. Mortensen, age 44
EVP Operations, Beth A. Wilson, age 59, $1,516,676 total compensation
VP Public Affairs Communications, Kent Jenkins Jr.
Vice Chairman, Paul R. St. Pierre, age 66
SVP Investor Relations and Corporate Communications, Anna Marie Dunlap
SVP and CIO, Carmella Cassetta
Group President, West, Robert D. Bosic
Group President, East, Mike Benvenuti

Group President, Online, Stephen (Steve) Quattrociocchi, age 48
SVP Marketing, Roger Van Duinen
Division President, Everest Canada, Rupert Altschuler
Chief Academic Officer, Richard B. Simpson
SVP Human Resources, Jim Wade
Auditors: Ernst & Young LLP

LOCATIONS

HQ: Corinthian Colleges, Inc.
6 Hutton Centre Dr., Ste. 400, Santa Ana, CA 92707
Phone: 714-427-3000   **Fax:** 714-724-5111
Web: www.cci.edu

PRODUCTS/OPERATIONS

2010 Sales

	$ mil.	% of total
Revenues from unaffiliated customers		
US operations	1,682.5	95
Canadian operations	81.3	5
Total	**1,763.8**	**100**

Selected Subsidiaries

Corinthian Schools, Inc.
Eton Education, Inc.
Florida Metropolitan University, Inc.
Grand Rapids Educational Center, Inc.
Pegasus Education, Inc.
Rhodes Colleges, Inc.
Sequoia Education, Inc.
Titan Schools, Inc.
Ward Stone College, Inc.

Selected Programs

Diploma programs
 Aircraft frame and power plant maintenance technology
 Automotive and diesel technology
 Electronics
 Information technology
 Massage therapy
 Medical assisting
 Medical insurance billing and coding
 Pharmacy technician
 Surgical technology
Degree programs
 Accounting
 Business administration
 Computer information technology
 Court reporting
 Criminal justice
 Film and video
 Hospitality
 Marketing
 Medical assisting
 Paralegal

COMPETITORS

Apollo Group
Argosy Education
Capella Education
Cardean Learning Group
Career Education
Concorde Colleges
DeVry
eCollege.com
Education Mana

EVCI Career Colleges
ITT Educational
Kaplan
Laureate Education
Lincoln Educational Services
The College Network
UTI

HISTORICAL FINANCIALS

Company Type: Public

Income Statement

FYE: June 30

	REVENUE ($ mil.)	NET INCOME ($ mil.)	NET PROFIT MARGIN	EMPLOYEES
06/11	1,868.8	(111.2)	—	16,600
06/10	1,763.8	146.0	8.3%	15,900
06/09	1,307.8	68.8	5.3%	11,100
06/08	1,068.7	21.3	2.0%	10,000
06/07	933.2	7.2	0.8%	8,950
Annual Growth	**19.0%**	**—**	**—**	**16.7%**

2011 Year-End Financials

Debt ratio: 58.5%
Return on equity: —
Cash ($ mil.): 107.4
Current ratio: 1.89
Long-term debt ($ mil.): 330.4

No. of shares (mil.): 84.6
Dividends
 Yield: —
 Payout: —
Market value ($ mil.): 360.4

	STOCK PRICE ($) FY Close	P/E High/Low		PER SHARE ($) Earnings	Dividends	Book Value
06/11	4.26	—	—	(1.30)	0.00	6.68
06/10	9.85	12	6	1.65	0.00	7.84
06/09	16.93	28	14	0.79	0.00	5.94
06/08	11.61	73	26	0.25	0.00	4.96
06/07	16.43	205	131	0.08	0.00	4.56
Annual Growth	**(28.6%)**	**—**	**—**	**—**	**—**	**10.0%**

Cornerstone OnDemand

At Cornerstone OnDemand class is always in session. The company provides on-demand workplace learning tools in a variety of subjects including enterprise social networking, performance management, and succession planning. Its training programs are meant to improve employee performance, communication, and collaboration, as well as foster professional development and assess employee skills. Cornerstone OnDemand's clients include multi-national corporations, public-sector organizations, higher education institutions, and not-for-profit entities. The company went public in 2011 through a $137 million IPO; CEO Adam Miller holds 15% of its stock.

The company makes most of its money through the sale of multi-year agreements (usually three years) with clients who have included Barclays Bank, Kelly Services, and Virgin Media. Cornerstone OnDemand uses a Software-as-a-Service (SAAS) model in which software applications are hosted and managed by a vendor (in this case Cornerstone OnDemand) and sold to customers via the Internet. Cornerstone OnDemand sells worldwide through direct sales teams in North America and Europe and through global distributor agreements.

Though multi-year agreements offer Cornerstone OnDemand a certain level of financial stability by guaranteeing that income for a certain period of time, it also means the company has a long sales cycle and must drum up new customers on a regular basis to bolster its income during the three-year contract cycle. Cornerstone OnDemand has experienced financial losses every year since its inception and expects to keep incurring losses as it continues to develop and expand the business.

Cornerstone OnDemand intends to use the funds from its IPO to do just that. It will further its growth strategy of adding new platforms and services to attract new customers (especially small businesses, a market it has not yet tapped), as well as to strengthen its sales channels in Europe, the Middle East, and Africa (EMEA) and the Asia-Pacific region. The company also intends to target new markets and grow in the markets in which it already operates. It currently serves the business services, energy, financial services and insurance, health care, higher education, manufacturing and automotive, retail and travel, and technology and media industries. It most recently entered the public sector market and intends to expand its operations in that area.

Cornerstone OnDemand was formed in 1999 under the name CyberU Inc. and operated as such until 2005 when it changed its name to Cornerstone OnDemand.

EXECUTIVES

CFO, Perry A. Wallack, age 42, $309,375 total compensation

President, CEO, and Director, Adam L. Miller, age 42, $378,125 total compensation

EVP, Strategic Accounts, Steven D. Seymour, age 42, $309,375 total compensation

VP, Sales, David J. (Dave) Carter, age 48, $325,205 total compensation

VP, Global Account Services, Frank A. Ricciardi, age 40

VP, Alliances and Strategy, David L. Somers, age 39

VP, Marketing, Julie Norquist Roy, age 44

VP, Consulting Services, Kirsten Maas Helvey, age 41

VP Technology, Ed Garber

CTO, Mark Goldin, age 50

Public Relations, Michelle Haworth

General Manager, Europe, Middle East and Africa, Vincent Belliveau, age 35, $350,267 total compensation

Auditors: PricewaterhouseCoopers LLP

LOCATIONS

HQ: Cornerstone OnDemand, Inc.
 1601 Cloverfield Blvd., Ste. 620 South, Santa Monica, CA 90404
Phone: 310-752-0200   **Fax:** 310-752-0199
Web: www.cornerstoneondemand.com

PRODUCTS/OPERATIONS

Selected Industries Served
Business Services
Energy
Financial Services and Insurance
Health Care
Higher Education
Manufacturing and Automotive
Public Sector
Retail and Travel
Technology and Media

COMPETITORS

Axel Springer	Learning Tree
Canterbury Consulting	New Horizons Worldwide
Cengage Learning	Oracle
Demand Media	Saba Software
Halogen Software	SAP
ITC Learning	SuccessFactors
ITT Educational	SumTotal
Jive Software	Taleo

HISTORICAL FINANCIALS

Company Type: Public

Income Statement

FYE: December 31

	REVENUE ($ mil.)	NET INCOME ($ mil.)	NET PROFIT MARGIN	EMPLOYEES
12/10	43.7	(48.4)	—	327
12/09	29.3	(8.4)	—	280
12/08	19.6	(10.2)	—	185
12/07	11.0	(5.7)	—	0
Annual Growth	58.4%	—	—	32.9%

2010 Year-End Financials

Debt ratio: —
Return on equity: —
Cash ($ mil.): 7.1
Current ratio: 0.65
Long-term debt ($ mil.): 6.6

No. of shares (mil.): —
Dividends
 Yield: —
 Payout: —
Market value ($ mil.): —

	STOCK PRICE ($) FY Close	P/E High/Low	PER SHARE ($)		
			Earnings	Dividends	Book Value
Annual Growth	—	— —	—	—	—

Cornerstone Therapeutics

Cornerstone Therapeutics wants to help clear things up for the asthmatic, the infected, and the inflamed. The drug company is focused on developing and commercializing therapeutic products to prevent and treat acute inflammation and other respiratory ailments. Its marketed products include CUROSURF, which is used to treat premature infants with respiratory distress syndrome, antibiotics FACTIVE and SPECTRACEF, and asthma treatment ZYFLO. It also is developing generic drugs through its Aristos Pharmaceuticals subsidiary. The company relies up on third parties to manufacture its marketed products and products in clinical trials. Italian drugmaker Chiesi Farmaceutici owns a majority stake in the company.

During 2010 the company pulled several of its generic products off of the market after receiving FDA notifications that the drugs were not properly approved. It withdrew several drugs containing propoxyphene, as well as some branded products which were caught in the FDA's 2009 market sweep that removed scores of products featuring older drugs in formulations that had never been through clinical trials. While its AlleRx and Hyomax products were not included in the sweep, Cornerstone Therapeutics chose to discontinue those lines.

To replace the drugs it pulled, the company is busily shepherding a handful of respiratory drug candidates through preclinical development, and building up a strong sales force to promote its fully-approved drugs. Cornerstone Therapeutics' sales force targets physicians who treat respiratory diseases, and hospitals with neonatal intensive care units that could stock CUROSURF.

The company built up its current product line through a series of acquisitions and licensing agreements. In mid-2009 the company acquired the North American and select European marketing rights to bronchitis and pneumonia antibiotic

FACTIVE from Oscient Pharmaceuticals for $5 million. Oscient, which was restructuring under bankruptcy protection, had originally licensed the drug from Korean drugmaker LG Life Sciences (part of the LG Group).

The company acquired worldwide rights from Abbott Laboratories for ZYFLO, an immediate-release zileuton that has FDA approval to treat chronic asthma. ZYFLO CR, which is marketed through the firm's direct sales force, has become a major seller.

Cornerstone Therapeutics was formed by the 2008 merger of Critical Therapeutics and privately held respiratory therapy firm Cornerstone Bio-Pharma. Cornerstone Therapeutics then struck a $70 million strategic agreement with Chiesi in 2009. The Italian firm gained a 51% share in Cornerstone, while Cornerstone received the rights to market Chiesi's CUROSURF, in the US market. The deal strengthened Cornerstone's finances, as well as broadened its product offerings and customer segments. President Craig Collard owns about 13% of the company.

EXECUTIVES

Chairman, President, and CEO, Craig A. Collard, age 45, $934,720 total compensation

EVP Finance and CFO, Vincent Morgus, age 45

EVP, General Counsel, and Secretary, Andrew K. W. Powell, age 53

EVP Manufacturing and Trade, Steven M. Lutz, age 44

VP Scientific Affairs, Alan T. Roberts, $1,019,719 total compensation

VP Corporate Strategy, Joshua B. Franklin, age 41, $1,121,310 total compensation

Director Accounting and Principal Accounting Officer, Ira Duarte

Auditors: Grant Thornton LLP

LOCATIONS

HQ: Cornerstone Therapeutics Inc.
 1255 Crescent Green Dr., Ste. 250, Cary, NC 27518
Phone: 919-678-6611   **Fax:** 866-443-3092
Web: www.crtx.com

PRODUCTS/OPERATIONS

2010 Sales

	$ mil.	% of total
Curosurf	33.6	27
Zyflo	30.6	24
Allerx	27.3	22
Hyomax	10.1	9
Spectracef	5.3	4
Factive	5.1	4
Other products	11.7	9
License & royalty agreements	1.6	1
Total	**125.3**	**100**

COMPETITORS

Abbott Labs	GlaxoSmithKline
AstraZeneca	Johnson & Johnson
Bayer HealthCare	Merck Sharp & Dohme
Bayer HealthCare Pharmaceuticals	Novartis Pharmaceuticals
Forest Labs	Pernix Therapeutics
Genentech	Teva

HISTORICAL FINANCIALS
Company Type: Public

Income Statement
FYE: December 31

	REVENUE ($ mil.)	NET INCOME ($ mil.)	NET PROFIT MARGIN	EMPLOYEES
12/10	125.3	6.2	4.9%	147
12/09	109.6	10.2	9.3%	162
12/08	64.9	9.0	13.9%	107
12/07	12.9	(37.0)	—	80
12/06	13.1	(48.8)	—	61
Annual Growth	75.9%	—	—	24.6%

2010 Year-End Financials
Debt ratio: 0.1%
Return on equity: 3.6%
Cash ($ mil.): 50.9
Current ratio: 1.66
Long-term debt ($ mil.): 0.1
No. of shares (mil.): 25.5
Dividends
  Yield: —
  Payout: —
Market value ($ mil.): 147.5

	STOCK PRICE ($) FY Close	P/E High/Low		PER SHARE ($) Earnings	Dividends	Book Value
12/10	5.79	32	20	0.24	0.00	6.77
12/09	6.10	23	3	0.54	0.00	6.55
12/08	2.65	13	1	1.14	0.00	6.79
12/07	12.70	—	—	(8.70)	0.00	3.96
12/06	20.40	—	—	(13.70)	0.00	11.88
Annual Growth	(27.0%)	—	—	—	—	(13.1%)

Cortex Pharmaceuticals

Cortex Pharmaceuticals develops drugs to treat neurodegenerative and psychiatric disorders. Its research focuses on the AMPA receptor, which facilitates communication between nerve cells; the firm's Ampakine compounds may enhance this receptor's activity. Cortex's tends to develop candidates and then license the technologies to larger firms for diseases that require clinical and commercialization infrastructure to develop drugs for large markets (Alzheimer's disease, for instance). In turn, it will focus its internal research efforts on developing more compounds for niche markets, which require a smaller sales organization and more limited clinical trials.

Cortex also hopes to obtain orphan drug designation on its compounds, which would give it a relatively quick regulatory pathway and a period of exclusive marketing rights.

Amid the global economic meltdown of 2009, Cortex announced it would cut 50% of its workforce, about a dozen people, and reduce executive salaries and spending on early-stage research efforts.

The next year, Cortex raised about $10 million (with the potential to earn another $15 million) by selling a number of its drug compounds meant to treat respiratory depression to Valeant Pharmaceuticals (formerly Biovail). The portfolio included lead candidate CX717, which is being developed for a number of indications including respiratory depression, as well as Alzheimer's disease, attention deficit hyperactivity disorder (ADHD), and daytime sleepiness.

Following the sale of that portfolio of candidates, Cortex intends to focus on developing a new batch of drugs aimed at treating attention deficit hyperactivity disorder and schizophrenia.

Organon (part of Schering-Plough, which is now known as Merck) has licensed Cortex's Ampakine technology to develop compounds (and commercialize them worldwide) to treat schizophrenia and depression.

EXECUTIVES
Chairman, Roger G. Stoll, age 68, $557,985 total compensation
President, CEO, and Director, Mark A. Varney, age 44, $728,041 total compensation
VP Preclinical Development, Steven A. Johnson, age 59
VP, CFO, and Corporate Secretary, Maria S. Messinger, age 43, $334,559 total compensation
SVP Business Development, James H. Coleman, age 69, $341,433 total compensation
Auditors: Haskell & White LLP

LOCATIONS
HQ: Cortex Pharmaceuticals, Inc.
  15231 Barranca Pkwy., Irvine, CA 92618
Phone: 949-727-3157   **Fax:** 949-727-3657
Web: www.cortexpharm.com

COMPETITORS
Cephalon	NeuroNova
Eisai	Novartis
Elan	Pfizer
Eli Lilly	Sanofi
GlaxoSmithKline	Shire
Neurocrine Biosciences	

HISTORICAL FINANCIALS
Company Type: Public

Income Statement
FYE: December 31

	REVENUE ($ mil.)	NET INCOME ($ mil.)	NET PROFIT MARGIN	EMPLOYEES
12/10	10.5	1.6	15.2%	11
12/09	0.0	(8.4)	—	13
12/06	1.2	(16.1)	—	25
12/05*	2.6	(11.6)	—	26
06/04	7.0	(6.0)	—	20
Annual Growth	7.0%	—	—	(9.5%)

*Fiscal year change

2010 Year-End Financials
Debt ratio: —
Return on equity: 68.4%
Cash ($ mil.): 1.0
Current ratio: 2.83
Long-term debt ($ mil.): —
No. of shares (mil.): 78.9
Dividends
  Yield: —
  Payout: —
Market value ($ mil.): 13.6

	STOCK PRICE ($) FY Close	P/E High/Low		PER SHARE ($) Earnings	Dividends	Book Value
12/10	0.17	12	5	0.02	0.00	0.03
12/09	0.10	—	—	(0.19)	0.00	(0.02)
12/06	0.57	—	—	(0.31)	0.00	0.07
12/05*	0.50	—	—	(0.31)	0.00	0.35
06/04	1.25	—	—	(0.47)	0.00	0.24
Annual Growth	(39.3%)	—	—	—	—	(40.2%)

*Fiscal year change

CPEX Pharmaceuticals

CPEX Pharmaceuticals has set out on its own to seek its fortunes in the drug industry. The company is developing prescription drugs using its CPE-215 drug delivery technology, which allows for drug absorption via the skin, nasal mucosa, and eyes. Auxilium Pharmaceuticals licensed the technology for its FDA-approved testosterone replacement gel Testim. And CPEX is using the technology to develop its own product, an intranasal insulin called Nasulin that is undergoing clinical trials. Formerly a unit of generic drugmaker Bentley Pharmaceuticals, the company was spun off in 2008. Then, after reviewing its strategic options, CPEX was acquired by investment entity FCB in 2011.

EXECUTIVES
President and CEO, John A. Sedor, age 66
VP and Chief Scientific Officer, Nils Bergenhem
VP and CFO, Robert P. (Bob) Hebert, age 38
SVP and Chief Medical Officer, Lance Berman, age 40
Auditors: BDO Seidman, LLP

LOCATIONS
HQ: CPEX Pharmaceuticals, Inc.
  2 Holland Way, Exeter, NH 03833
Phone: 603-658-6100   **Fax:** 603-658-6101
Web: www.cpexpharm.com

COMPETITORS
Abbott Labs	GlaxoSmithKline
Amylin Pharmaceuticals	MannKind
AstraZeneca	Nektar Therapeutics
Bayer Consumer Care	Novo Nordisk
Emisphere	Pfizer
Generex Biotechnology	Unigene Labs

HISTORICAL FINANCIALS
Company Type: Public

Income Statement
FYE: December 31

	REVENUE ($ mil.)	NET INCOME ($ mil.)	NET PROFIT MARGIN	EMPLOYEES
12/10	23.3	6.6	28.3%	13
12/09	18.7	(3.0)	—	17
12/08	15.6	(2.9)	—	18
12/07	11.1	(4.9)	—	15
12/06	8.4	(4.2)	—	0
Annual Growth	29.1%	—	—	(4.7%)

2010 Year-End Financials
Debt ratio: —
Return on equity: 21.0%
Cash ($ mil.): 22.2
Current ratio: 8.05
Long-term debt ($ mil.): —
No. of shares (mil.): 2.6
Dividends
  Yield: —
  Payout: —
Market value ($ mil.): 64.1

	STOCK PRICE ($) FY Close	P/E High/Low		PER SHARE ($) Earnings	Dividends	Book Value
12/10	24.50	12	4	2.46	0.00	12.10
12/09	11.02	—	—	(1.21)	0.00	9.08
12/08	9.75	—	—	(1.25)	0.00	9.60
Annual Growth	58.5%	—	—	—	—	12.3%

CPS Technologies

CPS Technologies makes thermal management components for electronics using aluminum silicon carbide (ALSiC) metal matrix composites. Products include substrates, baseplates, and heat spreaders that are used by customers in motor controller and wireless communications component applications. CPS is working with the US Army on using its composite technology in armor for military vehicles. The company also licenses its technology to other manufacturers; revenue from licenses and royalties, however, has dwindled away to virtually nothing. CPS Technologies makes more than two-thirds of its sales to locations outside the US, although the majority of its customers are actually based in the US.

EXECUTIVES

President, CEO, Treasurer, and Director, Grant C. Bennett, age 56, $156,349 total compensation
VP Operations and Engineering, Richard Adams
VP Sales, Cheryl Oliveira, $100,939 total compensation
VP Marketing and Technical Sales, and Research and Development Senior Scientist, Mark A. Occhionero, $109,731 total compensation
Sales Representative New England Regional, Jennifer Yee
Director Corporate Quality Assurance and HPB Operations Manager, Michael Staab
Manager Executive Sales, Bo Sullivan
Sales Representative European, Gio Schouten
Manager Production, Kim Richardson
Manager Engineering Design, Bruce Brown
Sales Representative India, Anand Nagarajan
Auditors: Wolf & Company, P.C.

LOCATIONS

HQ: CPS Technologies Corporation
 111 S. Worcester St., Norton, MA 02766
Phone: 508-222-0614   **Fax:** 508-222-0220
Web: www.alsic.com

PRODUCTS/OPERATIONS

HISTORICAL FINANCIALS
Company Type: Public

Income Statement
FYE: December 31

	REVENUE ($ mil.)	NET INCOME ($ mil.)	NET PROFIT MARGIN	EMPLOYEES
12/10	21.4	0.7	3.3%	194
12/09	13.0	0.6	4.6%	141
12/08	14.8	1.5	10.1%	133
12/07	12.4	0.9	7.3%	135
12/06	11.9	1.8	15.1%	133
Annual Growth	15.8%	(21.0%)	—	9.9%

2010 Year-End Financials
Debt ratio: 2.1%
Return on equity: 8.4%
Cash ($ mil.): 1.8
Current ratio: 3.94
Long-term debt ($ mil.): 0.2
No. of shares (mil.): 12.7
Dividends
 Yield: —
 Payout: —
Market value ($ mil.): 23.5

	STOCK PRICE ($) FY Close	P/E High/Low		PER SHARE ($) Earnings	Dividends	Book Value
12/10	1.85	33	18	0.06	0.00	0.67
12/09	1.15	40	18	0.04	0.00	0.60
12/08	1.39	23	10	0.11	0.00	0.55
12/07	2.60	57	20	0.07	0.00	0.43
12/06	1.50	14	5	0.14	0.00	0.35
Annual Growth	5.4%	—	—	(19.1%)	—	17.6%

Craft Brewers Alliance

Beer is a real craft for these brewers. Craft Brewers Alliance markets and sells the beers of The Redhook Ale Brewery (Seattle), Widmer Brothers Brewing Company (Portland, Oregon), and Kona Brewing Company (Kona, Hawaii). The Alliance, which is headquartered in Portland, offers approximately 20 craft beers that are available regionally and nationally. Its brands include Longhammer IPA, Wider Hefeweizen, Longboard Island Lager, and Oatmeal Stout. The company's beers are distributed nationally through a partnership with beverage giant Anheuser-Busch, which also owns about 35% of Craft Brewers Alliance.

Redhook Ale merged with Portland's Widmer Brothers in 2008 to form Craft Brewers Alliance (CBA). Previously, the two companies had operated a distribution joint venture serving customers in the western US. Included in the deal were Widmer's minority interests in Kona Brewing and Goose Island Beer (dba Fulton Street Brewery). In 2011 CBA sold its 42% stake in Fulton Street Brewery to Anheuser-Busch for about for $16 million. As part of the deal, CBA received additional retailing support and lower distribution fees from Anheuser-Busch.

To expand distribution of beverages made on the Big Island, CBA acquired the remaining interest it did not already own in Kona Brewing for nearly $18 million in cash and stock in mid-2010. Kona, which became a subsidiary as a result of the deal, looks to benefit from CBA's greater financial resources and broader marketing and distribution capabilities.

The company has boosted its sales volume by 3.5% to 607,800 barrels in 2010 as compared to 587,500 barrels in 2009. The additional shipment increase was due in large part to the company's contract brewing business and its contract with Chicago-based Fulton Street Brewing, LLC.

Consolidation in the beer industry has helped to reduce the number of rivals for CBA. While the craft brew market has been popular for years and has grown, some top US beer suppliers have merged with international brewers during the past decade to level the playing field for crafters.

EXECUTIVES

Chairman, Kurt R. Widmer, age 59
CEO, Terry E. Michaelson, age 56, $337,227 total compensation
President and CEO, Hawaii, Mattson Davis
CFO and Treasurer, Mark D. Moreland, age 46, $314,016 total compensation
VP Sales, Martin J. Wall IV, age 39
VP Marketing, Danielle A. Katcher, age 40
VP Brewing Operations and Technology, V. Sebastian Pastore, $232,915 total compensation

Manager Human Resources, Stacia Bird
Controller and Chief Accounting Officer, Joseph K. (Joe) O'Brien, age 53
Director SEC Reporting and Investor Relations, Patrick Green
Auditors: Moss Adams, LLP

LOCATIONS

HQ: Craft Brewers Alliance, Inc.
 929 N. Russell St., Portland, OR 97227-1733
Phone: 503-331-7270   **Fax:** 503-331-7373
Web: www.craftbrewers.com

PRODUCTS/OPERATIONS

2010 Sales

	% of total
Anheuser-Busch distribution	81
Alternating proprietorship	7
Contract brewing	2
Pubs & other	10
Total	**100**

Selected Breweries and Brands
Kona Brewing Company
 Big Wave Golden Ale
 Fire Rock Pale Ale
 Longboard Island Lager
 Pipeline Porter
 Wailua Wheat Ale
Redhook Ale Brewery
 Blackhook Porter
 Copperhook
 ESB Ale
 Late Harvest Autumn Ale
 Long Hammer IPA
 Slim Chance Light Ale
 Sunrye Golden Ale
 Winterhook Winter Ale
Widmer Brothers Brewing
 Broken Halo IPA
 Brr Seasonal Ale
 Drifter Pale Ale
 Drop Top Amber Ale
 OKTO Ale
 W Belgian-style Ale
 Widmer Hefeweizen

COMPETITORS

Anchor Brewers	New Belgium Brewing
As	North American
Boston Beer	Breweries
Deschutes Brewery	Pyramid Breweries
Diageo	Rogue Ales
Grupo Modelo	Shipyard Brewing
Heineken USA	Company
Magic Hat Brewing	Sierra Nevada
Mendocino Brewing	Stone Brewing
MillerCoors	

HISTORICAL FINANCIALS
Company Type: Public

Income Statement
FYE: December 31

	REVENUE ($ mil.)	NET INCOME ($ mil.)	NET PROFIT MARGIN	EMPLOYEES
12/10	131.7	1.7	1.3%	600
12/09	131.7	0.9	0.7%	400
12/08	79.8	(33.3)	—	400
12/07	41.5	(0.9)	—	221
12/06	35.7	0.5	1.4%	205
Annual Growth	38.6%	35.8%	—	30.8%

2010 Year-End Financials

Debt ratio: 26.2%
Return on equity: 1.8%
Cash ($ mil.): 0.2
Current ratio: 0.84
Long-term debt ($ mil.): 24.7

No. of shares (mil.): 18.8
Dividends
  Yield: —
  Payout: —
Market value ($ mil.): 139.1

	STOCK PRICE ($) FY Close	P/E High	P/E Low	PER SHARE ($) Earnings	PER SHARE ($) Dividends	PER SHARE ($) Book Value
12/10	7.39	99	22	0.10	0.00	5.01
12/09	2.40	84	17	0.05	0.00	4.72
12/08	1.20	—	—	(2.63)	0.00	4.68
12/07	6.65	—	—	(0.11)	0.00	7.19
12/06	5.20	89	52	0.06	0.00	7.34
Annual Growth	9.2%	—	—	13.6%	—	(9.1%)

Credit Acceptance

In the world of Credit Acceptance Corporation (CAC), to purchase a car is not an impossible dream for problem borrowers — just an expensive reality. Working with more than 3,000 independent and franchised automobile dealers in the US, CAC provides capital for auto loans to people with substandard credit. The company also provides other services to dealers, including payment servicing, receivables management, marketing, and service contracts. It typically funds around 1.5 million loans per year; Michigan, New York, Texas, Ohio, and Mississippi are the company's largest markets. Founder and chairman Donald Foss owns more than 50% of CAC.

The company funds loans in two ways: It advances money to its dealer-partners in exchange for the servicing rights to the underlying loan, or it purchases loans directly from dealers. CAC's revenues increased and its net income more than doubled in 2009, although its lending activity slowed due to lack of access to capital. In 2010 the company's loan portfolio began picking up, both in size and performance. Its bottom line has also gotten a boost from a spike in premiums earned on the reinsurance of vehicle service contracts, a new area of emphasis for the company.

HISTORY

Donald Foss was a used-car dealer in Detroit, where, to make sales, he sometimes financed cars out of his own pocket. As Foss' chain of dealerships grew, so did his financing business. In 1972 he established it as a separate company and 20 years later took it public.

For most of its history CAC stood alone in the field of subprime auto lending, but stagnating salaries made it a competitive growth business in the early 1990s. At mid-decade, the company entered Canada and the UK to tap similar markets there. In 1996 CAC acquired Montana Investment Group, a credit reporting service.

Even as rising consumer debt and bad credit continued to pump buyers into CAC's loan pipeline, the economic boom of the mid-1990s paradoxically made used cars less desirable. The soft used-car market squeezed several of CAC's competitors out of business; a staggering default rate — nearing 40% — also pressured CAC, whose auditors insisted it increase reserves to cover losses. The subsequent earnings dive spurred a shareholder lawsuit accusing CAC of hiding its poor fiscal health. Although bad loans had damaged its bottom line, the company adopted more stringent lending policies to reduce risk. Consumers filed class-action suits alleging unethical practices in 1998, but many claims were dismissed.

To pay off debt acquired through bad loans, CAC sold Montana Investment Group in 1999. In 2000 it launched CAC Leasing to further offset losses from a decrease in subprime lending, but in 2002 the company exited that line, deciding the lending field was more profitable. CAC stopped originating new loans in the UK and Canada in 2003.

In 2005 the SEC investigated CAC's accounting methods, specifically related to its loan portfolio, and the company restated portions of its past financial results.

The company found itself in hot water again in 2008 when it agreed to pay some 15,000 Missouri customers to settle a class action lawsuit. The lawsuit, filed more than a decade prior, alleged that CAC overcharged customers for fees and interest on their loans. As part of the settlement, CAC said it would write off $39 million in outstanding accounts and distribute another $13 million to customers.

EXECUTIVES

Chairman, Donald A. Foss, age 66, $477,450 total compensation
President, Steven M. Jones, age 47, $2,092,835 total compensation
CFO, Kenneth S. Booth, age 43, $592,978 total compensation
CEO and Director, Brett A. Roberts, age 44, $805,385 total compensation
CIO, John P. Neary, age 34
CTO, Michael P. Miotto, age 50, $572,231 total compensation
Chief Legal Officer and Corporate Secretary, Charles A. Pearce, age 46
SVP Loan Servicing, Michael W. Knoblauch, age 47
SVP and Treasurer, Douglas W. Busk, age 50
Auditors: Grant Thornton LLP

LOCATIONS

HQ: Credit Acceptance Corporation
25505 W. Twelve Mile Rd., Southfield, MI 48034-8339
Phone: 248-353-2700
Web: www.creditacceptance.com

PRODUCTS/OPERATIONS

2010 Sales

	$ mil.	% of total
Finance charges	388.0	88
Premium income	32.7	7
Other	21.4	5
Total	**442.1**	**100**

Selected Subsidiaries

Arlington Investment Company
Auto Funding America Inc.
Auto Lease Services, LLC
AutoNet Finance Company.com, Inc.
Buyers Vehicle Protection Plan, Inc.
CAC Leasing, Inc.
CAC Reinsurance, Ltd.
Credit Acceptance Motors, Inc.
Credit Acceptance Wholesale Buyers Club, Inc.
Vehicle Remarketing Services, Inc.
VSC Re Company

COMPETITORS

Ally Financial	Ford Motor Credit
American Honda Finance	GM Financial
Capital One Auto Finance	Mercedes-Benz Credit
Daimler Financial Services Americas	Toyota Motor Credit
First Investors Financial Services	Volkswagen Financial Services
	Volvo Car Finance

HISTORICAL FINANCIALS

Company Type: Public

Income Statement

FYE: December 31

	REVENUE ($ mil.)	NET INCOME ($ mil.)	NET PROFIT MARGIN	EMPLOYEES
12/10	442.1	170.1	38.5%	862
12/09	380.7	146.3	38.4%	911
12/08	312.2	67.2	21.5%	1,048
12/07	239.9	54.9	22.9%	971
12/06	219.3	58.6	26.7%	788
Annual Growth	19.2%	30.5%	—	2.3%

2010 Year-End Financials

Debt ratio: 115.7%
Return on equity: 35.8%
Cash ($ mil.): 3.8
Current ratio: 0.34
Long-term debt ($ mil.): 549.0

No. of shares (mil.): 27.3
Dividends
  Yield: —
  Payout: —
Market value ($ mil.): 1,713.9

	STOCK PRICE ($) FY Close	P/E High	P/E Low	PER SHARE ($) Earnings	PER SHARE ($) Dividends	PER SHARE ($) Book Value
12/10	62.77	11	7	5.67	0.00	17.38
12/09	42.10	10	3	4.62	0.00	15.99
12/08	13.70	15	5	2.16	0.00	11.01
12/07	20.67	18	9	1.76	0.00	8.79
12/06	33.33	21	10	1.66	0.00	6.99
Annual Growth	17.1%	—	—	35.9%	—	25.6%

Cree

Cree has its name in lights. Its blue, green, and near-ultraviolet light-emitting diodes (LEDs) — made from silicon carbide (SiC) and gallium nitride (GaN) — are used in products such as dashboard lights, architectural light fixtures, market tickers, and video screens, including the giant screen in New York City's Times Square. Cree also sells SiC wafers, which work better at higher temperatures and voltages than standard silicon devices, and SiC and GaN materials. Its power and radio-frequency (RF) products include Schottky diodes and transistors. Leading customers include Seoul Semiconductor, Arrow Electronics, and Sumitomo. More than 80% of sales come from outside the US.

Cree created the first blue LED, which, when combined with red and yellow LEDs, creates a full spectrum of colors. The technology has become an industry standard and expands the applications of LED lighting. To leverage this core technology, Cree has introduced the XLamp family of high-power packaged LEDs for specialty lighting applications, hoping to stay one step ahead of the competition. Cree's XLamp products have a wide array of residential and commercial uses, including appliance lighting and reading lamps, as well as backlighting for large flat-panel and retail displays.

The trends towards increased energy-efficient and environmental lighting, and the growing number of standard lighting products that use LEDs, have helped Cree weather a challenging economic environment better than many in the electronics industry. The company has combined external acquisitions and internal R&D to broaden its offerings — and increase its sales and market reach — into LED lighting fixtures, power switching, and RF products.

Sales for 2010 increased by an impressive 53% over 2009, driven by higher sales across all product lines. Within its core LED product line (more than 90% of sales), Cree benefited from higher average selling prices as it sold a larger proportion of LED components and LED lighting products. Sales of its power and RF products grew by 80% in the same period, primarily due to increased orders for Schottky diodes and GaN MMICs (monolithic microwave integrated circuits). On the strength of its sales, Cree's net income jumped to $152 million in 2010 from about $31 million the year before.

With strong financial results and a growing market for its products, Cree is investing in manufacturing capacity. It announced plans in 2010 to add a 150-mm LED wafer production line within its existing North Carolina facility. The wafers will be more than double the size of currently manufactured wafers, which increases the number of LEDs produced per wafer and reduces the cost of LED products. Cree hopes to have the first products from the new line qualified by June 2011.

Expansion means more jobs, and Cree has added more than 600 positions since 2009. It anticipates adding another 250 employees to staff the new wafer production line. As adoption of LED lighting accelerates, the company is focused on expanding its manufacturing capacity and plans to spend around $300 million in fiscal 2011 to expand and enhance its production capacity. In late 2009 it purchased a plant in Huizhou, China, to add capacity in the Asia/Pacific region.

Cree has also been successful in inking big deals. In 2010 Home Depot stores started carrying the company's six-inch downlights. In 2009 the Department of Defense began installing Cree luminaires in the Pentagon as part of a major renovation. The first eco-friendly McDonald's in North Carolina uses Cree downlights, bulbs, and other products for more than 97% of its lighting.

The company partnered with Habitat for Humanity in 2010 to provide LED downlights in the kitchens of all Habitat homes built in the US over the next three years. Another Cree program that promotes the uses of LED lighting is its LED City program, which encourages municipalities to install and promote LED lighting. LED City has added multiple US and international cities, including Austin, Texas; Anchorage, Alaska; Ann Arbor, Michigan; Gwanju, South Korea; Tianjin and Huizhou, China; Torraca, Italy; and Toronto, Ontario. Its LED University program similarly lets participants evaluate, promote, and deploy LED lighting across colleges and universities, enabling them to save on electricity and reduce maintenance costs.

On the acquisition side, Cree bought Ruud Lighting for about $583 million in 2011. The largest company purchase in Cree's history, the Ruud acquisition gives Cree more sales channels and more opportunities for product development. Ruud Lighting makes outdoor LED products, the logical complement to CREE's focus on indoor LED products. That combination may light the way for Cree's stride toward the top spot in the North American LED market.

Cree also acquired LED Lighting Fixtures in 2008 for about $77 million; the acquisition added lighting fixtures such as down lights and lumi-naires that use Cree's XLamp LEDs. Neal Hunter, CEO of LED Lighting Fixtures and a co-founder of Cree, rejoined Cree through the acquisition of his firm, which was renamed Cree LED Lighting Solutions. Hunter serves as president of the subsidiary.

HISTORY

Cree started at North Carolina State University, where brothers Eric and Neal Hunter and Calvin Carter researched silicon carbide (SiC) applications, in part with US government funding. In 1987 the trio founded Cree Research to continue their research. The company shipped its first-to-market blue light-emitting diode (LED) in 1991, and went public in 1993.

In 1995 the company began developing blue lasers — a project that continued for years to follow — via a 1999 pact with Microvision. Also that year Cree and Siemens formed a development and manufacturing agreement for blue and green LEDs. In 1997 Cree began supplying SiC crystals to gemstone manufacturer C3.

Cree in 1998 signed or extended pacts with Kansai Electric Power, Siemens, and Asea Brown Boveri (now ABB Ltd.). The next year the company shortened its name to Cree, Inc., and released its first radio-frequency transistor.

In 2000 Cree acquired semiconductor R&D boutique Nitres for $233 million and, to close out the year, purchased the UltraRF division of Spectrian (a maker of linear power amplifiers) for $113.5 million. (It later renamed the unit Cree Microwave.)

In 2004 Cree acquired the gallium nitride substrate and epitaxy assets of Advanced Technology Materials, a subsidiary of ATMI, for about $10 million, boosting its materials business and IP portfolio.

Co-founder Neal Hunter, who served as CEO of Cree from 1994 to 2001, resigned as chairman in 2005 after a decade in that post, and left the company's board of directors. Charles Swoboda, who had succeeded Hunter as CEO in 2001, succeeded him as chairman, as well.

Cree phased out its silicon-based RF and microwave semiconductor business in 2005, citing losses by its Cree Microwave subsidiary. The company refocused on its wide-bandgap RF and microwave devices fabricated on SiC and GaN substrates.

In 2006 the company opened a new engineering and production facility in Research Triangle Park, measuring 230,000 sq. ft., for making SiC and GaN devices.

That same year Cree acquired INTRINSIC Semiconductor for around $46 million, including $43.6 million in cash. INTRINSIC Semiconductor made low-defect-density SiC substrates, enabling high-power semiconductor devices and lower-cost LEDs.

In 2007 Cree acquired Hong Kong-based COTCO Luminant Device for about $200 million, giving Cree a broader range of LED components, access to a lower cost manufacturing facility, and established sales channels in the fast growing China market.

EXECUTIVES

Chairman, President, and CEO, Charles M. (Chuck) Swoboda, age 44, $4,266,764 total compensation
President, Cree LED Lighting, Neal Hunter, age 49
EVP and COO, Stephen D. (Steve) Kelley, age 49, $1,347,365 total compensation
EVP Finance, CFO, and Treasurer, John T. Kurtzweil, age 55, $1,291,371 total compensation

VP and General Manager, Cree LED Lighting, Ty Mitchell
VP; General Manager, LED Components, Norbert Hiller
VP and General Manager, Asia/Pacific, Soo Ghee Lee
VP Sales, LED Lighting, Mike Fallon
VP and General Manager, Power and RF, Cengiz Balkas
VP Global Manufacturing, Wayne K. Nesbit, age 47
VP Business Development, Chris James
VP Corporate Marketing, Greg Merritt
VP Market Development, Cree LED Lighting, Gary Trott
SVP Sales, Robert (Bob) Pollock, age 57
Director RF and Microwave Products, Jim Milligan
Director Investor Relations, Raiford Garrabrant
Director Advanced Optoelectronics, John Edmond
Product Line Manager, Cree LED Module, Scott Schwab
Director Marketing, LED Modules, Tom Roberts
Director National Accounts, Cree LED Lighting, Craig Lofton
Product Line Manager, Cree Materials, Vijay Balakrishna
Director Marketing, LED Components, Paul Thieken
LED Programs Manager, Deb Lovig
Secretary, Adam H. Broome
Director Sales and Marketing, RF Products, Tom Dekker
Corporate Communications, Michelle Murray
Director Business Development, Solid State Lighting, Mark McClear
Auditors: Ernst & Young LLP

LOCATIONS

HQ: Cree, Inc.
4600 Silicon Dr., Durham, NC 27703
Phone: 919-313-5300   Fax: 919-313-5558
Web: www.cree.com

2010 Sales

	% of total
China & Hong Kong	40
US	19
Europe	13
South Korea	10
Japan	9
Taiwan	4
Malaysia	2
Other countries	3
Total	**100**

PRODUCTS/OPERATIONS

2010 Sales

	$ mil.	% of total
LED products	790.0	91
Power & RF products	77.3	9
Total	**867.3**	**100**

Selected Products

Blue and green light-emitting diodes (LEDs; used in displays and indicators)
High-power packaged LEDs (XLamp)
Gallium nitride (GaN) products
  High electron mobility transistors (HEMT)
  Monolithic microwave integrated circuits (MMIC)
LED light fixtures (architectural lay-in, bulbs, downlights, housings, narrow beam spotlight)
Silicon carbide (SiC) products
  Radio-frequency and microwave transistors (used in communications applications)
  Rectifiers
  Switches
  Wafers (used in research programs)

COMPETITORS

Acuity Brands
Avago Technologies

Infineon Technologies
Kopin
Lighting Science Group
Nexxus Lighting
Nichia
OSRAM SYLVANIA
Philips Lumileds
Philips Solid-State Lighting Solutions, Inc.
RF Micro Devices
Sanken Electric
Sumitomo Electric Device
Toyoda Gosei

HISTORICAL FINANCIALS

Company Type: Public

Income Statement

FYE: Last Sunday in June

	REVENUE ($ mil.)	NET INCOME ($ mil.)	NET PROFIT MARGIN	EMPLOYEES
06/11	987.6	146.5	14.8%	4,753
06/10	867.3	152.3	17.6%	4,298
06/09	567.3	30.3	5.3%	3,172
06/08	493.3	33.4	6.8%	3,168
06/07	394.1	57.3	14.5%	2,578
Annual Growth	25.8%	26.5%	—	16.5%

2011 Year-End Financials

Debt ratio: —
Return on equity: 6.5%
Cash ($ mil.): 390.6
Current ratio: 10.38
Long-term debt ($ mil.): —

No. of shares (mil.): 109.6
Dividends
  Yield: —
  Payout: —
Market value ($ mil.): 3,681.7

	STOCK PRICE ($) FY Close	P/E High/Low		PER SHARE ($) Earnings	Dividends	Book Value
06/11	33.59	57	24	1.33	0.00	20.63
06/10	60.03	58	18	1.45	0.00	18.78
06/09	29.40	93	37	0.34	0.00	13.66
06/08	22.81	93	54	0.38	0.00	13.01
06/07	26.09	40	21	0.72	0.00	11.99
Annual Growth	6.5%	—	—	16.6%	—	14.5%

Crestwood Midstream Partners LP

The middle of the oil and gas stream is best for Crestwood Midstream Partners (formerly Quicksilver Gas Services). The company gathers and processes natural gas and natural gas liquids from the Barnett Shale formation near Fort Worth, Texas. Crestwood Midstream Partners' assets include a pipeline and a processing plant with 200 million cu. ft. a day capacity, a processing unit at the existing plant, extensions to the existing pipeline, and pipelines in other drilling areas in Texas. To raise cash, in 2010 parent Quicksilver Resources sold Quicksilver Gas Services to Crestwood Holdings Partners for $701 million.

EXECUTIVES

Chairman, President, and CEO, Robert G. Phillips, age 56
EVP, COO and Director, Paul J. Cook, age 54
VP Chief Accounting Officer, John C. Regan, age 41
VP and Treasurer, Vanessa Gomez, age 34

SVP and General Counsel, John C. (Chris) Cirone, age 61
SVP, CFO, and Director, Philip W. Cook, age 49
Auditors: Deloitte & Touche LLP

LOCATIONS

HQ: Crestwood Midstream Partners LP
  717 Texas Ave., Ste. 3150, Houston, TX 77002
Phone: 832-519-2200
Web: www.Crestwoodlp.com

PRODUCTS/OPERATIONS

2009 Sales

	$ mil.	% of total
Gathering & transportation	55.4	60
Gas processing	34.7	38
Other	1.6	2
Total	**91.7**	**100**

COMPETITORS

Crosstex Energy
DCP Midstream Partners
Energy Transfer Equity
Enterprise Products
Penn Virginia
Plains All American Pipeline
Regency Energy
Southern Natural Gas
Texas Gas Transmission

HISTORICAL FINANCIALS

Company Type: Public

Income Statement

FYE: December 31

	REVENUE ($ mil.)	NET INCOME ($ mil.)	NET PROFIT MARGIN	EMPLOYEES
12/10	113.6	34.9	30.7%	0
12/09	91.7	33.2	36.2%	0
12/08	78.1	26.4	33.8%	0
12/07	35.9	8.3	23.1%	0
12/06	13.9	2.4	17.3%	0
Annual Growth	69.1%	95.3%	—	—

2010 Year-End Financials

Debt ratio: —
Return on equity: —
Cash ($ mil.): 0.0
Current ratio: 1.39
Long-term debt ($ mil.): 283.5

No. of shares (mil.): 31.2
Dividends
  Yield: 6.0%
  Payout: 157.3%
Market value ($ mil.): 848.0

	STOCK PRICE ($) FY Close	P/E High/Low		PER SHARE ($) Earnings	Dividends	Book Value
12/10	27.19	29	16	1.03	1.62	(0.00)
12/09	20.97	19	8	1.21	1.50	(0.00)
12/08	9.48	28	5	0.96	1.32	4.44
12/07	25.02	129	101	0.20	0.17	4.74
Annual Growth	2.8%	—	—	72.7%	112.0%	—

Cubist Pharmaceuticals

Fighting infection is a modern art at Cubist Pharmaceuticals. The company is developing antimicrobial agents to treat drug-resistant infections, including methicillin-resistant *Staphylococcus aureus* (MRSA), typically found in hospitals and other health care institutions. Its flagship product Cubicin is an intravenous antibiotic that is FDA-approved to fight MRSA infections of the skin and blood. The drug has also received regulatory approval in Europe and a handful of non-European

countries. Cubist also maintains a pipeline of candidates in various stages of clinical and pre-clinical development.

Cubist markets Cubicin in the US using its own sales force. Internationally the company relies upon distribution agreements with other companies including Novartis in Europe and the Asia/Pacific, Merck in Japan, and AstraZeneca in China and other countries. The company relies upon third-party manufacturers to produce its active ingredients and finished products, and also outsources the warehousing and distribution.

Cubicin has been the company's main source of revenue since its launch in 2003, and with approval in more than 70 countries, sales of the drug have climbed steadily over the years. Cubist Pharmaceuticals continues to expand promotional efforts and territories for the drug, and it is also working to expand the number of approved indications for Cubicin.

To raise a little cash on the side, in 2011 Cubist formed an agreement to co-promote Optimer Pharmaceuticals' Dificid antibiotic for *C. difficile* associated diarrhea (CDAD) in the US through its existing hospital-focused sales force. Cubist had a similar agreement with AstraZeneca to co-promote that company's Merrem IV antibiotic in the US; however that partnership expired in 2010.

The company moved to add a second commercial product of its own in 2011 when it agreed to acquire struggling drug development firm Adolor. The purchase will add Entereg, a drug sold to hospitals in the US to speed patient recovery following bowel resection surgery. Adolor also has products under development, including a treatment for opioid induced constipation (OIC) in late-stage clinical trials. The $415 million deal includes $190 million in cash, plus a contingent payment right that Adolor's shareholders will recieve if certain regulatory and commercialization milestones are met for the OIC candidate.

Cubist's own R&D pipeline includes several drug candidates in various stages of development, including one aiming to treat CDAD, an IV antibiotic candidate for multi-drug resistant gram-negative infections, and a potential treatment for pneumonia. Other candidates in early research phases include pain and infection treatments. Cubist also maintains a research collaboration with Alnylam Pharmaceuticals to develop and market Alnylam's potential therapy for respiratory syncytial virus (RSV) infections in children; however, that program was put on hold during 2011 to wait on results from adult trials.

To expand its pipeline, while keeping focused on killing hospital-acquired infections, the company paid $100 million (plus milestone payments of up to $290 million) in 2009 to buy up privately held development firm Calixa Therapeutics. The purchase added candidates in clinical trials for the treatment of specific gram-negative bacterial infections.

EXECUTIVES

Chairman, Kenneth M. (Ken) Bate, age 60
President, CEO, and Director, Michael W. (Mike) Bonney, age 52, $2,321,405 total compensation
EVP Research and Development and Chief Scientific Officer, Steven C. (Steve) Gilman, age 58, $1,157,186 total compensation
EVP and COO, Robert J. Perez, age 46, $1,297,616 total compensation
VP Sales, Eric W. Kimble
VP Discovery Chemistry, Chester A. Metcalf III
VP, Chief Intellectual Property Counsel, and Head Litigation, Timothy J. Douros

SVP and Chief Medical and Development Officer, Santosh J. Vetticaden, age 51, $1,633,118 total compensation

SVP and CFO, David W. J. McGirr, age 56, $923,301 total compensation

SVP Technical Operations, Lindon M. Fellows, age 59, $675,343 total compensation

SVP Commercial Operations, Gregory (Greg) Stea, age 53

SVP, General Counsel, and Secretary, Tamara L. Joseph, age 48

Senior Director Corporate Communications, Eileen C. McIntyre

Auditors: PricewaterhouseCoopers LLP

LOCATIONS

HQ: Cubist Pharmaceuticals, Inc.
65 Hayden Ave., Lexington, MA 02421
Phone: 781-860-8660   **Fax:** 781-240-0256
Web: www.cubist.com

PRODUCTS/OPERATIONS

2010 Sales

	$ mil.	% of total
US products	599.6	94
International products	25.3	4
Service	8.5	1
Other	3.1	1
Total	**636.5**	**100**

COMPETITORS

Abbott Labs	Sanofi
Astellas Pharma	Shionogi & Co.
Eli Lilly	Teva
Forest Labs	The Medicines Company
Johnson & Johnson	Theravance
Merck	Trius Therapeutics
Pfizer	ViroPharma
Ranbaxy Laboratories	

HISTORICAL FINANCIALS

Company Type: Public

Income Statement

FYE: December 31

	REVENUE ($ mil.)	NET INCOME ($ mil.)	NET PROFIT MARGIN	EMPLOYEES
12/10	636.5	94.3	14.8%	638
12/09	562.1	79.6	14.2%	600
12/08	433.6	169.8	39.2%	554
12/07	294.6	48.1	16.3%	489
12/06	194.7	(0.4)	—	410
Annual Growth	**34.5%**	**—**	**—**	**11.7%**

2010 Year-End Financials

Debt ratio: 65.7%
Return on equity: 14.2%
Cash ($ mil.): 373.0
Current ratio: 6.75
Long-term debt ($ mil.): 435.8

No. of shares (mil.): 59.3
Dividends
  Yield: —
  Payout: —
Market value ($ mil.): 1,270.0

	STOCK PRICE ($) FY Close	P/E High/Low		PER SHARE ($) Earnings	Dividends	Book Value
12/10	21.40	16	12	1.55	0.00	11.18
12/09	18.97	19	10	1.36	0.00	8.12
12/08	24.16	11	6	2.56	0.00	5.47
12/07	20.51	31	20	0.83	0.00	1.76
12/06	18.11	—	—	(0.01)	0.00	0.74
Annual Growth	**4.3%**	**—**	**—**	**—**	**—**	**97.1%**

CUI Global

CUI Global (formerly Waytronx) offers its Way-Cool technology (liquid and air cooling in a wire mesh used to manage the temperature of components) for LED signage and its WayFast architecture (layers of woven electrical or optical wire mesh between chip surfaces increase speed in power management and data communications) for thermal management. It has also licensed the GasPT2 natural gas quality measurement system from GL Industrial Services. Subsidiary CUI distributes power electromechanical components and industrial controls to OEMs and design engineers. CUI Global changed its name to better reflect its focus on acquiring and developing technologies used in diverse markets and industries

CUI Global acquired CUI in 2008 for $37.5 million. The acquisition addressed the company's financial woes by bringing products to market and generating increased sales. It has also added a manufacturing, distribution, and marketing base. CUI Global plans to license and expand CUI's product lines.

In July 2009 the company acquired Comex Instruments as well as 49% of Comex Electronex. Comex Instruments and its distribution network, which includes Mitsubishi, Subaru, Hitachi, and Toshiba, will be known as CUI Japan, a 100% owned subsidiary of CUI Global. The acquisition also includes Comex's staff of hardware and software engineers who will support CUI Global's development of new technologies.

CUI co-founder and former CEO James McKenzie owns about 27% of CUI Global.

EXECUTIVES

Chairman, Colton R. Melby
CFO, Waytronx and CUI, Daniel Ford, $149,304 total compensation
President, CEO, General Counsel, and Director; CEO, CUI, William J. Clough, age 58, $536,270 total compensation
VP Worldwide Sales, CUI, Inc., Mark Adams
COO and President, CUI, Matthew (Matt) McKenzie, $143,684 total compensation
CTO, CUI, Duwang Li
SVP Business Development, Bradley J. (Brad) Hallock, age 51
Technical Fellow, Michael Schuette
Project Director and Lead Engineer, GASPT2, Terry Williams
Promotions Manager, Maggie Lefor
Director Administrative Services, Larry Rightmyer
Auditors:

LOCATIONS

HQ: CUI Global, Inc.
20050 SW 112th Ave., Tualatin, OR 97062
Phone: 503-612-2300   **Fax:** 503-612-2385
Web: www.cuiglobal.com

COMPETITORS

Arrow Electronics	IBM Microelectronics
Avnet	SprayCool
Cooligy	

HISTORICAL FINANCIALS

Company Type: Public

Income Statement

FYE: December 31

	REVENUE ($ mil.)	NET INCOME ($ mil.)	NET PROFIT MARGIN	EMPLOYEES
12/10	40.9	(7.0)	—	86
12/09	28.9	(4.2)	—	88
12/08	19.6	(1.8)	—	52
12/07	0.2	(5.7)	—	4
12/06	0.3	(14.5)	—	9
Annual Growth	**241.7%**	**—**	**—**	**75.8%**

2010 Year-End Financials

Debt ratio: 100.5%
Return on equity: —
Cash ($ mil.): 0.6
Current ratio: 0.94
Long-term debt ($ mil.): 12.4

No. of shares (mil.): 214.0
Dividends
  Yield: —
  Payout: —
Market value ($ mil.): 53.5

	STOCK PRICE ($) FY Close	P/E High/Low		PER SHARE ($) Earnings	Dividends	Book Value
12/10	0.25	—	—	(0.04)	0.00	0.06
12/09	0.09	—	—	(0.02)	0.00	0.03
12/08	0.10	—	—	(0.01)	0.00	0.06
12/07	0.27	—	—	(0.04)	0.00	0.01
12/06	0.28	—	—	(0.13)	0.00	0.04
Annual Growth	**(2.8%)**	**—**	**—**	**—**	**—**	**7.7%**

Curis

Curis's cancer patients and Sega's gamers might one day have an unlikely hero in common: Sonic the Hedgehog. Drug development firm Curis is studying hedgehog signaling pathways (including the sonic hedgehog pathway, named after the Sega mascot) to find treatments for oncology ailments and other conditions. Such signaling pathways regulate tissue growth and repair, and the company is looking for ways to either stimulate them or slow them down as a means of treating disease. Curis is collaborating with Genentech to develop cancer drugs using hedgehog pathways. The company also has internal development programs for cancer treatments using other signaling pathways.

Curis is a development-stage company (one with no marketed products) and as such relies on funding from its collaborations with larger firms to take its candidates into clinical trials. The company's main partnership with Genentech (and Genentech's parent, Roche) is focused on lead candidate GDC-0449, a potential treatment for basal cell carcinoma in late-stage clinical trials. The drug is also being tested for other oncology applications including breast, lung, and prostate cancers.

However, the company has had to end some development partnerships over the years due to disappointing trial results. Previous programs used the hedgehog and other pathway technologies to develop potential treatments for cancers and cardiovascular and neurological ailments.

As a result, the company is pursuing additional collaborative agreements, primarily for its cancer programs. It also intends to develop its own clinical capabilities in order to retain more rights to the candidates it discovers. In addition, Curis licenses out its technologies to third parties for use in their independent development efforts.

EXECUTIVES

Chairman, James R. McNab Jr., age 67
President, CEO, and Director, Daniel R. (Dan) Passeri, age 50, $855,184 total compensation
CFO, COO and Secretary, Michael P. (Mike) Gray, age 40, $568,516 total compensation
VP Technology Management and Intellectual Property, Mark W. Noel, age 52, $343,321 total compensation
SVP Discovery and Preclinical Development, Changgeng Qian, age 55, $467,339 total compensation
Auditors: PricewaterhouseCoopers LLP

LOCATIONS

HQ: Curis, Inc.
4 Maguire Rd., Lexington, MA 02421
Phone: 617-503-6500   **Fax:** 617-503-6501
Web: www.curis.com

PRODUCTS/OPERATIONS

2010 Sales

	% of total	% of total
License & maintenance fees	15.7	98
Research & development contracts & grants	0.3	2
Total	**16.0**	**100**

COMPETITORS

Amgen	Infinity
ArQule	Pharmaceuticals
Bristol-Myers Squibb	Kyowa Hakko Kirin
Celgene Signal	Merck
Research	Myrexis
Cell Therapeutics	Novartis
Eli Lilly	Pfizer
Exelixis	Semafore
Genentech	Pharmaceuticals
Geron	Synta Pharmaceuticals
Human Genome Sciences	

HISTORICAL FINANCIALS

Company Type: Public

Income Statement

FYE: December 31

	REVENUE ($ mil.)	NET INCOME ($ mil.)	NET PROFIT MARGIN	EMPLOYEES
12/10	16.0	(4.4)	—	32
12/09	8.6	(9.8)	—	33
12/08	8.4	(12.1)	—	34
12/07	16.4	(7.0)	—	42
12/06	14.9	(8.8)	—	51
Annual Growth	**1.8%**	**—**	**—**	**(11.0%)**

2010 Year-End Financials

Debt ratio: —
Return on equity: —
Cash ($ mil.): 7.8
Current ratio: 11.82
Long-term debt ($ mil.): —

No. of shares (mil.): 76.8
Dividends
Yield: —
Payout: —
Market value ($ mil.): 152.1

	STOCK PRICE ($) FY Close	P/E High/Low	PER SHARE ($) Earnings	Dividends	Book Value
12/10	1.98	— —	(0.06)	0.00	0.59
12/09	3.25	— —	(0.15)	0.00	0.49
12/08	0.75	— —	(0.19)	0.00	0.59
12/07	0.98	— —	(0.13)	0.00	0.74
12/06	1.26	— —	(0.18)	0.00	0.73
Annual Growth	**12.0%**		**—**	**—**	**(5.0%)**

CyberDefender Corporation

If the best defense is a good offense, then CyberDefender's got your lineup. Its CyberDefender line of Internet security software protects Windows-based PCs against identity theft, viruses, malware, and spyware. The company boasts about 600,000 active subscribers who renew its products on a monthly or yearly basis. CyberDefender markets its applications to consumers and small businesses through e-mails, banners, and search ads; it also runs a direct marketing campaign with Guthy-Renker. In addition, CyberDefender operates a tech-support call center called LiveTech, where its 500 help desk agents handle about 160,000 calls a month. Co-founder and CEO Gary Guseinov owns almost a quarter of the company's stock.

Call center operations are a relatively new business segment for CyberDefender. As the market for Internet security software is dominated by McAfee, Symantec (its SVP of product development is a former Symantec executive), and Trend Micro, the company noticed a need for general help desk support. Its tech support services were initially outsourced to India, where it costs less to run a call center, but customers weren't happy with the language barrier. CyberDefender began expanding its Los Angeles headquarters in 2010 to establish a US-based call center; customers pay about $300 a year for 24-hour assistance. At full capacity, the call center will be able to seat 600 agents and handle more than 1 million calls per month. By the second quarter of 2010, the LiveTech service accounted for 56% of CyberDefender's overall sales.

The company is also expanding its marketing channels to sell its line of security software. Up until 2009 it relied on e-mails, Web banners, and search ads to attract potential customers to its products' free week-long trials. That method ended up drawing hundreds of complaints with the Los Angeles Better Business Bureau when customers did not discontinue the service before their credit cards were charged. (In about 60% of those cases the customer received a full refund).

CyberDefender then teamed up with GR Match, a subsidiary of direct marketing giant Guthy-Renker, to create radio and TV commercials for home shopping channels in 28 countries. As part of the deal, Guthy-Renker Co-CEO Ben Van de Bunt is now CyberDefender's second-largest shareholder, controlling 22% of the company's stock. It also partnered with a subsidiary of publisher John Wiley & Sons to sell a line of anti-spyware software with the *For Dummies* trademark. Now *Anti-Spyware For Dummies* is available online in the familiar yellow box. Eventually its products will be sold in brick-and-mortar retail locations via a strategic alliance with retail distributor Allianex Corporation.

CyberDefender is small but growing. Its revenues increased a whopping 285% from 2008 to 2009, but the company is not yet profitable since it spends so much money on advertising — almost 70% of sales go back to marketing efforts. Preliminary 2010 revenues estimate growth of more than 135%, putting the company at $45 million for overall revenues.

The company was founded in 2003 as Network Dynamics. It began trading on the OTC market in 2007 and moved to the Nasdaq in June 2010.

EXECUTIVES

Chairman and CEO, Gary Guseinov, age 40
CFO, Secretary, and Director, Kevin Harris, age 41
VP Engineering and Threat Research, Brian Yoder
VP E-Commerce, Raffi Simonian
COO, Igor Barash, age 49
SVP Product Development, Sarah Hicks
SVP Call Center Operations, Jeff Gove
SVP Operations, Neil Evans
SVP Business and Legal Affairs, Gary Lloyd
Chief Revenue Officer, Steve Okun, age 46
Director, Ricardo A. Salas, age 47
Auditors: KMJ Corbin & Company, LLP

LOCATIONS

HQ: CyberDefender Corporation
617 W. 7th St., 10th Fl., Los Angeles, CA 90017
Phone: 213-689-8631   **Fax:** 213-689-8639
Web: www.cyberdefendercorp.com

PRODUCTS/OPERATIONS

Selected Products

AntiSpyware For Dummies
CyberDefenderCOMPLETE
CyberDefender Early Detection Center V2.0
CyberDefender FREE 2.0
CyberDefender Identity Theft Protection Service
CyberDefender Registry Cleaner
CyberDefenderULTIMATE
DoubleMySpeed
earlyNETWORK 3.0
MaxMySpeed
MyCleanPC
MyIdentityDefender Toolbar

COMPETITORS

Barracuda Networks	RSA Security
CA, Inc.	Sophos
F-Secure	Sunbelt Software
IBM Internet Security	Symantec
Systems	Trend Micro
Kaspersky Lab	Webroot Software
McAfee	Zone Labs
Panda Security	

HISTORICAL FINANCIALS

Company Type: Public

Income Statement

FYE: December 31

	REVENUE ($ mil.)	NET INCOME ($ mil.)	NET PROFIT MARGIN	EMPLOYEES
12/10	45.6	(39.6)	—	379
12/09	18.8	(13.7)	—	181
12/08	4.9	(11.3)	—	35
12/07	2.2	(5.9)	—	15
12/06	3.9	(5.5)	—	17
Annual Growth	**84.9%**	**—**	**—**	**117.3%**

2010 Year-End Financials

Debt ratio: —
Return on equity: —
Cash ($ mil.): 2.6
Current ratio: 0.46
Long-term debt ($ mil.): 10.0

No. of shares (mil.): 27.3
Dividends
Yield: —
Payout: —
Market value ($ mil.): 83.6

	STOCK PRICE ($) FY Close	P/E High/Low	PER SHARE ($) Earnings	Dividends	Book Value
12/10	3.06	— —	(1.49)	0.00	(0.86)
12/09	4.70	— —	(0.63)	0.00	(0.22)
12/08	1.27	— —	(0.72)	0.00	(0.47)
12/07	1.30	— —	(0.47)	0.00	(0.00)
Annual Growth	**33.0%**	**— —**	**—**	**—**	**—**

Cytori Therapeutics

Attention lovers of liposuction: Cytori Therapeutics wants your fat. The firm is developing therapies using regenerative adult stem cells derived from adipose, otherwise known as fat tissue. Cytori's Celution is an adipose tissue extraction system that is marketed in Europe and Asia for reconstructive and cosmetic surgery purposes. It also sells the PureGraft body contouring system in the US. The company is developing therapies based on the Celution system intended to treat cardiovascular disease, spine and orthopedic injuries, pelvic health conditions, and gastrointestinal disorders. Cytori has a joint venture with Olympus Corporation to develop future products based on its Celution system.

Cytori's products are marketed through direct sales organizations and independent distributors. The company began marketing the Celution system in Europe and Asia in 2008 for reconstructive surgery applications. Cytori launched its PureGraft system in the US market in 2010 after receiving FDA approval; the company is working to gain marketing approval to sell the Celution system in the US as well. In addition, the company sells its StemSource cell banking system, which collects and preserves stem and regenerative cells for research purposes, to customers around the globe.

Because Cytori is focused on regenerative cells, it has avoided much of the heat surrounding the embryonic stem cell debate. The company's main research project focuses on the use of adipose-derived cells to treat chronic heart disease and other heart attack patients. Cytori's cardiovascular research programs are part of its partnership with Olympus.

To focus on its core product offerings and R&D activities, Cytori has divested or phased out most of the products sold by its MacroPore Biosurgery unit, including a line of orthopedic implants. The unit continues to develop biological implant products in Japan.

Venture partner Olympus controls about 10% of the company. Affiliated distribution company Green Hospital Supply, which markets Cytori's products in Japan, also owns a minority stake in Cytori.

EXECUTIVES

Chairman, Lloyd H. Dean, age 60
President and Director, Marc H. Hedrick, age 48, $683,644 total compensation
CFO, Mark E. Saad, age 41, $652,016 total compensation
President, Asia Pacific, Seijiro N. Shirahama, age 57, $421,854 total compensation
CEO and Director, Christopher J. Calhoun, age 45, $867,290 total compensation
VP Clinical Development, Alexander M. Milstein, age 52
VP Emerging Market Sales, David C. Oxley
VP Regulatory Affairs and Quality Assurance, Kenneth K. Kleinhenz, age 47
SVP Operations, Douglas M. Arm, age 42
SVP US Sales, Bruce A. Reuter, age 62, $451,731 total compensation
Investor and Media Contact, Tom Baker
Auditors: KPMG LLP

LOCATIONS

HQ: Cytori Therapeutics, Inc.
3020 Callan Rd., San Diego, CA 92121
Phone: 858-458-0900   **Fax:** 858-458-0994
Web: www.cytori.com

2009 Sales

	$ mil.	% of total
US	9.8	67
Other countries	4.9	33
Total	**14.7**	**100**

PRODUCTS/OPERATIONS

2009 Sales

	$ mil.	% of total
Development revenues	8.9	61
Celution products	5.8	39
Total	**14.7**	**100**

COMPETITORS

Aastrom Biosciences	Geron
Advanced Cell Technology	Medtronic CardioVascular
Aldagen	MG Biotherapeutics
Baxter International	Osiris Therapeutics
Bioheart	StemCells
Celgene	ThermoGenesis
Fibrocell Science	ViaCord
Genzyme	

HISTORICAL FINANCIALS
Company Type: Public

Income Statement

FYE: December 31

	REVENUE ($ mil.)	NET INCOME ($ mil.)	NET PROFIT MARGIN	EMPLOYEES
12/10	10.6	(27.5)	—	124
12/09	14.7	(23.2)	—	93
12/08	4.5	(30.0)	—	126
12/07	6.0	(28.7)	—	143
12/06	7.9	(25.4)	—	133
Annual Growth	**7.6%**	**—**	**—**	**(1.7%)**

2010 Year-End Financials

Debt ratio: 58.0%	No. of shares (mil.): 52.0
Return on equity: —	Dividends
Cash ($ mil.): 52.7	Yield: —
Current ratio: 4.46	Payout: —
Long-term debt ($ mil.): 13.3	Market value ($ mil.): 269.6

	STOCK PRICE ($) FY Close	P/E High/Low		Earnings	PER SHARE ($) Dividends	Book Value
12/10	5.19	—	—	(0.60)	0.00	0.44
12/09	6.10	—	—	(0.65)	0.00	(0.09)
12/08	3.61	—	—	(1.12)	0.00	(0.26)
12/07	6.13	—	—	(1.25)	0.00	(0.39)
12/06	6.54	—	—	(1.53)	0.00	(0.58)
Annual Growth	**(5.6%)**	**—**	**—**	**—**	**—**	**—**

Datalink

Datalink serves up storage system smorgasbords. The company builds and implements high-end, custom-designed data storage systems for large corporations. Datalink's storage systems include disk- and tape-based storage devices, storage networking components, and data management software. The company employs an open-system standard, building networks from products made by leading manufacturers such as Brocade, EMC, and Hitachi Data Systems. Datalink also provides ongoing support and maintenance services. The company markets its products directly to customers in the US. It has designed systems for clients including AT&T, Harris Corporation, NAVTEQ, and St. Jude Medical. It has about 30 locations across the US.

Datalink fell just short of profitability in 2010 due to a double-digit decrease in revenues and increased operational expenses. The company's sales for the year got a boost from its acquisition of Incentra, but Datalink cited costs associated with the integration of those operations with its existing business as contributing to its loss for the year.

Datalink continues to focus on growing its service expertise and geographic presence largely through acquisitions. In 2009 the company bought the networking division of Minneapolis-based Cross Telecom for $2 million; the deal expanded Datalink's expertise in designing, implementing, and managing network storage and backup products. It also acquired IT systems distributor and managed services provider Incentra for $8.8 million in cash that year. The deal boosted the company's profile in Chicago and the Northeast, as well as in several western states.

Then in 2011 Datalink bought another Minneapolis business, Midwave, in a $17.6 million cash and stock deal. With the addition of Midwave's data center and IT infrastructure services, Datalink now claims to be the leading provider of such services in that region, doubling its Cisco-related revenue and Datalink's consulting services team.

Chairman and former CEO Greg Meland owns about 20% of Datalink.

HISTORY

Founded in 1963 as Stan Clothier, Datalink was originally a manufacturers' representative for technology products and components. Its name change to Datalink in 1987 reflected the company's growing role as a distributor of data storage products. Datalink opened a Chicago office in 1989 and expanded beyond the Midwest in 1992 with an office in Seattle. Greg Meland, formerly the company's VP of sales, was named president and CEO in 1993.

In 1995, with the introduction of its DataCare program, the company began to reposition itself as a provider of information management services rather than strictly a value-added distributor. Two years later Datalink began offering its consulting services to customers in the information management industry.

In 1998 Datalink initiated an IPO, which it later withdrew. That year the company expanded throughout the US, opening offices in Massachusetts, New Jersey, and California and adding five offices in the Southeast US with the acquisition of Georgia-based rival Direct Connect Systems. Datalink successfully went public in 1999. Its expansion continued in 2000, with additional offices opening in North Carolina and Oregon. In 2001 the company moved its headquarters from Edina, Minnesota to Chanhassen, a Minneapolis suburb.

Datalink raised more than $5 million in a 2002 private placement of stock, with institutional investors buying the shares.

Charlie Westling, previously the company's VP of market development, was promoted to president and COO in 2003 (he joined Datalink in 2001) and was named CEO of the company in 2005; Meland was made chairman. Director Paul Lidsky took over as CEO in 2009.

Datalink expanded its operations by acquiring systems integrator Midrange Computer Solutions for $14 million in 2007. The purchase extended Datalink's operations in the northeastern and midwestern regions, as well as in California.

EXECUTIVES

Chairman, Greg R. Meland, age 57
President, CEO, and Director, Paul F. Lidsky, age 57
EVP Strategy and Field Operations, Shawn O'Grady, age 48
VP Human Resources, Mary E. West, age 62
VP Technical Services, Tom Sylvester
VP Administration, CFO, and Secretary, Gregory T. Barnum, age 56, $443,490 total compensation
Vice Chairman, James E. (Jim) Ousley, age 65
CTO, Scott D. Robinson, age 51
Director Sales West Region, Mike Cannon
Media Relations, Bob Connolly
Engineering Director Eastern Region, Kevin Campbell
Secretary, Jeffrey C. Robbins
Director Sales North Central Region, Tim Rasmussen
Controller, Denise M. Westenfield
Investor Relations, Kim Payne
Auditors: McGladrey & Pullen, LLP

LOCATIONS

HQ: Datalink Corporation
8170 Upland Cir., Chanhassen, MN 55317-8589
Phone: 952-944-3462   **Fax:** 952-944-7869
Web: www.datalink.com

PRODUCTS/OPERATIONS

2009 Sales

	$ mil.	% of total
Product	94.7	53
Service	83.3	47
Total	**178.0**	**100**

COMPETITORS

Cranel	InterVision Systems
Dell	Technologies
Dot Hill	Midwave
EMC	NetApp
Forsythe Technology	Presidio, Inc.
Fujitsu	Qualstar
Hewlett-Packard	Sirius Computer
Hitachi Data Systems	Solutions
IBM	

HISTORICAL FINANCIALS

Company Type: Public

Income Statement

FYE: December 31

	REVENUE ($ mil.)	NET INCOME ($ mil.)	NET PROFIT MARGIN	EMPLOYEES
12/10	293.7	2.3	0.8%	299
12/09	178.1	(0.6)	—	307
12/08	195.6	3.4	1.7%	208
12/07	177.8	1.2	0.7%	199
12/06	146.0	8.5	5.8%	160
Annual Growth	**19.1%**	**(27.9%)**	**—**	**16.9%**

2010 Year-End Financials

Debt ratio: —	No. of shares (mil.): 13.6
Return on equity: 4.9%	Dividends
Cash ($ mil.): 9.0	Yield: —
Current ratio: 1.21	Payout: —
Long-term debt ($ mil.): —	Market value ($ mil.): 63.4

	STOCK PRICE ($) FY Close	P/E High/Low		PER SHARE ($) Earnings	Dividends	Book Value
12/10	4.67	28	16	0.18	0.00	3.50
12/09	4.33	—	—	(0.04)	0.00	3.27
12/08	3.20	24	8	0.27	0.00	3.28
12/07	3.69	96	36	0.10	0.00	3.07
12/06	7.52	16	5	0.76	0.00	2.43
Annual Growth	**(11.2%)**	**—**	**—**	**(30.2%)**	**—**	**9.5%**

Dataram

Dataram wants you to remember your DRAMs. The company makes add-in memory boards and memory modules that expand the capacity of computer servers and workstations running under the UNIX and Windows operating systems. Its products, which use DRAM memory devices, are compatible with systems from companies such as HP, IBM, and Dell, and with microprocessors made by AMD and Intel. Dataram has developed the Xcela-SAN storage optimization appliance, which accelerates data access for Fibre Channel storage area networks (SANs). About 80% of Dataram's sales come from customers in the US.

Continuing its growth and expansion strategy, in 2009 Dataram bought Micro Memory Bank (MMB), a privately held memory maker. MMB designs and manufactures memory upgrades, as well as sells new and refurbished memory upgrades manufactured by IBM and HP and buys excess memory inventories from other companies. It also sells factory original memory modules made by Micron, Hynix, Samsung, Elpida, and Nanya.

Dataram's sales rose in 2010, as the company revamped its sales and marketing strategy and the economy recovered. The MMB acquisition also contributed to higher revenues. The company was unprofitable, however, as it continued to invest in developing its new storage product line.

The company has made repeated big cuts to its workforce as part of restructuring efforts aimed at centralizing operations. Dataram has about one-quarter of the workforce it employed in fiscal 2001.

EXECUTIVES

Chairman, Roger C. Cady, age 73
President, CEO, and Director, John H. Freeman, age 62, $797,142 total compensation
VP Manufacturing and Engineering, Jeffrey H. Duncan, age 61, $240,632 total compensation
VP Finance and CFO, Mark E. Maddocks, age 59, $270,632 total compensation
VP Marketing and Strategy, Bruce Magath
Director Technology and Product Management, Paul Henke
Senior Marketing Manager, Phyllis Reiman
National Channel Sales Manager, Doug Doerhoff
Worldwide VP Sales, Philip P. Marino
Secretary, Thomas J. Bitar
Controller, Anthony M. Lougee, age 50, $136,208 total compensation
Auditors: J.H. Cohn LLP

LOCATIONS

HQ: Dataram Corporation
186 Princeton Rd., West Windsor, NJ 08550
Phone: 609-799-0071   **Fax:** 609-799-6734
Web: www.dataram.com

2010 Sales

	$ mil.	% of total
US	35.5	81
Europe	4.5	10
Asia/Pacific & other regions	4.0	9
Total	**44.0**	**100**

PRODUCTS/OPERATIONS

2010 Sales

	$ mil.	% of total
DRAM memory	30.0	68
Micro Memory Bank	14.0	32
Total	**44.0**	**100**

COMPETITORS

Buffalo Technology	Micron Technology
Centon Electronics	Mosel Vitelic
Dell	PNY Technologies
Elpida Memory	Samsung Electronics
Hewlett-Packard	Unigen
Hynix	Viking Modular
IBM	Solutions
Intel	Virtium
Kingston Technology	

HISTORICAL FINANCIALS

Company Type: Public

Income Statement

FYE: April 30

	REVENUE ($ mil.)	NET INCOME ($ mil.)	NET PROFIT MARGIN	EMPLOYEES
04/11	46.8	(4.6)	—	91
04/10	44.0	(10.7)	—	113
04/09	25.9	(3.1)	—	109
04/08	30.9	1.6	5.2%	89
04/07	38.4	0.8	2.1%	95
Annual Growth	**5.1%**	**—**	**—**	**(1.1%)**

2011 Year-End Financials

Debt ratio: —	No. of shares (mil.): 8.9
Return on equity: —	Dividends
Cash ($ mil.): 0.3	Yield: 0.0%
Current ratio: 1.42	Payout: —
Long-term debt ($ mil.): —	Market value ($ mil.): 17.1

	STOCK PRICE ($) FY Close	P/E High/Low		PER SHARE ($) Earnings	Dividends	Book Value
04/11	1.92	—	—	(0.52)	0.00	0.83
04/10	2.38	—	—	(1.21)	0.00	1.28
04/09	1.32	—	—	(0.35)	0.00	2.38
04/08	3.28	26	16	0.18	0.24	2.66
04/07	4.22	64	45	0.09	0.24	2.75
Annual Growth	**(17.9%)**	**—**	**—**	**—**	**—**	**(25.9%)**

DDi Corp.

DDi takes a dynamic approach to manufacturing. DDi provides time-critical, customized electronics design, fabrication, and assembly services for makers of communications and networking gear, computers, medical instruments, and military equipment. The company produces complete electronics systems, as well as subsystems, such as printed circuit boards (PCBs), backpanels, and wire harnesses. Its more than 1,000 customers include original electronics manufacturers and contract manufacturers worldwide. Nearly half of orders are filled within 10 days, and some are turned around in 24 hours. DDi gets over 90% of its business from customers in North America.

Late in 2009 DDi bought Toronto-based rival Coretec for about C$25 million (about $24 million). Coretec provided circuit board engineering and manufacturing services, which complement DDi's offerings. DDi combined the companies and integrated the Toronto operations into one facility. The acquisition increased DDi's North American capacity and extended its presence in the military, aerospace, and medical markets.

The company has divested itself of peripheral businesses except for its core PCB operations, and made parallel acquisitions of companies with industry strengths in circuit board manufacturing. The acquisitions have expanded the company's technical capabilities for flex and rigid-flex technologies, as well as moved it further into the military and aerospace markets.

DDi has manufacturing facilities located in the US and Canada that can provide low-volume production services, in addition to quick-turn prototype and pre-production fabrication. DDi also supports customers that have higher volume production needs by sourcing from contract manufacturers in Asia.

Investor Lloyd I. Miller III owns more than 22% of the company.

DDi was established in 1998 by the merger of two companies, Details and Dynamic, and became Dynamic Details. DDi was reincorporated as a Delaware corporation after its IPO in 2000.

EXECUTIVES

Chairman, Bryant R. Riley, age 44
President, CEO, and Director, Mikel H. Williams, age 54, $1,505,959 total compensation
VP and General Counsel, Kurt Scheuerman
VP Marketing, Peter Wetselaar
VP and CTO, Rajesh Kumar
SVP and CFO, J. Michael (Mike) Dodson, age 50
SVP and COO, Michael Mathews, age 50, $722,756 total compensation
Director Operations Accounting, Coleman C. Barner
Chief Accounting Officer, Wayne T. Slomsky, age 45
SVP Sales, Gerald P. Barnes, age 52, $536,356 total compensation
Auditors: PricewaterhouseCoopers LLP

LOCATIONS

HQ: DDi Corp.
1220 N. Simon Circle, Anaheim, CA 92806
Phone: 714-688-7200   **Fax:** 714-688-7400
Web: www.ddiglobal.com

2009 Sales

	$ mil.	% of total
North America	144.9	92
Asia/Pacific	10.6	7
Other regions	2.5	1
Total	**158.0**	**100**

PRODUCTS/OPERATIONS

2009 Sales by Market

	% of total
Military & aerospace	30
Communications	21
Industrial electronics	16
Computer	14
Instrumentation & medical	11
Consumer electronics	7
Business retail	1
Total	**100**

Selected Services

Backpanel, card cage, printed circuit board, and wire harness assembly
Complex printed circuit board design and fabrication
Customized engineering solutions
Electronic product development (quick-turn design, test, and launch)
Testing
Total system assembly and integration
Transition services

COMPETITORS

Benchmark Electronics	Plexus
Celestica	Sanmina-SCI
Eltek	SigmaTron
Endicott Interconnect	Suntron
Firan Technology Group	SYNNEX
Flextronics	TTM Technologies
IEC Electronics	Viasystems
Multek Flexible Circuits	

HISTORICAL FINANCIALS

Company Type: Public

Income Statement

	REVENUE ($ mil.)	NET INCOME ($ mil.)	NET PROFIT MARGIN	EMPLOYEES
				FYE: December 31
12/10	267.8	20.7	7.7%	1,676
12/09	158.0	1.8	1.1%	1,604
12/08	190.8	(33.4)	—	1,230
12/07	181.1	0.7	0.4%	1,300
12/06	198.1	(7.2)	—	1,300
Annual Growth	**7.8%**	**—**	**—**	**6.6%**

2010 Year-End Financials

Debt ratio: 10.9%	No. of shares (mil.): 20.2
Return on equity: 23.4%	Dividends
Cash ($ mil.): 28.3	Yield: 1.9%
Current ratio: 2.24	Payout: 21.8%
Long-term debt ($ mil.): 9.7	Market value ($ mil.): 237.3

	STOCK PRICE ($) FY Close	P/E High/Low		PER SHARE ($) Earnings	Dividends	Book Value
12/10	11.76	12	4	1.01	0.22	4.39
12/09	4.89	57	31	0.09	0.00	3.49
12/08	3.08	—	—	(1.60)	0.00	3.29
12/07	5.63	268	180	0.03	0.00	4.95
12/06	7.20	—	—	(1.21)	0.00	5.31
Annual Growth	**13.0%**	**—**	**—**	**—**	**—**	**(4.6%)**

Deckers Outdoor

There's no business like the specialty shoe business for Deckers Outdoor. It designs and markets the iconic UGG brand of luxury sheepskin footwear (66% of sales), and Teva sports sandals — a cross between a hiking boot and a flip-flop used for walking, hiking, and rafting, among other pursuits. Other product lines include Simple, TSUBO, MOZO, and Ahnu. While imitations flood the market, the company distinguishes UGG and Teva from its competitors by avoiding distribution in off-price outlets. Deckers Outdoor's products are made by independent contractors in Asia, Australia, and New Zealand. The company sells its footwear through about 25 retail stores worldwide, independent distributors, catalogs, and online.

Deckers Outdoor saw its total sales jump by about 23% in 2010 vs. 2009 (to top $1 billion), driven by an increase in UGG sales across all channels (wholesale, retail, and eCommerce) and by Teva wholesale sales. Teva's retail business suffered a 28% decline, while its online sales fell by more than 8%. Sales at the company's growing network of retail stores increased 59%, and Decker plans to continue to add stores both at home and abroad. While the company rings up about three-quarters of its sales in the US, its international sales grew by more than 40% in 2010 vs. 2009, more than twice the rate of its domestic sales growth. It was a profitable year for the company as well, with net income up about 35% over 2009.

With its Teva shoe business sliding, Deckers Outdoor has been working to fill the gap. To that end, in 2011 it agreed to acquire the Sanuk brand of sport footwear for at least $120 million. The purchase is expected to close in mid-2011. Previous acquisitions include the Anhu brand (2009) and TSUBO (2008). TSUBO was founded by a British designer in 1998; the name means "pressure point" in Japanese. The footwear firm complements Deckers Outdoor's existing brand portfolio and TSUBO boasts ergonomic sport and casual shoes, boots, sandals, and heels. They're sold in the US, primarily, but also in Canada, France, Australia, and Japan. In 2009 Deckers Outdoor also acquired Ahnu footwear, named for the goddess of balance and well-being in Celtic mythology. Sold in the US, the brand boasts active footwear that features traction, flexibility, cushioning, and flexibility.

The footwear maker continues to develop its heritage Teva brand. Pleased that the brand survived the downturn in the economy, Deckers Outdoor in 2010 has expanded the Teva product line in both performance and lifestyle markets and introduced shoes at several price points to attract additional men, women, and children who might be lured away by rival brands, such as Chaco and other shoes owned by Wolverine World Wide.

Deckers Outdoor's flagship UGG brand hit the ground running and has remained a cash cow, thanks to high-end retailers and China. Positioning the UGG sheepskin boot as upscale, the footwear firm peddles the brand mostly through high-end retailers. One of the company's top customers, Nordstrom, was responsible for a large portion of UGG sales in the US; the retailer accounted for 10% of sales for Deckers Outdoor overall. UGGs also sell through Neiman Marcus and Zappos.com. The shoe company's joint venture agreement with Stella International Holdings, inked in 2008, has been key for the increase, as well. The joint venture is 51%-owned by Deckers Outdoor; Stella, a major manufacturer for the company in China, owns the rest. As a result, the UGG brand has secured a foothold in China, where Deckers Outdoor has begun to open retail stores and distribute its products as a wholesaler. Soon after the venture was formed, the company opened its first UGG Australia-branded concept store in Beijing.

A continuing rise in UGG sales has extended debates over whether the name is generic or a trademark that could possibly be defended over international boundaries. Australian makers of the sheepskin boots, traditionally called uggs, contend that the name is generic, akin to trying to protect the name "sneaker" as a trademark.

HISTORY

Douglas Otto and his former partner, Karl Lopker, founded Styled Steers in 1973. But the small, obscure maker of leather sandals gained prominence with a line of multicolored rubber sandals. Surfers in Hawaii called them "deckers," and the company soon adopted the name. In 1985 Deckers Outdoor licensed Teva from river guide Mark Thatcher, who invented the Teva strapping system for rafters to ensure sandals remained attached in turbulent waters. Teva sport sandals became a popular form of casual footwear, largely through word of mouth. The company is the exclusive licensee of Teva shoes, the design of which Thatcher has defended repeatedly against would-be copycats.

In 1994 Deckers Outdoor expanded the Teva line to include closed footwear. With the popularity of Teva sandals seemingly on the wane, the next year it diversified, acquiring rival shoe companies Alp Sport Sandals and UGG Holdings and expanding into the women's and children's markets. A glut of sports sandals depressed sales the following year, but with new products and new marketing, Teva sales increased in 1997.

That year, targeting international expansion, the company acquired German distribution rights to Simple shoes from Vision Warenhandels. Also in 1997 Deckers Outdoor sold its interest in Trukke Winter Sports Products to focus on its core lines.

Thatcher settled with Wal-Mart Stores in 1998 after suing the company over patent and copyright infringement. The firm exited the manufacturing business that year and turned production over to suppliers, mainly in China. In mid-1999 Deckers Outdoor renewed its license with Thatcher through 2011. Continuing to divest noncore operations, in 2000 the company sold its 50% interest in Heirlooms, the makers of the Picante line. The company also hired an ex-adidas exec to help increase Teva's global business (26% in 1999).

In 2000 Otto gave up the president in his title to Peter Benjamin, who was charged with rejuvenating and giving each brand more individualized marketing. In 2001 sales slumped nearly 20% due in part to the weak economy and a bankruptcy filing by one of Deckers Outdoor's largest customers, Track n' Trail.

The company purchased Teva's total assets from its inventor and trademarks and patents holder, Mark Thatcher, in November 2002.

In 2004 Deckers inked licensing agreements for the manufacture of UGG handbags and outerwear, as well as gloves, hats, and scarves. The same year the company signed a separate licensing deal with RMP Athletic Locker for the manufacture of Teva sportswear.

In April 2005 Angel Martinez, a former Reebok executive, was named president and CEO of the company. (Doug Otto retained his position as chairman of the board.) Martinez became chairman of the board in May 2008.

Continued acquisitions and joint ventures have enabled Deckers Outdoor to ride out the recession that began in 2008.

EXECUTIVES

Chairman, President, and CEO, Angel R. Martinez, age 55, $5,951,782 total compensation
CFO, Thomas A. George, age 56
President, Europe, Middle East, and Africa, Stephen M. (Steve) Murray, age 50
President, UGG® Division, Constance X. (Connie) Rishwain, age 53, $2,105,661 total compensation
President, Teva® and Simple® Divisions, Peter K. (Pete) Worley, age 50
President, Ahnu and TSUBO, Jim Van Dine
VP Consumer Direct, John A. Kalinich, age 43
VP Information Technology, Yul Vanek
VP Marketing UGG Australia, Nancy Mamman
VP Human Resources, Graciela Montgomery
COO, Zohar Ziv, age 58, $2,330,555 total compensation
Chief Brand Officer, Jessica Buttimer
Director Corporate Social Responsibility, Mark Heintz
SVP Emerging Brands, Colin G. Clark, age 48, $1,783,711 total compensation
Director PR and Corporate Communications, Errin Cecil-Smith
General Counsel, Stephanie E. S. Cucurullo
SVP Supply Chain, Mark N. Fegley
Director Global Marketing, Teva, Joel Heath
Auditors: KPMG LLP

LOCATIONS

HQ: Deckers Outdoor Corporation
495-A S. Fairview Ave., Goleta, CA 93117
Phone: 805-967-7611   **Fax:** 805-967-7862
Web: www.deckers.com

2010 Sales

	$ mil.	% of total
US	764.1	76
International	236.9	24
Total	**1,001.0**	**100**

PRODUCTS/OPERATIONS

2010 Sales

	$ mil.	% of total
UGG wholesale	663.9	66
Retail stores	125.6	13
Teva wholesale	96.2	10
eCommerce	91.8	9
Other brands wholesale	23.5	2
Total	**1,001.0**	**100**

Selected Brands

Ahnu
MOZO
Simple Shoes
Teva
TSUBO
UGG Australia

COMPETITORS

adidas	LaCrosse Footwear
Birkenstock USA	NIKE
C&J Clark	North Face
Cole Haan	Patagonia, Inc.
Columbia Sportswear	PUMA AG
Converse	Quiksilver
Crocs	Skechers U.S.A.
Diesel SpA	Steven Madden
Fila	Timberland
Guess?	Vans
Keds	Wolverine World Wide
Kenneth Cole	

HISTORICAL FINANCIALS

Company Type: Public

Income Statement				FYE: December 31
	REVENUE ($ mil.)	NET INCOME ($ mil.)	NET PROFIT MARGIN	EMPLOYEES
12/10	1,001.0	158.2	15.8%	1,500
12/09	813.2	116.8	14.4%	1,000
12/08	689.4	73.9	10.7%	780
12/07	448.9	66.4	14.8%	370
12/06	304.4	31.5	10.3%	276
Annual Growth	34.7%	49.7%	—	52.7%

2010 Year-End Financials

Debt ratio: —	No. of shares (mil.): 38.6
Return on equity: 24.2%	Dividends
Cash ($ mil.): 445.2	Yield: —
Current ratio: 4.94	Payout: —
Long-term debt ($ mil.): —	Market value ($ mil.): 3,076.4

	STOCK PRICE ($) FY Close	P/E High/Low		PER SHARE ($) Earnings	Dividends	Book Value
12/10	79.74	22	8	4.03	0.00	16.93
12/09	33.91	12	4	2.96	0.00	12.73
12/08	26.62	26	8	1.87	0.00	9.80
12/07	51.69	33	11	1.69	0.00	7.67
12/06	19.98	25	12	0.82	0.00	5.68
Annual Growth	41.3%	—	—	48.9%	—	31.4%

Decorize

Rather than standardize, Decorize wants to spice things up in your living space. The company, founded in 2000, manufactures and wholesales imported home furnishings. In addition to furniture, Decorize imports accent pieces including lamps, frames, vases, mirrors, and baskets. It sources its wares directly to retailers from factories in China, Indonesia, the Philippines, and India. Decorize consolidated its brands in recent years. Products marketed to independent retailers (76% of 2008 revenue) maintain the GuildMaster brand, while products targeting large retailers (24% of 2008 revenue) are marketed under the Decorize brand name. Customers include Klaussner Furniture, Dillard's, OfficeMax, and Williams-Sonoma.

While the company's revenue mix favored independent retailers over large accounts by 3:1 in fiscal 2008, the firm is aiming for a more even split between the two channels. (Large retailers have accounted for up to 70% of the firm's annual revenues and independent retailers have comprised as low as 30%.) Decorize, however, has recently focused its attention to the independent retailer unit due to soft sales for large retail accounts.

Decorize owns two US subsidiaries, GuildMaster and Faith Walk, and two international subsidiaries, WestWay Enterprises and P.T. Niaga Merapi.

To boost sales at Broyhill, Decorize in late 2006 inked a deal with the furniture manufacturer to make and market a Broyhill-branded line of home accessories, lamps, wall decor, and accent furniture. In 2007 the company struck a similar deal with Klaussner Furniture Industries to make products to be marketed under the Klaussner's Complements brand.

EVP James Parsons and former president and CEO Jon Baker each own approximately 14% of the company's common stock.

EXECUTIVES

CFO, Daniel (Dan) Graham, age 48
President, CEO, and Director, Stephen R. (Steve) Crowder
EVP, James K. (Jim) Parsons, age 62
VP, John Michael Sandel
Auditors: BKD, LLP

LOCATIONS

HQ: Decorize, Inc.
1938 E. Phelps, Springfield, MO 65802
Phone: 417-879-3326
Web: www.decorize.com

COMPETITORS

Bassett Furniture	Herman Miller
Cost Plus	Newell Rubbermaid
DMI Furniture	Pier 1 Imports
Ethan Allen	Pinnacle Frames
Furniture Brands	Steelcase
International	Uniek

HISTORICAL FINANCIALS

Company Type: Public

Income Statement

FYE: June 30

	REVENUE ($ mil.)	NET INCOME ($ mil.)	NET PROFIT MARGIN	EMPLOYEES
06/08	15.2	(0.6)	—	554
06/07	15.9	(0.7)	—	432
06/06	9.2	(2.2)	—	324
06/05	10.8	(2.6)	—	131
06/04	12.1	(4.4)	—	133
Annual Growth	5.9%	—	—	42.9%

2008 Year-End Financials

Debt ratio: —	No. of shares (mil.): —
Return on equity: —	Dividends
Cash ($ mil.): 0.3	Yield: —
Current ratio: 0.70	Payout: —
Long-term debt ($ mil.): 1.2	Market value ($ mil.): —

	STOCK PRICE ($) FY Close	P/E High/Low	PER SHARE ($) Earnings	Dividends	Book Value
06/08	0.50	— —	(0.10)	0.00	(0.00)
06/07	2.50	— —	(0.15)	0.00	(0.00)
06/06	1.35	— —	(0.60)	0.00	(0.00)
06/05	3.35	— —	(1.00)	0.00	(0.00)
06/04	3.90	— —	(1.85)	0.00	(0.00)
Annual Growth	(40.2%)	—	—	—	—

DEI Holdings

If you try to steal a car protected by DEI's Viper, you just might get bit. DEI Holdings is the holding company of some of the most well-known consumer electronics brands in North America, including Directed Electronics' Viper, Python, and Clifford automobile security and remote start systems and Orion car audio systems. It is also a leading designer and manufacturer of premium home theater loudspeakers sold under the Polk Audio and Definitive Technology brands. DEI markets its products through several channels, including national retailers and specialty chains, among them Wal-Mart, Best Buy, and Sears. The company was acquired by private equity firm Charlesbank Capital Partners for about $305 million in 2011.

The company maintains its offices in the US and Canada, and it continues to be led by its existing management team. Charlesbank intends to expand DEI's business both in North America and internationally.

The company was founded as Directed Electronics in 1982 by Darrell Issa (now a US Congressman representing California's 49th District) and his wife Kathy. In 2008 it adopted a holding company structure, renaming the parent DEI Holdings, with Directed Electronics surviving as a business unit.

The following year the company was hurt by the recession, which cut into consumer demand for electronics. Its entry into the satellite radio market — selling equipment for the SIRIUS XM Radio network — also did not perform well, prompting DEI to voluntarily cease trading on the NASDAQ exchange. The move was designed to cut accounting, legal, and administrative costs associated with producing financial information required by the SEC.

Since then, the company has been busy touting some of its more technologically advanced products, namely the Viper SmartStart, the world's first smartphone application to remote start a car. In 2011 it set a world record by remote starting a car in New York from more than 10,000 miles away in Australia. The app can also be integrated into security services from Alarm.com to allow consumers to arm and disarm their home security systems using their smartphones. SmartStart is part of DEI's strategy to incorporate developing technologies into its products to enhance security and improve convenience for consumers.

EXECUTIVES

Chairman, Troy D. Templeton, age 50
President, Directed Electronics, Canada, Julien Joly
President, CEO, and Director, James E. (Jim) Minarik, age 57
EVP Definitive Technology, Dave E. Peet
EVP, Michael S. (Mike) Simmons
EVP and CFO, Kevin P. Duffy, age 35
VP Product Development, Polk Audio, Jeffrey Nemec
VP Sales, Polk Audio, Ben Newhall
SVP Marketing and Product Development, Paul DiComo
COO Polk Audio, Joe Tristani
Auditors: PricewaterhouseCoopers LLP

LOCATIONS

HQ: DEI Holdings, Inc.
1 Viper Way, Vista, CA 92081
Phone: 760-598-6200 **Fax:** 760-598-6400
Web: www.deiholdings.com

PRODUCTS/OPERATIONS

Selected Brands & Products

Directed Electronics
Astroflex AstroStart (vehicle alarm and remote start)
Automate (vehicle alarm, remote start, keyless entry, and GPS tracking)
Autostart (all-weather vehicle alarm and remote start)
Avital (vehicle alarm and remote start)
Clifford (vehicle alarm)
Orion (car audio)
Orion Wired (car audio)
Python (remote start and keyless entry)
Ready Remote and AutoCommand (do-it-yourself vehicle alarm and remote start)
Viper (vehicle alarm and remote start)
XpressKit (vehicle interface)
Polk Audio
Atrium (commercial and outdoor loudspeakers)
DSW (home theater subwoofers)
Hitmaster (gaming speakers)
I-Sonic (iPod sound system)
LSiM (home theater loudspeakers)
PA (car audio amplifiers)
Signature Reference (car audio speakers and subwoofers)
SurroundBar (single-speaker surround sound system)
Definitive Technology (home theater loudspeakers)
BiPolar
Mythos
ProCinema
ProMonitor

COMPETITORS

Alpine Electronics of	Pioneer Corporation
America	Rockford
Audiovox	Rodin
Bose	SANYO
Clarion	Sony
Harman International	Winner International
JVC KENWOOD	

HISTORICAL FINANCIALS

Company Type: Public

Income Statement

FYE: December 31

	REVENUE ($ mil.)	NET INCOME ($ mil.)	NET PROFIT MARGIN	EMPLOYEES
12/08	262.9	(55.0)	—	0
12/07	401.1	(140.0)	—	0
12/02	123.7	12.8	10.3%	210
12/01	120.0	—	—	190
12/00	101.0	—	—	170
Annual Growth	12.7%	—	—	11.1%

Debt ratio: —	No. of shares (mil.): —
Return on equity: —	Dividends
Cash ($ mil.): 0.3	Yield: —
Current ratio: 0.70	Payout: —
Long-term debt ($ mil.): 1.2	Market value ($ mil.): —

Demand Media

Demand Media knows that Web branding is in demand. Attracting more than 120 million unique visitors each month, the company operates through a variety of Web-related enterprises that exist to help drive Web traffic to its clients' sites. Subsidiaries include domain-name wholesaler eNom and Pluck, a blog syndicator and provider of social media tools used for integrating websites. Other Demand Media websites include online how-to tutorials provider eHow, humor site Cracked.com, and Trails.com, for outdoor enthusiasts. It also produces online video and written articles through its Demand Studios business, which employs freelancers to provide content for its websites. Demand Media launched an IPO in early 2011.

By going public, Demand Media raised about $151 million. It is using the cash to expand internationally and for general corporate purposes, such as augmenting its working capital and enhancing its sales and marketing activities. It is also using the proceeds to buy complementary technologies or businesses. One such acquisition was its 2011 purchase of CoverItLive, a blogging tool for publishers that complements its Pluck offering. The deal followed Demand Media's annual earnings results for 2010, when the company posted an increase in revenues (to about $253 million, up from some $198 million in 2009) and a decrease in net losses (to $5 million, compared with more than $22 million in 2009).

Around the time of its IPO filing, the company was forced to defend the quality of its output after being labeled a "content farm" by its critics. Demand Media's business model relies on being ranked highly on search results from Google. (For the year ending in 2010, the online search giant provided cost-per-click performance-based advertising that accounted for nearly 30% of Demand Media's total revenue.) Criticism of Demand Media was part of a larger discussion of how Google's search results are increasingly being filled with low-quality results. Such complaints led Google in 2011 to change its search algorithm to give low-content sites less visibility. Demand Media subsequently reported that Google's changes had no impact on its search results.

The company earns the majority of revenues (60%) through the sale of advertising in connection with its content and media segment. The segment includes Demand's owned and operated websites such as eHow.com (25% of total revenue), as well as more than 375 websites operated by customers such as USATODAY.com. The company produces videos through Demand Studios. The videos, primarily distributed to YouTube, earn revenue via targeted advertising. They are are shot in HD by freelance filmmakers, support Demand sites and third party sites, and are designed to appeal to YouTube viewers who are interested in niche subject matter (how hybrid cars work, healthy food choices, or how to grow eggplant).

Demand Media gets the rest of its revenues from its registrar segment, which operates primarily under its eNom brand and earns revenues through domain name registration subscriptions and other related value-added services. Demand manages about 11 million Internet domain names, and offers wholesale domain name registration services to roughly 7,000 resellers, including small businesses, large e-commerce websites, Internet service providers, and web-hosting companies. These resellers sell domains and provide online security, web hosting, and email services.

The company grew through a few key partnerships and acquisitions in 2008. That year Demand Media teamed with the Lance Armstrong Foundation to launch LIVESTRONG.com, a social networking website focused on health and fitness. The company's 2008 acquisition of Pluck added to its portfolio BlogBurst, which provides content from thousands of bloggers that newspapers and media sites can publish on their websites.

Demand Media was founded in 2006 by former Myspace.com chairman Richard Rosenblatt and Shawn Colo of Spectrum Equity Investors. Shortly after the company was formed, Demand Media purchased the assets of Internet marketing firm Intermix Media, which had owned and operated Myspace. Former Intermix Media assets now under Demand Media's control include the entertainment portal Grab.com and how-to site SoYouWanna.com.

In addition to its headquarters in Santa Monica, CA, the company has offices in Bellevue, Washington; Austin, Texas; New York City; and London. Demand Media investors include Oak Investment Partners (which owns a 27% share in the company) and Spectrum Equity (17%). They are represented on the company's board of directors by Fred Harman (Oak Investment) and Victor Parker (Spectrum).

EXECUTIVES

Chairman and CEO, Richard M. Rosenblatt, age 42
President and CFO, Charles S. Hilliard, age 48

EVP Media and Operations, Larry D. Fitzgibbon, age 42
EVP Technology and Engineering, Will Ballard
EVP Demand Studios, Steven Kydd
EVP Product Marketing and Community, Joe Perez
EVP Registrar Services, Michael L. Blend, age 44
EVP and Head Mergers and Acquisitions, Shawn J. Colo, age 39
EVP and General Counsel, Matthew P. Polesetsky, age 42
EVP People Operations, Courtney Montpas
EVP Branded Ad Sales, George Stewart
VP Human Resources, Nicolas Schoenlaub
VP European Sales and Business Development, Stephanie Himoff
VP Investor Relations, Julie C. MacMedan, age 45
Chief Marketing Officer, David E. (Dave) Panos, age 48
SVP and General Manager, typeF.com, Lisa Kraynak
SVP Content Partnership Development, Jeff Dossett
SVP Corporate Communications, Quinn Daly
General Manager, LIVESTRONG.COM, Dan Brian
General Manager, eHow.com, Gregory Boudewijn
Chief Innovation Officer, Byron Reese
General Manager, Demand Studio, Stewart Marlborough
SVP and General Manager, Pluck Enterprise, Steve Semelsberger
Chief Revenue Officer, Joanne K. Bradford, age 48
Auditors: PricewaterhouseCoopers LLP

LOCATIONS

HQ: Demand Media, Inc.
1299 Ocean Ave., Ste. 500, Santa Monica, CA 90401
Phone: 310-394-6400
Web: www.demandmedia.com

PRODUCTS/OPERATIONS

2010 Sales

	$ mil.	% of total
Content & Media		
Owned & operated websites	110.8	44
Network of customer websites	42.1	17
Registrar	100.0	39
Total	**252.9**	**100**

Selected Holdings

Domain Services
  eNom.com
Entertainment
  Cracked.com
Games
  Grab.com
Knowledge
  eHow.com
  ExpertVillage.com
  SoYouWanna.com
Outdoor Lifestyle
  Golflink.com
  LIVESTRONG.com
  Trails.com
Video Production and Written Content
  DemandStudio

COMPETITORS

About.com	Jive Software
AOL	Live Current Media
Connected Ventures	Marchex
Glam Media	Network Solutions
Go Daddy	Topica
HSW International	Tucows
IAC	ValueClick
IGN Entertainment	WebMD Health
Impulse Communications	Yahoo!
iVillage	

HISTORICAL FINANCIALS

Company Type: Public

Income Statement

FYE: December 31

	REVENUE ($ mil.)	NET INCOME ($ mil.)	NET PROFIT MARGIN	EMPLOYEES
12/10	252.9	(5.3)	—	600
12/09	198.5	(22.5)	—	550
12/08	170.3	(14.9)	—	0
12/07	102.3	(5.6)	—	0
Annual Growth	**35.2%**	**—**	**—**	**9.1%**

2010 Year-End Financials

Debt ratio: —	No. of shares (mil.): —
Return on equity: —	Dividends
Cash ($ mil.): 32.3	Yield: —
Current ratio: 0.96	Payout: —
Long-term debt ($ mil.): —	Market value ($ mil.): —

	STOCK PRICE ($) FY Close	P/E High/Low	PER SHARE ($) Earnings	Dividends	Book Value
Annual Growth	—	— —	—	—	—

Denbury Resources

Denbury Resources searches for the lucrative buried resources of oil and gas across the US. In 2010 the independent exploration and production company reported estimated proved reserves of 397.9 million barrels of oil equivalent in the Gulf Coast, Mid-Continent, Permian Basin, and the Rockies. In Mississippi and Montana it owns the top reserves of CO_2 used for tertiary oil recovery (hydrocarbon recovery using advanced techniques) east of the Mississippi River. CO_2 is transported to wellheads where it is used to force oil from abandoned wells. To expand its market share, in 2010 Denbury Resources acquired rival Encore Acquisition for $4.5 billion.

Denbury Resources' business strategy is to focus on tertiary oil activities and CO_2 production in core regions where it holds a strong track record and competitive advantage, and to make complementary acquisition that strengthen its portfolio. The Encore Acquisition deal positions Denbury Resources as one of the largest CO_2 enhanced oil recovery companies in the US with extensive holdings across the Gulf Coast and Rocky Mountains. In 2010 it boosted its CO_2 holdings, buying a 43% non-operated working stake in the Unit located in southwestern Wyoming for $115 million.

Growing its CO_2 assets further, in 2011 the company agreed to spend $191 million to buy the 57.5% working interest it did not already own in the Riley Ridge Federal Unit, in southwestern Wyoming, as well as a 33% stake in an additional 28,000 acres of leasehold property.

The global recession depressed commodity prices and the company's revenues and income in 2009. However, the downturn did not stop Denbury Resources from increasing its production, and from going ahead with the Encore Acquisition purchase.

In order to generate cash for investment in its tertiary oil operations and to pay down debt the company has been selling assets. In 2008 the company sold its gas operations in Louisiana for about $180 million, and in 2009 it sold 60% of its holdings in the Barnett Shale for about $270 million. The following year, Denbury sold the remainder of its Barnett Shale assets to Talon Oil & Gas for $210 million and acquired the Conroe Field property in Texas from Wapiti Energy for about $430 million in cash and stock. It also sold Haynesville Shale and other East Texas assets to a private buyer for $217.5 million, and sold its 46% stake in Encore Energy Partners (a master limited partnership acquired as part of the Encore Acquisition deal) for $380 million.

To raise cash, in 2010 the company also sold its interests in Genesis Energy L.P. for more than $101 million.

As a result of its expanded operations, increased production, higher oil and gas prices, and a gain from the sale of its Genesis Energy assets, Denbury Resources reported a major jump in revenues and net income in 2010.

EXECUTIVES

Chairman, Wieland F. Wettstein, age 61
President, CEO, and Director, Phil Rykhoek, age 54, $2,619,205 total compensation
VP and Chief Accounting Officer, Alan Rhoades, age 46
VP and Chief Information Officer, Steve McLaurin
VP Legal, Ray Dubuisson
VP North Region, Greg Dover, age 58
VP West Region, Charlie Gibson, age 52
VP Marketing, Dan E. Cole, age 58
VP CO2 Supply and Pipeline Operations, John Filiatrault
VP Drilling, Jeff Marcel, age 49
VP Business Development, Bradley (Brad) Cox, age 49
VP East Region, Barry Schneider, age 48
VP Legal and Secretary, H. Raymond (Ray) Dubuisson, age 60, $1,214,901 total compensation
VP Human Resources, Whitney Shelley, age 43
SVP Production Operations, Craig McPherson
Manager Investor and Public Relations, Laurie Burkes
SVP CO2 Operations, Robert L. (Bob) Cornelius, age 56, $2,132,434 total compensation
SVP, CFO, Treasurer, and Assistant Secretary, Mark C. Allen Sr., age 43, $1,995,080 total compensation
Auditors: PricewaterhouseCoopers LLP

LOCATIONS

HQ: Denbury Resources Inc.
5100 Tennyson Pkwy., Ste. 1200, Plano, TX 75024
Phone: 972-673-2000   **Fax:** 972-673-2150
Web: www.denbury.com

PRODUCTS/OPERATIONS

2010 Sales

	$ mil.	% of total
Oil, natural gas & related products	1,793.3	94
Gain on sale of interests in Genesis	101.5	5
CO2 sales and transportation fees	19.2	1
Other	7.8	-
Total	**1,921.8**	**100**

COMPETITORS

Abraxas Petroleum	Genesis Energy
Apache	McMoRan Exploration
BP	Murphy Oil
Chevron	Newfield Exploration
Delta Petroleum	Occidental Permian
Exxon Mobil	Royal Dutch Shell
Forest Oil	Swift Energy

HISTORICAL FINANCIALS
Company Type: Public

Income Statement
FYE: December 31

	REVENUE ($ mil.)	NET INCOME ($ mil.)	NET PROFIT MARGIN	EMPLOYEES
12/10	1,921.8	271.7	14.1%	1,195
12/09	882.5	(75.2)	—	830
12/08	1,365.7	388.4	28.4%	797
12/07	972.0	253.1	26.0%	686
12/06	731.5	202.5	27.7%	596
Annual Growth	**27.3%**	**7.6%**	**—**	**19.0%**

2010 Year-End Financials

Debt ratio: 55.2%
Return on equity: 6.2%
Cash ($ mil.): 381.9
Current ratio: 1.49
Long-term debt ($ mil.): 2,416.2
No. of shares (mil.): 400.2
Dividends
 Yield: —
 Payout: —
Market value ($ mil.): 7,640.1

	STOCK PRICE ($) FY Close	P/E High/Low		PER SHARE ($) Earnings	Dividends	Book Value
12/10	19.09	28	19	0.72	0.00	10.95
12/09	14.80	—	—	(0.30)	0.00	7.53
12/08	10.92	26	4	1.54	0.00	7.45
12/07	29.75	31	13	1.00	0.00	5.75
12/06	13.90	22	14	0.82	0.00	4.61
Annual Growth	**8.3%**	**—**	**—**	**(3.2%)**	**—**	**24.1%**

Dendreon

Dendreon wants to boost your immunity from the start. It is developing therapeutic vaccines that help the body's immune system fight cancer by targeting dendritic cells, which initiate an immune response to disease-causing antigens. Its sole commercial product, Provenge, is a therapeutic vaccine that targets prostate cancer. Provenge gained the status of being the first therapeutic cancer vaccine to receive FDA approval in 2010. Dendreon is also working on a therapeutic vaccine to treat breast, bladder, and ovarian cancers, and it has research programs investigating cancer-fighting monoclonal antibodies and small molecule drugs.

Following Provenge's FDA approval as a treatment for men with advanced prostate cancer in April 2010, treatments became available at the 50 centers in the US that also participated in the clinical trials. Dendreon then began to gradually increase manufacturing and treatment capacity for the difficult-to-make therapy; it greatly expanded its existing New Jersey manufacturing center in 2011, which allowed it the means to increase administration sites to about 225 clinics.

However early sales of Provenge have not rocketed quite as high and fast as the company had hoped. With an average round of treatment costing $93,000, insurers and Medicare have proven hesistant to reimburse for the drug, which studies have shown only extends patient's lives by about four months. Despite receiving the FDA's approval of its third manufacturing facility (in Atlanta), in mid-2011 the company assessed its cash and assets and announced a restructuring. It cut its workforce by 500 employees and brought in some fresh executive energy.

Dendreon's plans for Provenge don't stop with the US advanced prostate cancer market. The company is also developing Provenge as a treatment for early stage prostate cancer patients, and it is seeking commercialization partners to help the company seek approval for Provenge in international markets. Dendreon plans to first seek approval in Europe, where it will use a third-party manufacturer until it can build its own plant in Germany.

Provenge was developed under FDA fast track status as a treatment to extend the lives of patients in the advanced stages of prostate cancer. The vaccine, which represents a new kind of cancer therapy in which a patient's immune system is trained to fight disease, became the center of an FDA controversy in 2007 when the agency refused to approve the drug even after its expert advisory committee recommended approval. Instead, the FDA required Dendreon to put the drug through additional clinical testing, spurring patient advocacy groups and some investors to protest the decision. In 2009 the company announced that the trial results met their goals, and it successfully re-filed the drug for FDA approval later that year.

EXECUTIVES

Chairman, Richard B. Brewer, age 60
President, CEO, and Director, Mitchell H. Gold, age 44, $1,606,327 total compensation
EVP and COO, Hans Bishop
EVP, Chief Scientific Officer, and Director, David L. Urdal, age 61, $817,275 total compensation
EVP Human Resources, Richard J. (Rich) Ranieri, age 59
EVP and CFO, Gregory T. (Greg) Schiffman, age 53, $935,904 total compensation
EVP Research and Development, and Chief Medical Officer, Mark W. Frohlich, age 50, $617,518 total compensation
SVP Corporate Development, General Counsel, and Secretary, Richard F. (Rick) Hamm Jr., age 51, $786,655 total compensation
Auditors: Ernst & Young LLP

LOCATIONS

HQ: Dendreon Corporation
3005 1st Ave., Seattle, WA 98121
Phone: 206-256-4545   **Fax:** 206-256-0571
Web: www.dendreon.com

COMPETITORS

Abbott Labs	Northwest
Agenus	Biotherapeutics
AstraZeneca	Oncothyreon
AVAX	Onyvax
BioSante	Progenics
Celldex Therapeutics	Pharmaceuticals
MannKind	Sanofi
MediGene	Vaxon Biotech
Micromet	

HISTORICAL FINANCIALS
Company Type: Public

Income Statement
FYE: December 31

	REVENUE ($ mil.)	NET INCOME ($ mil.)	NET PROFIT MARGIN	EMPLOYEES
12/10	48.1	(439.5)	—	1,497
12/09	0.1	(220.2)	—	484
12/08	0.1	(71.6)	—	198
12/07	0.7	(99.3)	—	194
12/06	0.3	(91.6)	—	232
Annual Growth	**255.8%**	**—**	**—**	**59.4%**

2010 Year-End Financials

Debt ratio: 11.0%
Return on equity: —
Cash ($ mil.): 133.0
Current ratio: 6.60
Long-term debt ($ mil.): 54.3

No. of shares (mil.): 145.2
Dividends
  Yield: —
  Payout: —
Market value ($ mil.): 5,071.6

| | STOCK PRICE ($) | P/E | | PER SHARE ($) | |
	FY Close	High/Low	Earnings	Dividends	Book Value
12/10	34.92	— —	(3.18)	0.00	3.39
12/09	26.28	— —	(2.04)	0.00	3.84
12/08	4.58	— —	(0.79)	0.00	0.28
12/07	6.22	— —	(1.20)	0.00	0.48
12/06	4.17	— —	(1.27)	0.00	1.75
Annual Growth	70.1%	— —	—	—	18.0%

Depomed

For comedians and Depomed, it's all about the delivery. The drug company makes proprietary drug therapies using its patented delivery technology AcuForm, an extended-release technology that stretches out the time a pill stays in the stomach, thus reducing the number of necessary doses and potential side effects. Depomed's internal development efforts have yielded three FDA-approved and marketed products: Glumetza, an extended-release formulation of common diabetes drug metformin; Gralise to treat nerve pain; and, ProQuin XR, an extended-release version of antibiotic ciprofloxacin, used to treat urinary tract infections.

However, Depomed no longer manufactures or markets Proquin XR. Instead it is focused on getting Gralise to market. The treatment for postherpetic nerve pain (such as that caused by shingles) received FDA approval in 2011. Concurrent with its FDA approval, the company received a $48 million milestone payment with (now-former) development partner Abbott Products (part of Abbott Laboratories). At the same time the company terminated its licensing agreement with Abbott. Depomed expects to launch Gralise in the US sometime before 2012. Though the company will commercialize Gralise on its own if it has to, it is hoping to find a suitable promotional partner or licensee. As for its already-commercialized products, Valeant Pharmaceuticals markets Glumetza in Canada. Santarus co-promotes Glumetza in the US.

In addition to its marketed products, Depomed has several drug candidates in clinical development including Serada, another variation on gabapentin, in late-stage clinical trials as a treatment for menopausal hot flashes. Other products in development include DM-1992 for Parkinson's disease and DM-3458 to treat gastroesophageal reflux disease.

Depomed's product development strategy is three-fold. Its internal development activities focus on creating new formulations of off-patent drugs (such as metformin) that could benefit from AcuForm's extended-release delivery. It also out-licenses its product candidates once they have been formulated and are in clinical development. Finally, it enters into licensing and development partnerships with other pharmaceutical companies including Boehringer Ingelheim, Covidien, Janssen Pharmaceutical, and Merck.

Contract manufacturer Patheon and Valeant actually make the company's marketed products. De-

pomed's manufacturing capacity is limited to making supplies for its early stage trials.

In early 2011 Depomed named James Schoeneck as its president and CEO. Schoeneck replaced Carl Pelzel who resigned for personal reasons after serving at the company's helm for about four years.

EXECUTIVES

Chairman, Peter D. Staple, age 59
President, CEO, and Director, Carl A. Pelzel, age 60, $1,021,064 total compensation
President, CEO, and Director, James A. (Jim) Schoeneck, age 53
VP Finance, Tammy L. Cameron, age 45, $317,615 total compensation
VP Operations, William Callahan
VP Administration and Human Resources, Kera Alexander, age 54
VP Manufacturing Technology, John N. Shell, age 57
VP Research Development, Michael M. Sweeney, age 50, $489,464 total compensation
VP Marketing, Shay Weisbrich
VP and General Counsel, Matthew M. Gosling, age 40, $587,074 total compensation
SVP Business Development, Thadd M. Vargas, age 45
Investor Relations, Sheilah Serradell
Auditors: Ernst & Young LLP

LOCATIONS

HQ: Depomed, Inc.
1360 O'Brien Dr., Menlo Park, CA 94025-1436
Phone: 650-462-5900   **Fax:** 650-462-9993
Web: www.depomedinc.com

PRODUCTS/OPERATIONS

2010 Revenues

	$ mil.	% of total
Product sales		
Glumetza	45.5	57
Proquin XR	0.1	-
Royalties	0.3	-
License & collaborative revenues	34.8	43
Total	**80.7**	**100**

COMPETITORS

Bionovo	Pfizer
Bristol-Myers Squibb	Ranbaxy Laboratories
Flamel Technologies	Shionogi Pharma
GlaxoSmithKline	SkyePharma
Johnson & Johnson	Takeda Pharmaceutical
Merck	Teva
Mylan Pharmaceuticals	Watson Pharmaceuticals

HISTORICAL FINANCIALS

Company Type: Public

Income Statement

FYE: December 31

	REVENUE ($ mil.)	NET INCOME ($ mil.)	NET PROFIT MARGIN	EMPLOYEES
12/10	80.8	3.9	4.8%	69
12/09	57.7	(22.0)	—	73
12/08	34.8	(15.3)	—	81
12/07	65.6	49.2	75.0%	73
12/06	9.6	(39.7)	—	105
Annual Growth	70.3%	—	—	(10.0%)

2010 Year-End Financials

Debt ratio: —
Return on equity: 16.9%
Cash ($ mil.): 22.5
Current ratio: 2.41
Long-term debt ($ mil.): —

No. of shares (mil.): 53.0
Dividends
  Yield: —
  Payout: —
Market value ($ mil.): 336.8

| | STOCK PRICE ($) | P/E | | PER SHARE ($) | |
	FY Close	High/Low	Earnings	Dividends	Book Value
12/10	6.36	96 33	0.07	0.00	0.44
12/09	3.35	— —	(0.43)	0.00	0.30
12/08	1.65	— —	(0.32)	0.00	0.65
12/07	3.26	5 2	1.05	0.00	0.95
12/06	3.45	— —	(0.97)	0.00	(0.65)
Annual Growth	16.5%	— —	—	—	—

DeVry

It isn't exactly Ivy League, but DeVry is in the big leagues of technical, health care, and business schools. The for-profit company offers professional, undergraduate, and graduate programs through several subsidiary schools. Flagship DeVry University, with about 100 US locations and another in Canada, specializes in business and technology education. Its Keller Graduate School of Management unit offers MBA and other graduate programs while its Ross University offers medical and veterinary school training. The company also offers health care education through Chamberlain College of Nursing and Carrington College. In all, DeVry has more than 70,000 students through campus and online enrollment.

The company's Becker Professional Education subsidiary offers professional exam review and continuing education courses in accounting, finance, and project management. It operates in the US and several international markets.

In addition to its business, healthcare, and technical education services, DeVry offers middle school and high school programs online through its Advanced Academics unit. It is also laying the groundwork to expand into elementary education through its K-12 program.

Internationally, the company operates DeVry Brasil and its Ross University programs are based in the West Indies. DeVry Brasil began as Fanor and was acquired in 2009. It offers business, law, and engineering programs from about a half-dozen campuses in Brazil. Ross students take academic coursework at the university campuses in the Caribbean, then complete their degrees with clinical training at US teaching hospitals and affiliated veterinary colleges.

DeVry University's student population is generally older than those at traditional colleges. More than half of its students are older than 25 and represent the school's fastest-growing demographic; many are working adults. The school boasts an enrollment of more than 55,000 undergraduate students and some 18,000 graduate students.

Acquisitions to add to or expand upon its offerings have been a key part of the company's growth strategy. DeVry added to its health care offerings in 2008 with the acquisition of U.S. Education Company, which included about 20 Apollo College and Western Career College locations in the western US. The locations were later renamed Carrington College. It further expanded its medical training offerings through the $235 million purchase of American University of the Caribbean, a physician training school located on St. Maarten.

DeVry enjoyed a boost in enrollments during the economic recession — many unemployed workers took the opportunity to seek new technical training, and at the same time federal student loan purse strings loosened up, giving those workers access to loans for tuition. However, the rapid growth in the entire private education industry, including DeVry, drew attention from lawmakers during 2010, who were concerned that people were adding to their debt with student loans but receiving incomplete or low-quality education services.

Company co-founder and former chairman Dennis Keller, now a director emeritus, owns about 10% of DeVry.

HISTORY

DeVry Institutes was founded in 1931 by Herman DeVry as an electronics repair school. It was later acquired by Bell & Howell (now Voyager Learning Company). While working at Bell & Howell, Dennis Keller, a Princeton graduate, met Ronald Taylor, who had degrees from Harvard and Stanford. In 1973 they created a private business school targeting working adults. In 1987 Keller and Taylor bought DeVry and combined it with their graduate business school under the DeVry name; the company went public in 1991.

The company acquired Becker CPA Review in 1996. With plans to increase the number of DeVry campuses to 40 by the next decade, the company opened DeVry Institutes in New York City and Fremont, California, in 1998. The following year it bought Denver Technical College, which later was integrated into DeVry University. DeVry also began offering classes online.

The Becker Conviser Professional Review segment was bolstered in 2001 with the purchase of Argentum (which did business as Stalla Seminars), a firm engaged in the production of CFA (chartered financial analyst) test prep materials. DeVry Institutes and Keller Graduate School of Management merged to form DeVry University in 2002. DeVry acquired Ross University, a medical and veterinary school, in 2003.

In 2004 Keller turned over the CEO spot to fellow co-founder Ronald Taylor. He remained chairman for a couple of years before stepping down to become director emeritus.

DeVry's medical credentials were expanded in 2005 with the acquisition of Deaconess College of Nursing, renamed Chamberlain College of Nursing. Also that year, the company acquired Gearty CPE, a provider of continuing education programs in accounting and finance operating in New York and New Jersey.

Ronald Taylor retired as CEO at the end of 2006. He was succeeded by company COO Daniel Hamburger.

Keller Graduate School expanded its degree offerings in 2007 with the addition of a master's degree in educational technology.

EXECUTIVES

Chairman, Harold T. Shapiro, age 76
President, CEO, and Director, Daniel M. Hamburger, age 47, $6,058,205 total compensation
President, DeVry College of New York, Anthony A. Stanziani, age 51
President, Carrington Colleges Group, George Montgomery
President, Advanced Academics, Jeffrey Elliott
President, Philadelphia Metro, Adena Johnston
President, Tinley Park, Jamal J. Scott
President, Chamberlain College of Nursing, Susan L. Groenwald
President, Becker Professional Education, John P. Roselli, age 47
CFO, Medical and Healthcare Group, George Harbison

President, K-12, Professional and International Education, Steven P. (Steve) Riehs, age 51, $976,980 total compensation
President, DeVry Brasil, Carlos Filgueiras
EVP; President, Ross University, Thomas C. Shepherd, age 61, $714,688 total compensation
EVP; President, DeVry University, David J. (Dave) Pauldine, age 54, $1,565,349 total compensation
VP and Controller, Patrick J. Unzicker, age 40
VP Strategy and Business Development, Adriano Allegrini
SVP and CIO, Eric Dirst, age 44
SVP Government and Regulatory Affairs and Chief Compliance Officer, Sharon Thomas Parrott, age 61
SVP, General Counsel, and Secretary, Gregory S. Davis, age 49
SVP, CFO, and Treasurer, Richard M. (Rick) Gunst, age 55, $1,447,317 total compensation
SVP Human Resources, Donna N. Jennings, age 49
SVP; President, Healthcare Group, William Hughson, $874,794 total compensation
Center Dean, Glandale, AZ, DeVry University, Jeff H. Blake
Group VP Strategic Alliances, Fran Roberts
Director Investor Relations and Media Relations, Joan Bates
Auditors: PricewaterhouseCoopers LLP

LOCATIONS

HQ: DeVry Inc.
3005 Highland Pkwy, Downers Grove, IL 60515-5799
Phone: 630-571-7700
Web: www.devryinc.com

2010 Sales

	$ mil.	% of total
US	1,669.5	87
Dominica & St. Kitts/Nevis	193.0	10
Other countries	52.7	3
Total	**1,915.2**	**100**

PRODUCTS/OPERATIONS

2010 Sales by Segment

	$ mil.	% of total
Business, technology & management	1,263.6	66
Medical & healthcare	507.0	27
Professional education	84.8	4
Other educational services	59.8	3
Total	**1,915.2**	**100**

2010 Sales

	$ mil.	% of total
Tuition	1,795.8	94
Other	119.4	6
Total	**1,915.2**	**100**

Selected Fields of Study

Carrington College
   Dental assisting
   Diagnostic medical sonography
   Fitness training
   Medical assisting
   Medical laboratory technician
   Medical radiography
   Physical therapy assisting
   Practical nursing
   Respiratory care
   Veterinary assisting
Becker Professional Review
   CFA exam review
   CPA exam review
Chamberlain College of Nursing
   Nursing
DeVry University
   Accounting
   Biomedical engineering technology
   Business administration
   Computer engineering technology
   Computer information systems

Electrical engineering
Electronics and computer technology
Electronics engineering technology
Game and simulation programming
Health information technology
Network and communications management
Network systems administration
Technical management
DeVry Brasil
   Business management
   Engineering
   Law
Keller Graduate School of Management
   Accounting and finance
   Business administration
   Human resources
   Project management
   Public administration
   Technology management
Ross University
   Medicine
   Veterinary medicine

COMPETITORS

Apollo Group
Bridgepoint Education
Capella Education
Cardean Learning Group
Career Education
Concorde Colleges
Corinthian Colleges
Education Management

Heald College
ITT Educational
Kaplan
Laureate Education
Lincoln Educational
   Services
Strayer Education

HISTORICAL FINANCIALS

Company Type: Public

Income Statement

FYE: June 30

	REVENUE ($ mil.)	NET INCOME ($ mil.)	NET PROFIT MARGIN	EMPLOYEES
06/11	2,182.4	330.4	15.1%	12,599
06/10	1,915.2	279.9	14.6%	12,117
06/09	1,461.5	165.6	11.3%	10,200
06/08	1,091.8	125.5	11.5%	6,755
06/07	933.5	76.2	8.2%	5,400
Annual Growth	23.7%	44.3%	—	23.6%

2011 Year-End Financials

Debt ratio: —
Return on equity: 23.8%
Cash ($ mil.): 447.1
Current ratio: 1.97
Long-term debt ($ mil.): —

No. of shares (mil.): 68.6
Dividends
   Yield: 0.4%
   Payout: 5.1%
Market value ($ mil.): 4,058.4

	STOCK PRICE ($) FY Close	P/E High/Low		PER SHARE ($) Earnings	Dividends	Book Value
06/11	59.13	13	8	4.68	0.24	20.25
06/10	52.49	19	11	3.87	0.20	16.60
06/09	50.04	28	17	2.28	0.16	13.01
06/08	53.62	36	18	1.73	0.12	10.60
06/07	34.89	34	18	1.07	0.10	9.03
Annual Growth	14.1%	—	—	44.6%	24.5%	22.4%

DexCom

Dexterity and communication. Perhaps that is what DexCom is hoping to bring to mind with its choice of name. The company develops and manufactures a glucose monitoring system called SEVEN PLUS that measures and wirelessly transmits blood sugar levels from a sensor on the patient to the company's receiver. Real-time data is processed and displayed so patients can assess blood glucose trends. Patients are also alerted when levels are too high or too low. The company's other product, GlucoClear, is used in hospitals to monitor blood glucose levels in critical care patients. DexCom's products are marketed to physicians, endocrinologists, and diabetes educators in the US and select international markets.

DexCom's SEVEN PLUS blood glucose monitor is a next-generation version of its earlier SEVEN product. SEVEN PLUS is the only sensor approved for seven days of wear (as opposed to the standard three to five days). It is also designed to alert patients of both hyper- and hypoglycemia with a fixed alarm and show patients glucose trends over a three hour period.

When the company began marketing SEVEN PLUS (in 2009), it started phasing out the original version and eventually stopped marketing and supporting it altogether. In the future, DexCom intends to invest in the development of more next-generation products and to obtain additional FDA approvals for its continuous glucose monitoring systems for both the ambulatory and in-hospital markets. DexCom expects its next, next-generation SEVEN product to have improved sensor reliability, comfort, stability, and accuracy. The company also plans to seek approval for pediatric use of the device.

DexCom's in-hospital glucose monitoring product, GlucoClear, is being developed through an exclusive agreement with Edwards Lifesciences. DexCom is seeking US approval for GlucoClear, which is only sold in limited countries in Europe. The company is also working with Animas and Insulet to make integrated insulin pump/glucose monitoring systems in which DexCom's technology is used to transmit and display data on the insulin pump's screen.

DexCom's products are designed to complement, but not replace, standard home glucose monitoring devices. The short-term systems need replacement sensors and have to be recalibrated with a home device every seven days. The company has a small direct field sales force (that it intends to expand slightly in 2011) charged with the job of getting health care providers to adopt DexCom's technology and prescribe its products to their patients. DexCom also employs clinical specialists to educate and support its patients. SEVEN PLUS is sold throughout the US and in parts of Europe and Israel, but the company plans to expand its sales elsewhere in the future.

EXECUTIVES

President, CEO, and Director, Terrance H. (Terry) Gregg, age 62, $2,800,785 total compensation
VP and CFO, Jess Roper, age 46, $310,386 total compensation
VP Operations, Jeffrrey Moy, age 51
VP Intellectual Property, Laura Johnson, age 40
VP International Business Development, Peter Gerhardsson, age 57
VP Legal Affairs, John Lister
VP Sales, Richard B. Doubleday
VP Marketing, Claudia Graham, age 51
VP Research and Development, James H. (Jim) Brauker, age 60
Manager Human Resources, Cathy Alsaro
COO, Steven R. (Steve) Pacelli, age 40, $855,987 total compensation
CTO, Jorge A. Valdes, age 49, $663,168 total compensation

SVP Clinical and Regulatory Affairs and Quality Assurance, Andrew K. Balo, age 63, $515,949 total compensation
Auditors: Ernst & Young LLP

LOCATIONS

HQ: DexCom, Inc.
6340 Sequence Dr., San Diego, CA 92121
Phone: 858-200-0200   **Fax:** 858-200-0201
Web: www.dexcom.com

PRODUCTS/OPERATIONS

2010 Sales

	$ mil.	% of total
Products	40.1	83
Development grants & other	8.5	17
Total	**48.6**	**100**

COMPETITORS

Abbott Diabetes Care	LMP
Bayer Diabetes Care	Medtronic
Echo Therapeutics	Nipro Diagnostics
LifeScan	Roche Diagnostics

HISTORICAL FINANCIALS

Company Type: Public

Income Statement

FYE: December 31

	REVENUE ($ mil.)	NET INCOME ($ mil.)	NET PROFIT MARGIN	EMPLOYEES
12/10	48.6	(55.2)	—	520
12/09	29.7	(53.5)	—	385
12/08	9.8	(55.2)	—	304
12/07	4.6	(45.9)	—	252
12/06	2.2	(46.6)	—	260
Annual Growth	116.8%	—	—	18.9%

2010 Year-End Financials

Debt ratio: —
Return on equity: —
Cash ($ mil.): 4.9
Current ratio: 4.36
Long-term debt ($ mil.): —
No. of shares (mil.): 62.1
Dividends
Yield: —
Payout: —
Market value ($ mil.): 847.4

	STOCK PRICE ($) FY Close	P/E High/Low		Earnings	PER SHARE ($) Dividends	Book Value
12/10	13.65	—	—	(0.97)	0.00	0.98
12/09	8.07	—	—	(1.21)	0.00	(0.40)
12/08	2.76	—	—	(1.87)	0.00	(1.28)
12/07	8.83	—	—	(1.62)	0.00	0.25
12/06	9.86	—	—	(1.71)	0.00	2.02
Annual Growth	8.5%	—	—	—	—	(16.5%)

DFC Global

If your wallet is flat and payday is far away, DFC Global can tide you over. Formerly Dollar Financial Corp., the company owns some 1,300 check-cashing and payday loan stores (and franchises about 125 additional locations) in North America and Europe. The stores operate under such names as Money Mart, Money Shop, Money Corner, Loan Mart, Insta-Cheques, and The Check Cashing Store. In addition to check cashing and short-term loans, the stores offer money transfer services,

money orders, tax filing services, foreign exchange, and reloadable Visa and MasterCard debit cards to customers who choose not to use, or don't have access to, traditional banks or financial institutions.

DFC Global has more than 300 check-cashing and payday loan locations in about 15 states, more than half of which are in Florida and California. Another key market is Canada, where the company owns more than 400 National Money Mart locations and is one of the largest check-cashing services providers.

Amid increased regulatory pressures in the US and market saturation in Canada, though, the firm has increasingly looked overseas for expansion opportunities. Foreign operations now account for more than 80% of the company's revenue.

The company, which has more than 375 offices in the UK, purchased two pawn shops in Scotland in 2009. It opened its first store in Ireland in 2008. Continuing its growth into other parts of Europe in 2009, it acquired majority control of Polish lender Optima, which specializes in providing unsecured personal loans in the customer's home (as opposed to a retail location).

Growth came again in the UK with the 2010 purchase of Suttons & Robertsons, one of the oldest pawn shops in the UK. The acquired firm, which has three locations, specializes in pawn lending on high-end jewelry, watches, and diamonds. Building its Internet-based lending capabilities, Dollar Financial acquired UK firms Express Finance Limited (in 2009) and Purpose U.K. Holdings, which does business as PaydayUK (in 2011). The company expanded in Scandinavia in 2010 with the acquisition of Sweden-based pawn lender Sefina Finance. In 2011 it acquired Risicum Oyj, a leading provider of internet loans in Finland. It also pursued the acquisition of Swedish lender Folkia Group, but to no avail.

The firm plans to continue expanding in Canada and Europe by entering new markets, buying franchised and third-party locations, and opening new stores.

In 2009 the firm added to its service offerings with the purchase of Dealers' Financial Services, which provides fee-based services to military personnel applying for car loans through an agreement with a third-party bank. However, the company has been winding down the operations of its We The People franchise, which provides legal document processing services. The unit filed for bankruptcy in 2010 after being hit by two lawsuits from consumers who claimed it illegally advertised some of its services. Some franchisees then sued Dollar Financial and We the People for damages related to the consumer suits.

The company changed its name from Dollar Financial to DFC Global in 2011, reflecting the evolutionary changes it has made from its roots as a US pawn lender.

EXECUTIVES

Chairman and CEO, Jeffrey A. (Jeff) Weiss, age 68, $5,477,110 total compensation
President, US Retail, Mike Hudachek
EVP and CFO, Randall (Randy) Underwood, age 61, $3,114,950 total compensation
EVP and COO, Norman L. (Norm) Miller, age 50, $2,349,781 total compensation
EVP; Chairman, National Money Mart, Sydney F. Franchuck, age 59, $1,185,002 total compensation
CIO, Michael (Mike) Coury
SVP and Chief Credit Officer, Carl Spiker
Managing Director Global Strategy and Development, Jeff J. (Jeff) Wheatley

SVP Global Strategy and Development, Paul Mildenstein, age 49
SVP eCommerce, Carole Cross
SVP Finance and Treasurer, Peter Sokolowski, age 50
Managing Director Corporate Development, Ken Fisher
Principal Accounting Officer, William M. Athas, age 49
SVP Corporate Administration, Melissa Soper, age 45
SVP, General Counsel, and Secretary, Roy W. Hibberd, age 58
SVP; Managing Director, United Kingdom Operations, Silvio D. Piccini, age 48, $1,363,483 total compensation
Auditors: Ernst & Young LLP

LOCATIONS

HQ: DFC Global Corp.
1436 Lancaster Ave., Ste. 300, Berwyn, PA 19312-1288
Phone: 610-296-3400 **Fax:** 610-296-7844
Web: www.dfg.com

2011 Sales

	$ mil.	% of total
Europe	333.9	42
Canada	310.7	40
US retail	122.2	15
Other	21.7	3
Total	**610.9**	**100**

PRODUCTS/OPERATIONS

2011 Sales

	$ mil.	% of total
Consumer lending fees	429.2	55
Check cashing	144.1	18
Pawn service fees & sales	48.0	6
Gold sales	46.5	6
Money transfer fees	32.1	4
Other	88.5	11
Total	**788.4**	**100**

COMPETITORS

ACE Cash Express	Community Choice
Advance America	Financial
Albemarle & Bond	EZCORP
Cash America	First Cash Financial
Cash Plus	Services
Cash Store Financial	Provident Financial
Cattles	QC Holdings
Check 'n Go	World Acceptance
Check Into Cash	Xponential

HISTORICAL FINANCIALS

Company Type: Public

Income Statement

FYE: June 30

	REVENUE ($ mil.)	NET INCOME ($ mil.)	NET PROFIT MARGIN	EMPLOYEES
06/11	788.4	65.8	8.3%	5,375
06/10	610.9	(4.9)	—	4,966
06/09	527.9	1.8	0.3%	4,522
06/08	572.2	51.2	8.9%	5,490
06/07	409.9	(32.2)	—	4,795
Annual Growth	**17.8%**	**—**	**—**	**2.9%**

2011 Year-End Financials

Debt ratio: 196.6%
Return on equity: 15.4%
Cash ($ mil.): 189.0
Current ratio: 2.12
Long-term debt ($ mil.): 839.6

No. of shares (mil.): 43.7
Dividends
  Yield: —
  Payout: —
Market value ($ mil.): 947.1

STOCK PRICE ($) FY Close	P/E High/Low		PER SHARE ($) Earnings	Dividends	Book Value
06/11	21.65	14	6	1.66	0.00	9.76
06/10	13.19	—	—	(0.13)	0.00	5.97
06/09	9.19	313	69	0.05	0.00	4.74
06/08	10.07	16	7	1.39	0.00	5.32
06/07	19.00	—	—	(0.91)	0.00	4.03
Annual Growth	**3.3%**			**—**	**—**	**24.8%**

DG FastChannel

Commercials don't signify bathroom breaks for DG FastChannel (doing business as DG). The company provides digital distribution services for advertisers, agencies, newspaper publishers, and TV and radio broadcasters. Ad agencies and other content providers route their clients' audio and video spots to radio and TV stations and other traditional media outlets through DG's nationwide digital distribution network. The network connects more than 5,000 advertisers, advertising agencies, and content owners with more than 29,000 television, radio, cable, print, and online publishing destinations in the US, Canada, and Europe. Electronic transmissions are made across the Internet and via satellite.

While content distribution accounts for most of DG's business, the company also provides online business intelligence offerings and a searchable database of television advertisements; post-production services; digital asset management tools for archiving and collaboration; and media intelligence offerings, such as broadcast verification. The company also offers ad services through its Point.360 subsidiary. In addition, DG delivers digital video broadcast services for long-form programming (including syndicated television shows and movies) through its Digital Media Gateway (DMG).

The company saw its revenues and net income increase in 2010 as a result of a growth in new emerging digital technologies, the continued transition from analog to digital broadcast signal transmission, and the rapid adoption of high definition television by consumers. Corresponding with its positive earnings, DG has made several acquisitions in order to expand its digital distribution network, customer base, and product offerings.

In 2011 it purchased MediaMind Technologies, a provider of campaign management software used to develop and manage rich media content, including online, mobile, and in-game advertisements. DG bought MediaMind for $418 million in cash in a deal that extended its penetration into international markets and enhanced its online and TV advertising business. Continuing its efforts to expand its Internet advertising market presence, later in 2011 it acquired digital advertising business EyeWonder from Limelight Networks for $66 million. In 2010 DG purchased Match Point Media (along with its Treehouse Media Services and Voltage Video divisions) for $26 million in cash. Match Point provides digital distribution services for infomercials, and the deal gives DG a hand in digitizing the $5 billion-a-year direct response market.

These recent purchases add to a couple of prior key strategic acquisitions. DG expanded its distribution, post-production, and customer service operations with the 2009 acquisition of the Vyvx advertising business from Level 3 Communications for $129 million. Vyvx's services were similar to those of DG, and the company made the deal to grow its customer base and operations. And in 2008 DG purchased digital advertising firm Enliven Marketing Technologies Corporation for some $71 million in stock. The acquisition enhanced the company's digital media services, ad distribution, Internet marketing, and online and mobile advertising capabilities. Included in the deal was Enliven's Springbox subsidiary, an interactive, digital Web marketing firm.

The company became DG FastChannel in 2006 after purchasing competitor FastChannel Network for $37.5 million. It began doing business as DG in 2010.

EXECUTIVES

Chairman and CEO, Scott K. Ginsburg, age 58, $939,072 total compensation
President, Unicast, Adam Moore
President, COO, and Director, Neil H. Nguyen, age 37, $2,560,786 total compensation
CFO and Director, Omar A. Choucair, age 49, $548,171 total compensation
SVP SourceEcreative, Pamela (Pam) Maythenyi, age 55, $270,862 total compensation
SVP Engineering and IT, Brendan Sullivan
Auditors: Ernst & Young LLP

LOCATIONS

HQ: DG FastChannel, Inc.
750 W. John Carpenter Fwy., Ste. 700, Irving, TX 75039
Phone: 972-581-2000 **Fax:** 972-581-2001
Web: www.dgit.com

PRODUCTS/OPERATIONS

2010 Sales

	$ mil.	% of total
Audio & video content distribution	235.7	95
Other	11.8	5
Total	**247.5**	**100**

Selected Services

A/V production
Audio delivery
Conversion
Digital distribution
Duplication
Media asset management
Music distribution
Syndicated program distribution
Sweeps
Video delivery

COMPETITORS

Akamai	Google
Comcast	Limelight
Deluxe Entertainment	PointRoll
EDnet	Yangaroo
EyeWonder	

HISTORICAL FINANCIALS

Company Type: Public

Income Statement

FYE: December 31

	REVENUE ($ mil.)	NET INCOME ($ mil.)	NET PROFIT MARGIN	EMPLOYEES
12/10	247.5	41.6	16.8%	897
12/09	190.9	20.5	10.7%	739
12/08	157.1	15.1	9.6%	770
12/07	97.7	10.4	10.6%	552
12/06	68.7	(0.6)	—	376
Annual Growth	**37.8%**	**—**	**—**	**24.3%**

2010 Year-End Financials

Debt ratio: —	No. of shares (mil.): 27.9
Return on equity: 8.4%	Dividends
Cash ($ mil.): 73.4	Yield: —
Current ratio: 7.43	Payout: —
Long-term debt ($ mil.): —	Market value ($ mil.): 806.4

	STOCK PRICE ($) FY Close	P/E High/Low		PER SHARE ($) Earnings	Dividends	Book Value
12/10	28.88	29	10	1.50	0.00	17.80
12/09	27.93	33	14	0.88	0.00	14.47
12/08	12.48	31	15	0.79	0.00	12.69
12/07	25.64	43	21	0.61	0.00	10.75
12/06	13.48	—	—	(0.06)	0.00	11.24
Annual Growth	21.0%	—	—	—	—	12.2%

Diamond Foods

Shy, you ask? Not a bit. Diamond Foods is always coming out of its shell. The company sells a wide array of tree nuts and value-added nut products, as well as microwave popcorn and potato chips. Walnuts are its biggest selling nut but Diamond also offers almonds, Brazil nuts, hazelnuts, pecans, pine nuts, and peanuts for use in home cooking, snack foods, in-shell eating, and as ingredients for other food manufacturers. The company, whose primary nut brands are Diamond and Emerald, also is a supplier to restaurants and other foodservice operators. In addition to US markets, Diamond also does business internationally, mainly in the UK, Germany, Spain, the Netherlands, Turkey, Japan, and South Korea.

Diamond pursues a strategy of increasing its market share in the snack-food sector. It does this by expanding the number and kind of its snack-food offerings, mostly through acquisitions. To that end, it has agreed to acquire the world's largest potato chip brand — Pringles — from Procter & Gamble in a $1.5 billion stock transaction. The purchase, which includes the assumption of $850 million of Pringles debt, is a game changer for Diamond Foods. The addition of Pringles will more than triple the size of its snack business and boost the company's global presence. (Pringles is sold in about 140 countries.) Previously, Diamond's snack business more than doubled when it bought premium potato chip maker Kettle Foods in 2010. It paid $615 million to Lion Capital for the Salem, Oregon-based company. The acquisitions open up cross-promotional opportunities with Diamond's Emerald and Diamond nut products and its PopSecret popcorn brand.

The closing of the Pringles sale, originally slated for the end of 2011, has been postponed until 2012 due to an internal accounting investigation at Diamond Foods related to crop payments to walnut growers. The March 31, 2010 acquisition of Kettle has already proved profitable. Diamond's 2010 fiscal year (ended on July 31, 2010), total net sales were $680 million, compared to $571 million for fiscal 2009, an increase of 70%. The company attributed this uptick to increased snack sales, particularly the Kettle brand (which it had owned for only four months before the end of its fiscal year). Things had already begun to pop at Diamond in 2008, when the company acquired the operations of PopSecret from General Mills for $190 million in cash. PopSecret is the US's #2 popcorn

brand behind ConAgra's Orville Redenbacher products. (ConAgra also makes the popular Act II microwaveable popcorn.) In addition to popcorn, the company's other snack foods include roasted, glazed, and mixed nuts, trail mixes, and dried fruits.

The company's products are sold in more than 60,000 US retail locations and are available in some 100 other countries. Diamond plans to expand its retail distribution outlets to include more drug, convenience, and club stores, as well as mass merchandisers. Its biggest customer is Wal-Mart, which accounted for 17% of the company's 2010 sales; Costco accounted for 12%. The company owns no nut groves of its own; instead, it buys from growers. During 2010 all the walnuts, peanuts, and almonds, as well as most of its hazelnuts were sourced in the US; pecans came from the US and Mexico. It imported Brazil nuts from the Amazon basin; cashews from India, Africa, Brazil, and Southeast Asia; and pine nuts from China and Turkey. Other agricultural commodities it needs for production, such as corn and potatoes, were provided by US growers.

EXECUTIVES

Chairman, John J. (Jack) Gilbert, age 68
President and General Manager, Kettle Foods North America, Timothy G. (Tim) Fallon, age 54
President, CEO, and Director, Michael J. Mendes, age 48, $3,734,389 total compensation
EVP, CFO, Chief Administrative Officer, and Director, Steven M. (Steve) Neil, age 58, $1,485,336 total compensation
EVP and Chief Marketing Officer, Andrew Burke, age 45, $859,213 total compensation
EVP and Chief Sales Officer, Lloyd J. Johnson, age 48, $1,301,705 total compensation
VP Investor Relations and Treasurer, Robert (Bob) Philipps
VP Corporate Affairs and Communications, Stephen Sibert
SVP Human Resources and General Counsel, Stephen E. Kim, age 41, $624,524 total compensation
Managing Director, Kettle Foods UK, Jeremy Bradley
SVP Corporate Strategy and Communications, Linda B. Segre, age 50
Auditors: Deloitte & Touche LLP

LOCATIONS

HQ: Diamond Foods, Inc.
600 Montgomery St., 17th Floor, San Francisco, CA 94111-2702
Phone: 415-912-3180
Web: www.diamondfoods.com

2010 Sales

	$ mil.	% of total
US	554.0	81
Europe	65.0	10
Other	61.2	9
Total	**680.2**	**100**

PRODUCTS/OPERATIONS

2010 Sales

	$ mil.	% of total
Retail		
Snack	321.4	47
Culinary	217.5	32
In-shell	31.5	5
Ingredient & foodservice	38.0	6
Other	71.8	10
Total	**680.2**	**100**

COMPETITORS

AK Acres Popcorn	Dole Food
American Pop Corn	Frito-Lay
Arcade Industries	Golden Enterprises
Beer Nuts	Golden Peanut
Betsy Ann Candies	Golden West Nuts
Blue Diamond Growers	J & J Snack Foods
C.J. Vitner	John Sanfilippo &
Chiquita Brands	Kraft Foods
ConAgra	

HISTORICAL FINANCIALS

Company Type: Public

Income Statement

FYE: July 31

	REVENUE ($ mil.)	NET INCOME ($ mil.)	NET PROFIT MARGIN	EMPLOYEES
07/11	965.9	50.2	5.2%	1,797
07/10	680.2	26.2	3.9%	1,467
07/09	570.9	23.7	4.2%	855
07/08	531.5	14.8	2.8%	628
07/07	522.6	8.4	1.6%	754
Annual Growth	16.6%	56.4%	—	24.2%

2011 Year-End Financials

Debt ratio: 107.7%	No. of shares (mil.): 22.0
Return on equity: 11.0%	Dividends
Cash ($ mil.): 3.1	Yield: 0.3%
Current ratio: 1.49	Payout: 8.1%
Long-term debt ($ mil.): 490.0	Market value ($ mil.): 1,578.5

	STOCK PRICE ($) FY Close	P/E High/Low		PER SHARE ($) Earnings	Dividends	Book Value
07/11	71.59	36	17	2.22	0.18	20.63
07/10	44.54	34	19	1.36	0.18	17.36
07/09	28.20	22	13	1.44	0.18	10.47
07/08	24.32	30	17	0.91	0.18	9.04
07/07	16.66	38	25	0.53	0.12	7.83
Annual Growth	44.0%	—	—	43.1%	10.7%	27.4%

Diamond Hill Investment

Diamond Hill Investment Group takes a shine to investing. Operating through flagship subsidiary Diamond Hill Capital Management, the firm oversees approximately $5 billion in assets, most of it invested in mutual funds. Serving institutional and individual clients, the company administers several mutual funds and sells them mainly through independent investment advisors, broker-dealers, financial planners, investment consultants, and third-party marketing firms. It also manages separate accounts and hedge funds.

In 2008 the company said that it will establish a brokerage subsidiary that will offer statutory underwriting services to its own funds and to other mid-market funds.

President and CEO Ric Dillon owns about 7% of the company.

EXECUTIVES

President, CEO and Director; Co-Chief Investment Officer, Diamond Hill Capital Management, Inc., Roderick H. (Ric) Dillon Jr., age 54, $2,467,600 total compensation

Chairman, Diamond Hill Funds, Thomas E. (Tom) Line

CFO, Secretary and Treasurer; President, Diamond Hill Funds, James F. (Jim) Laird Jr., age 54, $744,000 total compensation

Managing Director, Planning and Operations, Randall J. Demyan

Managing Director, Strategic Income, Diamond Hill Investments, Kent K. Rinker, age 60

Managing Director, Equities, Diamond Hill Capital Management, Charles S. (Chuck) Bath, age 56

Coporate Controller and Chief Compliance Officer, Diamond Hills Funds, Gary R. Young

Portfolio Manager, Equities; Portfolio Manager, Diamond Hill Small-Mid Cap Fund and Co-Chief Investm, Christopher A. (Chris) Welch

Director Marketing, Patricia L. (Trish) Schindler

Portfolio Manager, Strategic Income, William P. Zox

Director Key Accounts, Tamala S. (Tammi) Gourley

Auditors: Plante & Moran, PLLC

LOCATIONS

HQ: Diamond Hill Investment Group, Inc.
325 John H. McConnell Blvd., Ste. 200, Columbus, OH 43215
Phone: 614-255-3333   **Fax:** 614-255-3363
Web: www.diamond-hill.com

PRODUCTS/OPERATIONS

2008 Sales

	$ mil.	% of total
Investment advisory	40.5	86
Mutual fund administration	6.1	13
Performance incentive	0.4	1
Total	**47.0**	**100**

COMPETITORS

AllianceBernstein	FMR
American Century	Franklin Templeton
Calamos Asset	GAMCO Investors
Management	Janus Capital
Cohen & Steers	MFS
Columbia Management	Putnam
Davis Advisers	T. Rowe Price
Duncan-Hurst	The Vanguard Group
Ed	Waddell & Reed
Edelman Financial	

HISTORICAL FINANCIALS

Company Type: Public

Income Statement

FYE: December 31

	REVENUE ($ mil.)	NET INCOME ($ mil.)	NET PROFIT MARGIN	EMPLOYEES
12/10	57.9	12.4	21.4%	77
12/09	43.6	11.4	26.1%	66
12/08	38.8	3.3	8.5%	57
12/07	42.2	9.9	23.5%	42
12/06	34.4	8.1	23.5%	32
Annual Growth	**13.9%**	**11.2%**	**—**	**24.5%**

2010 Year-End Financials

Debt ratio: —
Return on equity: 165.4%
Cash ($ mil.): 5.8
Current ratio: —
Long-term debt ($ mil.): —
No. of shares (mil.): 2.8
Dividends
Yield: —
Payout: —
Market value ($ mil.): 202.2

STOCK PRICE ($) FY Close	P/E High/Low		PER SHARE ($) Earnings	Dividends	Book Value
12/10	72.34	19	11	4.48	0.00	2.68
12/09	64.23	16	6	4.40	0.00	8.58
12/08	65.00	74	34	1.36	0.00	12.37
12/07	73.10	26	16	4.39	0.00	17.71
12/06	83.73	25	8	3.63	0.00	11.32
Annual Growth	**(3.6%)**	**—**	**—**	**5.4%**	**—**	**(30.2%)**

Digimarc

Digimarc makes its mark on media. The company provides digital watermarking software that embeds code in printed and digital content, including photographs, music, movies, and television content, as well as currency, documents, and packages. Customers — which include movie studios, record labels, broadcasters, creative professionals, and government agencies — use Digimarc's software to control copyrights, deter piracy, license online content, and manage digital assets. The company generates revenue from software development, consulting services, and technology licensing and subscription fees. Its licensees include Microsoft, Adobe Systems, The Nielsen Company, and Open Text.

Revenue increased about 14% in 2010 compared with 2009, and the company recorded net income of 13% in 2010 compared with a net loss of 14% the previous year. Digimarc attributes a big part of its healthy operating results to licensing income from Intellectual Ventures and Arbitron, which respectively account for 18% and 14% of revenue. Income from these two companies, as well as Nielsen (12% of revenue) and government contracts, increased domestic income 119% in 2010 over 2009. The company still counts its first successful product launch — counterfeiting prevention technology — as an important source of revenue. Government contracts account for 33% of the company's sales, and 90% of that business involves counterfeiting deterrence for banks.

Though the company first made a name for itself with anti-counterfeiting software, it has now branched out into new, growing markets. One recently launched product, the Digimarc Discover platform, targets the iTunes and Android markets by offering new media applications for smartphone users.

With more than a thousand US and foreign patents and patent applications in digital watermarking and related technologies, Digimarc faces competition primarily from alternative technologies, such as encryption, radio frequency tags, smart cards, and bar codes.

Prior to 2008, Digimarc also sold secure ID products used to create identification cards such as driver's licenses and office security badges. The company agreed to sell its ID systems business to L-1 Identity Solutions for $250 million in cash and stock in early 2008. Before the deal closed, French aerospace and defense giant SAFRAN offered a competing bid of $300 million for Digimarc. The company then accepted a second offer from L-1 for $310 million; the deal closed in August 2008.

When L-1 acquired Digimarc, its digital watermarking business was spun off as a separate entity initially called DMRC. The new, independent company later retained the Digimarc name.

EXECUTIVES

Chairman and CEO, Bruce Davis, age 58, $458,575 total compensation

EVP, Chief Legal Officer, and Secretary, Robert P. Chamness, age 58, $293,575 total compensation

EVP, CFO, and Treasurer, Michael E. McConnell, age 60, $293,575 total compensation

VP, Jeri Owen

Auditors: Grant Thornton LLP

LOCATIONS

HQ: Digimarc Corporation
9405 SW Gemini Dr., Beaverton, OR 97008
Phone: 503-469-4800   **Fax:** 503-469-4777
Web: www.digimarc.com

2010 Sales

	$ mil.	% of total
US	19.1	61
Other countries	12.1	39
Total	**31.2**	**100**

PRODUCTS/OPERATIONS

2010 Sales

	$ mil.	% of total
Service	12.4	40
License & subscription	18.8	60
Total	**31.2**	**100**

COMPETITORS

Aware, Inc.	Nielsen Holdings
Document Security	Philips Electronics
Systems	Widevine Technologies

HISTORICAL FINANCIALS

Company Type: Public

Income Statement

FYE: December 31

	REVENUE ($ mil.)	NET INCOME ($ mil.)	NET PROFIT MARGIN	EMPLOYEES
12/10	31.1	4.2	13.5%	98
12/09	19.1	(2.8)	—	93
12/08	19.8	1.5	7.6%	87
12/07	13.0	0.1	0.8%	99
12/06	11.1	(2.7)	—	0
Annual Growth	**29.4%**	**—**	**—**	**(0.3%)**

2010 Year-End Financials

Debt ratio: —
Return on equity: 8.2%
Cash ($ mil.): 6.3
Current ratio: 9.71
Long-term debt ($ mil.): —
No. of shares (mil.): 7.4
Dividends
Yield: —
Payout: —
Market value ($ mil.): 223.4

STOCK PRICE ($) FY Close	P/E High/Low		PER SHARE ($) Earnings	Dividends	Book Value
12/10	30.01	58	27	0.55	0.00	6.87
12/09	14.99	—	—	(0.39)	0.00	6.48
12/08	10.02	55	38	0.21	0.00	6.65
Annual Growth	**73.1%**	**—**	**—**	**61.8%**	**—**	**1.7%**

Digital Realty

Technically, Digital Realty Trust puts its chips in real estate. The real estate investment trust (REIT) owns properties that are leased to firms in the technology sector. Its portfolio includes more than 90 properties in the US, Europe, and Asia, including data communications hubs, electronic storage and processing centers, tech manufacturing facilities, and offices of tech companies. All told, the REIT owns about 17 million sq. ft. of rentable space, including space held for redevelopment. Digital Realty Trust focuses on properties in hot tech markets such as Chicago, Dallas, Phoenix, New Jersey, New York, northern Virginia, and California's San Francisco Bay area and Silicon Valley (its largest market).

The REIT's growth strategy includes real estate acquisitions and redevelopment of its existing properties. It has approximately 2 million sq. ft. of space under development. The company believes that upgrades to its properties lead to low tenant turnover and longer lease terms. Savvis Communications, Equinix, and Facebook are among its largest tenants.

Digital Realty Trust acquired 15 properties in 2010 (the busiest that the company had been since 2007), including some in new markets. The REIT added its first property in Asia when it bought a data center in Singapore. It entered Massachusetts and Connecticut with the acquisition of three data centers there, and purchased a portfolio of five data centers in California, Arizona, and Virginia. In separate deals, the REIT also acquired data centers and redevelopment properties in Silicon Valley. The additions helped to boost the company's revenues and net income in 2010.

Digital Realty Trust continued to enter new markets into 2011, as it acquired development sites in London and Sydney.

EXECUTIVES

Chairman, Richard A. Magnuson, age 53, $999,332 total compensation
CEO and Director, Michael F. Foust, age 55, $3,660,674 total compensation
CFO, Chief Investment Officer, and Secretary, A. William Stein, age 57, $2,021,230 total compensation
VP Global Sales, Brent Behrman
CTO, Jim Smith
SVP Portfolio Management, David J. Caron
Regional Head, Asia Pacific, Kris Kumar
SVP International Operations, Bernard Geoghegan
Chief Acquisitions Officer, Scott E. Peterson, age 49, $1,447,514 total compensation
Director Investor Relations, Pamela A. Matthews
General Counsel and Assistant Secretary, Joshua A. Mills
Auditors: KPMG LLP

LOCATIONS

HQ: Digital Realty Trust, Inc.
560 Mission St., Ste. 2900, San Francisco, CA 94105
Phone: 415-738-6500   **Fax:** 415-738-6501
Web: www.digitalrealtytrust.com

PRODUCTS/OPERATIONS

2010 Sales

	$ mil.	% of total
Rental	686.9	79
Tenant reimbursements	178.1	21
Other	0.4	-
Total	**637.1**	**100**

COMPETITORS

Brandywine Realty
CenterPoint Properties
CoreSite
Duke Realty
DuPont Fabros
EastGroup Properties
First Industrial Realty
Mack-Cali
Mission West Properties
ProLogis
Vornado Realty

HISTORICAL FINANCIALS

Company Type: Public

Income Statement

FYE: December 31

	REVENUE ($ mil.)	NET INCOME ($ mil.)	NET PROFIT MARGIN	EMPLOYEES
12/10	865.4	102.3	11.8%	454
12/09	637.1	87.7	13.8%	264
12/08	527.4	67.7	12.8%	210
12/07	395.2	40.6	10.3%	153
12/06	281.9	31.4	11.1%	109
Annual Growth	32.4%	34.3%	—	42.9%

2010 Year-End Financials

Debt ratio: 192.2%
Return on equity: 7.0%
Cash ($ mil.): 11.7
Current ratio: 1.15
Long-term debt ($ mil.): 2,807.0
No. of shares (mil.): 91.2
Dividends
  Yield: 3.9%
  Payout: 297.1%
Market value ($ mil.): 4,698.3

	STOCK PRICE ($) FY Close	P/E High/Low		PER SHARE ($) Earnings	Dividends	Book Value
12/10	51.54	94	68	0.68	2.02	21.53
12/09	50.28	83	41	0.61	1.47	20.30
12/08	32.85	125	44	0.41	1.26	20.46
12/07	38.37	130	94	0.34	1.17	16.12
12/06	34.23	79	47	0.47	1.08	15.61
Annual Growth	10.8%	—	—	9.7%	16.9%	8.4%

Diodes

Diodes Incorporated knows how important it is to be discrete in business. The company makes discrete semiconductors — fixed-function devices that are much less complex than integrated circuits. Diodes' products include diodes, transistors, and rectifiers; they are used by computer and consumer electronics manufacturers in products such as notebooks, LCD monitors, smartphones, and game consoles. Other applications include power supplies, climate control systems, GPS devices, and networking gear. Cisco, Honeywell, Samsung, and Hon Hai are among its more than 250 OEM and contract manufacturing customers. More than 80% of sales come from customers outside the US, primarily from China and Taiwan.

Lite-On Semiconductor, a company that is part of Taiwan's Lite-On Technology, owns about 20% of Diodes. Lite-On Semiconductor is also Diodes' biggest customer and its biggest supplier.

The global economic downturn hurt many of the company's customers, especially those in the computer and consumer electronics industries. In addition, the semiconductor industry is historically cyclical, as sales of products that incorporate electronic components are often subject to the whims of consumer demand. Diodes, which had experienced double digit sales growth in recent years, saw a sales increase of only 0.4% in 2009 over 2008. While the company remained profitable (unlike many of its peers), its 2009 net income was $7.5 million, a precipitous 73% drop from 2008. Diodes points to reduced demand for its products, along with lower average selling prices and lower interest and other income for the year, as reasons its bottom line suffered. The company has responded by cutting costs, which included making workforce reductions and moving its wafer probe and final testing operations from Taiwan to China.

Diodes is under continuous pressure from customers and competitors to reduce the prices of its products, which can result in significantly lower sales and profits for the company. The company has countered by expanding into higher-margin, proprietary product lines, such as high-density arrays and ultraminiature switching diodes used in mobile applications. It also continues to become more vertically integrated, which brings down cost and increases efficiency of operations. Diodes is looking to expand its manufacturing capacity, R&D capabilities, product development, and sales and marketing organizations in part through acquisitions.

In 2008 Diodes acquired a UK-based competitor, Zetex, for about $176 million in cash. Zetex specialized in discrete components and analog integrated circuits for power management and signal processing. Diodes bought the company for its strong European presence and its focus on automotive and industrial applications, among other factors.

EXECUTIVES

Chairman, Raymond Soong, age 69
President, CEO, and Director, Keh-Shew Lu, age 64, $3,458,936 total compensation
CFO, Secretary, and Treasurer, Richard D. White, age 63, $689,099 total compensation
VP Corporate Administration, Edmund (Ed) Tang, age 63
VP Packaging Operations, T.J. Lee, age 62
VP Worldwide Analog Products, Julie Holland, age 49
VP Worldwide Discrete Products, Francis Tang, age 56
Vice Chairman, C. H. Chen, age 68
SVP Sales and Marketing, Mark A. King, age 52, $920,183 total compensation
SVP Operations, Joseph Liu, age 69, $1,016,801 total compensation
Europe President and VP, Europe Sales and Marketing, Colin Greene, age 54
SVP Business Development, Hans Rohrer, age 62
Auditors: Moss Adams, LLP

LOCATIONS

HQ: Diodes Incorporated
15660 Dallas Pkwy., Ste. 850, Dallas, TX 75248
Phone: 972-385-2810
Web: www.diodes.com

2009 Sales

	$ mil.	% of total
Asia/Pacific	327.5	75
North America	59.8	14
Europe	47.1	11
Total	**434.4**	**100**

2009 Sales by Customer Location

	$ mil.	% of total
China	131.9	31
Taiwan	122.5	28
US	75.2	17
South Korea	27.2	6
UK	17.9	4
Germany	17.5	4
Singapore	14.4	3
Other countries	27.8	7
Total	**434.4**	**100**

PRODUCTS/OPERATIONS

2009 Sales by Market

	% of total
Computing	32
Consumer electronics	31
Industrial	18
Communications	16
Automotive	3
Total	**100**

Selected Products

Diodes
 Schottky diodes
 Switching diodes
 Zener diodes
High-density arrays
Metal oxide semiconductor field-effect transistors
 (MOSFETs)
Rectifiers
 Bridge rectifiers
 Schottky rectifiers
 Standard, fast, superfast, and ultrafast recovery
 rectifiers
Transient voltage suppressors
 Thyristor surge protection devices
 Zener transient-voltage suppressors
Transistors
 Bipolar transistors
 Darlington transistors
 Prebiased transistors

COMPETITORS

Advanced Photonix	NXP Semico
BCD Semiconductor	Sanken Electric
Fairchild	Shindengen Electric
Semiconductor	Manufacturing
Infineon Technologies	Siliconix
International	STMicroelectronics
Rectifier	Toshiba Semiconductor
IXYS	Vishay Intertechnology
Microsemi	

HISTORICAL FINANCIALS

Company Type: Public

Income Statement
FYE: December 31

	REVENUE ($ mil.)	NET INCOME ($ mil.)	NET PROFIT MARGIN	EMPLOYEES
12/10	612.9	76.7	12.5%	3,986
12/09	434.4	7.5	1.7%	3,501
12/08	432.8	39.0	9.0%	3,067
12/07	401.2	59.7	14.9%	2,612
12/06	343.3	48.1	14.0%	2,268
Annual Growth	**15.6%**	**12.4%**	**—**	**15.1%**

2010 Year-End Financials

Debt ratio: 0.9%
Return on equity: 14.2%
Cash ($ mil.): 270.9
Current ratio: 2.15
Long-term debt ($ mil.): 4.8

No. of shares (mil.): 44.7
Dividends
 Yield: —
 Payout: —
Market value ($ mil.): 1,205.4

	STOCK PRICE ($) FY Close	P/E High/Low		PER SHARE ($) Earnings	Dividends	Book Value
12/10	26.99	17	9	1.68	0.00	12.12
12/09	20.41	130	32	0.17	0.00	10.08
12/08	6.06	34	3	0.91	0.00	9.00
12/07	30.07	25	16	1.41	0.00	9.22
12/06	23.65	27	18	1.16	0.00	11.34
Annual Growth	**3.4%**	**—**	**—**	**9.7%**	**—**	**1.7%**

DJSP Enterprises

DJSP Enterprises is willing to do the paperwork on houses in foreclosure. Through a controlling interest in DAL LLC, the holding company provides mainly non-legal support services, such as document preparation and processing for mortgage lenders and servicers who are managing home foreclosures in Florida. DAL operating subsidiary DJS Processing prepares drafts of pleadings and other documentation in connection with residential foreclosures, bankruptcies, complex litigation, evictions, and sales of lender-owned real estate (REO) properties. In 2010 DJSP bought Timios, a provider of title insurance and settlement services throughout much of the US.

EXECUTIVES

Chairman, President, and CEO, Stephen J. Bernstein, age 44
VP and CIO, Norman E. Gottschalk III
VP Foreclosure Services DJS LLC, Miriam Mendieta, age 48
VP Business Development and Marketing DJS LLC, Philip Cobb, age 51
VP and COO DJS LLC, Cheryl Samons, age 43
Auditors: McGladrey & Pullen, LLP

LOCATIONS

HQ: DJSP Enterprises, Inc.
 900 South Pine Island Dr.,, Ste. 400, Plantation, FL 33324
Phone: 954-233-8000 **Fax:** 954-233-8570
Web: www.djspenterprises.com

COMPETITORS

Prommis

HISTORICAL FINANCIALS

Company Type: Public

Income Statement
FYE: December 31

	REVENUE ($ mil.)	NET INCOME ($ mil.)	NET PROFIT MARGIN	EMPLOYEES
12/08	199.2	42.9	21.5%	0
12/07	115.5	38.7	33.5%	0
12/06	40.4	8.6	21.3%	0
Annual Growth	**122.1%**	**123.3%**	**—**	**—**

Debt ratio: 0.9%
Return on equity: 14.2%
Cash ($ mil.): 270.9
Current ratio: 2.15
Long-term debt ($ mil.): 4.8

No. of shares (mil.): 44.7
Dividends
 Yield: —
 Payout: —
Market value ($ mil.): 1,205.4

Document Security Systems

Document Security Systems (DSS) caters to those who are insecure about their security, particularly on paper. The company develops anti-counterfeiting products. Its offerings include technology that prevents documents from being accurately scanned or copied and authentication coding that can be used in conjunction with a handheld reader to verify that a document is genuine. DSS also sells paper that displays words such as "void" or "unauthorized copy" if it goes through a copier, fax machine, or scanner. The company considers document security to be its core business, so it has been unloading units with unrelated objectives.

To this end, DSS in 2009 sold its Legalstore.com e-commerce business, which offered legal forms and office supplies, to Internet Media Services. As part of the deal, DSS received nearly 8 million shares of Internet Media Services' stock, or about a 40% stake. In 2007 DSS sold its retail copying and quick-printing business unit.

A handful of acquisitions in recent years has helped DSS to extend its reach in printing, packaging, and anti-counterfeiting and security technologies. In February 2010, DSS acquired Premier Packaging Corporation, based in Victor, New York, that specializes in providing packaging to clients in such industries as pharmaceutical, beverage, toy, and specialty foods. In December 2008 DSS, through its Secuprint subsidiary, acquired the assets of its bankrupt neighbor, DPI of Rochester, for about $940,000 in a bid to expand its security print production capabilities. (DPI filed for Chapter 11 bankruptcy in November to facilitate its sale to DSS.)

EXECUTIVES

Chairman, Robert B. Fagenson, age 62
President and COO, Robert B. Bzdick
CFO, Philip Jones, $133,600 total compensation
CEO and Director, Patrick White, age 58, $235,319
 total compensation
VP Operations and Technology and Director, David M. Wicker, age 51
CIO; Research and Development, Emerging Technologies, Michael S. Caton
Investor Relations, Jody Janson
Manager Marketing, Nicole Acton
Auditors: Freed Maxick & Battaglia CPA's, PC

LOCATIONS

HQ: Document Security Systems, Inc.
 28 E. Main St., Ste. 1525, Rochester, NY 14614
Phone: 585-325-3610 **Fax:** 585-325-2977
Web: www.documentsecurity.com

COMPETITORS

Appleton Papers	InkSure

Applied DNA Sciences
AuthentiDate
Canon
De La Rue
Digimarc
Eastman Kodak
Hewlett-Packard

L-1 Identity Solutions
LaserCard
Nocopi Technologies
Ricoh Company
Sharp Corp.
Standard Register
Xerox

HISTORICAL FINANCIALS
Company Type: Public

Income Statement
FYE: December 31

	REVENUE ($ mil.)	NET INCOME ($ mil.)	NET PROFIT MARGIN	EMPLOYEES
12/10	13.4	(4.6)	—	104
12/09	9.9	(4.0)	—	112
12/08	6.6	(8.3)	—	85
12/07	6.0	(7.0)	—	62
12/06	4.8	(4.8)	—	58
Annual Growth	29.3%	—	—	15.7%

2010 Year-End Financials

Debt ratio: 65.6%	No. of shares (mil.): 19.4
Return on equity: —	Dividends
Cash ($ mil.): 4.1	Yield: —
Current ratio: 1.72	Payout: —
Long-term debt ($ mil.): 2.3	Market value ($ mil.): 104.5

	STOCK PRICE ($) FY Close	P/E High/Low		PER SHARE ($) Earnings	Dividends	Book Value
12/10	5.39	—	—	(0.26)	0.00	0.18
12/09	2.45	—	—	(0.27)	0.00	0.14
12/08	1.83	—	—	(0.59)	0.00	0.14
12/07	6.49	—	—	(0.51)	0.00	0.54
12/06	11.10	—	—	(0.37)	0.00	0.87
Annual Growth	(16.5%)	—	—	—	—	(32.7%)

Dolan Company

Helping law firms is a big part of the process for this publisher. Formerly Dolan Media Company, The Dolan Company is a diversified professional services provider with a significant interest in local business news publishing. Through subsidiary National Default Exchange (NDeX), the company offers mortgage default processing services to lenders, loan servicers, and law firms around the country. Its Counsel Press and DiscoverReady units provide services for law firms, including outsourced document management to support litigation discovery. In addition, Dolan's publishing business includes a portfolio of more than 40 daily and weekly newspapers serving mostly markets on the East Coast and in the Midwest.

While professional services were once a small part of the business, Dolan Company has expanded that division through acquisitions focused on processing and other outsourcing services for customers in both the finance and legal sectors. It purchased an 85% interest in outsourced discovery-management provider DiscoverReady in 2009, for example. That shift in emphasis coincided with both the mortgage credit crisis and the decline in print advertising. The company changed its name from Dolan Media in 2010 to reflect its new focus as a provider of diversified professional services.

A few months later, Dolan expanded when it acquired Federal News Service (FNS), a provider of

transcripts from government events. FNS also tracks media coverage of current issues, and Dolan expects the deal to add significantly to its news publishing content.

Founder Jim Dolan, a former journalist turned investment banker, started the business in 1992 by acquiring the Minneapolis newspaper *Finance and Commerce* with backing from private equity firm Cherry Tree Investments. Dolan expanded through additional newspaper acquisitions. Its focus on law periodicals led the company to target acquisitions of legal services businesses. Dolan later went public through an IPO in 2007 to help fund its growth and acquisitions strategy.

EXECUTIVES

Chairman, President, and CEO, James P. (Jim) Dolan, age 61, $1,473,888 total compensation
Chairman and CEO, National Default Exchange, David A. Trott, age 50, $710,156 total compensation
EVP and CFO, Scott J. Pollei, age 50, $730,733 total compensation
EVP Business Information, Mark W. C. Stodder, age 51, $614,996 total compensation
VP, CFO, and Secretary, Vicki J. Duncomb, age 54, $525,935 total compensation
VP Technology, Vince Swartout, age 39
VP and General Counsel, Renee Jackson, age 44
Director Investor Relations, John W. Waelti, age 41
Auditors: McGladrey & Pullen, LLP

LOCATIONS

HQ: The Dolan Company
222 S. 9th St., Ste. 2300, Minneapolis, MN 55402
Phone: 612-317-9420   **Fax:** 612-321-0563
Web: www.dolanmedia.com

Selected Publishing Markets
Baltimore
Boise, ID
Boston
Charlotte, NC
Colorado Springs
Columbia, SC
Detroit
Jackson, MS
Kansas City
Milwaukee
Minneapolis
New Orleans
Oklahoma City
Phoenix
Portland, OR
Providence, RI
Raleigh, NC
Richmond, VA
Rochester, NY
St. Louis

PRODUCTS/OPERATIONS

2010 Sales

	$ mil.	% of total
Professional services	223.1	72
Publishing & business information	88.2	28
Total	**311.3**	**100**

COMPETITORS

American City Business Journals	Lee Enterprises
Crain Communications	Lender Processing Services
Daily Journal	McClatchy Company
First American	Media General
Gannett	MediaNe
GateHouse Media	News & Record
Herald Media	The Detroit News
Journal Communications	

HISTORICAL FINANCIALS
Company Type: Public

Income Statement
FYE: December 31

	REVENUE ($ mil.)	NET INCOME ($ mil.)	NET PROFIT MARGIN	EMPLOYEES
12/10	311.3	32.4	10.4%	2,034
12/09	262.9	30.8	11.7%	1,903
12/08	189.9	14.3	7.5%	1,812
12/07	152.0	(54.0)	—	1,237
12/06	111.6	(20.3)	—	1,177
Annual Growth	29.2%	—	—	14.7%

2010 Year-End Financials

Debt ratio: 47.2%	No. of shares (mil.): 30.5
Return on equity: 11.6%	Dividends
Cash ($ mil.): 4.9	Yield: —
Current ratio: 1.03	Payout: —
Long-term debt ($ mil.): 131.6	Market value ($ mil.): 424.7

	STOCK PRICE ($) FY Close	P/E High/Low		PER SHARE ($) Earnings	Dividends	Book Value
12/10	13.92	14	8	1.08	0.00	9.14
12/09	10.21	21	5	0.72	0.00	8.21
12/08	6.59	57	5	0.53	0.00	7.43
12/07	29.17	—	—	(3.41)	0.00	5.15
Annual Growth	(21.9%)	—	—	—	—	21.1%

Dolby

Talk about having a sound business model. Dolby Laboratories is the market leader in developing sound processing and noise reduction systems for use in professional and consumer audio and video equipment. Though it does make some of its own products, Dolby mostly licenses its technology to other manufacturers. (Licensing accounts for more than 75% of revenue.) The firm has about 1,900 patents and more than 990 trademarks worldwide. In film, the Dolby Digital format has become the de facto audio standard; its systems equip movie screens around the globe. The company has expanded into digital audio compression. American engineer and physicist Ray Dolby and his family own the more than 40-year-old company.

The company has managed to remain a technological ruler. The global transition to digital broadcast, the upgrade to high-definition (HD) technology, the increase in popularity of 3-D cinema, and the advancement in online and mobile delivery has helped Dolby's business. The company is the leading maker of the digital sound technology built into DVD, Blu-Ray Disc, and CD players, surround-sound theater systems, and HD TV sets. Its system records the sounds of nearly every movie, professional music performance, and radio and TV broadcast in the world. Dolby sells products and provide services in more than 85 countries, and about two-thirds of its sales come from outside the US.

In the licensing arena, the bulk of Dolby's customers come from the personal computer, broadcasting, and consumer electronics markets; in 2010 its largest customer group came from the PC market. Software giant Microsoft, a Dolby licensee, includes Dolby technologies in several editions of its Windows 7 operating system (Home Premium,

Ultimate, Professional, and Enterprise), and accounts for about 12% of the company's revenue. In addition to licensing, the company earns revenues from the sales of equipment and services to cinema operators (which provides technology for film soundtracks and cinema sound systems) and broadcasters (audio content for HDTV production and distribution and within broadcast programming).

The financially successful company has posted five consecutive years of increased revenues and net income, primarily due to the proliferation of all things digital. Its revenues grew in 2010 as a result of an increase in sales of Blu-ray Disc players and digital TVs, as well as an more sales of 3-D and digital cinema products. (For example, during 2010 movie-goers flocked to see *Avatar* at theaters equipped with Dolby 3-D.) The previous year the company expanded its offerings with the launch of Dolby Mobile. The product is designed to enhance the audio quality of media delivered on mobile devices.

In 2009 longtime Dolby executive Bill Jasper retired as president and CEO of the company. Jasper remains on the board of directors, and Kevin Yeaman, former CFO, replaced him as head of the company.

Ray Dolby founded the firm in London in 1965 and moved it to San Francisco in 1977. He controls more than 90% of the company's voting power.

EXECUTIVES

Chairman, Peter Gotcher, age 51
President, CEO, and Director, Kevin J. Yeaman, age 45, $2,077,610 total compensation
EVP and CFO, Murray J. Demo, age 49, $639,569 total compensation
EVP, General Counsel, and Secretary, Andy Sherman
EVP Sales and Marketing, Ramzi Haidamus, age 47
EVP Products and Technologies, Michael J. (Mike) Rockwell, age 43, $1,152,804 total compensation
VP International Sales, Broadcast, Tony Spath
VP Corporate Marketing, Paula Dunn
VP Financial Planning and Analysis, Michael Novelly, age 46
VP Marketing Planning, Francois Modarresse
VP International Sales, Cinema, Peter Seagger
SVP and CTO, Craig Todd
SVP Human Resources, Andrew Dahlkemper
SVP Sales, J. Stuart Mitchell
SVP and CIO, George Lin
SVP, Ioan Allen
SVP Research, Steven E. (Steve) Forshay, age 54
Media Relations, David Yang
Executive Director Marketing, Tom Daily
Senior Director Production Services, Bill Allen
Media Relations, Sean Durkin
Marketing Director, PC Segment, Mary Anderson
Director International Cinema Sales, Guy Hawley
Director Marketing, Mobile, Rolf Schmitz
Investor Relations, Alex Hughes
Senior Director Cinema Marketing, Page Haun
SVP Marketing, Robin Selden
Senior Marketing Manager, Games, Matt Tullis
SVP Corporate Development, Eric Cohen
Director Marketing, Connected Electronics, John Griffin
Auditors: KPMG LLP

LOCATIONS

HQ: Dolby Laboratories, Inc.
100 Potrero Ave., San Francisco, CA 94103-4813
Phone: 415-558-0200   **Fax:** 415-863-1373
Web: www.dolby.com

2010 Sales

	$ mil.	% of total
US	318.1	34
Other countries	604.6	66
Total	**922.7**	**100**

2010 Sales

	% of total
Asia/Pacific	49
Americas	34
Europe, Middle East & Africa	17
Total	**100**

PRODUCTS/OPERATIONS

2010 Sales

	$ mil.	% of total
Technology licensing	710.5	77
Product sales	180.4	20
Production services	31.8	3
Total	**922.7**	**100**

2010 Licensing Sales

	% of total
Personal computers	36
Broadcast	27
Consumer electronics	22
Other	15
Total	**100**

2010 Product Sales

	% of total
Cinema	90
Broadcast	9
Other	1
Total	**100**

Selected Dolby Technologies

Advanced Audio Coding (AAC, audio compression technology)
Dolby 3D (3-D image delivery)
Dolby AC-2 (digital audio processing for satellite and digital audio storage)
Dolby Digital (digital sound for film soundtracks and DVDs)
Dolby Digital Surround EX (expanded surround sound for theaters)
Dolby E (eight-channel digital sound systems)
Dolby Headphone (audio processing for headphone applications)
Dolby Mobile (digital audio processing for mobile devices)
Dolby SR (spectral recording, used in professional audio equipment)
Dolby Surround (four-channel sound for home theaters)

Selected Customers

ABC
AMC Entertainment
CBS
Cinemark USA
CyberLink
DreamWorks
Electronic Arts
HBO
Loews Cineplex
Microsoft
NBC
New Line Cinema
Nintendo
Paramount
Regal Cinemas
Walt Disney
Warner Brothers

COMPETITORS

DTS	Sony
Eastman Kodak	SRS Labs
QSound Labs	Technicolor
RealD	THX
RealNetworks	

HISTORICAL FINANCIALS

Company Type: Public

Income Statement

FYE: Last Friday in September

	REVENUE ($ mil.)	NET INCOME ($ mil.)	NET PROFIT MARGIN	EMPLOYEES
09/10	922.7	283.4	30.7%	1,244
09/09	719.5	243.0	33.8%	1,135
09/08	640.2	199.5	31.2%	1,153
09/07	482.0	142.8	29.6%	976
09/06	391.5	89.5	22.9%	864
Annual Growth	**23.9%**	**33.4%**	**—**	**9.5%**

2010 Year-End Financials

Debt ratio: —
Return on equity: 19.2%
Cash ($ mil.): 545.9
Current ratio: 6.40
Long-term debt ($ mil.): —
No. of shares (mil.): 112.1
Dividends
  Yield: —
  Payout: —
Market value ($ mil.): 6,367.5

	STOCK PRICE ($) FY Close	P/E High/Low		PER SHARE ($) Earnings	Dividends	Book Value
09/10	56.81	29	15	2.46	0.00	13.15
09/09	38.19	20	12	2.11	0.00	11.78
09/08	35.19	31	19	1.74	0.00	9.35
09/07	34.82	30	15	1.26	0.00	7.25
09/06	19.85	30	18	0.80	0.00	5.56
Annual Growth	**30.1%**	**—**	**—**	**32.4%**	**—**	**24.0%**

DTS

DTS (formerly Digital Theater Systems) surrounds movie lovers with sound. The company's multi-channel audio systems are used in consumer electronic devices such as audio/video receivers, DVD and Blu-ray HD players, PCs, car audio products, video game consoles, and home theater systems. DTS has licensing agreements with major consumer electronics manufacturers (Sony, Samsung, and Philips). It also provides DTS-encoded soundtracks in movies, TV shows, and music content. The firm was founded in 1990 as Digital Theater Systems by scientist Terry Beard. It received initial funding from Universal Pictures in 1993, and used that relationship to debut its audio system in the soundtrack to Universal's *Jurassic Park*.

The company saw higher revenues and profits in 2010 compared to the previous year, thanks to the proliferation of advanced home theater systems, which in turn led to an increase in sales of Blu-ray equipped players, game consoles, high-definition TVs, and PCs. Blu-ray related sales comprised more than 30% of DTS's total revenue for the year. And Sony and Samsung accounted for 17% and 15%, respectively, of total revenues in 2010.

Specializing in state-of-the-art audio technology, the company continues to expand via ongoing research and development. Through such efforts, in 2011 the company's high definition radio technology brought the home theater experience to the car. In addition, that year its high definition audio technology was integrated into the NFL's international HD broadcast of the Super Bowl in Dallas.

While DTS is headquartered in the US, it has a plethora of international offices, including locations in the UK, Japan, and China. Nearly 90% of DTS's revenues were derived internationally in

2010. Specifically, Japan is a significant source of revenues, accounting for nearly half of the company's business.

EXECUTIVES

Chairman, President, and CEO, Jon E. Kirchner, age 43, $1,581,854 total compensation
EVP Finance and CFO, Melvin L. (Mel) Flanigan, age 52, $675,138 total compensation
EVP Legal, General Counsel, and Corporate Secretary, Blake A. Welcher, age 49, $655,631 total compensation
EVP and CTO, Frederick (Fred) Kitson
EVP and COO, Brian D. Towne, age 46, $592,323 total compensation
VP North American Licensing Operations, Geir Skaaden
VP; Managing Director, Greater China, Kin Chan
Chief Scientist, James (JJ) Johnston
SVP Research and Development, Richard J. (Rick) Beaton, age 51
SVP Human Resources, Sharon K. Faltemier, age 55
SVP Research and Development, W. Paul Smith
SVP Corporate Strategy and Business Development, Patrick J. Watson, age 50, $516,825 total compensation
Corporate VP; President, DTS Japan, Nao Ohtake
Senior Audio Engineer, Edward Stein
Senior Manager Audio Processing, Jean-Marc Jot
Principal Audio Engineer, Martin Walsh
Director Marketing Communications, David Blasucci
Director Professional Audio, Ronny Katz
Auditors: Grant Thornton LLP

LOCATIONS

HQ: DTS, Inc.
5220 Las Virgenes Rd., Calabasas, CA 91302
Phone: 818-436-1000   **Fax:** 818-436-1999
Web: www.dts.com

2010 Sales

	$ mil.	% of total
Japan	41.4	48
South Korea	21.1	24
US	9.8	11
Other countries	14.8	17
Total	**87.1**	**100**

PRODUCTS/OPERATIONS

Selected Consumer Technology Licensing Applications
Audio/video receivers
Blu-ray HD DVD players
Car audio products
Home theater systems
Personal computers
Standard definition DVD players
Video game consoles

Selected Customer Segments
Consumer electronics manufacturers
Semiconductor manufacturers
Content providers

COMPETITORS

Dolby	Sony
ILM	SRS Labs
Microsoft	Technicolor
Philips Electronics	THX
QSound Labs	

HISTORICAL FINANCIALS

Company Type: Public

Income Statement

FYE: December 31

	REVENUE ($ mil.)	NET INCOME ($ mil.)	NET PROFIT MARGIN	EMPLOYEES
12/10	87.1	16.0	18.4%	228
12/09	77.7	10.6	13.6%	203
12/08	60.2	11.4	18.9%	193
12/07	53.1	(20.4)	—	159
12/06	78.3	3.0	3.8%	325
Annual Growth	**2.7%**	**52.0%**	**—**	**(8.5%)**

2010 Year-End Financials

Debt ratio: —
Return on equity: 10.9%
Cash ($ mil.): 41.7
Current ratio: 6.91
Long-term debt ($ mil.): —
No. of shares (mil.): 17.3
Dividends
Yield: —
Payout: —
Market value ($ mil.): 849.8

	STOCK PRICE ($) FY Close	P/E High/Low		PER SHARE ($) Earnings	Dividends	Book Value
12/10	49.05	56	29	0.90	0.00	8.52
12/09	34.21	59	22	0.60	0.00	8.09
12/08	18.35	57	20	0.63	0.00	7.25
12/07	25.57	—	—	(1.11)	0.00	6.86
12/06	24.19	169	91	0.16	0.00	8.63
Annual Growth	**19.3%**	**—**	**—**	**54.0%**	**—**	**(0.3%)**

Duke Realty

Duke Realty is royalty in the realm of US commercial real estate. The self-managed and self-administered real estate investment trust (REIT) owns and develops office, industrial, and health care properties primarily in major cities in the Midwest and East. Duke is building its holdings of industrial and medical office properties (about 50% of its portfolio). In addition to more than 790 rental properties totaling more than 140 million sq. ft., the company owns 4,800 acres of undeveloped land. Duke Realty's service operations include construction and development, asset and property management, and leasing. The company was founded in 1972.

Duke faced challenges during the economic recession as the commercial real estate market softened and the economy as a whole took a nosedive. Beginning in 2008 the company was forced to make several changes in order to protect its existing assets and grow capital. It limited new development, refocused on 20 core markets, and continued its strategy of diversifying itself by geography and property type.

In order to cope with the downturn the company also reduced its workforce by nearly 20% and froze salaries of top associates for 2009. Duke exited the retail and national build-to-suit development business. Previously, the REIT had been solicited by large corporations such as General Electric Company to construct facilities. That year also marked the closure of Duke's newest offices in Austin, Seattle, and Newport Beach, California. The company will consider returning to those markets when the economy improves.

Duke has been busy repositioning itself as the economy stabilizes. In order to freshen its asset portfolio, it is focused on selling older non-core suburban office properties in the Midwest. The company is using the money from those sales to invest in medical office buildings (which are in higher demand) and warehouse and distribution properties near seaports, such as Savannah, Baltimore, and Houston.

Duke is also limiting new development and listed about one-third of its land for sale, instead of holding it for future development. Although development projects have slowed, the company remains focused on leasing space in its existing buildings.

As part of Duke's strategy of building its industrial assets, the company in 2010 bought out its joint venture partner's 50% stake in Dugan Realty. The deal added more than 100 industrial buildings and 60 acres of undeveloped land in the Midwest and Southeast. Duke also arranged to acquire more than 50 bulk distribution/warehouse facilities and five office buildings in South Florida from Premier Commercial Realty.

The company's efforts, coupled with an improving economy, helped boost sales and reduce losses in 2010.

EXECUTIVES

Chairman and CEO, Dennis D. (Denny) Oklak, age 57, $2,859,415 total compensation
President, Healthcare, James D. Bremner, age 55
EVP and CFO, Christie B. Kelly, age 49, $1,154,439 total compensation
EVP Construction, Steven R. (Steve) Kennedy, age 54, $1,025,071 total compensation
EVP, General Counsel, and Secretary, Howard L. Feinsand, age 63, $1,016,170 total compensation
EVP Redevelopment and Logistics, William J. (Bill) DeBoer
VP Leasing, Atlanta, Brian Sutton
VP, Office Leasing, Atlanta, Craig Flanagan
VP Leasing, St. Louis, Whitaker Varley
VP Asset Management and Customer Service, Atlanta, Mark Dukes
VP Industrial Leasing, Dallas, Randy Wood
VP Asset Management and Customer Service, Dallas, Jeanne Coyle
VP Asset Management and Customer Service, Orlando, Scott Cipriani
VP Asset Management and Customer Service, Nashville, Jeffrey Stovall
VP Asset Management and Customer Service, Raleigh, Amy Mayer
VP, Industrial Leasing, Chicago, Susan Bergdoll
VP, Office Leasing, Chicago, Ryan O'Leary
VP, Office and Industrial Leasing and Development, Cincinnati, Jerry Royce
VP Leasing, Nashville, Coleman Aycock
VP Leasing, Nashville, Lonnie Russell
VP Industrial Leasing, St. Louis, John Hinds
VP Leasing, Tampa, Tim Hain
VP Leasing and Development , Washington DC, Battista Orcino
VP Leasing, Raleigh, Hooker Manning
VP Property Management, Washington DC, Kathy Knizner
VP Industrial, Columbus, Art Makris
VP, Property Management, Chicago, Matt Roberts
VP Property Management, Cincinnati, Jan Armstrong Cobb
VP Office Services, Cleveland, Bob Leibold
VP Asset Management, St. Louis, Mary Ellen Saenz
VP Industrial Leasing, Indianapolis, Jay W. Archer
VP Property Management, Indianapolis, Chris Yeakey
VP, Property Management, Columbus, Aimee D'Amore
VP, Office, Columbus, Ben Struewing
VP Office Leasing and Development, Indianapolis, Traci Kapsalis

VP Construction, Indianapolis, Jeff Stone
VP Leasing, Midwest, Healthcare, Indianapolis, Bruce Gordon
VP Industrial Leasing, Indianapolis, Mark Hosfeld
VP Asset Management and Customer Service, Ft. Lauderdale, Stephanie Rodriguez
VP Leasing, Ft. Lauderdale, Christopher Gallagher
Regional EVP, South and West Regions, Jeffrey D. (Jeff) Turner
SVP Phoenix Operations, Kevin T. Rogus
Senior Regional EVP, Southeast and East Regions, James B. (Jim) Connor, age 50
Regional EVP Southeast Region, J. Samue (Sam) O'Briant
SVP, Atlanta, Chris Brown
SVP Leasing and Development, Baltimore and Norfolk, John Macsherry
SVP Raleigh Operations, Jeff Sheehan
SVP Construction, Chicago Region, Petter Berntzen
SVP Atlanta Office, W. Kerry Armstrong
SVP, Strategic Execution Officer and CIO, Paul R. Quinn
SVP Human Resources, Denise K. Dank
SVP Marketing, Charles Vogt
SVP South Florida Operations, Ed Mitchell
Senior Leasing Representative, Industrial, Dallas, Curt Hefner
SVP St. Louis Operations, Toby Martin
SVP Dallas Operations, Jeff Thornton
SVP Central Florida Operations, Doug Irmscher
SVP Columbus Operations, Jim Clark
SVP Indiana Operations, Charlie Podell
SVP Leasing and Development, Houston, David Hudson
Media Contact, Jamie Jones
SVP, Corporate Controller, and Chief Accounting Officer, Mark A. Denien
Head, Investor Relations, Randy Henry
Media Contact, Jim Bremmer
SVP Nashville Operations, Jeff Palmquist
SVP, Chicago Operations, Steve Schnur
Leasing Representative, Cincinnati Office, Jeremy Kraus
SVP Washington DC Operations, Peter Scholz
SVP, Cincinnati Operations, Jon Burger
Senior Leasing Representative, Orlando, Tim Perry
Leasing Representative, Washington DC, Matt Bremner
Leasing Representative, Raleigh, Alban Barrus
Development Associate, Leasing, Phoenix, Chris Burns
SVP, Office Specialist, Cleveland, Douglas S. Leary
Senior Leasing Representative, Chicago Office, Josh Robbins
Senior Leasing Representative, Industrial, Atlanta, Corey Richardson
Senior Leasing Representative, Healthcare, Travis Tucker
Senior Leasing Representative, Industrial, Indianapolis, Glenn Davis
Senior Leasing Representative, Cory Driskill
Leasing Representative, Healthcare, Indianapolis, Tyson Chastain
Auditors: KPMG LLP

LOCATIONS

HQ: Duke Realty Corporation
600 E. 96th St., Ste. 100, Indianapolis, IN 46240
Phone: 317-808-6000   Fax: 317-808-6770
Web: www.dukerealty.com

PRODUCTS/OPERATIONS

2010

	$ in mil.	% of total
Rental and related services	878.2	63
General contractor and service fees	515.4	37
Total	**1,393.6**	**100**

2010 Properties

	No. of properties
Industrial properties	467
Office properties	290
Other properties (health care and retail)	36
Total	**793**

COMPETITORS

Boston Properties
Brandywine Realty
CenterPoint Properties
Colonial Properties
Cousins Properties
Equity Office
Highwoods Properties
Liberty Property Trust
Panattoni Development Company
Prime Group Realty
ProLogis

HISTORICAL FINANCIALS

Company Type: Public

Income Statement

FYE: December 31

	REVENUE ($ mil.)	NET INCOME ($ mil.)	NET PROFIT MARGIN	EMPLOYEES
12/10	1,393.6	65.8	4.7%	1,000
12/09	1,344.1	(260.1)	—	1,000
12/08	996.1	114.0	11.4%	1,200
12/07	923.2	279.5	30.3%	1,400
12/06	908.8	204.1	22.5%	1,250
Annual Growth	**11.3%**	**(24.6%)**	**—**	**(5.4%)**

2010 Year-End Financials

Debt ratio: 206.1%
Return on equity: 3.2%
Cash ($ mil.): 18.4
Current ratio: 0.69
Long-term debt ($ mil.): 4,207.1

No. of shares (mil.): 252.2
Dividends
Yield: 5.5%
Payout: —
Market value ($ mil.): 3,142.3

	STOCK PRICE ($) FY Close	P/E High/Low		PER SHARE ($) Earnings	Dividends	Book Value
12/10	12.46	—	—	(0.07)	0.68	11.68
12/09	12.17	—	—	(1.67)	0.76	13.06
12/08	10.96	72	10	0.38	1.93	19.15
12/07	26.08	31	16	1.55	1.91	18.89
12/06	40.90	41	31	1.07	1.89	18.51
Annual Growth	**(25.7%)**	**—**	**—**	**—**	**(22.6%)**	**(10.9%)**

DuPont Fabros

DuPont Fabros Technology owns, develops, operates, and manages wholesale data centers — the facilities that house, power, and cool computer servers for such technology companies as Facebook, Google, Microsoft, and Yahoo! The company establishes its rental rates based on the amount of power reserved for tenant use and the square footage they occupy. As a wholesale provider, the company targets clients with high power requirements and a preference for long-term leases. DuPont Fabros Technology develops its wholesale data centers to compete with more traditional colocation models in which managed services are bun-

dled with power and cooling. Wholesale customers typically install and maintain their own servers.

The company's three largest clients — Facebook, Microsoft, and Yahoo! — account for about two-thirds of its annualized base rental revenues.

DuPont Fabros Technology owns and operates eight data centers — six in northern Virginia, one in suburban Chicago, and one in New Jersey. It is developing two more data centers, one in Virginia and the other in California.

Depending on outside sources of capital to develop its data centers, DuPont Fabros is subject to disruptions and fluctuations in the credit markets. The company carries about $700 million in debt. It operates as a real estate investment trust (REIT) for federal income tax purposes. DuPont Fabros has been profitable from 2008 to 2010, the year it earned a net income of $43.7 million, but it has an accumulated deficit of $51.1 million. The company's tenants may choose to develop their own data centers, as Google is doing on a significant scale.

EXECUTIVES

Chairman, Lammot J. du Pont, age 44, $1,332,924 total compensation
President, CEO, and Director, Hossein Fateh, age 43, $2,050,529 total compensation
EVP, CFO, and Treasurer, Mark L. Wetzel, age 52, $1,131,197 total compensation
Chief Accounting Officer, Jeffrey H. Foster, age 48, $630,295 total compensation
SVP Construction, Robert J. Berlinsky, age 51
SVP Operations, Scott A. Davis, age 51
Investor Relations, Victoria (Vicki) Baker
Human Resources, Kathy Murphy
General Counsel and Secretary, Richard A. (Rick) Montfort Jr., age 50, $664,659 total compensation
SVP Sales and Leasing, M. Lee Kestler Jr., age 47
SVP Finance and Acquisitions, Maria Kenny, age 44
Auditors: Ernst & Young LLP

LOCATIONS

HQ: DuPont Fabros Technology, Inc.
1212 New York Ave. NW, Ste. 900, Washington, DC 20005
Phone: 202-728-0044   Fax: 202-728-0220
Web: www.dft.com

PRODUCTS/OPERATIONS

2010 Sales

	$ mil.	% of total
Base rent	154.3	64
Recoveries from tenant	78.4	32
Other revenues	9.8	4
Total	**242.5**	**100**

COMPETITORS

AT&T
CoreSite
Digital Realty
Equinix
Internap Network Services
Rackspace
SAVVIS
Terremark Worldwide
Verizon

Dynasil

HISTORICAL FINANCIALS
Company Type: Public

Income Statement			FYE: December 31
	REVENUE ($ mil.)	NET INCOME ($ mil.)	NET PROFIT MARGIN	EMPLOYEES
---	---	---	---	---
12/10	242.5	30.4	12.5%	83
12/09	200.3	1.8	0.9%	70
12/08	173.7	19.1	11.0%	67
12/07	25.9	(99.3)	—	52
12/06	54.8	0.8	1.5%	50
Annual Growth	45.0%	148.3%	—	13.5%

2010 Year-End Financials
Debt ratio: 78.2%	No. of shares (mil.): 59.8
Return on equity: 3.4%	Dividends
Cash ($ mil.): 227.0	Yield: 2.1%
Current ratio: 2.16	Payout: 86.3%
Long-term debt ($ mil.): 700.0	Market value ($ mil.): 1,272.5

	STOCK PRICE ($) FY Close	P/E High/Low		PER SHARE ($) Earnings	Dividends	Book Value
12/10	21.27	55	31	0.51	0.44	18.06
12/09	17.99	459	61	0.04	0.08	14.29
12/08	2.07	39	3	0.54	0.56	15.56
12/07	19.60	—	—	(2.80)	0.15	15.73
Annual Growth	2.8%	—	—	—	43.1%	4.7%

Dynasil Corporation of America likes playing with the dynamics of silica. The company manufactures custom synthetic-fused silica and quartz products primarily used in industrial optical materials. Its products include filters, lenses, prisms, reflectors, windows, and mirrors. Customers use the company's fabricated optical products in lasers, aircraft, optical equipment, analytical instruments, semiconductors, and electronics. Manufacturers Corning, Schott Glass Technologies, and General Electric supply the company with some fused silica, fused quartz, and optical materials. Dynasil sells its products in the US and overseas.

Looking for an investment opportunity across the Atlantic, Dynasil acquired UK-based Hilger Crystals from Newport Corporation in 2010. Hilger manufactures synthetic crystals with a variety of applications ranging from industrial to medical. The acquisition will open up distribution channels and give Dynasil greater access to the UK market. In mid-2008 the company acquired Radiation Monitoring Devices, Inc. (RMD) and specific assets of RMD Instruments, LLC, for $20 million in cash and stock. The purchase significantly added to the size of Dynasil, as RMD posted 2007 sales of more than $20 million. RMD performs research under government contracts and also makes photonics-related components and instruments.

Gerald Entine, one of RMD's owners and RMD's president, now owns more than 38% of Dynasil Corporation of America. President and CEO Craig Dunham holds nearly 27% of the company.

EXECUTIVES
Chairman, Peter Sulick, age 60
CFO, Richard A. (Rich) Johnson, age 56
President, Evaporated Metal Films, Paul Schulz

President, CEO, and Director, Craig T. Dunham, age 55
VP Commercialization, Paul Tyra, age 52
VP, Megan Shay
Director; President RMD Research, Gerald Entine, age 67
Corporate Secretary, Patricia L. Johnson
COO, Optometrics, Laura Lunardo
Auditors: Haefele, Flanagan & Co., p.c.

LOCATIONS
HQ: Dynasil Corporation of America
44 Hunt St., Watertown, MA 02472
Phone: 617-668-6800   **Fax:** 617-926-9980
Web: www.dynasilcorp.com

COMPETITORS
Asahi Glass	Heraeus Holding
Carl-Zeiss-Stiftung	II-VI
Coherent, Inc.	Minco
Gooch & Housego	

EACO

HISTORICAL FINANCIALS
Company Type: Public

Income Statement			FYE: September 30
	REVENUE ($ mil.)	NET INCOME ($ mil.)	NET PROFIT MARGIN	EMPLOYEES
---	---	---	---	---
09/10	43.0	3.2	7.4%	222
09/09	34.4	1.6	4.7%	191
09/08	17.1	1.2	7.0%	184
09/07	10.8	0.5	4.6%	80
09/06	6.9	0.5	7.2%	75
Annual Growth	58.0%	59.1%	—	31.2%

2010 Year-End Financials
Debt ratio: 54.2%	No. of shares (mil.): 11.7
Return on equity: 16.2%	Dividends
Cash ($ mil.): 4.1	Yield: —
Current ratio: 2.70	Payout: —
Long-term debt ($ mil.): 10.8	Market value ($ mil.): 49.0

	STOCK PRICE ($) FY Close	P/E High/Low		PER SHARE ($) Earnings	Dividends	Book Value
09/10	4.20	20	9	0.22	0.00	1.71
09/09	1.99	31	7	0.08	0.00	1.62
09/08	1.65	23	10	0.11	0.00	1.52
09/07	1.60	28	9	0.07	0.00	0.52
09/06	0.80	14	8	0.07	0.00	0.48
Annual Growth	51.4%	—	—	33.1%	—	37.4%

EACO Corporation lost its appetite for the buffet business. For a half-dozen years after selling its restaurant operations to pursue a new line of business, the company generated revenues from a handful of rental properties including restaurant and industrial properties. (Tenant NES Rentals accounts for about half of its rental revenues.) In 2010 the company acquired Bisco Industries, which distributes electronics components in the US and Canada. EACO was once the sole franchisee of Ryan's Restaurant Group restaurants in Florida; it also owned a chain of 16 Whistle Junction and Florida Buffet locations. CEO Glen Ceiley owns 98.9% of EACO.

EXECUTIVES
Chairman and CEO; CEO, Bisco, Glen F. Ceiley, age 65
President and COO, Bisco, Donald S. (Don) Wagner, age 49
Director; VP Technology, Bisco, William L. Means, age 67
Auditors: Squar, Milner, Peterson, Miranda & Williamson, LLP

LOCATIONS
HQ: EACO Corporation
1500 N Lakeview Ave., Anaheim, CA 92807
Phone: 714-876-2490   **Fax:** 714-876-2410
Web: www.eacocorp.com

COMPETITORS
Allied Electronics	Newark Corporation
Digi-Key	Realty Income
GE Franchise Finance	

HISTORICAL FINANCIALS
Company Type: Public

Income Statement			FYE: Wednesday nearest December 31
	REVENUE ($ mil.)	NET INCOME ($ mil.)	NET PROFIT MARGIN	EMPLOYEES
---	---	---	---	---
08/10*	92.6	(1.4)	—	329
12/08	1.2	(4.0)	—	0
12/07	1.2	(5.0)	—	0
12/06	0.8	(6.8)	—	0
12/05	0.2	9.4	4700.0%	4
Annual Growth	241.3%	—	—	141.6%

*Fiscal year change

2010 Year-End Financials
Debt ratio: 65.6%	No. of shares (mil.): 4.9
Return on equity: —	Dividends
Cash ($ mil.): 1.3	Yield: —
Current ratio: 1.24	Payout: —
Long-term debt ($ mil.): 7.1	Market value ($ mil.): 15.6

	STOCK PRICE ($) FY Close	P/E High/Low		PER SHARE ($) Earnings	Dividends	Book Value
08/10*	3.20	—	—	(0.30)	0.00	2.22
12/08	3.50	—	—	(26.25)	0.00	(25.25)
12/07	10.50	—	—	(32.00)	0.00	0.77
12/06	27.00	—	—	(43.25)	0.00	33.35
12/05	39.25	1	0	47.75	0.00	77.12
Annual Growth	(46.6%)	—	—	—	—	(58.8%)

*Fiscal year change

Eagle Bancorp (MD)

For those nest eggs that need a little help hatching, holding company Eagle Bancorp would recommend its community-oriented EagleBank subsidiary. The bank serves businesses and individuals through more than a dozen branches in Washington, DC, and its suburbs. Deposit products include checking, savings, and money market accounts; certificates of deposit; and IRAs. Commercial, residential, and construction real estate loans combined represent about 70% of its loan portfolio. The bank, which has significant expertise as a Small Business Administration lender, also writes business, consumer, and home equity loans. Eagle Bancorp is buying Alliance Bankshares for some $31 million.

The company has been focused on growing within its existing markets. In 2008 it acquired Fidelity & Trust Financial Corporation and its Fidelity & Trust Bank subsidiary. The $13 million deal broadened Eagle's reach in the Washington, DC, metro area by adding six branches in Maryland, Northern Virginia, and Washington, DC. Since the acquisition, Eagle has focused new growth for the company in the Northern Virginia and Maryland markets, as well as Washington, DC. In 2011 the company acquired a branch of OBA Bank in Washington, DC.

Eagle also is strengthening its International Banking Department (offering foreign currency exchange, among other services) in order to serve the international community and customers who travel or do business overseas.

The company managed to report record net income in 2009, despite the difficult economic conditions that wrecked many banks' results. Profits increased by some 40% from 2008 to 2009. The Washington, DC, market was less impacted by the recession and Eagle also was buoyed by a more than $38 million injection from the US Treasury under the TARP program. The money strengthened the company's capital levels, which in turn helped it grow its loan portfolio in 2009. Eagle's strict loan underwriting standards helped it have fewer problem loans (the downfall for many banks).

In 2010 Eagle expanded its residential mortgage lending division in efforts to increase mortgage production volume. The expansion also presented the opportunity for Eagle to increase non-interest income, as most of the mortgages will be sold on secondary markets and not held on the bank's books.

EXECUTIVES

Chairman, President, and CEO; Chairman and CEO, EagleBank, Ronald D. (Ron) Paul, age 55, $489,388 total compensation
President, EagleBank, Washington, DC and Virginia, Barry C. Watkins
President, Eagle Commercial Ventures, Richard D. Corrigan
President Community Banking, EagleBank, Thomas D. Murphy, age 63, $303,294 total compensation
EVP and CFO; EVP and CFO, EagleBank, James H. Langmead, age 62, $314,758 total compensation
EVP and Chief Credit Officer, EagleBank, Janice L. Williams, age 54
EVP; SEVP and COO, EagleBank, Susan G. Riel, age 61, $315,857 total compensation
EVP and COO, Michael T. (Mike) Flynn, age 63
EVP and Senior Operating Officer, Kim Ray
EVP, EagleBank, Martha Foulon-Tonat, age 55, $304,482 total compensation
EVP and Controller, Diane M. Begg
EVP and Interim Chief Lending Officer, EagleBank, Robert R. Hoffman
VP and Non-Profit Specialist, Malcolm S. Karl
VP and Branch Manager, Deborah J. Keller
VP and Manager Deposit Operations, Judy L. Callaway
VP and Market Manager, Juanita Douglas
VP and Commercial Loan Officer II, Timothy D. Hamilton
VP and Market Manager, James R. Chittock
VP and Business Development Officer, Linda A. Dawkins
VP and Manager Residential Mortgage Lending, Stephen L. Greene

VP and Workout, Recovery, and Liquidation Officer, Michele Capone
VP and Workout, Recovery, and Liquidation Officer, Jodee Lichtenstein
VP and Commercial Real Estate Loan Officer, Ryan A. Riel
VP and Commercial Real Estate Loan Officer, Matthew Leydig
VP and Commercial Loan Officer II, Kenneth S. Scales
VP and Commercial Real Estate Loan Officer, James R. Walker
VP and Business Development Officer, Jenny A. Shtipelman
VP and Commercial Loan Officer, Robin D. Powell
VP and Commercial Loan Officer, K. Russel Marsh
VP and Manager Wiire and Cash Room, Joan M. Grant
VP and Manager Loan Operations, Sharon A. Gray
VP and Credit Analyst II, Jane N. Willis
VP and Business Development Officer, Kai M. Hills
VP and Commercial Loan Officer II, Scott S. Kinlaw
VP and Director Compliance, Ludwell L. Miller III
VP and Credit Analyst II, Jackie Ho
VP and Manager Branch Operations, Susan M. Lewis
VP and Commercial Real Estate Loan Officer, Carisa D. Stanley
VP and Commercial Deposit Services Officer, Maria G. Acosta
VP and Manager Marketing and Advertising, Janette S. Shaw
VP and Manager Business Development Sales, Deborah C. Shumaker
VP and Business Development Officer, Andrew S. Bridge
VP and Commercial Loan Officer II, Horacio Chacon
VP and SBA Lender, Michael L. Devito
VP and Commercial Loan Officer II, John A. Bettini
VP and Business Development Officer, Jacqueline Ames
VP and Commercial Loan Real Estate Officer, Allan L. Acree
VP and Credit Analyst II, P. Lucas Flynn
Vice Chairman, Robert P. Pincus, age 64
SVP and Chief Risk Officer, Cynthia A. Pehl
SVP and Chief Risk Officer, Susan O. Kooker
SVP, Eagle Bancorp and EagleBank, Laurence E. (Larry) Bensignor
SVP and Manager Information Technology, Linda M. Lacy
SVP and Manager Commercial Deposit Services, Susan J. Schumacher
SVP and Group Leader Commercial Lending, Washington DC, John B. Richardson
SVP and Branch Administration Manager, Terry Clarke
SVP and Manager Branch Administration, Joseph L. Clarke
SVP and Director Customer Service, Elizabeth A. Ferrenz
SVP and Consumer Loan Manager, R. Frederick Marsden
SVP and Business Development Officer, Lawrence J. Bolton
SVP and Director Marketing, J. Mercedes Alvarez
SVP and Group Leader Commercial Real Estate Lending, Maryland, Thomas A. Mee
SVP and Manager Loan Administration, Joan Y. Pawloski
SVP and Controller, Terrence D. Weber
Auditors: Stegman & Company

LOCATIONS

HQ: Eagle Bancorp, Inc.
7815 Woodmont Ave., Bethesda, MD 20814
Phone: 301-986-1800   **Fax:** 301-986-8529
Web: www.eaglebankmd.com

PRODUCTS/OPERATIONS

2009 Sales

	$ mil.	% of total
Interest		
Loans	77.0	84
Securities	7.1	8
Other	0.2	-
Noninterest		
Service charges on deposits	2.9	3
Gain on sale of investment securities	1.5	2
Gain on sale of loans	1.1	1
Other	1.8	2
Total	**91.6**	**100**

Selected Subsidiaries

Bethesda Leasing LLC
EagleBank
   Eagle Land Title Company, LLC
   Fidelity Mortgage, Inc.
Eagle Commercial Ventures, LLC

COMPETITORS

Bank of America	OBA Financial Services
BB&T	PNC Financial
Capital One	Sandy Spring Bancorp
First Mariner Bancorp	SunTrust
M&T Bank	

HISTORICAL FINANCIALS

Company Type: Public

Income Statement

FYE: December 31

	ASSETS ($ mil.)	NET INCOME ($ mil.)	INCOME AS % OF ASSETS	EMPLOYEES
12/10	2,089.4	16.7	0.8%	292
12/09	1,805.5	10.4	0.6%	235
12/08	1,496.8	7.4	0.5%	235
12/07	846.4	7.7	0.9%	173
12/06	773.5	8.0	1.0%	171
Annual Growth	28.2%	20.2%	—	14.3%

2010 Year-End Financials

Equity as % of assets: 9.80%
Return on assets: 0.8%
Return on equity: 9.1%
Long-term debt ($ mil.): 49.3
No. of shares (mil.): 19.7
Dividends
  Yield: 0.0%
  Payout: —
Market value ($ mil.): 284.3
Sales ($ mil.): 105.9

	STOCK PRICE ($) FY Close	P/E High/Low		PER SHARE ($) Earnings	Dividends	Book Value
12/10	14.43	19	13	0.77	0.00	10.39
12/09	10.47	20	10	0.55	0.00	9.64
12/08	5.75	21	9	0.62	0.11	11.17
12/07	11.00	22	14	0.71	0.22	7.59
12/06	15.82	26	20	0.74	0.21	7.03
Annual Growth	(2.3%)	—	—	1.0%	—	10.3%

Eagle Bulk Shipping

Some eagles soar through the skies, but Eagle Bulk Shipping rides the waves. The company owns a fleet of about 40 Handymax dry bulk carriers that it charters to customers, typically on one- to three-year contracts. Most of its vessels are classified as Supramaxes — large Handymaxes, essentially. The Supramaxes range in capacity from 50,000 to 60,000 deadweight tons (DWT) and feature on-board cranes for cargo loading and unloading.

Overall, the company's fleet has a carrying capacity of more than 1.1 million DWT. Cargo carried by charterers of Eagle Bulk Shipping's vessels includes cement, coal, fertilizer, grain, and iron ore.

Eagle Bulk Shipping continues to increase the size of its fleet. After adding several ships in 2010, the company's operating days (the number of days vessels actually generate revenues) increased nearly 50%. The company will add eight additional vessels by the end of 2011 and increase its potential DWT by more than 450,000. The company began utilizing chartered in (ships leased for a specified period of time) in late 2010 to meet shipping demands.

EXECUTIVES

Chairman and CEO, Sophocles N. Zoullas, age 45, $20,741,976 total compensation

CFO and Secretary, Alan S. Ginsberg, age 52, $1,942,679 total compensation

COO, Eagle Shipping International (USA), Claude G. Thouret Jr.

Director; President, Eagle Shipping International, Alexis P. Zoullas, age 40

Auditors: PricewaterhouseCoopers LLP

LOCATIONS

HQ: Eagle Bulk Shipping Inc.
477 Madison Ave., Ste. 1405, New York, NY 10022
Phone: 212-785-2500   **Fax:** 212-785-3311
Web: www.eagleships.com

PRODUCTS/OPERATIONS

Selected Vessels & Year Built

Avocet (2010)
Bittern (2009)
Canary (2009)
Cardinal (2004)
Condor (2001)
Crane (2010)
Crested Eagle (2009)
Crowned (2008)
Egret Bulker (2010)
Falcon (2001)
Gannet Bulker (2010)
Golden Eagle (201)0)
Goldeneye (2002)
Grebe Bulker (2010)
Harrier (2001)
Hawk I (2001)
Heron (2001)
Ibis Bulker (2010)
Imperial Eagle (2010)
Jaeger (2004)
Jay (2010)
Kestrel I (2004)
Kingfisher (2010)
Kite (1997)
Kittiwake (2002)
Martin (2010)
Merlin (2001)
Osprey I (2002)
Peregrine (2001)
Redwing (2007)
Shrike (2003)
Skua (2003)
Sparrow (2000)
Stellar Eagle (2009)
Tern (2003)
Thrasher (2010)
Woodstar (2008)
Wren (2008)

COMPETITORS

A.P. M ller - M rsk	Kawasaki Kisen
DryShips Inc.	Mitsui O.S.K. Lines
Excel Maritime	Overseas Shipholding
Carriers	Group
Genco Shipping and	Pacific Basin Shipping
Trading	Star Bulk
Hanjin Shipping	

HISTORICAL FINANCIALS
Company Type: Public

Income Statement
FYE: December 31

	REVENUE ($ mil.)	NET INCOME ($ mil.)	NET PROFIT MARGIN	EMPLOYEES
12/10	265.0	26.8	10.1%	800
12/09	192.6	33.3	17.3%	568
12/08	185.4	61.6	33.2%	495
12/07	124.8	52.2	41.8%	387
12/06	104.6	33.8	32.3%	339
Annual Growth	26.2%	(5.6%)	—	23.9%

2010 Year-End Financials

Debt ratio: 172.1%	No. of shares (mil.): 62.6
Return on equity: 4.0%	Dividends
Cash ($ mil.): 129.1	Yield: 0.0%
Current ratio: 4.94	Payout: —
Long-term debt ($ mil.): 1,151.4	Market value ($ mil.): 311.6

	STOCK PRICE ($) FY Close	P/E High/Low		PER SHARE ($) Earnings	Dividends	Book Value
12/10	4.98	14	9	0.43	0.00	10.70
12/09	4.95	16	5	0.60	0.00	9.98
12/08	6.82	28	2	1.31	2.00	10.05
12/07	26.55	29	14	1.24	1.98	11.02
12/06	17.34	18	12	0.98	2.08	8.96
Annual Growth	(26.8%)	—	—	(18.6%)	—	4.5%

East West Bancorp

East West Bancorp is the holding company for East West Bank, which operates more than 100 branches in California, mainly in and around Los Angeles, the San Francisco Bay area, Orange County, and Silicon Valley. The bank has more than 25 additional branches in the Atlanta, Boston, Houston, New York, and Seattle metropolitan areas, as well as locations in China, Hong Kong, and Taiwan. Catering to the Asian-American community, it provides international banking and trade financing to importers/exporters doing business in the Asia/Pacific region. East West Bank offers multilingual service in English, Cantonese, Mandarin, Vietnamese, and Spanish.

The bank also offers standard services such as personal and business loans, checking and savings accounts, insurance, and merchant credit card processing services. Catering to the manufacturing, wholesale trade, and service sectors, East West Bank focuses its lending activities on commercial and industrial real estate loans, which account for about 60% of the company's loan portfolio. The bank also writes multifamily real estate, residential mortgage, construction, business, and consumer loans. Although East West Bancorp is highly involved in California's slumping commercial real estate market and it suffered its first yearly loss in nearly three decades in 2008, the company's strong liquidity and reserves has helped it weather the economic downturn.

East West Bancorp has expanded its market area through acquisitions. In 2009 the company acquired more than 60 branches and most of the banking operations of larger rival United Commercial Bank, which had been seized by regulators. The deal gave East West Bank about 40 more California branches, plus some 20 additional US locations beyond the state. Pre-tax gains from the transaction, which included a loss-sharing agreement with the FDIC, helped East West Bancorp return to profitability in fiscal 2009. The company kept the momentum going into 2010 as net interest margins improved.

Also in 2010 East West Bancorp made an unsolicited bid to acquire bankrupt real estate company Meruelo Maddux, which owns about 50 properties in Southern California, but the offer was rebuffed by both the target company and a bankruptcy court judge. East West Bancorp inherited some $27 million in loans to Meruelo Maddox as part of its takeover of United Commercial Bank, and had hoped to turn convert the credit into an ownership stake in the property company.

In another 2010 deal, East West Bancorp acquired the failed Washington First International Bank, adding six branches in Seattle; the transaction also included a loss-sharing agreement with the FDIC.

EXECUTIVES

Chairman and CEO, East West Bancorp and East West Bank, Dominic Ng, age 52, $2,374,462 total compensation

EVP, Chief Risk Officer, General Counsel, and Secretary, East West Bancorp and East West Bank, Douglas P. Krause, age 54

EVP and Director Business Banking, East West Bank, Andy Yen, age 53

EVP and Head Retail, Banking and Technology, Karen Fukumura, age 46

EVP and CFO, Irene Oh

EVP and Head International Banking, East West Bank, Agatha Fung, age 51

EVP and Director International Trade Banking, East West Bank, Kwok-Yin Cheng, age 58

EVP and Director Corporate Banking, East West Bank, Wellington Chen, age 51, $404,898 total compensation

EVP and Chief Credit Officer, East West Bank, William J. Lewis, age 67

EVP and Head North California Commercial Lending Division, William H. Fong, age 63

EVP, Donald S. Chow, age 60, $569,932 total compensation

EVP and Director Loan Operations, Ming Lin Chen, age 50

EVP and Director Credit Risk Management, Lawrence B. Schiff

Vice Chairman, East West Bancorp and East West Bank, John Lee, age 79

Vice Chairman; President and COO, East West Bancorp and East West Bank, Julia S. Gouw, age 51

Auditors: KPMG LLP

LOCATIONS

HQ: East West Bancorp, Inc.
135 N. Los Robles Ave., Pasadena, CA 91101
Phone: 626-768-6000   **Fax:** 626-799-3167
Web: www.eastwestbank.com

PRODUCTS/OPERATIONS

2010 Sales

	$ mil.	% of total
Interest		
Loans receivable, including fees	998.6	82
Investment securities	70.1	6
Other	27.2	2
Noninterest		
Branch fees	32.6	3
Net gain on sales of investment securities	31.2	3
Gain on acquisition	22.9	2
Net gain on sales of loans	18.5	1
Decrease in FDIC indemnification asset & receivable	(83.2)	–
Other	17.2	1
Total	**1,135.1**	**100**

COMPETITORS

Bank of America	Hanmi Financial
Bank of East Asia	JPMorgan Chase
Cathay General Bancorp	Nara Bancorp
Citibank	U.S. Bancorp
City National	Wells Fargo
Comerica	Wilshire Bancorp

HISTORICAL FINANCIALS

Company Type: Public

Income Statement

FYE: December 31

	ASSETS ($ mil.)	NET INCOME ($ mil.)	INCOME AS % OF ASSETS	EMPLOYEES
12/10	20,700.5	164.6	0.8%	2,142
12/09	20,559.2	76.6	0.4%	2,679
12/08	12,422.8	(49.7)	—	1,346
12/07	11,852.2	161.2	1.4%	1,361
12/06	10,823.7	143.4	1.3%	1,312
Annual Growth	**17.6%**	**3.5%**	**—**	**13.0%**

2010 Year-End Financials

Equity as % of assets: 10.21%	Dividends
Return on assets: 0.8%	Yield: 0.2%
Return on equity: 8.1%	Payout: 4.8%
Long-term debt ($ mil.): 1,449.7	Market value ($ mil.): 2,904.0
No. of shares (mil.): 148.5	Sales ($ mil.): 1,135.1

	STOCK PRICE ($) FY Close	P/E High/Low		PER SHARE ($) Earnings	Dividends	Book Value
12/10	19.55	25	17	0.83	0.04	14.23
12/09	15.80	53	10	0.33	0.05	20.78
12/08	15.97	—	—	(0.94)	0.40	24.36
12/07	24.23	16	9	2.60	0.40	18.59
12/06	35.42	18	15	2.35	0.20	16.65
Annual Growth	**(13.8%)**	**—**	**—**	**(22.9%)**	**(33.1%)**	**(3.8%)**

EasyLink

EasyLink Services International makes sure clients get the message. The company provides electronic data interchange (EDI) and telex software and services through its Supply Chain Messaging division. Its data translation systems allow trading partners with incompatible information systems to exchange invoices, purchase orders, shipping notices, and other documents. EasyLink's On Demand Messaging segment provides a document delivery system that handles fax, e-mail, and messaging communications. The company offers services ranging from consulting and training to outsourced document processing.

Formerly called Internet Commerce Corporation (ICC), the company purchased EasyLink Services, a provider of document conversion and messaging services, in 2007; after the acquisition ICC changed its name to EasyLink Services International. York Capital Management financed the transaction, which was valued at $67 million. Operations gained from the purchase augmented the company's existing EDI business (which now makes up the bulk of its Supply Chain division); they also formed the entirety of its On Demand division.

EDI, the electronic exchange of documents between computer systems, still is the data format used in most e-commerce transactions. The format differs from ordinary e-mail messages in that companies exchange such documents as bills of lading and checks through EDI. The format predates the Internet and will likely be phased out in time in favor of using XML-based Web services and more sophisticated data formats, rather than the ASCII-based format employed in EDI.

As part of its strategy to acquire complementary businesses in its existing markets, in late 2010 EasyLink bought the Xpedite Systems subsidiary of Premiere Global Services for $105 million. Xpedite includes the PGiSend messaging service that lets users fax from their desktops. After the deal, EasyLink has around 30,000 customers on five continents, along with an advanced enterprise messaging service portfolio that bolsters its On Demand Messaging offering. The company cites contributions from Xpedite as an important factor in the 102% year-over-year rise in revenue it enjoyed in fiscal 2011.

EasyLink serves companies in the biotech, financial services, government, health care, industrial manufacturing, and pharmaceutical sectors. Customers include Home Properties and USDA.

EasyLink's supply chain segment competes with such companies as GXS and Sterling Commerce. The company cites its early adoption of Internet-based systems instead of more costly private EDI networks as a competitive advantage. It has added new features for data handling (such as XML capabilities) to its package of services.

York Capital Management and Wynnefield Capital each own about 10% of EasyLink Services International. All officers and directors together hold 27% of the company.

HISTORY

EasyLink Services International traces its roots to Infosafe, a firm started in 1991 by Thomas Lipscomb, a veteran of the publishing industry and co-founder of data security innovator Wave Systems. Lipscomb teamed with computer scientist and brain researcher Robert Nagel to develop a system to provide digital information, while keeping track of the content used, without going through a commercial online service. Initial customers included the American Trucking Associations, which wanted one of the company's systems to sell training and regulatory information to its members, and International Typeface Corporation, which used the system to license its fonts.

Infosafe went public in 1995. That year it introduced the Design Palette desktop system (a pay-per-use graphics library). In 1996 Arthur Medici succeeded Lipscomb as CEO. The firm's strategy shifted to focus more on Internet technology, and in 1997 Infosafe scrapped its Design Palette and Mark III hardware, deeming its technology dated due to the rapid development of the Internet. It acquired Internet Commerce Corporation, a developer of products for the e-commerce market, and

took that company's name in 1998. Medici remained as president, but financier Richard Berman was brought in as CEO.

ICC worked to develop a commercial electronic data interchange (EDI) system for the secure delivery of electronic documents in support of online transactions. It signed its first contract with New York's Board of Education in 1999. Geoffrey Carroll became CEO later that year.

As interest in online commerce heated up, so too did investor interest. UK-based Cable and Wireless took a stake in ICC and agreed to market its services to international customers. (Cable and Wireless sold most or all of its ICC stock in 2005.) Service agreements with blue-chip customers such as Barnes & Noble, OfficeMax, and Revlon came in 2000, and ICC began acquiring other EDI technology startups to grow its business. The company's stock took off like a rocket and peaked at $90 per share when the dot-com bubble burst.

ICC continued to sign up new customers for its services, but with the dot-conomy meltdown came new business realities. A reorganization to focus the business on achieving profitability brought Michael Cassidy as CEO in 2001. The Department of Defense signed on as a client, and the business continued to grow its top line despite continued losses.

ICC's lower costs and growing popularity with customers began to threaten rival EDI providers such as GE Global Exchange (later Global eXchange Services and GXS) and Sterling Commerce, both of which cut the company off from exchanging data with their EDI systems by 2002.

In 2004 COO Thomas Stallings was elevated to CEO. Arthur Medici, who left ICC in 1999, returned to the company as COO. Also in 2004 ICC acquired Electronic Commerce Systems (ECS) of Norcross, Georgia, adding some 600 clients to its portfolio. Following the ECS acquisition, ICC relocated its corporate headquarters to Atlanta from New York City. The company maintained an office on Long Island.

In 2005 the company acquired the Managed EC business of Inovis, adding some 1,500 customers to its clientele base. ICC also acquired The Kodiak Group, a supplier of e-commerce and data synchronization services, widening its portfolio of professional services. The company acquired Enable, a provider of electronic marketplace software and services, in 2006.

After acquiring EasyLink Services in 2007, ICC changed its name to EasyLink Services International.

EXECUTIVES

CFO and Secretary, Glen E. Shipley, age 60, $500,341 total compensation
CEO and Director, Thomas J. Stallings, age 63, $876,402 total compensation
EVP Production Operations, Chris A. Parker, age 40
EVP Product Development and Support, Teresa A. (Terri) Deuel, age 49
VP Global Product Management, John Mecke
VP Sales, Asia Pacific, Jeremy Fox
SVP Global Sales and Marketing, Kevin Maloney, age 56, $515,134 total compensation
Director Corporate Communications, Pamela Bernardino
Auditors: Friedman LLP

LOCATIONS

HQ: EasyLink Services International Corporation
6025 The Corners Pkwy., Ste. 100, Norcross, GA
30092
Phone: 678-533-8000
Web: www.easylink.com

2011 Sales

	$ mil.	% of total
US	96.2	59
Europe	30.3	18
Asia/Pacific & other regions	38.3	23
Total	**164.8**	**100**

PRODUCTS/OPERATIONS

2011 Sales

	$ mil.	% of total
On Demand		
Fax services	94.6	57
Production email	16.3	10
Notification	8.6	6
Fax services	1.9	-
Other on demand	5.3	3
EDI services	31.8	20
Telex services	6.3	4
Total	**164.8**	**100**

COMPETITORS

BT Radianz	Onvia
Fenestrae	Open EC
Graphnet	Open Text
GXS	Silanis Technologies
IntraLinks	SPS Commerce
j2 Global	Sterling Commerce
Omtool	Swisscom

HISTORICAL FINANCIALS

Company Type: Public

Income Statement			FYE: July 31
	REVENUE ($ mil.)	NET INCOME ($ mil.)	NET PROFIT MARGIN	EMPLOYEES
07/11	164.8	24.7	15.0%	541
07/10	81.4	17.1	21.0%	282
07/09	85.4	(11.2)	—	293
07/08	92.2	16.3	17.7%	359
07/07	21.9	2.7	12.3%	368
Annual Growth	**65.6%**	**73.9%**	**—**	**10.1%**

2011 Year-End Financials

Debt ratio: 80.9%
Return on equity: 24.9%
Cash ($ mil.): 30.2
Current ratio: 1.21
Long-term debt ($ mil.): 80.2
No. of shares (mil.): 31.4
Dividends
  Yield: —
  Payout: —
Market value ($ mil.): 166.6

	STOCK PRICE ($) FY Close	P/E High/Low		PER SHARE ($) Earnings	Dividends	Book Value
07/11	5.30	9	3	0.72	0.00	3.15
07/10	2.34	5	3	0.53	0.00	2.28
07/09	1.74	—	—	(0.46)	0.00	2.18
07/08	3.10	9	5	0.50	0.00	2.41
07/07	2.85	37	20	0.11	0.00	0.91
Annual Growth	**16.8%**	**—**	**—**	**60.0%**	**—**	**36.4%**

Ebix

Ebix knows a lot about the insurance biz. The company sells insurance industry software products and professional services to property/casualty insurers, brokerages, and individuals in Asia, Australia, Europe, and North America. The company's EbixExchange service acts as an online auction house where buyers and carriers can exchange bids for auto, home, health, life, and other types of insurance, while paying Ebix a fee on each transaction. Ebix also provides agency management software that includes workflow and customer relationship management (CRM) capabilities, as well as other back-office functions, for insurance brokers and insurance carriers.

In addition to its insurance exchanges and software products, Ebix also offers custom software development and business process outsourcing services. Ebix serves clients worldwide, operating from a development center in India and offices in the US, Australia, Brazil, New Zealand, Singapore, Japan, and China.

The company has used selective acquisitions throughout its history to expand its product lines and customer base. Ebix paid about $66 million in stock and cash to buy Atlanta-based A.D.A.M. The deal gave Ebix a boost in the health care and insurance markets. In 2010 Ebix acquired the assets of Connective Technologies, a provider of exchange services for the property and casualty insurance industry in the US. In 2009 the company boosted its hosted CRM offerings for insurance companies, brokers, and agents when it purchased E-Z Data for about $50 million. It also bought insurance software provider Peak Performance Solutions for $8 million and Facts, Inc. (automated claims processing software for health care payers) for $7 million.

In 2008 the company acquired Telstra eBusiness Services for about $44 million, Acclamation Systems for $22 million; other smaller deals included the purchased of ConfirmNet and Periculum Services Group. The deals expanded Ebix's offerings for clients involved with the health care industry and boosted its presence in foreign markets such as Australia.

EXECUTIVES

Chairman, President, and CEO, Robin Raina, age 45, $2,781,769 total compensation
VP System Development Group, Infinity Carrier, John L. Schmitt
SVP EbixExchange, Dan Delity
SVP Ebix Health, Jim Senge
SVP, CFO and Secretary, Robert (Bob) Kerris, age 57, $167,249 total compensation
SVP, Infinity Carrier, Kathryn S. Cay
SVP Ebix P&C, Christine M. Denham
Managing Director Ebix New Zealand, Anthony (Tony) Wisniewski
SVP International Business and Intellectual Poperty, Graham Prior
Managing Director Ebix Singapore, Andy Wakefield
Auditors: Habif, Arogeti, & Wynne, LLP

LOCATIONS

HQ: Ebix, Inc.
  5 Concourse Pkwy., Ste. 3200, Atlanta, GA 30328
Phone: 678-281-2020   **Fax:** 678-281-2019
Web: www.ebix.com

PRODUCTS/OPERATIONS

2009 Sales

	$ mil.	% of total
Exchanges	60.8	62
BPO	14.7	15
Broker systems	11.6	12
Carrier systems	10.6	11
Total	**97.7**	**100**

COMPETITORS

Answer Financial	Cover-All
Applied Systems	Crawford & Company
BenefitMall	InsWeb
CCC Information	Intuit
Computer Sciences	Life Quotes
Corp.	SunGard

HISTORICAL FINANCIALS

Company Type: Public

Income Statement			FYE: December 31
	REVENUE ($ mil.)	NET INCOME ($ mil.)	NET PROFIT MARGIN	EMPLOYEES
12/10	132.2	59.0	44.6%	1,179
12/09	97.7	38.8	39.7%	958
12/08	74.8	27.3	36.5%	637
12/07	42.8	12.7	29.7%	391
12/06	29.3	6.0	20.5%	292
Annual Growth	**45.7%**	**77.1%**	**—**	**41.8%**

2010 Year-End Financials

Debt ratio: 10.9%
Return on equity: 25.5%
Cash ($ mil.): 23.4
Current ratio: 1.56
Long-term debt ($ mil.): 25.2
No. of shares (mil.): 36.0
Dividends
  Yield: —
  Payout: —
Market value ($ mil.): 852.5

	STOCK PRICE ($) FY Close	P/E High/Low		PER SHARE ($) Earnings	Dividends	Book Value
12/10	23.67	19	4	1.51	0.00	6.42
12/09	16.28	22	6	1.03	0.00	4.96
12/08	7.97	18	8	0.76	0.00	2.34
12/07	8.13	21	7	0.40	0.00	2.04
12/06	3.11	16	8	0.21	0.00	1.05
Annual Growth	**66.1%**	**—**	**—**	**63.8%**	**—**	**57.3%**

Echo Global

By land, air, or sea, Echo Global Logistics can help you deliver the goods. The company provides a wide range of transportation and logistics services, such as carrier management, rate negotiation, freight bill audit and payment, routing compliance, and shipment execution and tracking. In addition, its Evolved Transportation Manager (ETM) software analyzes clients' transportation needs and helps reduce costs, as well as manages all procedures in shipping. Established in 2005, Echo Global Logistics customer base are primarily companies in the manufacturing and consumer products industries.

About 24,000 transportation providers make up Echo Global Logistics' carrier network, which consists of small and midsized fleets, trucking companies, and single-truck owners. The company has two types of clients, enterprise (under multiyear contracts) and transactional (services provided on a shipment-by-shipment basis). The number of enterprise clients increased nearly 30% in 2010 compared to 2009 (which was also up more than 25% compared to 2008). Similarly, the number of transactional clients improved from 15,259 in 2009 to 22,617 in 2010 (a 48% increase). As a result of the increase in the number of customers, revenue was up nearly 65% in 2010. In spite of an increase in transportations costs, Echo Global Logistics has been able to keep expenses down. Total operating expenses declined from over 19% of the company's revenue in 2009 to less than 16% in 2010.

Although Echo Global Logistics' focus is on truckload (TL), less than truckload (LTL), and small parcel delivery; the company also offers intermodal (combination of rail and truck) air delivery. The company will continue to expand its geographic reach, both through air and ocean modes of delivery.

Truckload operations have also been a target for growth. Echo Global Logistics expanded its US presence in mid 2011 with the purchase of the assets owned by Advantage Transport, an Arizona-based truckload transportation brokerage company. In 2009 the company acquired brokerage firm Raytrans Distribution Services. Raytrans, which became a division of Echo, specializes in flatbed, over-sized, auto-haul and other specialty dry van brokerage services.

A group of company executives, including directors Henry Weller, Eric Letkofsky, and Bradley Keywell, control more than half of Echo Global Logistics. Echo Global Logistics went public in late 2009.

EXECUTIVES

Chairman, Samuel K. Skinner, age 72
CEO and Director, Douglas R. (Doug) Waggoner, age 52
CFO, David B. (Dave) Menzel, age 49
VP Station Sales, Marty Sinicrope
COO, Orazio Buzza, age 38
CTO, David C. Rowe, age 44
SVP Sales, Vipon Sandhir, age 39
Regional Branch Manager, Atlanta, Anne Wyrsch
Regional Branch Manager, Dallas, Mike Bryan
SVP Operations, Michael Mobley
Manager Human Resources, Debbie Bowen
Marketing Coordinator and Investor Relations, Heather Mills
Director, Business Development, Scott A. Frisoni, age 38
Auditors: Ernst & Young LLP

LOCATIONS

HQ: Echo Global Logistics, Inc.
 600 W. Chicago Ave., Ste. 725, Chicago, IL 60610
Phone: 800-354-7993   **Fax:** 888-796-4445
Web: www.echo.com

COMPETITORS

ABF Freight System
C.H. Robinson Worldwide
Con-way Inc.
Expeditors
FedEx
J.B. Hunt
MIQ Logistics
Ozburn-Hessey Logistics
Roadrunner Transportation Services
Ryder System
Schneider Logistics
Total Quality Logistics
Transplace
UPS

HISTORICAL FINANCIALS

Company Type: Public

Income Statement

FYE: December 31

	REVENUE ($ mil.)	NET INCOME ($ mil.)	NET PROFIT MARGIN	EMPLOYEES
12/10	426.4	8.4	2.0%	709
12/09	259.6	5.2	2.0%	663
12/08	202.8	2.9	1.4%	553
12/07	95.5	1.7	1.8%	245
12/06	33.2	(0.2)	—	0
Annual Growth	**89.3%**	**—**	**—**	**42.5%**

2010 Year-End Financials

Debt ratio: 6.9%
Return on equity: 8.0%
Cash ($ mil.): 43.2
Current ratio: 2.31
Long-term debt ($ mil.): 7.2

No. of shares (mil.): 22.0
Dividends
 Yield: —
 Payout: —
Market value ($ mil.): 265.4

	STOCK PRICE ($) FY Close	P/E High/Low		PER SHARE ($) Earnings	Dividends	Book Value
12/10	12.04	42	26	0.38	0.00	4.76
12/09	12.69	53	41	0.29	0.00	4.31
Annual Growth	**(5.1%)**	**—**	**—**	**31.0%**	**—**	**10.5%**

EDAC Technologies

At EDAC Technologies, aerospace products really make the rounds. Comprising both aerospace and commercial sectors, the company designs, manufactures, and services complex rotating aircraft engine and other precision industrial components and assemblies (such as rotating seals, disks, shafts, and turbine cases) for leading engine OEMs. It offers three major product lines: EDAC AERO, EDAC Machinery, and Apex Machine Tool (one of the company's two subsidiaries, along with GrosIte). EDAC also provides grinding, welding, painting, and assembly services, and its facilities include computerized, numerically controlled (CNC) machining centers. United Technologies generates about 45% of EDAC's sales.

United Technologies (UTC) has the distinction of being EDAC's largest customer. It contracts the company to make jet engine components for the Joint Strike Fighter. UTC's subsidiary, Pratt & Whitney, is also a client, along with Boeing, General Electric, and Mitsubishi — more than 75% of the company's business is generated by its aerospace customers. Additionally, most of EDAC's customer base is in the US, though it is making headway into Canada and Mexico, and certain countries in Asia and Europe.

EDAC AERO is a relative newcomer to the company. In mid-2009 EDAC paid more than $250,000 to acquire the assets of the manufacturing unit of Connecticut-based MTU Aero Engines North America, a subsidiary of MTU Aero Engines Holding. EDAC reorganized its related operations into a single product line by combining AERO with its Precision Components and Engine Components Repair units — the combined entity was renamed EDAC AERO.

The company has made a number of acquisitions, allowing it to actively grow its product lines to strengthen its business in the aerospace industry. In 2010 it acquired New Hampshire-based Ac-

cura Technics, a grinding machinery specialist, for $300,000. In 2009 the company purchased the assets of Service Network Incorporated (SNI) for $775,000; SNI manufactures and rebuilds precision grinders. These acquisitions reflect the company's understanding that diversification and adaptation are instrumental in weathering economic downturns. Accura Technics, AERO, and SNI give the company new capabilities and technologies that expand its market share in the aerospace industry.

Due to the new acquisitions, EDAC experienced a 34% rise in 2010 sales over 2009. The company's net income did not fare so well; it suffered an almost 90% loss — going from more than $7 million in 2009 to a low $845,000 in 2010. EDAC cited problems with initial production runs for a major aerospace order, as well as difficulties starting up its SNI operations, as the reasons for the intense decline. According to EDAC, customers are still recovering from the economic crisis and remain cautious in making major capital equipment purchases.

President, CEO, and director Dominick Pagano owns more than 14% of the company.

EXECUTIVES

Chairman, Daniel C. Tracy, age 70
President, CEO, and Director, Dominick A. Pagano, age 67, $389,177 total compensation
VP Business Development, Luciano M. Melluzzo, age 47, $234,130 total compensation
VP Finance, CFO, and Secretary, Glenn L. Purple, age 55, $180,843 total compensation
Manager, Human Resources, Carol Foley
Auditors: CCR LLP

LOCATIONS

HQ: EDAC Technologies Corporation
 1806 New Britain Ave., Farmington, CT 06032
Phone: 860-677-2603   **Fax:** 860-674-2718
Web: www.edactechnologies.com

PRODUCTS/OPERATIONS

2010 Sales by Market

	$ mil.	% of total
Aerospace	56.6	77
Other	16.5	23
Total	**73.1**	**100**

2010 Sales by Product Line

	$ mil.	% of total
EDAC AERO	50.2	69
Apex Machine Tool	17.0	23
EDAC Machinery	5.9	8
Total	**73.1**	**100**

Selected Product Lines

Aerospace
 EDAC AERO
  Disks
  Fan case
  Housings
  Hubs
  Rings
  Seals
  Shrouds
  Spacers
  Sync rings
  Turbine cases
Commercial
 Accura Technics
  CNC (computerized numerical control) grinding and
   machining systems
 Apex Machine Tool
  Close tolerance plastic injection molds
  Fixtures

Molds for composite parts and specialized machinery
Precision gages
Gros-Ite Precision Engineered Components
Aircraft welding and riveting
Assembly of jet engine sync rings and medical devices
Post assembly machining
Sutton barrel finishing
Gros-Ite Precision Engineered Spindles
Low pressure turbine cases, hubs, rings, and disks
Spindle manufacture
Spindle repair
Service Network International (SNI)
Precision grinding machines

COMPETITORS

GE
Goodrich Corp.
Precision Castparts
SIFCO
Volvo Aero

HISTORICAL FINANCIALS

Company Type: Public

Income Statement

FYE: Saturday nearest December 31

	REVENUE ($ mil.)	NET INCOME ($ mil.)	NET PROFIT MARGIN	EMPLOYEES
12/10	73.1	0.8	1.1%	384
12/09	54.6	7.6	13.9%	345
12/08	44.7	1.1	2.5%	224
12/07	50.0	3.4	6.8%	223
12/06	38.3	1.6	4.2%	228
Annual Growth	17.5%	(15.9%)	—	13.9%

2010 Year-End Financials

Debt ratio: 39.7%
Return on equity: 3.4%
Cash ($ mil.): 1.0
Current ratio: 1.84
Long-term debt ($ mil.): 9.9

No. of shares (mil.): 4.9
Dividends
Yield: —
Payout: —
Market value ($ mil.): 16.5

	STOCK PRICE ($) FY Close	P/E High/Low	PER SHARE ($) Earnings	Dividends	Book Value
12/10	3.38	40 16	0.17	0.00	5.10
12/09	3.10	3 1	1.54	0.00	4.91
12/08	1.79	42 4	0.23	0.00	3.25
12/07	9.78	16 4	0.70	0.00	3.29
12/06	3.05	14 8	0.32	0.00	2.35
Annual Growth	2.6%	— —	(14.6%)	—	21.4%

Edd Helms

Like a friend's sentiment in your junior high yearbook, the Edd Helms Group wants you to "stay cool." The contracting group provides electrical and HVAC maintenance and retrofitting services for commercial, marine (primarily private yachts), and residential customers in South Florida. It also offers temporary power and lighting installation for tradeshows and conventions; the group markets its temporary power services for emergency restoration in emergency situations such as hurricanes. Additionally, the group provides structural and radio frequency services for wireless and cellular towers. CEO and founder W. Edd Helms, Jr., owns 84% of the company.

EXECUTIVES

Chairman, President, and CEO, W. Edd Helms Jr., age 65
CFO, Dean A. Goodson, age 43
EVP, Secretary, Treasurer, and Director, L. Wade Helms, age 54
Auditors: Dohan and Company, PA

LOCATIONS

HQ: Edd Helms Group, Inc.
17850 NE 5th Ave., Miami, FL 33162-1008
Phone: 305-653-2520   **Fax:** 305-651-5527
Web: www.eddhelms.com

PRODUCTS/OPERATIONS

2008 Sales

	$ mil.	% of total
Electric	12.3	57
HVAC	9.3	43
Total	**21.6**	**100**

COMPETITORS

Honshy Electric
Jorda Enterprises
Megatran
Tri-City Electrical Contractors
Uniweld Products
W.W. Gay Mechanical Contractor

HISTORICAL FINANCIALS

Company Type: Public

Income Statement

FYE: May 31

	REVENUE ($ mil.)	NET INCOME ($ mil.)	NET PROFIT MARGIN	EMPLOYEES
05/03	16.8	(0.1)	—	129
05/02	24.5	1.0	4.1%	175
05/99	0.3	(0.1)	—	1
Annual Growth	173.6%	—	—	237.0%

Debt ratio: 39.7%
Return on equity: 3.4%
Cash ($ mil.): 1.0
Current ratio: 1.84
Long-term debt ($ mil.): 9.9

No. of shares (mil.): 4.9
Dividends
Yield: —
Payout: —
Market value ($ mil.): 16.5

eHealth

eHealth brought e-commerce to the insurance business. Through its eHealthInsurance Services subsidiary, the company sells health insurance online to more than 700,000 individual, family, and small business members. The company is licensed to sell in all 50 states and Washington, DC, and it has partnerships with some 180 health insurance carriers. It offers more than 10,000 products online — including health, dental, and vision insurance products from the likes of Aetna, Humana, Kaiser Permanente, and Wellpoint, as well as more than 40 Blue Cross and Blue Shield licensees. The company was founded in 1997.

eHealth is trying to fill a gap in the health insurance brokerage business, left by large brokers who cater to large and midsized companies and local agents who sell to individuals and small businesses but offer plans from a limited number of carriers. eHealth's technology platform and nationwide presence allow customers to get online rate quotes

and side-by-side plan comparisons from a much wider range of providers. The company's online applications are delivered electronically to insurance carriers' information systems, reducing the time it takes to process and enroll new members.

The company gets most of its revenue from commissions off sales of policies. A much smaller amount comes from advertising sponsorships on its website and licensing agreements with agents and carriers who use the company's e-commerce technology. The company launched its online advertising business in 2006.

eHealth is working to build greater brand awareness with consumers and drive more traffic to its website. The company has marketing partnerships with online financial services firms and medical information providers to help get potential customers to its site. By making more people aware of the company's offerings, enhancing its technologies, and providing more products from an ever-growing network of carriers, the company hopes to expand its membership.

To follow through on its strategies, eHealth broadened its Medicare offerings when it acquired privately-held PlanPrescriber in 2010 for roughly $30 million. PlanPrescriber provides online and pharmacy-based tools to help seniors navigate Medicare health insurance options. The acquisition will help accelerate eHealth's penetration of the large and steadily growing senior market. As the Baby Boomer generation continues to reach retirement age, more companies like eHealth are seeking ways to take advantage of that potentially lucrative market. eHealth also intends to expand its online Medicare enrollment capabilities following the buy.

Though the company operates a technology center in China, almost all its revenues come from the US. However, it has launched a pilot program in China to sell insurance online in select markets within the country.

EXECUTIVES

Chairman, President, and CEO, Gary L. Lauer, age 58, $2,297,107 total compensation
President, eHealth Government Systems, Samuel C. (Sam) Gibbs III, age 53, $293,169 total compensation
EVP Technology and CTO, Sheldon X. Wang, age 51, $1,035,190 total compensation
EVP Business and Corporate Development, Bruce A. Telkamp, age 43, $903,547 total compensation
VP Public Policy and Government Affairs, John D. Desser
VP Communications, Brian Mast
SVP Sales and Operations, Robert S. Hurley, age 51, $525,256 total compensation
SVP and CFO, Stuart M. Huizinga, age 48, $806,606 total compensation
Director Investor Relations, Kate Sidorovich
Director Public Relations, Nate Purpura
Senior Media Consultant, Sande Drew
Auditors: Ernst & Young LLP

LOCATIONS

HQ: eHealth, Inc.
440 E. Middlefield Rd., Mountain View, CA 94043
Phone: 650-584-2700   **Fax:** 650-961-2153
Web: https://www.ehealthinsurance.com

PRODUCTS/OPERATIONS

2009 Sales

	$ mil.	% of total
Commissions	119.3	88
Sponsorships, licensing & other	15.6	12
Total	**134.9**	**100**

Selected Insurance Carriers

Aetna
Altius
Anthem Blue Cross and Blue Shield
Assurant Health
Bay Dental Plan
BlueCross BlueShield of Texas
Blue Shield of California
CareFirst BlueCross BlueShield
CIGNA
ConnectiCare
Coventry Health Care
HealthAmerica
HealthNet
Humana
Kaiser Permanente
LifeWise Health Plans
Mountain State BlueCross BlueShield
Regence BlueCross BlueShield
Scott & White Health Plan
Security Life Insurance Company of America
UniCare
UnitedHealthcare
WellPath Select
WellPoint

COMPETITORS

Aflac	InsWeb
Answer Financial	Life Quotes
Aon	Marsh Inc.
BenefitMall	Matrix Direct
Bollinger, Inc.	Wells Fargo Insurance
Ebix	Services

HISTORICAL FINANCIALS

Company Type: Public

Income Statement

FYE: December 31

	REVENUE ($ mil.)	NET INCOME ($ mil.)	NET PROFIT MARGIN	EMPLOYEES
12/10	160.4	17.5	10.9%	641
12/09	134.9	15.3	11.3%	520
12/08	111.7	14.2	12.7%	482
12/07	87.8	31.6	36.0%	437
12/06	61.3	16.5	26.9%	357
Annual Growth	**27.2%**	**1.5%**	**—**	**15.8%**

2010 Year-End Financials

Debt ratio: —
Return on equity: 10.8%
Cash ($ mil.): 128.1
Current ratio: 7.36
Long-term debt ($ mil.): —
No. of shares (mil.): 21.6
Dividends
  Yield: —
  Payout: —
Market value ($ mil.): 306.1

	STOCK PRICE ($) FY Close	P/E High/Low		PER SHARE ($) Earnings	Dividends	Book Value
12/10	14.19	26	13	0.73	0.00	7.52
12/09	16.43	32	19	0.61	0.00	6.47
12/08	13.28	66	15	0.55	0.00	6.18
12/07	32.11	30	14	1.22	0.00	5.61
12/06	20.11	36	25	0.80	0.00	4.40
Annual Growth	**(8.3%)**	**—**	**—**	**(2.3%)**	**—**	**14.3%**

El Paso Pipeline Partners

While El Paso Pipeline Partners might seem like the way El Paso gets great Mexican food across the border, it's actually a natural gas pipeline and storage company. The firm, which consists primarily of Wyoming Interstate Company (WIC), Colorado Interstate Gas Company (CIG), and Southern Natural Gas Company (SNG), has 12,500 miles of pipeline, and storage facilities totaling 89 billion cu. ft. El Paso Pipeline Partners' customers include local distribution companies, industrial users, electricity generators, and natural gas marketing and trading companies. Parent El Paso Corp. controls about 51% of the company.

The partnership's strategy is to increase the efficiency of its pipelines while making complementary asset acquisitions from its parent and from third parties.

In 2010 it expanded its liquefied natural gas (LNG) assets, acquiring from its parent a 51% stake in Southern LNG Company and El Paso Elba Express Company for $810 million. It subsequently acquired the remaining stakes in these companies, plus an additional 15% stake in SNG for $1.1 billion. After further purchases, in 2011 El Paso Pipeline Partners held 100% of Southern LNG and El Paso Elba Express, 100% of SNG, and 86% of CIG.

EXECUTIVES

Chairman, Ronald L. Kuehn Jr., age 75
President, CEO, and Director, James C. (Jim) Yardley, age 59
EVP and General Counsel, Robert W. Baker, age 54
VP, Controller, and Principal Accounting Officer, Rosa P. Jackson, age 57
SVP, Daniel B. (Dan) Martin, age 54
SVP, Norman G. Holmes, age 55
SVP, James J. Cleary, age 56
SVP, CFO, and Director, John R. (J. R.) Sult, age 51
Auditors: Ernst & Young LLP

LOCATIONS

HQ: El Paso Pipeline Partners, L.P.
  1001 Louisiana St., Houston, TX 77002
Phone: 713-420-2600   **Fax:** 713-420-4417
Web: www.eppipelinepartners.com

COMPETITORS

ANR Pipeline	Southern Union
Bridgeline	Transcontinental Gas
Duncan Energy	Pipe Line
Gulf South Pipeline	U.S. Transmission

HISTORICAL FINANCIALS

Company Type: Public

Income Statement

FYE: December 31

	REVENUE ($ mil.)	NET INCOME ($ mil.)	NET PROFIT MARGIN	EMPLOYEES
12/10	1,344.1	378.5	28.2%	0
12/09	537.6	213.5	39.7%	0
12/08	141.1	114.5	81.1%	0
12/07	110.0	66.0	60.0%	0
12/06	97.0	65.0	67.0%	0
Annual Growth	**92.9%**	**55.3%**	**—**	**—**

2010 Year-End Financials

Debt ratio: —
Return on equity: —
Cash ($ mil.): 68.8
Current ratio: 0.79
Long-term debt ($ mil.): 3,400.3
No. of shares (mil.): 177.2
Dividends
  Yield: 4.6%
  Payout: 81.6%
Market value ($ mil.): 5,926.3

	STOCK PRICE ($) FY Close	P/E High/Low		PER SHARE ($) Earnings	Dividends	Book Value
12/10	33.45	19	12	1.90	1.55	(0.00)
12/09	25.96	16	9	1.64	1.33	(0.00)
12/08	15.60	20	10	1.22	1.01	5.63
12/07	25.05	197	156	0.13	0.00	6.84
Annual Growth	**10.1%**	**—**	**—**	**144.5%**	**—**	**—**

Electric & Gas Technology

Oil and water may not mix, but electric and metal does — in the business plan of Electric & Gas Technology (EGTI). EGTI operates as a holding company. Its subsidiary Logic Metals Technology offers contract precision sheet metal fabrication of electronic metal enclosures and equipment panels. The company caters to communications and electronics industries, as well as a variety of aesthetic design applications. The father and son team, Chairman S. Mort Zimmerman and CEO Daniel Zimmerman control the company.

EXECUTIVES

President, CEO, and Director, Daniel A. Zimmerman
Auditors: Turner, Stone & Company, L.L.P.

LOCATIONS

HQ: Electric & Gas Technology, Inc.
  3233 W. Kingsley Rd., Garland, TX 75041
Phone: 972-840-3223   **Fax:** 972-271-8925
Web: www.elgt.com

PRODUCTS/OPERATIONS

2006 Sales

	$ mil.	% of total
Contract manufacturing	10.6	83
Utilities products	2.1	17
Total	**12.7**	**100**

Subsidiaries

Logic Metals Technology, Inc.
Reynolds Equipment Company

COMPETITORS

Badger Meter	Maysteel
Electro Industries	PowerSecure
Elster American Meter	International
Falstrom	Schlumberger
Itron	Thomas & Betts

HISTORICAL FINANCIALS

Company Type: Public

Income Statement

	REVENUE ($ mil.)	NET INCOME ($ mil.)	NET PROFIT MARGIN	EMPLOYEES
07/06	12.7	(1.5)	—	122
07/05	8.5	0.1	1.2%	78
07/04	6.4	(3.0)	—	47
07/03	13.6	(1.2)	—	84
07/02	9.7	(2.5)	—	78
Annual Growth	7.0%	—	—	11.8%

FYE: July 31

2006 Year-End Financials

Debt ratio: —
Return on equity: —
Cash ($ mil.): 0.5
Current ratio: 0.82
Long-term debt ($ mil.): 4.4

No. of shares (mil.): —
Dividends
  Yield: —
  Payout: —
Market value ($ mil.): —

	STOCK PRICE ($) FY Close	P/E High/Low		PER SHARE ($) Earnings	Dividends	Book Value
07/06	1.02	—	—	(0.19)	0.00	(0.00)
07/05	0.75	63	8	0.02	0.00	(0.00)
07/04	0.21	—	—	(0.44)	0.00	(0.00)
07/03	1.50	—	—	(0.19)	0.00	(0.00)
07/02	0.18	—	—	(0.40)	0.00	(0.00)
Annual Growth	54.3%	—	—	—	—	—

Electro Rent

Electro Rent isn't the electronic version of the popular Broadway musical — it's a company that rents, leases, and resells electronic test and measurement equipment, computers, and related equipment. The company's suppliers include Agilent Technologies and Tektronix, while its personal computers and workstations come from such manufacturers as Dell, Hewlett-Packard, IBM, Apple, and Toshiba. Electro Rent provides new and used equipment to government agencies and companies in the electronics and military/aerospace industries. The company gets around 85% of its sales in the US, but it also has operations in Canada and Europe.

True to its name, Electro Rent makes around two-thirds of its revenues from rentals and leases; the rest comes from selling equipment. The company's test and measurement unit accounts for 87% of total revenues.

Sales for the company increased by some 12% in 2010 over the prior year; although its net income was down slightly, the company remained profitable. The increase in sales was due to a 61% increase in equipment sales and other revenues, offset by a decrease in rentals and leases due to lower demand for data products. Electro Rent saw higher sales of used equipment and an increase in finance leases; the company is looking to flexible financing alternatives to drive growth in its lease and rental business.

In March 2010 Electro Rent bought the assets of Telogy for nearly $25 million in cash. Telogy (which had filed for bankruptcy protection from creditors) leased, rented, and sold electronic test equipment. Electro Rent expected that the acquisition would help it achieve substantial cost savings by integrating the Northern California company's inventory and the relocation of Telogy's operations to Electro Rent's Southern California headquarters. The acquisition is broadening the company's equipment base and expanding its customer base.

In 2011 the company acquired Las Vegas-based Equipment Management Technology, which specializes in the sale and rental of electronic test equipment to companies in the aerospace and defense sectors.

Chairman and CEO Daniel Greenberg and his brother, Phillip, own about 30% of Electro Rent outright and through several trusts.

HISTORY

Formed in 1965 to lease high-tech instruments, Electro Rent was bought in 1973 by Telecor. That year Daniel Greenberg joined Electro Rent; he became chairman and CEO in 1979. Electro Rent was spun off and went public in 1980 and continued to thrive during the growth of the defense industry in the early 1980s. In 1985 the company formed a joint venture in Japan. Then sales began to slip as a result of cutbacks in federal spending for defense and aerospace. Greenberg overhauled the company, which branched into the leasing of PCs and workstations in 1987. It worked. A surge in demand for PCs and workstations helped to offset the decline in revenues from test and measurement equipment.

Electro Rent's revenues rebounded in 1994 as growth in the communications industry helped boost demand for complex test equipment. Also that year Electro Rent bought rival Genstar Rental Electronics of Canada. In 1996 the company bought LDI Computer Rentals, and the following year it doubled in size when it acquired General Electric Technology Management Services, another computer and test equipment rental business. To cut costs, the company reduced its workforce by 8% in 1998 and sold its Japanese operations.

Because of slipping demand for PC rentals in 2000, the company shifted focus to its test and measurement equipment rentals and began to offer telecommunications and fiber-optic test equipment in 2001.

It opened its rental center in China in 2005. That same year, the company established a European outpost through its relationship with a Belgian rental firm, Everest ES. Electro Rent later acquired Everest ES and made it part of its ER Europe subsidiary.

Electro Rent completed its acquisition of Rush Computer Rentals in 2006 and its acquisition of Telogy in 2010.

EXECUTIVES

Chairman and CEO, Daniel Greenberg, age 70
President and COO, Steven Markheim, age 58
VP, Sales, Eastern Region and Canada, Thomas A. Curtin, age 56
VP, Distribution and Technical Services, Ronald J. Deming, age 60
VP, Administrative and Information Services, Meryl D. Evans, age 52
VP Sales, Rush Computer Rentals, Peter Oman
VP, Sales, Western Region, John Hart, age 60
VP; General Manager, Computer Products and Services Group, Rush Computer Rentals, Dennis M. Clark, age 55
VP, Product Management, Richard E. Bernosky, age 53
VP, Human Resources, Peter M. Shapiro, age 65
VP and CFO, Craig R. Jones, age 65
VP Operations, Computer Products, Rush Computer Rentals, Craig R. Burgi, age 56

National Sales Director, Advanced Technology Partner Channel, Herb Ostenberg, age 62
General Manager, Electro Rent Europe, David Saeys
Sales Manager, Distribution Products Group, Scott Wrinkle
General Manager, Electro Rent (Tianjin) China, Paul Pang
Auditors: Deloitte & Touche LLP

LOCATIONS

HQ: Electro Rent Corporation
6060 Sepulveda Blvd., Van Nuys, CA 91411-2512
Phone: 818-787-2100   **Fax:** 818-786-4354
Web: www.electrorent.com

2010 Sales

	$ mil.	% of total
US	124.6	85
Other countries	21.3	15
Total	**145.9**	**100**

PRODUCTS/OPERATIONS

2010 Sales

	$ mil.	% of total
Rentals & leases	94.2	65
Sales of equipment & other	51.7	35
Total	**145.9**	**100**

2010 Sales

	$ mil.	% of total
Test & Measurement	127.2	87
Data Products	18.7	13
Total	**145.9**	**100**

Selected Products

Test and Measurement
  Cellular, mobile, and satellite
  Data acquisition
  Digital design
  Electronic
  Insulation
  Network analyzers
  Optical spectrum analyzers
  Power monitors
  Synthesized signal sources
  Telecommunications
  Test equipment calibration
  Transformer
  Video broadcasts
  Wavelength meters
Data Products
  Desktop computers
  Hubs, routers, and switches
  Peripherals
  PCs
  PC displays
  Projection devices
  Network devices
  Notebook computers
  Servers
  UNIX workstations

COMPETITORS

CalFirst
Continental Resources
McGrath RentCorp
MetricTest

ORIX
Transcat
Trek Equipment

HISTORICAL FINANCIALS

Company Type: Public

Income Statement

FYE: May 31

	REVENUE ($ mil.)	NET INCOME ($ mil.)	NET PROFIT MARGIN	EMPLOYEES
05/11	228.7	23.8	10.4%	371
05/10	145.9	11.6	8.0%	335
05/09	130.5	11.8	9.0%	296
05/08	144.5	21.1	14.6%	0
05/07	125.3	21.0	16.8%	301
Annual Growth	16.2%	3.2%	—	5.4%

2011 Year-End Financials

Debt ratio: —
Return on equity: 9.9%
Cash ($ mil.): 41.4
Current ratio: 1.10
Long-term debt ($ mil.): —

No. of shares (mil.): 24.0
Dividends
Yield: 3.9%
Payout: 60.6%
Market value ($ mil.): 367.9

	STOCK PRICE ($) FY Close	P/E High/Low		PER SHARE ($) Earnings	Dividends	Book Value
05/11	15.34	18	11	0.99	0.60	10.02
05/10	13.59	32	18	0.48	0.60	9.60
05/09	9.65	34	14	0.47	0.60	9.55
05/08	14.12	20	15	0.81	0.45	9.87
05/07	14.41	22	16	0.81	0.00	9.42
Annual Growth	1.6%	—	—	5.1%	—	1.6%

Electro Scientific Industries

Electro Scientific Industries (ESI) and its subsidiaries use science — and a lot of engineering — to help customers produce electronics. The company's laser-based equipment is used to manufacture and test semiconductors, interconnect devices, LEDs, and other electronic components. Its offerings include yield improvement, optical inspection, and high-capacity test equipment. Outside of manufacturing, applications include forensics, bioimaging, and environmental research. ESI's customers have included Canon, Hynix, Kulicke and Soffa, Kyocera, Samsung Electronics, and STMicroelectronics. More than 80% of sales come from customers in the Asia/Pacific region.

With most of its business in Asia, the company is moving some of its production capacity there to be nearer its customers and to reduce costs. The company has a manufacturing facility in Singapore, as well as research and development offices in China and Taiwan. The company's top ten customers account for more than half of sales; sales to Apple make up 30%.

The global economic downturn, along with a limited number of customers, negatively impacted results for ESI in 2009 and 2010. Consumer and business spending improved in 2010, which improved the overall health of the capital equipment markets worldwide. For that year, sales fell by 5% over the prior period. While orders for its passive components and interconnect products rose, its semiconductor group continued to be impacted by weakness in the memory markets. ESI reported a net loss of $12 million for 2010, compared to a net loss of $51 million for 2009, which included re-

structuring expenses, merger transaction costs, and high expenses related to the impairment of its auction rate securities. ESI cut costs in 2009 by reducing its headcount by 84 employees, an 11% reduction in workforce.

ESI continues to bolster its portfolio and core competences by acquiring new businesses. As part of its strategy, ESI looks to buy companies that allow it to enter or strengthen its position in multiple markets by adding applications. In 2010 the company bought Canada-based PyroPhotonics Lasers, a maker of tailored-pulse fiber lasers used in DRAM repair and other applications. In 2008 the company picked up New Wave Research (NWR), which develops laser-based systems used in the semiconductor market for applications such as sapphire wafer scribing for high-brightness LED lighting, flat-panel display repair, and semiconductor failure analysis.

Director David Nierenberg, through his firm Nierenberg Investment Management, owns nearly 14% of Electro-Scientific.

HISTORY

Electro Scientific Industries (ESI) was founded in 1944 by former vice chairman Douglas Strain, his father Clayton, and two classmates. It was incorporated in 1949. ESI initially produced high-precision resistance measurement instruments and reference standards. In 1970 it introduced laser systems for trimming resistors. Ten years later ESI developed memory repair laser systems. The company purchased capacitor test equipment expert Palomar Systems in 1982 and went public the next year. In 1991 it formed a division with the acquisition of Intelledex Vision Products.

Mechanical Technology executive Donald Van-Luvanee took over as CEO in 1992. ESI acquired companies in markets where it prospered. In 1994 it bought its top laser trimming competitor, Chicago Laser Systems. The next year the company purchased XRL, its key memory repair rival.

Acquisitions continued to drive expansion of ESI's product line throughout the 1990s. The company moved into the vision systems market with the purchases of Cybernetic Systems (1996), Automation (1996), and Applied Intelligent Systems (1997). ESI also highlighted its presence in the electronic packaging business in 1997 with the purchases of Dynamotion and Chip Star. In 1998 the company acquired Testec, a maker of electrical test systems for passive components.

The next year it bought MicroVision, a provider of vision-based inspections systems for semiconductor companies. Also in 1999 Strain retired.

VanLuvanee retired in 2002; longtime ESI chairman David Bolender succeeded him as acting president and CEO. CFO James Dooley became president and CEO later that year; Bolender remained chairman.

A performance review of its financial statements spurred several changes in 2003. ESI moved to stop making mechanical drills for electronics production. The service unit connected with the drill business was transferred to a subsidiary of Esterline Technologies in 2003. Chairman Bolender also stepped down as chairman and Dooley was placed on administrative leave. Director Jon Tompkins succeeded Bolender as chairman; fellow board member Barry Harmon was named president and CEO. Several weeks later, the company terminated Dooley's employment.

At the start of 2004, Advantest executive Nick Konidaris succeeded Harmon as president and CEO. (Harmon remained a director.) Later that year the company reached legal settlements with

rivals GSI Lumonics (now GSI Group) and Cognex over patent infringement claims. In 2004 ESI laid off 9% of its workforce and implemented other cost-cutting measures in response to lower sales and a plunge in orders.

ESI opened an R&D facility at its corporate headquarters in 2005. In 2007 the company decided to change its fiscal yearend from the end of May to the end of March, effective in 2008.

In 2008 ESI agreed to merge with competitor Zygo, but the deal fell apart in 2009 as the global financial crisis took hold and the companies were unable to agree on revising terms of their merger agreement.

Also in 2008, the company acquired New Wave Research (NWR) for $36 million. NWR develops high-end laser-based systems used in multiple applications for the semiconductor market. Two years later, the company bought Canada-based PyroPhotonics Lasers, a maker of tailored-pulse fiber lasers used in DRAM repair and other applications.

EXECUTIVES

Chairman, Jon D. Tompkins, age 71
President, CEO, and Director, Nicholas (Nick) Konidaris, age 66, $1,364,560 total compensation
VP Finance, Controller, and Chief Accounting Officer, Kerry L. Mustoe, age 54, $344,593 total compensation
VP Operations, Robert M. (Bob) DeBakker, age 53, $512,495 total compensation
VP, New Wave Research Division, Pei Hsien Fang
VP Customer Operations, Sidney B. F. Wong, age 52, $246,399 total compensation
VP Administration, CFO, and Secretary, Paul Oldham, age 48, $573,509 total compensation
VP; General Manager, Semiconductor Products Division, Louis Vintro
Director Research and Development, Bob Hainsey
Director Customer Support, Paul Rex
General Manager, Interconnect and Micromachining Division, Jeff Albelo
General Manager, Component Test and Inspection Division, Sean Phillips
Director Public and Investor Relations, Brian Smith
Director Human Resources, Tracey Jerijervi
Auditors: KPMG LLP

LOCATIONS

HQ: Electro Scientific Industries, Inc.
13900 NW Science Park Dr., Portland, OR 97229
Phone: 503-641-4141   **Fax:** 503-671-5551
Web: www.esi.com

2010 Sales

	$ mil.	% of total
Asia/Pacific	124.1	83
Americas	14.2	10
Europe	10.6	7
Total	**148.9**	**100**

PRODUCTS/OPERATIONS

2010 Sales

	$ mil.	% of total
Interconnect/Micromachining	88.7	60
Passive Components	31.7	21
Semiconductor	28.5	19
Total	**148.9**	**100**

Selected Products

Automatic semiconductor inspection and sorting systems
Circuit fine-tuning systems
Electrical testers
Electronic packaging systems
Flat-panel display repair and failure analysis

Interconnect
Laser ablation
Laser fuse processing
Laser trimming
LED wafer scriber
Machine tooling
Micromaching laser drills
Replacement belts
Termination systems (for passive components)
Wafer dicing

COMPETITORS

Adept Technology	Hoya Corp.
Cognex	Mitsubishi Electric
CyberOptics	Orbotech
Disco Corp.	Zygo
GSI Group	
Hitachi	
High-Technologies	

HISTORICAL FINANCIALS

Company Type: Public

Income Statement

FYE: Saturday nearest March 31

	REVENUE ($ mil.)	NET INCOME ($ mil.)	NET PROFIT MARGIN	EMPLOYEES
03/11	256.8	7.9	3.1%	648
03/10	148.9	(12.0)	—	581
03/09	157.3	(51.0)	—	567
03/08*	247.2	16.6	6.7%	0
05/07	250.8	23.5	9.4%	585
Annual Growth	0.6%	(23.9%)	—	2.6%

*Fiscal year change

2011 Year-End Financials

Debt ratio: —
Return on equity: 2.2%
Cash ($ mil.): 116.4
Current ratio: 4.81
Long-term debt ($ mil.): —

No. of shares (mil.): 28.2
Dividends
 Yield: —
 Payout: —
Market value ($ mil.): 489.4

	STOCK PRICE ($) FY Close	P/E High/Low		PER SHARE ($) Earnings	Dividends	Book Value
03/11	17.36	65	37	0.28	0.00	12.85
03/10	12.81	—	—	(0.44)	0.00	12.43
03/09	5.92	—	—	(1.89)	0.00	12.68
03/08*	16.41	43	26	0.59	0.00	14.23
05/07	20.65	29	22	0.80	0.00	14.03
Annual Growth	(4.2%)	—	—	(23.1%)	—	(2.2%)

*Fiscal year change

Electromed

Electromed aims to clear the way for patients suffering from respiratory ailments. A medical device maker, the company manufactures respiratory products designed to treat patients with cystic fibrosis, chronic obstructive pulmonary disease (COPD), and other ailments that affect respiratory systems. Its FDA-approved SmartVest System is a vest worn by patients that helps loosen lung congestion. A self-administered therapy, the vest works by administering high frequency pulsations that compress and release the patient's chest area. Electromed sells its SmartVest and related products primarily in the US to patients, home health care professionals, and hospitals. Founded in 1992, the company went public in 2010.

Electromed intends to use the $6.8 million raised in its IPO to expand its workforce, repay debt, and fund general corporate activity. As a key part of its workforce expansion efforts, the company wants to bolster its sales and marketing staff, an effort intended to facilitate the company's strategic move into new domestic markets. Specifically, it wants to increase its sales to institutional customers like hospitals, clinics, and other health care organizations. It is also looking to increase its direct sales to patients (its largest customer segment).

Electromed's other growth efforts include expansion into international markets, particularly Europe and Asia, where the company already has a limited presence. Electromed, which sells mainly through distributors in international markets, plans to bolster its presence in these regions by fostering existing and new relationships with distributors.

Prior to filing its IPO, the company gradually increased its funding to its sales and marketing, international expansion, and R&D operations. In 2009 its efforts paid off after an increase in its sales volume led to a sharp rise in profits.

Company executives, including co-founders and brothers Robert and Craig Hansen, collectively own more than 35% of Electromed.

EXECUTIVES

Chairman and CEO, Robert D. Hansen, age 70, $340,469 total compensation
CFO, Terry M. Belford, age 60, $258,123 total compensation
Strategic Marketing Counsel, Eileen M. Manning
Regulatory and Clinical Affairs Counsel, Chet E. Sievert Jr.
Manager Quality Assurance, Gregory A. Spurlock
Product Operations Manager, Lonnie J. Helgeson
Regional Manager Central U.S., Sherie Wheeler
National Sales Manager, Martin J. Davig
Manufacturing Manager, Brad Blaszciek
Manager Patient Services, Clara M. Buri
Secretary, William J. George, age 60
Regional Manager Western U.S., William R. Grimm
Auditors: McGladrey & Pullen, LLP

LOCATIONS

HQ: Electromed, Inc.
 500 6th Ave. NW, New Prague, MN 56071
Phone: 952-758-9299   **Fax:** 866-758-5077
Web: www.electromed.com

PRODUCTS/OPERATIONS

2010 Sales

	$ mil.	% of total
Home Care	13.1	92
International	0.6	4
Government/Institutional	0.6	4
Total	**14.3**	**100**

HISTORICAL FINANCIALS

Company Type: Public

Income Statement

FYE: June 30

	REVENUE ($ mil.)	NET INCOME ($ mil.)	NET PROFIT MARGIN	EMPLOYEES
06/11	19.0	1.1	5.8%	92
06/10	14.3	0.9	6.3%	70
06/09	13.0	1.3	10.0%	62
06/08	8.8	0.3	3.4%	0
Annual Growth	29.2%	54.2%	—	21.8%

2011 Year-End Financials

Debt ratio: 10.8%
Return on equity: 7.2%
Cash ($ mil.): 4.1
Current ratio: 3.77
Long-term debt ($ mil.): 1.6

No. of shares (mil.): 8.1
Dividends
 Yield: —
 Payout: —
Market value ($ mil.): 26.7

	STOCK PRICE ($) FY Close	P/E High/Low		PER SHARE ($) Earnings	Dividends	Book Value
06/11	3.30	33	23	0.13	0.00	1.82
Annual Growth	—	—	—	—	—	—

Ellington Financial

Mortgage-related assets are music to Ellington Financial's ears. The specialty finance company manages a portfolio of primarily non-agency residential mortgage-backed securities, valued at more than $366 million. It also seeks to acquire other target assets, such as residential whole mortgage loans, commercial mortgage-backed securities, commercial real estate debt, and asset-backed securities. Riskier residential whole mortgage loans, which are generally not guaranteed by the US government, include subprime, non-performing, and sub-performing mortgage loans. Founded in 2007, Ellington Financial went public in 2010 in hopes of taking advantage of the current credit environment.

The company is using a substantial portion of the proceeds from its initial public offering to acquire more target assets. It plans to use the balance for interest-bearing, short-term investments — such as money market accounts — as well as for working capital and general corporate expenses.

In its attempt to acquire target assets, Ellington Financial will compete with other specialty finance companies, mortgage REITs, public and private funds, and commercial and investment banks. Keeping its portfolio diverse may help it weather downturns among certain geographic regions or property types that are subject to higher risk of foreclosure.

Ellington Financial executive officers and directors together own about a quarter of the company's stock.

EXECUTIVES

Chairman and Co-Chief Investment Officer, Michael W. Vranos, age 49
President, CEO, and Director, Laurence Penn
COO, Eric Bothwell, age 42
Interim CFO, Paul Asaro
General Counsel and Secretary, Paul Saltzman, age 50
Co-Chief Investment Officer, Mark Tecotzky, age 49
Director, Edward (Ed) Resendez, age 54
Auditors: PricewaterhouseCoopers LLP

LOCATIONS

HQ: Ellington Financial LLC
 53 Forest Ave., Old Greenwich, CT 06870
Phone: 203-698-1200   **Fax:** 203-698-0869
Web: www.ellingtonfinancial.com

COMPETITORS

Annaly Capital Management	MFA Financial
Chimera	MFResidential
Galiot Capital	Sutherland
	Western Asset Mortgage

HISTORICAL FINANCIALS

Company Type: Public

Income Statement

FYE: December 31

	REVENUE ($ mil.)	NET INCOME ($ mil.)	NET PROFIT MARGIN	EMPLOYEES
12/10	61.4	40.6	66.1%	0
12/09	126.7	93.4	73.7%	100
12/08	14.7	(2.4)	—	0
12/07	5.9	3.3	55.9%	0
Annual Growth	118.3%	130.9%	—	—

2010 Year-End Financials

Debt ratio: —
Return on equity: 10.1%
Cash ($ mil.): 35.8
Current ratio: —
Long-term debt ($ mil.): —

No. of shares (mil.): 16.5
Dividends
  Yield: 3.6%
  Payout: 26.3%
Market value ($ mil.): 366.9

	STOCK PRICE ($) FY Close	P/E High/Low		PER SHARE ($) Earnings	Dividends	Book Value
12/10	22.24	7	7	3.04	0.80	24.47
Annual Growth	—	—	—	—	—	—

---

eMagin

eMagin is imagining eye-opening technology. The company develops virtual imaging and organic light-emitting diodes (OLEDs) that can be used in applications ranging from wearable PCs and virtual imaging devices to more mundane products such as DVD headset systems, video games, and high-definition televisions. The technology also extends to military uses. eMagin's products use microcircuits and displays to magnify images of text or video. Subsidiary Virtual Vision develops near-eye and virtual image display products, including headset viewer systems. eMagin markets to OEMs and directly to customers in the government, industrial, and medical sectors.

EXECUTIVES

Chairman, Thomas Paulsen, age 74
President, CEO, and Director, Andrew Sculley, $449,073 total compensation
VP, Government Programs, Rob Sainsbury
SVP Research and Development, Amal Ghosh
SVP, Display Operations, Design, and Development, Olivier Prache
SVP, CFO, and Treasurer, Paul C. Campbell, age 55, $203,539 total compensation
Auditors:

LOCATIONS

HQ: eMagin Corporation
  10500 NE 8th St., Ste. 1400, Bellevue, WA 98004
Phone: 425-749-3600   **Fax:** 425-749-3601
Web: www.emagin.com

PRODUCTS/OPERATIONS

2009 Sales

	$ mil.	% of total
Product	19.8	83
Contract	4.0	17
Total	**23.8**	**100**

COMPETITORS

Cambridge Display Technology
Eastman Kodak
Kopin
Microvision
Sony
Sumitomo Electric
Universal Display

HISTORICAL FINANCIALS

Company Type: Public

Income Statement

FYE: December 31

	REVENUE ($ mil.)	NET INCOME ($ mil.)	NET PROFIT MARGIN	EMPLOYEES
12/10	30.5	14.8	48.5%	67
12/09	23.8	4.3	18.1%	64
12/08	18.7	(1.9)	—	59
12/07	17.6	(18.5)	—	65
12/06	8.2	(15.3)	—	67
Annual Growth	38.9%	—	—	0.0%

2010 Year-End Financials

Debt ratio: —
Return on equity: 53.9%
Cash ($ mil.): 7.8
Current ratio: 3.63
Long-term debt ($ mil.): —

No. of shares (mil.): 21.2
Dividends
  Yield: —
  Payout: —
Market value ($ mil.): 127.3

	STOCK PRICE ($) FY Close	P/E High/Low		PER SHARE ($) Earnings	Dividends	Book Value
12/10	6.00	12	3	0.49	0.00	1.30
12/09	1.88	12	2	0.17	0.00	0.58
12/08	0.54	—	—	(0.13)	0.00	0.24
12/07	1.28	—	—	(1.59)	0.00	(0.31)
12/06	1.04	—	—	(1.52)	0.00	(0.11)
Annual Growth	55.0%	—	—	—	—	—

Emergent BioSolutions

Emergent BioSolutions protects your thorax against anthrax. The company develops and produces vaccines that treat or protect against infectious diseases and bio-agents. The company supplies BioThrax (the US's only FDA-approved anthrax vaccine) primarily to the departments of Defense and Health and Human Services (HHS). Its biodefense unit is also developing a post-exposure treatment for anthrax and a preventive vaccine for botulinum toxin. For commercial markets, Emergent BioSolutions is working on therapies and vaccines for such infectious diseases as typhoid, tuberculosis, hepatitis B, and chlamydia. Chairman and CEO Fuad El-Hibri controls half of the company.

Nearly all of Emergent BioSolutions' revenue comes from sales of BioThrax to its US government customers. Under its Defense and HHS contracts, it has supplied millions of doses for vaccination of military personnel and to replenish the nation's stockpile of medical treatments for terrorist attacks and other disasters.

The company benefited from the spike in biodefense spending that followed the attacks of September 11, 2001, and the still unsolved cases of anthrax infection of the same year. In particular, the Project Bioshield law, which took effect in 2004, authorized billions of dollars in additional funds for procurement of countermeasures to bioterror agents.

Emergent BioSolutions wants to move beyond its US government customer base by targeting state and local governments (who may want stockpiles for inoculating first responders), as well as foreign governments. It has established marketing operations in Singapore and Germany to target international markets. And while it depends on biodefense markets for most of its revenue currently, it is trying to balance its drug development efforts between biodefense and commercial candidates. The company has built its commercial vaccine business through acquisitions of vaccine and biotech firms in Germany, the UK, and the US.

In 2010 Emergent BioSolutions grew its human vaccine operations further by forming a joint venture with Temasek Life Science Ventures called EPIC BIO. The partnership was designed to develop, manufacture, and commercialize vaccines to protect against a broad range of influenza strains. The joint venture also enhanced Emergent Biosolutions' presence in the Asia/Pacific region.

To move entirely outside of its comfort-zone, Emergent BioSolutions added to its oncology and autoimmunity pipeline by acquiring and absorbing Trubion Pharmaceuticals in a deal worth about $135 million in late 2010. The acquisition gave Emergent Trubion's two clinical-stage candidates for the treatment of rheumatoid arthritis and a chronic, inflammatory autoimmune disorder called systemic lupus erythematosus it developed in partnership with Pfizer. Emergent also gained Small Modular Immunopharmaceutic (SMIP) and Scorpion technologies for developing therapeutic candidates. In 2011, the company continued with its oncology roll-up strategy and acquired a late-stage candidate from TenX BioPharma. It paid an initial $2.5 million in cash to secure the rights to develop and commercialize zanolimumab as a treatment for cancer, autoimmune and inflammatory diseases.In addition, Emergent has agreed to pay upwards of $5.5 million in possible milestone payments.

When it doesn't buy a company outright or form partnerships with other pharmaceuticals companies, Emergent BioSolutions' product development strategy involves acquiring or in-licensing candidates in the later stages of clinical development and seeing them through the clinical regulatory process. It has also established development collaborations, including one with the UK's Health Protection Agency for its botulinum toxin program. A joint venture with researchers at the University of Oxford is conducting trials on a tuberculosis vaccine candidate. In 2008 a struggling VaxGen sold its rival anthrax program, which used next-generation recombinant protective antigen (rPA) proteins, to Emergent BioSolutions.

The company's 2006 initial public offering raised funds for clinical trials and the construction of a large-scale production facility in Lansing, Michigan. Emergent BioSolutions contracts with a filling company to measure BioThrax into dosage vials.

EXECUTIVES

Chairman and CEO, Fuad El-Hibri, age 53, $1,964,364 total compensation
President, COO, and Director, Daniel J. Abdun-Nabi, age 56, $1,212,152 total compensation
VP Corporate Communications, Tracey Schmitt
VP Investor Relations, Robert G. Burrows
Chief Quality Officer, Denise Landry
SVP Finance and Administration, CFO, and Treasurer, R. Don Elsey, age 57, $787,448 total compensation
SVP and Chief Scientific Officer, W. James Jackson, age 50

SVP Product Development, Stephen Lockhart, age 54, $452,532 total compensation
Chief Business Officer and SVP Strategic Investments, Steven N. Chatfield
SVP Manufacturing Operations, Kyle W. Keese, age 49, $647,575 total compensation
SVP Corporate Affairs, Allen Shofe
Auditors: Ernst & Young LLP

LOCATIONS

HQ: Emergent BioSolutions Inc.
2273 Research Blvd., Ste. 400, Rockville, MD 20850
Phone: 301-795-1800 **Fax:** 301-795-1899
Web: www.emergentbiosolutions.com

PRODUCTS/OPERATIONS

2009 Sales

	$ mil.	% of total
Products	217.2	92
Contracts & grants	17.6	8
Total	**234.8**	**100**

Selected Products

Licensed
BioThrax (Anthrax Vaccine Adsorbed)
Investigational
Anthrax IG Therapeutic
Anthrax Monoclonal Antibody Therapeutic
Chlamydia vaccine
Recombinant Anthrax Vaccine (rPA)
Tuberculosis vaccine
Typhella (Typhoid Vaccine Live Oral ZH9)
Universal flu vaccine

COMPETITORS

Cangene
Crucell
DiagnoCure
Elusys Therapeutics
Human Genome Sciences
Panacea Pharmaceuticals
PharmAthene
Soligenix

HISTORICAL FINANCIALS

Company Type: Public

Income Statement

FYE: December 31

	REVENUE ($ mil.)	NET INCOME ($ mil.)	NET PROFIT MARGIN	EMPLOYEES
12/10	286.2	51.7	18.1%	767
12/09	234.8	31.1	13.2%	652
12/08	178.6	20.7	11.6%	587
12/07	182.9	22.9	12.5%	560
12/06	152.7	22.8	14.9%	494
Annual Growth	17.0%	22.7%	—	11.6%

2010 Year-End Financials

Debt ratio: 8.2%
Return on equity: 14.0%
Cash ($ mil.): 169.0
Current ratio: 3.22
Long-term debt ($ mil.): 30.2
No. of shares (mil.): 35.0
Dividends
  Yield: —
  Payout: —
Market value ($ mil.): 821.4

	STOCK PRICE ($) FY Close	P/E High/Low		PER SHARE ($) Earnings	Dividends	Book Value
12/10	23.46	15	8	1.59	0.00	10.55
12/09	13.59	27	9	0.99	0.00	7.82
12/08	26.11	39	8	0.68	0.00	6.66
12/07	5.06	23	6	0.77	0.00	5.75
12/06	11.16	14	10	0.93	0.00	5.05
Annual Growth	20.4%	—	—	14.3%	—	20.2%

Encore Capital Group

Credit junkies, beware: Encore Capital Group has your number. The firm and its Midland Credit Management subsidiary purchase, at a discount, defaulted consumer receivables that credit card issuers, telecommunications, and other lenders have given up on. The group then does its best to collect the money via phone, direct mail, third-party collection agencies, and legal action. Utilizing a "friendly, but firm approach" its account managers evaluate customers' ability to pay, then develop tailored payment programs; the company also uses skip-tracers to track down stubborn debtors. In addition, subsidiary Ascension Capital Group provides bankruptcy services to the finance industry.

The global economic crisis and high unemployment levels in the US created a rise in credit delinquencies and charge-offs between 2008 and 2010. As a result, the company invested in new portfolios of credit card, telecom, and consumer bankruptcy charge-offs at deeply discounted rates. As Encore increased its portfolio, its gross collections also increased (by more than 20% in 2010 alone).

Encore Capital operates call centers in California, Arizona, Minnesota, Texas and another in India. In 2009 the company moved its India call center to a larger location, allowing it to increase its collection staff. The company considers its operations in India key to its future growth. The India call center represents half of Encore's call center collections and company expects that contribution to increase. In addition to growing the call center in India, Encore is developing software, managing IT infrastructure, handling analytics, and processing back-office tasks from its India offices.

In 2011 Encore Capital agreed to settle several class-action lawsuits that accused the company of using falsified affidavits to collect money. The settlement could reach as much as $5.7 million. Encore also is cooperating with the states of Texas and California, which are investigating the company's collection methods.

Investment firms J.C. Flowers & Co. and FPK Capital acquired around 25% of Encore Capital in 2007; Red Mountain Capital Partners took an approximately 15% stake. Each of the three companies gained a seat on Encore Capital's board, as well.

EXECUTIVES

President, CEO, and Director, J. Brandon Black, age 43, $1,238,078 total compensation
EVP, CFO, Treasurer, and Secretary, Paul J. Grinberg, age 50, $930,949 total compensation
VP Consumer Marketing, Brian Enneking
Executive Chairman, George Lund, age 47, $3,537,686 total compensation
SVP Operations and Chief Marketing Officer, Jim Syran
SVP, General Counsel, and Corporate Secretary, Ronald E. (Ron) Naves Jr.
SVP Information Technology and CIO, Olivier Baudoux
SVP Human Resources, Steven B. (Steve) Gonabe, age 58
SVP Corporate Strategy and Analytics, Christopher Trepel
SVP and General Manager, Ascension Capital Group, Blair Korschun
Auditors: BDO USA, LLP

LOCATIONS

HQ: Encore Capital Group, Inc.
8875 Aero Dr., Ste. 200, San Diego, CA 92123
Phone: 858-560-2600
Web: www.encorecapital.com/

PRODUCTS/OPERATIONS

2010 Sales

	$ mil.	% of total
Receivable portfolios, net	364.3	96
Servicing fees & other	17.0	4
Total	**381.3**	**100**

Selected Subsidiaries

Ascension Capital Group, Inc.
Midland Credit Management, Inc.
Midland Funding LLC
Midland Funding NCC-2 Corporation
Midland India LLC
Midland International LLC
Midland Portfolio Services, Inc.
MRC Receivables Corporation

COMPETITORS

Asset Acceptance Capital
Asta Funding
FirstCity Financial
GC Services
Genesis Financial Solutions
Leland Scott & Associates
Nationwide Recovery Systems
NCO Group
Portfolio Recovery

HISTORICAL FINANCIALS

Company Type: Public

Income Statement

FYE: December 31

	REVENUE ($ mil.)	NET INCOME ($ mil.)	NET PROFIT MARGIN	EMPLOYEES
12/10	381.3	49.1	12.9%	1,900
12/09	316.4	33.0	10.4%	1,500
12/08	255.9	18.8	7.3%	1,100
12/07	254.0	15.0	5.9%	1,000
12/06	255.1	24.0	9.4%	893
Annual Growth	10.6%	19.6%	—	20.8%

2010 Year-End Financials

Debt ratio: 127.3%
Return on equity: 16.2%
Cash ($ mil.): 10.9
Current ratio: 0.54
Long-term debt ($ mil.): 385.3
No. of shares (mil.): 24.0
Dividends
  Yield: —
  Payout: —
Market value ($ mil.): 563.1

	STOCK PRICE ($) FY Close	P/E High/Low		PER SHARE ($) Earnings	Dividends	Book Value
12/10	23.45	12	8	1.95	0.00	12.61
12/09	17.40	15	2	1.37	0.00	10.41
12/08	7.20	18	8	0.80	0.00	8.50
12/07	9.68	20	14	0.64	0.00	7.46
12/06	12.60	19	9	1.03	0.00	6.64
Annual Growth	16.8%	—	—	17.3%	—	17.4%

Endologix

Medical device maker Endologix strengthens weak arteries with its PowerLink Systems, which use a catheter and stent cage to treat abdominal aortic aneurysm (or weakening of the aortic wall).

The device, which reduces blood pressure on the weakened portion of the aorta, is delivered to the site through the femoral artery which is a less invasive alternative to conventional surgery. Endologix sells the products in the US through its own team of sales representatives and internationally through a dozen independent distributors. PowerLink products are pitched primarily to vascular surgeons, and, to a lesser extent, interventional cardiologists and radiologists.

Endologix manufactures its own products at a single US facility. Outside of the US, PowerLink products have received approval for sale in 25 other countries in Asia, Europe, and parts of South America.

While PowerLink is used to treat regular abdominal aortic aneurysm, Endologix has turned part of its attention to developing a system to repair percutaneous endovascular abdominal aortic aneurysm, for which there are no approved treatment devices. In 2010 it launched a clinical trial of its IntuiTrack endovascular delivery system to carry PowerLink stent grafts to repair such aneurysms.

The company agreed in late 2010 to acquire fellow medical device maker, Nellix in a deal worth up to $40 million. Nellix complements Endologix's current product line with its own treatments for abdominal aortic aneurysms.

EXECUTIVES

Chairman, Franklin D. Brown, age 67
President, CEO, and Director, John McDermott, age 50, $674,421 total compensation
President, Global Strategic Initiatives, Robert D. Mitchell, age 48
CFO and Secretary, Robert J. (Bob) Krist, age 62, $414,710 total compensation
VP Technology, Stefan G. Schreck, age 51, $417,176 total compensation
VP Sales, Joseph A. DeJohn, age 50, $163,642 total compensation
VP Operations, Todd Abraham
VP Quality, Gary I. Sorsher, age 46
VP Regulatory, Quality, and Clinical Affairs, Janet Fauls, age 48, $262,852 total compensation
VP Global Marketing, Martin Tyler
Medical Director, Edward B. Diethrich, age 75
Auditors: PricewaterhouseCoopers LLP

LOCATIONS

HQ: Endologix, Inc.
11 Studebaker, Irvine, CA 92618
Phone: 949-595-7200   **Fax:** 949-457-9561
Web: www.endologix.com

2009 Sales

	$ mil.	% of total
US	43.7	83
Europe	2.9	6
Asia	2.9	6
South America	2.7	5
Other countries	0.2	-
Total	**52.4**	**100**

PRODUCTS/OPERATIONS

COMPETITORS

Cook Group	Terumo
Lombard Medical	W.L. Gore
Medtronic	

HISTORICAL FINANCIALS

Company Type: Public

Income Statement

FYE: December 31

	REVENUE ($ mil.)	NET INCOME ($ mil.)	NET PROFIT MARGIN	EMPLOYEES
12/10	67.3	10.7	15.9%	297
12/09	52.4	(2.4)	—	197
12/08	37.7	(12.0)	—	190
12/07	27.8	(15.1)	—	168
12/06	14.7	(17.5)	—	164
Annual Growth	**46.3%**	**—**		**16.0%**

2010 Year-End Financials

Debt ratio: —
Return on equity: 11.3%
Cash ($ mil.): 38.2
Current ratio: 5.32
Long-term debt ($ mil.): —

No. of shares (mil.): 56.4
Dividends
  Yield: —
  Payout: —
Market value ($ mil.): 403.3

	STOCK PRICE ($) FY Close	P/E High/Low		PER SHARE ($) Earnings	Dividends	Book Value
12/10	7.15	36	16	0.21	0.00	1.66
12/09	5.28	—	—	(0.05)	0.00	0.88
12/08	1.20	—	—	(0.28)	0.00	0.59
12/07	2.80	—	—	(0.35)	0.00	0.81
12/06	3.50	—	—	(0.44)	0.00	1.09
Annual Growth	**19.6%**	**—**	**—**	**—**	**—**	**11.2%**

Ener1

Ener1 is on a quest to energize the world. The company develops and manufactures lithium-ion batteries and battery packs, primarily for grid energy storage, transportation, and small electronics applications. Its EnerDel unit makes lithium-ion batteries and battery cells in the US and South Korea. The subsidiary has an agreement with Norway-based Think Global to supply batteries for its Think City electric vehicle (EV). It is also developing batteries for the Volvo C30 EVs. Ener1's EnerFuel unit develops fuel cell components and its NanoEner subsidiary develops technology for depositing materials onto battery electrodes. Ener1 manufactures in the US and South Korea; more than half of sales come from its US operations.

Sales for 2010 rose 122% over 2009, driven primarily by demand for small format battery packs. Sales for the small battery packs were up more than 50%, and were sold to Motorola Solutions for use in handheld scanners. Other factors contributing to increased sales for the year included the initiation of commercial sales of EV battery packs to Think Global and an increase in EV prototype battery packs to other customers. Like many companies, Ener1 continues to rack up large losses as it moves from development stage into production. Its net loss for 2010 was 34% higher than the prior year.

Ener1 raised about $55 million in capital in 2010 from a group of investors led by Goldman Sachs, and it took a $10 million investment from ITOCHU. The influx of funds followed a $65 million investment from top shareholder Ener1 Group earlier that year, and a $20 million investment from ITOCHU late the previous year. The company has slated these funds, along with a previous grant from the Department of Energy, to expand its manufacturing capacity and increase output of EV batteries at its three facilities in Indianapolis, Indiana.

In turn, Ener1 made investments in Think Holdings in 2010 that resulted in an ownership stake of 48% stake in the company; Think Holdings is the parent company of electric car maker Think Global.

In 2010 Ener1 took steps to further its international ambitions. The company formed Ener1 Europe, a subsidiary based in France, that will focus on its European business development and partnership programs. It also agreed to form a joint venture with the EV division of Wangxiang, a leading auto parts supplier in China, with plans to start producing battery systems for passenger and heavy-duty vehicles later in the year to meet Wangxiang's existing backlog of customers. Ener1 has been manufacturing small format lithium-ion cells in South Korea since 2008 through its Ener1 Korea (formerly Enertech International) subsidiary.

Moving beyond cars, in 2010 Ener1 agreed to work with Russia's Federal Grid Company (FGC) to develop the use of high-performance battery systems for energy storage in conjunction with smart grids with the hope of improving that country's aging electricity system. One of the largest electricity markets in the world, the Russian government is spending billions of dollars to upgrade its generating and transmission system. FGC alone plans to spend around $15 billion through 2012 updating its transmission facilities.

HISTORY

Ener1 began as Boca Research, a business founded by Timothy Farris in 1985. With just a small office and a production room in the back, the company produced a memory board the next year, offering it at half the price of a similar model made by IBM.

Through the late 1980s the company expanded its memory board selection and added video boards, and in the early 1990s it unveiled its first data communications product, a 2,400 bps modem. Boca went public in 1993. That year it entered the networking market with Ethernet adapters and purchased peripherals and software producer Complete PC.

Motorola executive Anthony Zalenski was named president and CEO of Boca in 1994. He increased retail distribution, and by 1997 Boca was shipping to major retailers such as Best Buy, Computer City, and Costco.

To combat harsh price wars and a weakening market for Boca's slower modems, in 1997 Zalenski streamlined operations, cut 10% of the workforce, and diversified the product mix with Internet appliances. Despite these moves, Boca suffered a loss that year.

In 1998 the company bought the modem business and brand name of Global Village Communications. The purchase contributed to another loss. A financial boost came in 1999 when National Instruments and Infomatec Integrated Information Systems made significant investments in Boca. That year the company began offering thin-client/server computing devices and information appliances.

In early 2000 Zalenski resigned as president and CEO; chairman Robert Ferguson stepped in to replace him. Later that year, the company sold its modem business and changed its name to Inprimis. It also ended a brief foray into the application service provider market, ceasing development of its AppsCom subsidiary. Ferguson later announced he would resign as CEO and Eduard Will was brought in to take his place in 2001. The next year Florida-based Ener1 Holdings took an 80% stake in the company. Will resigned from Inprimis shortly afterward (COO Larry Light was tapped as interim chief) and the company changed its name to EnerNow. Later in 2002 the company announced the formation of EnerLook Healthcare Solutions, its 51%-owned joint venture to develop interactive TV systems for hospitals; it also made another name change, this time to Ener1.

Ener1 discontinued business through EnerLook Solutions in 2003. Also that year, Ener1 and Japan's ITOCHU formed EnerStruct to develop rechargeable batteries and fuel cells for such applications as hybrid automobiles. Ener1 held a 49% stake in EnerStruct. Kevin Fitzgerald, a former CEO of Neff Corp., was named chairman and CEO of Ener1 in 2003.

In mid-2004, the company merged one of its non-active subsidiaries into Splinex Technology Inc., a visual computing technology provider.

The assets of EnerLook Healthcare Solutions were transferred to TVRC Communications in late 2004 in exchange for an equity stake in TVRC.

Ener1 in 2005 said it was considering spinning off three subsidiaries — EnerDel, EnerFuel, and NanoEner — as separate companies. Later that year, the company started restructuring EnerDel to focus on developing lithium ion batteries for hybrid electric vehicles. EnerDel discontinued work on Bellcore technology it had received from Delphi, saying it could not profitably manufacture the technology.

Victor Mendes was named chairman and CEO in late 2006. Just weeks later, he resigned from those posts. Before the end of the year, CTO Peter Novak was promoted to CEO. Novak added the title of president in late 2007, following the resignation of Subhash Dhar.

Novak resigned as CEO in 2008; he remained with the company as president and resumed the title of CTO. Chairman Charles Gassenheimer added the post of CEO to his responsibilities, succeeding Novak.

Ener1 added South Korean manufacturing operations with its 2008 purchase of a majority interest in Enertech International, a South Korea-based maker of lithium-ion battery cells, from TVG Capital Partners.

EXECUTIVES

Chairman and CEO; CEO, Ener1 Group, Charles Gassenheimer, age 38, $500,000 total compensation
President; CEO, EnerDel, Christopher (Chris) Cowger
CFO, Jeffrey (Jeff) Seidel, age 48
Chairman and CEO, Ener1 Korea, Tae-Hee Yoon
President, Transportation Group, Thomas C. Goesch
President, Grid Energy Storage, Bruce Curtis
EVP; President, Ener1 Europe, Ulrik Grape, age 50, $470,003 total compensation
VP Human Resources, Eddie Luedke
VP Manufacturing Engineering, Robert R. Kamischke, age 56
VP, General Counsel, and Secretary, Nicholas Brunero, age 32
COO; President, EnerDel, Richard L. Stanley, age 54
CTO, Ener1 and EnerDel, Naoki Ota, age 44
SVP Finance and Chief Accounting Officer, Melissa Debes
SVP Operations and Procurement, Dan Allen
Senior Director Manufacturing, EnerDel, David Hahn
Auditors: PricewaterhouseCoopers LLP

LOCATIONS

HQ: Ener1, Inc.
1540 Broadway, Ste. 25C, New York, NY 10036
Phone: 212-920-3500
Web: www.ener1.com

2010 Sales

	$ mil.	% of total
US	69.2	56
South Korea	54.4	44
Adjustments	(46.2)	-
Total	**77.4**	**100**

PRODUCTS/OPERATIONS

2010 Sales

	$ mil.	% of total
Battery	77.3	100
Fuel cell & other	0.1	-
Total	**77.4**	**100**

COMPETITORS

A123 Systems	NEC
Ballard Power	Panasonic Corp
Electrovaya	Plug Power
Evonik Industries	Samsung SDI
GS Yuasa	SANYO
Hitachi	Toyota
Hydrogenics	Ultralife
Johnson Controls	Valence Technology
Mitsubishi Power Systems	

HISTORICAL FINANCIALS

Company Type: Public

Income Statement

FYE: December 31

	REVENUE ($ mil.)	NET INCOME ($ mil.)	NET PROFIT MARGIN	EMPLOYEES
12/10	77.4	(68.8)	—	769
12/09	34.8	(51.0)	—	515
12/08	6.8	(43.0)	—	486
12/07	0.3	(51.7)	—	104
12/06	0.1	(41.3)	—	73
Annual Growth	**427.5%**	**—**	**—**	**80.2%**

2010 Year-End Financials

Debt ratio: 27.3%
Return on equity: —
Cash ($ mil.): 60.3
Current ratio: 1.74
Long-term debt ($ mil.): 56.0
No. of shares (mil.): 163.8
Dividends
Yield: —
Payout: —
Market value ($ mil.): 620.7

	STOCK PRICE ($) FY Close	P/E High/Low		PER SHARE ($) Earnings	Dividends	Book Value
12/10	3.79	—	—	(0.51)	0.00	1.25
12/09	6.34	—	—	(0.45)	0.00	0.93
12/08	7.15	—	—	(0.42)	0.00	0.91
12/07	5.63	—	—	(0.84)	0.00	(0.09)
12/06	1.61	—	—	(0.77)	0.00	(0.84)
Annual Growth	**23.9%**	**—**	**—**	**—**	**—**	**—**

Energy Focus

The Illuminator may be coming to a theater near you, but it isn't a movie— its what Energy Focus does. The company makes products such as energy-efficient fiber-optic, light-emitting diode, ceramic metal halide, and high-intensity discharge lighting systems. Serving the commercial/industrial and pool lighting markets, Energy Focus' systems illuminate cinemas, shopping malls, parking garages, performing arts centers, restaurants, pools/spas, and homes. Its lighting products include acrylic accent fixtures, downlight fixtures, spotlights, and display-case lighting. The company's Stones River Companies (SRC) unit concentrates on turnkey lighting projects and solar retrofit jobs.

Energy Focus was in the right place at the right time with its energy-efficient products when the Energy Independence and Security Act (EISA) was enacted in 2007; the controversial act federally mandates that all incandescent bulbs by use 25% to 30% less energy by 2012. (EISA has come under fire as the so-called "light bulb ban" comes closer to going into effect.) This gives Energy Focus a competitive edge, as many of its products already meet lighting efficiency standards set for 2020. The company claims that many of its products use 80% less energy than present-day incandescent bulbs. Also in Energy Focus's favor is its qualification for federal and state tax incentives and funding; the Energy Independence and Security Act will offer billions in government grants for energy conservation programs.

The company is transitioning to become a turnkey lighting systems provider. In 2009 to further its growth and profitability, Energy Focus launched a restructuring plan that calls for the development of mainstream lighting technologies to compete with fluorescent and general illumination lamps, as well as the divestiture of non-core, nonstrategic business units. In December 2009 the company sold its German-based subsidiary LBM Lichtleit Fasertechnik, with possible plans to divest its Fiberstars pools and United States commercial businesses.

Cost reduction initiatives brought about the relocation of manufacturing and assembly operations from the company's Ohio plant to a contract manufacturing facility in Mexico. Final assembly plants are located in Australia, India, Japan, and Taiwan. Energy Focus is also building its energy services business. In December 2009 it acquired Stones River Companies (SRC), a Nashville-based lighting systems retrofitter for $5 million. Energy Focus will continue to be on the lookout for similar additions as it seeks a national sales and delivery conduit into the existing building market.

Following its long-term strategy plan, the company is focusing on solar technology development and will continue its involvement with the US government's Very High Efficiency Solar Cell (VHESC) Consortium. The VHESC expects to develop a solar cell for US military applications that offers 40% or greater efficiency, but also plans to market the product to the public.

EXECUTIVES

President and Director, John M. Davenport, age 66, $462,448 total compensation
CEO and Director, Joseph G. (Joe) Kaveski, age 50, $241,638 total compensation
VP Operations and COO, Eric Hilliard, age 43, $294,767 total compensation
VP Sales and Marketing, Steve Gasperson
VP Sales, Gerrit Reinders
VP, CTO, and General Manager, Roger Buelow, age 38, $229,433 total compensation
Interim Chief Accounting Officer, Frank LaManna, age 47
National Sales Manager, Energy Focus, Paul Schooley
Account Executive and OEM Specialist, Michael E. Weber
General Manager, Pool and Spa Division, Barry R. Greenwald, age 65
Office Facility Manager, Donna Prunetti
Director, David N. Ruckert, age 73
Auditors: Plante & Moran, PLLC

LOCATIONS

HQ: Energy Focus, Inc.
32000 Aurora Rd., Solon, OH 44139
Phone: 440-715-1300   **Fax:** 440-715-1314
Web: www.energyfocusinc.com

2010 Sales

	$ mil.	% of total
US	31.3	89
Other countries	3.8	11
Total	**35.1**	**100**

PRODUCTS/OPERATIONS

2010 Sales

	$ mil.	% of total
Stones River Companies (SRC)	19.7	56
Traditional commercial lighting	12.3	35
Government products & R&D services	3.1	9
Total	**35.1**	**100**

Selected Products and Operations

Fiber-optic cable (stranded and large core)
Fixtures
  Accent lighting
  Decorative fixtures
  Downlighting
  LED products
  Merchandise and display lighting
  Outdoor, outdoor feature, and landscape lighting
  Specialty lighting
Illuminators (the source of light in a fiber-optic system)
Pool and spa lighting
Signage lighting
Solar retrofit projects

Selected Subsidiaries and/or Divisions

Crescent Lighting Limited (decorative and specialty lighting products)
Energy Focus Government Contracts and Sales (lighting technologies and products for the US military)
Energy Focus National Accounts (energy-efficient lighting products)
Fiberstars Commercial (decorative LED and fiber optic lighting products)
Fiberstars Pool and Spa (decorative lighting for swimming pools)
Stones River Companies, LLC (design, engineering, project management of lighting and solar retrofits)

COMPETITORS

Astronics	LSI Industries
Bridgestone	Mitsubishi Corp.
Havells Sylvania	Nexxus Lighting
Hayward Industries	OSRAM
Intermatic	Pentair
Juno Lighting	Philips Lighting
Lighting Science Group	Toray Industries

HISTORICAL FINANCIALS

Company Type: Public

Income Statement

FYE: December 31

	REVENUE ($ mil.)	NET INCOME ($ mil.)	NET PROFIT MARGIN	EMPLOYEES
12/10	35.1	(8.5)	—	68
12/09	12.5	(11.0)	—	78
12/08	23.0	(14.4)	—	92
12/07	22.9	(11.3)	—	102
12/06	27.0	(9.6)	—	160
Annual Growth	**6.8%**	**—**	**—**	**(19.3%)**

2010 Year-End Financials

Debt ratio: 32.6%
Return on equity: —
Cash ($ mil.): 4.1
Current ratio: 1.17
Long-term debt ($ mil.): 2.2

No. of shares (mil.): 24.0
Dividends
  Yield: —
  Payout: —
Market value ($ mil.): 22.8

	STOCK PRICE ($) FY Close	P/E High/Low		PER SHARE ($) Earnings	Dividends	Book Value
12/10	0.95	—	—	(0.37)	0.00	0.28
12/09	0.64	—	—	(0.70)	0.00	0.54
12/08	1.15	—	—	(1.02)	0.00	1.13
12/07	7.25	—	—	(0.98)	0.00	1.87
12/06	6.51	—	—	(0.85)	0.00	2.71
Annual Growth	**(38.2%)**	**—**	**—**	**—**	**—**	**(43.4%)**

Energy Services of America

When energy companies don't want to get their hands dirty, they can call on Energy Services of America (ESA). The service company provides installation, repair, and maintenance work primarily for natural gas and electricity providers. It also installs water and sewer lines for government agencies. ESA operates mostly in the Mid Atlantic region; its customers include Spectra Energy, Hitachi, Columbia Gas Transmission, Toyota, MarkWest Energy, and American Electric Power. Typically the pipes, steel plates, wire, and fittings used by the company are supplied by their customer, keeping costs low. The company operates through subsidiaries ST Pipeline and C.J. Hughes Construction, which it purchased in 2008.

Prior to 2008 ESA was a blank check or shell company with no operations. It was formed in 2006 and went public that year, using the proceeds to purchase its operating subsidiaries.

Marshall Reynolds, chairman, and Douglas Reynolds, director, together own about 40% of the company. They are father and son, respectively. Jack Reynolds, brother of Douglas, is president, CFO, and a director. He holds about 4%.

EXECUTIVES

Chairman, Marshall T. Reynolds, age 74
President, CEO, and Director, Edsel R. Burns, age 60
CFO, Secretary, and Treasurer, Larry A. Blount, age 61
President, ST Pipeline and Director, James Shafer, age 67
VP, Jim Poling
Manager, Fleet and Equipment, Homer Rose
Controller, Charles Crimmel
Auditors: Arnett & Foster, P.L.L.C.

LOCATIONS

HQ: Energy Services of America Corporation
100 Industrial Lane, Huntington, WV 25702
Phone: 304-399-6300   **Fax:** 304-399-1096
Web: www.energyservicesofamerica.com

COMPETITORS

Babcock International Group	Holloman
Dycom	Insituform Technologies
EMS USA	Miller Group
Garney Holding	SUMMIT Electric Supply
Halliburton	

HISTORICAL FINANCIALS

Company Type: Public

Income Statement

FYE: September 30

	REVENUE ($ mil.)	NET INCOME ($ mil.)	NET PROFIT MARGIN	EMPLOYEES
09/10	218.3	5.8	2.7%	1,190
09/09	106.8	(5.9)	—	393
09/08	28.5	2.8	9.8%	269
Annual Growth	**176.8%**	**43.9%**	**—**	**110.3%**

2010 Year-End Financials

Debt ratio: 20.3%
Return on equity: 9.6%
Cash ($ mil.): 2.6
Current ratio: 1.30
Long-term debt ($ mil.): 12.2

No. of shares (mil.): 12.1
Dividends
  Yield: —
  Payout: —
Market value ($ mil.): 42.6

	STOCK PRICE ($) FY Close	P/E High/Low		PER SHARE ($) Earnings	Dividends	Book Value
09/10	3.52	10	4	0.48	0.00	4.97
09/09	3.00	—	—	(0.49)	0.00	4.49
09/08	5.45	30	25	0.21	0.00	5.61
00/00	5.62	54	48	0.11	0.00	3.72
Annual Growth	**(14.4%)**	**—**	**—**	**63.4%**	**—**	**10.1%**

EnerNOC

EnerNOC knocks on the door of large energy customers and kindly asks them to dim the lights. Not literally of course, but the company has added its technology to utility companies' traditional demand response model. Rather than manually calling up their largest end users, EnerNOC's Network Operations Center (NOC) through its DemandSMART program remotely monitors their customers' energy assets and has the capability to adjust their electrical use. It caters to commercial, industrial, and institutional organizations, as well as electric power grid operators and utilities. EnerNOC operates across the US and in Australia, Canada, New Zealand, and the UK.

At the end of 2010 the company was serving 3,600 commercial, institutional, and industrial accounts on 8,600 customer sites tied into its demand response network, managing more than 5,300 MW of demand response capacity.

Other energy management applications and services provided by EnerNOC include EfficiencySMART (data-based energy efficiency options), SupplySMART (energy pricing and risk management services), and CarbonSMART (carbon emission management).

The company is seeking to respond to the industry trends of increasing automation of power grids and stricter environmental controls on power production. It is leveraging its track record and scale of operations to expand into other states in the US, and grow its international profile. (EnerNOC moved into the UK in 2009, providing services to National Grid's Short-Term Operating Reserve program).

As part of this push, in 2010 it bought energy management and demand response wireless technology services provider M2M Communications, which manages hundreds of MW of demand response across the US.

In 2011 the company acquired California-based Global Energy Partners. By adding Global Energy Partners' client list of major utilities, and expertise its in utility energy efficiency and demand response programs, EnerNOC expanded its market reach with a broader portfolio of services.

In 2011 EnerNOC also expanded its global coverage, buying Energy Response Pty Ltd, the largest demand response provider in Australia and New Zealand.

The company saw a spike in revenues and net income in 2009 thanks to an increase in its power capacity under management, led by a major growth in its sales of demand response solutions to PJM Interconnection. Revenues and income grew at an even higher rate in 2010 for the same reasons (sales to PJM jumped by more than $69.2 million).

EXECUTIVES

Chairman and CEO, Timothy G. (Tim) Healy, age 42, $1,705,824 total compensation
President and Director, David B. Brewster, age 39, $1,179,107 total compensation
CFO and Treasurer, Timothy Weller, age 38, $2,151,039 total compensation
EVP, David M. Samuels, age 48, $1,129,381 total compensation
VP Enterprise Energy Management, Nick d'Arbeloff
VP Energy Efficiency and Carbon Solutions, Tom Arnold
VP Engineering, Hugh Scandrett
VP Product Development and Engineering, Terry Sick
Media Relations, Brian Bowen
Chief Accounting Officer, Kevin Bligh, age 56
SVP Marketing and Sales, Gregg M. Dixon, age 39, $894,468 total compensation
Media Relations, Sarah McAuley
Investor Relations, Will Lyons
Auditors: Ernst & Young LLP

LOCATIONS

HQ: EnerNOC, Inc.
75 Federal St., Ste. 300, Boston, MA 02110
Phone: 617-224-9900   **Fax:** 617-224-9910
Web: www.EnerNOC.com

PRODUCTS/OPERATIONS

2010 Sales

	$ mil.	% of total
Demand response solutions	264.6	94
Energy management solutions	15.6	6
Total	**280.2**	**100**

COMPETITORS

Ambient Corp.	Itron
Comverge	National Grid USA
eMeter	SmartSynch
ESCO Technologies	

HISTORICAL FINANCIALS

Company Type: Public

Income Statement

FYE: December 31

	REVENUE ($ mil.)	NET INCOME ($ mil.)	NET PROFIT MARGIN	EMPLOYEES
12/10	280.2	9.6	3.4%	484
12/09	190.7	(6.8)	—	418
12/08	106.1	(36.7)	—	345
12/07	60.8	(23.6)	—	253
12/06	26.1	(5.8)	—	131
Annual Growth	**81.0%**	**—**	**—**	**38.6%**

2010 Year-End Financials

Debt ratio: —	No. of shares (mil.): 25.2
Return on equity: 4.2%	Dividends
Cash ($ mil.): 153.4	Yield: —
Current ratio: 2.75	Payout: —
Long-term debt ($ mil.): —	Market value ($ mil.): 601.5

	STOCK PRICE ($) FY Close	P/E High/Low		PER SHARE ($) Earnings	Dividends	Book Value
12/10	23.91	100	62	0.37	0.00	8.99
12/09	30.39	—	—	(0.32)	0.00	8.05
12/08	7.44	—	—	(1.88)	0.00	4.90
12/07	49.10	—	—	(1.80)	0.00	6.58
Annual Growth	**(21.3%)**	**—**	**—**	**—**	**—**	**11.0%**

Entropic Communications

Entropic Communications is far from sluggish when it comes to broadband. The fabless semiconductor company designs specialized chipsets for video and broadband multimedia applications. Through the Multimedia over Coax Alliance (MoCA) networking standard, Entropic is targeting digital home entertainment networks linked by coaxial cable connections, a market being promoted by cable TV services providers and others. The company's c.LINK technology enables networking among high-definition TVs, digital video recorders, and set-top boxes. Leading customers include Actiontec Electronics, Samsung, Motorola Mobility (17% of sales), and Wistron NeWeb (21%). The Asia/Pacific region accounts for most sales.

Having never made a profit, Entropic's luck finally changed in 2010 when it jumped into the black to the tune of $64.7 million from revenues that increased 81% to $210.2 million. An increased demand for its home networking products and DBS (digital broadcast satellite) outdoor unit products, along with the addition of service providers drove the positive result. That reduces its accumulated deficit to less than $180 million.

The company has a limited number of customers, four of which accounted for 56% of sales in 2010. Entropic is a charter member of MoCA, an industry group standardizing technologies for home networking of consumer electronics. Major service providers that have announced an alignment with MoCA standard include Verizon, Time Warner Cable, Comcast, and Cox, while companies such as AT&T, Motorola Solutions, Pace, and Analog Devices participate in the Home Phoneline Networking Alliance (HPNA). Entropic's DBS outdoor products are used mainly by DISH Network and DIRECTV.

The major contributors to the company's 2010 revenues were Verizon's FiOS push and DIRECTV's multi-room DVR and SWiM deployments. Entropic expects, however, that other MoCA-committed service providers will help it get its eggs into more baskets.

Entropic outsources production of its chips to Taiwan Semiconductor Manufacturing and TowerJazz, which accounted for 32% and 17%, respectively, of Entropic's purchases in 2010. Another vendor, Amkor Technology, accounted for 27% of purchases that year.

EXECUTIVES

Chairman, Umesh Padval, age 53
President, CEO, and Director, Patrick C. Henry, age 48, $1,322,754 total compensation
CFO, David Lyle, age 46, $1,053,911 total compensation
VP Technology, Anton Monk
VP Engineering, Dale Hancock
VP Operations, Timothy (Tim) Pappas, age 46
VP and General Counsel, Lance W. Bridges, age 49, $717,360 total compensation
VP Corporate Marketing and Communications, Susan Huberman
VP Business Development, Stephen Blake
VP and General Manager Entropic Israel, Jonathan Masel
VP Human Resources, Suzanne (Suzy) Zoumaras
VP Marketing, John Graham
SVP Engineering and Operations, Michael R. (Mike) Farese, age 64
CTO, Tom Lookabaugh
SVP Worldwide Sales, William R. (Bill) Bradford, age 47
SVP Marketing and Business Development, Vinay Gokhale, age 47
Director Investor Relations, Debra K. Hart
Director Technology Initiatives, Itzhak Gurantz, age 65, $407,284 total compensation
Corporate Controller and Principal Accounting Officer, Trevor Renfield, age 40
Auditors: Ernst & Young LLP

LOCATIONS

HQ: Entropic Communications, Inc.
6290 Sequence Dr., San Diego, CA 92121
Phone: 858-768-3600   **Fax:** 858-768-3601
Web: www.entropic.com

2010 Sales

	$ mil.	% of total
Asia	195.1	93
North America		
US	3.0	1
Other countries	9.0	5
Europe	3.1	1
Total	**210.2**	**100**

COMPETITORS

Broadcom	LSI Corp.
Freescale Semiconductor	Sierra Monolithics

HISTORICAL FINANCIALS

Company Type: Public

Income Statement

FYE: December 31

	REVENUE ($ mil.)	NET INCOME ($ mil.)	NET PROFIT MARGIN	EMPLOYEES
12/10	210.2	64.7	30.8%	300
12/09	116.3	(13.2)	—	262
12/08	146.0	(136.4)	—	297
12/07	122.5	(32.0)	—	281
12/06	41.5	(7.1)	—	220
Annual Growth	**50.0%**	**—**	**—**	**8.1%**

2010 Year-End Financials

Debt ratio: —	No. of shares (mil.): 85.1
Return on equity: 26.0%	Dividends
Cash ($ mil.): 98.1	Yield: —
Current ratio: 7.88	Payout: —
Long-term debt ($ mil.): —	Market value ($ mil.): 1,027.9

STOCK PRICE ($)		P/E		PER SHARE ($)		
	FY Close	High/Low		Earnings	Dividends	Book Value
12/10	12.08	15	4	0.82	0.00	2.92
12/09	3.07	—	—	(0.19)	0.00	0.97
12/08	0.50	—	—	(2.01)	0.00	1.02
12/07	7.28	—	—	(2.47)	0.00	2.82
Annual Growth	18.4%	—	—	—	—	1.2%

Environmental Tectonics

Environmental Tectonics Corporation (ETC) believes virtual environments can teach us a lot about real life. Through its Training Services Group, the company makes software-driven aircrew training systems, flight simulators, and disaster simulators. Through its Control Systems Group, it designs, manufactures, and sells industrial steam and gas sterilizers for the pharmaceutical, medical device, and animal research industries, hyperbaric chambers for the medical industry, and environmental testing products for the automotive and HVAC industries. ETC has operating subsidiaries in Turkey and Poland and regional offices in the UK, the Middle East, Asia, and Canada.

ETC markets and sells its products and services through its own sales force and about 100 independent sales representatives around the world. The company has branch offices in the UK, Egypt, Turkey, the United Arab Emirates, and Malaysia, as well as representatives in India and China. NASTAR Center LLC is a wholly-owned Delaware subsidiary that operates the NASTAR Center, a non-government, commercial aerospace training and research facility. Another wholly-owned subsidiary Entertainment Technology Corporation (EnTCo) operates a developmental proving ground called The Ride Works, which designs and develops motion-based simulation rides for the amusement industry.

Historically, in any given fiscal year, a substantial portion of ETC's revenues are generated by key contracts with a small number of customers. In fiscal 2011 and prior years, its core business, aircrew training systems, was awarded three large, multiyear contracts from the US Department of Defense. Its aircrew training systems are generally sold to US and foreign governmental agencies. Its disaster management simulators are sold domestically primarily to municipalities and quasi-governmental agencies and internationally to training schools and academies. Most of its sterilizer sales are domestic, while hyperbaric and environmental system sales are domestic and international.

Company director H.F. Lenfest, a veteran of the cable TV industry, controls ETC with about a 67% stake. Chairman and CEO William Mitchell, who founded ETC in 1969, owns about 14% of the company.

EXECUTIVES

Chairman, President, and CEO, William F. Mitchell, age 69, $293,000 total compensation
CFO, Duane D. Deaner, age 63, $119,000 total compensation
President, ETC Simulation Division, Marco van Wijngaarden
President and Creative Director, Entertainment Technology Corporation, Robert E. M. (Rob) Lloyd
President, Biomedical, Steve Wood
President, Biomedical Systems; Regional Sales, South America and Sub-Sahara, Gene E. Davis
EVP, Contract Administration, Richard E. McAdams, age 75
VP, Engineering, Bernhard H. Richter
VP International Sales and Marketing; Regional Sales, Turkey, Middle East, and North Africa, Husnu Onus
VP, Administration and Secretary, Ann M. Allen
VP, Aircrew Training Systems, Dick Leland
VP BioMedical Sales, Don R. Webber
Manager and Chief Engineer, ETC High Performance Composites, Robert B. Henstenburg
Business Unit Manager, Testing and Simulation Systems, Theresa Wagner
Software Division Manager, ETC Information Systems, Alper Kus
Business Unit Manager, ETC Information Systems, Larry Beavan
Regional Sales, Western Europe, Keith George
Regional Sales, Eastern Europe, Dariusz Olowski
Regional Sales, Egypt, Essam El Taib
Commercial and Marketing Director, ETC PZL - USA, Anna Brzozwoska
General Manager, Shanghai, David Kong
Director Business Development, BioMedical Systems Division, David Steimle
Sales Coordinator, BioMedical Systems; Commercial and Marketing Director, ETC PZL - USA, Ann McMaster
Technical Director, Sterilization Systems; Head Professional Services Group, Sterilization Systems G, John Fay
Sales Director, Mid-West, R. Todd Giager
Sales Engineer, Steam and Retrofits, Sterilization Systems, John Bucar
Technical Director, BioMedical Systems, Russell E. (Russ) Peterson
Regional Sales, Asia, Eric Sprague
International Service, ILS/COMS, Mark Peterson
Manager, Corporate Marketing, Donna M. Averell
Regional Sales, Western Europe; European Operations, Testing and Simulation Systems, Allan Firth
Sales Director, ETC Tactical Flight Simulation, Ernest L. (Ernie) Lewis
Applications Manager, Aircrew Training Systems, Glenn King
European Operations, Testing and Simulation Systems, Roger Macklin
Sales Engineer, EtO & Control System Upgrades, Paul Reckner
Sales Manager, Sterilization Systems Group, David (Dave) Mitchell
COO, ETC Simulation; Sales Manager, ETC PZL USA, Christine Stephenson
Auditors:

LOCATIONS

HQ: Environmental Tectonics Corporation
125 James Way, Southampton, PA 18966-3877
Phone: 215-355-9100   **Fax:** 215-357-4000
Web: www.etcusa.com

2011 Sales

	$ mil.	% of total
US government	23.3	42
International	20.0	36
Domestic	12.2	22
Total	**55.5**	**100**

PRODUCTS/OPERATIONS

2011 Sales

	$ mil.	% of total
Training Services Group@2col Table head A:		
Pilot training services	33.8	61
Simulation	1.9	3
ETC-PZL & other	1.0	2
Control Systems Group@2col Table head A:		
Environmental	7.7	14
Sterilizers	7.0	13
Service & spares	2.2	4
Hyperbaric	1.9	3
Total	**55.5**	**100**

Selected Products

Training Services Group
  Aircrew training systems
  Commercial flight simulators
  Disaster management simulation systems
  Disorientation training equipment
  Vehicle simulators
  Motion-based simulation amusement rides
  Tactical fighting simulation systems
  Upset recovery training
Control Systems Group
  Environmental testing and control devices
  Hyperbaric chambers
  Sterilizers

COMPETITORS

Aero Simulation	FlightSafety
Boeing Training &	Parker-Hannifin
Flight Services	QualMark
CAE Inc.	Rockwell Collins
Cubic Simulation	STERIS
Systems	

HISTORICAL FINANCIALS

Company Type: Public

Income Statement

FYE: Last Friday in February

	REVENUE ($ mil.)	NET INCOME ($ mil.)	NET PROFIT MARGIN	EMPLOYEES
02/11	55.5	14.5	26.1%	323
02/10	42.3	6.5	15.4%	273
02/09	36.7	(2.0)	—	240
02/08	22.7	(13.9)	—	259
02/07	17.4	(8.9)	—	257
Annual Growth	33.6%	—	—	5.9%

2011 Year-End Financials

Debt ratio: 51.8%   No. of shares (mil.): 9.1
Return on equity: 244.0%   Dividends
Cash ($ mil.): 1.4   Yield: —
Current ratio: 2.03   Payout: —
Long-term debt ($ mil.): 3.1   Market value ($ mil.): 26.2

STOCK PRICE ($)		P/E		PER SHARE ($)		
	FY Close	High/Low		Earnings	Dividends	Book Value
02/11	2.88	6	4	0.59	0.00	3.08
02/10	2.86	12	2	0.30	0.00	1.91
02/09	1.30	—	—	(0.32)	0.00	(1.30)
02/08	1.85	—	—	(1.61)	0.00	(0.98)
02/07	3.54	—	—	(1.02)	0.00	1.64
Annual Growth	(5.0%)	—	—	—	—	17.1%

eOn

eOn Communications knows it's been ages since you've had a good customer service experience. The company's products integrate voice and Internet communications for large call centers and e-commerce customer contact centers. eOn's communications servers feature automatic call distribution, e-mail queuing, and customer identification. It also sells the Millennium voice switching hardware platform, a private branch exchange (PBX) system with computer telephony integration. Customers include Lillian Vernon and Rockhurst University. eOn gets more than 90% of sales from the US. Chairman David Lee owns about 27% of the company.

In 2009 eOn acquired Cortelco Systems Holding, a manufacturer of traditional and IP-based phones controlled by David Lee, for $11 million in cash. In addition to selling products in the US, Cortelco focuses on sales to Latin America and other international markets.

eOn had expected to see greater sales growth rates in Asian markets such as China and South Korea. Sales in China fell to about 2% of sales in fiscal 2010 from 11% in 2008.

EXECUTIVES

Chairman, David S. Lee, age 74, $157,500 total compensation
CEO and Director, James W. (Jim) Hopper, age 67, $36,968 total compensation
CFO, Lee M. Bowling, age 56, $14,577 total compensation
VP Channel Sales, Jack Dienno
COO, Robert Schnabl
Director Millennium Engineering, Jim Taylor
Director eQueue Engineering, Gary P. Schaefer
Director eQueue Sales, Keith Nansteel
Auditors: GHP Horwath, PC

LOCATIONS

HQ: eOn Communications Corporation
185 Martinvale Ln., San Jose, CA 95119
Phone: 408-694-9500   **Fax:** 408-694-9600
Web: www.eoncc.com

2010 Sales

	$ mil.	% of total
US	15.6	91
Puerto Rico	1.2	7
China	0.3	2
Total	**17.1**	**100**

PRODUCTS/OPERATIONS

2010 Sales

	$ mil.	% of total
Telephony products	12.1	71
Communications systems & services	3.7	22
Puerto Rico	1.3	7
Total	**17.1**	**100**

Selected Products

Multimedia contact center software (eQueue)
Voice switching hardware platform (Millennium)

COMPETITORS

Aastra Technologies
Aspect Software
Avaya
Cisco Systems
eGain Communications
Interactive
LivePerson
Mitel Networks
NEC
Oracle
Polycom
Siemens AG
Intelligence
KANA
KGP Logistics
Syntellect
Toshiba
VTech Holdings

HISTORICAL FINANCIALS

Company Type: Public

Income Statement

FYE: July 31

	REVENUE ($ mil.)	NET INCOME ($ mil.)	NET PROFIT MARGIN	EMPLOYEES
07/11	23.4	(1.4)	—	86
07/10	17.1	0.5	2.9%	104
07/09	10.6	(0.3)	—	61
07/08	7.0	(3.5)	—	43
07/07	10.7	(1.3)	—	92
Annual Growth	**21.6%**	**—**	**—**	**(1.7%)**

2011 Year-End Financials

Debt ratio: 61.7%
Return on equity: —
Cash ($ mil.): 1.5
Current ratio: 2.52
Long-term debt ($ mil.): 3.1
No. of shares (mil.): 2.9
Dividends
  Yield: —
  Payout: —
Market value ($ mil.): 4.8

	STOCK PRICE ($) FY Close	P/E High/Low	PER SHARE ($) Earnings	Dividends	Book Value
07/11	1.66	— —	(0.48)	0.00	1.76
07/10	1.56	44 5	0.17	0.00	2.28
07/09	0.85	— —	(0.12)	0.00	2.12
07/08	0.70	— —	(1.27)	0.00	2.21
07/07	4.20	— —	(0.50)	0.00	3.39
Annual Growth	**(20.7%)**	**— —**	**—**	**—**	**(15.2%)**

Epoch

Epoch Holding is the holding company of Epoch Investments Partners (EIP), a boutique investment manager and advisor serving corporations, endowments, foundations, and high-net-worth individuals. EIP also acts as a sub-advisor for several mutual funds for John Hancock and MainStay Investments, an affiliate of New York Life; the latter relationship accounts for more than 15% of Epoch's annual revenue. The company sells its products through investment consultants, private banks, asset managers, and other third-party distributors. It serves clients in the US, Australia, Canada, Japan, and the UK.

Investing mainly in common stock of publicly traded companies, EIP employs strategies focused on US equities, global equities, and international small-cap firms. It has approximately $12 billion of assets under management, a figure that has about doubled since 2007.

Formerly known as J Net Enterprises, Epoch was once one of Nevada's largest gaming-machine operators and even tried its hand at Internet-based e-commerce before acquiring EIP in 2004.

Executive officers and board members of Epoch and institutional investors hold a majority of the company's stock. CEO and co-founder William Priest owns approximately 12%, as does Chicago-based money manager Keeley Asset Management.

EXECUTIVES

Chairman, Allan R. Tessler, age 74
President and COO, Timothy T. (Tim) Taussig, age 53
CFO, Adam Borak, age 43
CEO and Director, William W. Priest, age 69
EVP, Head of U.S. Equities and Portfolio Manager, David N. Pearl, age 51
EVP and Head of Client Relations, J. Philip Clark, age 58
VP Consultant Relations, Robert V. Martin
VP, Business Administration and Assistant Compliance Officer, Neeraj Garg
VP Performance, Jason Root
VP Analyst, Thuy Tran
VP International Trader, Nishu Trivedi
Managing Director Sub-advisory Relations, Jeff Ulness
Managing Director Public Funds Relations, Ronan J. Burke
Senior Associate Client Service, Melissa Boryk
Managing Director Client Relations, Kathleen P. Dunlap
Managing Director Client Relations, T. Jon Williams
Managing Director, Portfolio Manager and Senior Analyst, Emily Baker
Managing Director, Portfolio Manager, and Senior Analyst, Joseph W. Donaldson
Managing Director, Portfolio Manager, and Senior Analyst, Daniel Geber
Managing Director Consultant Relations, Andrea Taske Glogoff
Auditors: CF & Co., LLP

LOCATIONS

HQ: Epoch Holding Corporation
640 5th Ave., 18th Fl., New York, NY 10019
Phone: 212-303-7200   **Fax:** 212-202-4948
Web: www.eipny.com

2010 Sales by Region

	$ mil.	% of total
US	37.8	71
Canada	7.0	13
Europe	4.7	9
Asia/Australia	3.9	7
Total	**53.4**	**100**

PRODUCTS/OPERATIONS

2010 Sales

	$ mil.	% of total
Advisory & management fees	52.6	99
Performance fees	0.8	1
Total	**53.4**	**100**

COMPETITORS

AllianceBernstein
BlackRock
Goldman Sachs
JPMorgan Asset Management
Legg Mason
Morgan Stanley Investment Management
Old Mutual (US)

HISTORICAL FINANCIALS

Company Type: Public

Income Statement

FYE: June 30

	REVENUE ($ mil.)	NET INCOME ($ mil.)	NET PROFIT MARGIN	EMPLOYEES
06/11	70.6	21.6	30.6%	57
06/10	53.4	11.6	21.7%	52
06/09	31.2	5.9	18.9%	46
06/08	33.8	9.0	26.6%	46
06/07	23.9	7.9	33.1%	43
Annual Growth	**31.1%**	**28.6%**	**—**	**7.3%**

2011 Year-End Financials

Debt ratio: —
Return on equity: 34.9%
Cash ($ mil.): 29.1
Current ratio: 5.94
Long-term debt ($ mil.): —

No. of shares (mil.): 23.4
Dividends
  Yield: 1.2%
  Payout: 23.7%
Market value ($ mil.): 417.1

	STOCK PRICE ($) FY Close	P/E High/Low		PER SHARE ($) Earnings	Dividends	Book Value
06/11	17.85	19	10	0.93	0.22	2.64
06/10	12.27	26	14	0.52	0.16	2.44
06/09	8.64	46	16	0.26	0.12	2.24
06/08	9.11	41	20	0.41	0.08	2.23
06/07	13.39	57	10	0.35	0.00	1.76
Annual Growth	7.5%	—	—	27.7%	—	10.7%

Equinix

Founded in 1998, Equinix provides data and network hosting and colocation facilities (it calls them Internet Business Exchanges, or IBXs) where ISPs, telecommunications carriers, and content providers can locate equipment and interconnect networks and operations. The company also offers colocation-related services that include providing clients with cabinets, operating space, and storage. Its clients have included Apple, eBay, IBM, and Bank of America. Equinix operates dozens of IBXs in international markets including Chicago, Hong Kong, Los Angeles, New York, and Tokyo. The company makes more than one third of its sales overseas.

The company's revenue grew in 2010, as it has done each year of the past decade, while profits slipped by nearly half compared to 2009. The boost in sales was attributable to a growing customer base (larger by about 50% in 2010) driven by acquisitions and organic expansion of its global facilities network. Profits were down due to increased expenses related to the acquisitions and data center expansion activities. The company's costs for sales and marketing, among other areas, rose in 2010 as well.

In anticipation of a continued increase in demand for commercial data center services, Equinix is investing in its infrastructure in the Americas and Europe. In 2011 the company acquired 90% of ALOG Data Centers of Brazil for $83 million in cash, $15 million of which was slated for future data center expansion. The deal extended the company's reach to South America, bringing its total number of data centers to 95 in 37 markets worldwide. ALOG has data centers in Rio de Janeiro and Sao Paolo.

In 2010 Equinix acquired Switch and Data Facilities for about $683 million in a move that boosted its number of data centers to about 90. As part of the deal it paid around $134 million in cash and issued approximately 5.5 million shares of common stock for the rival collocation and Internet exchange services provider with operations in more than 20 markets in North America.

The company spent $30 million in 2009 to acquire and equip an additional data center in Frankfurt and it put another $100 million into its New York facilities.

EXECUTIVES

Chairman, Peter F. Van Camp, age 55
President, CEO, and Director, Stephen M. (Steve) Smith, age 55, $3,302,958 total compensation
CFO, Keith D. Taylor, age 49, $2,016,131 total compensation
President, Equinix Asia-Pacific, Samuel Lee
President, North America, Charles Meyers, age 41
President, Equinix Europe, Eric Schwartz, age 44, $1,698,669 total compensation
VP Sales, North America, Dan Walker
VP Sales, Equinix Asia-Pacific, Doug Oates
COO, Sushil (Sam) Kapoor, age 64, $1,912,857 total compensation
CIO, Brian Lillie
CTO, David Pickut
Chief Sales Officer, Peter T. Ferris, age 53, $1,258,278 total compensation
SVP Global Human Resources, Keri Crask
SVP Global Real Estate, Howard B. Horowitz
Managing Director, Equinix Japan, Kei Furuta
Managing Director, Equinix Greater China, Jonathan Leung
Managing Director, Equinix Australia, Darren Mann
Chief Technologist, Lane Patterson
Chief Marketing Officer; VP Marketing, Asia Pacific, Todd Handcock
General Manager, The Netherlands, Michiel Eielts
General Manager, Germany, Jorg Rosengart
Managing Director, Equinix Singapore, Clement Goh
General Manager, United Kingdom, Russell Poole
General Counsel and Corporate Secretary, Brandi L. Galvin Morandi
Senior Director Investor Relations, Jason Starr
General Manager, France, Michel Brignano
Chief Development Officer, Mark Adams
Auditors: PricewaterhouseCoopers LLP

LOCATIONS

HQ: Equinix, Inc.
  1 Lagoon Dr., 4th Fl., Redwood City, CA 94465
Phone: 650-598-6000   **Fax:** 650-598-6900
Web: www.equinix.com

2010 Sales

	$ mil.	% of total
North America	776.2	64
Europe	281.8	23
Asia-Pacific	162.3	13
Total	**1,220.3**	**100**

PRODUCTS/OPERATIONS

Selected Services

Central switching connections
Colocation-related equipment, operating space, and storage
Installation and maintenance of customer equipment
Power supply services
Private and shared cages

COMPETITORS

AboveNet	NaviSite
AT&T	NTT
COLT Group	Rackspace
Digital Realty	SAVVIS
DuPont Fabros	SingTel
Everest Interlink Broadband	SunGard Availability Services
Hostway	TeleCity
Internap Network Services	Telx Group
Level 3 Communications	Terremark W
	Verizon Business

HISTORICAL FINANCIALS

Company Type: Public

Income Statement
FYE: December 31

	REVENUE ($ mil.)	NET INCOME ($ mil.)	NET PROFIT MARGIN	EMPLOYEES
12/10	1,220.3	36.9	3.0%	1,921
12/09	882.5	69.4	7.9%	1,301
12/08	704.7	131.5	18.7%	1,115
12/07	419.4	(5.2)	—	911
12/06	286.9	(6.4)	—	616
Annual Growth	43.6%	—		32.9%

2010 Year-End Financials

Debt ratio: 107.5%
Return on equity: 2.0%
Cash ($ mil.): 442.8
Current ratio: 2.45
Long-term debt ($ mil.): 2,020.6

No. of shares (mil.): 46.2
Dividends
  Yield: —
  Payout: —
Market value ($ mil.): 3,751.5

	STOCK PRICE ($) FY Close	P/E High/Low		PER SHARE ($) Earnings	Dividends	Book Value
12/10	81.26	135	85	0.82	0.00	40.73
12/09	106.15	62	24	1.75	0.00	30.08
12/08	53.19	31	10	3.31	0.00	23.90
12/07	101.07	—	—	(0.16)	0.00	22.44
12/06	75.62	—	—	(0.22)	0.00	12.17
Annual Growth	1.8%	—	—	—	—	35.3%

Essex Rental

Unless you employ construction workers who moonlight as super heroes, you may need to rent one of Essex Rental's cranes to hoist those steel beams and concrete pipes. Specializing in lattice-boom crawler cranes (large, heavy-duty cranes with dynamic lifting capabilities), Essex Rental rents a fleet of some 350 Manitowoc and Liebherr brand cranes and attachments to North American construction and industrial companies and municipalities. Its cranes are typically used in the construction of power plants, petrochemical plants, water treatment and purification facilities, as well as in commercial and infrastructure construction. Essex also sells used equipment and offers crane transportation and repair services.

The company operates five main regional service centers in Alabama, Texas, Colorado, California, and Florida that serve customers across the US and Canada. It intends to grow its presence in North America primarily through acquisitions of other crane companies and organic fleet expansion. Ultimately Essex's business strategy centers on optimizing its fleet, mainly by strategically placing its rental operations in certain markets and by purchasing and selling equipment to maintain a modern fleet that's also proportioned to market demand. The company has, in recent years, been working to diversify the end markets it serves in order to reduce its dependency on any one sector in the construction industry.

Essex Rental, formed in 2006 as a shell company, acquired the assets of Essex Crane in 2008. Before it was acquired, Essex Crane had been in business since the 1960s. The decades-old company is Essex Rental's primary operating subsidiary. Another key subsidiary, Essex Finance, was formed in 2009 to handle acquisitions of cranes and other equipment.

Company chairman Laurence S. Levy owns a 19% stake in Essex Rental.

EXECUTIVES

Chairman, Laurence S. Levy, age 55
CFO, Martin Kroll, age 55
CEO, Coast Crane Company, Dan Goodale
President, CEO, and Director, Ronald Schad, age 52
VP Sales and Customer Account Management,
  William O'Rourke
VP Customer Support and Operations, Bill Erwin
Secretary, Carol Zelinski, age 56
Auditors: Grant Thornton LLP

LOCATIONS

HQ: Essex Rental Corp.
  1110 Lake Cook Rd., Ste. 220, Buffalo Grove, IL
  60089
Phone: 847-215-6500   **Fax:** 847-215-6535
Web: www.essexcrane.com

COMPETITORS

AMECO   RSC Equipment Rental
Maxim Crane Works   United Rentals

HISTORICAL FINANCIALS

Company Type: Public

Income Statement
FYE: December 31

	REVENUE ($ mil.)	NET INCOME ($ mil.)	NET PROFIT MARGIN	EMPLOYEES
12/10	41.5	(9.6)	—	276
12/09	52.1	1.2	2.3%	111
12/08	14.5	(11.9)	—	128
Annual Growth	69.2%	—	—	46.8%

2010 Year-End Financials

Debt ratio: 278.3%
Return on equity: —
Cash ($ mil.): 3.5
Current ratio: 2.15
Long-term debt ($ mil.): 222.9

No. of shares (mil.): 20.5
Dividends
  Yield: —
  Payout: —
Market value ($ mil.): 112.6

	STOCK PRICE ($) FY Close	P/E High/Low		PER SHARE ($) Earnings	Dividends	Book Value
12/10	5.50	—	—	(0.59)	0.00	3.91
12/09	6.20	87	38	0.08	0.00	5.25
12/08	4.50	—	—	(0.88)	0.00	5.33
00/00	7.29	57	54	0.13	0.00	5.09
Annual Growth	(9.0%)	—	—	—	—	(8.4%)

EVCI Career Colleges

EVCI provides on-campus college education through three institutions: the Interboro Institute, Technical Career Institutes, and Pennsylvania School of Business. Interboro (2,700 students) offers associate degrees to students who have GEDs or did not graduate from high school. Students earn an associate of occupational studies degree in areas such as accounting, medical assistant, executive assistant, paralegal studies, ophthalmic dispensing, and security. Technical Career (3,000 students) degrees include office technology, facilities

management technology, and industrial technology. The Pennsylvania School of Business (325 students) offers training in office and medical billing operations, among others.

In 2008, the the Board of Directors took the company private, saying the cost and administrative burdens of maintaining a listing on the NASDAQ exchage were too high for a company with fewer than 300 shareholders.

The company ran into trouble in 2007 over how it determined students were eligible for financial aid. An investigation by the New York State Education Department indicated the company cheated; EVCI said that the errors were mostly clerical. The company was fined more than $2.5 million by the federal government.

Robert F. Kennedy Jr., son of Bobby, joined EVCI's board in 2007.

EXECUTIVES

President and CEO, John J. McGrath, age 58
CFO, Henry Hetherington
EVP Finance and Administration, William (Bill) Talbot
VP Corporate Affairs and General Counsel, Joseph D. Alperin, age 67
Auditors: McGladrey & Pullen, LLP

LOCATIONS

HQ: EVCI Career Colleges Holding Corp.
  1 Van Der Donck St., 2nd Fl., Yonkers, NY 10701
Phone: 914-623-0700   **Fax:** 914-964-8222
Web: www.evcinc.com

COMPETITORS

Apollo Group   Corinthian Colleges
Argosy Education   DeVry
Career Education   Strayer Education

HISTORICAL FINANCIALS

Company Type: Public

Income Statement
FYE: December 31

	REVENUE ($ mil.)	NET INCOME ($ mil.)	NET PROFIT MARGIN	EMPLOYEES
12/06	65.4	(13.5)	—	700
12/05	50.7	0.4	0.8%	849
12/04	33.1	6.3	19.0%	464
12/03	19.9	3.2	16.1%	252
12/02	15.3	(2.0)	—	237
Annual Growth	43.8%	—	—	31.1%

2006 Year-End Financials

Debt ratio: 72.9%
Return on equity: —
Cash ($ mil.): 2.2
Current ratio: 0.64
Long-term debt ($ mil.): 9.8

No. of shares (mil.): —
Dividends
  Yield: —
  Payout: —
Market value ($ mil.): —

	STOCK PRICE ($) FY Close	P/E High/Low		PER SHARE ($) Earnings	Dividends	Book Value
12/06	1.35	—	—	(3.24)	0.00	(0.00)
12/05	4.80	368	50	0.09	0.00	(0.00)
12/04	28.80	30	11	1.50	0.00	(0.00)
12/03	16.17	20	1	0.93	0.00	1.95
12/02	1.95	—	—	(1.95)	0.00	(0.00)
Annual Growth	(8.8%)	—	—	—	—	—

Evercore Partners

Evercore Partners provides advisory services on mergers and acquisitions, restructurings, divestitures, and financing to corporate clients. Subsidiary Evercore Asset Management serves institutional investors and focuses on small- and mid-cap stocks of publicly traded US firms, while Evercore Wealth Management serves high-net-worth individuals. All told, Evercore Partners has some $15 billion of assets under management. Subsidiary Protego, a boutique investment bank founded by Pedro Aspe, Mexico's former Minister of Finance, specializes in financing municipal infrastructure and energy projects there. Evercore Europe serves clients from its London office. Evercore Partners also makes private equity investments.

As an independent investment banking firm that is not involved in commercial banking or proprietary trading, the company believes that it operates without conflicts of interest that may occur at larger firms that both underwrite and invest in their clients. Evercore is also hoping to capitalize on turmoil in the industry that has seen some of its bulge-bracket competitors go bankrupt (Lehman Brothers) or get acquired (Merrill Lynch, Bear Stearns). The company has participated in several high-profile transactions in recent years, including the recapitalizations of GM and CIT Group and the acquisition of Burlington Northern Santa Fe by Berkshire Hathaway. An increase in recapitalizations and large mergers boosted the company's advisory services revenue in fiscal 2009.

Japan's Mizuho Corporate Bank has invested some $120 million in Evercore and plans to invest up to $150 million in Evercore-affiliated funds. By partnering with Mizuho, Evercore hopes to strengthen its international business, particularly in Japan. The company has also been making acquisitions in efforts to expand its services and geographic reach. (Protego and Evercore Europe, formerly Braveheart Financial Services, were both brought in via acquisitions in 2006.)

In 2009, Evercore entered into a strategic agreement with Citic Securities International to facilitate its clients' access to Chinese markets. The partnership will focus on cross-border merger and acquisition advisory and investment management between China and other countries. In 2010 Evercore Partners acquired a 50% stake in Brazilian boutique investment bank G5 advisors to increase its presence there. The partners of G5 retained the other 50% stake in the company, though Evercore has an option to acquire it outright in the future.

Also in 2009, Evercore purchased Bank of America's Special Fiduciary Services division. The business, now called Evercore Trust, provides investment management and trustee services to employee benefits plans. Evercore strengthened its advisory services operations with the 2010 acquisition of the private funds placement business of asset manager Neuberger Berman. It entered the real estate advisory business when it bought MJC Associates. Evercore also purchased a 49% stake in investment manager Atalanta Sosnoff Capital for some $69 million; Atalanta management retained majority ownership in the firm.

Evercore made yet another acquisition in 2011. It bought Lexicon Partners, an independent investment banking advisory firm in the UK. Lexicon, which has offices in London, Hong Kong, New York, and Aberdeen, provides investment advisory services for large and midsize corporations.

Evercore has also been growing internally, expanding its coverage of the chemicals and energy and mining, minerals, and materials sectors, and adding financial institutions and technology, telecommunications, and media groups. The company also has divisions devoted to the aerospace and defense, automotive, consumer products, and general industrial sectors.

Evercore was launched in 1996 (it went public 10 years later) by Roger Altman, who formerly led investment banking and merger advisory practices at Lehman Brothers and The Blackstone Group. Altman resigned as CEO in 2009 and was succeeded by Ralph Schlosstein, co-founder of asset management giant BlackRock; Altman remained executive chairman.

EXECUTIVES

President, CEO, and Director, Ralph L. Schlosstein, age 60
CEO, Evercore Wealth Management, Jeffrey S. (Jeff) Maurer
CFO, Robert B. Walsh, age 54, $2,396,404 total compensation
CEO and Director, Protego Asset Management Business, Sergio Sanchez
VP, Corporate Advisory, Rafael Polanco
VP, Corporate Advisory, Scott Newman
VP Corporate Advisory, Jeffrey M. Reisenberg
VP Corporate Advisory, Mayer Bick
VP, Evercore Europe and Corporate Advisory, Neal Shah
VP Corporate Advisory, David Cox
VP Corporate Advisory, Christopher J. Sieger
VP Corporate Advisory, Brendan Panda
VP Corporate Advisory, Mark Brofka
VP Corporate Advisors, Gus Christensen
VP Evercore Europe and Corporate Advisory, Tiarnán O'Rourke
VP, Privatge Equity, Justin W. Steil
VP, Evercore Europe and Corporate Advisory, Lee Hayes
Executive Chairman and Co-Chairman, Roger C. Altman, age 65, $7,124,344 total compensation
Senior Managing Director and Co-Head, Private Equity, Neeraj Mital
Senior Managing Director and Head, Equities Division, Charles Myers
Senior Managing Director and Head, Real Estate Advisory, Martin J. Cicco, age 55
Senior Managing Director and Co-Head, Private Equity, James R. Matthews
Senior Managing Director, Mining, Metals, and Materials Advisory, F. Perkins (Perk) Hixon, age 52
Co-Vice Chairman, Europe, Bernard Taylor, age 54
Co-Vice Chairman, Corporate Advisory Business, Eduardo G. Mestre, age 62, $4,660,329 total compensation
COO, Equities Division, Terri Fortuna
Senior Managing Director, Evercore Europe and Corporate Advisory, Ian Ferguson
Senior Managing Director, Evercore Europe and Corporate Advisory, Anthony Swift
Senior Managing Director, Evercore Europe and Corporate Advisory, Michael Forsyth
Senior Managing Director and COO, Private Equity, Kathleen G. Reiland, age 46
Senior Managing Director, Evercore Europe and Corporate Advisory, Anthony Fry, age 54
Senior Managing Director and COO, Corporate Advisory Business, Timothy G. LaLonde
Head Sales and Marketing, Evercore Asset Management, Gail S. Landis
Senior Managing Director, Strategy and Business Development, Ciara A. Burnham
General Counsel, Adam B. Frankel, age 43

Senior Managing Director, Evercore Europe, Philippe Camus, age 63
Senior Managing Director, Evercore Europe, Robert Gillespie
Co-Chairman; Chairman and CEO, Protego, Pedro Aspe, age 60, $2,060,313 total compensation
Senior Managing Director, Evercore Europe and Corporate Advisory, Edward (Ed) Banks
Client Services Manager, Evercore Wealth Management, Karen Francois
Senior Managing Director, Evercore Europe and Corporate Advisory, Julian Oakley
Principal Accounting Officer and Controller, Paul Pensa
Director, Protego, Antonio Souza
Director, Protego, Jorge Marcos
Director, Protego, Augusto Arellano
Director, Protego, Fernando Aportela
Director, Protego, Hugo Garza
Managing Director, Restructuring Advisory, Stephen Hannan
Senior Managing Director, Corporate Advisory, Naveen Nataraj
Auditors: Deloitte & Touche LLP

LOCATIONS

HQ: Evercore Partners Inc.
55 E. 52nd St., 43rd Fl., New York, NY 10055
Phone: 212-857-3100   **Fax:** 212-857-3101
Web: www.evercore.com

PRODUCTS/OPERATIONS

2009 Sales

	$ mil.	% of total
Advisory revenue	293.3	94
Investment management & other	19.8	6
Total	**313.1**	**100**

COMPETITORS

Allen & Company	Greenhill
Barclays Capital	JPMorgan Chase
Blackstone Group	Lazard
Citigroup Global Markets	Merrill Lynch
	Morgan Stanley
Credit Suisse	UBS Investment Bank
Goldman Sachs	

HISTORICAL FINANCIALS

Company Type: Public

Income Statement

FYE: December 31

	REVENUE ($ mil.)	NET INCOME ($ mil.)	NET PROFIT MARGIN	EMPLOYEES
12/10	401.7	9.0	2.2%	610
12/09	337.4	(1.6)	—	335
12/08	224.9	(4.7)	—	335
12/07	321.6	(34.5)	—	290
12/06	209.7	69.7	33.2%	247
Annual Growth	**17.6%**	**(40.1%)**	**—**	**25.4%**

2010 Year-End Financials

Debt ratio: 32.6%	No. of shares (mil.): 20.0
Return on equity: 3.0%	Dividends
Cash ($ mil.): 141.3	Yield: 1.9%
Current ratio: 1.68	Payout: 161.5%
Long-term debt ($ mil.): 98.1	Market value ($ mil.): 679.4

	STOCK PRICE ($) FY Close	P/E High/Low		PER SHARE ($) Earnings	Dividends	Book Value
12/10	34.00	98	54	0.39	0.63	15.05
12/09	30.40	—	—	(0.10)	0.39	16.30
12/08	12.49	—	—	(0.36)	0.48	17.27
12/07	21.55	—	—	(3.38)	0.41	15.51
12/06	36.85	53	32	0.76	0.00	24.52
Annual Growth	**(2.0%)**	**—**	**—**	**(15.4%)**	**—**	**(11.5%)**

Evergreen Solar

In the theater of alternative energy, Evergreen Solar is a rising star. Using a proprietary, low-cost silicon wafer manufacturing technology called String Ribbon, the company makes and markets solar power products, including solar cells, panels, and systems. Residential and commercial applications for Evergreen's solar modules (assemblies of photovoltaic solar cells) range from highway call boxes to street and billboard lighting, and on-grid and off-grid rural electrification. Key customers include Ralos Vertriebs, IBC Solar, and Wagner & Co. Solartechnik. Three-fourths of Evergreen Solar's revenue comes from overseas, with Germany accounting for the majority. Evergreen filed for Chapter 11 bankruptcy in 2011.

The company intends to sell its assets at auction to raise $485.6 million to repay creditors. Evergreen's bankruptcy is part of a trend driven by plummeting global prices of solar panels due to increasing competition from international manufacturers, particularly in China. The stalled progress of clean energy legislation in the US is also contributing to an unfavorable business environment for domestic solar companies.

Evergreen Solar's growth was fueled by a new manufacturing process; the company makes solar cells using less silicon than industry peers. It draws sheets of molten silicon between two strings and processes it into cells. Others cut silicon into wafers, losing up to half in silicon sawdust — Evergreen Solar's method eliminates the waste. The company's third-generation double ribbon technology approximately doubled its wafer capacity and reduced its manufacturing costs. Development of a fourth-generation technology, called quad ribbon, could double output again.

Success is also driven by demand for its products. Evergreen Solar has a $1.2 billion deal with German solar-panel distributor IBC Solar (17% of sales). On the supply side, the company has multiyear silicon supply agreements with OCI Company (which holds a 13% ownership stake in Evergreen Solar), Wacker Chemie AG, Colaricos Trading, and Silicium de Provence S.A.S. These agreements gave the company sufficient amounts of silicon under contract to reach desired annual production levels during a global silicon shortage.

Evergreen Solar more than doubled its sales in 2009. It remains unprofitable, however, with an accumulated deficit of nearly $489 million. The company expects to continue incurring operating losses until its Chinese factory reaches full capacity around mid-2012. It is exploring alternatives for outsourcing a portion of its wafers into solar cells; outsourcing would enable Evergreen Solar to fulfill contract obligations while cutting its expenses.

Sovello, a joint venture between Evergreen, Q-Cells, and Renewable Energy Corporation, operates two facilities that manufacture and market products based on Evergreen Solar's technology, and use fabrication processes combining the technologies of the three partners. Due to financial difficulties at Sovello, its three owners agreed to sell the German firm to Ventizz Capital Fund IV in 2010.

Evergreen Solar CEO Richard Feldt left the company to head another business in 2010. He was replaced by Michael El-Hillow who had previously served as chairman, CFO, and COO of the company.

EXECUTIVES

Chairman, Edward C. (Ed) Grady, age 64
President, CEO, and Director, Michael (Mike) El-Hillow, age 59, $970,862 total compensation
CFO, Donald W. Reilly, age 51
President and General Manager, Asia Operations, Yeok (Henry) Chan Ng
VP Marketing, Ian Gregory
VP Global Sales, Peter Rusch
VP Human Resources, Gary T. Pollard, age 51
VP and General Manager, US Manufacturing, Daniel Welch
VP Sales and Marketing, Scott J. Gish
VP and Corporate Controller, Paul Kawa, age 49
VP Construction Management and Facilities Engineering, Carl Stegerwald, age 59, $689,063 total compensation
CTO, Lawrence (Larry) Felton, age 49, $465,818 total compensation
Chief Strategy Officer, Richard G. Chleboski, age 45, $640,827 total compensation
Director Sales, Americas, Barrett Silver
Manager Applications Engineering, John Wilson
Director Investor Relations, Michael W. (Mike) McCarthy
Director Sales, Europe, Thomas Hofmann
Director Marketing Communications, Christopher (Chris) Lawson
Auditors: PricewaterhouseCoopers LLP

LOCATIONS

HQ: Evergreen Solar, Inc.
138 Bartlett St., Marlboro, MA 01752
Phone: 508-357-2221   **Fax:** 508-229-0747
Web: www.evergreensolar.com

COMPETITORS

BP Solar	LDK Solar
China Sunergy	MEMC Electronic
Conergy	Materials
Energy Conversion	Mitsubishi Electric
Devices	Nanosolar
First Solar	Q-Cells
GE Energy	SANYO Semiconductor
JA Solar	SCHOTT Solar
Konarka Technologies	Sharp Corp.
Kyocera Solar	Suntech Power

HISTORICAL FINANCIALS

Company Type: Public

Income Statement

FYE: December 31

	REVENUE ($ mil.)	NET INCOME ($ mil.)	NET PROFIT MARGIN	EMPLOYEES
12/10	338.8	(465.4)	—	1,034
12/09	271.8	(265.2)	—	1,112
12/08	112.0	(84.9)	—	801
12/07	69.9	(16.6)	—	400
12/06	103.1	(26.7)	—	330
Annual Growth	34.6%	—	—	33.0%

2010 Year-End Financials

Debt ratio: —	No. of shares (mil.): 34.8
Return on equity: —	Dividends
Cash ($ mil.): 61.6	Yield: —
Current ratio: 3.79	Payout: —
Long-term debt ($ mil.): 427.0	Market value ($ mil.): 121.7

	STOCK PRICE ($) FY Close	P/E High/Low	Earnings	PER SHARE ($) Dividends	Book Value
12/10	3.50	— —	(13.59)	0.00	(1.76)
12/09	9.06	— —	(8.46)	0.00	11.42
12/08	19.14	— —	(3.90)	0.00	18.91
12/07	103.62	— —	(1.14)	0.00	19.50
12/06	45.42	— —	(2.46)	0.00	8.19
Annual Growth	(47.3%)	— —	—	—	—

ExamWorks

ExamWorks Group examines whether people should qualify for certain types of insurance. Through subsidiary ExamWorks, Inc., the holding company is a leading North American provider of independent medical examinations (IMEs). IMEs are physical exams conducted by independently contracted physicians to verify illness and injury claims for individuals seeking workers' compensation, automotive and personal injury liability, and disability insurance coverage. Its network consists of more than 13,500 doctors and medical providers. ExamWorks also offers medical record and medical bill reviews. Clients include insurance companies and law firms. The group filed to go public in mid-2010 after a series of acquisitions.

ExamWorks began operating in 2008 with the acquisition of three US IME businesses in New Jersey, New York, and Texas. It acquired more than 20 additional IME businesses, including operations in Canada and a leading provider of IME software, by mid-2010. The group subsequently filed a $172.5 million initial public offering and plans to use certain net proceeds to fund further acquisitions amidst a fragmented industry consisting mainly of smaller, local and regional companies. Other net proceeds from its offering will go towards repaying loan and credit facility amounts.

The company in 2011 bought MES Group for $175 million in cash, 1.4 million shares of common stock, and about $10 million in debt. The buy enhanced ExamWorks' portfolio of independent medical examinations, peer reviews and utilization reviews for the automotive, disability, liability, and workers' compensation markets. The acquisition excludes MES' Veterans Evaluation Services business.

ExamWorks maintains a direct sales force that markets its services to both clients who request IMEs and the physicians and medical providers who perform them. Clients who request IMEs include claims adjusters and in-house counsel for major insurance companies covering workers' compensation, injury liability, and disability; attorneys who litigate claims; third-party claims administrators working for large self-insured corporations that outsource claims management; government health and labor agencies; and state funds that provide mandatory workers' compensation insurance to companies.

Physicians and other medical professionals generally perform IME services to supplement their primary incomes. IMEs are considered a low-risk source of additional revenue as physicians are paid on a per-service basis at a pre-negotiated rate. ExamWorks' specialized IME*Centric technology platform equips participating medical providers with appointment scheduling, case tracking, and client reporting systems to reduce administrative costs and increase efficiency.

Chairman Richard Perlman owns about one-third of ExamWorks Group.

EXECUTIVES

Chairman, Richard E. Perlman, age 65, $22,057 total compensation
President, Wesley J. (Wes) Campbell, age 45, $349,688 total compensation
CEO and Director, James K. (Jim) Price, age 53, $21,840 total compensation
VP and CIO, Kevin J. Kozlowski, age 48, $269,764 total compensation
VP Sales and Marketing, Joshua W. LeMaire, age 37
VP, General Counsel, and Assistant Secretary, Clare Y. Arguedas, age 29
VP Human Resources and Secretary, Crystal B. Patmore, age 39, $193,006 total compensation
SVP and CFO, J. Miguel Fernandez de Castro, age 38, $349,688 total compensation
CTO, Brian K. Denton, age 44
Chief Medical Director, Robert C. Porter, age 61
Auditors: KPMG LLP

LOCATIONS

HQ: ExamWorks Group, Inc.
3280 Peachtree Rd., N.E., Suite 2625, Atlanta, GA 30305
Phone: 404-952-2400   **Fax:** 404-846-1554
Web: www.examworks.com

HISTORICAL FINANCIALS

Company Type: Public

Income Statement

FYE: December 31

	REVENUE ($ mil.)	NET INCOME ($ mil.)	NET PROFIT MARGIN	EMPLOYEES
12/10	163.5	(6.0)	—	1,485
12/09	49.6	(4.4)	—	780
12/08	14.7	(2.2)	—	0
12/07	0.0	0.2	—	0
Annual Growth	—	—	—	90.4%

2010 Year-End Financials

Debt ratio: 3.8%	No. of shares (mil.): 32.2
Return on equity: —	Dividends
Cash ($ mil.): 33.6	Yield: —
Current ratio: 1.98	Payout: —
Long-term debt ($ mil.): 7.5	Market value ($ mil.): 595.4

	STOCK PRICE ($) FY Close	P/E High/Low	Earnings	PER SHARE ($) Dividends	Book Value
12/10	18.48	— —	(0.33)	0.00	6.22
Annual Growth	—	— —	—	—	—

Excel Trust

Excel Trust likes to buy retail space off the clearance rack. Based in San Diego, the self-managed, self-administered real estate investment trust has a penchant for acquiring high-value retail properties at a reduced cost — including anchored and "power" shopping centers and freestanding retail properties — located in the Northwest, Northeast, and the Sunbelt regions. Excel went public in 2010. The company raised some $194 million in order to acquire more properties. Excel owns about 30 retail and commercial properties totaling more than 1 million sq. ft. of leasable space. Tenants include Walgreens, Publix and Dollar Tree.

EXECUTIVES

Chairman and CEO, Gary B. Sabin, age 56
President, COO, and Director, Spencer G. Plumb, age 35
CFO and Treasurer, James Y. Nakagawa, age 45
SVP Acquisitions and Chief Investment Officer; Director, Mark T. Burton, age 50
SVP, Capital Markets, Matthew S. Romney, age 39
SVP, Asset Management and Development, William J. Stone, age 67
SVP, General Counsel and Secretary, S. Eric Ottesen, age 55
Auditors: Deloitte & Touche LLP

LOCATIONS

HQ: Excel Trust, Inc.
17140 Bernardo Center Dr., Ste. 300, San Diego, CA 92128
Phone: 858-613-1800   **Fax:** 858-487-9890
Web: www.excelreit.com

COMPETITORS

Cedar Shopping Centers
Colonial Properties
Donahue Schriber
Equity One
Feldman Mall Properties
Glimcher Realty
Kimco Realty

HISTORICAL FINANCIALS

Company Type: Public

Income Statement

FYE: December 31

	REVENUE ($ mil.)	NET INCOME ($ mil.)	NET PROFIT MARGIN	EMPLOYEES
12/10	17.5	(3.9)	—	31
12/09	5.0	0.2	4.0%	20
12/08	3.8	(0.4)	—	0
12/07	4.5	0.1	2.2%	0
Annual Growth	57.3%	—	—	55.0%

2010 Year-End Financials

Debt ratio: 118.6%
Return on equity: —
Cash ($ mil.): 6.5
Current ratio: 1.54
Long-term debt ($ mil.): 222.4
No. of shares (mil.): 15.7
Dividends
Yield: 1.7%
Payout: —
Market value ($ mil.): 189.5

	STOCK PRICE ($) FY Close	P/E High/Low	PER SHARE ($) Earnings	Dividends	Book Value
12/10	12.10	— —	(0.24)	0.20	11.97
Annual Growth	—	— —	—	—	—

Exelixis

We've come a long way, baby, but we still have a lot in common with the fruit fly. Exelixis, a pharmaceutical research and development firm, got its start analyzing genetic data from fruit flies and other organisms as a means to speed the development of drugs and other products. Its early genomic work has yielded a pipeline of drug candidates primarily in the area of cancer therapies, as well as some potential treatments for metabolic and cardiovascular diseases. The company's drug candidates in clinical trials include treatments for solid tumors, thyroid cancer, and non-small cell lung cancer. Development and licensing partners include Bristol-Myers Squibb, Genentech, GlaxoSmithKline, and Sanofi.

Exelixis, which takes its name from the Greek word for evolution, has been building upon its past in genomics research to become a full-fledged drug development company, focusing increasingly on its pharmaceuticals pipeline. The company is led by CEO Michael Morrissey who replaced George Scangos when he left the company in 2010 to take the helm at Biogen. Morrissey is also a member of the company's board of directors.

Exelixis largely relies on licensing and co-development partnerships to fund its operations. While the company has several independent cancer therapy candidates under development, it is focusing future growth plans on the collaborative side of its business. The company is partnering on several cancer drug trials with Bristol-Myers Squibb (BMS). It also has licensed out development programs for potential cancer therapies and medicines for metabolic and cardiovascular diseases to companies including GlaxoSmithKline, BMS, Boehringer Ingelheim, Pfizer, and Daiichi Sankyo.

In 2008 Exelixis enhanced its partnership with BMS by granting it co-development and co-marketing rights to Exelixis' lead cancer candidate (XL184 for thyroid and other cancers), as well as full development rights to another drug, for $195 million plus future potential milestone payments. As a result, BMS accounted for more than half of Exelixis' 2009 revenues. The company also struck a new collaboration deal worth some $140 million (plus possible milestone fees) with Sanofi (then known as Sanofi-Aventis) to develop two solid tumor cancer therapies in 2009.

Along with increasing its partnerships, the company is taking steps to cut costs in other areas. Exelixis laid off about 10% of its workforce in late 2008, and began cutting funding for noncore development programs. Then, in 2010, the company reduced its employee count by another 40%, primarily in the discovery-stage research division, to further curb expenses. It is focused on the development of key candidates in advanced phases of clinical trials, and it is looking to form new collaborations on additional proprietary candidates.

To better focus on its drug discovery work, in late 2007 Exelixis sold off the majority of its mouse genomics subsidiary Artemis Pharmaceuticals to Taconic Farms. At the same time, it sold off its Exelixis Plant Sciences business to Dow Chemical's Agrigenetics subsidiary.

EXECUTIVES

Chairman, Stelios Papadopoulos, age 62
President, CEO, and Director, Michael M. Morrissey, age 50, $1,661,308 total compensation
EVP and Chief Medical Officer, Gisela M. Schwab, age 54, $1,083,144 total compensation
EVP Operations, Lupe M. Rivera, age 44
EVP Discovery Research and Chief Scientific Officer, Peter Lamb, age 50
EVP and CFO, Frank L. Karbe, age 42, $1,272,785 total compensation
EVP and General Counsel, Pamela A. Simonton, age 61, $1,054,362 total compensation
EVP Business Development, Frances K. (Fran) Heller, age 44
VP Plant Biotechnology, Exelixis Plant Sciences, D. Ry Wagner, age 54
VP Corporate Communications and Investor Relations, Charles Butler
VP Corporate Legal Affairs and Secretary, James B. Bucher
SVP Chemistry, John M. Nuss, age 52
Associate Director Investor Relations, DeDe Sheel
SVP Translational Research, Dana Aftab
Senior Manager Corporate Communications, Soleil Maxwe Harrison
Auditors: Ernst & Young LLP

LOCATIONS

HQ: Exelixis, Inc.
210 E. Grand Ave., South San Francisco, CA 94080
Phone: 650-837-7000   **Fax:** 650-837-8300
Web: www.exelixis.com

PRODUCTS/OPERATIONS

2009 Sales

	$ mil.	% of total
License fees	97.6	64
Contract		
Research & development funding	36.6	24
Milestone payments	17.6	12
Total	**151.8**	**100**

2009 Sales

	$ mil.	% of total
Bristol-Myers Squibb	81.4	54
Sanofi-Aventis	46.9	31
Genentech	12.0	8
Boehringer Ingelheim	10.8	7
GlaxoSmithKline	0.5	-
Other	0.2	-
Total	**151.8**	**100**

Selected Drug Candidates

XL139 (cancer, with BMS)
XL147 (solid tumors, lung cancer; licensed to Sanofi-Aventis)
XL184 (solid tumors, lung and thyroid cancer; with BMS)
XL281 (cancer, licensed to BMS)
XL518 (solid tumors, licensed to Genentech)
XL652 (metabolic and cardiovascular diseases, licensed to BMS)
XL765 (solid tumors, glioblastoma, non small-cell lung cancer; licensed to Sanofi-Aventis)
XL880 (renal cell carcinoma, gastric cancer, head and neck cancer; licensed to GlaxoSmithKline)

COMPETITORS

Amgen
Array BioPharma
AstraZeneca
Bayer HealthCare Pharmaceuticals Inc.
Biogen Idec
Bristol-Myers Squibb
Eli Lilly
Genentech
Genmab
Genzyme
GlaxoSmithKline
Keryx Biopharmaceuticals
Millennium: The Takeda Oncology Company
Novartis
Onyx Pharmaceuticals
OSI

HISTORICAL FINANCIALS

Company Type: Public

Income Statement

FYE: Friday nearest December 31

	REVENUE ($ mil.)	NET INCOME ($ mil.)	NET PROFIT MARGIN	EMPLOYEES
12/10	185.0	(92.3)	—	240
12/09	151.8	(135.2)	—	676
12/08	117.9	(162.9)	—	676
12/07	113.5	(86.4)	—	735
12/06	98.7	(101.5)	—	651
Annual Growth	17.0%	—	—	(22.1%)

2010 Year-End Financials

Debt ratio: —
Return on equity: —
Cash ($ mil.): 97.4
Current ratio: 0.92
Long-term debt ($ mil.): 170.7

No. of shares (mil.): 109.3
Dividends
  Yield: —
  Payout: —
Market value ($ mil.): 897.2

	STOCK PRICE ($) FY Close	P/E High/Low		PER SHARE ($) Earnings	Dividends	Book Value
12/10	8.21	—	—	(0.85)	0.00	(2.09)
12/09	7.37	—	—	(1.26)	0.00	(1.52)
12/08	5.02	—	—	(1.54)	0.00	(0.54)
12/07	8.63	—	—	(0.87)	0.00	0.69
12/06	9.00	—	—	(1.17)	0.00	0.55
Annual Growth	(2.3%)	—	—	—	—	—

EXL

Have an extra-large task you'd rather not take on? Outsource it to ExlService Holdings. The company, known as EXL, offers business process outsourcing (BPO), research and analytics, and consulting services. EXL's BPO offerings, which generate most of its sales, include claims processing, collections, customer support, and finance and accounting. Customers come mainly from the banking, financial services, and insurance industries, but also from sectors such as utilities and telecommunications. Two customers, The Travelers Indemnity Company and natural gas supplier Centrica, collectively accounted for 34% of EXL's sales in 2009. EXL owns 15 delivery centers and was established in 1999.

EXL markets and sells its services through offices in the US, the UK, and Singapore and delivery facilities in the Czech Republic, India, Romania, and the Philippines. Business has been brisk for EXL and other BPO firms as the global economic downturn has caused many companies to cut costs and outsource operations.

The company hopes to grow primarily by selling more services to existing customers and by adding more Global 1,000 companies to its client list. In addition, EXL will continue to evaluate acquisition opportunities. EXL officials are looking at BPO firms in Eastern Europe or the US with capabilities in insurance, utilities, compliance, and risk management as acquisition targets.

Sticking to this strategy, in mid-2011 EXL acquired Outsource Partners International (OPI), a provider of finance and accounting outsourcing services serving about 80 clients. OPI has expertise in such areas as payroll, and tax compliance, SEC financial reporting, and risk management. The deal substantially bolstered EXL's existing fi-

nance and accounting offerings and allowed it to better cater to CFOs. It also enhanced its footprint in the Asia/Pacific and in Europe.

In 2009 EXL acquired the back-office operations of Schneider Logistic's Czech Republic facility. The unit offers accounting and transaction processing services along with multi-lingual capabilities. The deal gave EXL an outpost to extend and diversify its outsourcing operations in Europe. In March 2010, EXL paid $29 million for Global Travel Service Center (GTSC), the back-office operations belonging to American Express located in Gurgaon, India.

Affiliates of investment firm Oak Hill Capital Partners — represented on EXL's board by managing partner Steven Gruber, director Edward Dardani, executive chairman Vikram Talwar, and president and CEO Rohit Kapoor — control a 36% stake in the company.

EXECUTIVES

Chairman, Vikram Talwar, age 61, $1,846,138 total compensation
President, CEO, and Director, Rohit Kapoor, age 46, $1,796,501 total compensation
CFO, Vishal Chhibbar, $811,871 total compensation
EVP Global Client Services, Bill Bloom
VP and Head Strategic Account Management, North America, Bruce Polsky
VP and Global Head Corporate Communications and Brand, Shruti Jain
COO, Pavan Bagai, age 49, $689,274 total compensation
Chief Sales and Marketing Officer, Krishna Nacha, age 41, $551,165 total compensation
SVP and Head Global Technology, Baljinder Singh
SVP, UK and Europe, Kulpreet Singh
Assistant VP Marketing Communications, Shailendra Singh
SVP; Center Head, EXL Philippines, Jaideep Pradhan
Head Outsourcing Services, Vikas Bhalla, age 39
General Counsel and Secretary, Amit Shashank, age 41, $644,360 total compensation
Global Head Human Resources, Amitabh Hajela, age 42
Global Head Human Resources, Sanjay Gupta, age 49
Head Investor Relations and Corporate Development and Treasurer, Jarrod Yahes
Auditors: Ernst & Young LLP

LOCATIONS

HQ: ExlService Holdings, Inc.
280 Park Ave., 38th Fl., New York, NY 10017
Phone: 212-277-7100   **Fax:** 212-277-7111
Web: www.exlservice.com

2009 Sales

	$ mil.
% of total	
US	121.9
64	
UK	64.7
34	
Other countries	4.4
2	
Total	191.0
100	

PRODUCTS/OPERATIONS

2009 Sales

	$ mil.
% of total	
Outsourcing services	152.6
80	
Transformation services	38.4
20	
Total	191.0
100	

COMPETITORS

Accenture
Affiliated Computer Services
Genpact
HP Enterprise Services
IBM Global Services
Infosys
Jefferson Wells International
Tata Consultancy
Wipro
WNS (Holdings)

HISTORICAL FINANCIALS

Company Type: Public

Income Statement

FYE: December 31

	REVENUE ($ mil.)	NET INCOME ($ mil.)	NET PROFIT MARGIN	EMPLOYEES
12/10	252.8	26.6	10.5%	12,700
12/09	191.0	15.7	8.2%	10,700
12/08	181.7	14.4	7.9%	9,995
12/07	179.9	27.0	15.0%	10,000
12/06	121.8	14.1	11.6%	8,200
Annual Growth	20.0%	17.2%	—	11.6%

2010 Year-End Financials

Debt ratio: 0.2%
Return on equity: 10.7%
Cash ($ mil.): 111.2
Current ratio: 3.44
Long-term debt ($ mil.): 0.4

No. of shares (mil.): 29.4
Dividends
  Yield: —
  Payout: —
Market value ($ mil.): 632.3

	STOCK PRICE ($) FY Close	P/E High/Low		PER SHARE ($) Earnings	Dividends	Book Value
12/10	21.48	25	8	0.88	0.00	8.44
12/09	18.15	35	11	0.53	0.00	7.09
12/08	8.57	53	9	0.49	0.00	5.94
12/07	23.08	31	17	0.93	0.00	6.07
12/06	21.04	50	27	0.58	0.00	4.53
Annual Growth	0.5%	—	—	11.0%	—	16.9%

Express-1 Expedited Solutions

Express-1 Expedited Solutions specializes in arranging expedited ground transportation. Customers' freight is transported throughout the US by independent contractors, who give the company's Express-1 unit access to a fleet of vehicles that includes cargo vans, trucks, and tractor-trailers. Express-1 Expedited offers domestic and international freight forwarding through Concert Group Logistics, as well as truckload freight brokerage services through Bounce Logistics. With operations centers in the Midwest and in Florida, Express-1 Expedited provides services to more than 1,500 customers across the US, Canada, and Mexico.

In an effort to diversify beyond the expedited freight transportation model, Express-1 Expedited acquired LRG International, an international forwarding company with ocean and air freight services expertise. Express-1 Expedited integrated LRG into its Concert Group Logistics operations in order to add international markets. As a result of the acquisition, international markets account for 48% of Concert Group Logistics' revenues in 2010. The company bought Concert Group Logistics, a provider of freight forwarding and logistics services, in 2008. The acquisition closed just weeks after Express-1 Expedited announced the formation of Bounce Logistics, which specializes in premium truckload freight brokerage. The goal is to sell more bundles of higher-value services to the company's customers.

In early 2009 Express-1 Expedited discontinued its contract dedicated transportation services business, after its contract with Ford ended.

Director Daniel Para, the founder of Concert Group Logistics, holds a 12% stake in Express-1 Expedited.

EXECUTIVES

Chairman, James J. (Jim) Martell, age 56
CEO and Director, Michael R. (Mike) Welch, age 48, $297,200 total compensation
President, Bounce Logistics, Tim Hindes
President, Express-1 Dedicated, Brian J. Glaser, age 36
President and Secretary, Jeffrey A. (Jeff) Curry, age 49
VP Information Technology, Joseph C. (Joe) Campbell, age 49
VP Operations, James M. (Jim) Welch, age 54
VP Sales, Dennis M. McCaffrey, age 41
VP Operations, Bounce Logistics, Kurt LaDow
VP Sales, Concert Group Logistics, Dominick Muzi
Interim CFO, John D. Welch, age 50
Director Capacity Management, Keith P. Avery, age 48
Director Safety, Robert J. Tracey, age 60
Director; CEO, Concert Group Logistics Freight Forwarding, Daniel (Dan) Para, age 58
Auditors: Pender Newkirk & Company

LOCATIONS

HQ: Express-1 Expedited Solutions, Inc.
429 Post Rd., Buchanan, MI 49107
Phone: 269-695-2700   **Fax:** 269-695-7458
Web: www.express-1.com

PRODUCTS/OPERATIONS

2010 Sales

	$ mil.	% of total
Express-1	76.7	48
Concert Group Logistics	65.2	40
Bounce Logistics	20.0	12
Adjustments	(3.9)	-
Total	**158.0**	**100**

COMPETITORS

Alliance Air	Panther Expedited
Daylight Transport	Services
DHL	Schneider National
FedEx	Towne Air Freight
Forward Air	UPS
New Penn Motor Express	

HISTORICAL FINANCIALS

Company Type: Public

Income Statement

FYE: December 31

	REVENUE ($ mil.)	NET INCOME ($ mil.)	NET PROFIT MARGIN	EMPLOYEES
12/10	158.0	4.9	3.1%	190
12/09	100.1	1.7	1.7%	137
12/08	109.5	3.2	2.9%	150
12/07	52.8	2.2	4.2%	132
12/06	42.2	3.9	9.2%	129
Annual Growth	**39.1%**	**5.9%**	**—**	**10.2%**

2010 Year-End Financials

Debt ratio: 14.2%
Return on equity: 14.4%
Cash ($ mil.): 0.6
Current ratio: 1.81
Long-term debt ($ mil.): 4.8
No. of shares (mil.): 8.1
Dividends
 Yield: —
 Payout: —
Market value ($ mil.): 83.2

	STOCK PRICE ($) FY Close	P/E High/Low		PER SHARE ($) Earnings	Dividends	Book Value
12/10	10.24	19	8	0.60	0.00	4.19
12/09	5.12	26	13	0.20	0.00	3.55
12/08	4.60	15	8	0.40	0.00	3.31
12/07	4.92	20	13	0.32	0.00	2.72
12/06	5.08	10	4	0.60	0.00	2.33
Annual Growth	**19.2%**	**—**	**—**	**(0.0%)**	**—**	**15.8%**

Exterran Partners

Exterran Partners is the largest operator of contract compression equipment in the US. Its services include designing, installing, operating, repairing, and maintaining compression equipment. The company operates a fleet of more than 3,400 compressor units, comprising more than 1.3 million horsepower. Global compression unit provider Exterran Holdings holds a majority stake in Exterran Partners. Exterran Partners and Exterran Holdings manage their respective US compression fleets as one pool of compression equipment in order to more easily fulfill their respective customers' needs.

Exterran Partners grows through accretive acquisitions of assets and business lines from its parent company, third-party compression providers, and natural gas producers or transporters.

In 2009 the company reported a growth in revenues as the properties of earlier acquisitions came into service. However, increased costs brought down income that year.

Further growing its portfolio, in 2010 the company acquired contracts serving 43 customers and 580 related compressor units from Exterran Holdings for $214 million. In 2011 Exterran Partners acquired compression and processing assets (contracts serving 34 customers, and 407 compressor units) from its parent for $228 million.

Universal Compression Holdings held a 50% stake in the company (spun off in 2006) until Universal Compression merged with Hanover Compressors to form Exterran Holdings in 2007.

EXECUTIVES

Chairman and CEO, Ernie L. Danner, age 57
VP, CFO and Director, Michael J. Aaronson, age 36
VP Investor Relations, David Oatman
VP Finance and Accounting, Kenneth R. Bickett, age 49

SVP and Director, J. Michael Anderson, age 48
SVP, General Counsel, and Secretary, Donald C. Wayne, age 44
Director; VP and CFO Eastern Hemisphere, David S. Miller, age 47
SVP and Director, Daniel K. Schlanger, age 37
SVP and Director, D. Bradley (Brad) Childers, age 46
Auditors: Deloitte & Touche LLP

LOCATIONS

HQ: Exterran Partners, L.P.
16666 Northcase Dr., Houston, TX 77060
Phone: 281-836-7000
Web: www.exterran.com

COMPETITORS

Cameron International	Enerflex
Compressor Systems	J-W Operating
Dresser-Rand	

HISTORICAL FINANCIALS

Company Type: Public

Income Statement

FYE: December 31

	REVENUE ($ mil.)	NET INCOME ($ mil.)	NET PROFIT MARGIN	EMPLOYEES
12/10	237.6	(23.3)	—	0
12/09	181.7	14.8	8.1%	0
12/08	163.7	29.8	18.2%	0
12/07	107.7	19.4	18.0%	0
12/05	36.8	8.3	22.6%	0
Annual Growth	**45.2%**	**—**	**—**	**—**

2010 Year-End Financials

Debt ratio: —
Return on equity: —
Cash ($ mil.): 0.1
Current ratio: 2.08
Long-term debt ($ mil.): 449.0
No. of shares (mil.): 32.1
Dividends
 Yield: 6.9%
 Payout: —
Market value ($ mil.): 862.4

	STOCK PRICE ($) FY Close	P/E High/Low		PER SHARE ($) Earnings	Dividends	Book Value
12/10	26.86	—	—	(0.90)	1.86	(0.00)
12/09	22.22	34	16	0.68	1.85	(0.00)
12/08	11.23	21	5	1.68	1.74	(0.00)
12/07	32.00	31	20	1.29	1.38	8.70
Annual Growth	**(5.7%)**	**—**	**—**	**—**	**10.5%**	**—**

EZCORP

No mere pawn in the game, EZCORP is one of the largest operators of pawnshops in the US. The company operates some 400 EZPAWN and Value Pawn locations in the US and more than 110 stores in Mexico under the banners Empe o Fácil and Empe e Su Oro. The stores offer standard pawnshop fare such as second-hand jewelry, tools, electronics, sports equipment, and musical instruments. The company's inventory is built from items forfeited by customers who used them as collateral for small, short-term, high-interest loans. EZCORP also offers customers unsecured loans, commonly referred to as payday loans or payroll advances, through some of its pawnshops and from its nearly 500 EZMONEY stores in the US and Canada.

Most of its EZMONEY stores are located in Texas, the company's largest market by far. These locations ceased marketing payday loans and instead began providing fee-based advice and third-party loans in 2005. The company doesn't actually make or fund these loans, but typically earns a fee of 20% on each loan amount. If a borrower defaults on his or her loan, EZCORP pays the lender the principal and accrued interest, plus an insufficient funds fee. The company then attempts to collect these monies from the borrower.

EZCORP's pawnshops feature a retail ambience intended to dispel the industry's seedy image. The stores' services come at a price: monthly interest rates of up to 20% on loans that typically range from $80 to $120. Some three in four borrowers redeem their property or renew or extend the terms of their loans. Nonetheless, more than half of the company's revenues come from reselling forfeited merchandise. EZCORP also offers larger, longer-term consumer installment loans and loans secured by automobile titles.

The company owns about a third each of international pawnshop operators Albemarle & Bond (UK) and Cash Convertors (Australia). EZCORP has targeted Mexico for growth: It has added more than 100 locations since opening its first store there in 2006 and is opening 50 to 60 more. In 2009 the company established its first two payday loan stores in Canada under the CASHMAX brand; it added about 50 more in fiscal 2010 alone and hopes to nearly double that figure.

EZCORP also continues to build its pawnshop empire through acquisitions. In 2010 the company bought some 15 pawnshops in Florida, Illinois, Nevada, and Texas from separate sellers, including its first five locations in Chicago. The following year, it acquired 30 Mister Money pawn stores in Iowa, Illinois, Wisconsin, and Texas; and seven Jumping Jack Cash stores in Salt Lake City, Utah.

Since regulation of payday lending is in flux and varies from state to state, EZCORP is often compelled to exit or reduce its presence in markets such as Colorado and Wisconsin when new laws that restrict the company's activities are enacted. In order to reduce its reliance on payday lending, the company has added services in recent years such as auto title lending, fee-based credit consulting, and jewelry scrapping. EZCORP again added to its product menu and expanded geographically with the 2011 acquisition of Cash Converters, which employs a buy/sell business model rather than a pawn model. The deal included seven stores in Pennsylvania and Virginia, as well as the right to use the Cash Converters name in several other states.

After a decade at the helm of the company, EZCORP CEO Joseph Rotunda retired in 2010. He was succeeded by president Paul Rothamel.

HISTORY

Courtland Logue opened the first EZ Pawn in Austin, Texas, in 1974. By 1989 there were 16 U-Pawn-It and EZ Pawn stores. (All of them took the latter name in 1991.) Bankrolled by private investors, Logue began expanding nationally.

After going public in 1991, EZCORP tightened loan valuation standards, beefed up internal audit procedures to decrease shrinkage, set up a centralized jewelry center to refurbish forfeited collateral, and expanded retail sales.

In 1995 inventory reductions contributed to plummeting earnings. EZCORP closed 15 stores and combined 17 units with others; it also instituted a more restrictive lending policy to boost the number of repaid loans. Amid the turmoil, Logue was ousted as chairman and succeeded by Sterling Brinkley.

The company's first JewelryLand Outlet, a low-priced jewelry store, opened in Georgia in 1996. Four new EZ Pawns opened in 1997, and 1998 saw EZCORP go international, buying about 30% of Albemarle & Bond Holdings, a pawnshop operator in the UK.

EZCORP made headlines in 1998 and 1999 with its bid to keep small-caliber handguns off the streets; it gave guns from its stores to local police departments (although it continues to sell such "sporting long guns" as rifles and shotguns). As the booming US economy made it easier for the company's traditional clients to get mainstream credit, the company eyed expansion of its retail business, launching website EZPAWN.com.

In 2000 the company decided to shut down more than 50 underperforming stores. By year's end almost 25 had been closed, and an additional 15 were closed in 2001.

EZCORP began expanding again in 2006. It opened its first Mexico location that year, and in 2007 acquired 15 Colorado pawnshops operating under the name Jumping Jack Cash.

The company gained about 70 locations with its 2008 acquisition of Value Financial Services. Also that year it acquired about a dozen Pawn Plus and ASAP Pawn pawnshops in Nevada. That deal expanded its presence in Las Vegas, which is considered a good pawn market.

EZCORP ran into legal problems in 2008. It was forced to close 11 EZMONEY stores in Florida after state regulators filed action against EZCORP alleging that its stores violated state law. (The company's Florida pawn shops were not affected.) Also that year EZCORP paid a $600,000 settlement with the Texas attorney general, who'd charged that the company failed to adequately protect customers' private information. EZCORP disputed the claims.

EXECUTIVES

Chairman, Sterling B. Brinkley Jr., age 59
President, CEO, and Director, Paul E. Rothamel, age 46
President, Signature Loans, Joe Borbely
President, Pawn Americas, Eric Fosse, age 47
VP EZMONEY, Michael Volpe, age 46
VP and CIO, Robert Jackson, age 55
VP Strategic Development, John R. Kissick, age 68
VP Property Management, James Rose, age 56
SVP, General Counsel, and Secretary, Thomas H. (Tom) Welch Jr.
SVP Strategic Development, Mark E. Kuchenrither, age 49
SVP Human Resources, Tony Sanders
Vp and Chief Accounting Officer, Daniel M. (Danny) Chism, age 42
SVP EZPAWN Operations, Fred L. Fox, age 52
SVP Human Resources, Anthony (Tony) Sanders
Auditors: BDO USA, LLP

LOCATIONS

HQ: EZCORP, Inc.
1901 Capital Pkwy., Austin, TX 78746
Phone: 512-314-3400   **Fax:** 512-314-3404
Web: www.ezcorp.com

2010 Locations

	No.
US	
Texas	476
Florida	85
Colorado	72
Wisconsin	35
Oklahoma	26
Idaho	20
Utah	17
Alabama	16
Nevada	16
Indiana	15
Kansas	13
Missouri	13
South Dakota	7
Tennessee	7
Nebraska	6
Illinois	5
Georgia	4
Louisiana	3
Mississippi	3
Arkansas	1
Mexico	115
Canada	51
Total	**1,006**

PRODUCTS/OPERATIONS

2010 Sales

	$ mil.	% of total
Merchandise sales	399.5	55
Pawn service charges	163.7	22
Signature loan fees	139.3	19
Auto title loan fees	17.7	2
Other	12.8	2
Total	**733.0**	**100**

Selected Subsidiaries

EZCORP International, Inc.
EZCORP Online, Inc.
EZMONEY Alabama, Inc.
EZMONEY Canada, Inc.
EZMONEY Colorado, Inc.
EZMONEY Holdings, Inc.
EZMONEY Idaho, Inc.
EZMONEY Kansas, Inc.
EZMONEY Management, Inc.
EZMONEY Missouri, Inc.
EZMONEY Nebraska, Inc.
EZMONEY Nova, Inc.
EZMONEY South Dakota, Inc.
EZMONEY Tario, Inc.
EZMONEY Toba, Inc.
EZMONEY Utah, Inc.
EZMONEY Wisconsin, Inc.
EZPAWN Alabama, Inc.
EZPAWN Arkansas, Inc.
EZPAWN Colorado, Inc.
EZPAWN Florida, Inc.
EZPAWN Holdings, Inc.
EZPAWN Illinois, Inc.
EZPAWN Indiana, Inc.
EZPAWN Louisiana, Inc.
EZPAWN Mexico Holdings, Inc.
EZPAWN Mexico Ltd., Inc.
EZPAWN Nevada, Inc.
EZPAWN Oklahoma, Inc.
EZPAWN Services Mexico, SRL de CV (Holdings)
EZPAWN Tennessee, Inc.
Payday Loan Management, Inc.
Texas EZPAWN Management, Inc.

COMPETITORS

ACE Cash Express	DGSE Companies
Advance America	First Cash Financial
Cash America	Services
Cash Plus	World Acceptance
Check Into Cash	Xponential
DFC Global	

HISTORICAL FINANCIALS

Company Type: Public

Income Statement

FYE: September 30

	REVENUE ($ mil.)	NET INCOME ($ mil.)	NET PROFIT MARGIN	EMPLOYEES
09/10	733.0	97.3	13.3%	4,900
09/09	597.5	68.5	11.5%	4,350
09/08	457.4	52.4	11.5%	3,300
09/07	372.2	37.9	10.2%	3,200
09/06	315.9	29.3	9.3%	3,100
Annual Growth	23.4%	35.0%	—	12.1%

2010 Year-End Financials

Debt ratio: 2.9%	No. of shares (mil.): 49.2
Return on equity: 18.7%	Dividends
Cash ($ mil.): 25.9	Yield: 0.0%
Current ratio: 4.35	Payout: —
Long-term debt ($ mil.): 15.0	Market value ($ mil.): 986.5

	STOCK PRICE ($) FY Close	P/E High/Low		PER SHARE ($) Earnings	Dividends	Book Value
09/10	20.04	12	5	1.96	0.00	10.55
09/09	13.66	13	7	1.42	0.00	8.54
09/08	18.80	16	8	1.21	0.00	6.59
09/07	13.47	20	11	0.88	0.00	5.23
09/06	12.89	22	6	0.69	0.00	4.29
Annual Growth	11.7%	—	—	29.8%	—	25.2%

FBL Financial

Insurance holding company FBL Financial Group is the parent of Farm Bureau Life and EquiTrust Life. Through these subsidiaries the firm sells life insurance, annuities, and investment products to farmers, ranchers, and agricultural businesses. Farm Bureau Life sells its insurance and annuities through an exclusive network of some 2,000 agents in the Midwest and West. The company markets its products through an affiliation with the American Farm Bureau Federation. The Iowa Farm Bureau Federation owns about two-thirds of the company. It has announced plans to sell its EquiTrust Life business.

EquiTrust Life sells annuity products through more than 14,500 independent agents across the US, but FBL Financial has decided to focus on its Farm Bureau Life business. Financial services firm Guggenheim Partners has agreed to pay some $440 million for EquiTrust Life. Before agreeing to sell the business, FBL first worked to reduce risk and diversify EquiTrust Life. First it halted new sales of variable annuities (it still sells fixed rate and index annuities) and then introduced new life insurance products in 2010.

The company also manages two Farm Bureau-affiliated property/casualty insurers, Farm Bureau Property & Casualty and Western Agricultural Insurance. The two affiliates underwrite auto, crop, and other property/casualty policies for individuals and groups in the midwestern and western US. FBL expands its penetration in both the life and property/casualty markets by encouraging existing policyholders to purchase other insurance products through the agents they already know.

FBL expanded its territory over the years through acquisitions, and has traditionally kept an eye out for other consolidation opportunities. However, unstable conditions in the US financial markets in 2008 and 2009 caused the company to focus on strengthening its capital operations, restoring its financial ratings, and reducing risk in its businesses. Like many insurance companies, in 2008 FBL suffered from losses on investments in mortgage and asset-backed securities.

James Noyce stepped down as CEO in April 2009 and Allstate veteran James Hohmann was named interim CEO. In early 2010 Hohmann was named to the CEO post on a permanent basis.

EXECUTIVES

Chairman, Craig A. Lang, age 59
CEO and Director, James E. (Jim) Hohmann, age 55
CFO, Chief Administrative Officer, and Treasurer, James P. (Jim) Brannen, age 48, $807,116 total compensation
EVP Farm Bureau Life, Richard J. (Rich) Kypta, age 58, $608,396 total compensation
EVP, Farm Bureau Life, JoAnn W. Rumelhart, age 57, $3,158,117 total compensation
EVP and Chief Investment Officer, Charles T. Happel, age 49
EVP Marketing and Distribution, Kevin R. Slawin
VP, EquiTrust, Tom May
VP Strategy and Business Development, David T. Sebastian, age 58
VP Finance, Donald J. Seibel, age 47
VP Investor Relations, Kathleen Till Stange
VP Information Technology, Douglas W. Gumm, age 56
VP Human Resources, Mark Mincks
VP, General Counsel and Secretary, David A. McNeill
Vice Chairman, Jerry L. Chicoine, age 68
Chief Actuary, Russell J. (Russ) Wiltgen
Media, Nancy Doll
Auditors: Ernst & Young LLP

LOCATIONS

HQ: FBL Financial Group, Inc.
5400 University Ave., West Des Moines, IA 50266-5997
Phone: 515-225-5400   **Fax:** 515-226-6053
Web: www.fblfinancial.com

PRODUCTS/OPERATIONS

2010 Sales

	$ mil.	% of total
Life & annuity		
Traditional annuity, independent distribution	459.4	41
Traditional & universal life	341.7	31
Traditional annuity, exclusive distribution	169.1	15
Variable life & annuity	67.7	6
Gains on investments	30.6	3
Gains on derivatives	21.0	2
Corporate & other	19.1	2
Total	**1,108.6**	**100**

Selected Subsidiaries

Insurance
  EquiTrust Life Insurance Company
  Farm Bureau Life Insurance Company
Noninsurance
  EquiTrust Assigned Benefit Company
  EquiTrust Financial Group
  EquiTrust Investment Management Services, Inc.
  EquiTrust Marketing Services, LLC
  FBL Financial Services, Inc.

COMPETITORS

AIG
Allstate
American Equity Investment Life Holding Company
American Farmers & Ranchers Mutual Insurance Co.
COUNTRY Financial
Farm Family Holdings
Great American Financial Resources
MetLife
Midland National Life
Nationwide
Nationwide Agribusiness
Pruden

HISTORICAL FINANCIALS

Company Type: Public

Income Statement
FYE: December 31

	ASSETS ($ mil.)	NET INCOME ($ mil.)	INCOME AS % OF ASSETS	EMPLOYEES
12/10	15,334.1	120.7	0.8%	1,679
12/09	14,259.3	69.8	0.5%	1,714
12/08	14,060.8	(18.1)	—	1,866
12/07	14,003.0	86.3	0.6%	1,818
12/06	12,154.0	90.1	0.7%	1,858
Annual Growth	6.0%	7.6%	—	(2.5%)

2010 Year-End Financials

Equity as % of assets: 7.48%	Dividends
Return on assets: 0.8%	Yield: 0.9%
Return on equity: 10.6%	Payout: 6.4%
Long-term debt ($ mil.): 271.2	Market value ($ mil.): 887.1
No. of shares (mil.): 30.9	Sales ($ mil.): 1,108.6

	STOCK PRICE ($) FY Close	P/E High/Low		PER SHARE ($) Earnings	Dividends	Book Value
12/10	28.67	8	4	3.92	0.25	37.05
12/09	18.52	10	1	2.31	0.31	28.59
12/08	15.45	—	—	(0.61)	0.50	8.56
12/07	34.53	15	11	2.84	0.48	29.94
12/06	39.08	14	10	3.01	0.46	30.98
Annual Growth	(7.5%)	—	—	6.8%	(14.1%)	4.6%

FiberTower

FiberTower rises to great heights to provide wireless backhaul and access services. Its offerings include spectrum leasing, backhauling of mobile phone traffic, and the provision of broadband connectivity and extensions to fiber-optic networks. Customers include mobile, fiber, and other high-speed telecommunications carriers, large-volume enterprise users, and government agencies. The company owns wireless spectrum licenses in high-frequency 24 GHz and 39 GHz bands that cover virtually all of the US. FiberTower provides backhaul services in more than a dozen markets across the country.

FiberTower's largest customer, AT&T Mobility, accounted for more than half of its sales in 2007.

The company deploys its infrastructure at sites (towers, rooftops, etc.) that often host several carriers. Part of FiberTower's growth strategy includes serving multiple customers at each site.

The company took its current form in 2006 when First Avenue Networks combined its operations with San Francisco-based FiberTower in an all-stock deal valued at $1.5 billion.

EXECUTIVES

Chairman, John D. Beletic, age 59, $925,923 total compensation
President, CEO, and Director, Kurt J. Van Wagenen, age 47, $907,692 total compensation
VP and Treasurer, Ornella Napolitano
SVP and COO, Ravi Potharlanka, age 43, $1,056,546 total compensation
SVP Technology, Michael Finlayson, age 44, $701,343 total compensation
SVP, CFO, Treasurer, and Secretary, Thomas A. Scott, age 35, $1,324,565 total compensation

SVP Regulatory and Government Affairs, Joseph M.
Sandri Jr., age 47, $587,847 total compensation
SVP Network Services, David L. (Dave) Jones, age 47
SVP Sales and Marketing, Patrick J. Coughlin, age 46
Investor Relations, Gus Okwu
Auditors: Ernst & Young LLP

LOCATIONS

HQ: FiberTower Corporation
185 Berry St., Ste. 4800, San Francisco, CA 94107
Phone: 415-659-3500   **Fax:** 415-659-0007
Web: www.fibertower.com

PRODUCTS/OPERATIONS

COMPETITORS

AT&T	PPL Corporation
Cox Communications	Time Warner Cable
IDT	Verizon
Level 3 Communications	XO Holdings

HISTORICAL FINANCIALS

Company Type: Public

Income Statement

FYE: December 31

	REVENUE ($ mil.)	NET INCOME ($ mil.)	NET PROFIT MARGIN	EMPLOYEES
12/10	76.1	(49.4)	—	160
12/09	63.2	(2.1)	—	144
12/08	49.2	(249.8)	—	152
12/07	27.1	(272.1)	—	221
12/06	13.8	(57.3)	—	219
Annual Growth	53.2%	—	—	(7.5%)

2010 Year-End Financials

Debt ratio: 58.6%
Return on equity: —
Cash ($ mil.): 21.3
Current ratio: 2.46
Long-term debt ($ mil.): 168.5

No. of shares (mil.): 50.0
Dividends
Yield: —
Payout: —
Market value ($ mil.): 222.9

	STOCK PRICE ($) FY Close	P/E High/Low		PER SHARE ($) Earnings	Dividends	Book Value
12/10	4.46	—	—	(1.05)	0.00	5.75
12/09	4.18	—	—	(0.13)	0.00	7.27
12/08	1.60	—	—	(17.30)	0.00	11.30
12/07	22.80	—	—	(19.00)	0.00	28.27
12/06	58.80	—	—	(11.10)	0.00	46.61
Annual Growth	(47.5%)	—	—	—	—	(40.7%)

Fifth Street Finance

Fifth Street Finance is hoping to put the companies it lends money to on easy street. A business development company, Fifth Street lends capital to and invests in small and midsized firms with annual revenues between $25 million and $250 million. The company typically invests $5 million to $60 million in the form of senior debt or equity per transaction. It favors established firms over start-ups and prefers to participate actively in its investments as advisors. Fifth Street's portfolio comprises more than 35 companies, many of which operate in the health care, manufacturing, IT services, and business services sectors. Formed in

2007, the company has more than $1 billion in assets under management.

As a business development company, Fifth Street's overarching strategy includes infusing debt capital in businesses that show growth potential and then exiting its investments after businesses repay their debt or go through recapitalization. As part of its own growth strategy, the company intends to continue doing what has helped it grow so far: Focusing its lending activity on small and midsized companies, which it believes to be underserved by many finance companies. Fifth Street will also continue to originate its own loans in order to maintain control over the structuring of its investments and generate revenue from origination and exit fees.

Fifth Street is externally managed and advised by Fifth Street Management LLC.

EXECUTIVES

Chairman and CEO, Leonard M. Tannenbaum, age 39
CFO, William H. (Bill) Craig, age 54
President, Chief Compliance Officer, Secretary, and Director, Bernard D. Berman, age 39
Partner and Co CIO, Fifth Street Management LLC, Ivelin M. Dimitrov
Chief Investment Officer, Marc A. Goodman, age 52
Managing Director and Head Capital Markets, John Trentos
Managing Director Origination, Fifth Street Management LLC, Sunny K. Khorana
Managing Director and Co-CIO, Fifth Street Management LLC, Chad S. Blakeman
Executive Director Marketing and Brand Management, Fifth Street Management LLC, James F. Velgot
Executive Director Investor Relations, Fifth Street Management LLC, Stacey L. Thorne
Executive Director and Controller, Steven M. Noreika
Auditors: PricewaterhouseCoopers LLP

LOCATIONS

HQ: Fifth Street Finance Corp.
10 Bank St., 12th Fl., White Plains, NY 10606
Phone: 914-286-6800   **Fax:** 914-328-4214
Web: www.fifthstreetfinance.com

PRODUCTS/OPERATIONS

Selected Portfolio Companies

ADAPCO
Advanced Pain Management Holdings, Inc.
Caregiver Services
Cenegenics
CRGT, Inc.
DISA Inc.
Dominion Diagnostics LLC
Eagle Hospital Physicians
Enhanced Recovery Corporation
Epic MedStaff Services, Inc.
Filet of Chicken
Fitness Edge
Flatout
HealthDrive
idX
IZI
JTC Education Holdings
Lighting by Gregory
MedKnowledge Group
Miche Bag LLC
NDS Surgical Imaging
Nicos Polymers & Ginding
O'Currance Teleservices
Pacific Production Technologies
Premier Trailer Leasing
Rail Acquisition Corp.
ReBath
Specialty Bakers LLC
Tegra

Traffic Control and Safety Corporation
Trans-Trade
Welocalize, Inc.
Western Emulsions
WhatCounts

COMPETITORS

American Capital	MCG Capital
Ares Capital	MVC Capital
Gladstone Capital	Solar Capital

HISTORICAL FINANCIALS

Company Type: Public

Income Statement

FYE: September 30

	REVENUE ($ mil.)	NET INCOME ($ mil.)	NET PROFIT MARGIN	EMPLOYEES
09/10	51.8	22.4	43.2%	19
09/09	24.7	6.2	25.1%	16
09/08	33.3	3.3	9.9%	21
Annual Growth	24.7%	160.5%	—	(4.9%)

2010 Year-End Financials

Debt ratio: —
Return on equity: 3.9%
Cash ($ mil.): 76.8
Current ratio: —
Long-term debt ($ mil.): —

No. of shares (mil.): 54.6
Dividends
Yield: 9.8%
Payout: 222.4%
Market value ($ mil.): 607.7

	STOCK PRICE ($) FY Close	P/E High/Low		PER SHARE ($) Earnings	Dividends	Book Value
09/10	11.14	28	19	0.49	1.09	10.43
09/09	10.93	45	20	0.25	1.15	10.84
09/08	10.05	63	36	0.21	0.61	13.02
Annual Growth	5.3%	—	—	52.8%	33.7%	(10.5%)

Financial Engines

Like the little engine that could, Financial Engines does. What it does is provide financial advice, portfolio management, and retirement assessment services. The company serves US retirement-plan participants, sponsors, and service providers across a wide range of industries that includes more than 100 *FORTUNE* 500 companies and several of the largest retirement plan operators. It delivers its services online, as well as by telephone. Financial Engines has more than $375 billion in assets under management and serves some 5 million individual retirement-plan participants. The company went public in 2010 with an offering worth $127.2 million.

Financial Enginers generates revenue from professional management fees and subscription-based platform fees — that is, fees paid for access to its online information and services. It markets itself to new employers through existing relationships with plan administrators. Financial Engines also markets its management services to passive plan participants to beef up fee revenues. The company used funds from its offering to help pay operating costs, which increased as it ramped up marketing, hired personnel, and set up new clients. As such, revenues have more than doubled in the past five year.

Founder Bill Sharpe is a notable innovator in the analysis and valuation of investments and has written books on topics including portfolio theory and investment fundamentals. He received the Nobel Prize in Economics in 1990.

EXECUTIVES

Chairman, Paul G. Koontz, age 50
President, CEO, and Director, Jeffrey N. (Jeff) Maggioncalda, age 41, $963,610 total compensation
EVP Investment Management and Chief Investment Officer, Christopher L. (Chris) Jones, age 43, $675,619 total compensation
EVP Sales and Client Services, Lawrence M. (Larry) Raffone, age 47, $987,981 total compensation
EVP and CFO, Raymond J. (Ray) Sims, age 60, $503,230 total compensation
EVP Technology and Service Delivery, Garry W. Hallee, age 49, $567,044 total compensation
EVP Marketing, Kenneth M. (Ken) Fine, age 42
EVP Service Delivery, Manjari Lewis
EVP General Counsel and Secretary, Anne S. Tuttle, age 49
VP Retirement Plan Providers and Plan Sponsors, Paul Gamble
VP Portfolio Management, Omar Aguilar
VP Human Resources, Deborah J. (Debbi) Behrman, age 53
VP Risk and Technical Operations and Chief Security Officer, Matthew Todd
Regional Director, West, Chris Cooney
Regional Director, Midwest, Damon Dunkel
Regional Director, Southeast, Southwest, and Mid-Atlantic, Mark Stasch
Media Relations, Asma Emneina
Managing Director, Retiree Research Center, Jason Scott
Director of Investor Services, David Ankrom
Consultants and ERISA Relations, Joe Parlavecchio
Sales Specialist, Northeast, Maria Indeglia
Auditors: KPMG LLP

LOCATIONS

HQ: Financial Engines, Inc.
1804 Embarcadero Rd., Palo Alto, CA 94303
Phone: 650-565-4900   **Fax:** 650-565-4905
Web: www.financialengines.com

PRODUCTS/OPERATIONS

2010 Sales

	$ mil.	% of total
Professional management	79.2	71
Platform fees	29.7	26
Other	2.9	3
Total	**111.8**	**100**

COMPETITORS

Ameriprise	FMR
BlackRock	Merrill Lynch
Charles Schwab	Morningstar
Fidelity Financial	The Vanguard Group

HISTORICAL FINANCIALS

Company Type: Public

Income Statement

FYE: December 31

	REVENUE ($ mil.)	NET INCOME ($ mil.)	NET PROFIT MARGIN	EMPLOYEES
12/10	111.8	63.6	56.9%	303
12/09	85.0	5.7	6.7%	264
12/08	71.3	(3.6)	—	256
12/07	63.3	(1.8)	—	0
12/06	48.2	(8.0)	—	0
Annual Growth	**23.4%**	**—**	**—**	**8.8%**

2010 Year-End Financials

Debt ratio: —	No. of shares (mil.): 43.1
Return on equity: 34.3%	Dividends
Cash ($ mil.): 114.9	Yield: —
Current ratio: 5.09	Payout: —
Long-term debt ($ mil.): —	Market value ($ mil.): 855.0

	STOCK PRICE ($) FY Close	P/E High/Low		PER SHARE ($) Earnings	Dividends	Book Value
12/10	19.83	16	9	1.30	0.00	4.30
Annual Growth	—	—	—	—	—	—

Finisar

Finisar helps put the "work" in network with equipment that enables high-speed data communications over LANs or metro-area and storage-area networks (MANs/SANs). Finisar's optical components and subsystems include data links (transmitters, receivers, and transceivers) and link extenders. While the company's customers have included US information technology leaders such as Cisco Systems, EMC, and IBM, Finisar makes the bulk of its sales to customers outside the US. In 2008 the company merged with rival Optium in a stock-swap deal valued at approximately $243 million.

Combining Optium's expertise in telecommunications and CATV with Finisar's experience in storage and data networking, the merger created one of the largest suppliers of optical components in the world.

In mid-2009 Finisar sold its Network Tools business to archrival JDS Uniphase for about $40 million in cash, becoming a pure supplier of optical components in the process. A year earlier Finisar spun off some assets of its Network Tools and NetWisdom business to an investor group led by Mark Urdahl, Jim Davidson, and Steve Mankoff. The NetWisdom product line is used to monitor and analyze storage-area networks in enterprise data centers.

The company has a limited number of customers for its optical components and subsystems, with the top five representing about 50% of sales. It does not have long-term contracts with its customers and must remain competitive with its product line to keep most of them. Finisar must also struggle to keep up with the challenge of ever-evolving technological demands from its customers, requiring new products. Additionally, pressures from several factors, including greater competition and oversupply, can drag down the prices of optical subsystems.

Amid these tough market conditions, revenue for Finisar grew more than 50% in fiscal 2011 — a record year, in fact — compared with 2010 thanks mainly to telecom companies and other businesses taking on more infrastructure projects to create more bandwidth. The company counted a gain in market share for higher-speed products as another factor in the year's strong sales. Gross profit also increased over the same period, growing more than 73%.

Finisar has grown in part through an aggressive acquisition strategy. In the century's first decade the company acquired more than 10 firms and bought assets and businesses from six other companies. More recently the company acquired Norwegian optical components maker Ignis to expand

in Europe in 2011. Before that it bought fiber-optic transceiver product maker Broadway Networks in 2010. Finisar made that purchase to add complementary products to its line of digital diagnostics components, and to build its customer roster.

The company won a patent infringement case against The DIRECTV Group, with the jury awarding Finisar nearly $79 million in damages. The judge in the case awarded another $38 million in damages and interest to Finisar, and ordered DIRECTV to pay a licensing fee of $1.60 per set-top box to Finisar for the life of the patent in question, which expires in 2012. DIRECTV appealed the verdict and damages. In 2008 the US Court of Appeals for the Federal Circuit vacated the jury's verdict of infringement and sent the case back to the trial court to consider the validity of six patent claims. In 2009 the trial court entered final judgment for DIRECTV in response to motions filed by both parties. Finisar filed a notice of appeal.

EXECUTIVES

Chairman, Jerry S. Rawls, age 66, $1,616,400 total compensation
CEO and Director, Eitan Gertel, age 49, $1,174,789 total compensation
VP Employee Services, Katherine Watt
VP and Controller, John E. Drury, age 49
VP, General Counsel, and Secretary, Christopher E. Brown, age 42
SVP Operations and Engineering, Mark Colyar, age 48, $762,359 total compensation
SVP Finance and CFO, Kurt Adzema, age 41, $596,512 total compensation
Director Product Line Management, John DeMott
Director New Product Development, Jim Tatum
Senior Manager Corporate Communications, Victoria McDonald
SVP Operations and Engineering, Joseph A. Young, age 55, $914,363 total compensation
SVP Corporate Development and Investor Relations, Stephen K. Workman, age 61, $719,749 total compensation
SVP Sales and Marketing, Todd Swanson, age 38, $809,578 total compensation
Auditors: Ernst & Young LLP

LOCATIONS

HQ: Finisar Corporation
1389 Moffett Park Dr., Sunnyvale, CA 94089-1134
Phone: 408-548-1000   **Fax:** 408-541-6138
Web: www.finisar.com

2011 Sales

	$ mil.	% of total
US	279.5	29
China	218.6	23
Malaysia	150.1	16
Other countries	300.6	32
Total	**948.8**	**100**

PRODUCTS/OPERATIONS

2011 Sales

	$ mil.	% of total
Transceivers, transponders, & components	782.7	82
ROADM linecards & WSS modules	150.9	16
CATV	15.2	2
Total	**948.8**	**100**

COMPETITORS

ADVA	JDS Uniphase
Agilent Technologies	LeCroy
Alliance Fiber Optic	Mitsubishi Electric

Products	MRV Communications
Avago Technologies	NeoPhotonics
Brocade Communications	Oclaro
Cisco Systems	Oki Semiconductor
EMC	Oplink Communications
EMCORE	Opnext
Intel	

HISTORICAL FINANCIALS
Company Type: Public

Income Statement
FYE: April 30

	REVENUE ($ mil.)	NET INCOME ($ mil.)	NET PROFIT MARGIN	EMPLOYEES
04/11	948.8	88.1	9.3%	8,065
04/10	629.9	14.1	2.2%	6,893
04/09	541.2	(254.8)	—	5,004
04/08	440.2	(76.4)	—	4,476
04/07	418.5	(46.6)	—	3,908
Annual Growth	22.7%	—		19.9%

2011 Year-End Financials

Debt ratio: 5.7%	No. of shares (mil.): 89.9
Return on equity: 12.6%	Dividends
Cash ($ mil.): 314.8	Yield: —
Current ratio: 5.18	Payout: —
Long-term debt ($ mil.): 40.0	Market value ($ mil.): 2,525.4

	STOCK PRICE ($) FY Close	P/E High/Low		PER SHARE ($) Earnings	Dividends	Book Value
04/11	28.09	46	12	1.00	0.00	7.78
04/10	14.96	78	16	0.22	0.00	4.60
04/09	5.28	—	—	(4.88)	0.00	1.93
04/08	10.80	—	—	(2.00)	0.00	3.16
04/07	29.52	—	—	(1.20)	0.00	4.83
Annual Growth	(1.2%)	—	—	—	—	12.7%

First Bancorp of Indiana

First Bancorp of Indiana wants to be second to none. It's the holding company for First Federal Savings Bank, which serves individuals and local businesses through nine branches in the Evansville, Indiana, area. The bank offers standard retail products and services like checking, savings, and money market accounts; certificates of deposit; and retirement savings plans. Its lending activities primarily consist of mortgage and consumer loans (approximately 50% and 40% of the company's loan portfolio, respectively). The bank also offers savings account loans and business loans.

EXECUTIVES

Chairman, First Bancorp of Indiana and First Federal Savings Bank, Harold Duncan, age 70
President, CEO, and Director; President and CEO, First Federal Savings Bank, Michael H. Head, age 53
CFO and Treasurer; EVP and CFO, First Federal Savings Bank, George J. (Jeffrey) Smith, age 55
VP; EVP and COO, First Federal Savings Bank, Kirby W. King, age 57
Auditors: BKD, LLP

LOCATIONS
HQ: First Bancorp of Indiana, Inc.
5001 Davis Lant Dr., Evansville, IN 47715
Phone: 812-492-8100
Web: www.firstfedevansville.com

COMPETITORS

Fidelity Federal	MainSource Financial
Fifth Third	Old National Bancorp
German American Bancorp	

HISTORICAL FINANCIALS
Company Type: Public

Income Statement
FYE: June 30

	ASSETS ($ mil.)	NET INCOME ($ mil.)	INCOME AS % OF ASSETS	EMPLOYEES
06/07	363.0	0.5	0.1%	83
06/06	294.6	1.3	0.4%	88
06/05	277.4	1.5	0.5%	83
06/04	264.1	0.3	0.1%	80
06/03	188.5	1.6	0.8%	80
Annual Growth	17.8%	(25.2%)	—	0.9%

2007 Year-End Financials

Equity as % of assets: 9.43%	Dividends
Return on assets: 0.1%	Yield: 4.0%
Return on equity: 1.5%	Payout: 200.0%
Long-term debt ($ mil.): 72.5	Market value ($ mil.): 27.6
No. of shares (mil.): 1.8	Sales ($ mil.): 21.3

	STOCK PRICE ($) FY Close	P/E High/Low		PER SHARE ($) Earnings	Dividends	Book Value
06/07	15.07	69	50	0.30	0.60	18.67
06/06	18.72	26	21	0.87	0.60	18.13
06/05	19.77	22	19	0.98	0.59	18.65
06/04	20.15	117	95	0.20	0.56	17.82
06/03	18.39	18	13	1.04	0.40	18.70
Annual Growth	(4.9%)	—	—	(26.7%)	10.7%	(0.0%)

First Financial Bancorp

First Financial spreads itself thick. The holding company's flagship subsidiary, First Financial Bank, operates through around 140 branches in Indiana, Kentucky, and Ohio. Founded in 1863, the bank offers checking and savings accounts, money market accounts, CDs, credit cards, private banking, wealth management, and trust services. Commercial loans, including real estate and construction loans, make up about 70% of First Financial's total loan portfolio; the bank also offers residential mortgage and consumer loans. Another subsidiary, First Financial Capital Advisors, acts as the investment advisor to the company's proprietary mutual funds, The First Funds Group.

In 2009 First Financial acquired the branches and deposits of the failed Peoples Community Bancorp in an FDIC-assisted transaction, adding about 20 locations in the Cincinnati area. It also purchased three Indiana branches from Irwin Financial, along with a package of loans and deposits. That deal gave First Financial a larger foothold in Indiana. Irwin Financial's Irwin Union Bank and Irwin Union Bank and Trust subsidiaries later failed and were seized by regulators, and First Financial Bancorp assumed all of the institutions' de-

posits and gained more than two dozen branches, also in a FDIC-brokered deal. The transaction included restaurant franchisee lender Irwin Franchise Capital (now First Franchise Capital). The acquisitions boosted the bottom line of First Financial, which remained profitable throughout the recession.

Meanwhile, the company announced in 2010 that would exit the Michigan and Louisville, Kentucky markets (areas it entered via the Irwin deal) in order to focus on its core markets of Indiana and southwestern Ohio. To that end, it acquired 16 branches in western Ohio from Liberty Savings Bank and agreed to buy 22 Indianapolis-area branches from Flagstar Bank in 2011.

EXECUTIVES

Chairman, Murph Knapke, age 63
President, CEO, and Director; Chairman, President, and CEO, First Financial Bank, Claude E. Davis, age 50
Chairman, President, and CEO, First Financial Insurance, Mark A. Willis
EVP and CFO, J. Franklin (Frank) Hall, age 42
EVP and COO, C. Douglas (Doug) Lefferson, age 46
EVP Banking Markets, Samuel J. (Sam) Munafo, age 60
VP and Controller, Elizabeth E. Fontaine, age 46
VP and Retail Market Manager, Dayton and Middletown, Jason Newport
VP and Commercial Bank Manager, First Financial Bank, Dan Kane
VP, Commercial Lending, Clark and Greene Counties, First Financial Bank, Herb Greer
VP Investor Relations and Corporate Development, Kenneth Lovik
SVP Sales and Marketing, Jill L. Wyman, age 49
SVP and Chief Credit Officer, Richard S. Barbercheck, age 52
SVP and General Counsel, Gregory A. Gehlmann, age 49
SVP, Retail Credit and Product Management, John C. Hoying
SVP, Chief Accounting Officer, and Controller, Anthony M. Stollings, age 56
SVP and Managing Director, Wealth Resource Group, First Financial Bank, David C. Brooks
SVP and President, Indiana, First Financial Bank, Al Roszczyk
Assistant VP, Investor Relations; Secretary, First Financial Bancorp and First Financial Bank, Terri J. Ziepfel
Market President, Lafayette, First Financial Bank, Bradley W. (Brad) Marley
Market President, Hastings, First Financial Bank, Cortney Collison
Market President, Celina and Van Wert, First Financial Bank, George Brooks
Market President, Southeastern Indiana, First Financial Bank, Michael A. Sorrells
Market President, Northern Kentucky, First Financial Bank, Thomas R. Saelinger
Market President, Northwestern Indiana, First Financial Bank, David S. Harvey
Market President, North Manchester, First Financial Bank, Michael R. Terrone
Market President, Hartford City, First Financial Bank, James M. (Jim) Weiseman
Market President, Cincinnati, First Financial Bank, John Marrocco
Market President, Butler and Warren, First Financial Bank, Adrian O. Breen
SVP and Chief Risk Officer, John Sabath
SVP and Chief Investment Officer, First Financial Capital Advisors, Alfred Shepard
Auditors: Ernst & Young LLP

LOCATIONS

HQ: First Financial Bancorp
  4000 Smith Rd., Ste. 400, Cincinnati, OH 45209
Phone: 877-322-9530
Web: bankatfirst.com

PRODUCTS/OPERATIONS

2010 Sales

% of total	$ mil.
Interest	
Loans, including fees	306.1
62	
Taxable investment securities	21.7
4	
Other	15.7
3	
Noninterest	
FDIC loss-sharing income	51.8
11	
Accelerated discount on covered loans	29.1
6	
Service charges on deposit accounts	22.2
5	
Trust & wealth management fees	13.9
3	
Bankcard income	8.5
2	
Other	21.3
4	
Total	**674.5**
100	

COMPETITORS

AMB Financial	Logansport Financial
Commercial Bancshares	MutualFirst Financial
Farmers National	Peoples Community
Fifth Third	Bancorp
First Defiance	Peoples-Sidney
Financial	PNC Financial
First Franklin	Rurban Financial
LCNB	U.S. Bancorp
Liberty Capital	

HISTORICAL FINANCIALS

Company Type: Public

Income Statement

FYE: December 31

	ASSETS ($ mil.)	NET INCOME ($ mil.)	INCOME AS % OF ASSETS	EMPLOYEES
12/10	6,250.2	59.3	0.9%	1,664
12/09	6,681.1	246.5	3.7%	1,748
12/08	3,699.1	23.0	0.6%	1,127
12/07	3,369.3	35.7	1.1%	1,159
12/06	3,301.6	21.3	0.6%	1,283
Annual Growth	17.3%	29.2%	—	6.7%

2010 Year-End Financials

Equity as % of assets: 11.16%
Return on assets: 0.9%
Return on equity: 8.5%
Long-term debt ($ mil.): 149.5
No. of shares (mil.): 58.1

Dividends
  Yield: 2.2%
  Payout: 40.4%
Market value ($ mil.): 1,073.0
Sales ($ mil.): 490.3

	STOCK PRICE ($) FY Close	P/E High/Low		PER SHARE ($) Earnings	Dividends	Book Value
12/10	18.48	22	14	0.99	0.40	12.01
12/09	14.56	3	1	5.33	0.40	13.13
12/08	12.39	30	13	0.61	0.68	9.29
12/07	11.40	18	11	0.93	0.65	7.40
12/06	16.61	34	26	0.54	0.64	7.24
Annual Growth	2.7%	—	—	16.4%	(11.1%)	13.5%

First Hartford

First Hartford puts real estate first. The company, operating through subsidiary First Hartford Realty, invests in and develops commercial and other real estate. Its portfolio is located primarily in the Northeast and includes shopping centers, a restaurant, and a business and technology school campus. First Hartford has also built single-family homes, public housing units, government facilities, and several industrial properties. It is a preferred developer for CVS Caremark in areas of Texas, New Jersey, New York, and Lousiana. The company's largest tenants include Stop & Shop, Big Y Foods, and Kmart. Subsidiary Lead Tech provides lead and asbestos inspection and remediation services.

EXECUTIVES

President and Director, Neil H. Ellis, age 83, $251,053 total compensation
VP, John Toic, age 39
VP, David B. Harding, age 64, $176,053 total compensation
Auditors: Carlin, Charron & Rosen LLP

LOCATIONS

HQ: First Hartford Corporation
  149 Colonial Rd., Manchester, CT 06040
Phone: 860-646-6555   **Fax:** 860-646-8572
Web: firsthartford.com

PRODUCTS/OPERATIONS

2008 Sales

	$ mil.	% of total
Rent	9.3	78
Service income	1.5	13
Real estate sales	0.7	6
Other	0.4	3
Total	**11.9**	**100**

COMPETITORS

Benderson Development	Gilbane Development
Centro Properties	Horizon Group
CPI	Properties
DDR	Kushner Companies
Garden Commercial	Picerne
Properties	Simon Property Group
General Growth	Urstadt Biddle
Properties	

HISTORICAL FINANCIALS

Company Type: Public

Income Statement

FYE: April 30

	REVENUE ($ mil.)	NET INCOME ($ mil.)	NET PROFIT MARGIN	EMPLOYEES
04/10	23.4	(2.1)	—	119
04/09	15.4	(4.1)	—	75
04/08	11.9	(1.3)	—	59
04/07	12.2	—	—	65
04/06	33.9	0.7	2.1%	32
Annual Growth	(8.9%)	—	—	38.9%

2010 Year-End Financials

Debt ratio: —
Return on equity: —
Cash ($ mil.): 5.2
Current ratio: 1.43
Long-term debt ($ mil.): 141.5

No. of shares (mil.): 3.0
Dividends
  Yield: —
  Payout: —
Market value ($ mil.): 5.8

	STOCK PRICE ($) FY Close	P/E High/Low		PER SHARE ($) Earnings	Dividends	Book Value
04/10	1.90	—	—	(0.70)	0.00	(3.89)
04/09	1.50	—	—	(1.36)	0.00	(3.32)
04/08	2.25	—	—	(0.44)	0.00	(0.88)
04/07	2.15	—	—	(0.00)	0.00	(0.38)
04/06	1.70	19	8	0.21	0.00	(0.29)
Annual Growth	2.8%	—	—	—	—	—

First Investors Financial Services

They're not the first investors in the subprime auto loan market, but they're coming on. First Investors Financial Services originates subprime auto loans (made to people with blemished or nonexistent credit) indirectly through auto dealers or directly to consumers. The dealer indirect program consists of loans originated through hundreds of franchised auto dealers in nearly 30 states. First Investors Financial Services drums up business for its direct lending through direct mail campaigns in about 15 states. The company also purchases portfolios of auto loans from other lenders. It has some 40,000 customers and $600 million in receivables. Texas is its largest market.

Citing the prohibitive cost and the fact that the company has fewer than 300 beneficial shareholders (the minimum required), First Investors Financial Services deregistered its stock and ceased reporting to the SEC in 2008.

HISTORY

Banker Tommy Moore and oilman Walter Stockard founded First Investors Financial in 1989 to capitalize on the growing market for subprime auto loans. At first they bought loans and repackaged them for sale to banks and other lenders. More investors came on in 1992 and capitalized the company's move into buying loans for its own account. This initiative took First Investors beyond Texas, and it has expanded quickly into a nationwide presence.

The recession in which the company was born spurred the growth of the used car market by making people more careful about their spending. But even though more people were shopping for used cars, the rise in personal bankruptcies hurt the subprime loan market, forcing lenders to charge off more loans. In 1998 First Investors took a pretax charge, since softer used car prices were yielding lower returns on its repossessed autos.

The company acquired Fortis subsidiary Auto Lenders Acceptance later that year. The deal doubled First Investors' assets and added in-house collections and servicing capabilities, allowing First Investors to terminate its prior servicing agreement with GE Capital.

EXECUTIVES

Chairman, President, and CEO, Tommy A. Moore Jr., age 54
EVP, CFO, Secretary, and Treasurer, Bennie H. Duck, age 47
VP Portfolio Risk Management and Director, Roberto Marchesini, age 67

SVP and COO, Blaise G. Rodon, age 50
Director Human Resources, Mary Dela Cruz
Auditors: Grant Thornton LLP

LOCATIONS

HQ: First Investors Financial Services Group, Inc.
675 Bering Dr., Ste. 710, Houston, TX 77057
Phone: 713-977-2600   **Fax:** 800-528-2384
Web: www.fifsg.com

COMPETITORS

Capital One Auto	Credit Acceptance
Finance	GM Financial
Consumer Portfolio	United PanAm Financial

HISTORICAL FINANCIALS

Company Type: Public

Income Statement

FYE: April 30

	REVENUE ($ mil.)	NET INCOME ($ mil.)	NET PROFIT MARGIN	EMPLOYEES
04/07	62.5	3.2	5.1%	198
04/06	46.7	2.4	5.1%	193
04/05	36.2	0.7	1.9%	148
04/04	38.6	—		163
04/03	35.6	0.3	0.8%	166
Annual Growth	15.1%	80.7%	—	4.5%

2007 Year-End Financials

Debt ratio: 614.9%   No. of shares (mil.): —
Return on equity: 10.1%   Dividends
Cash ($ mil.): 1.7   Yield: —
Current ratio: —   Payout: —
Long-term debt ($ mil.): 195.2   Market value ($ mil.): —

	STOCK PRICE ($) FY Close	P/E High/Low		PER SHARE ($) Earnings	Dividends	Book Value
04/07	7.11	12	10	0.67	0.00	(0.00)
04/06	7.45	16	8	0.53	0.00	(0.00)
04/05	4.75	40	27	0.14	0.00	(0.00)
04/04	5.35	625	347	0.01	0.00	(0.00)
04/03	4.10	61	29	0.07	0.00	(0.00)
Annual Growth	14.8%	—	—	75.9%	—	—

First Niagara Financial

A lot of water and a few barrels have gone over Niagara Falls since First Niagara Bank was founded. Tracing its roots to 1870, the flagship subsidiary of acquisitive First Niagara Financial operates about 300 branches in upstate New York, Connecticut, Massachusetts, and Pennsylvania. The bank offers financial services like deposits, loans, insurance, investments, and wealth management. Commercial real estate loans, business loans, and residential mortgages account for most of the bank's loan portfolio. Subsidiary First Niagara Commercial Bank accepts municipal deposits.

In 2011 First Niagara Financial completed its acquisition of NewAlliance Bancshares; the $1.5 billion deal added some 90 bank branches and extended the company's franchise into Connecticut and Massachusetts. Also that year First Niagara agreed to pay $1 billion for 195 HSBC branches in Upstate New York and Connecticut; it will divest more than 25 Buffalo-area locations acquired in the deal to satisfy antitrust concerns.

First Niagara Financial previously entered Pennsylvania in a big way: It acquired more than 50 branches from PNC Financial in 2009 and bought bank holding company Harleysville National the next year. The PNC acquisition, which expanded First Niagara's operations into western Pennsylvania, included locations that PNC was compelled to divest to satisfy antitrust concerns regarding its takeover of National City. Harleysville National Bank added some 80 branches in central and eastern Pennsylvania. First Niagara Bank is emphasizing consumer-oriented products and services such as home equity loans in its new markets to help foment customer relationships.

First Niagara expanded its insurance business in Pennsylvania in 2010 with the acquisition of Summit Insurance Group's operations in the state. The new business, which took the First Niagara Risk Management name, offers risk management, employee benefits consulting, and investment services. That deal was combined with previous acquisitions of RTI Insurance Services and Three Rivers Financial Services, which expanded First Niagara's footprint in western Pennsylvania. First Niagara bought another Pennsylvania-based employee benefits, risk management, and investment services firm, Banyan Consulting, later that year. That company was also merged with First Niagara Risk Management.

To facilitate its expansion, First Niagara Financial converted from a thrift holding company to a bank holding company and First Niagara Bank converted from a savings institution to a commercial bank in 2010, a move that gives the company more flexibility in making acquisitions.

Prior to entering Pennsylvania, First Niagara Financial had already more than doubled its size with an acquisition spree; it had fewer than 50 branches operating under its banner at the end of 2003. That year, the company acquired Finger Lakes Bancorp. It bought Troy Financial in 2004 and Hudson River Bancorp the following year. In 2008 the company bought Great Lakes Bancorp, the parent of Greater Buffalo Savings Bank.

EXECUTIVES

Chairman, G. Thomas Bowers, age 67
CFO, Gregory W. Norwood
President, CEO, and Director, John R. Koelmel, age 58, $2,526,618 total compensation
EVP and COO, Gary M. Crosby, age 57
EVP Operations, Frank J. Polino, age 51, $700,523 total compensation
EVP Commercial Real Estate, G. Gary Berner, age 63
EVP Commercial Business; Regional President, Western New York, Daniel E. Cantara III, age 51, $996,951 total compensation
Vice Chairman, David M. Zebro, age 60
SVP and CIO, John Petrey
Treasurer and Chief Investment Officer, Michael W. Harrington, age 47, $954,742 total compensation
SVP and Chief Administrative Officer, Elizabeth A. (Beth) Bauman, age 50
Regional President, Eastern New York, Thomas L. Amell
SVP Retail Banking, Mark R. Rendulic
Manager Investor Relations, Anthony M. Alessi
Investor Relations, Linda Mussen
Manager Public Relations and Corporate Communications, Leslie G. Garrity
Auditors: KPMG LLP

LOCATIONS

HQ: First Niagara Financial Group, Inc.
726 Exchange St., Ste. 618, Buffalo, NY 14210
Phone: 716-819-5500
Web: www.fnfg.com

PRODUCTS/OPERATIONS

2010 Sales

	$ Mil.	% of Total
Interest		
Loans & leases	496.0	53
Investment securities & other	249.6	27
Noninterest		
Banking services	80.8	9
Insurance & benefits consulting	51.6	6
Wealth management	19.8	2
MortgAge banking	12.2	1
Lending & leasing	11.5	1
Other	10.7	1
Total	**932.2**	**100**

COMPETITORS

Capital One	KeyCorp
Citigroup	M&T Bank
Citizens Financial	NBT Bancorp
Group	PNC Financial
Community Bank System	SEFCU
HSBC USA	TD Bank USA
JPMorgan Chase	

HISTORICAL FINANCIALS

Company Type: Public

Income Statement

FYE: December 31

	ASSETS ($ mil.)	NET INCOME ($ mil.)	INCOME AS % OF ASSETS	EMPLOYEES
12/10	21,083.9	140.4	0.7%	3,791
12/09	14,584.8	79.4	0.5%	3,000
12/08	9,331.4	88.4	0.9%	1,909
12/07	8,096.2	84.1	1.0%	1,824
12/06	7,945.5	91.9	1.2%	1,922
Annual Growth	27.6%	11.2%	—	18.5%

2010 Year-End Financials

Equity as % of assets: 13.11%   Dividends
Return on assets: 0.7%   Yield: 4.1%
Return on equity: 5.1%   Payout: 81.4%
Long-term debt ($ mil.): 3,104.9   Market value ($ mil.): 2,923.4
No. of shares (mil.): 209.1   Sales ($ mil.): 932.2

	STOCK PRICE ($) FY Close	P/E High/Low		PER SHARE ($) Earnings	Dividends	Book Value
12/10	13.98	21	16	0.70	0.57	13.22
12/09	13.91	35	21	0.46	0.56	12.61
12/08	16.17	28	12	0.81	0.56	14.57
12/07	12.04	19	14	0.81	0.54	12.83
12/06	14.86	18	16	0.85	0.46	12.53
Annual Growth	(1.5%)	—	—	(4.7%)	5.5%	1.4%

First Republic (CA)

First Republic Bank offers private banking, wealth management, trust, and brokerage services for businesses and high-net-worth clients though about 60 branches. Its main geographic focus is on urban markets including San Francisco, Los Angeles, New York, Boston, Portland, and San Diego.

The bank's lending focuses on commercial and residential real estate and personal loans, including vacation home mortgages and aircraft and yacht financing. Trust services are offered through the bank's First Republic Trust Company division.

An investor group led by First Republic's management team bought the bank from Bank of America in 2010; it went public later that year. First Republic raised some $280 million from its stock offering. It plans to use proceeds to fund its lending activities and to make investments. The bank was previously publicly traded before it was acquired by Merrill Lynch for some $1.8 billion in 2007. Bank of America assumed ownership of First Republic as part of its 2009 acquisition of Merrill Lynch.

A conservative lender, First Republic has been relatively unscathed by the financial problems plaguing the banking industry. The company has a solid asset portfolio with few delinquencies.

First Republic is focused on growing its business banking and wealth management business, which spurs fee income. The bank is expanding its wealth management unit through hiring and cross-selling.

In 2011 First Republic expanded its service capabilities by adding bankers with experience in the entertainment industry. The bank now caters to film and television companies by offering lending, deposit, and wealth management services.

EXECUTIVES

Chairman and CEO, James H. Herbert II
President, First Republic Securities, David Tateosian
President, First Republic Investment Management, Bob Thornton
President, First Republic Trust Company, San Francisco, Michael J. Harrington
President, COO, and Director, Katherine August-deWilde, age 60
EVP and Chief Marketing Officer, Dianne Snedaker
EVP and Chief Credit Officer, David B. Lichtman
EVP and CFO, Willis H. Newton Jr., age 61
EVP, Secretary, and General Counsel, Edward J. Dobranski, age 60
EVP and CIO, Dale A. Smith
EVP Deposit Sales, Product, and Strategy, Joseph M. (Joe) Petitti
VP and Investment Consultant, First Republic Private Wealth Management, Southern California, R. Brooks Brydges
VP and Senior Trust Officer, First Republic Trust, San Francisco, Jacqueline E. (Jackie) De Anda
VP and Senior Trust Officer, First Republic Trust, New York, Jennifer Anne Charlebois
VP and Portfolio Manager, First Republic Investment Management, Southern California, Stephanie Pham
VP, First Republic Private Wealth Management, San Francisco, John Froley
VP, First Republic Investment Management, Hawaii, Sheri Ann T. Chang Yamaguchi
VP and Senior Trust Officer, First Republic Trust, New York, Christina M. Barton
VP and Senior Trust Officer, First Republic Trust, Los Angeles, Stephanie L. Wheeler
Chief Administrative Officer, First Republic Investment Management, Yale Kofman
Chief Investment Officer, First Republic Investment Management, Michelle Watson
SVP, First Republic Trust, San Francisco, Raul I. Galano
Senior Managing Director, Foreign Exchange Department, Richard (Rich) Lombardozzi Jr.
Senior Managing Director and Regional Manager, First Republic Securities, San Francisco, Laura Harri Ward
Senior Managing Director and Portfolio Manager, First Republic Investment Management, Southern Calif, Jon S. Bull
Senior Managing Director, First Republic Investment Management, Northern California, Anne B. Golden
Senior Managing Director and Chief Credit Officer, First Republic Securities, San Francisco, Catherine L. (Cathy) Sweeney
Managing Director and Fixed Income Portfolio Manager, First Republic Investment Management, Alan Remedios
Senior Relationship Manager, Napa, California, Bill Marseilles
Senior Relationship Manager, Portland, Stacy Benner
Chief Compliance Officer, First Republic Investment Management, Charles A. Christofilis
Senior Relationship Manager, Rockefeller Center, New York, Theresa Yoon
Senior Relationship Manager, Palo Alto, Gigi Chellamy
Senior Trust Officer, First Republic Trust, Portland, Kathleen Host
Memer, Fixed Income Investment Management Team, First Republic Investment Management, Michael Martini
Managing Director and Relationship Manager, Iris Chavarria
Trust Officer, First Republic Trust, Los Angeles, Michael Laubenstein
Product and Risk Manager, Foreign Exchange Department, First Republic Securities, Kate Kent-Sheehan
Senior Commercial Lender, Business Banking Group, Palo Alto, California, Julie Schneider
Manager, Foreign Exchange Trading Desk, FX Group, First Republic Securities, Ted H. Gould
Relationship Manager, Santa Barbara, Linda Cheresh
Senior Construction Loan Officer, Cynthia Leghorn
Trust Officer, First Republic Trust, Nevada, Elaine Frazier
Senior Trust Officer First Republic Trust, Portland, Scott Duttenhaver
Trust Officer, First Republic Trust, San Francisco, Lawrence Wong
Senior Trust Officer and Investment Coordinator, First Republic Trust, San Francisco, Peter A. Harrison
Chief Equity Strategist, First Republic Investment Management, Northeast, J. Robert (Bob) Bloom Jr.
Member, Fixed Income Investment Management Team, First Republic Investment Management, William W. (Bill) Marden III
Member, Fixed Income Investment Management Team, First Republic Investment Management, Jonathan Crowley
Relationship Manager, Santa Barbara, Karin Napel
Manager Preferred Banking, Rockefeller Center, New York, Martin Gibson
Assistant Team Leader and Senior Preferred Banker, Rockefeller Center, New York, Todd Valoff
SVP Strategy and Business Development, First Republic Private Wealth Management, Nicolas Gentin
Senior Relationship Manager, Portland, Chuck Collopy
Team Leader, Construction Lending, San Francisco, Richard Israel
Managing Director, Foreign Exchange, Boston, Erich Zarnfaller
Managing Director, Construction Lending, San Francisco, Michael Zazzara
Managing Director, Construction Lending, San Diego, Jason Kaimer
Managing Director, Construction Lending, San Francisco, Stefani Phipps
Senior Trust Officer and SVP, Wealth Management, Terry Kane
Auditors: KPMG LLP

LOCATIONS

HQ: First Republic Bank
111 Pine St., San Francisco, CA 94111
Phone: 415-392-1400   **Fax:** 415-392-1413
Web: www.firstrepublic.com

PRODUCTS/OPERATIONS

2010 Sales

	$ in mil.	% of total
Interest income, other	1,055.9	92
Noninterest income	95.9	8
Total	**1,151.5**	**100**

Selected Affiliates

First Republic Investment Management, Inc.
First Republic Securities Company, LLC
First Republic Trust Company

COMPETITORS

Bank of New York Mellon	City National
Boston Private	JPMorgan Private Bank
Citigroup Private Bank	Morgan Stanley
	UnionBanCal

HISTORICAL FINANCIALS

Company Type: Public

Income Statement

FYE: December 31

	REVENUE ($ mil.)	NET INCOME ($ mil.)	NET PROFIT MARGIN	EMPLOYEES
12/10	1,151.5	271.2	23.6%	1,502
12/06	685.7	69.2	10.1%	1,112
12/05	496.3	60.8	12.3%	793
12/04	351.8	46.5	13.2%	793
12/03	314.2	37.0	11.8%	333
Annual Growth	**20.4%**	**32.9%**	—	**24.0%**

2010 Year-End Financials

Debt ratio: 31.3%
Return on equity: 12.7%
Cash ($ mil.): 1,528.1
Current ratio: —
Long-term debt ($ mil.): 668.4

No. of shares (mil.): 128.9
Dividends
  Yield: —
  Payout: —
Market value ($ mil.): —

	STOCK PRICE ($) FY Close	P/E High/Low		PER SHARE ($) Earnings	Dividends	Book Value
12/10	0.00	—	—	(0.00)	0.00	16.59
12/06	39.08	21	16	2.21	0.55	(0.00)
12/05	37.01	19	15	2.08	0.45	(0.00)
12/04	35.33	21	13	1.72	0.35	(0.00)
Annual Growth	—	—	—	—	—	—

First Savings Financial

First Savings Financial Group was formed in 2008 to be the holding company for First Savings Bank, a community bank serving consumers and small businesses in southern Indiana. Through more than a dozen branches, the bank offers standard deposit services like savings, checking, and retirement accounts, as well as a variety of lending services. One- to four- family residential loans make up about 60% of First Savings Bank's loan portfolio; other loans in the bank's portfolio include commercial real estate, construction, consumer, and commercial business. In 2009 the company bought Community First Bank, which kept its name after the acquisition and now operates as a division of First Savings Bank.

EXECUTIVES

Chairman, Michael F. Ludden, age 61
CFO, Anthony A. (Tony) Schoen
President, CEO, and Director, Larry W. Myers, age 52, $186,054 total compensation
COO and Director, John P. Lawson Jr., age 53, $129,248 total compensation
Assistant VP and Branch Manager, Jeffersonville, Nancy Boman
Assistant VP and Branch Manager, Charlestown, Lois Sperzel
Assistant VP and Branch Manager, Georgetown, Cheryl Sawyer
Assistant VP and Branch Manager, Sellersburg, Beth Roberts
Assistant VP and Branch Manager, Clarksville, Staci Flispart
Assistant VP and Branch Manager, Jeffersonville Court Avenue, DeeDee Ragland
Treasurer and Corporate Secretary, M. Sue Johnson, age 63
Auditors: Monroe Shine & Co., Inc.

LOCATIONS

HQ: First Savings Financial Group, Inc.
501 E. Lewis and Clark Pkwy., Clarksville, IN 47129
Phone: 812-283-0724   **Fax:** 812-288-2558
Web: www.fsbbank.net

PRODUCTS/OPERATIONS

2008 Sales

	$ mil.	% of total
Interest		
Loans, including fees	11.6	85
Taxable securities	0.7	5
Other	0.3	2
Noninterest		
Service charges on deposit accounts	0.5	4
Other	0.5	4
Total	**13.6**	**100**

COMPETITORS

Community Bank Shares of Indiana	JPMorgan Chase
First Capital	MainSource Financial
Indiana Community Bancorp	PNC Financial
	Regions Financial
	River Valley Bancorp

HISTORICAL FINANCIALS

Company Type: Public

Income Statement   FYE: September 30

	ASSETS ($ mil.)	NET INCOME ($ mil.)	INCOME AS % OF ASSETS	EMPLOYEES
09/10	508.4	2.6	0.5%	158
09/09	480.8	—	—	158
09/08	228.9	(0.2)	—	80
09/07	203.3	0.8	0.4%	84
09/06	206.4	0.4	0.2%	0
Annual Growth	**25.3%**	**59.7%**	**—**	**23.4%**

2010 Year-End Financials

Equity as % of assets: —
Return on assets: 0.5%
Return on equity: 4.8%
Long-term debt ($ mil.): 67.2
No. of shares (mil.): 2.4
Dividends
Yield: —
Payout: —
Market value ($ mil.): 31.6
Sales ($ mil.): 29.2

	STOCK PRICE ($) FY Close	P/E High/Low	Earnings	PER SHARE ($) Dividends	Book Value
09/10	13.08	12 9	1.17	0.00	22.84
09/09	10.70	1100 825	0.01	0.00	20.80
Annual Growth	**22.2%**	**—**	**—11600.0%**	**—**	**9.8%**

First South Bancorp (SC)

First South Bancorp knows a thing or two about firsts. It is the holding company for First South Bank (no relation to North Carolina's First South Bancorp) and serves the area around Spartanburg, South Carolina (a state that was among the first 13 American colonies and the first one to secede prior to the Civil War). The five-branch bank offers such traditional retail-banking products as checking and savings accounts, CDs, money market accounts, and IRAs. Funds from deposits are used to write real estate, business, and consumer installment loans. Mortgages account for more than two-thirds of the bank's loan portfolio.

EXECUTIVES

Chairman, First South Bancorp and First South Bank, Roger A. F. Habisreutinger, age 69
President, CEO, and Director; President and CEO, First South Bank, Barry L. Slider, age 58
EVP and CFO, First South Bancorp and First South Bank, V. Lewis Shuler, age 67
Auditors: Cherry, Bekaert & Holland, LLP

LOCATIONS

HQ: First South Bancorp, Inc.
1450 John B. White Sr. Blvd., Spartanburg, SC 29306
Phone: 864-595-0455   **Fax:** 864-587-2781
Web: www.firstsouthbancorp.com

COMPETITORS

Bank of America	Southern First Bancshares
BB&T	SunTrust
First Citizens Bancorporation	Synovus
Palmetto Bancshares	Wells Fargo
Regions Financial	

HISTORICAL FINANCIALS

Company Type: Public

Income Statement   FYE: December 31

	ASSETS ($ mil.)	NET INCOME ($ mil.)	INCOME AS % OF ASSETS	EMPLOYEES
12/07	378.9	3.2	0.8%	73
12/06	353.4	4.6	1.3%	65
12/05	324.7	3.4	1.0%	58
12/04	296.4	3.0	1.0%	59
12/03	251.7	2.1	0.8%	52
Annual Growth	**10.8%**	**11.1%**	**—**	**8.9%**

2007 Year-End Financials

Equity as % of assets: 10.42%
Return on assets: 0.8%
Return on equity: 8.0%
Long-term debt ($ mil.): 38.3
No. of shares (mil.): —
Dividends
Yield: —
Payout: —
Market value ($ mil.): —
Sales ($ mil.): 30.2

	STOCK PRICE ($) FY Close	P/E High/Low	Earnings	PER SHARE ($) Dividends	Book Value
12/07	18.05	20 12	1.45	0.00	(0.00)
12/06	27.25	14 12	2.11	0.00	(0.00)
12/05	27.50	20 14	1.57	0.00	(0.00)
12/04	29.17	20 12	1.47	0.00	(0.00)
12/03	17.50	16 13	1.22	0.00	(0.00)
Annual Growth	**0.8%**	**— —**	**4.4%**	**—**	**—**

First Trust Bank

Tar Heels might put their trust in First Trust Bank. It provides retail and commercial banking services through five locations in the North Carolina communities of Charlotte, Concord, Monroe, and Mooresville. The bank provides standard deposit services and products, including checking and savings accounts, IRAs, CDs, and debit cards. Commercial mortgages make up approximately half of First Trust Bank's loan portfolio, followed by construction and land development loans (more than a quarter) and commercial and industrial loans (about 15%). Residential mortgages, farmland loans, and personal loans round out the bank's lending activities.

EXECUTIVES

Chairman, William C. Godley
President, CEO, and Director, Jim Bolt
VP and Branch Administrator, Queens Rd., Wendy Isaac
VP and Commercial Loan Officer, Mooresville, Tim Anderson
VP and Business Development Officer, Aaron Smith
VP and Commercial Loan Officer, Alan Sulek
VP and Branch Development Officer, SouthPark, Mark Edinger
VP and Commercial Loan Officer, Karl G. Cahoon Jr.
VP and Branch Administrator, Headquarters, Rosemary Harrington
VP and Commercial Banking Officer, Mooresville, Greg Silliman
VP and Commercial Banking Officer, Mooresville, David Steen
VP and Commercial Loan Officer, SouthPark, Eleanor M. (Ellie) McIntire
VP, Business Development Officer and Branch Administrator, Queens Road, Diane Blackmon
VP and Commercial Loan Officer, SouthPark, Chris Sharpe
VP and Business Development Officer, Mooresville, Trudi A. Zangardi
VP and Commercial Banking Officer, Queens Road, Sheldon Hilaire
VP and Commercial Banking Officer, SouthPark, Warren Miller
Vice Chairman, Thomas M. Barnhardt III
SVP and Senior Loan Officer, William D. (Bill) Elder
SVP and Chief Credit Officer, John Keane
SVP and CFO, Jean Galloway
Assistant VP, Deborah J. Rouse
Auditors:

LOCATIONS

HQ: First Trust Bank
1420 E. Third St., Charlotte, NC 28204
Phone: 704-377-3936   **Fax:** 704-377-8869
Web: www.firsttrustnc.com

COMPETITORS

Bank of America	Peoples Bancorp (NC)
BB&T	SunTrust
First Citizens	Wells Fargo
BancShares	

HISTORICAL FINANCIALS

Company Type: Public

Income Statement

FYE: December 31

	ASSETS ($ mil.)	NET INCOME ($ mil.)	INCOME AS % OF ASSETS	EMPLOYEES
12/07	411.4	4.4	1.1%	48
12/06	364.8	3.9	1.1%	45
12/05	303.0	3.2	1.1%	42
12/04	239.1	2.4	1.0%	35
12/03	206.1	2.0	1.0%	28
Annual Growth	18.9%	21.8%	—	14.4%

2007 Year-End Financials

Equity as % of assets: 9.02%	Dividends
Return on assets: 1.1%	Yield: —
Return on equity: 11.8%	Payout: —
Long-term debt ($ mil.): —	Market value ($ mil.): —
No. of shares (mil.): —	Sales ($ mil.): 28.7

	STOCK PRICE ($) FY Close	P/E High/Low		PER SHARE ($) Earnings	Dividends	Book Value
12/07	12.90	18	13	1.01	0.00	(0.00)
12/06	17.92	22	15	0.89	0.00	(0.00)
12/05	13.26	23	16	0.74	0.00	(0.00)
12/04	14.32	25	15	0.63	0.00	(0.00)
12/03	10.10	23	11	0.53	0.00	(0.00)
Annual Growth	6.3%	—	—	17.5%	—	—

FirstCity Financial

FirstCity Financial helps loans deal with performance issues. Through operating subsidiaries, the company buys, manages, and sells primarily nonperfoming loans from financial institutions, government agencies, and other lenders. It typically buys nonperforming loans at a deep discount but purchases performing loans, as well. The company or one of its affiliates services the loans it acquires. FirstCity Financial manages a portfolio worth approximately $11 billion. In addition to buying loans, the company invests in special situations such as restructurings, turnarounds, and executive buyouts through its majority-owned FirstCity Denver subsidiary.

FirstCity Financial sees an advantage in not being picky. It doesn't limit itself to any one type of loan but rather buys loans of varying qualities, both unsecured and secured by diverse collateral and real estate. The firm also originates and services Small Business Administration loans through subsidiary American Business Lending.

Nor does FirstCity limit itself geographically. It has acquired portfolio assets throughout the US

and in Latin America, Asia, and Europe. The company has offices throughout the US and Mexico.

EXECUTIVES

Chairman, Richard E. Bean, age 67
President, CEO, and Director, James T. Sartain, age 62
EVP and Managing Director U.S. Operations, James C. Holmes, age 54
EVP, COO, and Treasurer, Jim W. Moore, age 61
Vice Chairman, C. Ivan Wilson, age 84
SVP, Terry R. DeWitt, age 54
SVP and CFO, J. Bryan Baker, age 50
SVP and Tax Director, Joe S. Greak, age 62
Auditors: KPMG LLP

LOCATIONS

HQ: FirstCity Financial Corporation
6400 Imperial Dr., Waco, TX 76712
Phone: 254-761-2800
Web: www.fcfc.com

COMPETITORS

Asta Funding	Ocwen Financial
Consumer Portfolio	Portfolio Recovery
Encore Capital Group	Rampart Capital
NCO Portfolio Management	

HISTORICAL FINANCIALS

Company Type: Public

Income Statement

FYE: December 31

	REVENUE ($ mil.)	NET INCOME ($ mil.)	NET PROFIT MARGIN	EMPLOYEES
12/10	104.8	12.5	11.9%	264
12/09	87.9	18.7	21.3%	365
12/08	45.4	(46.7)	—	265
12/07	54.6	2.2	4.0%	241
12/06	42.6	9.8	23.0%	208
Annual Growth	25.2%	6.3%	—	6.1%

2010 Year-End Financials

Debt ratio: 345.1%	No. of shares (mil.): 10.3
Return on equity: 14.2%	Dividends
Cash ($ mil.): 46.6	Yield: —
Current ratio: —	Payout: —
Long-term debt ($ mil.): 304.8	Market value ($ mil.): 83.3

	STOCK PRICE ($) FY Close	P/E High/Low		PER SHARE ($) Earnings	Dividends	Book Value
12/10	8.10	7	4	1.23	0.00	8.59
12/09	7.48	5	0	1.83	0.00	7.78
12/08	1.99	—	—	(4.55)	0.00	5.11
12/07	8.13	60	39	0.19	0.00	9.90
12/06	11.08	15	10	0.83	0.00	9.63
Annual Growth	(7.5%)	—	—	10.3%	—	(2.8%)

Flint Telecom Group

Flint Telecom Group fans the flame of advanced communications. Through eight subsidiaries, the holding company provides a host of products and technologies to US and international communications service providers, including cable companies, ISPs, and telcos. It distributes advanced broad-

band, hosted digital phone, voice and data, and wireless products, as well as prepaid cellular and calling card products. The company's Digital Phone Solutions subsidiary offers VoIP services to independent cable companies, a niche that is showing strong market growth, particularly in the US.

Flint acquired prepaid debit card services provider Ingedigit International in late 2010 to expand its interanational business and improve its ability provide application development and support services related to electronic transaction processing to the financial services industry. Ingedigit serves clients in Africa, the Americas, the Asia Pacific region, and the UK. Ingedigit was renamed as Power2Process.

Flint acquired six US subsidiaries from China Voice Holding Corp. at the beginning of 2009 and integrated those operations into its business. The deal gave it additional capabilities to distribute prepaid calling cards within the US. The company also enacted cost-cutting measures that year to bring down overhead.

EXECUTIVES

President and COO, Bernard A. Fried, age 65
Chairman and CEO, Vincent Browne, age 43
Auditors: L.L. Bradford & Company

LOCATIONS

HQ: Flint Telecom Group, Inc.
375 N. Stephanie St., Ste. 1411, Henderson, NV 89014
Phone: 561-394-2748
Web: www.flinttel.com

PRODUCTS/OPERATIONS

Selected Subsidiaries

Cable & Voice Corporation (advanced broadband products & services)
CVC International, Inc. (VoIP services)
Dial-Tone Communication Inc. (discount international calling cards)
Digital Phone Solutions, Inc. (digital VoIP services)
Phone House, Inc. (discount international calling cards)
Phone House of Florida Inc. (discount international calling cards)
StarCom Alliance, Inc. (prepaid cellular products)
Wize Communications, Inc. (prepaid cellular products & calling cards)

HISTORICAL FINANCIALS

Company Type: Public

Income Statement

FYE: June 30

	REVENUE ($ mil.)	NET INCOME ($ mil.)	NET PROFIT MARGIN	EMPLOYEES
06/10	34.1	(28.9)	—	7
06/09*	34.3	(14.6)	—	21
03/08	1.0	(2.1)	—	14
03/07	1.6	(2.1)	—	19
03/06	2.4	(1.4)	—	26
Annual Growth	94.1%	—	—	(28.0%)

*Fiscal year change

2010 Year-End Financials

Debt ratio: —	No. of shares (mil.): 6.5
Return on equity: —	Dividends
Cash ($ mil.): 0.0	Yield: —
Current ratio: 0.12	Payout: —
Long-term debt ($ mil.): 1.0	Market value ($ mil.): 0.5

	STOCK PRICE ($) FY Close	P/E High/Low	PER SHARE ($) Earnings	Dividends	Book Value
06/10	0.08	— —	(7.00)	0.00	(1.75)
06/09*	11.00	— —	(6.20)	0.00	0.38
03/08	5.00	— —	(21.40)	0.00	13.57
03/07	44.00	— —	(24.00)	0.00	32.75
03/06	84.00	— —	(20.00)	0.00	50.08
Annual Growth	(82.4%)	— —	—	—	—

*Fiscal year change

Fluidigm

When Fluidigm's microfluidic systems measure volume by the *nanoliter*, they're not using itty bitty Erlenmeyer flasks. Based on the fabrication technology that brought forth semiconductors, Fluidigm develops integrated fluidic circuits (IFCs) and strings them together as systems to automate certain tasks in life sciences research. Fluidigm's BioMark and EP1 systems are used for genetic analysis including genotyping and gene expression. Its Access Array system is used to prepare samples for DNA sequencing. The company's customers range across the agricultural biotechnology, molecular diagnostics, and other life sciences research industries. Fluidigm completed an IPO in 2011.

Fluidigm first filed to make its initial public offering in 2008, but, faced with turbulent economy, withdrew the filing later that year. Encouraged by its own sales growth and a more stable economy, the company filed anew in 2010, and it finally completed the offering early the following year. Fluidigm intends to use the proceeds (about $70 million) to build up a sales force to help commercialize its products, continue to fund its research and development activities, and expand its manufacturing facilities.

Fluidigm believes it has a market advantage because its systems perform faster than standard microplate gene expression systems. Once a system is sold, the company continues to bring in money through the sale of the single-use and reusable microfluidic chips, chemical reagents, and other consumables used in its systems. The firm is also looking to expand its customer base by promoting its systems for new life science applications, such as molecular diagnostics.

One way that the company is able to reach new market segments is by developing and launching new products. Its Access Array system, for instance, was introduced in 2009, and in late 2010 Fluidigm released a line of multi-use chips for genotyping purposes. The company has also been working on custom-designed assays that will target specific sections of DNA or genes.

In addition, Fluidigm has expanded by striking marketing and development agreements with other life sciences companies. One agreement allows for bundled marketing of Fluidigm's Access Array systems with 454 Life Sciences' DNA sequencing technology. Under another agreement with Novartis, the company is working to develop in-vitro diagnostics.

The company maintains distribution agreements in Asia, Australia and New Zealand, Europe, and North and South America. It manufactures its products at a facility in Singapore and the company has received development grants from the Singapore government in exchange for operating in that country. Entities affiliated with the Singapore government also hold just over 10% of the company.

EXECUTIVES

Chairman, Samuel D. (Sam) Colella, age 70
CFO, Vikram Jog, age 54, $591,060 total compensation
President, CEO, and Director, Gajus V. Worthington, age 41, $558,190 total compensation
EVP Research and Development, Robert C. (Bob) Jones, age 55, $460,499 total compensation
VP North American Sales, Service, and Support, Pam Morley
VP Legal Affairs, General Counsel, and Secretary, William M. Smith, age 59, $530,590 total compensation
VP Worldwide Manufacturing; Managing Director, Fluidigm Singapore Pte., Mai Chan (Grace) Yow, age 51, $463,470 total compensation
VP European Sales and Support; General Manager, Fluidigm Europe BV, Dominique Remy-Renou
Media Relations, Howard High
Chief Business Officer, Fredric T. (Fred) Walder, age 53
Auditors: Ernst & Young LLP

LOCATIONS

HQ: Fluidigm Corporation
7000 Shoreline Ct., Ste. 100, South San Francisco, CA 94080
Phone: 650-266-6000   **Fax:** 650-871-7152
Web: www.fluidigm.com

2009 Product Revenues

	% of total
US	54
Europe	21
Japan	13
Asia/Pacific	9
Other	3
Total	**100**

PRODUCTS/OPERATIONS

2009 Revenues

	$ mil.	% of total
Product sales		
Instruments	17.3	68
Consumables	6.3	25
Grant revenue	1.8	7
Total	**25.4**	**100**

COMPETITORS

Affymetrix
Agilent Technologies
Caliper Life Sciences
Illumina
Life Technologies Corporation
Luminex
Roche Diagnostics
Sequenom

HISTORICAL FINANCIALS

Company Type: Public

Income Statement

FYE: December 31

	REVENUE ($ mil.)	NET INCOME ($ mil.)	NET PROFIT MARGIN	EMPLOYEES
12/10	33.6	(16.9)	—	206
12/09	25.4	(19.1)	—	198
12/08	15.3	(29.5)	—	0
12/07	7.3	(25.5)	—	131
12/06	6.4	(23.6)	—	0
Annual Growth	51.4%	—	—	16.3%

2010 Year-End Financials

Debt ratio: —	No. of shares (mil.): —
Return on equity: —	Dividends
Cash ($ mil.): 5.7	Yield: —
Current ratio: 1.13	Payout: —
Long-term debt ($ mil.): 10.1	Market value ($ mil.): —

	STOCK PRICE ($) FY Close	P/E High/Low	PER SHARE ($) Earnings	Dividends	Book Value
Annual Growth	—	— —	—	—	—

Fortinet

Fortinet secures the fortress against Internet marauders. The company makes network security appliances (sold under its FortiGate line) and software that integrate antivirus, firewall, content filtering, intrusion prevention systems (IPS), and antispam functions to protect against computer viruses, worms, and inappropriate Web content. Its FortiGuard subscription services offer continuous updates on all new threats to provide real-time network protection. The company also offers complementary products that include its FortiMail e-mail security system and FortiAnalyzer logging, reporting, and analysis systems. More than 60% of sales come from outside the Americas.

Fortinet acquired enterprise Internet telephony systems maker TalkSwitch in 2011 to expand its product selection and boost its profile in the multiservice gateway market. The company also extended the reach of its sales organization with the purchase; TalkSwitch has relationships with resellers and distributors worldwide. Past acquisitions included the purchase of the assets of IPLocks in 2008, a deal that expanded Fortinet's database security and compliance technologies.

The company's sales increased by 19% in 2009 over 2008, as its services revenues continued to grow. Services, an important source of recurring revenue, account for more than half of sales. Fortinet achieved profitability in the third quarter of 2008, and its net income jumped from $7.4 million that year to $60 million in 2009, due in part to a large tax benefit related to prior period losses. Fortinet used the proceeds from a 2009 IPO for general corporate purposes, product development, and to pursue potential acquisitions.

Fortinet was founded in 2000 by CEO Ken Xie, who also founded leading firewall appliance provider NetScreen Technologies (acquired in 2004 by Juniper Networks). Xie holds an equity stake of nearly 16% in the company. CTO Michael Xie, a co-founder of Fortinet and Ken Xie's younger brother, owns about 11% of the company.

EXECUTIVES

Chairman, John L. Walecka, age 51
President, CEO, and Director, Ken Xie, age 48, $664,816 total compensation
VP Channel Sales, Kendra Krause
VP and CFO, Kenneth A. (Ken) Goldman, age 61, $654,760 total compensation
VP Americas Sales and Support, Michael Valentine
VP Corporate Communications, Michelle Spolver
VP Products, Anthony James
VP International Sales and Support, Patrice Perche

VP Corporate Development, Strategic Alliances,
  General Counsel, and Corporate Secretary, John
  Whittle, age 43, $517,207 total compensation
VP Human Resources, Sherry Pulvers
VP Strategy and New Technology, Jens Andreassen
VP Engineering, CTO, and Director, Michael Xie, age
  42, $617,129 total compensation
Media Contacts Americas, Rick Popko
Media Contact EMEA, Barbara Maigret
Analyst Contact, Jennifer Leggio
Media Contact APAC, Georgina Tan
Auditors: Deloitte & Touche LLP

LOCATIONS

HQ: Fortinet, Inc.
  1090 Kifer Rd., Sunnyvale, CA 94086
Phone: 408-235-7700   Fax: 408-235-7737
Web: www.fortinet.com

2009 Sales

	$ mil.	% of total
Europe, Middle East & Africa	95.9	38
Americas	92.6	37
Asia/Pacific	63.6	25
Total	**252.1**	**100**

PRODUCTS/OPERATIONS

2009 Sales

	$ mil.	% of total
Services	139.2	55
Product	98.7	39
Ratable product & services	14.2	6
Total	**252.1**	**100**

Selected Products

Database security appliance (FortiDB)
E-mail antispam (FortiMail)
Endpoint security software (FortiClient)
Endpoint vulnerability management appliance
  (FortiScan)
Network event correlation and content archiving
  (FortiAnalyzer)
Network security appliances (FortiGate)
Security management (FortiManager)
Web application firewall appliance (FortiWeb)

COMPETITORS

Bivio Networks	McAfee
Blue Coat	Microsoft
CA, Inc.	NetWolves
Check Point Software	SonicWALL
Cisco Systems	SRA International
Crossbeam	SteelCloud
e-DMZ Security	Symantec
F5 Networks	Trend Micro
Fortrex	VeriSign
Infoblox	WatchGuard Technolo
Juniper Networks	

HISTORICAL FINANCIALS

Company Type: Public

Income Statement   FYE: December 31

	REVENUE ($ mil.)	NET INCOME ($ mil.)	NET PROFIT MARGIN	EMPLOYEES
12/10	324.7	41.2	12.7%	1,336
12/09	252.1	60.2	23.9%	1,223
12/08	211.8	7.4	3.5%	1,151
12/07	155.4	(21.8)	—	1,000
12/06	123.5	(5.3)	—	0
Annual Growth	**27.3%**	**—**	**—**	**10.1%**

2010 Year-End Financials

Debt ratio: —
Return on equity: 17.7%
Cash ($ mil.): 66.9
Current ratio: 1.92
Long-term debt ($ mil.): —

No. of shares (mil.): 148.8
Dividends
  Yield: —
  Payout: —
Market value ($ mil.): 2,406.2

	STOCK PRICE ($) FY Close	P/E High/Low	PER SHARE ($) Earnings	Dividends	Book Value
12/10	16.17	69 28	0.26	0.00	1.56
12/09	8.78	24 21	0.39	0.00	1.07
Annual Growth	**84.2%**	**— —**	**(33.3%)**	**—**	**46.6%**

FragranceNet.com

FragranceNet.com has set its sights on the sweet
smell of success through its fragrance site. Customers can buy — but not sample — more than
10,000 discounted brand-name fragrances, hair
and skin care products, aromatherapy items, and
scented candles at FragranceNet.com. The company carries products under designer names Ralph
Lauren, Christian Dior, Hermes, Nicole Miller, Yves
Saint Laurent, Oscar de la Renta, Fendi, and others. In addition to the website, the fragrance firm
operates a wholesale business called FragranceNet
Wholesales. FragranceNet.com got its start in 1995
by selling fragrances via an 800 number, which it
still uses.

EXECUTIVES

Chairman, CEO, and CFO, Dennis M. Apfel, age 61
President, COO, and Director, Jason S. Apfel, age 33
VP, Secretary, and Director, Eric J. Apfel, age 32
Auditors: Margolin, Winer & Evens LLP

LOCATIONS

HQ: FragranceNet.com, Inc.
  104 Parkway Dr. South, Hauppauge, NY 11788
Phone: 631-582-5204   Fax: 631-582-8433
Web: www.FragranceNet.com

PRODUCTS/OPERATIONS

Selected Products

Aromatherapy
Candles
Gift sets
Haircare
Men's fragrances
Skincare
Women's fragrances

COMPETITORS

Bloomingdale's	Sephora USA
Marilyn Miglin	Target Corporation
Nordstrom	Wal-Mart
Perfumania Holdings	Walgreen
Saks	

HISTORICAL FINANCIALS

Company Type: Public

Income Statement   FYE: March 31

	REVENUE ($ mil.)	NET INCOME ($ mil.)	NET PROFIT MARGIN	EMPLOYEES
03/06	31.9	0.4	1.3%	0
03/05	23.3	0.3	1.3%	0
03/04	14.7	0.4	2.7%	40
03/03	10.5	0.1	1.0%	28
03/02	7.5	0.2	2.7%	20
Annual Growth	**43.6%**	**18.9%**	**—**	**41.4%**

Debt ratio: —
Return on equity: 17.7%
Cash ($ mil.): 66.9
Current ratio: 1.92
Long-term debt ($ mil.): —

No. of shares (mil.): 148.8
Dividends
  Yield: —
  Payout: —
Market value ($ mil.): 2,406.2

Francescas Holdings

Customers of Francesca's Holdings are left holding the bag - one full of trendy wares. The company sells apparel and accessories to 18- to 35-year
old women at some 250 Francesca's Collections
shops in 40 states. It opens about 70 new stores
a year, yet promotes an independent, upscale boutique image by allowing store managers to person-
alize shops. Francesca's Collections also deliber-
ately carries limited quantities of certain items to
foster a "treasure hunt atmosphere." It relies on
a mix of half apparel and half jewelry and accessories along with rapid product turnover to encourage customers to return often. Formed in 1999, the
company issued an initial public offering and entered the stock market in 2011.

Although the majority of shares sold came from
previous owners (and didn't benefit the company),
Francesca's Holdings netted $44.1 million from
the offering (way ahead of expectations). Funds
were used to repay debt and for general corporate
purposes, including opening new stores and increasing its online sales. Store growth, a key part
of the company's strategy, calls for 75 new bou-
tiques in 2011 and 2012 and about 900 total US
locations eventually. The company opened 62
stores in fiscal 2011; earnings jumped about 60%
in 2011 over the prior year on a 70% increase in
sales, driven more than doubling store count.

In keeping with its independent boutique image,
the company eschews traditional advertising for
viral and in-boutique efforts. Francesca's Collections intends to expand the contribution from online sales, but through general consumer awareness rather than advertising.

The company's major stockholder, private-equity
firm CCMP Capital continues to hold a 65% stake,
down from its pre-IPO interest of about 84% of the
company.

EXECUTIVES

Chairman, Greg Brenneman, age 49
President, CEO, and Director, John De Meritt, age 40
EVP and COO, Theresa Backes, age 53
EVP and CFO, Gene S. Morphis, age 62
EVP, General Counsel and Corporate Secretary, Kal
  Malik, age 50
VP Accounting, Cindy Thomassee
Vice Chairperson, Kyong Gill, age 46
Auditors: Ernst & Young LLP

LOCATIONS

HQ: Francesca's Holdings Corporation
3480 W. 12th St., Houston, TX 77008
Phone: 713-864-1358
Web: www.francescascollections.com

2010 Stores

	No.
Texas	28
California	24
Florida	16
Illinois	14
New Jersey	10
Georgia	9
North Carolina	9
Tennessee	9
Arizona	8
Ohio	8
Alabama	7
South Carolina	6
Connecticut	5
Louisiana	5
Massachusetts	5
Minnesota	5
Missouri	5
New York	5
Wisconsin	5
Colorado	4
Maryland	4
Michigan	4
Nevada	4
Oklahoma	4
Arkansas	3
Indiana	3
Kansas	3
Kentucky	3
Nebraska	3
Pennsylvania	3
Virginia	3
Washington	3
Iowa	2
Mississippi	2
Rhode Island	2
Delaware	1
Maine	1
New Mexico	1
Total	**236**

PRODUCTS/OPERATIONS

2011 Sales

	$ mil.	% of total
Apparel	70.3	52
Jewelry	27.1	20
Accessories	19.6	15
Gifts	17.4	13
Total	**134.4**	**100**

COMPETITORS

Ann Taylor	H&M
Caché	J. Jill Group
Charlotte Russe	Target Corporation
Chico's FAS	Urban Outfitters

HISTORICAL FINANCIALS

Company Type: Public

Income Statement

	REVENUE ($ mil.)	NET INCOME ($ mil.)	NET PROFIT MARGIN	EMPLOYEES	FYE: Saturday closest to January 31st
01/11	135.2	16.9	12.5%	1,560	
01/10	79.4	10.6	13.4%	0	
01/09	52.3	4.6	8.8%	0	
Annual Growth	**60.8%**	**91.7%**	**—**	**—**	

Debt ratio: —
Return on equity: 17.7%
Cash ($ mil.): 66.9
Current ratio: 1.92
Long-term debt ($ mil.): —

No. of shares (mil.): 148.8
Dividends
  Yield: —
  Payout: —
Market value ($ mil.): 2,406.2

Franklin Wireless

Franklin Wireless is a founding father of the mobile nation. The company makes connectivity products for wireless devices. Its products include USB, embedded, and standalone modems, as well as PC cards. Customers use its products to connect their mobile computers to wireless broadband networks. Franklin Wireless sells directly to wireless operators and through distributors. Its customers include consumer electronics makers, cellular operators, and end users.

EXECUTIVES

Chairman, Gary Nelson, age 70
President, Acting CFO, and Director, O. C. Kim, age 48
VP Finance, Richard Walker
COO, Yun J. (David) Lee, age 49
Auditors: Choi, Kim & Park, LLP

LOCATIONS

HQ: Franklin Wireless Corp.
9853 Pacific Heights Blvd., Ste. J, San Diego, CA 92121
Phone: 858-623-0000   **Fax:** 858-623-0050
Web: www.fklt.com

HISTORICAL FINANCIALS

Company Type: Public

Income Statement

	REVENUE ($ mil.)	NET INCOME ($ mil.)	NET PROFIT MARGIN	EMPLOYEES	FYE: June 30
06/11	46.5	4.5	9.7%	68	
06/10	101.9	4.8	4.7%	58	
06/09	24.0	3.6	15.0%	20	
06/08	34.7	3.9	11.2%	13	
06/07	10.4	1.3	12.5%	9	
Annual Growth	**45.4%**	**36.4%**	**—**	**65.8%**	

2011 Year-End Financials

Debt ratio: —
Return on equity: 25.2%
Cash ($ mil.): 11.4
Current ratio: 3.91
Long-term debt ($ mil.): —

No. of shares (mil.): 11.8
Dividends
  Yield: —
  Payout: —
Market value ($ mil.): 28.9

	STOCK PRICE ($) FY Close	P/E High	P/E Low	PER SHARE ($) Earnings	PER SHARE ($) Dividends	PER SHARE ($) Book Value
06/11	2.45	9	3	0.36	0.00	1.53
06/10	2.10	8	1	0.35	0.00	1.06
06/09	0.70	7	1	0.27	0.00	0.70
06/08	1.99	70	2	0.30	0.00	0.42
06/07	1.47	—	—	(0.00)	0.00	(0.00)
Annual Growth	**13.6%**			**—**	**—**	**—**

Full House Resorts

When it comes to gaming outside Sin City, nothing beats a Full House. Full House Resorts owns 50% of Harrington Raceway and Casino (formerly called Midway Slots and Simulcast) in Delaware. Harrington offers more than 2,100 slot machines and gaming devices, a 450-seat buffet, a 50-seat diner, and an entertainment lounge area. The company also owns Stockman's Casino in Fallon, Nevada, featuring 280 slot and gaming machines, four table games, and keno. In addition, Full House has collaborated with a Native American tribe in Battle Creek, Michigan, to manage the FireKeepers Casino. The property has 2,680 slot machines, nearly 80 table games, and 12 poker tables along with five restaurants and lounges.

Full House Resorts operates under the goal of pursuing acquisitions in regional gaming markets, and its business has significantly expanded through a few key recent purchases and partnerships. In 2011 it acquired the Grand Victoria Casino & Resort in Rising Son, Indiana for approximately $19 million in cash and $33 million in credit. The property includes 40,000 square feet of gaming space, a 200-room hotel, a theater, and several restaurants. It subsequently changed the name of Grand Victoria to Rising Star Casino Resort. Previously, the company's FireKeepers Casino opened in 2009, and Full House Resorts' management agreement with the property runs through 2016.

EXECUTIVES

Chairman and CEO, Andre M. Hilliou, age 63, $586,653 total compensation
CFO, COO, Treasurer, and Director, Mark J. Miller, age 54, $537,853 total compensation
VP Development, Jim Dacey
VP Operations and Project Management, T. Wesley (Wes) Elam, age 57, $340,545 total compensation
VP Finance, James D. Meier, age 46
Vice Chairman, Carl G. Braunlich, age 58
General Manager, FireKeepers Casino, R. Bruce McKee
Secretary and General Counsel, Barth F. Aaron, age 62
Integrated Corporate Relations, William Schmitt
Auditors: Piercy Bowler Taylor & Kern

LOCATIONS

HQ: Full House Resorts, Inc.
4670 S. Fort Apache Rd., Ste. 190, Las Vegas, NV 89147
Phone: 702-221-7800   **Fax:** 702-221-8101
Web: www.fullhouseresorts.com

COMPETITORS

Boyd Gaming	Mashantucket Pequot
Caesars Entertainment	MGM Resorts
Dover Downs Gaming	Pinnacle Entertainment

HISTORICAL FINANCIALS

Company Type: Public

Income Statement

	REVENUE ($ mil.)	NET INCOME ($ mil.)	NET PROFIT MARGIN	EMPLOYEES	FYE: December 31
12/10	32.9	7.7	23.4%	2,069	
12/09	19.0	4.8	25.3%	1,965	
12/08	9.7	1.6	16.5%	630	
12/07	9.6	0.9	9.4%	10	
12/06	3.9	0.6	15.4%	9	
Annual Growth	**70.4%**	**89.3%**	**—**	**289.4%**	

Debt ratio: —	No. of shares (mil.): 18.0
Return on equity: 16.2%	Dividends
Cash ($ mil.): 13.3	Yield: —
Current ratio: 11.11	Payout: —
Long-term debt ($ mil.): —	Market value ($ mil.): 61.0

	STOCK PRICE ($) FY Close	P/E High	P/E Low	PER SHARE ($) Earnings	PER SHARE ($) Dividends	PER SHARE ($) Book Value
12/10	3.39	9	5	0.43	0.00	2.62
12/09	3.44	15	3	0.26	0.00	2.19
12/08	1.12	33	12	0.08	0.00	1.87
12/07	2.80	94	40	0.05	0.00	1.74
12/06	3.80	98	64	0.04	0.00	2.83
Annual Growth	(2.8%)	—	—	81.1%	—	(1.9%)

Fusion-io

Fusion-io has a data storage solution that boggles the mind. Its proprietary ioMemory offers more than 100 times the density of DRAM and allows users to use significantly fewer servers and handle more data. ioMemory, a form of flash memory, allows for more efficient data processing since it can replace a computer's hard drive, eliminating the need for power-draining server rooms and associated cooling and infrastructure costs. The company's ioMemory Virtual Storage Layer software connects operating systems and flash memory in its ioDrive products. It counts Facebook, HP, Dell, and IBM among its customers. Fusion-io was formed in 2005, and the company went public in 2011.

Fusion-io intends to use its anticipated $150 million in IPO proceeds primarily to expand its sales and marketing and to expand its product offerings. The company's strategy includes leveraging its visibility as a public company to capitalize on its first-to-market position and its creation of the data decentralization niche. It plans to develop more ioMemory-based software applications and continue expanding internationally. It may also make technology or business acquisitions though nothing specific is in the works.

In addition to its Virtual Storage Layer (VSL) software, Fusion-io's other software products include directCache data-tiering, which allows users to benefit from ioMemory while still using existing storage servers, and ioSphere data center management software. It also offers support services in hardware, software, and combination packages in yearly terms. The company's software is developed in-house, while vendors AlphaEMS and Jabil Circuit supply its hardware.

Directors Forest Baskett and Scott Sandell, through venture capital firm New Enterprise Associates, together control about a third of Fusion-io. Apple co-founder Steve Wozniak is its chief scientist.

EXECUTIVES

President, CEO, and Director, David A. Flynn, age 41
EVP and CTO, Neil A. Carson, age 34
EVP and CFO, Dennis P. Wolf, age 58
EVP Business Development, Saul H. Zales, age 49
EVP and COO, Lance L. Smith, age 47
EVP Worldwide Sales, James L. Dawson, age 49
EVP, Chief Legal Officer, and Secretary, Shawn J. Lindquist, age 41

EVP, Chief Marketing Officer, and Director, Rick C. White, age 41
VP Alliances, Tyler Smith
Chief Scientist, Stephen G. Wozniak, age 60
Media Relations, Robert Brumfield
Manager, EMEA OEM and Alliances, Mat Young
Auditors: Ernst & Young LLP

LOCATIONS

HQ: Fusion-io, Inc.
2855 E. Cottonwood Pkwy., Ste. 100, Salt Lake City, UT 84121
Phone: 801-424-5500
Web: www.fusionio.com

2010 Sales

	% of total
US	76
Other countries	24
Total	**100**

COMPETITORS

EMC	Oracle
Hitachi Data Systems	Samsung Electronics
Intel	Seagate Technology
LSI Corp.	STEC
Micron Technology	Toshiba
NetApp	Western Digital
OCZ Technology	

HISTORICAL FINANCIALS

Company Type: Public

Income Statement

FYE: June 30

	REVENUE ($ mil.)	NET INCOME ($ mil.)	NET PROFIT MARGIN	EMPLOYEES
06/11	197.2	4.6	2.3%	441
06/10	36.2	(31.7)	—	348
06/09	10.1	(25.6)	—	0
06/08	0.6	(10.0)	—	0
Annual Growth	590.1%	—	—	26.7%

2011 Year-End Financials

Debt ratio: —	No. of shares (mil.): 81.1
Return on equity: 1.7%	Dividends
Cash ($ mil.): 219.6	Yield: —
Current ratio: 9.09	Payout: —
Long-term debt ($ mil.): —	Market value ($ mil.): 2,441.8

	STOCK PRICE ($) FY Close	P/E High	P/E Low	PER SHARE ($) Earnings	PER SHARE ($) Dividends	PER SHARE ($) Book Value
06/11	30.09	616	321	0.06	0.00	3.38
Annual Growth	—	—	—	—	—	—

FX Energy

FX Energy is not exactly fixated on energy in Poland, but it is in western Poland's Permian Basin where it is hoping to make its big breakthrough. In 2008 the independent exploration and production company reported proved reserves of 45.9 billion cu. ft. of natural gas equivalent in Poland, and 45,000 barrels of oil equivalent in the US (from properties in Montana and Nevada). Partners include state-owned Polish Oil and Gas and CalEnergy Gas, which have served as operators for exploration wells in Poland. FX Energy holds about 5.4 million net acres in western Poland.

EXECUTIVES

Chairman and EVP, Thomas B. Lovejoy, age 75, $440,629 total compensation
President, CEO, and Director, David N. Pierce, age 65, $643,551 total compensation
VP Finance, Treasurer, and Chief Accounting Officer, Clay Newton, age 54, $366,433 total compensation
VP Investor Relations and Secretary, Scott J. Duncan, age 62
VP Operations, Andrew W. (Andy) Pierce, age 63, $514,056 total compensation
VP International Exploration and Director, Jerzy B. Maciolek, age 61, $521,731 total compensation
Auditors: PricewaterhouseCoopers LLP

LOCATIONS

HQ: FX Energy, Inc.
3006 Highland Dr., Ste. 206, Salt Lake City, UT 84106
Phone: 801-486-5555   **Fax:** 801-486-5575
Web: www.fxenergy.com

2008 Oil & Gas Sales

	$ mil.	% of total
Poland	7.8	58
US	5.7	42
Total	**13.5**	**100**

PRODUCTS/OPERATIONS

2008 Sales

	$ mil.	% of total
Oil & gas	13.5	76
Oilfield services	4.3	24
Total	**17.8**	**100**

HISTORICAL FINANCIALS

Company Type: Public

Income Statement

FYE: December 31

	REVENUE ($ mil.)	NET INCOME ($ mil.)	NET PROFIT MARGIN	EMPLOYEES
12/10	25.0	(0.8)	—	49
12/09	14.7	(0.5)	—	49
12/08	17.8	(54.7)	—	47
12/07	18.0	(11.7)	—	40
12/06	8.2	(13.8)	—	42
Annual Growth	32.1%	—	—	3.9%

2010 Year-End Financials

Debt ratio: 146.8%	No. of shares (mil.): 45.3
Return on equity: —	Dividends
Cash ($ mil.): 19.7	Yield: —
Current ratio: 3.57	Payout: —
Long-term debt ($ mil.): 35.0	Market value ($ mil.): 278.5

	STOCK PRICE ($) FY Close	P/E High	P/E Low	PER SHARE ($) Earnings	PER SHARE ($) Dividends	PER SHARE ($) Book Value
12/10	6.15	—	—	(0.02)	0.00	0.53
12/09	2.85	—	—	(0.01)	0.00	0.25
12/08	2.79	—	—	(1.35)	0.00	0.36
12/07	5.68	—	—	(0.32)	0.00	0.99
12/06	6.27	—	—	(0.39)	0.00	0.91
Annual Growth	(0.5%)	—	—	—	—	(12.8%)

G-III Apparel

G-III Apparel Group has the leather part of Stevie Nicks' leather and lace wrapped up. The company is best known for making leather jackets under the G-III, Marvin Richards, Black Rivet, Winlit, Siena Studio, and other labels (such as Andrew Marc), as well as under licensed names. It also makes pants, skirts, and sportswear from leather and other materials. Some 65% of G-III's sales are generated from licensed apparel it makes for the NFL, NBA, NHL, and MLB teams, as well as for Jones New York, Nine West, and Kenneth Cole. The company's customers include department stores such as Macy's, Nordstrom, Lord & Taylor, and Kohl's. Chairman and CEO Morris Goldfarb own some 17% of G-III.

Additionally, Buckingham Capital Management and FMR each hold about a 12% stake.

The company formed a joint venture with The Camuto Group to develop a chain of stores devoted to footwear and accessories operating under the Vince Camuto banner. The chain leverages G-III's retail infrastructure (real estate, distribution, information, and administrative systems), with Camuto providing its growing family of big-name brands, including Vince Camuto, Jessica Simpson, BCBG Max Azria, BCBGeneration, Kensiegirl, Lucky Brand, and Arturo Chiang. The first Vince Camuto store opened in early 2011.

Having been big in licensing for a decade, the company has inked several deals that maintain its strategy and revenue mix of licensed and non-licensed products. A particular purchase it has used as a foundation for this effort is its acquisition of Andrew Marc for $42 million in 2008. The deal gave G-III handbags and upscale specialty and department store distribution. Andrew Marc then entered a licensing agreement with Camuto to make and market women's footwear under the Andrew Marc and Marc New York brands. G-III's Jessica Howard license extends its reach into dresses with its Jessica Howard and Eliza J names. G-III's purchase of Industrial Cotton also expanded its junior denim products. The purchases also gave G-III a foothold in new retail outlets, with the brands selling in Dillard's, Nordstrom, Sears, Kohl's, and Coldwater Creek, among others.

Beyond the department store channel, G-III operates about 120 retail stores, most of which are outlet stores. The company's retail business generated about 16% of its sales in 2010. G-III had extended its reach into retail in 2008, when the apparel wholesaler acquired the Wilsons The Leather Experts' outlet stores, as well as the Wilsons brand name and distribution center operations for about $22 million. The move represented G-III's effort to boost its retail presence.

G-III conducts most of its business in the US, with 98% of its revenue generated within the country's borders. Its products are produced by independent manufacturers, however, located primarily in China, as well as in India, Indonesia, Sri Lanka, Taiwan, Thailand, Vietnam, and Central and South America. Some of its garments are made in the US.

EXECUTIVES

Chairman and CEO, Morris Goldfarb, age 60, $2,373,854 total compensation
President, Jeanette Nostra, age 59, $855,373 total compensation
CFO and Treasurer, Neal S. Nackman, age 51, $515,335 total compensation
COO and Secretary, Wayne S. Miller, age 53, $1,037,755 total compensation
Group President, Women's Leather Fashions, Deborah Gaertner, age 56
Vice Chairman, Sammy Aaron, age 51, $623,320 total compensation
Investor Relations, James Palczynski
Auditors: Ernst & Young LLP

LOCATIONS

HQ: G-III Apparel Group, Ltd.
512 7th Ave., New York, NY 10018
Phone: 212-403-0500   **Fax:** 212-403-0551
Web: www.g-iii.com

2010 Sales

	$ mil.	% of total
US	782.3	98
Other countries	18.6	2
Total	**800.9**	**100**

PRODUCTS/OPERATIONS

2010 Sales

	$ mil.	% of total
Wholesale licensed apparel	523.6	62
Wholesale non-licensed apparel	188.3	23
Retail	126.6	15
Adjustments	(37.6)	-
Total	**800.9**	**100**

Divisions

Outerwear
  Andrew Marc
  Black Rivet
  Calvin Klein
  Cole Haan
  Dockers
  Ellen Tracy
  Guess
  Jones New York
  Kenneth Cole
  Levi's
  Marc New York
  Nine West
  Sean John
  Tommy Hilfiger
Ready to Wear
  Andrew Marc Dresses
  Calvin Klein Dresses
  Calvin Klein Performance Wear
  Calvin Klein Sportswear
  Calvin Klein Women Suits
  Eliza J Dresses
  Ellen Tracy Dresses
  Jessica Howard Dresses
  Jessica Simpson Dresses
  Marc New York Dresses
Sports
  G-III for Her
  G-III Sports by Carl Banks
  Major League Baseball
  National Basketball Association
  National Football League
  National Hockey League
  Officially Licensed Collegiate Products
  Touch by Alyssa Milano
Retail
  Wilsons Outlets

Selected Licenses

Calvin Klein
Cole Haan
Ellen Tracy
IZOD
Jones New York
Kenneth Cole Productions
Major League Baseball
National Basketball Association
National Football League
National Hockey League
Nine West
Tommy Hilfiger

COMPETITORS

Amerex	L.L. Bean
Armani	NIKE
Burberry	North Face
Burlington Coat Factory	Phat Fashions
Columbia Sportswear	Roc Apparel
Diesel SpA	Sean John
FUBU	Tandy Leather
J. Crew	The Gap
	Wal-Mart

HISTORICAL FINANCIALS

Company Type: Public

Income Statement

FYE: January 31

	REVENUE ($ mil.)	NET INCOME ($ mil.)	NET PROFIT MARGIN	EMPLOYEES
01/11	1,063.4	56.7	5.3%	2,154
01/10	800.9	31.7	4.0%	1,880
01/09	711.1	(14.0)	—	1,245
01/08	518.9	17.5	3.4%	573
01/07	427.0	13.2	3.1%	510
Annual Growth	**25.6%**	**44.0%**	**—**	**43.4%**

2011 Year-End Financials

Debt ratio: —
Return on equity: 18.7%
Cash ($ mil.): 10.0
Current ratio: 2.72
Long-term debt ($ mil.): —
No. of shares (mil.): 19.7
Dividends
  Yield: —
  Payout: —
Market value ($ mil.): 686.9

	STOCK PRICE ($) FY Close	P/E High/Low		PER SHARE ($) Earnings	Dividends	Book Value
01/11	34.89	13	6	2.88	0.00	15.41
01/10	17.41	12	2	1.83	0.00	12.33
01/09	5.50	—	—	(0.85)	0.00	9.81
01/08	13.37	25	10	1.05	0.00	10.59
01/07	22.14	24	8	0.94	0.00	7.21
Annual Growth	**12.0%**	**—**	**—**	**32.3%**	**—**	**20.9%**

Geeknet

This company is fanning the flames of the open source software movement. Geeknet (formerly SourceForge) produces websites aimed primarily at open source software developers and other technology enthusiasts. The company's websites include SourceForge.net (an online collaborative development site), Slashdot.org (peer-produced and -moderated technology news), and freshmeat.net (catering to Linux users). It also operates ThinkGeek, an online shop for apparel, books, and tech gadgets. The company sold its enterprise software business in 2007. Founded by former chairman Larry Augustin in 1993, the business adopted the Geeknet name in late 2009.

During the past couple years, Geeknet has seen some worn carpet in its executive suite. Scott Kauffman, a veteran of several digital entertainment and Internet companies, joined the firm as president and CEO in January 2009 to transform the online media and e-commerce company into a major presence on the Internet. However, when Geeknet in August 2010 announced its lukewarm second-quarter financial results, the firm also announced Kauffman's resignation. Chairman Ken Langone then assumed the title of interim CEO. Along with the executive shift, Geeknet announced plans to complete a 1:10 reverse stock split and changed its ticker symbol to GKNT effective August 5, 2010.

Kauffman had helped the firm close a deal to acquire Ohloh Corporation, a private company that runs open source data and community Ohloh.net. The move gave Geeknet greater insight into the open source development community and allowed it to target its advertising. The Ohloh purchase was quickly followed by the acquisition of Geek.com, an online information resource and community for techies and professionals, for the sum of $1 million. Geek.com features news and reviews of hardware, software, and games, along with computer buying guides and forums. Geeknet hopes the acquisition increases traffic and boosts its access to mainstream consumer advertising categories.

In October 2010 the company sold Ohloh to Black Duck Software; at the same time, its ThinkGeek unit released two new products to commemorate the 30th anniversary of *Star Wars: Episode V The Empire Strikes Back* — a Star Wars Wampa Rug and a C-3PO Bespin Backpack.

The company plans relocated in 2011, moving its headquarters from California to Fairfax, Virginia, in March.

HISTORY

Unable to afford a high-end Sun Microsystems workstation in 1991, Larry Augustin decided to build a Linux-based version in his living room so he could finish his dissertation at Stanford. When his experiment yielded a machine that was a third the price and twice as fast as Sun's, his fellow graduate students took notice. Instead of pursuing the business model Augustin co-wrote with friends Jerry Yang and David Filo (which eventually became Yahoo!), Augustin stuck to his engineering roots and continued to build workstations out of his house.

In 1993, still a doctoral student in electrical engineering, he started VA Research along with pal James Vera (VA comes from the initials of their surnames) with financing from their credit cards. The company incorporated in 1995. (Vera remained a researcher at Stanford.)

Because VA Research designed and built its systems from the ground up (and because Linux itself was continuously morphing into something else), it wasn't until 1997 that the company released its first high-end workstations. With funding from venture investment firm Sequoia Capital in 1998, VA Research began building its staff by hiring Linux veterans such as Leonard Zubkoff, whom Augustin lured away from Oracle to be his CTO. The company also began to target the high-end server market, offering $200,000 systems to ISPs.

In 1999 VA Research changed its name to VA Linux Systems and formed alliances with Linux software vendors Red Hat and SuSE Linux to preinstall its software on its systems. The company also bought out its closest rival, Linux Hardware Solutions, as well as a Linux consulting company and a graphical user interface specialist. VA Linux went public that December — its stock price soaring a record 698% during its first day of trading.

The company acquired Linux information portal Andover.Net in 2000 and later launched the Open Source Development Network (OSDN). It also bought privately held TruSolutions and NetAttach in two deals with a combined value of about $230 million.

The next year — citing sluggish hardware spending and high costs — VA Linux announced that it would cut about 35% of its workforce and exit its core server and workstation business in order to focus on Linux-based development software and services. The company changed its name to VA Software late in 2001.

Company president and COO Ali Jenab was promoted to CEO the next year, while Augustin remained chairman (he left in 2007). In 2004 the company renamed OSDN the Open Source Technology Group and redesigned many of its online publications in an effort to expand the audience for its Web sites.

In December 2005, VA Software sold its Animation Factory subsidiary to WebMediaBrands for about $9.4 million. Two years later, VA Software changed its name to SourceForge.

In April 2007 the company sold its SourceForge software development suite, which offered a Web-based environment for collaborative programming teams to manage their work. CollabNet, a fellow collaboration facilitator, picked up the software for an equity stake in that company. The software business accounted for about 23% of the firm's sales. While a graduate student at Stanford in 1993, Augustin (who owns 5% of the company) chose to help start VA Software rather than become a co-founder of Yahoo!. The company changed its name from VA Software to SourceForge in May 2007.

In June 2008 Robert Neumeister succeeded Jenab as president and CEO of the firm on an interim basis in June 2008. In January 2009 Scott Kauffman succeeded Neumeister, who remained chairman of the company. In May the firm bought privately held Ohloh Corporation, a provider of open source data based in Bellevue, Washington. In November 2009 the company changed its name from SourceForge to Geeknet, Inc. to better communicate its mission as the online network for the global geek community.

In May 2010 Geeknet acquired Geek.com for $1 million. Kauffman resigned in August 2010 amid lukewarm 2Q results and Ken Langone, chairman, assumed the title of interim CEO. The company moved from California to Virginia in 2011.

EXECUTIVES

Chairman, President, and CEO, Kenneth G. (Ken) Langone, age 75
President and CEO, ThinkGeek, Caroline Offutt, age 47
EVP and CFO, Kathryn K. (Katy) McCarthy, age 42
VP Sales, Chris Dobbrow
VP Platform, Jeff (Hemos) Bates, age 35
VP, SourceForge.net and SourceForge.net Marketplace, Michael Rudolph, age 46
VP, Corporate Secretary, and General Counsel, James Jay Seirmarco, age 46
COO, Jason Baird
Corporate Controller, Jeffrey Chalmers, age 48
Chief Revenue Officer, Matthew (Matt) Sweeney
Auditors: Stonefield Josephson, Inc.

LOCATIONS

HQ: Geeknet, Inc.
11216 Waples Mill Rd., Ste. 100, Fairfax, VA 22030
Phone: 650-694-2100   **Fax:** 650-694-2111
Web: geek.net

PRODUCTS/OPERATIONS

2009 Sales

	$ mil.	% of total
E-commerce	49.1	75
Media	16.5	25
Total	**65.6**	**100**

Selected Products and Operations

E-commerce (ThinkGeek)
  Apparel
  Caffeinated products
  Electronics
  Office products
Online media
  Freshmeat.net
  Linux.com
  Slashdot.org
  SourceForge.net

COMPETITORS

Amazon.com	International Data
AOL	Group
Bloomberg Businessweek	MSN
CBS Interactive	Newegg
Forbes	Tucows
Fry's Electronics	Yahoo!
Google	Ziff Davis Media

HISTORICAL FINANCIALS

Company Type: Public

Income Statement

FYE: December 31

	REVENUE ($ mil.)	NET INCOME ($ mil.)	NET PROFIT MARGIN	EMPLOYEES
12/10	94.6	(4.4)	—	122
12/09*	65.6	(14.0)	—	127
07/08	55.3	(4.3)	—	120
07/07	45.6	8.7	19.1%	101
07/06	43.6	11.0	25.2%	121
Annual Growth	**21.4%**	**—**	**—**	**0.2%**

*Fiscal year change

2010 Year-End Financials

Debt ratio: —
Return on equity: —
Cash ($ mil.): 35.3
Current ratio: 3.01
Long-term debt ($ mil.): —
No. of shares (mil.): 6.3
Dividends
  Yield: —
  Payout: —
Market value ($ mil.): 157.0

	STOCK PRICE ($) FY Close	P/E High/Low		Earnings	Dividends	Book Value
12/10	25.03	—	—	(0.73)	0.00	7.63
12/09*	11.90	—	—	(2.30)	0.00	7.97
07/08	13.90	—	—	(0.60)	0.00	9.30
07/07	37.10	43	24	1.30	0.00	9.51
07/06	39.70	35	8	1.70	0.00	7.78
Annual Growth	**(10.9%)**	**—**	**—**	**—**	**—**	**(0.5%)**

*Fiscal year change

Genomic Health

Genomic Health believes the genome is key to good health. The company conducts genomic research to develop molecular diagnostics and assays that can predict the likelihood of disease recurrence and response to therapy and treatments. Genomic Health's Onco*type* DX breast cancer test predicts the likelihood of chemotherapy effectiveness and cancer recurrence in women with newly diagnosed, early stage invasive breast cancer. Genomic Health's research efforts are targeted at providing a wider base of cancer-related tests, and in 2010 it launched a new Oncotype DX colon cancer test to predict recurrence rates for stage II colon cancer patients. The company sells its products to oncologists and pathologists.

Genomic Health uses a direct sales force to market its products; it also operates a clinical pathology lab in California to process the test results. The company relies heavily on reimbursements from health plans and managed care companies to pay for its products and services, and as such, is dependent on insurance companies' reimbursement approvals of its products. Its largest customer is Centers for Medicare and Medicaid Services (CMS), which accounts for 20% of sales.

While more than 90% of its revenues come from the US market, Genomic Health is widening its distribution network for the Oncotype DX breast cancer test into international markets by establishing partnerships with regional drug representatives. It is focused on sales in the Americas, Europe, and Asia, and it is working to expand its colon cancer tests into international markets as well. Genomic Health achieved its first profitable year in 2010 and, as a result, is increasing investments in marketing expansion and research and development efforts.

The company is working to apply its breast cancer product to late-stage breast cancer patients, as well as to evaluate the effectiveness of other treatment methods besides chemotherapy. It also plans to expand the patient applications for its colon cancer test, and it is developing additional tests for prostate, lung, and renal cell cancer and melanoma patients. The renal cancer test is being developed in partnership with Pfizer.

Genomic Health has a research partnership with Bristol-Myers Squibb and ImClone Systems to develop a test evaluating the effectiveness of the companies' Erbitux colorectal treatment. Genomic Health has a similar affiliation with Sanofi-Aventis to predict the likelihood of benefit for Aventis' Taxotere breast cancer treatment. In addition, the firm is working on a new next-generation gene sequencing technology to provide for faster, more efficient diagnostic services.

Investment firm Baker Brothers Advisors owns about a quarter of the company's stock.

EXECUTIVES

Chairman, Randal W. (Randy) Scott, age 53, $315,500 total compensation
CFO, Dean Schorno, age 47
President, CEO, and Director, Kimberly J. (Kim) Popovits, age 52, $457,000 total compensation
EVP Worldwide Commercialization, David Logan
CIO, Paul Aldridge
Chief Medical Officer, Steven (Steve) Shak, age 60, $413,400 total compensation
Chief Scientific Officer, Joffre B. Baker, age 63, $397,100 total compensation
SVP Human Resources, Tricia Tomlinson
SVP Corporate Communications, Laura Leber, age 46
SVP and General Counsel, Kathy L. Hibbs, age 48
COO and Secretary, G. Bradley (Brad) Cole, age 55, $391,700 total compensation
Auditors: Ernst & Young LLP

LOCATIONS

HQ: Genomic Health, Inc.
301 Penobscot Dr., Redwood City, CA 94063
Phone: 650-556-9300   **Fax:** 650-556-1132
Web: www.genomichealth.com

PRODUCTS/OPERATIONS

2010 Sales

	$ mil.	% of total
Product revenues	174.9	98
Contract revenues	3.2	2
Total	**178.1**	**100**

COMPETITORS

Celera	Med BioGene
deCODE genetics	Myriad Genetics
GE Healthcare	Novartis
Genoptix	Precision Therapeutics
Genzyme	QIAGEN
Hologic	Quest Diagnostics
Johnson & Johnson	Response Genetics
LabCorp	Roche Diagnostics
Life Technologies	Siemens Healthca
Corporation	

HISTORICAL FINANCIALS

Company Type: Public

Income Statement

FYE: December 31

	REVENUE ($ mil.)	NET INCOME ($ mil.)	NET PROFIT MARGIN	EMPLOYEES
12/10	178.1	4.3	2.4%	472
12/09	149.5	(9.4)	—	453
12/08	110.6	(16.1)	—	387
12/07	64.0	(27.3)	—	288
12/06	29.2	(28.9)	—	191
Annual Growth	**57.2%**	**—**	**—**	**25.4%**

2010 Year-End Financials

Debt ratio: —	No. of shares (mil.): 29.0
Return on equity: 5.0%	Dividends
Cash ($ mil.): 31.2	Yield: —
Current ratio: 4.53	Payout: —
Long-term debt ($ mil.): —	Market value ($ mil.): 620.5

	STOCK PRICE ($) FY Close	P/E High/Low		PER SHARE ($) Earnings	Dividends	Book Value
12/10	21.39	169	85	0.14	0.00	2.97
12/09	19.56	—	—	(0.33)	0.00	2.39
12/08	19.48	—	—	(0.57)	0.00	2.33
12/07	22.64	—	—	(1.02)	0.00	2.53
12/06	18.85	—	—	(1.18)	0.00	1.71
Annual Growth	**3.2%**	—	—	**—**	**—**	**14.9%**

GeoEye

Much like a celestial being, GeoEye keeps watch over the planet. The company provides satellite-collected Earth imagery and geospatial information for commercial and government organizations. It operates high-resolution imaging satellites that collect detailed land, sea, and atmospheric images, which the company processes and distributes. The company's imagery and information is used for a variety of applications, including mapping, disaster response, environmental monitoring, resource management, national security, and infrastructure and asset management. GeoEye also offers aerial imaging, advanced image processing, and production software and services. The company generates more than 70% of its sales in the US.

Accounting for about two-thirds of GeoEye's revenues, the US government is GeoEye's largest customer — specifically the National Geospatial-Intelligence Agency (NGA). The company's NextView imagery contract with the NGA was modified in 2008 to accommodate satellite launch delays and to bill GeoEye's work by specific products and services rather than by square kilometers of imagery. In mid-2010 it was awarded a $3.8 billion contract from the NGA under the Enhanced-View program (the follow-on program to NextView) to provide products and services to support the increased geospatial intelligence needed by the Department of Defense and the intelligence community.

GeoEye's sales grew by around 85% in 2009, primarily due to a large increase in imagery revenues related to its contract with the NGA. Its net income for the year was $32 million, which included a non-recurring loss from early extinguishment of debt offset by an income tax benefit related to a change in accounting. The company continued to report record results on a quarterly basis in fiscal 2010. However, satellites have a limited operational lifespan and are expensive and time-consuming to replace. GeoEye's business model depends on the sale of imagery from its satellites; if one of its older satellites fails, the company currently has no plans to replace it.

Google uses images from the GeoEye-1 satellite (launched in 2008) for its Web-based Google Earth and Google Maps services. GeoEye has three satellites in orbit and is planning to launch another satellite, the GeoEye-2, which is expected to be operational in late 2013. GeoEye has contracted with Lockheed Martin Space Systems to complete construction of the satellite. ITT developed the camera for the GeoEye-2, which will be able to discern objects on the Earth's surface as small as nearly 10 inches in size.

In late 2010 GeoEye expanded its information services for defense customers when it made an offer to buy SPADAC Inc. for $46 million in cash and stock. SPADAC offers geospatial predictive analysis — it studies the satellite imagery and offers insight based on a customers' needs. Once the acquisition is complete, SPADAC will be renamed GeoEye Analytics.

During 2010 the company added a large, multiyear order from its Russian reseller, ScanEx Research and Development Center. It also launched its EyeQ subscription-based Web mapping information service. With EyeQ, the company plans to expand sales of imagery for use in the engineering, oil and gas, construction, and mining industries.

GeoEye got its start in 1993, originally as an operating division of Orbital Sciences; it became a separate company in 1997, when Orbital Sciences spun off the division. The company underwent restructuring under Chapter 11 bankruptcy protection due to expenses related to legal disputes with Orbital Sciences over license agreements with the former parent. The company settled its differences with Orbital Sciences and emerged from bankruptcy in 2003.

In 2006 the company (then called ORBIMAGE) acquired rival Space Imaging in a deal valued at $58.5 million. The combined company then began operating as GeoEye. A year later it purchased M.J. Harden Associates, a digital aerial imagery specialist, from General Electric.

EXECUTIVES

Chairman, James A. Abrahamson, age 77
President, CEO, and Director, Matthew M. O'Connell, age 58, $1,644,203 total compensation
EVP and CFO, Joseph F. Greeves, age 54, $1,071,691 total compensation
VP Product Integration, Steven P. Wallach
VP International Sales, Paolo E. Colombi, age 62
VP Corporate Communications, Mark E. Brender, age 61
VP Business Development, Dean Edmundson
VP Finance and Planning and Principal Financial Officer, Steven R. Balthazor, age 46, $295,099 total compensation
VP North American Sales, U.S. Government Sales, Thornton W. (Bill) Wilt Jr., age 65, $313,372 total compensation
VP Investor Relations, Randall J. Scherago
COO, William Schuster, age 59, $755,062 total compensation
SVP Marketing, Tony Frazier
SVP, General Counsel, and Secretary, William L. Warren, age 45, $646,733 total compensation
Senior Director International Sales Channel Support, International Channel Partners, Michael Rugala
Senior Account Representative, SeaStar Sales in Spain, SeaStar Fisheries Information Serivces, Liliana Serpa
Manager Partner Development, U.S. and Canada Partners, Shaun Callaghan
Sales Associate, SeaStar Sales (North America), SeaStar Fisheries Information Services, Matthew Galston
Director North American Partners, U.S. and Canada Channel Partners, Tara Byrnes
Senior Director International Sales Operations, International Channel Partners, Michelle Noonan
Senior Channel Sales Manager, Latin America and the Caribbean, Mack Koepke
International Sales Director, Information Services, Hanna Kubiak
Consultant, SeaStar Sales in Latin America, SeaStar Fisheries Information Services, Pedro Noriega
Senior Regional Sales Director, Asia, Andy Stephenson
Senior Regional Sales Director, Middle East, Africa, India, Nepal, and Sri Lanka, Rao Ramayanan
Senior Regional Sales Director, Europe, Andy Hanna
Director Government Programs, NGA, U.S. Government Sales, Christopher (Chris) Incardona
Senior Director, NGA Programs, U.S. Government Sales, Erol Morey
Manager Corporate Communications, Valerie (Val) Webb
CTO, Brian O'Toole, age 47, $573,141 total compensation
SVP Sales, Christopher R. (Chris) Tully, age 54
Director Sales and Marketing, SeaStar Sales in Asia & Oceania, SeaStar Fisheries Information Service, Chris Wilson
Director Commercial Sales, Lori Ward
Director Air and Marine Transportation, U.S. Government Sales, Dejan Damjanovic
Senior Director, Federal Sales, U.S Government Sales, Steve Miller
Senior Sales Manager, SeaStar Sales in Europe & Africa, SeaStar Fisheries Information Services, Richard Holmquist
Auditors: KPMG LLP

LOCATIONS

HQ: GeoEye, Inc.
21700 Atlantic Blvd., Dulles, VA 20166
Phone: 703-480-7500   **Fax:** 703-450-9570
Web: www.geoeye.com

2009 Sales

	$ mil.	% of total
US	196.7	73
Other countries	74.4	27
Total	**271.1**	**100**

PRODUCTS/OPERATIONS

2009 Sales

	$ mil.	% of total
Imagery	206.4	76
NextView cost share	21.1	8
Production & other services	43.6	16
Total	**271.1**	**100**

COMPETITORS

DigitalGlobe	Integrity Applications
Earth Search Sciences	Orbital Sciences
Getmapping	Trimble Navigation

HISTORICAL FINANCIALS

Company Type: Public

Income Statement
FYE: December 31

	REVENUE ($ mil.)	NET INCOME ($ mil.)	NET PROFIT MARGIN	EMPLOYEES
12/10	330.3	24.6	7.4%	723
12/09	271.1	32.1	11.8%	534
12/08	146.7	26.6	18.1%	484
12/07	183.8	42.4	23.1%	410
12/06	151.2	23.4	15.5%	318
Annual Growth	**21.6%**	**1.3%**	—	**22.8%**

2010 Year-End Financials

Debt ratio: 114.6%
Return on equity: 5.6%
Cash ($ mil.): 283.2
Current ratio: 3.36
Long-term debt ($ mil.): 508.2

No. of shares (mil.): 22.1
Dividends
  Yield: —
  Payout: —
Market value ($ mil.): 935.2

	STOCK PRICE ($) FY Close	P/E High/Low	Earnings	Dividends	Book Value
12/10	42.39	47 23	1.02	0.00	20.09
12/09	27.88	21 10	1.55	0.00	14.06
12/08	19.23	27 11	1.36	0.00	12.60
12/07	33.65	17 7	2.14	0.00	12.33
12/06	19.35	20 9	1.08	0.00	9.33
Annual Growth	**21.7%**	— —	**(1.4%)**	—	**21.1%**

Georgia Bancshares

Georgia Bancshares is (peachy) keen on community banking. Based in Peachtree City, it's the holding company for The Bank of Georgia, which operates nearly 10 branches in the Peach State, southwest of Atlanta. Specializing in community-oriented financial services for individuals and small to midsized businesses, the bank offers checking and savings accounts; CDs; money market accounts; and IRAs. Commercial mortgage, construction, and land development loans account for approximately two-thirds of the company's loan portfolio. The bank also offers investment services through an agreement with a third-party provider. Directors and executive officers of Georgia Bancshares own more than half of the company.

EXECUTIVES

Chairman, Enrico A. Stanziale, age 68
President, CEO, and Director, Ira (Pat) Shepherd III, age 61
Director; EVP and Director, The Bank of Georgia, Malcolm R. Godwin, age 53
Director; EVP and Senior Loan Officer, The Bank of Georgia, Rick A. Duncan, age 56
SVP and CFO, The Bank of Georgia, C. Lynn Gable, age 56
Auditors: Porter Keadle Moore, LLP

LOCATIONS

HQ: Georgia Bancshares, Inc.
100 Westpark Dr., Peachtree City, GA 30269
Phone: 770-631-9488   **Fax:** 770-487-4098
Web: www.georgiabancshares.com

COMPETITORS

Bank of America	Regions Financial
BB&T	SunTrust
Fidelity Southern	Synovus
Heritage Financial Group	United Community Banks

HISTORICAL FINANCIALS

Company Type: Public

Income Statement
FYE: December 31

	ASSETS ($ mil.)	NET INCOME ($ mil.)	INCOME AS % OF ASSETS	EMPLOYEES
12/04	249.6	1.8	0.7%	64
12/03	205.1	1.3	0.6%	44
12/02	171.6	0.6	0.3%	37
12/01	118.8	0.3	0.3%	0
Annual Growth	**28.1%**	**81.7%**	—	**31.5%**

2004 Year-End Financials

Equity as % of assets: —
Return on assets: 0.7%
Return on equity: 8.7%
Long-term debt ($ mil.): 8.7
No. of shares (mil.): —

Dividends
  Yield: —
  Payout: —
Market value ($ mil.): —
Sales ($ mil.): 14.2

	STOCK PRICE ($) FY Close	P/E High/Low	Earnings	Dividends	Book Value
12/04	15.00	29 22	0.55	0.00	(0.00)
12/03	15.00	58 30	0.36	0.00	(0.00)
12/02	13.60	81 55	0.17	0.00	(0.00)
Annual Growth	**5.0%**	— —	**79.9%**	—	—

Gevo

Putting sugar in a gas tank is generally not a good idea, but Gevo has figured out a way to make it beneficial. A renewable chemical and biofuels company, Gevo produces isobutanol, a multi-purpose chemical derived from glucose and other cellulosic biomass extracted from plant matter. Its isobutanol can be used as a blendstock (additive used during the refining process) for gasoline and jet fuel production and as a chemical used in the production of plastics, fibers, and rubber. Gevo does not yet produce isobutanol on a commercial scale, but it is in the process of building its customer and partnership base in preparation of commencing production. Formed in 2005, the company went public in early 2011.

Gevo plans to use the majority of the proceeds raised in its IPO (about $150 million) to acquire and refurbish production facilities. The company's ideal facilities are existing ethanol plants that it would either acquire or gain access to through joint ventures with other companies.

Using its IPO funds, Gevo entered a joint venture with Redfield Energy in 2011 to retrofit Redfield's existing ethanol plant into an isobutanol plant with a production capacity of 38 million gallons per year. The retrofit, using Gevo technology, will start in late 2011 and commercial production of isobutanol will begin in late 2012.

Gevo also began retrofitting its own ethanol plant in Luverne, Minnesota in early 2011 and will begin producing isobutanol in the first half of 2012. The plant's initial capacity is expected to hover around 18 million gallons of isobutanol per year. The company's long-term plans include ramping up production by 2014 to around 350 million gallons annually.

While Gevo is working to get its production operations online, it is also making an effort to secure demand for its product by pursuing potential customers and partners. The company has already signed non-binding agreements with some customers, including rubber-producer LANXESS and oil and gas company Total Petrochemicals, both of which also hold a small ownership stake in Gevo (Total Petrochemicals holds an indirect stake.). Other potential customers include Toray Industries, a fiber and plastic maker, and United Airlines, which would purchase jet fuel made with the company's isobutanol. The company's partners would include petroleum companies that produce and sell petroleum made with the company's isobutanol, and Cargill, which would supply biomass to Gevo.

The company is relying on the successful coordination of its customers, partners, and commercial production operations to generate income and, ultimately, become profitable. Gevo has been unprofitable since its inception, mainly because it has been focused primarily on research and development of isobutanol and has not generated enough income to offset its expenses.

Prior to its IPO, Gevo was owned by entities affiliated with Khosla Ventures (more than 40%), Virgin Green Fund (15%), and other investment firms.

EXECUTIVES

CFO, Mark L. Smith, age 49, $375,198 total compensation
CEO and Director, Patrick R. Gruber, age 51, $923,307 total compensation
EVP Corporate Development and Public Affairs, Jack Huttner, age 57, $347,206 total compensation
EVP Technology, David A. Glassner, age 53, $412,604 total compensation
EVP, General Counsel, and Secretary, Brett Lund, age 35
EVP Business Development, Christopher Ryan, age 50, $787,161 total compensation
VP Regulatory Affairs, Glenn Johnston
VP Human Resources, Paula A. Dinwiddie
Auditors: Deloitte & Touche LLP

LOCATIONS

HQ: Gevo, Inc.
345 Inverness Dr. South, Bldg. C, Ste. 310, Englewood, CO 80112
Phone: 303-858-8358
Web: www.gevo.com

COMPETITORS

Amyris
Dow Chemical
DuPont
Exxon Mobil
METabolic EXplorer

HISTORICAL FINANCIALS

Company Type: Public

Income Statement

FYE: December 31

	REVENUE ($ mil.)	NET INCOME ($ mil.)	NET PROFIT MARGIN	EMPLOYEES
12/10	16.4	(40.1)	—	91
12/09	0.7	(19.9)	—	57
12/08	0.2	(14.5)	—	0
12/07	0.3	(7.2)	—	0
Annual Growth	279.5%	—		59.6%

2010 Year-End Financials

Debt ratio: 94.1%
Return on equity: —
Cash ($ mil.): 15.3
Current ratio: 1.97
Long-term debt ($ mil.): 18.6
No. of shares (mil.): —
Dividends
　Yield: —
　Payout: —
Market value ($ mil.): —

	STOCK PRICE ($) FY Close	P/E High/Low	PER SHARE ($) Earnings	Dividends	Book Value
Annual Growth	—	— —	—	—	—

GigOptix

GigOptix hopes its light shines bright in an optical universe. The company develops polymer materials and products for use in wireless and optical communications networks. Products include optical and radio-frequency (RF) amplifiers, compact panel wireless antennas, and electro-optic modulators and optical interconnects for use in telecommunications. Its products are used in fiber-optic communications networks and for connecting to other types of electronic equipment. GigOptix also develops custom electro-optic devices for the US government, particularly the Department of Defense, which accounts most of sales. Customers have included Multiplex, Inc. and ZTE Corporation.

GigOptix has used acquisitions to expand its product portfolio. In its most recent deal, in 2011 the company acquired Endwave, a maker of RF components for wireless networks, for around $25 million in an all-stock transaction. By integrating Endwave's product lines and manufacturing capacity into its own product portfolio, GigOptix is looking to become a one-stop shop for optical network and mobile backhaul components.

In 2009 GigOptix acquired ChipX, a private supplier of analog and mixed signal integrated circuits. ChipX, which will continue as a product line, brings cross-selling opportunities, as well as a tier-one customer base (it is major supplier to National Instruments), and its technologies complement those of GigOptix. Both companies are located in the Silicon Valley and will be consolidated into one location at the GigOptix Palo Alto headquarters. ChipX investors received around 3.5 million of GigOptix's common stock shares (about 26%).

EXECUTIVES

Chairman, President, and CEO, Avi Katz, age 53
VP Engineering and CTO, Andrea Betti-Berutto, age 47
VP Optical Communications Sales, Jay de la Barre
VP and General Manager, GigOptix-Helix, Jörg Wieland
VP, RF and ASIC Sales, Elie Massabki
VP and General Manager, GigOptix-Bothell, Raluca Dinu
Acting CFO and Controller, Jeff Parsons
SVP Operations, Julie Tipton, age 47
Scientific Advisor, Bahram Jalali
Marketing Communications Manager, Parker Martineau
Auditors: PricewaterhouseCoopers LLP

LOCATIONS

HQ: GigOptix, Inc.
2400 Geng Rd., Ste. 100, Palo Alto, CA 94303
Phone: 650-424-1937　　**Fax:** 650-424-1938
Web: www.gigoptix.com

PRODUCTS/OPERATIONS

Selected Products

Biotechnology disposables (NanoCapture microarray slides)
Electro-optic devices
Instrument systems for biomarker research (ProteomicProcessor)
Polymer materials
Wireless antennas and systems

COMPETITORS

Affymetrix
Agilent Technologies
Fujitsu Semiconductor
JDS Uniphase
Laird Technologies
New Focus
SkyCross
Sumitomo Osaka Cement
Thermo Fisher Scientific

HISTORICAL FINANCIALS

Company Type: Public

Income Statement

FYE: December 31

	REVENUE ($ mil.)	NET INCOME ($ mil.)	NET PROFIT MARGIN	EMPLOYEES
12/10	26.9	(4.4)	—	83
12/09	14.8	(10.0)	—	98
12/08	9.7	(7.7)	—	67
12/07	3.2	(6.4)	—	65
12/06	2.3	(10.3)	—	56
Annual Growth	84.9%	—	—	10.3%

2010 Year-End Financials

Debt ratio: —
Return on equity: —
Cash ($ mil.): 4.5
Current ratio: 1.08
Long-term debt ($ mil.): —
No. of shares (mil.): 12.2
Dividends
　Yield: —
　Payout: —
Market value ($ mil.): 33.6

	STOCK PRICE ($) FY Close	P/E High/Low	PER SHARE ($) Earnings	Dividends	Book Value
12/10	2.75	— —	(0.41)	0.00	1.26
12/09	2.10	— —	(1.75)	0.00	1.51
12/08	1.00	— —	(5.78)	0.00	(0.00)
Annual Growth	65.8%	— —	—	—	—

Gleacher & Company

Gleacher & Company provides advisory services, capital raising, research, and securities and brokerage services to institutional clients in the US and Europe. The investment bank's MBS/ABS & Rates arm sells and trades asset and mortgage-backed securities. Gleacher's Corporate Credit division offers sales and trading on a range of debt securities. Another subsidiary, FA Technology Ventures, provides growth capital to technology firms. Gleacher & Company has offices in New York, Illinois, California, and New Jersey.

The company is focused on diversifying its product mix as a way to bring in other streams of revenue. A large portion of Gleacher & Company's revenues come from its sales and trading business (MBS/ABS & Rates and Corporate Credit). Those units suffered as markets declined during the recession. Net revenue for the company was down by more than 20% in 2010 alone.

Gleacher & Company launched a residential mortgage banking business in 2011 after it acquired ClearPoint Funding, a residential mortgage lender based in Massachusetts. The deal extended Gleacher's mortgage platform and diversified its business.

The company exited its underperforming equities division in 2011 and realigned its investment banking division. The strategic shift underscores the firm's commitment to its core fixed income operations and its investment banking, mortgage origination, and other stronger or promising operations. The company will also continue seeking new lines of business.

Gleacher & Company is reorganizing its business to better serve key industries such as real estate, financial services, aerospace and defense, and manufacturing.

Gleacher & Company was formed in 2009 after Broadpoint Securities acquired Gleacher Partners, a firm best known for its M&A advisory practice. The company officially changed its name to Gleacher & Company the following year.

Private equity firm MatlinPatterson owns more than 26% of Gleacher & Company. Chairman Eric Gleacher owns about 10%.

EXECUTIVES

Chairman, Eric J. Gleacher, age 70, $200,577 total compensation
CEO and Director, Thomas J. (Tom) Hughes, age 53
President, Equity Capital Markets, Curt Snyder
CEO, Equity Capital Markets, Robert (Bob) Meier
President, DESCAP, Robert M. (Rob) Fine
VP Advisory Services, William Cooling
VP, Matt Pennino
VP and Senior Research Analyst, Nam Sung Ji
COO, John Griff, age 55
Chief Administrative Officer, Laurence Mascera
Executive Managing Director; Head, Debt Capital Markets, Joseph Mannello
Managing Director; Head, Real Estate, Steve Hentschel
Managing Director and Co-Head, Restructuring and Recapitalization Advisory Group, Richard NeJame
Managing Director; Head, Capital Markets Origination, Keith (Lex) Malas
Head Trading, Equity Capital Markets, Richard Brown
Managing Director and Head, Investment Banking, Tim O'Connor
Managing Director and Co-Head, Restructuring Advisory Group, Robert Kost
Managing Director; Head, Equity Capital Markets Origination, J. Scott Coburn
Managing Director; Co-Head Investment-Grade Fixed-Income Sales, Richard J. Crescenzo
Managing Director; Co-Head Trading, Debt Capital Markets, Riaz Haidri
Managing Director; Co-Head Trading, Debt Capital Markets, John Hale
Managing Director; Co-Head Investment-Grade Fixed-Income Sales, Douglas J. Scales
Managing Director; Head Investment-Grade Trading, Robert Gorham
Managing Director, Investment-Grade Fixed Income Trading, Robert B. Cox
Managing Director, Investment-Grade Fixed Income Desk Analyst, Douglas R. Colandrea
Managing Director; Head Bank Loan Trading, Marc Berg
Managing Director; Head High Yield, Bank Loan, and Convertible Institutional Sales, Gregory Sullivan
Head Research, Equity Capital Markets, Mark Conley
Managing Director Mergers and Acquisitions, Advisory Services, David M. Reed Jr.
Acting CFO; Controller and COO, Broadpoint Capital, Jeffrey H. Kugler, age 51
Head Trading, DESCAP, Robert Tirschwell
Vice Chairman, Equity Capital Markets, Richard Prati
Managing Director and Head Sales, Equity Capital Markets, Myles Lavelle
Managing Director, Investment-Grade Fixed Income Sales, William F. (Bill) Parry
Secretary and General Counsel, Broadpoint Gleacher Securities Group and Broadpoint Capital, Patricia A. Arciero-Craig, age 43, $750,000 total compensation
Principal, Advisory Services, Sunny Cheung
Auditors: PricewaterhouseCoopers LLP

LOCATIONS

HQ: Gleacher & Company, Inc.
1290 Avenue of the Americas, 4th and 5th Fl., New York, NY 10017
Phone: 212-273-7100
Web: www.gleacher.com

PRODUCTS/OPERATIONS

2010 Sales

	$ mil.	% of total
Principal transactions	154.8	55
Interest income	57.3	20
Investment banking	43.4	15
Commissions	19.4	7
Investment banking revenue from related party	2.0	1
Fees and other	5.3	2
Total	**282.2**	**100**

COMPETITORS

Cowen Group	Robert W. Baird & Co.
Jefferies Group	Stifel Financial
Ladenburg Thalmann	Wedbush Securities
Oppenheimer Holdings	William Blair

HISTORICAL FINANCIALS

Company Type: Public

Income Statement

FYE: December 31

	REVENUE ($ mil.)	NET INCOME ($ mil.)	NET PROFIT MARGIN	EMPLOYEES
12/10	282.2	(20.6)	—	368
12/09	357.4	54.9	15.4%	342
12/08	145.0	(17.4)	—	255
12/07	47.1	(19.5)	—	211
12/06	130.7	(44.4)	—	284
Annual Growth	**21.2%**	**—**	**—**	**6.7%**

2010 Year-End Financials

Debt ratio: 0.3%
Return on equity: —
Cash ($ mil.): 40.0
Current ratio: —
Long-term debt ($ mil.): 0.9
No. of shares (mil.): 130.8
Dividends
 Yield: 0.0%
 Payout: —
Market value ($ mil.): 310.0

	STOCK PRICE ($) FY Close	P/E High/Low		PER SHARE ($) Earnings	Dividends	Book Value
12/10	2.37	—	—	(0.17)	0.00	2.65
12/09	4.46	17	4	0.53	0.00	2.65
12/08	2.97	—	—	(0.25)	0.00	1.23
12/07	1.18	—	—	(0.71)	0.00	1.52
12/06	2.32	—	—	(2.90)	0.00	3.12
Annual Growth	**0.5%**	**—**	**—**	**—**	**—**	**(4.1%)**

Global Power Equipment

Global Power Equipment Group doesn't let global power go to its head but to its bottom line. Through its subsidiaries, the company designs and manufactures power generation equipment for OEMs, engineering, construction, and power generation customers. Its products include auxiliary parts for natural gas-fired turbines, which are sold under its Braden Manufacturing and Consolidated Fabricators brands. It also sells heat recovery boilers under its Deltak brand. In addition, subsidiary Williams Industrial Services offers upgrades and maintenance services to industrial and utility companies, as well as to nuclear and hydroelectric power plants. North America represents more than 90% of Global Power's sales.

Instability in the US economy in recent years, coupled with weak demand from gas-fired power generation plant customers, has left the company with declining revenues. The declines are most pronounced in its power generation products segment, where annual revenues have been sliding year after year (in some cases by double-digit percentages).

Global Power's growing services segment has been picking up some of the slack, however. The unit has seen an uptick in services needed for capital improvements at aging power plants. Solid revenues generated by its services segment, as well as low operating costs, have enabled the company as a whole to remain profitable.

The company is expecting continued growth in its services segment as aging plants, including nuclear power plants built decades ago, seek to upgrade and modernize their facilities. Global Power is also confident that demand for its gas turbines and other equipment will rebound as the anticipated recovery in the natural gas industry —evident in increased gas exploration and production activity — takes hold in coming years.

EXECUTIVES

Chairman, Charles Macaluso, age 67
President, CEO, and Director, David L. (Dave) Keller, age 56
VP Business Development, General Counsel, and Secretary, Tracy D. Pagliara, age 48
SVP and CFO, David Willis, age 38
SVP; President, Braden Manufacturing, Gene Schockemoehl, age 62
SVP; President, Services Division, Ken Robuck, age 50
SVP; President, Products Division and Deltak, Dean Glover, age 44
Auditors: BDO Seidman, LLP

LOCATIONS

HQ: Global Power Equipment Group Inc.
6120 S. Yale St., Ste. 1480, Tulsa, OK 74136
Phone: 918-488-0828   **Fax:** 918-488-8389
Web: www.globalpower.com

2010 Sales

	% of total
North America	92
US and Canada	91
Mexico	1
Europe	6
Asia	1
Total	**100**

PRODUCTS/OPERATIONS

2010 Sales

	$ mil.	% of total
Services	377.4	73
Products	142.7	27
Total	**520.1**	**100**

Selected Products and Services

Power Generation Equipment
  Aftermarket products
  Auxiliary equipment for gas turbines
  Heat recovery steam generators
Maintenance Services
  Fossil fuel and hydroelectric power plant maintenance
  Industrial painting and coatings
  Insulation replacement and abatement
  Nuclear power plant maintenance
  Retrofit of auxiliary equipment for gas turbines
  Roofing removal and replacement
  Specialty fabrications and welding

COMPETITORS

ALSTOM	GEA Group
Blount International	Global Thermoelectric
Dril-Quip	Siemens Energy
Ferrotec USA	SpiraxSarco
Foster Wheeler	Vapor Power
GE Energy	Webco Industries

HISTORICAL FINANCIALS

Company Type: Public

Income Statement

FYE: December 31

	REVENUE ($ mil.)	NET INCOME ($ mil.)	NET PROFIT MARGIN	EMPLOYEES
12/10	520.1	40.6	7.8%	687
12/07	403.4	(14.9)	—	0
12/06	357.4	(56.1)	—	0
12/04	233.7	(0.7)	—	1,805
12/03	263.8	19.8	7.5%	949
Annual Growth	**10.2%**	**10.8%**	**—**	**(4.5%)**

2010 Year-End Financials

Debt ratio: —
Return on equity: 22.7%
Cash ($ mil.): 55.5
Current ratio: 2.45
Long-term debt ($ mil.): —

No. of shares (mil.): 15.5
Dividends
  Yield: —
  Payout: —
Market value ($ mil.): —

	STOCK PRICE ($) FY Close	P/E High/Low	PER SHARE ($) Earnings	Dividends	Book Value
12/10	0.00	— —	2.49	0.00	11.57
12/07	0.00	— —	(0.00)	0.00	(0.00)
Annual Growth	**—**	**— —**	**—**	**—**	**—**

Globe Specialty

Globe Specialty Metals is an apt name for a company that peddles its metals around the world. The specialty metals manufacturer sells silicon metal and silicon-based alloys to customers in the Americas, Asia, and Europe from facilities in the US, Argentina, China, and Poland. Its silicon metal and alloys are used to make a variety of industrial products, from aluminum and automotive parts to steel and semiconductors. It holds about one-fifth of the Western market share for magnesium ferrosilicon. Globe also recycles by-products such as silica fume, a dust-like material known as microsilica that is collected in air filtration systems, which it sells for use as a concrete additive.

Globe's revenues grew 11% in 2010, the result of a significant increase in metric tons sold. Sales of silicon-based alloys increased 28% while silicon metals were up 18%. Increased demand in the automotive sector also drove sales. Net income swung to a $34 million profit from a net loss the previous year.The company produces silicon, foundry alloys, steelmaking alloys, electrodes and silica fume through its subsidiaries, including Globe Metallurgical, Inc.(GMI), Globe Metais Industria e Comercio S.A. (Globe Metais), Globe Metales S.A. (Globe Metales), Solsil, Inc. (Solsil), and Ningxia Yonvey Coal Industrial Co. Ltd. (Yonvey).

In 2011 Globe acquired Alden Resources, a miner, processor, and supplier of specialty coal to the silicon and silicon-based alloy industries and thermal coal to the power industry. Alden operated several underground mines in Kentucky and Tennessee that had a combined 32 million tons of coal reserves.

Globe acquired Core Metals Group from Ospraie Funds for $52 million in 2010. Core is a Pennsylvania-based firm that produces and markets high-purity ferrosilicon and other specialty steel ingredients. The move will enhance Globe's fer-

rosilicon business and help diversify its product line.

In 2009 Dow Corning bought two of Globe's facilities, one in Brazil and the other in the US, for about $175 million. The US facility was part of a joint venture deal with Dow Corning, with Globe holding onto a 51% stake. The sale of the Brazilian plant marked Globe's pull-out from the country, though the company remains committed to its South American business through plants in Argentina.

EXECUTIVES

Chairman, Alan Kestenbaum, age 49, $7,884,400 total compensation
CEO and COO, Jeff Bradley, age 51, $1,888,753 total compensation
CFO, Malcolm Applebaum, age 49, $1,368,620 total compensation
Chief Legal Officer, Stephen Lebowitz, age 46, $481,522 total compensation
SVP, Theodore A. (Ted) Heilman Jr., age 53, $278,094 total compensation
Executive Director, Globe Metales, S.A., Delfin Rabinovich, age 62
Executive Director, Globe Metais, S.A., Bruno Santos Parreiras, age 43
Auditors: KPMG LLP

LOCATIONS

HQ: Globe Specialty Metals, Inc.
1 Penn Plaza, Ste. 2514, 250 W. 34th St., New York, NY 10119
Phone: 212-798-8122   **Fax:** 212-798-8185
Web: www.glbsm.com

2010 Sales

	$ mil.	% of total
US	407.6	86
Argentina	42.1	9
Brazil	12.8	3
Poland	9.7	2
China	0.6	-
Total	**472.7**	**100**

PRODUCTS/OPERATIONS

2010 Sales

	$ mil.	% of total
Silicon metal and related alloys	444.9	94
Silica fume and other	27.8	6
Total	**472.7**	**100**

Selected Subsidiaries

Globe Metais Industria e Comercio S.A. (Brazil)
Globe Metales S.A. (Argentina)
Globe Metallurgical, Inc. (US)
Ningxia Yongvey Coal Industrial Co., Ltd. (China)
Solsil, Inc. (US)

COMPETITORS

Elkem AS	Simcala
Orkla	Timminco

HISTORICAL FINANCIALS

Company Type: Public

Income Statement

FYE: June 30

	REVENUE ($ mil.)	NET INCOME ($ mil.)	NET PROFIT MARGIN	EMPLOYEES
06/11	641.9	52.8	8.2%	1,213
06/10	472.7	34.1	7.2%	1,136
06/09	426.3	(42.0)	—	828
06/08	452.6	36.5	8.1%	1,373
06/07	221.9	11.1	5.0%	1,064
Annual Growth	30.4%	47.7%	—	3.3%

2011 Year-End Financials

Debt ratio: —	No. of shares (mil.): 75.0
Return on equity: 11.1%	Dividends
Cash ($ mil.): 166.2	Yield: —
Current ratio: 4.16	Payout: —
Long-term debt ($ mil.): —	Market value ($ mil.): —

	STOCK PRICE ($) FY Close	P/E High/Low		PER SHARE ($) Earnings	Dividends	Book Value
06/11	0.00	—	—	0.69	0.00	6.36
Annual Growth	—	—	—	—	—	—

Globecomm

Globecomm Systems sends data flying. The company designs, assembles, and installs satellite earth stations, complete uplink centers, and media broadcast centers. It also builds Internet protocol-based communications networks. Its Globecomm Network Services subsidiary provides broadband satellite-delivered Internet and intranet access, Web hosting, video broadcasting, and network management services. Globecomm markets to communications carriers, government agencies, equipment makers, content providers, and broadcasters. The company has served agencies of the US government, military contractors like top client Northrop Grumman Information Technology, as well as commercial clients, which have included CBS and Reuters.

Globecomm increased its revenue and profit for 2010 due largely to a boost of more than $30 million in sales contributed by businesses it acquired in 2009 and 2010. Meanwhile, cost of services rose by nearly 40% in 2010, limiting its profit performance.

The company, which has historically done much of its business overseas (US sales accounted for less than one-third of revenues in 2005, for example), built its domestic business up to account for more than half of its sales in 2008 and 2009. This was made possible by increased sales to the US government, which was the company's largest customer in those years. Revenue from US clients slipped, however, to just over 40% for 2010, with the Middle East coming in as Globecomm's second busiest region, accounting for nearly 30% of sales.

In 2011 Globecomm boosted its wireless technology business with the $20 million acquisition of ComSource, a provider of independent test and evaluation of telecom equipment and software applications. The deal provides for an additional payment of up to $21 million to ComSource, which provides its software and services on a recurring basis as a complement to equipment sales. For

Globecomm, the acquisition provides access to cross-selling opportunities in the fast-growing mobile market and lets it continue to expand beyond its core satellite-based applications.

In 2010 the company purchased Netherlands-based Carrier to Carrier Telecom BV and the assets of Evolution Communication Ltd. for about $15 million in cash. These acquisitions helped Globecomm fill out its portfolio of managed services and extend its geographic reach in Europe and other regions. Globecomm extended its managed wireless services to Africa in 2010 when it won a contract in Freetown, Sierra Leone.

The previous year Globecomm bought Mach6, a privately held satellite services provider also headquartered in the Netherlands, as well as Telaurus Communications for $6.5 million in cash in a move to boost its presence in the maritime market.

EXECUTIVES

Chairman and CEO, David E. Hershberg, age 74, $709,161 total compensation
President and COO, Keith Hall, age 42, $709,161 total compensation
VP Human Resources, Paul Eterno, age 58
VP Network Services, Globecomm Services Maryland, Jeff Winkler
VP Hosted Services, Andrew (Andy) Silberstein
VP Operations, Globecomm Services Maryland, Stephen Wilson
SVP and CTO, Stephen C. Yablonski, age 64
SVP Sales and Marketing, William Raney Jr., age 50, $705,997 total compensation
SVP, CFO, and Treasurer, Andrew C. Melfi, age 58, $709,161 total compensation
SVP Customer Relations and Contracts and Corporate Secretary, Paul J. Johnson, age 56
SVP and General Manager, Tom Coyle, age 62, $389,115 total compensation
Investor Relations, Matthew Byron
Auditors: Ernst & Young LLP

LOCATIONS

HQ: Globecomm Systems Inc.
45 Oser Ave., Hauppauge, NY 11788-3816
Phone: 631-231-9800 **Fax:** 631-231-1557
Web: www.globecommsystems.com

2010 Sales

	% of total
Americas	
US	42
Other countries	3
Middle East	28
Europe	12
Africa	9
Asia	6
Total	**100**

PRODUCTS/OPERATIONS

2010 Sales

	$ mil.	% of total
Services	144.4	63
Infrastructure solutions	92.8	40
Adjustments	(9.4)	-
Total	**227.8**	**100**

Selected Products and Services

Earth stations
  Antennas
  Modulation/demodulation equipment
  Monitor and control systems
  Radio transmitters and receivers
  Voice, data, and video networking equipment
High-speed wide-area networking
Local-area network (LAN) data transmission

Satellite Internet access
Satellite multimedia content delivery

COMPETITORS

Alcatel-Lucent	GlobeCast
Ascent Media	Intelsat
AT&T	L-3 GCS
CommScope	Loral Space
Convergent Media	SES WORLD SKIES
Exelis	Thales
General Dynamics	Verizon
Gilat Satellite	ViaSat

HISTORICAL FINANCIALS

Company Type: Public

Income Statement

FYE: June 30

	REVENUE ($ mil.)	NET INCOME ($ mil.)	NET PROFIT MARGIN	EMPLOYEES
06/11	274.2	9.0	3.3%	475
06/10	227.8	7.9	3.5%	416
06/09	170.2	3.3	1.9%	347
06/08	196.5	27.0	13.7%	316
06/07	150.7	8.3	5.5%	282
Annual Growth	16.1%	2.0%	—	13.9%

2011 Year-End Financials

Debt ratio: 11.2%	No. of shares (mil.): 22.5
Return on equity: 4.9%	Dividends
Cash ($ mil.): 48.0	Yield: —
Current ratio: 2.03	Payout: —
Long-term debt ($ mil.): 20.7	Market value ($ mil.): 349.5

	STOCK PRICE ($) FY Close	P/E High/Low		PER SHARE ($) Earnings	Dividends	Book Value
06/11	15.56	39	16	0.41	0.00	8.18
06/10	8.25	24	17	0.38	0.00	7.74
06/09	7.19	68	25	0.16	0.00	7.42
06/08	8.26	12	6	1.34	0.00	7.38
06/07	15.00	30	13	0.50	0.00	4.29
Annual Growth	0.9%	—	—	(4.8%)	—	17.5%

Golden Star Resources

Gold gets top billing at Golden Star Resources. The company's producing assets — the Bogoso and Wassa properties — are in Ghana, in West Africa's Ashanti gold belt. (The Ghanaian government owns 10% of each of those properties.) The company has proved and probable reserves of about 3.75 million ounces of gold and produces about 350,000 ounces annually. Golden Star has open-pit gold mines and processing operations at two sites, Bogoso/Prestea and Wassa/HBB, and it processes both non-refractory and refractory ores. The company explores other mineral properties in Ghana and other parts of West Africa, including Sierra Leone, Burkina Faso, Niger, and Côte d'Ivoire, as well as in South America.

Golden Star reported gold revenues of $432.7 million in 2010 and grew its reserves and resources by focusing on drilling. However, the company's costs were affected by unusually wet weather, which resulted in delays in minning and lower grades of ore being recovered. That year the company realized a price of $1,219 per ounce, but its operating costs per ounce were $766. In 2010 Golden Star experienced a net loss of $8.3 million.

Although the company anticipated 2011's performance to be similar to that of the previous year, by the third quarter it was seeing signs of progress in both mining and processing operations. Metallurgical recovery was improving significantly and gold production was higher than forecast. The company attributed its focus on delivering an optimal blend of sulfide and transition ore to the Bogoso/Prestea mill as key to the increase in metallurgical recovery. Golden Star also focused on cost efficiencies and sought to streamline operations and ramp up production even more in 2011.

EXECUTIVES

Chairman, Christopher M.T. Thompson
President , CEO, and Director, Thomas G. (Tom) Mair, age 54, $1,603,251 total compensation
EVP and COO, Sam Coetzer, age 51
VP Sustainability, Mark Thorpe
VP and General Manager, Bogoso/Prestea, Nigel Tamlyn
VP Corporate Development, Bruce Higson-Smith, age 50, $319,438 total compensation
VP Technical Operations, Peter Bourke
VP Exploration, S. Mitchel (Mitch) Wasel, age 46, $400,733 total compensation
VP Operations, Ghana, Daniel M. A. Owiredu, age 42
VP Finance and Controller, Roger Palmer, age 61, $457,629 total compensation
SVP and CFO, John A. Labate, age 62, $281,728 total compensation
Treasurer and Interim Corporate Secretary, Bryant Veazey
Manager Investor Relations, Anne Hite
General Manager, Golden Star (Wassa) Limited, Richard Q. Gray
Auditors: PricewaterhouseCoopers LLP

LOCATIONS

HQ: Golden Star Resources Ltd.
10901 W. Toller Dr., Ste. 300, Littleton, CO 80127-6312
Phone: 303-830-9000   **Fax:** 303-830-9094
Web: www.gsr.com

HISTORICAL FINANCIALS

Company Type: Public

Income Statement

FYE: December 31

	REVENUE ($ mil.)	NET INCOME ($ mil.)	NET PROFIT MARGIN	EMPLOYEES
12/10	432.7	(8.3)	—	2,490
12/09	400.7	16.5	4.1%	2,200
12/08	257.4	(135.3)	—	2,800
12/07	175.6	(36.4)	—	2,150
12/06	128.7	64.7	50.3%	1,800
Annual Growth	35.4%	—	—	8.5%

2010 Year-End Financials

Debt ratio: 22.6%
Return on equity: —
Cash ($ mil.): 178.0
Current ratio: 2.13
Long-term debt ($ mil.): 117.3

No. of shares (mil.): 258.5
Dividends
Yield: —
Payout: —
Market value ($ mil.): 1,186.6

	STOCK PRICE ($) FY Close	P/E High/Low		PER SHARE ($) Earnings	Dividends	Book Value
12/10	4.59	—	—	(0.03)	0.00	2.00
12/09	3.12	64	13	0.07	0.00	2.02
12/08	1.00	—	—	(0.51)	0.00	1.82
12/07	3.16	—	—	(0.16)	0.00	2.33
12/06	2.95	13	8	0.31	0.00	2.22
Annual Growth	11.7%	—	—	—	—	(2.6%)

Government Properties Income Trust

If Government Properties Income Trust had one request of Uncle Sam it would be this: "I want you to lease our properties." As a real estate investment trust (REIT), Government Properties Income Trust invests in properties that are leased to government tenants. It owns 3 million sq. ft. of leasing space at some 30 properties, many of which are located in the Washington, D.C. area and other states. The company leases mostly to federal agencies (such as the FBI, IRS, and FDA), but it does lease to some state-run agencies as well. Government Properties Income Trust went public in 2009. Former majority owner HRPT Properties Trust owns about 30% of the company following the IPO.

EXECUTIVES

President and COO, David M. Blackman, age 48
CFO and Treasurer, Mark L. Kleifges, age 50
VP Investor Relations, Timothy A. (Tim) Bonang
Director Internal Audit and Compliance, William J. Sheehan
Secretary, Jennifer B. Clark, age 49
Auditors: Ernst & Young LLP

LOCATIONS

HQ: Government Properties Income Trust
400 Centre St., Newton, MA 02458-2076
Phone: 617-219-1440   **Fax:** 617-219-1441
Web: www.govreit.com

COMPETITORS

Boston Properties
CapLease
Corporate Office Properties Trust
First Potomac Realty
piedmont office realty trust
USFP Trust

HISTORICAL FINANCIALS

Company Type: Public

Income Statement

FYE: December 31

	REVENUE ($ mil.)	NET INCOME ($ mil.)	NET PROFIT MARGIN	EMPLOYEES
12/10	116.8	27.8	23.8%	0
12/09	79.0	26.0	32.9%	0
12/08	75.4	31.8	42.2%	570
12/07	73.1	32.1	43.9%	0
Annual Growth	16.9%	(4.7%)	—	—

2010 Year-End Financials

Debt ratio: —
Return on equity: 3.7%
Cash ($ mil.): 2.4
Current ratio: 0.15
Long-term debt ($ mil.): —

No. of shares (mil.): 40.5
Dividends
Yield: 4.6%
Payout: 150.6%
Market value ($ mil.): 1,085.0

	STOCK PRICE ($) FY Close	P/E High/Low		PER SHARE ($) Earnings	Dividends	Book Value
12/10	26.79	35	27	0.81	1.22	18.70
12/09	22.98	15	10	1.72	0.80	16.39
Annual Growth	16.6%	—	—	(52.9%)	52.5%	14.1%

Grand Canyon Education

Grand Canyon Education (dba Grand Canyon University) spans a broad educational horizon. The regionally accredited educator offers graduate and undergraduate degrees online, at its bricks-and-mortar campus in Phoenix, and onsite at corporate facilities. Grand Canyon University's degree programs are career-oriented and focus on the core disciplines of business, education, health care, and liberal arts. The school's student body is composed primarily of working adults. Grand Canyon enrolls more than 41,000 students annually; approximately 90% are enrolled in online programs, and about half of those students are pursuing master's or doctorate degrees. It has a student-teacher ratio of about 25:1.

Grand Canyon University keeps its enrollment numbers up by marketing itself to working adults (whom the company defines as 25 years and older) seeking to complete their education, switch careers, or earn a higher degree in the field in which they already work. Grand Canyon University attracts adult students with the flexibility and convenience of online classes, and conversely, adult students are attractive to Grand Canyon University because they are generally more stable, able to finance their education, and have higher completion rates than younger students.

In order to continue to attract students, Grand Canyon University keeps tabs on industry trends and adjusts its course offerings accordingly. For example, increased demand for nursing programs led the school to establish satellite locations at multiple hospitals where nursing students can complete their clinical education while also completing other course work online. It has similar on-site arrangements with certain employers, such as schools and school districts, through which students can pursue a profession in teaching.

Grand Canyon University derives about 85% of its income from tuition that is financed under Title IV programs (federal grants and loans to students awarded on the basis of their financial need). Other sources of income come from private loans, other financial aid programs, and employer tuition reimbursements.

Originally founded as Grand Canyon College, a private, not-for-profit college, in 1949, the university moved to its existing campus in Phoenix in 1951. In 2004 several of its stockholders acquired Grand Canyon University and converted it to a for-profit institution. The company then raised about

$126 million through a public offering, which was completed in 2008 after a four-month-long IPO drought in the US. The company also named Brian Mueller, former president of the Apollo Group, as CEO that year.

Chairman (and former CEO) Brent Richardson controls about 11% of Grand Canyon College. Venture finance firm Endeavour Capital owns another 11% stake.

EXECUTIVES

Chairman, Brent D. Richardson, age 49, $345,038 total compensation
CEO and Director, Brian E. Mueller, age 57, $1,965,023 total compensation
President Grand Canyon University, Kathy Player, age 48, $455,514 total compensation
CFO, Daniel E. Bachus, age 40, $254,667 total compensation
EVP, W. Stan Meyer, age 50, $282,365 total compensation
CIO, Michael S. Lacrosse, age 56, $372,724 total compensation
General Counsel and Director, Christopher C. Richardson, age 39, $323,250 total compensation
Chief University Relations and Student Success Officer, Faith A. Weese
Auditors: Ernst & Young LLP

LOCATIONS

HQ: Grand Canyon Education, Inc.
3300 W. Camelback Rd., Phoenix, AZ 85017
Phone: 602-639-7500 **Fax:** 602-589-2717
Web: www.gcu.edu

2010 Enrollment by Location

	# of students	% of total
Online	37,734	91
Ground (Phoenix campus, corporate studies)	3,748	9
Total	**41,482**	**100**

PRODUCTS/OPERATIONS

2010 Student Enrollment by Degree

	No. of students	% of total
Undergraduate degree	23,750	57
Graduate degree	17,732	43
Total	**41,482**	**100**

COMPETITORS

Apollo Group	Capella Education
Arizona State University	Career Education
Azusa Pacific University	Northern Arizona University
Baylor University	Strayer Education
Bridgepoint Education	University of Arizona

HISTORICAL FINANCIALS

Company Type: Public

Income Statement

FYE: December 31

	REVENUE ($ mil.)	NET INCOME ($ mil.)	NET PROFIT MARGIN	EMPLOYEES
12/10	385.8	44.4	11.5%	2,600
12/09	261.9	27.3	10.4%	1,899
12/08	161.3	6.7	4.2%	1,365
12/07	99.3	1.5	1.5%	702
12/06	72.1	0.6	0.8%	0
Annual Growth	**52.1%**	**193.3%**	**—**	**54.7%**

2010 Year-End Financials

Debt ratio: 16.1%
Return on equity: 32.5%
Cash ($ mil.): 33.6
Current ratio: 1.16
Long-term debt ($ mil.): 22.0
No. of shares (mil.): 45.8
Dividends
  Yield: —
  Payout: —
Market value ($ mil.): 896.5

	STOCK PRICE ($) FY Close	P/E High/Low		PER SHARE ($) Earnings	Dividends	Book Value
12/10	19.59	30	16	0.96	0.00	2.99
12/09	19.01	35	21	0.60	0.00	1.88
12/08	18.78	112	56	0.17	0.00	(0.00)
Annual Growth	**2.1%**	**—**	**—**	**137.6%**	**—**	**—**

Green Dot

If you've got the green but not the plastic, Green Dot would like to help. The company offers prepaid debit cards through more than 55,000 retail locations in the US. The MasterCard- and Visa-branded reloadable cards function like credit cards for purchases and cash withdrawals. Green Dot, which has more than 3 million cards in circulation, partners with PayPal, Wal-Mart, Walgreens, 7-Eleven, and other retailers to enable its customers to add funds to their accounts. The company's products are designed for people who aren't able or choose not to utilize traditional credit card and banking services. It makes most of its money from new card, monthly maintenance, and ATM fees. Green Dot went public in 2010.

The company's debut on the market exceeded its own expectations, raising nearly $165 million. Although the initial public offering (IPO) of secondary shares raised a significant amount, Green Dot did not keep any of the money for itself. Instead, the money was distributed to existing shareholders, the most prominent being Wal-Mart. Prior to the IPO the retail giant took a minority stake in Green Dot — a move that cemented the pair's partnership. Green Dot gets more than 60% of its revenues through sales at Wal-Mart.

Unlike its nearest competitors, which focus on check cashing and payday loans, Green Dot has partnered with three of the top five retailers and other mainstream companies such as Radio Shack, Kmart, and Rite Aid. It also offers co-branded cards in some locations. The company plans to grow by increasing both its network and customer usage by offering improved services. As the electronics payments industry evolves and competitors continue to introduce new products such as contactless cards, Green Dot is exploring its various technological options. In addition to technological innovations along the lines of mobile commerce, card companies like Green Dot are also focusing on maintaining a stable and secure technology infrastructure.

The company makes about half of its money in card revenues, which include new card and monthly maintenance fees, optional extras including additional cards, and ATM fees. Interchange fees (charges paid to the company when its cards are used) and cash transfer fees make up the rest of Green Dot's revenues. The company saw growth in all three areas in 2010.

Green Dot hopes to become a bank holding company through its planned acquisition of Utah-based Bonneville Bancorp and its Bonneville Bank

subsidiary. As a bank holding company, Green Dot could cut operating costs by issuing cards directly to customers rather than going through third-party banks. Green Dot and Bonneville are also participating in a pilot program through which they distribute federal tax refunds to prepaid debit cards.

Sequoia Capital controls 49% of Green Dot. The venture capital firm also has board representation in Michael Moritz, who has served as a director since 2003.

EXECUTIVES

Chairman, President, and CEO, Steven W. Streit, age 49, $528,209 total compensation
CFO, John L. Keatley, age 37, $1,651,446 total compensation
President, Cards and Network, Mark T. Troughton, age 42, $489,231 total compensation
VP Special Projects; General Manager, Government Programs, Mark Shifke
COO, William D. Sowell, age 45, $378,186 total compensation
General Counsel and Secretary, John C. Ricci, age 45, $930,600 total compensation
Auditors: Ernst & Young LLP

LOCATIONS

HQ: Green Dot Corporation
605 East Huntington Dr., Ste. 205, Monrovia, CA 91016
Phone: 626-775-3400
Web: www.mygreendot.com

PRODUCTS/OPERATIONS

2010 Sales

	$ mil.	% of total
Card revenues	167.4	44
Interchange revenues	108.4	29
Cash transfer revenues	101.5	27
Adjustments	(13.4)	-
Total	**363.9**	**100**

COMPETITORS

Amscot Financial	FSV Payment Systems
Blackhawk Network	NetSpend
Citi Prepaid Services	nFinanSe
DFC Global	

HISTORICAL FINANCIALS

Company Type: Public

Income Statement

FYE: December 31

	REVENUE ($ mil.)	NET INCOME ($ mil.)	NET PROFIT MARGIN	EMPLOYEES
12/10*	363.9	42.2	11.6%	352
07/09	234.8	37.2	15.8%	256
07/08	168.1	17.3	10.3%	0
07/07	83.6	4.6	5.5%	0
Annual Growth	**63.3%**	**109.3%**	**—**	**37.5%**

*Fiscal year change

2010 Year-End Financials

Debt ratio: —
Return on equity: 25.6%
Cash ($ mil.): 167.5
Current ratio: 2.24
Long-term debt ($ mil.): —
No. of shares (mil.): 41.9
Dividends
  Yield: —
  Payout: —
Market value ($ mil.): 2,374.7

	STOCK PRICE ($)	P/E		PER SHARE ($)		
	FY Close	High/Low	Earnings	Dividends	Book Value
12/10*	56.74	125 79	0.52	0.00	3.95
Annual Growth	—	— —	—	—	—

*Fiscal year change

Green Mountain Coffee

Green Mountain Coffee Roasters' business amounts to more than a hill of beans. The company offers about 200 varieties of coffee, cocoa, and tea, which it sells wholesale to supermarkets, convenience (c-) stores, resorts, and office-delivery services. Its roster of customers has included ExxonMobil c-stores and McDonald's restaurants. The company's coffee is marketed under the Newman's Own Organics, Tully's, and its namesake Green Mountain Coffee labels. In addition, Green Mountain sells the K-Cup single-cup brewing systems for office and home use, made by its subsidiary Keurig. Following a string of acquisitions in 2009, the company bought California's Diedrich Coffee and Canada's Van Houtte in 2010.

The two purchases coupled with alliances and product innovations are part of Green Mountain's aggressive growth strategy. Year-over-year earnings in 2009 and 2010 have soared roughly 135% and 30%, respectively, on an increase in sales of approximately 60% and 70%. Marking a record high, the improvement in 2010 was driven mainly by sales from the Keurig single-cup brewing system, which account for more than 50% of total revenues. Green Mountain in 2011 has continued to build its position in single-serve beverage market by securing licensing deals to sell single-serve pods of Dunkin' Donuts and Starbucks brand coffees and Tazo teas in the US and Canada.

Most recently, the company looked north to Canada to expand its specialty coffee brand business. It purchased Van Houtte in a deal valued at CAD$915 million (roughly a whopping $905 million) from Connecticut-based private equity Littlejohn & Co. Van Houtte has partnered with Green Mountain as a Keurig licensee since 2001, selling Keurig and K-Cup coffee-brewing equipment and gourmet coffee. The move garnered Van Houtte's own brand, and the names Brulerie St. Denis, Les Cafes Orient Express Coffee, and Brulerie Mont Royal, as well as opened up multiple distribution channels to the retail store, restaurant, and online markets. At the time of the deal Green Mountain signaled its intent to sell Van Houtte USA Holdings, the US coffee-service business known as Filterfresh, to reduce redundancies. In fall 2011 Aramark scooped up the office-coffee business from Green Mountain for about $145 million. (Its coffee business operates via subsidiary Aramark Refreshment Services.)

At a price of $35 per share for Diedrich, that acquisition — valued at some $300 million — was in part fueled by an intense bidding war sparked in 2009 between Peet's Coffee & Tea and Green Mountain. Peet's Coffee originally offered to acquire the business for $210 million, intending to pair Diedrich's brands and K-Cup production with its rising portfolio of retail and wholesale brands. After a series of sweetened bids, however, Green Mountain took possession of Diedrich, along with Coffee People, and the rights to the Gloria Jean's

brand. New additions to its coffee offerings also included development of Brista Prima Coffeehouse, a super-premium product in K-Cups.

Green Mountain initially shifted into expansion mode in 2009. It scooped up the brand and domestic wholesale business of Tully's Coffee for some $40 million. The deal gave Green Mountain a well-known specialty coffee brand name, a 200,000-sq.-ft. coffee roasting plant, and strengthened its presence on the West Coast. Tully's retail coffee shops continue to operate under license and supply agreements with Green Mountain. (Tully's retail and international business remains independent, operating under the name TC Global.)

Among other acquisitions in 2009, Green Mountain's took over the brand and wholesale business of Timothy's Coffees of the World, for approximately $157 million. (Bruegger's Enterprises bought Timothy's retail coffee shops, which numbered about 140.) As part of the deal, Green Mountain gained an entry into Canada, along with a coffee-roasting facility in Toronto, and a contract to supply the shops with coffee for five years.

To help finance its growth, Green Mountain in mid-2010 entered into a stock purchase agreement with Luigi Lavazza. The Italian firm bought about $250 million of newly issued Green Mountain stock, about 7% of Green Mountain's shares, with an option to raise its stake. Concurrently, Lavazza is looking to use Green Mountain's Keurig subsidiary as a platform for challenging Nestle in the high-growth capsule coffee market. Founder and chairman Robert Stiller retains control of about 15% of the company's stock.

HISTORY

In 1981 Robert Stiller had his first cup of Green Mountain coffee at a small Vermont coffee shop. He was so impressed, he bought the one-store company (using proceeds from the sale of E-Z Wider, the marijuana-rolling-paper-business he co-founded in 1971). Stiller sought a wider market, and in 1984 he began generating word-of-mouth business by donating coffee to charities and civic groups and placing mail-order ads. By 1985 Green Mountain Coffee had four stores and was turning a profit.

Using direct-mail sales as a vanguard, Green Mountain continued its efforts to build a multi-channel distribution network. It was successful: Supermarkets began selling Green Mountain coffees, and institutions such as the Harvard Club began serving them. The company added retail locations in the late 1980s and early 1990s and went public in 1993. It had 12 stores by 1994, but earnings suffered as Green Mountain's expansion outpaced its sales growth.

The company began selling its products online in 1995, and Business Express Airlines began serving Green Mountain coffee on its flights in the US and Canada. Delta Air Lines' shuttle service followed suit the next year. Green Mountain signed a five-year agreement with Mobil Oil (later, Exxon-Mobil) in 1997 to provide coffee at its On The Run convenience stores.

Green Mountain inked a deal in 1998 with American Skiing Company to supply its nine US ski resorts, including Vermont's Killington and Sugarbush resorts. Also that year it expanded its organic coffee line, revamped its website, and began closing or selling its retail operations to concentrate on its wholesale business; all stores were closed by August 1999. Also in 1999 Green Mountain partnered with Keurig to offer one-cup brewing varieties of its coffees.

In 2000 the company agreed to supply coffee to more than 900 (up from nearly 500) ExxonMobil corporately owned convenience stores; as part of the deal, Green Mountain also became the recommended coffee to about 13,000 ExxonMobil dealer and franchise store locations. In mid-2001 Green Mountain purchased the Frontier Organic Coffee brand from Frontier Natural Products Co-op for about $2.4 million.

Green Mountain began selling coffee under the Newman's Own name in 2003. That year the company signed an agreement with Hain Celestial Group to sell a line of teas.

In 2004 the company expanded its Vermont manufacturing and distribution facility with a 52,000-sq.-ft. warehouse and packaging plant. The added space boosted Green Mountain's annual production capacity from 17 million pounds of coffee to 50 million pounds. Also in 2004 the company announced plans to sell Heifer Hope Blend, an organic coffee that generates income for Heifer Project International. The organization provides support and training for coffee farmers in Guatemala.

Green Mountain has pinned its growth hopes to the trend of "single-cup" brewers. The company had been a minority owner of single-cup brewing-system manufacturer Keurig since 2002. In 2006 Green Mountain acquired the remaining 65% of Keurig that it did not already own for $104 million.

In 2007, in conjunction with International Paper, it created an environmentally friendly coffee cup made of corn, natural paper, and water, which, unlike traditional paper cups, breaks down into organic matter after use. Green Mountain uses the cup in all of its US outlets.

In May 2010 Green Mountain acquired Diedrich Coffee at a price of $35 per share following an intense bidding war for the company. In December, Green Mountain acquired Canada-based Van Houtte for CAD$915 million (or about $900 million). Van Houtte roasts and markets gourmet coffee for home and office consumption, and distributes it through its direct-to-store delivery and coffee services networks in Canada and the US.

EXECUTIVES

Chairman, Robert P. (Bob) Stiller, age 67
President, CEO, and Director, Lawrence J. (Larry) Blanford, age 57, $2,133,092 total compensation
President, Keurig, Michelle V. Stacy, age 54, $599,154 total compensation
President, Specialty Coffee Business Unit, R. Scott McCreary, age 52, $657,314 total compensation
VP and Chief Human Resources Officer, Linda T. Kazanova, age 58
VP Development, Stephen J. (Steve) Sabol, age 50, $334,042 total compensation
VP and CIO, James K. (Jim) Prevo, age 57
VP, CFO, and Treasurer, Frances G. (Fran) Rathke, age 51, $735,997 total compensation
VP Corporate Social Responsibility, Michael (Mike) Dupee, age 42
VP Environmental Affairs, Paul Comey, age 60
VP, Corporate General Counsel, and Secretary, Howard Malovany, age 60
Investor Relations Coordinator, Kathleen Shaffer
Public Relations Coordinator, Kristen Mercure
Director Public Relations, Sandy Yusen
Director Creative, Rick Slade
Auditors: PricewaterhouseCoopers LLP

LOCATIONS

HQ: Green Mountain Coffee Roasters, Inc.
33 Coffee Ln., Waterbury, VT 05676
Phone: 802-244-5621 **Fax:** 802-244-5436
Web: www.greenmountaincoffee.com

PRODUCTS/OPERATIONS

2010 Sales

	$ mil.	% of total
Keurig	727.8	54
Specialty coffee	629.0	46
Total	**1,356.8**	**100**

Selected Brands

Barista Prima Coffeehouse
Br lerie Mont Royal
Br lerie St. Denis
Cafe Escape
Caribou
Celestial
Coffee People
Diedrich Coffee
Donut House Collection
Emeril's
Green Mountain Coffee
Green Mountain Naturals
Gloria Jean's
K-Cup (portion packs for Keurig brewing system)
Kahlúa
Les Cafes Orient Express Coffee
Newman's Own Organics
revv
Timothy's Coffee
Timothy's World Cup (portion packs for Keurig brewing system)
Tully's Coffee
Van Houtte

COMPETITORS

Cafe Britt Coffee	Nestlé
Caribou Coffee	Peet's Coffee & Tea
Community Coffee	Republic of Tea
Dunkin	Sara Lee North
Farmer Bros.	American Retail
Fireside Coffee	Smucker
Hawaii Coffee	Starbucks
Kraft Foods	The Coffee Bean
Mars, Incorporated	

HISTORICAL FINANCIALS

Company Type: Public

Income Statement

FYE: Last Saturday in September

	REVENUE ($ mil.)	NET INCOME ($ mil.)	NET PROFIT MARGIN	EMPLOYEES
09/10	1,356.8	79.5	5.9%	2,380
09/09	803.0	55.9	7.0%	1,517
09/08	500.3	22.3	4.5%	1,220
09/07	341.7	12.8	3.7%	995
09/06	225.3	8.4	3.7%	849
Annual Growth	**56.7%**	**75.4%**	**—**	**29.4%**

2010 Year-End Financials

Debt ratio: 48.0%
Return on equity: 11.4%
Cash ($ mil.): 4.4
Current ratio: 2.08
Long-term debt ($ mil.): 335.5
No. of shares (mil.): 132.8
Dividends
  Yield: —
  Payout: —
Market value ($ mil.): 4,142.8

	STOCK PRICE ($) FY Close	P/E High/Low		PER SHARE ($) Earnings	Dividends	Book Value
09/10	31.19	65	34	0.58	0.00	5.26
09/09	24.61	55	11	0.46	0.00	4.51
09/08	8.74	51	29	0.19	0.00	1.28
09/07	7.57	83	23	0.12	0.00	0.94
09/06	2.73	42	29	0.08	0.00	0.73
Annual Growth	**83.8%**	**—**	**—**	**64.1%**	**—**	**63.6%**

Green Plains

It's plain to Green Plains Renewable Energy that, with stratospheric oil prices, there is green to be made in ethanol production. Formed in 2004, the company operates eight ethanol facilities in Indiana, Iowa, Nebraska, Michigan, and Tennessee. With a combination of plants it has both constructed and acquired, the vertically integrated Green Plains has the annual capacity to produce 735 million gallons of ethanol. It also sells ethanol produced by others, bringing the company's total to more than 1 billion gallons. In addition, Green Plains' plants, when operating at full capacity, produce animal feed known as distillers grains, the primary by-product of ethanol production.

The company also has an Agribusiness segment with operations in bulk grain, agronomy, and petroleum, as well as a Marketing and Distribution unit. Its grain business operates 13 elevators with more than 30 million bushels of capacity, as well as sales of fertilizers and petroleum products. Its marketing and distribution operation sells and ships Green Plains' own ethanol products, as well as those from other companies.

Green Plains had a solid 2010, with revenues jumping some 64% over the previous year. The significant increase in business activity was attributable to a number of the company's recent acquisitions completing their first full year of operations, resulting in a significant jump in sales. Ethanol sales was up 43%, while sales of distillers grains gained 42%; grain and fertilizer sales were up 95% in the Agribusiness segment, while the Marketing and Distribution group reported a 66% jump in sales. Net income was up 143%, driven by increased sales volumes and prices combined with federal and state incentives for ethanol production.

The company's strategy is to become a market-leading, vertically-integrated, low-cost producer of ethanol and agricultural products, growing primarily through targeted acquisitions (as well as strategic capital investments where appropriate). The company seeks to lock in the cost of its raw materials in long-term contracts to minimize the risk of commodity market fluctuations, works to continually improve the efficiency of its operations, works to expand its third-party marketing volumes, and invests in the next generation of biofuels.

Pursuing its growth strategy, in 2008 the company acquired ethanol producers Great Lakes Cooperative and VBV LLC. The next year it acquired a majority interest in biofuels terminal company Blendstar. That company operates a number of terminal facilities throughout the southern US. Green Plains is already a customer of Blendstar and will remain so. It also benefitted from VeraSun's liquidation sale in 2009, when Green Plains bought two

of the bankrupt ethanol producer's former facilities for about $125 million.

In 2010 it acquired five grain elevators (with a storage capacity of 11.7 million bushels) all located within 50 miles of the company's Obion, Tennessee, ethanol production plant. It also acquired Global Ethanol LLC, which operates facilities in Lakota, Iowa, and Riga, Michigan, for $170 million. It added to its storage capacity in 2011 by acquiring 2 million bushels of storage in Missouri from Horizon Grain of Hopkins, Inc and GS Grain.

Green Plains acquired Otter Tail Ag Enterprises, a 55-million gallon annual capacity dry mill ethanol plant in Minnesota, in 2011. Green Plains' $55 million offer for the plant was approved by a bankruptcy court. The deal significantly increased Green Plains' annual production capacity and made it North America's fourth largest ethanol producer.

EXECUTIVES

Chairman, Wayne B. Hoovestol, age 52, $396,565 total compensation
President, CEO, and Director, Todd A. Becker, age 45, $1,625,585 total compensation
CFO, Jerry L. Peters, age 53, $647,653 total compensation
EVP Ethanol Marketing, Carl S. (Steve) Bleyl, age 52, $398,818 total compensation
EVP, General Counsel, and Secretary, Michelle S. Mapes, age 44
EVP Commercial Operations, Michael (Mike) Orgas
EVP Plant Operations, Edgar E. Seward Jr., age 44, $303,993 total compensation
EVP Finance and Treasurer, Ron Gillis, age 61
COO, Jeffrey S. (Jeff) Briggs, age 46
Auditors: KPMG LLP

LOCATIONS

HQ: Green Plains Renewable Energy, Inc.
9420 Underwood Ave., Ste. 100, Omaha, NE 68114
Phone: 402-884-8700 **Fax:** 402-884-8776
Web: www.gpreinc.com

PRODUCTS/OPERATIONS

2010 Sales

	$ mil.	% of total
Marketing & distribution	1,822.6	55
Ethanol	1,115.2	34
Agribusiness	370.3	11
Eliminations	(1,175.1)	-
Total	**2,133.0**	**100**

COMPETITORS

Abengoa Bioenergy	GreenShift Corp
ADM	Lake Area Corn
Aventine	Processors
Badger State Ethanol	Little Sioux Corn
Cargill	Processors

HISTORICAL FINANCIALS

Company Type: Public

Income Statement

FYE: December 31

	REVENUE ($ mil.)	NET INCOME ($ mil.)	NET PROFIT MARGIN	EMPLOYEES
12/10	2,133.0	48.0	2.3%	605
12/09	1,304.2	19.8	1.5%	438
12/08*	188.8	(6.9)	—	308
11/07	24.2	(7.1)	—	50
11/04	0.0	(0.1)	—	0
Annual Growth	**—**	**—**	**—**	**129.6%**

2010 Year-End Financials

Debt ratio: 108.1%	No. of shares (mil.): 35.8
Return on equity: 9.8%	Dividends
Cash ($ mil.): 233.2	Yield: —
Current ratio: 1.71	Payout: —
Long-term debt ($ mil.): 527.9	Market value ($ mil.): 403.0

	STOCK PRICE ($) FY Close	P/E High/Low		PER SHARE ($) Earnings	Dividends	Book Value
12/10	11.26	12	5	1.51	0.00	13.64
12/09	14.87	20	1	0.79	0.00	12.08
12/08*	1.84	—	—	(0.56)	0.00	35.76
11/07	10.48	—	—	(1.18)	0.00	15.25
11/04	28.25	334	88	0.19	0.00	14.31
Annual Growth	(20.5%)	—	—	67.9%	—	(1.2%)

*Fiscal year change

Groupon

Savvy consumers get their coupon on with Groupon. Tapping into the power of collective buying, the company helps businesses attract customers by offering them a unique way to save on things to eat, see, and do in more than 500 markets worldwide. In each participating city, Groupon advertises a daily deal, typically a half-off coupon for anything from a local restaurant or retail store to a hotel or spa; if enough consumers buy the coupon online by midnight, the deal is on and the featured business can achieve a nice chunk in sales. In late 2010, the company rejected a reported $5.3 billion buyout offer from Internet search giant Google. Groupon went public instead in late 2011.

Groupon filed its IPO shortly after online networking service LinkedIn's initial public offering flew off the shelves. Looking to capitalize on the market momentum generated by LinkedIn and other social online services, Groupon initially expected to raise about $750 million by going public. Eventually the offering raised around $700 million. The company will use the IPO proceeds to invest in growing its global brand and improving its technology.

Looking to corner a key market, in 2011 Groupon teamed up with Live Nation, the world's largest ticket seller, to form a joint venture, GrouponLive, that offers group discounts and promotions for local tickets to concerts, sporting events, and other attractions. Groupon also rolled out a mobile version of its service (Groupon Now!) in 2011.

Launched in 2008, Groupon experienced explosive growth in a short period of time and is now the market leader in the group buying industry. The company's first year revenues were just $94,000 (it didn't have a full year of operations until 2009), but that figure jumped enormously to $713 million for 2010. Although Groupon posted a net loss of more than $400 million in 2010 and the company has yet to realize a profit. Groupon's biggest operating expense is marketing. The company spent more than $260 million promoting its service in 2010.

Groupon now reaches more than 80 million subscribers worldwide and uses its website (searchable by locale) and opt-in e-mails to help businesses market their goods or services. The group buying model is a red-hot trend with smaller competitors and startups racing to gain some of the company's market share. The Groupon model was designed as a lower-risk alternative to traditional advertising. Whereas most marketing campaigns — print ads, radio spots, and TV commercials — require upfront payment, Groupon costs businesses nothing out-of-pocket. Once a daily deal reaches its buyer quota, also called a tipping point, Groupon takes a cut and the company takes the remainder.

Groupon evolved out of privately-owned The Point, a technology platform that organizes not only group discounts but other campaigns that require group action, such as organizing events, creating petitions, and raising money. Today, Groupon serves a wide range of industries, including automotive, beauty and fitness, consumer goods, electronics, entertainment, fashion, financial services, food and beverage, health, and travel. Businesses can sign on to be featured on Groupon through the GrouponWorks portal. A feature on the Groupon website can attract thousands of subscribers in each city, who then can share the offer through Facebook, Twitter, and other social media to create even more buzz. Demographically, Groupon tends to attract younger, Internet friendly consumers. The majority of its subscribers are college educated and fall between the ages of 18 and 34.

Geographically, the US is Groupon's largest market, followed by Canada and Europe. The service has expanded into more than 40 countries, partly through acquisitions. An international management team, acquired in Groupon's 2010 purchase of Berlin-based CityDeal, oversees operations of Groupon Latin America. In early 2011, Groupon swallowed up SoSasta, Grouper, and Twangoo, local online coupon discount sites catering to India, Israel, and South Africa. The moves are part of a broader sustained effort to make Groupon a global Internet brand.

Co-founder and chairman Eric Lefkofsky and his wife own more than 20% of the company.

EXECUTIVES

Chairman, Eric P. Lefkofsky, age 42
CFO, Jason E. Child, age 42
CEO and Director, Andrew D. Mason, age 30
VP Product, David Jesse
Vice Chairman, Theodore J. (Ted) Leonsis, age 55
SVP Customer Marketing, Aaron Cooper
SVP Corporate Development, Jason Harinstein
SVP Engineering and Operations, Brian K. Totty, age 44
SVP Sales, Darren Schwartz
Public Relations Manager, Julie Mossler
Auditors: Ernst & Young LLP

LOCATIONS

HQ: Groupon, Inc.
600 W. Chicago Ave., Ste. 620, Chicago, IL 60654
Phone: 312-676-5773   **Fax:** 312-676-2728
Web: www.groupon.com

2010 Sales

	$ mil.	% of total
North America	448.3	63
International	265.1	37
Total	**713.4**	**100**

COMPETITORS

Catalina Marketing	Microsoft
Facebook	Valpak Direct
Google	Marketing Systems
LivingSocial	

HISTORICAL FINANCIALS

Company Type: Public

Income Statement   FYE: December 31

	REVENUE ($ mil.)	NET INCOME ($ mil.)	NET PROFIT MARGIN	EMPLOYEES
12/10	713.4	(413.4)	—	7,107
12/09	30.5	(1.3)	—	350
12/08	0.1	(1.5)	—	0
Annual Growth	8346.3%	—	—	1930.6%

Debt ratio: 108.1%	No. of shares (mil.): 35.8
Return on equity: 9.8%	Dividends
Cash ($ mil.): 233.2	Yield: —
Current ratio: 1.71	Payout: —
Long-term debt ($ mil.): 527.9	Market value ($ mil.): 403.0

GSE Systems

GSE Systems is into the appearance of power and control. The company provides simulation software to train power plant operators, engineers, and managers. Its systems, used primarily for the nuclear power, fossil energy, and chemical industries, can also be used to test new plant systems before they are installed. GSE Systems also offers training services through a partnership with General Physics. Customers include Slovenske electrarne, American Electric Power, Emerson Process Management, Statoil ASA, and Westinghouse Electric. With international offices in China, India, Sweden, and the UK, GSE Systems generates about 70% of sales from customers located outside the US.

Contract revenues were up 18% in 2010 over 2009. The company, which has not been profitable since 2007, saw its losses grow for the year on higher operating expenses and losses from ongoing simulator projects. At the end of 2010, GSE had cash and equivalents of nearly $27 million and an accumulated deficit of close to $32 million. The company was in default on two revolving credit agreements, and though it received a written waiver from its lender, GSE is required to collateralize future borrowings with cash.

GSE Systems targets customers in emerging markets for growth — specifically those located in Slovakia, Russia, and China — as well as those in established regions such as the US, the UK, and Japan. It had $9.2 million in backlog related to upgrades at two nuclear facilities in Japan at the end of 2010. Though neither of the plants was damaged in the 2011 earthquake and tsunami, the company is unsure whether the events will have an effect on its operations; it expects to recognize $5.4 million in revenues for the year from the contracts. In fact, 85% of GSE's backlog is related to the nuclear power industry, which had been experiencing a bit of a renaissance.

In early 2011 GSE Systems expanded with the acquisition of EnVision Systems, a maker of interactive multimedia tutorials and simulation models, for $1.2 million in cash, plus an additional $3 million if EnVision meets certain revenue targets through December 2014. The purchase provides entry-level training that complements GSE's more advanced simulators, which GSE can use to add new customers, cross-sell to existing customers, and create a new revenue stream from resale of EnVision's library of refining models.

The $2.3 million purchase of TAS Holdings (renamed TAS Engineering Consultants) in 2010 expanded GSE Systems' non-nuclear energy business with engineering consulting, electrical system design, controls and automation engineering, and electrical distribution systems modeling services. The acquisition also added opportunities for training as a part of engineering and consulting projects; extended the company's modeling and simulation operations into renewable energy, electrical distribution, and grid systems; and expanded its presence in the UK with an existing customer portfolio that includes BP and ConocoPhillips.

Also in 2010 GSE Systems formed a joint venture in China with Beijing UNIS Investment. GSE owns 49% of the JV, named GSE-UNIS Simulation Technology, which has not begun commercial operations.

EXECUTIVES

Chairman, Jerome I. (Jerry) Feldman, age 82, $333,445 total compensation
CEO and Director, James A. (Jim) Eberle, age 42
President, Chin-Our Jerry Jen, age 62, $249,474 total compensation
EVP and Director, Michael D. Feldman, age 43
SVP, CFO, Treasurer, and Secretary, Jeffery G. Hough, age 56, $220,517 total compensation
SVP, Gill R. Grady, age 53, $211,163 total compensation
Auditors: KPMG LLP

LOCATIONS

HQ: GSE Systems, Inc.
   1332 Londontown Blvd., Ste. 200, Sykesville, MD 21784
Phone: 410-970-7800   **Fax:** 410-970-7997
Web: www.gses.com

2010 Sales

	$ mil.	% of total
US	37.2	79
Europe	9.7	20
Asia	0.3	1
Total	**47.2**	**100**

PRODUCTS/OPERATIONS

2010 Sales by Industry

	% of total
Nuclear power	72
Fossil fuel power	18
Process	8
Training & education	2
Total	**100**

Selected Products

Java-based applications (JADE)
Plant information systems (Vista PIN)
Semi-automatic plant surveillance and diagnosis systems (Pegasus)
Real-time simulation control systems (OpenSim and SimExec)
Software modeling tools (eXtreme)
Workstations for monitoring boiling water reactor plants (SIMON)

Selected Services

Application engineering
Consulting
Maintenance
Project management
Training

COMPETITORS

CAE Inc.
Emerson Electric
Honeywell
   International
Invensys
L-3 Communications

Maxager Technology
OSIsoft
Schlumberger
Siemens AG
Thales

HISTORICAL FINANCIALS
Company Type: Public

Income Statement
FYE: December 31

	REVENUE ($ mil.)	NET INCOME ($ mil.)	NET PROFIT MARGIN	EMPLOYEES
12/10	47.2	(2.2)	—	248
12/09	40.1	(0.8)	—	201
12/08	29.0	(0.7)	—	178
12/07	31.9	1.2	3.8%	153
12/06	27.5	(0.3)	—	135
Annual Growth	**14.5%**	**—**	**—**	**16.4%**

2010 Year-End Financials

Debt ratio: —
Return on equity: —
Cash ($ mil.): 26.6
Current ratio: 2.89
Long-term debt ($ mil.): —

No. of shares (mil.): 19.2
Dividends
   Yield: —
   Payout: —
Market value ($ mil.): 69.4

	STOCK PRICE ($) FY Close	P/E High/Low		PER SHARE ($) Earnings	Dividends	Book Value
12/10	3.62	—	—	(0.12)	0.00	1.93
12/09	5.48	—	—	(0.05)	0.00	1.96
12/08	5.90	—	—	(0.04)	0.00	1.30
12/07	10.24	154	70	0.08	0.00	1.35
12/06	6.65	—	—	(0.07)	0.00	0.77
Annual Growth	**(14.1%)**	—	—	—	—	**25.6%**

GSI Technology

GSI Technology makes some very fast chips. The company designs and markets specialized SRAM (static random-access memory) integrated circuits used in high-speed networking equipment. Its chips allow routers, switches, and other gear from the likes of Alcatel-Lucent and Cisco Systems to retrieve data at the speeds needed for broadband transmission. The fabless semiconductor company does most of its business through contract manufacturers, such as Jabil Circuit, and through distributors, including Avnet and Nu Horizons. Other top customers include SMART Modular Technologies, which buys memory chips for products it makes on behalf of Cisco. More than two-thirds of GSI's sales come from outside the US.

The company divides its marketing efforts between the US and developing countries, principally China and Malaysia. In an industry battered by a prolonged slump and global economic downturn, GSI has maintained steady growth in sales and continued profitability. It doesn't hurt that the company has a blue-chip networking customer like Cisco. Outside of the networking and telecommunications industries, other markets that use GSI's high-performance chips include military, medical, and test equipment.

In 2009 the company acquired the assets of Sony Electronics' SRAM product line, hoping to gain additional market share by boosting GSI's product portfolio and customer base.

GSI relies on Taiwan Semiconductor Manufacturing, a silicon foundry, to provide the manufacturing of its products. The semiconductors are primarily tested and packaged by Advanced Semiconductor Engineering (ASE). King Yuan Electronics performs most of the burn-in and functional testing on the parts, though low-volume products are tested in-house at GSI's California and Taiwan facilities.

Chairman, president, and CEO Lee-Lean Shu, who co-founded the company in 1995, owns more than 9% of GSI Technology.

EXECUTIVES

Chairman, President, and CEO, Lee-Lean Shu, age 56, $542,210 total compensation
CFO, Douglas Schirle, age 56, $287,326 total compensation
VP US Operations, Ping Wu, age 54
VP Taiwan Operations, Bor-Tay Wu, age 58
VP Sales, Didier Lasserre, age 46, $320,104 total compensation
VP Engineering, Secretary, and Director, Robert Yau, age 58, $284,919 total compensation
VP Marketing, David Chapman, age 55, $277,454 total compensation
VP Telecommunications Division, Suengliang (Leon) Lee, age 57
Auditors: PricewaterhouseCoopers LLP

LOCATIONS

HQ: GSI Technology, Inc.
   1213 Elko Dr., Sunnyvale, CA 94089
Phone: 408-331-8800   **Fax:** 408-331-9795
Web: www.gsitechnology.com

2010 Sales

	$ mil.	% of total
US	21.0	31
Malaysia	18.2	27
China	15.4	23
Singapore	7.9	12
Other countries	5.1	7
Total	**67.6**	**100**

PRODUCTS/OPERATIONS

2010 Sales

	% of total
Foreign & domestic distributors	50
Contract manufacturers & consignment warehouses	39
Others	11
Total	**100**

COMPETITORS

Cypress Semiconductor
IBM Microelectronics
Integrated Device
   Technology
Integrated Silicon
   Solution

Renesas Electronics
Samsung Electronics
STEC

HISTORICAL FINANCIALS
Company Type: Public

Income Statement
FYE: March 31

	REVENUE ($ mil.)	NET INCOME ($ mil.)	NET PROFIT MARGIN	EMPLOYEES
03/11	97.8	18.9	19.3%	133
03/10	67.6	10.4	15.4%	127
03/09	62.1	9.3	15.0%	108
03/08	53.2	6.8	12.8%	103
03/07	58.2	7.4	12.7%	100
Annual Growth	**13.9%**	**26.4%**	**—**	**7.4%**

2011 Year-End Financials

Debt ratio: —
Return on equity: 15.1%
Cash ($ mil.): 26.0
Current ratio: 6.11
Long-term debt ($ mil.): —

No. of shares (mil.): 28.6
Dividends
   Yield: —
   Payout: —
Market value ($ mil.): 260.4

	STOCK PRICE ($) FY Close	P/E High/Low		PER SHARE ($) Earnings	Dividends	Book Value
03/11	9.09	16	7	0.64	0.00	4.35
03/10	4.66	16	6	0.38	0.00	3.58
03/09	2.54	13	6	0.33	0.00	3.16
03/08	2.65	25	9	0.24	0.00	2.79
03/07	5.29	17	16	0.32	0.00	1.08
Annual Growth	14.5%	—	—	18.9%	—	41.7%

GT Advanced Technologies

GT Advanced Technologies (formerly GT Solar International) is a beacon on the path of the solar power supply chain. The company manufactures the equipment used by other companies to produce silicon wafers and solar cells. Key products include chemical vapor deposition (CVD) reactors used to produce polysilicon, the raw material in solar cells; and directional solidification systems (DSS), the furnaces used to transform polysilicon into ingots, which are sliced into silicon wafers to become solar cells. GT Advanced Technologies does most of its business in Asia, primarily in China. The company changed its name from GT Solar to GT Advanced Technologies in 2011 to reflect its ambitions beyond the solar industry.

The company's revenue rose 65% in fiscal 2011 over the year before because of strong demand from solar component manufacturers. Its customer base extends outside of the solar components sector, however, to include chemical companies that manufacture polysilicon, including longtime customer OCI Company.

In 2010 GT Advanced Technologies further expanded its customer base with the purchase of Crystal Systems for $24 million in cash and 5 million shares of GT Advanced Technologies stock. Crystal Systems, located in Salem, Massachusetts, manufactures sapphire substrates used in the LED (light-emitting diode), defense, medical, and aerospace industries. GT Advanced Technologies is tapping the growing LED market, a component in flat-screen TVs and light bulbs.

In 2011 the company bought Missouri-based Confluence Solar in an all-cash transaction worth up to $80 million. Confluence Solar developed a technology called HiCz that GT Advanced Technologies expects will improve the efficiency of its DSS equipment in making monocrystalline wafers. It also plans on creating a commercial equipment product based on the technology for release in 2013.

The company outsources most of its manufacturing process to third-party companies in Asia. It operates manufacturing centers in Massachusetts, Montana, and New Hampshire that assemble and test its final products, which are then shipped out to customers — more than 80% of which are back in Asia. GT Advanced Technologies has operations in Shanghai, Beijing, Taiwan, and Hong Kong.

EXECUTIVES

Chairman, J. Bradford Forth, age 46
President, CEO, and Director, Thomas (Tom) Gutierrez, age 62
CFO, Richard J. Gaynor, age 50
VP and General Manager, Photovoltaic (PV) Equipment Division, John (Rick) Tattersfield, age 48, $427,437 total compensation
VP Technology, Peter Bihuniak
VP Human Resources, Brian Logue
VP Finance and Corporate Controller, Richard E. Johnson, age 48
VP Sales, Keith Matthei
VP and General Manager, Polysilicon Division, David W. Keck, age 46, $1,719,210 total compensation
VP and General Manager, Turnkey Division, Ron Jones
VP, General Counsel, and Secretary, Hoil Kim, age 53
VP and General Manager, Asia, Jeffrey J. Ford, age 55, $521,005 total compensation
VP Strategic Development, David C. Gray, age 45
Media Relations, Susan Vaillancourt
Investor Relations, Bob Blair
Country Manager, Taiwan, Eric M. T. Hsu
Director Turnkey Sales, Scott Kroeger
Deputy General Counsel, Daniel F. Lyman
Director, R. Chad Van Sweden
Auditors: Deloitte & Touche LLP

LOCATIONS

HQ: GT Advanced Technologies Inc.
243 Daniel Webster Hwy., Merrimack, NH 03054
Phone: 603-883-5200   **Fax:** 603-595-6993
Web: www.gtsolar.com

2011 Sales

	$ mil.	% of total
China	635.8	71
Korea	119.3	13
Europe	51.3	6
US	9.4	1
Other	83.2	9
Total	**899**	**100**

PRODUCTS/OPERATIONS

2011 Sales

	$ mil.	% of total
Photovoltaic equipment	716.4	80
Polysilicon business	143.6	16
Photovotaic services, parts, and other	23.7	3
Sapphire business	15.3	1
Total	**899**	**100**

COMPETITORS

Advanced Metallurgical Group	Mitsubishi Electric
Amtech Systems	Oerlikon
Applied Materials	OTB Group
BTU International	Roth & Rau
centrotherm	Spire Corp.
Ferrotec	Sumitomo Electric
Manz Automation	Tokuyama
MEMC Electronic Materials	ULVAC
	Veeco Instruments

HISTORICAL FINANCIALS

Company Type: Public

Income Statement
FYE: March 31

	REVENUE ($ mil.)	NET INCOME ($ mil.)	NET PROFIT MARGIN	EMPLOYEES
03/11	899.0	174.8	19.4%	622
03/10	544.2	87.3	16.0%	384
03/09	541.0	88.0	16.3%	332
03/08	244.1	36.1	14.8%	305
03/07	60.1	(18.4)	—	248
Annual Growth	96.7%	—	—	25.8%

2011 Year-End Financials

Debt ratio: 50.3%   No. of shares (mil.): 124.9
Return on equity: 86.5%   Dividends
Cash ($ mil.): 362.7   Yield: —
Current ratio: 1.52   Payout: —
Long-term debt ($ mil.): 101.6   Market value ($ mil.): 1,333.2

	STOCK PRICE ($) FY Close	P/E High/Low		PER SHARE ($) Earnings	Dividends	Book Value
03/11	10.67	10	4	1.24	0.00	1.62
03/10	5.23	15	7	0.60	0.00	1.25
03/09	6.64	28	3	0.61	0.00	0.57
Annual Growth	26.8%	—	—	42.6%	—	67.9%

GTx

GTx knows hormones are just as important to men as they are to women. The company develops therapies targeting estrogens and androgens for prostate cancer and other diseases in the arena of men's health. GTx is developing a potential therapy that could be useful in treating side effects of androgen-deprivation therapy (a treatment for advanced prostate cancer) including osteoporosis and hot flashes. Another candidate could prevent men who have been identified with certain precancerous conditions from developing prostate cancer. To fund its work, GTx sells Fareston, a drug for metastatic breast cancer.

Fareston has the same key ingredient (toremifene) as several of the company's lead prostate cancer-related candidates. GTx licenses rights to develop other toremifene compounds from Finnish drug maker Orion. The company in turn licenses rights to Ipsen for development and marketing of the toremifene compounds in Europe and the Asia/Pacific region.

The company also has a development program exploring another class of drugs to treat muscle and musculoskeletal wasting in cancer patients. GTx had been collaborating with Merck on the project, but it reacquired full rights to the program in 2010.

GTx was working to commercialize its toremifene 80mg candidate to prevent bone fractures in men with prostate cancer in 2009; however, delays in FDA approval of the drug caught the company up a bit short of cash. To weather the delays, the company cut nearly 30% of its workforce at the end of 2009. The company is working to control costs and raise additional funding to pursue regulatory approval of the candidate; it has expanded its development agreement with Ipsen to further these goals.

Chairman Joseph Hyde III owns 30% of GTx, while CEO Mitchell Steiner owns about 10%.

EXECUTIVES

Chairman, Joseph R. (J. R.) Hyde III, age 68
President, COO, and Director, Marc S. Hanover, age 48, $806,854 total compensation
VP Sales, Christopher K. West, age 44
VP and Chief Medical Officer, Ronald A. Morton, age 52, $801,198 total compensation
VP Preclinical Research and Development, James T. (Jim) Dalton, age 48, $594,348 total compensation
VP Regulatory Affairs, Jeffrey G. (Jeff) Hesselberg, age 52
VP Clinical Research and Development Strategy, K. Gary Barnette, age 43
VP Medical Affairs, Shontelle Dodson
VP, CFO, and Treasurer, Mark E. Mosteller, age 48, $574,412 total compensation
VP, General Counsel, and Secretary, Henry P. Doggrell, age 62
VP Clinical Operations, Domingo Rodriguez, age 49
VP Marketing and Managed Care, Michael D. Brown
VP Sales and Marketing, Gregory A. (Greg) Deener, age 49
Vice Chairman and CEO, Mitchell S. Steiner, age 50, $710,967 total compensation
Executive Director Medical Affairs and Clinical Development, Michael K. Brawer
Director Drug Safety, Robert S. Boger, age 64
Director Corporate Communications and Financial Analysis, McDavid Stilwell
Director Preclinical Development, Karen A. Veverka, age 43
Director Corporate Quality, T. Gary Bird, age 58
Auditors: Ernst & Young LLP

LOCATIONS

HQ: GTx, Inc.
175 Toyota Plaza, 7th Fl., Memphis, TN 38103
Phone: 901-523-9700 **Fax:** 901-523-9772
Web: www.gtxinc.com

PRODUCTS/OPERATIONS

2009 Sales

	$ mil.	% of total
Collaboration revenue	11.4	78
Product sales	3.3	22
Total	**14.7**	**100**

COMPETITORS

Abbott Labs
Amgen
Boehringer Ingelheim
Bristol-Myers Squibb
Cytokinetics
Eli Lilly
GlaxoSmithKline
Ligand Pharmaceuticals
Merck
Novartis
Pfizer
Procter & Gamble
Sanofi

HISTORICAL FINANCIALS

Company Type: Public

Income Statement FYE: December 31

	REVENUE ($ mil.)	NET INCOME ($ mil.)	NET PROFIT MARGIN	EMPLOYEES
12/10	60.6	15.3	25.2%	111
12/09	14.7	(46.3)	—	120
12/08	13.5	(51.8)	—	147
12/07	7.1	(40.4)	—	111
12/06	7.5	(35.5)	—	91
Annual Growth	68.6%	—	—	5.1%

2010 Year-End Financials

Debt ratio: —
Return on equity: 29.6%
Cash ($ mil.): 58.2
Current ratio: 11.38
Long-term debt ($ mil.): —
No. of shares (mil.): 51.7
Dividends
Yield: —
Payout: —
Market value ($ mil.): 137.1

	STOCK PRICE ($) FY Close	P/E High	P/E Low	PER SHARE ($) Earnings	Dividends	Book Value
12/10	2.65	11	5	0.39	0.00	1.00
12/09	4.20	—	—	(1.27)	0.00	(0.24)
12/08	16.84	—	—	(1.43)	0.00	0.88
12/07	14.35	—	—	(1.16)	0.00	2.26
12/06	17.84	—	—	(1.14)	0.00	3.13
Annual Growth	(37.9%)	—	—	—	—	(24.8%)

Hallador Energy

Despite its *Harry Potter*-like name, Hallador Petroleum could find no magic in oil and natural gas exploration and production – just a lot of hard and dirty work. It therefore decided to focus on its coal operations. Hallador sells coal from its Carlisle Mine in Indiana to three utilities in the Midwest. First commercial production began at the mine in 2007. That year it sold 972,500 tons at an average price of $28 per ton. Hallador has recoverable coal reserves of 36 million tons. It is exploring the possibility of other contracts with a number of coal purchasers.

The company was founded in 1949. In 1997 investment company Yorktown Energy Partners II and affiliates invested $5 million in Hallador. The company acquired control of Sunrise Coal, co-developer of the Carlisle Mine, in 2008.

EXECUTIVES

Chairman, David Hardie, age 60
President, Hallador Petroleum and Sunrise Coal and Director, Brent K. Bisland, age 37, $1,287,000 total compensation
CFO, William A. (Andy) Bishop, age 58
CFO, Sunrise Coal, Larry Martin, age 46, $178,000 total compensation
CEO and Director, Victor P. Stabio, age 63, $2,064,000 total compensation
Auditors: Ehrhardt Keefe Steiner & Hottman PC

LOCATIONS

HQ: Hallador Energy Company
1660 Lincoln St., Ste. 2700, Denver, CO 80264-2701
Phone: 303-839-5504 **Fax:** 303-832-3013
Web: www.halladorenergy.com

PRODUCTS/OPERATIONS

2009 Sales

	$ mil.	% of total
Coal sales	117.4	100
Equity loss	(1.6)	-
Other	0.5	-
Total	**116.3**	**100**

COMPETITORS

Alpha Natural Resources
Arch Coal
CONSOL Energy
Foresight Energy
Peabody Energy

HISTORICAL FINANCIALS

Company Type: Public

Income Statement FYE: December 31

	REVENUE ($ mil.)	NET INCOME ($ mil.)	NET PROFIT MARGIN	EMPLOYEES
12/10	129.2	22.4	17.3%	332
12/09	116.3	20.2	17.4%	300
12/08	70.7	8.9	12.6%	6
12/07	27.2	(2.4)	—	148
12/06	2.5	(0.8)	—	90
Annual Growth	168.1%	—	—	38.6%

2010 Year-End Financials

Debt ratio: 13.8%
Return on equity: 17.7%
Cash ($ mil.): 11.6
Current ratio: 1.35
Long-term debt ($ mil.): 17.5
No. of shares (mil.): 27.9
Dividends
Yield: —
Payout: —
Market value ($ mil.): 292.9

	STOCK PRICE ($) FY Close	P/E High	P/E Low	PER SHARE ($) Earnings	Dividends	Book Value
12/10	10.49	18	8	0.78	0.00	4.54
12/09	7.85	20	4	0.83	0.00	3.91
12/08	3.00	13	4	0.46	0.00	3.25
12/07	3.50	—	—	(0.18)	0.00	2.39
12/06	3.00	—	—	(0.07)	0.00	2.32
Annual Growth	36.7%	—	—	—	—	18.3%

Halozyme

Halozyme Therapeutics is searching for cures to the world's "ologys." The company is developing treatments for endocrinology, oncology, and dermatology. It is also creating products for the drug delivery market. Halozyme's portfolio is based on its Enhanze technology which includes the family of human enzymes called hyaluronidases. There are two marketed products using Halozyme's technology: Hylenex and Cumulase. Hylenex is used as an adjuvant for drug and fluid infusions and Cumulase is used for in-vitro fertilization. Halozyme receives limited income from sales of the active pharmaceutical ingredients to the third party that makes Cumulase, as well as revenues from its partnerships with ViroPharma and Roche.

The firm's commercial products are marketed through distribution agreements, primarily in the US and Europe. It also receives revenue from its development partnerships. Halozyme has a development and marketing agreement with Baxter International to develop an under-the-skin delivery technology for Baxter's Gammagard Liquid immunodeficiency treatment using Halozyme's Enhanze platform. The two companies did partner on sales of Hylenex as well, however, in early 2011 Baxter returned its marketing rights back to Halozyme. Halozyme intends to take advantage of the inroads already made by Baxter to commercialize the product further. However, it will have to wait until Hylenex is introduced back onto the market after being voluntary recalled in 2010. Hylenex was recalled after a portion of the drug, which was then being manufactured by Baxter, was found not to be compatible with the vial in which it was packaged. Halozyme has drawn up a corrective plan and market relaunch strategy.

Halozyme has an exclusive distribution agreement for Cumulate with a distributor of IVF reagents that sells to IVF clinics in the US and Europe. Sales of Cumulate bring in less than half a million dollars annually. Cumulate is more expensive than its animal-derived counterpart, which has made market penetration difficult.

Halozyme also has a collaboration with Roche to apply its Enhanze technology to Roche's therapeutic biological compounds in areas including oncology and immunology.

Halozyme's lead proprietary program is its Ultrafast Insulin, which combines the company's enzyme with mealtime insulins to increase absorption, speed of action, and glycemic control. Additional candidates target bladder cancer, solid tumors, and aesthetic dermatology conditions.

Director Randal J. Kirk, founder of New River Pharmaceuticals (which is now part of Shire plc), owns about 15% of Halozyme.

EXECUTIVES

Chairman, Kenneth J. (Ken) Kelley, age 52
President, CEO, and Director, Gregory I. Frost, age 39, $467,556 total compensation
VP Alliance Management and Portfolio Development, Michael Haller
VP Product Development, Michael J. LaBarre
VP Business Development, William F. (Bill) Daly
VP Endocrinology Clinical Development, Douglas B. Muchmore
VP Preclinical Development, Walter Bee
VP Regulatory Affairs and Quality Assurance, Don A. Kennard, age 64
VP and CFO, Kurt A. Gustafson, age 43
VP Manufacturing and Operations, William J. Fallon, age 54, $354,308 total compensation
VP and Chief Scientific Officer, H. Michael Shepard
VP Legal and Secretary, James E. (Jim) Cartoni
VP Corporate Development, David A. Ramsay, age 46, $370,835 total compensation
Senior Director, Investor Relations, Robert H. Uhl
Auditors: Ernst & Young LLP

LOCATIONS

HQ: Halozyme Therapeutics, Inc.
11388 Sorrento Valley Rd., San Diego, CA 92121
Phone: 858-794-8889   **Fax:** 858-704-8311
Web: www.halozyme.com

PRODUCTS/OPERATIONS

2010 Revenues

	$ mil.	% of total
Collaborative agreements	12.7	93
Product sales	1.0	7
Total	**13.7**	**100**

COMPETITORS

Access Pharmaceuticals	Genencor International
Amphastar	Irvine Scientific
Biodel	ISTA Pharmaceuticals
Cook Group	Novo Nordisk
CooperSurgical	Phase Bioscience
Dyadic	

HISTORICAL FINANCIALS

Company Type: Public

Income Statement

FYE: December 31

	REVENUE ($ mil.)	NET INCOME ($ mil.)	NET PROFIT MARGIN	EMPLOYEES
12/10	13.6	(53.2)	—	102
12/09	13.7	(58.4)	—	139
12/08	8.8	(48.7)	—	129
12/07	3.8	(23.9)	—	92
12/06	1.0	(14.8)	—	40
Annual Growth	**92.0%**	**—**	**—**	**26.4%**

2010 Year-End Financials

Debt ratio: —
Return on equity: —
Cash ($ mil.): 83.3
Current ratio: 5.83
Long-term debt ($ mil.): —

No. of shares (mil.): 100.6
Dividends
  Yield: —
  Payout: —
Market value ($ mil.): 796.6

	STOCK PRICE ($) FY Close	P/E High/Low	PER SHARE ($) Earnings	Dividends	Book Value
12/10	7.92	— —	(0.56)	0.00	0.20
12/09	5.87	— —	(0.67)	0.00	0.08
12/08	5.60	— —	(0.61)	0.00	0.19
12/07	7.11	— —	(0.32)	0.00	0.74
12/06	8.05	— —	(0.24)	0.00	0.36
Annual Growth	**(0.4%)**	**— —**	**—**	**—**	**(13.3%)**

Hampton Roads Bankshares

Hampton Roads Bankshares is the holding company for the Bank of Hampton Roads and Shore Bank, which together have about 40 offices in southeastern Virginia and eastern Maryland. Its Gateway Bank & Trust division has about 25 locations in Virginia and North Carolina. Serving area consumers and businesses, the banks offer standard services such as checking and savings accounts, CDs, retirement accounts, and loans. The company has struggled with big losses due to real estate lending. In 2011 Hampton Roads announced the sale of seven of its Gateway Bank branches in North Carolina to ECB Bancorp. The company is selling other outlying branches. It sold its insurance and mortgage banking units in 2011.

Construction loans make up the largest portion of Hampton Roads Bankshares' loan portfolio (more than 33%), which is not surprising considering several company board members are also executives of construction firms. Commercial mortgages comprise about a quarter of the company's loan book, and residential mortgages and business loans are around 20% each.

EXECUTIVES

Chairman, Richard F. Hall III, age 57
President, CEO, and Director; CEO, Bank of Hampton Roads, John A. B. (Andy) Davies, age 59
President and CEO, Shore Bank, W. Thomas Mears
EVP and CFO, Stephen P. Theobald
EVP and Chief Operations Officer, Reneé R. McKinney, age 46
EVP and Chief Credit Risk Officer, Julie R. Anderson, age 52
EVP and Investor Relations Officer and Secretary; EVP, Marketing Officer, and Secretary, Bank of Ham, Tiffany K. Glenn, age 41
EVP; President and CEO, Gateway Bank, David R. Twiddy, age 53
EVP, COO, General Counsel, and Director, Douglas J. Glenn, age 44
SVP and Director Products and Business Line Strategy, Robert M. (Bob) Cooper
SVP and Treasurer, Mark D. Bedard
SVP and Chief Accounting Officer, Lorelle L. Fritsch, age 44, $213,475 total compensation
Chief Credit Officer, Douglas D. (Doug) Wall
Director; President and COO, Bank of Hampton Roads, Ronald A. Day
Auditors: KPMG LLP

LOCATIONS

HQ: Hampton Roads Bankshares, Inc.
999 Waterside Dr., Ste. 200, Norfolk, VA 23510
Phone: 757-217-1000   **Fax:** 757-217-3656
Web: www.bankofhamptonroads.com

COMPETITORS

Bank of America	Old Point Financial
BB&T	SunTrust
Commonwealth Bankshares	TowneBank
Heritage Bankshares	Xenith Bankshares
Monarch Financial Holdings inc	

HISTORICAL FINANCIALS

Company Type: Public

Income Statement

FYE: December 31

	ASSETS ($ mil.)	NET INCOME ($ mil.)	INCOME AS % OF ASSETS	EMPLOYEES
12/10	2,900.2	(211.3)	—	767
12/09	2,975.6	(145.5)	—	699
12/08	3,085.7	7.2	0.2%	721
12/07	563.8	6.8	1.2%	182
12/06	476.3	6.0	1.3%	176
Annual Growth	**57.1%**	**—**	**—**	**44.5%**

2010 Year-End Financials

Equity as % of assets: —
Return on assets: 211.3
Return on equity: —
Long-term debt ($ mil.): 263.2
No. of shares (mil.): 33.4

Dividends
  Yield: 0.0%
  Payout: —
Market value ($ mil.): 434.0
Sales ($ mil.): 140.8

	STOCK PRICE ($) FY Close	P/E High/Low	PER SHARE ($) Earnings	Dividends	Book Value
12/10	13.00	— —	(12.75)	0.00	5.70
12/09	43.25	— —	(176.75)	5.50	204.24
12/08	218.25	24 11	14.75	11.00	651.87
12/07	314.00	23 18	16.25	2.75	179.33
12/06	300.00	20 16	16.25	0.00	170.81
Annual Growth	**(54.4%)**	**— —**	**—**	**—**	**(57.3%)**

Hartville Group

Whether your heart belongs to a Fluffy or a Duke, Hartville can serve your pet insurance needs. Its Petsmarketing Insurance.com Agency subsidiary markets and sells health coverage for household pets across the US on behalf of insurance underwriters. Another unit, Hartville Re, provides reinsurance for pet health policies. Petsmarketing's products cover only cats and dogs, but range from the basic (illnesses, injuries, and neutering) to the deluxe (long-term and chronic illnesses, dental cleanings, and vaccinations). Proving itself no mere runt, Hartville insures over 60,000 pets and has been in business since 1997. The company sells its products by telephone and online.

Through investment companies Islandia and Midsummer Investment, director Michel Amsalem controls about 57% of the company's stock.

The company has been focusing on effective marketing campaigns to boost its customer count, partially through branding agreements with pet organizations like the ASPCA. Hartville doubled the number of pets covered by its marketed insurance products during 2007.

EXECUTIVES

Chairman, Nicholas John Leighton, age 50
CFO, Secretary, and Director, Christopher R. Sachs, age 58
President, CEO, and Director, Dennis C. Rushovich, age 60
CIO, Michael Kalman
Chief Marketing Officer and Director, Christopher C. (Chris) Edgar, age 46
Investor Relations, Vicki Pratt
Auditors: BDO Seidman, LLP

LOCATIONS

HQ: Hartville Group, Inc.
3840 Greentree Ave. SW, Canton, OH 44706
Phone: 330-484-8080   **Fax:** 330-484-8081
Web: www.hartvillegroup.com

PRODUCTS/OPERATIONS

2007 Sales

	$ mil.	% of total
Reinsurance company	6.8	64
Insurance agency	3.8	36
Total	**10.6**	**100**

COMPETITORS

American Kennel Club	Matrix Direct
Answer Financial	Veterinary Pet
esure	Insurance

HISTORICAL FINANCIALS

Company Type: Public

Income Statement   FYE: December 31

	ASSETS ($ mil.)	NET INCOME ($ mil.)	INCOME AS % OF ASSETS	EMPLOYEES
12/07	6.9	(21.1)	—	67
12/06	6.2	(11.2)	—	83
12/05	9.4	(8.0)	—	46
12/04	14.9	(8.0)	—	48
12/03	10.5	0.9	8.6%	44
Annual Growth	**(10.0%)**	**—**	**—**	**11.1%**

Equity as % of assets: —
Return on assets: 21.1
Return on equity: —
Long-term debt ($ mil.): 263.2
No. of shares (mil.): 33.4
Dividends
Yield: 0.0%
Payout: —
Market value ($ mil.): 434.0
Sales ($ mil.): 140.8

Hatteras Financial

Hatteras Financial hopes for smooth sailing on the sometimes tumultuous seas of mortgage investing. The company is a real estate investment trust (REIT) that invests in adjustable-rate and hybrid adjustable-rate single-family residential mortgages guaranteed by a US government agency or a government-backed company such as Ginnie Mae, Fannie Mae, or Freddie Mac. Hatteras Financial's investment portfolio, valued at some $7 billion, consists mostly of hybrid adjustable-rate loans with terms of three to five years. Hatteras Financial is externally managed by Atlantic Capital Advisors.

The manager is responsible for Hatteras Financial's day-to-day operations, including buying and selling investments, financing, risk management, and advisory services. It also oversees another mortgage REIT, ACM Financial Trust. The two REITs and Atlantic Capital all share CEO Michael Hough and other top executives.

Though the mortgage market has been battered, analysts have likened Hatteras' strategy of only buying government-backed loans to one of investing in bonds since the government would cover any defaults. The REIT prefers to invest in mortgage securities backed by Fannie Mae, which pays principal and interest sooner than Freddie Mac.

EXECUTIVES

Chairman and CEO, Michael R. Hough, age 50
President, COO, and Director, Benjamin M. (Ben) Hough, age 46
CFO, Secretary, and Treasurer, Kenneth A. Steele, age 47
EVP and Co-Chief Investment Officer, Frederick J. Boos II, age 57
EVP and Co-Chief Investment Officer, William H. Gibbs Jr., age 51
Auditors: Ernst & Young LLP

LOCATIONS

HQ: Hatteras Financial Corp.
110 Oakwood Dr., Ste. 340, Winston-Salem, NC 27103
Phone: 336-760-9331
Web: hatfin.com

COMPETITORS

AG Mortgage Investment Trust	Capstead Mortgage
Annaly Capital Management	Redwood Trust
Anworth Mortgage Asset	Walter Investment Management
ARMOUR Residential REIT	

HISTORICAL FINANCIALS

Company Type: Public

Income Statement   FYE: December 31

	REVENUE ($ mil.)	NET INCOME ($ mil.)	NET PROFIT MARGIN	EMPLOYEES
12/10	278.6	169.5	60.8%	9
12/09	283.1	174.4	61.6%	9
12/08	192.3	79.1	41.1%	8
12/07	7.3	1.2	16.4%	6
Annual Growth	**236.7%**	**420.8%**	**—**	**14.5%**

2010 Year-End Financials

Debt ratio: —	No. of shares (mil.): 46.1
Return on equity: 14.8%	Dividends
Cash ($ mil.): 112.6	Yield: 14.5%
Current ratio: —	Payout: 102.3%
Long-term debt ($ mil.): —	Market value ($ mil.): 1,395.9

	STOCK PRICE ($) FY Close	P/E High/Low		PER SHARE ($) Earnings	Dividends	Book Value
12/10	30.27	7	3	4.30	4.40	24.84
12/09	27.96	7	4	4.82	4.50	25.74
12/08	26.60	8	5	3.48	2.80	27.50
Annual Growth	**6.7%**	**—**	**—**	**11.2%**	**25.4%**	**(5.0%)**

Healthways, Inc.

For health insurers, healthy plan members are cheap plan members; that's where Healthways comes in. The health services company provides disease management and wellness programs to managed care companies, self-insured employers, governments, and hospitals, with the ultimate goals of improving members' health and lowering health care costs. Its disease management programs help members manage chronic illnesses like diabetes and emphysema, making sure they keep up with treatment plans and maintain healthy behaviors. Healthways' wellness offerings, including its SilverSneakers program for seniors, encourage fitness and other good lifestyle choices.

The company provides services to more than 35 million people worldwide. It operates in all 50 US states, as well as Washington DC and Puerto Rico, through about a dozen service centers. Its biggest customer is health insurer CIGNA, which accounts for about 20% of the company's total revenue.

Since healthy people require expensive medical services less often, Healthways' strategy consists of finding new and better ways of controlling health care costs by improving members' well-being. It has added services through partnerships with other health care companies, including a collaboration with pharmacy benefits manager Medco. Healthways actively pursues such partnerships, which it uses as a way to open up new distribution channels and establish new markets in which to sell its products.

The firm also occasionally pursues acquisitions as a means of growth. For instance, in 2011 it acquired Navvis, a provider of change management and consulting services for health care systems, in a $29 million deal. The purchase allowed Healthways to enhance its involvement in cost-control initiatives at the provider level by offering clinical integration, leadership training, and partnering strategy services to medical systems working to adapt to health reform measures.

The company is also adding custom programs for targeted markets, such as its Senior Care Management (SCM) program which identifies and manages the care of high-risk Medicare Advantage members; the SCM program can be integrated with the SilverSneakers fitness program.

Along with expanding its service options, Healthways attracts customers by using convenience as a marketing point. The company offers a myriad of ways to take part in its programs including via phone, mobile devices, direct mail, the Internet, through face-to-face consultations, and by visiting care centers.

In North America, Healthworks' relies primarily on its contracts with health plans for the majority of its income. It also contracts with governments, employers, pharmacy benefit managers, and hospitals. Additionally it administers health improvement programs and services in Brazil and Australia and is seeking to grow its overseas operations, especially in Asia, Africa, and Europe.

HISTORY

In 1981 Thomas Cigarran and Henry Herr (alumni of a company that later became part of HCA) joined with venture capitalist Martin Koldyke to found American Healthcorp to buy hospitals. The company diversified, entering the diabetes market in 1984 and arthritis care in 1987.

With profitability lagging, the company sold its hospitals to focus on niche care. In the same spirit, it de-emphasized arthritis care in 1990. The company went public in 1991.

After a brief foray into obesity treatment, the company in 1994 invested in AmSurg, a manager of ambulatory surgery centers. (AmSurg was spun off in 1997.)

By the late 1990s the company increasingly targeted HMOs. It signed its first contract with Principal Health Care (1996, ended in 1998 after Coventry Health Care bought the HMO). Contracts with such HMOs as John Deere Health Care and Health Options of Blue Cross & Blue Shield of Florida followed in 1998.

To standardize income, the company in 1998 converted all of its contracts from shared savings arrangements (in which the company's earnings were based on the payers' savings) to fee-based arrangements. In 1999 American Healthcorp began offering a cardiac health management program to its hospital and HMO clients; that year it changed its name to American Healthways to reflect its expanded product line.

American Healthways in 2000 signed a deal with Agilent Technologies to offer that company's home heart monitoring systems to American Healthways' patients. It also launched MY-HEALTHWAYS, a Web-based application, which offers disease-prevention plans to health plan members.

In 2001 American Healthways launched Comprehensive Care Enhancement Programs, under which all health plan members are screened and provided with any needed health care programs.

The company acquired Company StatusOne Health Systems in 2003 to expand its health management service offerings for high-risk populations. American Healthways changed its name to Healthways in early 2006.

In late 2006 the firm acquired preventive health services provider AXIA Health Management for more than $450 million. The acquisition added a host of wellness services, such as fitness and nutrition programs, to Healthways' service offering. Among them were the SilverSneakers program, as well as an online smoking cessation support group called QuitNet.

Healthways set up shop overseas at the beginning of 2008, with a contract to provide disease management and wellness services to members of German health insurer Deutsche Angestellten Krankenkasse. That year it also entered the Brazil market via a partnership with Brazilian health services company Fleury. In 2009 the company established a presence in Australia when it entered into a wellness contract with insurer Hospitals Contribution Fund.

EXECUTIVES

Chairman, Thomas G. (Tom) Cigarran, age 69
President, CEO, and Director, Ben R. Leedle Jr., age 50, $4,812,790 total compensation
President, International Business, Matthew E. Kelliher, age 56, $1,197,169 total compensation
EVP, Mary D. Hunter, age 66
EVP Operations Services, Robert L. Chaput, age 61
VP and CFO, Alfred Lumsdaine, age 46
VP Innovations and Chief Wellness Officer, John Harris
VP and COO, Thomas F. Cox
VP and Chief Science Officer, James E. (Jim) Pope, age 58, $1,282,077 total compensation
VP, Robert E. Stone, age 65, $939,575 total compensation
Vice President Employer Market, Christopher (Chris) Cigarran
Senior Advisor, Stefen F. (Steve) Brueckner, age 62
Media Relations, Todd Hasting
Media Relations, Melissa Wyllie
Auditors: Ernst & Young LLP

LOCATIONS

HQ: Healthways, Inc.
701 Cool Springs Blvd., Franklin, TN 37067
Phone: 615-614-4929
Web: www.healthways.com

PRODUCTS/OPERATIONS

Selected Products and Services
Disease management programs
Asthma
Back pain
Cancer
Chronic kidney disease/end-stage renal disease (CKD/ESRD)
Chronic obstructive pulmonary disease (COPD)
Coronary artery disease
Depression
Diabetes
Heart failure
Hepatitis C
Obesity
Osteoporosis
Gallup-Healthways Well-Being Index (collection and measurement of national health)
Prime Fitness (fitness program for adults under 65 years of age)
QuitNet (smoking cessation program)
SilverSneakers (fitness program for older adults)
WholeHealth (alternative and complementary medicine and therapy program)

COMPETITORS

Accordant Health Services, Inc.	CIGNA
Accredo Health	Comprehensive Care
ActiveHealth	Express Scripts
Management	Fresenius Medical Care
Aetna	Health Dialog
Alere	Humana
APS Healthcare	iMetrikus
Catalyst Health	Magellan Health
Solutions	Medco He
	OptumHealth

HISTORICAL FINANCIALS

Company Type: Public

Income Statement

FYE: December 31

	REVENUE ($ mil.)	NET INCOME ($ mil.)	NET PROFIT MARGIN	EMPLOYEES
12/10	720.3	47.3	6.6%	2,800
12/09	717.4	10.4	1.4%	3,000
12/08*	244.7	734.0	300.0%	0
08/08	736.2	54.8	7.4%	3,500
08/07	615.6	45.1	7.3%	3,800
Annual Growth	5.4%	1.6%	—	(9.7%)

*Fiscal year change

2010 Year-End Financials

Debt ratio: 56.5%	No. of shares (mil.): 34.0
Return on equity: 11.0%	Dividends
Cash ($ mil.): 1.1	Yield: —
Current ratio: 1.00	Payout: —
Long-term debt ($ mil.): 243.4	Market value ($ mil.): 379.6

	STOCK PRICE ($) FY Close	P/E High/Low		PER SHARE ($) Earnings	Dividends	Book Value
12/10	11.16	14	7	1.36	0.00	12.66
12/09	18.34	65	23	0.30	0.00	11.14
12/08*	19.05	47	12	1.50	0.00	10.55
08/08	0.00	—	—	(0.00)	0.00	(0.00)
Annual Growth	—			—	—	—

*Fiscal year change

Heckmann Corporation

Heckmann is completely absorbed with water. The holding company produces bottled water for Coca-Cola's Chinese operations through its China Water and Drinks subsidiary and disposes of, transports, and treats waste water from oil and gas operations in Texas and Louisiana through Heckmann Water Resources. Its Heckmann Water Solutions is a 50/50 joint venture with Energy Transfer Partners to develop waste water pipelines and treatments for shale field oil and gas producers. Minority interests include water pipeline supplier Underground Solutions in the US and Chinese bottling equipment maker China Bottles. Heckmann was formed in 2007 as a blank check company; it made its first purchase, China Water, in 2008.

Heckmann's Chinese water unit has seven production facilities in mostly eastern China. It makes mineral, spring, purified, flavored, and oxygenated water in several sizes under the brands Darcunk and Grand Canyon. The company also supplies branded water for Coca-Cola China (the company's largest customer with nearly 60% of sales), Uni-President, and Jian Li Bao, and private label bottled water for hotels and casinos.

In 2008 the Heckmann purchased China Water from its chairman and president Xu Hong Bin for $505 million. The following year the company later sued Xu, settled a lawsuit with China Water's former CEO, and took a second look at the assets, which lead to goodwill impairment of $357.5 million causing a net income loss of $395.5 million for the year. In 2011 the company sold its China Water holdings to Pacific Water & Drinks for an undisclosed amount in amove to return to its core operations..

As part of the company's strategy to expand its service offerings in the shale oil and gas production industry, it entered its Energy Transfer Water Solutions joint venture with Energy Transfer Partners in early 2010. The JV plans to develop infrastructure and water treatments similar to its HWR business for companies in Texas and Louisiana and, eventually, seven northeastern states. Early the following year Heckmann purchased Complete Vacuum and Rental, an oilfield water disposal and transport company, for about $64 million.

EXECUTIVES

Chairman and CEO, Richard J. (Dick) Heckmann, age 67

President and COO, Charles R. (Chuck) Gordon, age 52

President, China Division, J. John Cheng

EVP Corporate Development and Chief Legal Officer, Damian C. Georgino, age 50

VP and CFO, Brian R. Anderson, age 56, $1,027,900 total compensation

VP, General Counsel, and Secretary, Donald G. Ezzell, age 47, $1,027,900 total compensation

Director, Kevin L. Spence

Director, Alfred E. Osborne Jr., age 66

Auditors: GHP Horwath, PC

LOCATIONS

HQ: Heckmann Corporation
75080 Frank Sinatra Dr., Palm Desert, CA 92211
Phone: 760-341-3606
Web: heckmanncorp.com

PRODUCTS/OPERATIONS

2009 Sales

	$ mil.	% of total
China Water	32.1	89
Heckmann Water Resources	3.8	11
Total	**35.9**	**100**

COMPETITORS

Baker Hughes	Key Energy
Basic Energy	Nestlé
Coca-Cola	Schlumberger
Danone Water	Siemens AG
GE Water and Process Technologies	Uni-President
	Veolia Environnement

HISTORICAL FINANCIALS

Company Type: Public

Income Statement
FYE: December 31

	REVENUE ($ mil.)	NET INCOME ($ mil.)	NET PROFIT MARGIN	EMPLOYEES
12/10	45.7	(14.7)	—	1,148
12/09	36.0	(395.4)	—	1,074
12/08	10.5	(14.9)	—	1,181
Annual Growth	**108.6%**	**—**	**—**	**(1.4%)**

2010 Year-End Financials

Debt ratio: 6.8%
Return on equity: —
Cash ($ mil.): 91.2
Current ratio: 3.72
Long-term debt ($ mil.): 20.5
No. of shares (mil.): 114.2
Dividends
  Yield: —
  Payout: —
Market value ($ mil.): 574.3

	STOCK PRICE ($) FY Close	P/E High/Low	PER SHARE ($) Earnings	Dividends	Book Value
12/10	5.03	— —	(0.14)	0.00	2.64
12/09	4.99	— —	(3.61)	0.00	2.93
12/08	5.65	— —	(0.19)	0.00	10.99
00/00	7.35	245 240	0.03	0.00	4.16
Annual Growth	**(11.9%)**	**— —**	**—**	**—**	**(14.0%)**

Hecla Mining

Not all that glitters at Hecla Mining is gold — in fact, most of it is silver. Hecla explores for and mines gold, silver, lead, and zinc. It produces some 10.5 million ounces of silver and 69,000 ounces of gold annually; silver accounts for more than half of the company's sales. Hecla operates mines in the US (Alaska and Idaho) and Mexico. Half of the company's sales are to Teck Resources, which processes the minerals at its smelter in British Columbia. The company's Greens Creek gold/silver/zinc/lead mine in Alaska had been a joint venture with Rio Tinto until Hecla bought it outright in 2008. Hecla sold properties in Venezuela to help pay for its acquisition of the Greens Creek property that year.

Hecla's revenues hit record levels in 2010, up 34% on the strength of higher gold production and increased metals prices across the board. Net income was down 28% in 2010, due to increased exploration costs and a significant charge from the settlement of environmental litigation.

The company's strategy is to expand its operations through investing in its four current exploration projects, expanding its reserves, operating efficiently, and seeking opportunities to acquire new mining properties.

The rising price of metals had Hecla looking at reopening three mines in 2011 that had been closed in previous years: the Star Mine in Idaho's Silver Valley, the San Juan silver mine in Colorado, and the Hugh Zone at the company's San Sebastian project in Mexico. The mines had been closed in the early 2000s as silver prices dropped below $10, but by mid-2011, they had risen to around $40.

EXECUTIVES

President, CEO, and Director, Phillips S. Baker Jr., age 51, $2,113,611 total compensation

VP Corporate Development, Don Poirier, age 52

VP Investor Relations, Mélanie Hennessey

VP and General Counsel, David C. Sienko

VP Exploration, Dean W. A. McDonald, age 53, $620,741 total compensation

SVP and CFO, James A. (Jim) Sabala, age 56, $672,918 total compensation

Auditors: BDO Seidman, LLP

LOCATIONS

HQ: Hecla Mining Company
6500 N. Mineral Dr., Ste. 200, Coeur d'Alene, ID 83815
Phone: 208-769-4100   **Fax:** 208-769-7612
Web: www.hecla-mining.com

2010 Sales

	$ mil.	% of total
Canada	124.9	30
South Korea	94.1	22
China	73.3	17
Japan	62.7	15
Belgium	25.9	6
US	24.7	6
Mexico	16.2	4
Adjustments	(3.0)	-
Total	**418.8**	**100**

PRODUCTS/OPERATIONS

2010 Sales

	$ mil.	% of total
Greens Creek	313.3	75
Lucky Friday	105.5	25
Total	**418.8**	**100**

Selected Properties

Greens Creek mine (silver, Alaska)
Lucky Friday mine (silver and lead, Idaho)
San Sebastian mine (silver, Mexico)

COMPETITORS

Agnico-Eagle	Newmont Mining
Barrick Gold	Pan American Silver
Coeur d'Alene Mines	Pe oles
Golden Minerals Company	Silverado Gold Mines

HISTORICAL FINANCIALS

Company Type: Public

Income Statement
FYE: December 31

	REVENUE ($ mil.)	NET INCOME ($ mil.)	NET PROFIT MARGIN	EMPLOYEES
12/10	418.8	49.0	11.7%	686
12/09	312.5	67.8	21.7%	656
12/08	192.7	(54.5)	—	742
12/07	222.6	53.2	23.9%	871
12/06	217.4	69.1	31.8%	1,163
Annual Growth	**17.8%**	**(8.2%)**	**—**	**(12.4%)**

2010 Year-End Financials

Debt ratio: 0.4%
Return on equity: 5.1%
Cash ($ mil.): 283.6
Current ratio: 1.68
Long-term debt ($ mil.): 3.8
No. of shares (mil.): 258.5
Dividends
  Yield: 0.0%
  Payout: —
Market value ($ mil.): 2,910.5

	STOCK PRICE ($) FY Close	P/E High/Low	PER SHARE ($) Earnings	Dividends	Book Value
12/10	11.26	89 33	0.13	0.00	3.72
12/09	6.18	32 5	0.23	0.00	3.63
12/08	2.80	— —	(0.57)	0.00	3.83
12/07	9.35	29 15	0.43	0.00	4.08
12/06	7.66	14 7	0.57	0.00	1.88
Annual Growth	**10.1%**	**— —**	**(30.9%)**	**—**	**18.6%**

hhgregg

hhgregg has evolved from black-and-white to digital. The appliance and electronics retailer began as a small storefront selling washing machines, refrigerators, and black-and-white TVs. Today the fast-growing firm sells name-brand products at more than 170 stores in about 15 mostly southern states and online. Its offerings include TV and video products (LED TVs, Blu-ray disc players), home and car audio gear (CD players, home theater systems), appliances (refrigerators, washers and dryers), computers, gaming consoles, digital cameras, GPS navigators, and mattresses. Founded in 1955, hhgregg has been growing aggressively amid tough economic conditions in the US.

In a bid to capitalize on the demise of rival Circuit City, which shuttered more than 700 stores in 2009, hhgregg announced an accelerated growth strategy, which calls for the opening of up to 70 stores in existing and new markets over two years. During fiscal 2011 (ended March) the company added about 40 locations and debuted in four new states: Delaware, Maryland, New Jersey, and Pennsylvania. hhgregg also opened a distribution center in Philadelphia to serve the new stores. The retailer is slated to open 35 to 40 locations in fiscal 2012 and will extend its presence to Illinois. hhgregg's accelerated plan to expand its store network comes at a time when consumer spending has weakened as a result of the deep recession in the US. (In the long term, the company hopes to operate about 600 locations from coast to coast.)

Despite the risk involved, expansion has helped hhgregg's business. In 2011 sales topped $2 billion, a more than 35% year-over-year improvement, driven by demand from the new stores. (Same-store sales fell by 4% that year, suggesting that hhgregg may be focusing on opening new outlets at the expense of those already in business.) TV and video products accounted for more than 45% of revenue while appliances brought in about 35%; other products, such as cell phones, computers, and mattresses, generated nearly 20% of sales. The strong top-line performance boosted profits to $48 million in 2011, a more than 20% gain from the year before.

The investment firm Freeman Spogli & Co. owns 35% of the company's shares.

EXECUTIVES

Chairman, Gerald W. (Jerry) Throgmartin, age 56, $572,304 total compensation
CFO, Jeremy J. Aguilar, age 36, $854,792 total compensation
President, CEO, and Director, Dennis L. May, age 43, $1,526,581 total compensation
EVP and COO, Gregg W. Throgmartin, age 33, $1,015,019 total compensation
VP Employee Services and Development, Thomas W. Westcott
VP Marketing, Jeff Pearson
Chief Information Officer, Stephen R. Nelson, age 58, $423,737 total compensation
Chief Merchandising Officer, Michael G. Larimer, age 57, $914,477 total compensation
Chief Human Resources Officer, Charles B. Young, age 47
Chief Administrative Officer, Michael D. (Mike) Stout, age 57, $762,291 total compensation
SVP Appliance Merchandising, Jeffrey J. McClintic, age 55
Director Finance and Investor Relations, Andy Giesler
National Training Manager, Matthew Straub
Auditors: KPMG LLP

LOCATIONS

HQ: hhgregg, Inc.
4151 E. 96th St., Indianapolis, IN 46240
Phone: 317-848-8710   **Fax:** 317-848-8723
Web: www.hhgregg.com

2011 Stores

	No.
Ohio	26
Florida	23
Indiana	17
North Carolina	17
Georgia	15
Virginia	15
Pennsylvania	14
Maryland	11
Tennessee	11
Kentucky	6
South Carolina	6
Alabama	5

Delaware	3
New Jersey	3
Mississippi	1
Total	**173**

PRODUCTS/OPERATIONS

2011 Sales

	% of total
Video	46
Appliances	36
Other	18
Total	**100**

COMPETITORS

Amazon.com	Kmart
Best Buy	Lowe's
BrandsMart USA	RadioShack
Costco Wholesale	Sears
Fry's Electronics	Target Corporation
Home Depot	Wal-Mart
J. C. Penney Company	

HISTORICAL FINANCIALS

Company Type: Public

Income Statement

FYE: March 31

	REVENUE ($ mil.)	NET INCOME ($ mil.)	NET PROFIT MARGIN	EMPLOYEES
03/11	2,077.7	48.2	2.3%	5,600
03/10	1,534.3	39.2	2.6%	4,900
03/09	1,396.7	36.5	2.6%	3,500
03/08	1,256.7	21.4	1.7%	3,808
03/07	1,059.4	21.4	2.0%	3,171
Annual Growth	**18.3%**	**22.5%**	**—**	**15.3%**

2011 Year-End Financials

Debt ratio: —
Return on equity: 15.2%
Cash ($ mil.): 72.8
Current ratio: 2.00
Long-term debt ($ mil.): —
No. of shares (mil.): 39.7
Dividends
 Yield: —
 Payout: —
Market value ($ mil.): 531.9

	STOCK PRICE ($) FY Close	P/E High/Low		PER SHARE ($) Earnings	Dividends	Book Value
03/11	13.39	26	11	1.19	0.00	7.97
03/10	25.24	26	13	1.03	0.00	6.58
03/09	14.15	14	3	1.10	0.00	3.86
03/08	11.64	26	12	0.67	0.00	2.53
Annual Growth	**4.8%**	**—**	**—**	**21.1%**	**—**	**46.6%**

Hi-Tech Pharmacal

Hi-Tech Pharmacal combines imitation with innovation, making and distributing dozens of liquid and semi-solid prescription, over-the-counter (OTC), and vitamin products. The company primarily produces generic forms of prescription drugs, including versions of allergy medicine Flonase (from GlaxoSmithKline). Hi-Tech's ECR Pharmaceuticals business makes branded over-the-counter products, including Bupap analgesic tablets and Zolpimist insomnia spray. Its Health Care Products division markets OTC products, including nutritional products and devices for people with diabetes, and the Zostrix line of pain and arthritis medications.

Hi-Tech's expertise is with difficult-to-manufacture liquid and semi-solid dosage products, including ophthalmic and inhaled pharmaceuticals. It provides contract manufacturing services to other drug firms needing this specialty. The company's products are marketed across the US through large retailers and wholesale distributors.

Sales from its generic drugs and contract manufacturing bring in more than 80% of Hi-Tech's revenue. Its generic product line focuses on oral solutions and suspensions, creams and ointments, and nasal sprays. The company maintains a steady pipeline of new products seeking approval. In 2011 it launched generic versions of Pfizer's Neurontin and Vistakon's Quixin, among others.

To enter the branded drug game, the company purchased privately held ECR Pharmaceuticals for $5.1 million in 2009. ECR manufactures branded specialty prescription drugs (allergy, headache, and dermatitis) and promotes them through an in-house force of sales representatives active in the mid-Atlantic and southern US. Most of ECR's products are made by contract manufacturers. A price hike in 2010 helped boost the division's sales.

An FDA crack-down on unapproved products in 2011 bit deep into the ECR product line. Along with other manufacturers, Hi-Tech Pharmacal had presumed the products — which had been on the market for over six decades — did not require new drug applications. However, the FDA got extra particular and yanked over 500 drugs off shelves, including ECR's antihistamine Lodrane which had accounted for 85% of its sales.

To offset the loss, Hi-Tech Pharmacal refilled ECR's offerings later in 2011 with the $3.6 million purchase of a portfolio of pain medications from private drugmaker Atley Pharmaceuticals. It further added to the ECR line by acquiring marketing and distribution rights for OTC cough medicine TussiCaps from Covidien's Mallinckrodt unit. To further reclaim its lost sales, the company is also considering filing a new drug approval for its Lodrane products with the FDA.

The firm's Health Care Products division, which handles its branded OTC business, targets diabetic patients with such products as DiabetiSweet (sugar substitute) and DiabetiDerm (moisturizing lotion). Hi-Tech Pharmacal added to the division with the 2010 purchase of the Mag-Ox line of magnesium supplements from Blaine Pharmaceuticals.

CEO David Seltzer and his brother, director Reuben Seltzer, own more than 20% of the firm their grandfather and father founded.

HISTORY

Reuben Seltzer started Hi-Tech Pharmacal's predecessor, Success Chemical, around 1930 in the back of his brother's drugstore in Brooklyn, New York. His son, Bernard, joined the company in the late 1940s and continued the business after his father died. The firm was acquired in 1967 by drug wholesaler Ketchum & Co. and adopted the name Ketchum Labs.

Seltzer and an associate bought the liquid and ointment division from Ketchum in 1981 and started the new company as Hi-Tech Pharmacal to make generic drugs. It went public in 1992 and started its Health Care Products division the next year to market hemorrhoid pads, cough remedies, and skin creams. In 1994 the company purchased Dr. Rose, Inc., a maker of generic over-the-counter and prescription suppositories, creams, and lotions.

Hi-Tech Pharmacal's 1995 product introductions included generic equivalents of constipation medications developed by what is now Sanofi-Aventis. In 1996 the company began marketing DiabetiSweet sugar substitute for diabetics and other people on special diets. That year the company opened a facility for making sterile ophthalmic and ear medication products. In 1996 and 1997 Hi-Tech Pharmacal won FDA approval for six new products, including a generic substitute for hair-growth stimulant Rogaine. The next year it added a painkiller and pediatric antibiotic to its roster.

In 2000 Hi-Tech Pharmacal signed a co-marketing agreement with Diabetic.com, a website that targets the needs of individuals with diabetes. The company also launched its Kosher Care brand of products (cough, allergy, and pain treatments), aimed at the kosher consumer market. The following year the firm further bolstered its Internet presence with its acquisition of diabetic support site SweetThoughts.com.

In 2007 the company acquired Midlothian Laboratories, gaining specialization in cough and cold medicines and prescription vitamins. It only held Midlothian a short while before selling the business in 2011 to focus on its other generic product lines.

EXECUTIVES

Chairman, President, CEO, Secretary, and Treasurer, David S. Seltzer, age 51, $603,000 total compensation
President, Health Care Products Division and Divisional VP, Sales, Gary M. April, age 54, $254,000 total compensation
EVP and Chief Scientific Officer, Kamel Egbaria
VP and CFO, William Peters, age 43, $384,000 total compensation
VP Operations, Eyal Mares, age 48
VP Information Systems, James P. Tracy, age 67
VP Pharmaceutical Operations, ECR Pharmaceuticals, Davis Caskey, age 63, $40,000 total compensation
VP and Controller, Margaret M. Santorufo, age 45
VP Corporate Development, Christopher LoSardo, age 45
VP Sales and Marketing, Edwin A. Berrios, age 58
Senior Director Quality Assurance, Jesse Kirsh, age 52
Senior Director, Strategic Planning and Product Development and Director New Business Development, Tanya Akimova, age 57
Senior Director Science, Pudpong Poolsuk, age 67
Director Regulatory Affairs, Joanne Curri, age 70
Senior Director Research and Development, Polireddy Dondeti, age 46
Auditors:

LOCATIONS

HQ: Hi-Tech Pharmacal Co., Inc.
369 Bayview Ave., Amityville, NY 11701
Phone: 631-789-8228   **Fax:** 631-789-8429
Web: www.hitechpharm.com

PRODUCTS/OPERATIONS

2011 Sales

	$ mil.	% of total
Hi-Tech Generics	157.3	83
ECR Pharmaceuticals	19.6	10
Health Care Products	13.9	7
Total	**190.8**	**100**

COMPETITORS

Bayer HealthCare	Pfizer
Caraco Pharmaceutical	Ranbaxy Laboratories
GlaxoSmithKline	Roche Holding
Johnson & Johnson	Sandoz International
Merck	GmbH
Mylan	Shionogi Pharma

Par Pharmaceutical Companies	Teva Pharmaceuticals USA
Perrigo	Watson Pharmaceuticals

HISTORICAL FINANCIALS
Company Type: Public

Income Statement
FYE: April 30

	REVENUE ($ mil.)	NET INCOME ($ mil.)	NET PROFIT MARGIN	EMPLOYEES
04/11	190.8	41.5	21.8%	408
04/10	163.7	31.1	19.0%	391
04/09	108.7	9.8	9.0%	375
04/08	62.0	(5.1)	—	288
04/07	58.9	(2.0)	—	262
Annual Growth	**34.2%**	**—**	**—**	**11.7%**

2011 Year-End Financials
Debt ratio: 0.3%
Return on equity: 22.9%
Cash ($ mil.): 62.3
Current ratio: 7.12
Long-term debt ($ mil.): 0.6
No. of shares (mil.): 12.7
Dividends
  Yield: —
  Payout: —
Market value ($ mil.): 351.5

	STOCK PRICE ($) FY Close	P/E High/Low		PER SHARE ($) Earnings	Dividends	Book Value
04/11	27.66	9	5	3.19	0.00	14.25
04/10	24.33	12	3	2.50	0.00	10.73
04/09	7.55	15	4	0.84	0.00	7.62
04/08	8.75	—	—	(0.45)	0.00	6.66
04/07	13.24	—	—	(0.17)	0.00	7.26
Annual Growth	**20.2%**	**—**	**—**	**—**	**—**	**18.3%**

Higher One

Higher One Holdings' higher ambition is to facilitate higher education payments. The company provides payment processing and disbursement services to colleges and universities and their students. Designed to make financial transactions in higher education settings more efficient, the company's suite of offerings includes OneDisburse, which more than 400 US schools use to electronically distribute financial aid and other funds to students. For students, it offers the OneAccount banking service, a deposit account and debit card. The company also provides online billing and payment services to make tuition payments convenient. Higher One Holdings went public in June 2010 after several years of steady growth.

The company raised some $171 million in the offering, which it has used to pay down debts and other obligations. By taking itself public, Higher One expects to further expand its market position as a service provider in the higher education industry, targeting schools whose in-house disbursement and payment systems may be outdated or inefficient. It also intends to pursue cross-selling opportunities presented by its 2009 acquisition of CASHNet (formerly Informed Decision Corporation), a provider of cashiering and payment services for higher education.

Since its 2000 inception, the company has experienced overall growth in revenue, cash flow, and net income. The majority of its revenues comes from ATM, intechange, and other service fees charged through its OneAccount service for students. Other revenues are generated from conven-

ience fees charged to parents and students who make online tuition payments and annual subscription fees charged to schools. Recent federal legislation has passed limiting bank overdraft and related fees, which translates to lower fee-per-account revenues. However, Higher One has continued to expand the number of accounts it services, so those revenues are still growing.

Higher One sells itself as a "one-stop shop" of technology and payment services to keep a leg up on such competitors as Nelnet, Sallie Mae, and TouchNet, which offer similar payment software and services. In addition to serving student banking needs, it addresses the needs of its educational institution clients by helping them to streamline administrative processes, reduce paper and other expenses, and remain compliant with federal regulations governing financial aid transactions. Higher One's strategic attention to customer service and brand development has helped it grow a diverse base of clients.

Private equity firm Lightyear Capital invested in Higher One in 2008 and helped take the company public. It owns 25% of the company and has board representation through director Stewart Gross.

EXECUTIVES

Chairman and CFO, Mark Volchek, age 33
President, CEO, and Director, Dean Hatton, age 50
COO and Director, Miles Lasater, age 33
Chief Sales Officer, Robert (Rob) Reach, age 54
Chief Service Officer, Casey McGuane, age 36
Director, F. Patrick McFadden Jr., age 73
Auditors: PricewaterhouseCoopers LLP

LOCATIONS

HQ: Higher One Holdings, Inc.
25 Science Park, New Haven, CT 06511
Phone: 203-776-7776
Web: www.higherone.com

PRODUCTS/OPERATIONS

2010 Sales

	$ mil.	% of total
Account revenue	113.5	78
Payment transaction revenue	15.7	11
Higher education institution revenue	12.6	9
Other	3.2	2
Total	**145.0**	**100**

COMPETITORS

American Student Assistance	Mohela
Bank of America	Nelnet
Core3	Sallie Mae
First Marblehead	U.S. Bancorp
Great Lakes Higher Education	Wells Fargo

HISTORICAL FINANCIALS
Company Type: Public

Income Statement
FYE: December 31

	REVENUE ($ mil.)	NET INCOME ($ mil.)	NET PROFIT MARGIN	EMPLOYEES
12/10	145.0	25.1	17.3%	450
12/09	75.5	14.2	18.8%	380
12/08	44.0	6.4	14.5%	0
12/07	28.0	2.3	8.2%	0
Annual Growth	**73.0%**	**121.8%**	**—**	**18.4%**

2010 Year-End Financials

Debt ratio: —
Return on equity: 30.1%
Cash ($ mil.): 34.5
Current ratio: 2.28
Long-term debt ($ mil.): —

No. of shares (mil.): 56.1
Dividends
  Yield: —
  Payout: —
Market value ($ mil.): 1,135.1

	STOCK PRICE ($) FY Close	P/E High/Low	PER SHARE ($) Earnings	Dividends	Book Value
12/10	20.23	50 25	0.44	0.00	1.49
Annual Growth	—	— —	—	—	—

HMS Holdings

HMS Holdings makes sure health benefits providers are paying only as much as they have to. Through its Health Management Systems subsidiary, the company specializes in helping providers determine participant eligibility, coordinate benefits, and identify and recover claims that were paid in error or should have been paid by another party. It serves state Medicaid agencies and Children's Health Insurance Programs in some 40 states, as well as federal agencies including Centers for Medicare & Medicaid Services and Veterans Health Administration. The company also provides services to commercial insurers, employer groups, and pharmacy benefits managers.

HMS has experienced strong revenue growth in recent years as government agencies pressure medical providers to cut health care costs and drive out process inefficiencies. It first received a boost from federal mandates under the 2006 Deficit Reduction Act, and then again with the Patient Protection and Affordable Care Act in 2010. State Medicaid enrollment rates, health insurance exchanges, and employer-sponsored heath benefits programs are all expected to swell as a result, and coordination of benefits and cost containment services will be in high demand.

HMS's revenue charts have a nice slant upwards through the years, due, in part, to a successful series of acquisitions that have widened its customer base and its service offerings. To build up its fraud detection services, the company purchased IntegriGuard for $5 million in 2009 and Allied Management Group — Special Investigation Unit in 2010.

HMS entered the employer-sponsored benefits market beginning with its $8 million, 2009 purchase of Verify Solutions, a provider of dependent eligibility audits and other human resource services for group health plans. It continued building up that segment with the 2010 acquisition of Chapman Kelly which provides dependent eligibility audits and claims audits to large self-insured employers.

In late 2011 the company announced plans to acquire HealthDataInsights for some $400 million. HMS made the move to expand its Recovery Audit Contractor services to government and commercial health plans.

EXECUTIVES

Chairman, Robert M. Holster, age 64, $911,673 total compensation
President, CEO, and Director, William C. (Bill) Lucia, age 53, $2,156,883 total compensation
EVP Operations, Sean Curtin
EVP Government Markets, Maria Perrin
EVP Corporate Development, Christina Dragonetti
VP, Controller, and Principal Accounting Officer, Joseph M. (Joe) Donabauer, age 48
VP Human Resources, John D. Schmid, age 53, $473,066 total compensation
Chief Security Officer, Scott Pettigrew
Chief Compliance Officer, Alexandra Holt
General Counsel, Edith Marshall
Media Relations, Francesca Marraro
SVP, CFO, and Corporate Secretary, Walter D. Hosp, age 53, $1,600,030 total compensation
Investor Relations, Christine Rogers Saenz
Auditors: KPMG LLP

LOCATIONS

HQ: HMS Holdings Corp.
  401 Park Ave. South, New York, NY 10016
Phone: 212-857-5000   **Fax:** 212-857-5973
Web: www.hms.com

PRODUCTS/OPERATIONS

Selected Subsidiaries

AMG-SIU
Health Management Systems, Inc.
HMS Business Services, Inc.
IntegriGuard
Permedion Inc.
Reimbursement Services Group, Inc.

COMPETITORS

ActiveHealth Management	Magellan Medicaid Administration
Affiliated Computer Services	McKesson
Argus	NCO Group
CorVel	NHXS
HP Enterprise Services	OptumnInsight
	PRGX

HISTORICAL FINANCIALS

Company Type: Public

Income Statement

FYE: December 31

	REVENUE ($ mil.)	NET INCOME ($ mil.)	NET PROFIT MARGIN	EMPLOYEES
12/10	302.9	40.1	13.2%	1,736
12/09	229.2	30.0	13.1%	1,306
12/08	184.5	21.4	11.6%	922
12/07	146.7	15.0	10.2%	760
12/06	87.9	5.3	6.0%	578
Annual Growth	36.2%	65.9%	—	31.6%

2010 Year-End Financials

Debt ratio: —
Return on equity: 13.0%
Cash ($ mil.): 94.8
Current ratio: 5.54
Long-term debt ($ mil.): —

No. of shares (mil.): 83.4
Dividends
  Yield: —
  Payout: —
Market value ($ mil.): 1,799.6

	STOCK PRICE ($) FY Close	P/E High/Low	PER SHARE ($) Earnings	Dividends	Book Value
12/10	21.59	48 31	0.47	0.00	3.69
12/09	16.23	46 26	0.36	0.00	2.96
12/08	10.51	46 23	0.27	0.00	2.36
12/07	11.07	60 28	0.19	0.00	1.90
12/06	5.05	74 33	0.07	0.00	1.54
Annual Growth	43.8%	— —	61.0%	—	24.5%

Holly Energy Partners

Holly Energy Partners is having a jolly good time piping petroleum products and crude oil from refineries. It operates petroleum product and crude gathering pipelines (in New Mexico, Oklahoma, Texas, and Utah), distribution terminals (in Arizona, Idaho, New Mexico, Oklahoma, Texas, Utah, and Washington) and refinery tankage in New Mexico and Utah. It operates 1,330 miles of refined petroleum pipelines (340 miles leased), 10 distribution terminals, one jet fuel terminal, and two truck-loading facilities. It also has three 65-mile pipelines that ship feedstocks and crude oil. HollyFrontier, the parent of the company's general partner (Holly Logistics), holds a 34% stake in Holly Energy Partners.

Holly Energy Partners' strategy is to make acquisitions that complement its existing portfolio, both in tandem with HollyFrontier and independently.

Holly Energy Partners is integral to HollyFrontier's business growth by developing and extending that company's assets. In 2008 Holly Energy Partners acquired crude oil pipelines and tankage assets from HollyFrontier for $180 million. In 2009 it picked up the Roadrunner pipeline, a 65-mile pipeline connecting HollyFrontier's refining facilities in Lovington, New Mexico, to the terminus of a Centurion pipeline linking West Texas and Cushing, Oklahoma. In 2010 it acquired petroleum storage tanks at HollyFrontier's Tulsa refinery (2 million barrels of capacity) and other assets from HollyFrontier for $93 million.

Building the largest refinery complex in the area, in 2009 HollyFrontier acquired refineries and related assets in Tulsa from Sunoco and Sinclair. In 2011 HollyFrontier's acquisition of Frontier Oil (with refineries in Kansas and Wyoming) boosted its total refining capacity to 443.000 barrels per day.

Despite a down economy Holly Energy Partners posted a sharp jump in revenues in 2009, primarily due to increased product volumes through its expanded pipeline system. However, net income went down by about 15% as increased costs, and depreciation and amortization related to its recent expansions cut into profits. Higher oil prices and volumes helped to lift the company's results in 2010.

Building its portfolio, in 2011 Holly Energy Partners acquired pipeline, tankage, loading rack and crude receiving assets from HollyFrontier's El Dorado and Cheyenne refineries for $340 million.

EXECUTIVES

Chairman and CEO, Matthew P. (Matt) Clifton, age 59
President, Holly Energy Partners and Holly Logistic Services, David G. Blair, age 52, $744,232 total compensation
VP Investor Relations, Holly Energy Partners and Holly Corporation, M. Neale Hickerson, age 58
VP and Treasurer, Stephen D. Wise
VP and Controller, Holly Logistic Services, Scott C. Surplus
VP Human Resources, Nancy F. Hartmann
VP Pipeline Operations, James G. Townsend, age 56
VP, Secretary, and General Counsel, W. John Glancy, age 69
SVP and CFO, Bruce R. Shaw, age 43
Auditors: Ernst & Young LLP

LOCATIONS

HQ: Holly Energy Partners, L.P.
2828 N. Harwood, Ste. 1300, Dallas, TX 75201
Phone: 214-871-3555 **Fax:** 214-871-3560
Web: www.hollyenergy.com

PRODUCTS/OPERATIONS

2009 Sales

	$ mil.	% of total
Pipelines		
Refined products	76.5	42
Crude oil	38.9	21
Intermediates	21.0	11
Terminals & truck loading racks	45.7	25
Total	**182.1**	**100**

COMPETITORS

ExxonMobil Pipeline	Shell Pipeline
Magellan Midstream	Wolverine Pipe Line
NuStar Energy	Company

HISTORICAL FINANCIALS

Company Type: Public

Income Statement

FYE: December 31

	REVENUE ($ mil.)	NET INCOME ($ mil.)	NET PROFIT MARGIN	EMPLOYEES
12/10	182.1	58.9	32.3%	148
12/09	146.6	66.0	45.0%	140
12/08	118.1	25.4	21.5%	121
12/07	105.4	39.3	37.3%	106
12/06	89.2	27.5	30.8%	89
Annual Growth	**19.5%**	**21.0%**	**—**	**13.6%**

2010 Year-End Financials

Debt ratio: —	No. of shares (mil.): 22.1
Return on equity: —	Dividends
Cash ($ mil.): 0.4	Yield: 6.4%
Current ratio: 0.75	Payout: 154.7%
Long-term debt ($ mil.): 491.6	Market value ($ mil.): 1,124.0

	STOCK PRICE ($) FY Close	P/E High/Low		PER SHARE ($) Earnings	Dividends	Book Value
12/10	50.91	25	18	2.12	3.28	(0.00)
12/09	39.84	13	7	3.18	3.12	(0.00)
12/08	21.35	35	11	1.34	2.96	(0.00)
12/07	43.75	25	18	2.26	2.79	3.40
12/06	40.25	27	22	1.60	2.59	4.43
Annual Growth	**6.0%**	**—**	**—**	**7.3%**	**6.1%**	**—**

HomeAway

There's no place like a home away from home for fun or functionality. HomeAway boasts more than 500,000 paid listings for vacation rental properties across 145 countries worldwide and helps property owners rent out their shack, condo, or château. Its HomeAway.com website is free to travelers, who are typically affluent, and is searchable by destination. Its listings include information on weekly rates, availability, and amenities, as well as photographs, descriptions, and contact information. HomeAway also maintains 30 other travel-related websites. Founded in 2005 as WVR Group, the company changed its name in 2006 to Home-

Away, launched its flagship website that year, and went public in mid-2011.

Raising $216 million through its initial offering, HomeAway plans to use the proceeds to not only pay off investors, but to continue its strategy of buying businesses, expanding into new global markets, adding more product lines, and increasing the functionality and relevance of its websites. The company has grown organically and by acquiring several US-centric vacation rental websites. It logged a year-over-year growth rate of nearly 40% in 2010 despite the global economy recovering from a downturn. The renter's resource also has reached outside the US to develop its business abroad. In 2010, for instance, the company purchased Brazilian-based website AlugueTemporada.com.br.

To better cater to property management professionals, the firm has been adding software providers to its portfolio. In late 2010 it acquired industry-leading developers Escapia and Instant Software, which together represent about 1,700 property managers in the US. HomeAway hopes that by bolstering its software operations, it will simplify property-management duties and drive traffic to listings through partner platforms.

Property listings accounted for about 91% of the company's 2010 revenue. HomeAway charges fees to property owners to market their properties through online listings. Property managers, vacation rental sellers and buyers, and relatively larger landlords (owners of between one and five vacation rentals) enlist the help of HomeAway to help them peddle their properties. The more listings, the more cash in HomeAway's pocket. To this end, the company offers a variety of listing packages and services, including online payments, for one-time smaller clients to customers with multiple listings.

HomeAway also generates a growing percentage of its revenue from advertising. In 2006, the company's "other revenue," which includes money generated through online advertising, accounted for 2% of its sales. HomeAway's other revenue in 2010 reached 9% of its overall sales, thanks to a 142% increase in online advertising revenue as more companies returned to the medium. The company also attributes the boost in non-listing sales to changes it has made to its websites to cater to advertisers, revenue from its software acquisitions, money received from the sale of gift cards, and royalties from the sale of travel insurance, among other items.

With property owners and managers paying for online marketing, HomeAway looks to attract tech-savvy travelers who regularly book vacation rentals. Its websites also showcase temporary housing for those who are having a home remodeled and need another place to hang their hat. Compared to the average leisure traveler, the firm cites that vacation rental bookers spend more and travel more frequently and for longer periods of time. To make it easier for customers to find properties while traveling, HomeAway in 2010 launched an iPhone application.

EXECUTIVES

President, CEO, and Director, Brian Sharples, age 50
CFO, Lynn Atchison, age 51
President Europe, Petra Friedmann
VP Partner Channels, Martin Slagter
VP North America, Alexis de Belloy
VP Customer Experience, Jeffrey (Jeff) Mosler
VP Hosting Operations and Technology, Steve Davis
COO, Brent Bellm, age 39
CTO, Ross A. Buhrdorf, age 46
Chief Product Officer, Thomas (Tom) Hale, age 42

Director Global Public Relations, Eileen Buesing
Chief Strategy and Development Officer and Director, Carl G. Shepherd, age 59
Auditors: PricewaterhouseCoopers LLP

LOCATIONS

HQ: HomeAway, Inc.
1011 W. 5th St., Ste. 300, Austin, TX 78703
Phone: 512-493-0382
Web: www.homeaway.com

2010 Sales

	$ mil.	% of total
US	104.3	62
France	27.4	16
UK	23.7	14
Other international	12.5	8
Total	**167.9**	**100**

PRODUCTS/OPERATIONS

2010 Sales

	$ mil.	% of total
Listings	152.9	91
Other	15.0	9
Total	**167.9**	**100**

Company Trademarks

Abritel.fr
Aluguetemporada BedandBreakfast.com
Clearstay
CyberRentals.com
Entech
Escapia
FeWo-Direkt
First Resorts
Holiday-Rentals
HomeAway
Homelidays
InstantSoftware
OwnersDirect
PropertyPlus
Rezovation
V12
VacationRentals.com
Villanao.fr
VRBO
Webervations

Selected Websites

Abritel.fr (France)
AlugueTemporada.com.br (Brazil)
BedandBreakfast.com
HomeAway.co.uk (UK)
HomeAway.com (US)
HomeAway.de (Germany)
HomeAway.es (Spain)
HomeAwayRealEstate.com
Homelidays.com (France)
OwnersDirect.co.uk (UK)
VacationRentals.com (US)
VRBO.com (US)

COMPETITORS

Century 21 Real Estate	Interval Leisure Group
Coldwell Banker	Kayak Software
craigslist	MSN
eBay	Orbitz Worldwide
Expedia	priceline.com
Fairfax Media	Prudential
Google	RE/MAX
Hotels.com	Telecom Italia
Hotwire, Inc.	Telete
Internet Brands	Wyndham Worldwide

Company Type: Public

Income Statement FYE: December 31

	REVENUE ($ mil.)	NET INCOME ($ mil.)	NET PROFIT MARGIN	EMPLOYEES
12/10	167.9	16.9	10.1%	781
12/09	120.2	7.7	6.4%	540
12/08	82.3	(5.7)	—	350
Annual Growth	42.8%	—	—	49.4%

Debt ratio: —
Return on equity: —
Cash ($ mil.): 0.4
Current ratio: 0.75
Long-term debt ($ mil.): 491.6

No. of shares (mil.): 22.1
Dividends
 Yield: 6.4%
 Payout: 154.7%
Market value ($ mil.): 1,124.0

HomeFed

HomeFed won't provide you with room and board, but it can help you get a home. The company earns *its* keep by investing in and developing residential real estate in California. Through subsidiaries, HomeFed is developing a master-planned community in San Diego County called San Elijo Hills, which contains approximately 3,500 residences, as well as commercial space and a town center. The company is responsible for design engineering; infrastructure such as streets, utilities, and public facilities; and the completion of individual lots. It owns a 68% stake in the development.

EXECUTIVES

Chairman, Joseph S. Steinberg, age 67
President and Director, Paul J. Borden, age 62, $661,761 total compensation
VP, Curt R. Noland, age 54, $287,739 total compensation
VP, Treasurer, and Controller, Erin N. Ruhe, age 45, $272,117 total compensation
Secretary, Corinne A. Maki
Auditors: PricewaterhouseCoopers LLP

LOCATIONS

HQ: HomeFed Corporation
 1903 Wright Place, Ste. 220, Carlsbad, CA 92008
Phone: 760-918-8200 **Fax:** 760-918-8210

PRODUCTS/OPERATIONS

2009 Sales

	$ mil.	% of total
Sales of real estate	14.7	99
Co-op marketing & advertising fees	0.2	1
Total	14.9	100

COMPETITORS

Brookfield Homes
Corky McMillin
Irvine Company
Newhall Land
Tejon Ranch

Company Type: Public

Income Statement FYE: December 31

	REVENUE ($ mil.)	NET INCOME ($ mil.)	NET PROFIT MARGIN	EMPLOYEES
12/10	35.9	3.5	9.7%	13
12/09	14.9	2.8	18.8%	13
12/08	10.4	(9.9)	—	13
12/07	23.7	6.8	28.7%	24
12/06	69.4	17.2	24.8%	23
Annual Growth	(15.2%)	(32.8%)	—	(13.3%)

2010 Year-End Financials

Debt ratio: 6.3%
Return on equity: 2.3%
Cash ($ mil.): 43.8
Current ratio: —
Long-term debt ($ mil.): 9.7

No. of shares (mil.): 7.9
Dividends
 Yield: 0.0%
 Payout: —
Market value ($ mil.): 171.8

	STOCK PRICE ($) FY Close	P/E High/Low		PER SHARE ($) Earnings	Dividends	Book Value
12/10	21.80	73	41	0.45	0.00	19.42
12/09	24.50	71	31	0.36	0.00	18.95
12/08	16.50	—	—	(1.21)	0.00	18.58
12/07	62.00	83	67	0.82	0.00	19.59
12/06	66.00	34	29	2.08	0.50	18.71
Annual Growth	(24.2%)	—	—	(31.8%)	—	0.9%

Houston American Energy

Houston-based, with North and South American properties, and energy focused, Houston American Energy explores for and produces oil and natural gas, primarily in Colombia, but also along the US Gulf Coast. In 2008 the company reported proved reserves of 18.8 million cu. ft. of natural gas and about 213,000 barrels of oil. Of its 5,360 gross acres of proved developed leasehold, about 30% is in Colombia. The bulk of the balance is in Louisiana and Texas, although the oil and gas independent also holds some acreage in Oklahoma. President and CEO John Terwilliger owns 31% of Houston American Energy; director Orrie Tawes, 12%.

EXECUTIVES

Chairman, President, CEO, COO, and Secretary, John F. Terwilliger, age 63, $315,000 total compensation
CFO, James J. (Jay) Jacobs, age 33, $347,831 total compensation
SVP Exploration, Kenneth A. Jeffers
Auditors: GBH CPAs, PC

LOCATIONS

HQ: Houston American Energy Corp.
 801 Travis St., Ste. 1425, Houston, TX 77002
Phone: 713-222-6966 **Fax:** 713-222-6440
Web: www.houstonamericanenergy.com

2008 Sales

	$ mil.	% of total
South America	10.2	96
North America	0.4	4
Total	10.6	100

PRODUCTS/OPERATIONS

2008 Sales

	$ mil.	% of total
Oil	10.4	98
Gas	0.2	2
Total	10.6	100

COMPETITORS

Ecopetrol
Emerald Energy
Global Energy
 Development
HKN
Nexen
Pacific Rubiales
Petrobank Energy and
 Resources
Talisman Energy

Company Type: Public

Income Statement FYE: December 31

	REVENUE ($ mil.)	NET INCOME ($ mil.)	NET PROFIT MARGIN	EMPLOYEES
12/10	19.5	21.0	107.7%	4
12/09	8.1	(0.7)	—	3
12/08	10.6	0.5	4.7%	3
12/07	5.0	0.5	10.0%	2
12/06	3.2	(0.5)	—	2
Annual Growth	57.1%	—	—	18.9%

2010 Year-End Financials

Debt ratio: —
Return on equity: 41.8%
Cash ($ mil.): 26.7
Current ratio: 7.74
Long-term debt ($ mil.): —

No. of shares (mil.): 31.1
Dividends
 Yield: 0.1%
 Payout: 3.0%
Market value ($ mil.): 562.3

	STOCK PRICE ($) FY Close	P/E High/Low		PER SHARE ($) Earnings	Dividends	Book Value
12/10	18.09	31	10	0.66	0.02	1.62
12/09	6.16	—	—	(0.02)	0.04	1.08
12/08	3.38	599	101	0.02	0.04	0.75
12/07	3.05	345	115	0.02	0.00	0.73
12/06	7.36	—	—	(0.02)	0.00	0.70
Annual Growth	25.2%	—	—	—	—	23.4%

Hudson Pacific

Hudson Pacific Properties wants to be the landlord to the stars. The company buys and manages office space in Northern and Southern California, in cities such as Los Angeles, Orange County, San Diego, and San Francisco. It owns about 10 properties totaling some 2 million sq. ft., including the Technicolor Building and two production studios on Hollywood's Sunset Boulevard. It also owns about 1.5 million sq. ft. of undeveloped land adjacent to its Hollywood production studios. Tenants include ABC, CBS, NBC, Fox, and Technicolor. Hudson went public in a 2010 initial public offering (IPO) and intends to operate as a self-administered and self-managed real estate investment trust (REIT).

Chairman and CEO, Victor J. Coleman, age 49
CFO, Mark T. Lammas, age 45
President and Director, Howard S. Stern, age 49
EVP Operations and Development, Christopher Barton, age 46
EVP Finance, Dale Shimoda, age 43
VP Asset Management, Alexander Vouvalides, age 32
Auditors: Ernst & Young LLP

LOCATIONS

HQ: Hudson Pacific Properties, Inc.
11601 Wilshire Blvd.,, Ste. 1600, Los Angeles, CA 90025
Phone: 310-445-5700
Web: hudsonpacificproperties.com

COMPETITORS

Douglas Emmett	Meruelo Maddux
Irvine Company	MPG Office Trust
J. H. Snyder	Newhall Land
Kilroy Realty	Pacific Office
Majestic Realty	Properties Trust
Meredith Enterprises	Watson Land Co.

HISTORICAL FINANCIALS

Company Type: Public

Income Statement

FYE: December 31

	REVENUE ($ mil.)	NET INCOME ($ mil.)	NET PROFIT MARGIN	EMPLOYEES
12/10	60.6	(3.3)	—	66
12/09	39.3	—	—	60
12/08	35.6	(1.7)	—	0
12/07	7.0	(2.3)	—	0
Annual Growth	105.3%	—	—	10.0%

2010 Year-End Financials

Debt ratio: 5.1%	No. of shares (mil.): 22.4
Return on equity: —	Dividends
Cash ($ mil.): 48.9	Yield: 1.3%
Current ratio: 0.18	Payout: —
Long-term debt ($ mil.): 21.0	Market value ($ mil.): 337.7

	STOCK PRICE ($) FY Close	P/E High/Low	PER SHARE ($) Earnings	Dividends	Book Value
12/10	15.05	— —	(0.00)	0.19	22.10
Annual Growth	—	— —	—	—	—

Human Genome Sciences

Human Genome Sciences (HGS) knows that the path to good health starts at the molecular level. Using its expertise in human genetics, the biopharmaceutical discovery and development firm is working on therapies for infectious and autoimmune diseases, cardiovascular disease, and cancer. In 2011 lead candidate Benlysta gained FDA approval to treat systemic lupus. Previously, the company's only product approved for sale was an antibody treatment for inhaled anthrax. Benlysta was developed through a partnership with GlaxoSmithKline, which also covers other products in HGS's pipeline, including heart disease and Type 2 diabetes candidates. In addition, the company has several anticancer drugs in development stages.

HGS earned its first revenues from sales of a product in 2009 when it delivered 20,000 doses of anthrax treatment raxibacumab to the US government for its bioterrorism stockpile. The company reported $154 million in revenues that year related to raxibacumab. Also in 2009, the government ordered another 45,000 doses, to be delivered by mid-2012; the company earned $47 million in 2010 related to the order.

The company has high hopes that Benlysta will skyrocket HGS into the big leagues among biopharma companies. Benlysta is expected to become a blockbuster seller (reaching over $1 billion in sales), as it is the first new lupus drug approved by the FDA in more than 50 years. To support the drug's launch, HGS has been building up a sales organization to market Benlysta in the US and Europe; GSK will also sell the product in global markets. (Benlysta is awaiting European Union approval and has been submitted in additional international markets). Aimed first at treating lupus, the drug may eventually be used to treat a variety of immune disorders and to help kidney transplant patients.

The key to developing and marketing biological drugs is having a manufacturing facility that can brew up the finicky potions in sufficient quantity, quality, and speed. HGS currently manufactures all of its drugs at its facility in the US, but to expand its capacity in preparation for Benlysta's approval, it entered an agreement in 2010 to transfer its technology to biologics manufacturer Lonza to conduct larger-scale contract manufacturing overseas by mid-2012.

In late 2010 HGS dropped development of hepatitis C candidate Zalbin, which it had been developing with Novartis, when the drug's application to the FDA was turned down. The company plans to continue to evaluate collaborative and licensing partnership opportunities for future product development efforts.

HISTORY

When Human Genome Sciences (HGS) was founded in 1992, with funding from Wallace Steinberg's HealthCare Ventures, it was clear that the Department of Energy's Human Genome Project was viable and that private industry ought to get on the bandwagon. Steinberg tapped Harvard don William Haseltine to lead the new company. HGS was to fund research performed by The Institute for Genomic Research (TIGR), which was led by Craig Venter. A star of the Project, Venter's method for speeding up the Project (mapping small gene sequences for later assembly in a completed map) had been rejected by colleagues.

TIGR began using gene sequencers from Applied Biosystems to churn out DNA sequences. The next year Haseltine licensed the resulting data to SmithKline Beecham (now GlaxoSmithKline) for possible product development. Other data licensing — as well as product development — agreements followed.

In 1997 Haseltine's drive to commercialize TIGR's results clashed with Venter's desire to publish his research results immediately, and the relationship between the two entities was severed. Under the terms of the split, HGS stopped funding TIGR and renounced rights to future genetic information. Venter continued his quest to map the entire genome at Celera, while Haseltine, with his own complement of sequencers, zeroed in on expressive genes and then on product development.

In 1998 HGS initiated clinical trials of two drugs: Mirostipen, aimed at reducing the toxicity of certain cancer chemotherapies, and Repifermin, which targeted mucosal and skin tissue repair.

The firm continued to uncode DNA in 1999, with discoveries in the fields of Hodgkin's lymphoma causation and immunology offering possible applications to AIDS (in 2000 it was awarded a patent for uncovering a possible genetic mechanism for AIDS infection). In 2000 HGS was caught up in the euphoria caused by the race to complete the gene map and the subsequent biotech plunge when President Clinton and UK Prime Minister Blair endorsed open access to raw genome data (which isn't patentable anyway). Also that year it bought privately held Principia Pharmaceutical, from which it gained a drug delivery technology using the blood protein albumin that it began developing for hepatitis C uses in 2001.

When licensing agreements with major drugmakers for its gene database expired in June 2001, HGS opted not to make any more agreements, keeping the information largely for its own drug development activities. Anticipating the approval of its drug candidates, the company began building a manufacturing plant to make commercial products in October of that year.

In 2002 the company, like many drug developers, hit a snag. HGS stopped development of Mirostipen, a potential therapy for chemotherapy-induced neutropenia, after early clinical trials showed the drug candidate was not as effective as its developers had hoped it would be. Instead, the company forwarded Albugranin, a different type of drug for the same condition, into clinical trials.

To reduce costs, the company in 2004 halted work on about half of its drug candidates. HGS also streamlined its operations, consolidated facilities, and fired about 20% of its staff. The downsizing was an indication that using gene-based therapies to address unmet medical needs might not be as successful as scientists had originally hoped. Two of the company's most promising drug candidates had failed to meet expectations. Later that year, founding chairman and CEO William Haseltine retired to make way for more business-oriented leaders.

In order to focus on its later-stage development projects, in 2006 the company spun off its CoGenesys unit, which it had formed to handle early drug development efforts and to out-license some assets the company wasn't interested in developing itself. HGS retained a 14% stake in the unit until 2008, when CoGenesys was acquired by Israeli drugmaker Teva. In addition to receiving $52.6 million from the sale, HGS retained the right to receive a portion of the revenue that Teva may receive from future sales of the products it gained.

EXECUTIVES

Chairman, Argeris N. (Jerry) Karabelas, age 58
President, CEO, and Director, H. Thomas (Tom) Watkins, age 58, $3,427,736 total compensation
EVP and CFO, David P. Southwell, age 50
EVP, General Counsel, and Secretary, James H. Davis, age 59, $1,247,178 total compensation
EVP Research and Development, David C. Stump, age 61, $1,608,001 total compensation
EVP and Chief Commercial Officer, Barry A. Labinger, age 47, $1,563,186 total compensation
VP Intellectual Property, Michele M. Wales
VP Manufacturing Operations, Randy Maddux
VP Engineering, Joseph A. (Joe) Morin
VP Quality, Sarah Thomas

VP BioPharmaceutical Development, Thomas M. Spitznagel
VP Corporate Communications and Public Policy, Jerry Parrott
VP Clinical Operations, Ann L. Wang
VP Clinical Research, Immunology, Rheumatology, and Infectious Diseases, William W. Freimuth
VP Medical Affairs, Gregory F. Keenan
VP Sales, Scott Habig
VP HGS Europe, Tuomo Pätsi
VP Clinical Research, Oncology, Gilles Gallant
VP Clinical Research, General Medicine, Daniel J. Odenheimer
VP Sales and Marketing, Kevin P. McRaith, age 46
SVP Human Resources, Susan Bateson, age 56
SVP Operations, Curran M. Simpson, age 49
SVP Development and Regulatory Affairs, Sally D. Bolmer
Auditors: Ernst & Young LLP

LOCATIONS

HQ: Human Genome Sciences, Inc.
14200 Shady Grove Rd., Rockville, MD 20850-7464
Phone: 301-309-8504 **Fax:** 301-309-8512
Web: www.hgsi.com

PRODUCTS/OPERATIONS

2010 Sales

	$ mil.	% of total
R&D collaborations	87.5	56
Product sales	47.2	30
Manufacturing & development services	22.7	14
Total	**157.4**	**100**

COMPETITORS

Amgen	Genzyme Oncology
Anthera	Gilead Sciences
Pharmaceuticals	Immunomedics
Aradigm	Johnson & Johnson
Bayer HealthCare	Maxygen
Biogen Idec	Merck
Cangene	Merck Serono
Elusys Therapeutics	Teva
Emergent BioSolutions	TolerRx
Genentech	

HISTORICAL FINANCIALS

Company Type: Public

Income Statement
FYE: December 31

	REVENUE ($ mil.)	NET INCOME ($ mil.)	NET PROFIT MARGIN	EMPLOYEES
12/10	157.4	(233.2)	—	1,100
12/09	275.7	5.7	2.1%	850
12/08	48.4	(244.9)	—	880
12/07	41.9	(262.4)	—	850
12/06	25.8	(251.2)	—	770
Annual Growth	**57.2%**	**—**	**—**	**9.3%**

2010 Year-End Financials

Debt ratio: 74.2%
Return on equity: —
Cash ($ mil.): 155.7
Current ratio: 1.89
Long-term debt ($ mil.): 434.7
No. of shares (mil.): 189.0
Dividends
Yield: —
Payout: —
Market value ($ mil.): 4,514.8

	STOCK PRICE ($) FY Close	P/E High/Low		PER SHARE ($) Earnings	Dividends	Book Value
12/10	23.89	—	—	(1.24)	0.00	3.10
12/09	30.58	785	11	0.04	0.00	4.08
12/08	2.12	—	—	(1.81)	0.00	(1.78)
12/07	10.44	—	—	(1.95)	0.00	(0.09)
12/06	12.44	—	—	(1.91)	0.00	1.61
Annual Growth	**17.7%**	**—**	**—**	**—**	**—**	**17.7%**

IBERIABANK

Rather than crawdads, gumbo, and boudin, IBERIABANK Corporation serves up financial services. Through its flagship bank subsidiary, also called IBERIABANK, the holding company operates about 200 branches in the South. It also has about 25 title insurance offices in Louisiana and Arkansas, in addition to more than 50 mortgage loan offices in a dozen states. Offering deposit products such as checking and savings accounts, CDs, and IRAs, the bank uses funds gathered mainly to make loans. Business operating loans and commercial mortgages make up more than two-thirds of the company's loan portfolio, which also includes consumer loans and residential mortgages.

Acquisitions have been a big part of IBERIA-BANK's growth strategy. It expanded eastward from its Louisiana base by acquiring the failed CapitalSouth Bank in an FDIC-assisted transaction in 2009. The deal, which included a loss-sharing agreement with the regulator, comprised about a dozen locations in Alabama and Florida. IBERIA-BANK later added more than 30 branches in the Sunshine State by acquiring failed institutions Orion Bank, Century Bank, and Sterling Bank in similar deals with the FDIC.

IBERIABANK continued making acquisitions in 2011 when it bought Omnibank, based in the New Orleans suburb of Metairie; and Cameron State Bank, a 22-branch bank based in Lake Charles. It also bought the assets of Florida Trust Company, a subsidiary of the failed Bank of Florida Corporation. All of the acquisition activity has expanded the company's asset holdings and branch network and provided entry into new states.

In 2010 the bank formed IBERIA Wealth Advisors in an effort to build its trust and asset management operations. Other subsidiaries brokerage unit Iberia Financial Services, IBERIABANK Insurance Services, and Lenders Title Company.

EXECUTIVES

Chairman, William H. Fenstermaker, age 62
President, CEO, and Director; President and CEO, IBERIABANK, Daryl G. Byrd, age 56, $1,403,916 total compensation
President Mortgage Market, Alabama and Georgia, IBERIABANK, Barry Carroll
President and CEO, IBERIABANK Mortgage, Chuck M. Quick Jr.
EVP, Corporate Secretary, and Director Corporate Operations, George J. Becker III, age 70
EVP and Chief Credit Officer, H. Gregg Strader, age 52
EVP and Director Communications, Beth Ardoin
EVP and Chief Risk Officer, James B. Gburek
EVP and President, Mobile, Alabama, Lawrence G. (Russ) Ford Jr.

EVP; President Birmingham, Alabama, IBERIABANK, Gregory A. King
EVP and Internal Audit Manager, Lewis P. Rogers, age 58
EVP and Director Enterprise Risk Management, Elise Latimer
Vice Chairman, E. Stewart Shea III, age 59
Vice Chairman and COO, Michael J. (Mike) Brown, age 54
SEVP and CFO, Anthony J. Restel, age 41, $420,900 total compensation
SEVP, Florida Markets, Michael A. Naquin, age 50, $645,513 total compensation
SEVP and Director Financial Strategy and Mortgage, John R. Davis, age 50, $727,282 total compensation
Market President, Northeast Louisiana, Paul E. Hutcheson Jr.
Market President, Lafayette, Pete M. Yuan
Market President, New Iberia and Community Markets, Taylor F. Barras
Market President, New Orleans, Karl E. Hoefer
Market President, Baton Rouge, J. Keith Short
Vice Chairman and Managing Director Brokerage, Trust and Wealth Management, Jefferson G. (Jeff) Parker, age 58
Market President, Shreveport, Mark D. Evans
Auditors: Ernst & Young LLP

LOCATIONS

HQ: IBERIABANK Corporation
200 W. Congress St., Lafayette, LA 70501
Phone: 337-521-4012 **Fax:** 337-364-1171
Web: www.iberiabank.com

PRODUCTS/OPERATIONS

2010 Sales

	$ mil.	% of total
Interest		
Loans, including fees	353.2	65
Securities	49.4	9
Other	6.8	1
Noninterest		
Gain on sale of loans, net	47.7	9
Service charges on deposit accounts	24.4	5
Title revenue	18.1	3
ATM/debit card fees	10.1	2
Broker commissions	7.5	1
Net gain on sale of investments	5.3	1
Other	22.5	4
Adjustments	(14.7)	-
Total	**603.4**	**100**

Selected Subsidiaries

IBERIA Capital Partners, LLC
IBERIABANK
   Acadiana Holdings, LLC
   CB Florida RRE Holdings, LLC
   Finesco, LLC
   Iberia Financial Services, LLC
   IBERIABANK Insurance Services, LLC
   Jefferson Insurance Corporation
Lenders Title Company
   American Abstract and Title Company, Inc.
   Asset Exchange, Inc.
   United Title & Abstract, LLC
   United Title of Louisiana, Inc.

COMPETITORS

Bank of America	JPMorgan Chase
Bank of the Ozarks	Louisiana Bancorp
Capital One	MidSouth Bancorp
Hancock Holding	Regions Financial
Home Bank	Teche Holding

HISTORICAL FINANCIALS

Company Type: Public

Income Statement

FYE: December 31

	ASSETS ($ mil.)	NET INCOME ($ mil.)	INCOME AS % OF ASSETS	EMPLOYEES
12/10	10,026.8	48.8	0.5%	2,193
12/09	9,700.4	151.3	1.6%	1,685
12/08	5,583.2	39.9	0.7%	1,356
12/07	4,917.0	41.3	0.8%	1,319
12/06	3,203.0	35.7	1.1%	754
Annual Growth	33.0%	8.1%	—	30.6%

2010 Year-End Financials

Equity as % of assets: 13.00%
Return on assets: 0.5%
Return on equity: 3.7%
Long-term debt ($ mil.): 432.3
No. of shares (mil.): 26.9

Dividends
Yield: 2.3%
Payout: 72.3%
Market value ($ mil.): 1,589.1
Sales ($ mil.): 530.3

	STOCK PRICE ($) FY Close	P/E High/Low		PER SHARE ($) Earnings	Dividends	Book Value
12/10	59.13	34	26	1.88	1.36	48.50
12/09	53.81	7	4	8.03	1.36	45.99
12/08	48.00	23	12	3.04	1.36	56.57
12/07	46.75	18	12	3.27	1.34	39.08
12/06	59.05	18	14	3.57	1.22	32.93
Annual Growth	0.0%	—	—	(14.8%)	2.8%	10.2%

ICG Group

B2B or not B2B? That is the question for ICG Group, Inc. (formerly Internet Capital Group). The company invests in firms in the business-to-business (B2B) market, working with its holdings to develop strategy. ICG owns stakes in about a dozen companies involved in technology-enabled business process outsourcing, Internet marketing, and software as a service. Its core holdings include scheduling software and services company StarCite, international trade facilitator FreeBorders, and ICG Commerce, which offers procurement outsourcing services. ICG closely works with its core companies, and often helps them with day-to-day management.

ICG has been working to build ICG Commerce for more than a decade. In 2010 it increased its ownership in ICG Commerce from 64% to 80%. The deal helped ICG more closely align with the acquired company's management.

ICG also owns significant stakes in data management software company Investor Force; White-Fence, which allows consumers to compare utilities providers; and Channel Intelligence, which helps consumers to connect online with manufacturer, retailers, and publishers.

In 2011 the company sold business process management software maker Metastorm to Open Text Corporation. The sale yielded more than $50 million for ICG. It uses the proceeds from such transactions towards other software and services investments.

In 2010 ICG acquired an 89% stake in GovDelivery for $20 million. The acquired firm provides digital subscription management software that enables government organizations to provide citizens with information through email, mobile text alerts, and other channels.

ICG plan son making more acquisitions and seeking bolt-on acquisitions for its portfolio companies. Demand in for business outsourcing and software as a service has increased as companies look to cut costs by automating or improving processes.

EXECUTIVES

Chairman and CEO, Walter W. Buckley III, age 51, $984,436 total compensation
President, Douglas A. (Doug) Alexander, age 50, $994,128 total compensation
CFO, R. Kirk Morgan, age 44, $453,356 total compensation
VP, Bertrand (Bert) Navarrete
VP, Matthew J. Safaii
VP Treasury and Tax, Philip A. (Phil) Rooney
VP Investor Relations and Corporate Communications, Karen Greene
Corporate Counsel, Scott Powers
Managing Director, John Loftus
Managing Director, Paul Slaats
Managing Director, General Counsel, and Secretary, Suzanne L. Niemeyer
Managing Director, Vincent P. (Vince) Menichelli
Managing Director, Darren Sandberg
Managing Director, Kamal Advani, age 50
Auditors: KPMG LLP

LOCATIONS

HQ: ICG Group, Inc.
690 Lee Rd., Ste. 310, Wayne, PA 19087
Phone: 610-727-6900   **Fax:** 610-727-6901
Web: www.internetcapital.com

PRODUCTS/OPERATIONS

Selected Holdings

Acquirgy (25%, search engine marketing and direct response TV)
Channel Intelligence, Inc. (49%, e-commerce sourcing)
Freeborders, Inc. (31%, international trade)
GoIndustry-DoveBid plc (26%, auction sales of industrial machinery, UK)
GovDelivery, Inc. (93%, government-to-citizen communication platform)
ICG Commerce Holdings, Inc. (81%, procurement services and sourcing)
Investor Force Holdings, Inc. (78%, online applications for the financial services industry)
SeaPass (25%, insurance services)
StarCite, Inc. (36%, scheduling software and services)
WhiteFence (36%, residential services)

COMPETITORS

Accel Partners	Kleiner Perkins
Alloy Ventures	Matrix Partners
Benchmark Capital	Menlo Ventures
Hummer Winblad	Safeguard Scientifics
Idealab	Sevin Rosen
IVP	SOFTBANK

HISTORICAL FINANCIALS

Company Type: Public

Income Statement

FYE: December 31

	REVENUE ($ mil.)	NET INCOME ($ mil.)	NET PROFIT MARGIN	EMPLOYEES
12/10	115.7	46.6	40.3%	773
12/09	90.3	15.5	17.2%	648
12/08	71.2	(22.9)	—	509
12/07	52.9	(30.6)	—	410
12/06	64.7	15.6	24.1%	336
Annual Growth	15.6%	31.5%	—	23.2%

2010 Year-End Financials

Debt ratio: 6.9%
Return on equity: 20.8%
Cash ($ mil.): 92.4
Current ratio: 3.78
Long-term debt ($ mil.): 15.5

No. of shares (mil.): 37.0
Dividends
Yield: —
Payout: —
Market value ($ mil.): 527.2

	STOCK PRICE ($) FY Close	P/E High/Low		PER SHARE ($) Earnings	Dividends	Book Value
12/10	14.25	11	5	1.26	0.00	6.05
12/09	6.65	21	8	0.42	0.00	7.72
12/08	5.45	—	—	(0.60)	0.00	6.48
12/07	11.74	—	—	(0.81)	0.00	7.89
12/06	10.26	27	18	0.41	0.00	7.64
Annual Growth	8.6%	—	—	32.4%	—	(5.7%)

Iconix Brand Group

Once a shoemaker, Iconix Brand Group has stepped it up as a licensing and brand management company. Its company-owned consumer and home brands are licensed to third parties that make and sell apparel, footwear, and a variety of other fashion and home products. Consumer brands in the Iconix stable include Badgley Mischka, Danskin, Ocean Pacific, Mossimo, London Fog, Mudd, and Rocawear; among the company's home brands are Cannon, Fieldcrest, and Waverly. The firm diversified through its high-profile purchase of the Peanuts cartoon brand from E. W. Scripps in mid-2010. Along with licensing the brands, Iconix markets and promotes them through its in-house advertising and public relations services.

Iconix made industry news in June 2010 when it acquired a majority stake in United Media Licensing, the owner of Charles M. Schulz's world-famous Peanuts brand and its cast of characters including Charlie Brown and Snoopy. Iconix and the Schulz family teamed up to buy the business for $175 million. (Iconix owns 80% of the company and the Schulz family owns the rest.) In addition, the deal included properties such as disgruntled office worker Dilbert and children's book heroine Fancy Nancy. The deal was a strong play by Iconix to expand its business beyond fashion brands. It expects to earn about $75 million in annual revenues from licensing Peanuts. Iconix also hopes that the worldwide Peanuts presence will open up new international markets for its existing fashion business. (E. W. Scripps' United Media Syndicate subsidiary will continue to syndicate the *Peanuts* comic strip.)

The Peanuts deal is just the latest (and highest profile) acquisition for highly acquisitive Iconix, which collects brands the way some people collect shoes. The company has made 15 acquisitions in the past five years and hopes to one day grow to a collection of 25-30 brands. In late 2009 Iconix snatched up a 51% controlling interest in the brand portfolio of urban fashion firm Marc Ecko Enterprises. The firm manages such brands as Ecko Unlimited, Marc Ecko, the Rhino logo, and Zoo York. Iconix paid an overall purchase price of about $109 million for the brands. A year earlier, Iconix acquired Waverly, a home furnishing brand, from NexCen Brands. The Waverly acquisition opened up partnerships with retail giants such as Target, Lowe's, and J. C. Penney.

As another means for growth, Iconix expects to grow through its licensing agreements with Wal-Mart to sell Ocean Pacific, Danskin Now, and Starter apparel and accessories. The company also is looking to international markets to boost revenues as the US economy weakens. In 2008 Iconix formed joint ventures in China and Latin America to advance its brands.

Iconix, formerly a footwear company known as Candie's Inc., changed its name in 2005 to reflect a shift in focus from manufacturing to brand management. The company continues to keep a toe in the footwear business with the Candie's brand and through its subsidiary Bright Star, which oversees the design and arranges for the manufacturing and distribution of men's shoes sold under private labels, primarily by Wal-Mart.

Iconix is led by chairman, president, and CEO Neil Cole, brother of fashion icon Kenneth Cole.

EXECUTIVES

Chairman, President, and CEO, Neil Cole, age 53, $10,852,400 total compensation
CEO, Ecko.Complex, Seth Gerszberg, age 37
EVP and CFO, Warren Clamen, age 46, $1,710,369 total compensation
EVP and Head Strategic Development, David Blumberg, age 51, $1,592,380 total compensation
EVP and General Counsel, Andrew Tarshis, age 44, $1,710,369 total compensation
COO, Yehuda Shmidman, $1,453,007 total compensation
Chief Merchandising Officer, Lanie List
Chief Creative Officer, Ecko.Complex, Marc Ecko, age 39
SVP Brand Management, Home Division, Carolyn D'Angelo
Chief Marketing Officer, Dari Marder
Auditors: BDO Seidman, LLP

LOCATIONS

HQ: Iconix Brand Group, Inc.
1450 Broadway, 4th Fl., New York, NY 10018
Phone: 212-730-0030   **Fax:** 212-391-2057
Web: iconixbrand.com

2009 Sales

	$ mil.	% of total
US	218.7	94
Other countries	13.4	6
Total	**232.1**	**100**

PRODUCTS/OPERATIONS

2009 Sales

	$ mil.	% of total
Direct-to-retail license	110.9	48
Wholesale license	108.1	46
Other (commissions, sales of trademarks, etc.)	13.1	6
Total	**232.1**	**100**

Selected Brands

Consumer
  Badgley Mischka
  Bongo
  Candie's
  Danskin
  Dilbert
  Fancy Nancy
  Joe Boxer
  London Fog
  Mossimo
  Mudd
  Ocean Pacific
  Peanuts
  Rampage
  Rocawear
  Starter

Home
  Cannon
  Charisma
  Fieldcrest
  Royal Velvet

COMPETITORS

Ann Taylor	Limited Brands
Billabong	Liz Claiborne
Calvin Klein	NIKE
Cherokee Inc.	Pacific Sunwear
Collective Licensing	Polo Ralph Lauren
Guess?	Quiksilver
H&M	The Gap
Hanesbrands	Vera Wang
J. C. Penney	VF Corporation
Jones Group	Williamson-Dickie
Kellwood	

HISTORICAL FINANCIALS

Company Type: Public

Income Statement				FYE: December 31
	REVENUE ($ mil.)	NET INCOME ($ mil.)	NET PROFIT MARGIN	EMPLOYEES
12/10	332.6	98.8	29.7%	133
12/09	232.1	75.1	32.4%	66
12/08	216.8	70.2	32.4%	82
12/07	160.0	63.8	39.9%	94
12/06	80.7	32.5	40.3%	46
Annual Growth	**42.5%**	**32.0%**	**—**	**30.4%**

2010 Year-End Financials

Debt ratio: 52.9%
Return on equity: 9.5%
Cash ($ mil.): 121.9
Current ratio: 2.26
Long-term debt ($ mil.): 548.0

No. of shares (mil.): 72.5
Dividends
  Yield: —
  Payout: —
Market value ($ mil.): 1,400.4

	STOCK PRICE ($) FY Close	P/E High/Low		PER SHARE ($) Earnings	Dividends	Book Value
12/10	19.31	16	9	1.32	0.00	14.29
12/09	12.67	17	6	1.10	0.00	12.71
12/08	9.78	20	4	1.15	0.00	10.53
12/07	19.66	24	17	1.04	0.00	9.28
12/06	19.39	28	13	0.72	0.00	11.44
Annual Growth	**(0.1%)**	**—**	**—**	**16.4%**	**—**	**5.7%**

ICU Medical

ICU Medical sees the future of infection prevention. The company's devices protect health care workers and patients from the spread of diseases such as HIV and hepatitis. Its primary products are intravenous (IV) connection devices, called Clave needleless connectors, that reduce the risk of needle sticks and disconnections. The firm also makes custom IV sets, many of which use Clave connectors and other ICU products, for third parties. Additionally, ICU Medical makes critical care equipment, such as angiography kits and heart monitors. ICU Medical sells its products to other equipment makers and distributors throughout the US and internationally.

ICU Medical has a long-standing relationship with medical device maker Hospira. Way back in 2005, ICU Medical purchased Hospira's Salt Lake City manufacturing plant, which produces catheters, angiography kits, and cardiac monitors, among other devices. At that time the two entered a 20 year agreement under which ICU Medical will manufacture the products and Hospira will purchase them. Then, in 2009, ICU Medical purchased the commercial rights and physical assets from Hospira's critical care product line giving ICU Medical complete control of manufacturing and marketing rights of the critical care line.

Through yet another agreement with Hospira, ICU Medical makes and co-promotes custom IV systems under the name SetSource. That agreement is set to last through 2014. All told, sales to Hospira account for more than 40% of ICU Medical's yearly income.

Aside from bringing home the bacon, ICU Medical's dealings with Hospira provide ICU Medical access to the IV set market in the US, in which Hospira has a significant share. The company expects Hospira will be important to growth its CLAVE line (which already accounts for about 35% of sales), custom infusion sets, and its other products worldwide.

Outside of its dealings with Hospira, ICU Medical's growth strategy hinges upon its ability to continue to develop and introduce new products to its customers, particularly in the face of upcoming patent expirations on some of its products. Much like pharmaceutical companies, medical device manufacturers enjoy a certain amount of market exclusivity on their patented products, but once those patents expire, competitors are free to introduce their own versions of the devices. ICU Medical has patents expiring at the end of 2011 (for its biggest selling Clave connectors) up until 2023 (the Orbit 90 infusion set). Once those patents expire, ICU Medical can expect a substantial drop in sales for the product or products losing patent expiration.

It's getting itself ready for those losses by diversifying its product line, internally developing products and systems, and by acquiring product lines. Internally developed products, including those for use in oncology therapy, dialysis, and diabetes, accounted for close to 10% of its sales in 2010. These products include the TEGO for use in dialysis, the Orbit 90 diabetes set, and a line of oncology products including the Spiros male luer connector device, the Genie vial access device, custom IV sets, and ancillary products specifically designed for chemotherapy.

On the sales side, the company is increasingly directing its marketing efforts toward securing long-term contracts with large buying organizations. ICU Medical is reacting to an increasingly consolidated health care provider marketplace, because the providers have more buying power as they get larger. Long-term contracts help the company lock in prices even as the market changes around them.

ICU Medical has sought to save on manufacturing costs by moving more of its production to Mexico, where it operates a plant with about 1,100 workers in Ensenada.

CEO George Lopez and his family own more than a quarter of ICU Medical.

EXECUTIVES

Chairman, President, and CEO, George A. Lopez, age 63, $2,458,987 total compensation
President, Europe, Gabriele Giovanelli
CFO, Secretary, and Treasurer, Scott E. Lamb, age 48, $803,275 total compensation
VP International, Greg Pratt
VP Operations, Steven C. (Steve) Riggs, age 52, $808,768 total compensation

VP Sales and Marketing, Richard A. (Richie) Costello, age 47, $801,450 total compensation

VP Product Development, Alison D. Burcar, age 38, $453,108 total compensation

Manager, Animal Health, Scott St. Germain

Product Specialist, Renal Systems, Tennessee, North Carolina, South Carolina, Georgia, Alabama, and, J D Shuff

European Product Specialist, UK and Ireland, David Chantry

European Product Specialist, Italy, Mirco Bordoni

Senior Product Specialist, Renal Systems, Ohio, Michigan, Wisconsin, Minnesota, Iowa, Illinois, Kent, Bill Grimes

Product Manager, Oncology Systems, Tim Shannon

Western Region Manager, Hospital Sales, Gary Soileau

Director Critical Care Systems, Rob Kraal

Sales Manager, Critical Care Systems, Andrew Wickersham

Manager Sales, Northern Asia, Masayoshi Iwata

International Product Specialist, Brazil, Valter J. Loio

Critical Care Product Manager, Tage Grant

Senior Critical Care Device Specialist, Glen Hill

Senior Product Specialist, Renal Systems, Colorado, Wyoming, Montana, Idaho, Utah, Arizona, Californ, Billy Huard

Western US Sales Manager, Critical Care Systems, Mike Schoonover

Southern Region Manager, Alternate Site Sales, Tim Lefort

Manager International Sales, Mexico, Xalixia Larrea

Eastern Region Manager, Hospital Sales, Bruce Dragish

Central Region Manager, Alternate Site Sales, Dan Marten

Product Specialist, Renal Systems, Maine, Vermont, New Hampshire, Massachusetts, New York, Pennsylva, Jim Wickersham

Controller, Kevin McGrody

National Manager, Western Canada, Neil Perrett

Product Specialist, Eastern Canada, Don McDonald

European Product Specialist, Northern Europe, Andre Schepers

Director National Accounts, Mark Jorgensen

Central Region Manager, Hospital Sales, Randy Clark

European Product Specialist, Spain and Portugal, Roberto Zambrano

Manager International Sales, South East Asia and India, Jason Kuan

Manager Oncology Systems Sales, Mike Lester

Director Human Resources, James J. (Jim) Reitz

Director Media Relations, James McCusker

Director Renal Systems Sales, Louisiana, Arkansas, Texas, Oklahoma, Kansas, Mississippi, Nebraska, N, Greg Walpole

Director Oncology Systems Sales, Rob Houde

Senior Marketing Manager and International Marketing Manager, IV Systems, Global, Latin America, and, Michelle Olivo

Manager International Marketing, Southeast Asia, Middle East, India, and Africa, Mike Sweeney

Manager Sales and Marketing, Asia Pacific, Russell Nicholson

Eastern Region Manager, Alternate Site Sales, Dave Bolesta

Auditors: McGladrey & Pullen, LLP

LOCATIONS

HQ: ICU Medical, Inc.
951 Calle Amanecer, San Clemente, CA 92673
Phone: 949-366-2183   Fax: 949-366-8368
Web: www.icumed.com

2010 Sales

	% of total
Medical product manufacturers	41
Domestic distributors/direct	36
International	23
Total	**100**

PRODUCTS/OPERATIONS

2010 Sales

	% of total
Clave	35
Custom products	35
Standard critical care products	18
Standard oncology products	3
Other	9
Total	**100**

Selected Products

Clave (needleless IV connector)
CLC2000 (connector preventing the backflow of blood)
Io2 Valve (one- or two-way drug delivery system)
Lopez Valve (valve permitting intermittent injections without disconnection)
Orbit 90 (diabetes set)
SetMaker (IV set)
Smart Y (animal health, valves)
TEGO Connector (connector for use in hemodialysis)

COMPETITORS

B. Braun Melsungen
Baxter International
Becton, Dickinson
Cardinal Health
Covidien
Edwards Lifesciences
Fresenius
Merit Medical Systems
Navilyst Medical

HISTORICAL FINANCIALS

Company Type: Public

Income Statement   FYE: December 31

	REVENUE ($ mil.)	NET INCOME ($ mil.)	NET PROFIT MARGIN	EMPLOYEES
12/10	284.6	30.9	10.9%	2,237
12/09	231.5	26.6	11.5%	1,936
12/08	204.7	24.3	11.9%	1,829
12/07	188.1	23.1	12.3%	1,796
12/06	201.6	25.7	12.7%	1,819
Annual Growth	**9.0%**	**4.7%**	**—**	**5.3%**

2010 Year-End Financials

Debt ratio: —
Return on equity: 11.3%
Cash ($ mil.): 78.9
Current ratio: 8.07
Long-term debt ($ mil.): —
No. of shares (mil.): 13.7
Dividends
Yield: —
Payout: —
Market value ($ mil.): 498.6

	STOCK PRICE ($) FY Close	P/E High/Low		PER SHARE ($) Earnings	Dividends	Book Value
12/10	36.50	18	14	2.23	0.00	20.08
12/09	36.44	25	15	1.77	0.00	18.61
12/08	33.14	23	13	1.67	0.00	17.16
12/07	36.01	30	21	1.51	0.00	15.41
12/06	40.68	30	20	1.64	0.00	15.32
Annual Growth	**(2.7%)**	**—**	**—**	**8.0%**	**—**	**7.0%**

Idaho Independent Bank

Idaho Independent Bank has about a dozen branches located throughout the state. Targeting individuals and small to midsized businesses, the bank provides such traditional products as checking and savings accounts, certificates of deposit, and credit cards. The bank also offers a variety of products and services aimed specifically at business customers, including cash management and working capital loans. Real estate loans make up more than half of the bank's loan portfolio. Idaho Independent Bank also originates business, construction, and consumer loans.

EXECUTIVES

Chairman and CEO, Jack W. Gustavel, age 71
President, COO, and Director, Kurt R. Gustavel
EVP, Chief Credit Officer, and Director, Rod B. Colwell, age 52
SVP, Cashier, and Secretary, Paul H. Montreuil
Auditors: Moss Adams, LLP

LOCATIONS

HQ: Idaho Independent Bank
1260 W. Riverstone Dr., Coeur d'Alene, ID 83814
Phone: 208-765-3619   Fax: 208-765-6091
Web: www.theidahobank.comIdaho Independent Bank has operations in the Idaho communities of Boise, Caldwell, Coeur d'Alene, Hayden Lake, Ketchum, Meridian, Mountain Home, Nampa, and Star.

COMPETITORS

Bank of America
Sterling Financial (WA)
U.S. Bancorp
Washington Trust Bancorp

HISTORICAL FINANCIALS

Company Type: Public

Income Statement   FYE: December 31

	ASSETS ($ mil.)	NET INCOME ($ mil.)	INCOME AS % OF ASSETS	EMPLOYEES
12/06	615.1	11.0	1.8%	194
12/05	510.3	7.4	1.5%	181
12/04	394.7	5.0	1.3%	164
12/03	355.3	4.6	1.3%	158
12/02	325.6	4.0	1.2%	164
Annual Growth	**17.2%**	**28.8%**	**—**	**4.3%**

2006 Year-End Financials

Equity as % of assets: —
Return on assets: 1.8%
Return on equity: 19.2%
Long-term debt ($ mil.): 31.8
No. of shares (mil.): 6.2
Dividends
Yield: —
Payout: —
Market value ($ mil.): 192.2
Sales ($ mil.): 50.1

	STOCK PRICE ($) FY Close	P/E High/Low		PER SHARE ($) Earnings	Dividends	Book Value
12/06	31.21	21	11	1.64	0.00	9.30
12/05	19.36	18	12	1.11	0.00	7.53
12/04	13.10	18	16	0.77	0.00	6.40
12/03	12.24	20	13	0.71	0.00	5.99
12/02	9.63	16	12	0.62	0.00	4.91
Annual Growth	**34.2%**	**—**	**—**	**27.5%**	**—**	**17.3%**

Identive Group

Identive Group (formerly SCM Microsystems) grants secure access to the digital world. The company provides hardware and software for securely accessing digital content and services. Its products include smart card readers designed to work with electronic IDs and driver's licenses, as well as health care, computer network, and facility access cards. Its digital media readers, used primarily in digital photo kiosks, transfer data to and from flash media. Identive sells to computer manufacturers, large enterprises, government contractors, systems integrators, financial institutions, and photo processing equipment makers. SCM Microsystems changed its name to Identive Group in 2010.

Prior to its name change that year, the company acquired Switzerland's Bluehill ID AG in a stock-swap transaction. Bluehill ID makes radio-frequency identification (RFID) and other ID equipment for applications in inventory tracking and security, among other uses. The combination built upon the identification technology portfolio that SCM expanded with the 2009 purchase of Hirsch Electronics. The merger gave Bluehill ID's shareholders a 38% stake in the combined company, with the majority of shares in the hands of SCM's previous stockholders. Bluehill has four subsidiaries — ACiG AG, Arygon Technologies AG, Multicard AG, and TagStar Systems GmbH. SCM Microsystems subsequently changed its name to Identive Group. Late in 2010 the company bought Smartag, a designer of high frequency radio transponders and tags used for RFID applications.

Cost-cutting efforts that followed the acquisitions included the consolidation of operations, closing an office in Mainz, Germany, and combining two subsidiaries, SCM Microsystems India and SCOLIS Technologies, based in Chennai, India. The restructuring led to the elimination of about 13% of the global workforce. The restructuring also included changes in top management and the board of directors. Ayman Ashour, executive chairman of the board, added the post of CEO, succeeding Felix Marx, who became the company's COO.

In 2011 the company bought polyright SA, a provider of multifunction RFID cards for the education and health care industries. Headquartered in Switzerland, polyright has offices in Austria and Germany. The company will become part of Bluehill's subsidiary Mulitcard.

Identive bought Hirsch in 2009. Already one of its distribution partners, Hirsch specialized in access control security systems. The purchase, which nearly doubled the size of the company, added physical security systems to the company's product portfolio; such systems are used to protect buildings, campuses, and military facilities. Key markets for Hirsch included banking, critical infrastructure, education, government, and health care.

EXECUTIVES

Chairman and CEO, Ayman S. Ashour
CFO and Secretary, Melvin Denton-Thompson
EVP Strategic Sales and Business Development; CEO, SCM Microsystems GmbH, Manfred Mueller, age 41
EVP and Director; President, Hirsch Electronics, Lawrence W. Midland
EVP Technology and Product Management, Joseph Tassone
EVP Transition Management and Acquisition Integration, John S. Rogers

VP Group Operations and Supply Chain, Brent C. Archer
VP Government and Standards, Robert C. (Rob) Zivney Jr.
VP, Martin Wimmer
VP Americas, David (Dave) Holmes, age 37
Media Contact, Europe, Fabien B. Nestmann
Media Contact, US, Darby Dye
Auditors: Deloitte & Touche GmbH

LOCATIONS

HQ: Identive Group, Inc.
1900 Carnegie Ave., Ste. B, Santa Ana, CA 92705
Phone: 949-250-8888   **Fax:** 949-250-7263
Web: www.identive-group.com

2008 Sales

	$ mil.	% of total
US	12.2	43
Europe	9.9	35
Asia/Pacific	6.3	22
Total	**28.4**	**100**

PRODUCTS/OPERATIONS

2008 Sales

	$ mil.	% of total
Secure authentication	23.7	84
Digital media & connectivity	4.6	16
Total	**28.3**	**100**

COMPETITORS

Automated Logic
Chazak Valu
Dust Networks, Inc.
Echelon Corporation
Gemalto
HID Global
Honeywell International
Ingenico
Johnson Controls
L-1 Enterprise Access Solutions
LaserCard
NDS Group
O2Micro
Oberthur Technologies
SMDK
STMicroelectronics
Wave Systems

HISTORICAL FINANCIALS

Company Type: Public

Income Statement

FYE: December 31

	REVENUE ($ mil.)	NET INCOME ($ mil.)	NET PROFIT MARGIN	EMPLOYEES
12/10	84.8	(9.5)	—	387
12/09	41.3	(14.2)	—	225
12/08	28.4	(10.1)	—	147
12/07	30.4	(1.9)	—	153
12/06	33.6	1.0	3.0%	156
Annual Growth	**26.0%**	**—**	**—**	**25.5%**

2010 Year-End Financials

Debt ratio: 1.1%
Return on equity: —
Cash ($ mil.): 10.8
Current ratio: 1.32
Long-term debt ($ mil.): 0.8
No. of shares (mil.): 47.7
Dividends
  Yield: —
  Payout: —
Market value ($ mil.): 120.1

	STOCK PRICE ($) FY Close	P/E High/Low		Earnings	Dividends	Book Value
12/10	2.52	—	—	(0.22)	0.00	1.63
12/09	2.37	—	—	(0.64)	0.00	1.51
12/08	2.25	—	—	(0.64)	0.00	1.79
12/07	3.34	—	—	(0.12)	0.00	2.35
12/06	3.15	56	40	0.07	0.00	2.25
Annual Growth	**(5.4%)**	**—**	**—**	**—**	**—**	**(7.7%)**

IEC Electronics

IEC makes products you may never see. Most of IEC Electronics' sales come from the contract manufacturing of printed circuit boards. The company makes a mix of boards, including models that use surface-mount technology, pin-through-hole connections, and more advanced interconnection techniques. Customers come from the aerospace, communications, medical, and military industries. Like many contract electronics manufacturers, IEC also offers a variety of auxiliary services, including design and prototyping, materials procurement and management, engineering, testing, packaging, and distribution. The company has four manufacturing plants in the US; nearly all sales are to customers located in the US.

IEC Electronics has weathered plenty of economic ups and downs in its four decades as a contract electronics manufacturer. While high-volume electronics manufacturing has been shipped overseas, IEC specializes in the custom manufacture of complex circuit cards, system level assemblies, custom cable and wire harness assemblies, and precision sheet metal. All of its manufacturing is done in the US. Together, top customers GE, Ultralife, and ViaSat account for about a third of sales.

The company has essentially been recovering from the tech bust at the turn of the century, when it struggled with a weak market for telecom equipment, had fewer orders, and bid farewell to a major customer, the former Motorola, Inc. IEC Electronics resurrected itself over the years by streamlining its operations and paring down debt; in addition, it gained new customers in the aerospace and military industries, which rely on US suppliers. Sales pushed the $100 million mark in 2010, up more than 40% from a year before, and the company expects to hit $150 million in 2012.

IEC Electronics has used acquisitions to expand its product lines and customer base. In 2010 it bought two companies — first, Rochester, New York-based Celmet Corporation for about $2 million. Celmet makes metal chassis and assemblies; the deal enables IEC to handle chassis assemblies in-house instead of outsourcing as it had in the past. Celmet is located about 30 miles east of IEC's headquarters. In December IEC paid $25 million for Southern California Braiding Company, which makes cable and wire harnesses for defense contractors and government agencies.

In 2009 it bought contract manufacturer General Technology Corporation (GTC) from Crane Co. for a little over $14 million. GTC serves the military and defense sectors, a market that now accounts for about 60% of its revenues. Past purchases include Val-U-Tech, a privately held supplier of wire harness assemblies, which was renamed IEC Electronics Wire and Cable and now makes up IEC's manufacturing capabilities outside New York. The Southern California Braiding Company complements IEC Electronics Wire and Cable and will boost its offerings to the military and defense market.

The company has no major individual or institutional shareholders. Chairman and CEO Barry Gilbert owns about 4% of IEC Electronics.

HISTORY

General Dynamics veteran Roger Main and others founded IEC in 1966 to make components for handheld two-way radios and other electronic devices. IEC went public in 1967 and sold its radio business in 1979 in order to concentrate on contract electronics manufacturing. IEC began a partnership with Compaq in 1983 when the latter started building PCs. Main and other executives took IEC private in an LBO in 1988.

As Compaq's orders slowed during the recession of the early 1990s, IEC's profits fell. When Compaq rebounded, IEC did likewise. It acquired Texas-based Calidad Electronics in 1992, and went public again in 1993. In 1995 IEC expanded its production facilities and services, but component shortages and customer scheduling demands led to a drop in sales. After Main died in 1996, EVP Russell Stingel (Main's former General Dynamics co-worker) was named CEO. That year IEC's earnings slipped as computer equipment sales fell and the market for electronic components became saturated.

The company closed its money-losing Alabama plant in 1998, taking a restructuring charge that contributed to a loss for the year. In early 1999 IEC opened a manufacturing facility in Mexico. The following year IEC closed its operation in Ireland and began to diversify its customer base, decreasing its dependence on PC makers and targeting the telecommunications equipment and industrial instrumentation markets. Also in 2000 turnaround specialist Thomas Lovelock succeeded Stingel as president and CEO; Stingel remained as chairman until 2001, when director W. Barry Gilbert took over the position.

As the economic downturn in the telecom equipment market resulted in fewer orders for IEC in 2001, the company responded with more restructuring, closing its Texas facility and transferring those operations to its plant in Mexico. In 2002 the company laid off employees, and Lovelock resigned. (Gilbert became president and CEO, in addition to chairman.) Later that year, in response to continuing losses, the company sold the assets of its manufacturing plant in Mexico.

Sales continued to drop in 2004 and 2005, as IEC lost the business of two top customers. The company tried to make up the lost business by signing up many smaller customers. In 2006 IEC had around 25 customers and was able to reverse the sales decline. Its top five customers, however, accounted for around two-thirds of sales.

While IEC was able to stop a long decline in sales and return to profitability, its annual revenues in fiscal 2006 were less than one-tenth of what they were a decade earlier; its headcount, while rebounding from a low in 2005, was one-sixth that of 10 years before.

The company definitively reversed the decline in fiscal 2007, increasing revenues by 81% over the prior year, by adding a number of new customers. IEC's five largest customers, however, account for about 60% of sales.

EXECUTIVES

Chairman and CEO, W. Barry Gilbert, age 64, $419,306 total compensation
President; President, IEC Contract Manufacturing, Jeffrey T. (Jeff) Schlarbaum, age 44, $321,341 total compensation
EVP Operations, Donald S. (Don) Doody, age 42, $264,644 total compensation
VP and CFO, Susan E. Topel-Samek
Business Unit and Field Sales Manager, Tracy Humphrey
Director Business Development, New England and East Coast, Scott Barone
Corporate Secretary, Martin S. Weingarten

Director Business Development, New York, Midwest, and West Coast, Timothy S. (Tim) Fox
Auditors: Rotenberg & Co. LLP

LOCATIONS

HQ: IEC Electronics Corp.
105 Norton St., Newark, NY 14513
Phone: 315-331-7742   **Fax:** 315-331-3547
Web: www.iec-electronics.com

PRODUCTS/OPERATIONS

Services

Complete systems building
Design services
Distribution
Engineering support for manufacturing
Final packaging
Material procurement and management
Printed circuit board assembly
Prototype assembly
Resources management
Statistical quality assurance
Testing

COMPETITORS

Ansen	Jabil
AsteelFlash	Nam Tai
Benchmark Electronics	Nortech Systems
Celestica	Plexus
DDi Corp.	Sanmina-SCI
Eltek	SigmaTron
Entorian	Suntron
Flextronics	SYNNEX
Green St. Energy	Wellex
HEI	

HISTORICAL FINANCIALS

Company Type: Public

Income Statement

FYE: September 30

	REVENUE ($ mil.)	NET INCOME ($ mil.)	NET PROFIT MARGIN	EMPLOYEES
09/10	96.7	4.7	4.9%	567
09/09	67.8	5.0	7.4%	368
09/08	51.1	10.5	20.5%	350
09/07	40.9	0.9	2.2%	229
09/06	22.6	0.2	0.9%	240
Annual Growth	43.8%	120.2%	—	24.0%

2010 Year-End Financials

Debt ratio: 62.9%	No. of shares (mil.): 9.1
Return on equity: 18.3%	Dividends
Cash ($ mil.): —	Yield: —
Current ratio: 2.24	Payout: —
Long-term debt ($ mil.): 16.0	Market value ($ mil.): 47.8

	STOCK PRICE ($) FY Close	P/E High/Low		PER SHARE ($) Earnings	Dividends	Book Value
09/10	5.26	13	7	0.48	0.00	2.80
09/09	5.65	15	2	0.52	0.00	2.32
09/08	1.87	2	1	1.12	0.00	1.72
09/07	2.00	21	11	0.10	0.00	0.48
09/06	1.09	41	13	0.03	0.00	0.37
Annual Growth	48.2%	—	—	100.0%	—	66.0%

Ikanos

Ikanos Communications hopes to become an icon in the field of networking semiconductors. The fabless semiconductor company designs broadband DSL products that allow networks to achieve speeds of 100 megabits per second over existing copper wires and high-speed programmable single- and multi-port chipsets for wide area network systems that include DSL, wireless broadband, and Ethernet. Ikanos products also allow service providers to offer a hybrid of copper and fiber that can cost about 10% of the typical charge for deploying a full fiber system. In 2009 Ikanos acquired the Broadband Access product lines of Conexant Systems for more than $53 million in cash.

The acquisition more than doubled Ikanos' sales and headcount and greatly expanded its sales of broadband access ports in China, Japan, and North America. As part of the deal, Tallwood Venture Capital invested $42 million in Ikanos, giving Tallwood about a 45% equity stake in Ikanos at the time. Tallwood now owns 43% of Ikanos (or 49% assuming the full exercise of 7.8 million warrants).

Thanks mostly to that acquisition, revenue at Ikanos increased 47% in 2010 over 2009. Also as a result of that acquisition, Asian sales went from more than $75 million in 2009 to more than $115 million in 2010.

The Fusiv processor line Ikanos acquired earlier from Analog Devices got Ikanos into the home Internet gateway market, now its leading line of business. The Conexant product lines added ADSL and VDSL chips — more than 350 million delivered so far — to the company's portfolio.

The company has a limited number of customers. Ikanos derives about 18% of sales from Alcatel-Lucent, and some 16% from Sagem (part of SAFRAN). Other customers have included 2Wire, Huawei, and NEC. Asian customers provide about 60% of the company's sales.

As a fabless company that outsources fabrication, sorting, assembly, and testing of its semiconductors, Ikanos is able to concentrate resources on designing and developing its products.

EXECUTIVES

Chairman, Interim President, and CEO, Diosdado P. (Dado) Banatao, age 65
President, CEO, and Director, John Quigley, age 55
VP Worldwide Human Resources, Jim Murphy
VP Finance and CFO, Dennis A. Bencala, age 56
VP Program Management, Shay Conway
VP Worldwide Sales, Michael Kelly
VP Worldwide Sales, Nick N. Shamlou, age 50, $771,985 total compensation
VP Corporate Development, Mitch Kahn
COO, Craig J. Garen, age 52, $213,267 total compensation
SVP Worldwide Sales, Daniel (Dan) Karr, age 51
SVP and CTO, Debajyoti (Debu) Pal
Director Human Resources Worldwide, Tammy Carr
Media Relations, Margo Westfall
Investor Relations, Bonnie Mott
Auditors: PricewaterhouseCoopers LLP

LOCATIONS

HQ: Ikanos Communications, Inc.
47669 Fremont Blvd., Fremont, CA 94538
Phone: 510-979-0400   **Fax:** 510-438-5377
Web: www.ikanos.com

2010 Sales

	$ mil.	% of total
China	53.6	28
France	46.4	24
Japan	29.8	16
US	4.7	2
Other	57.2	30
Total	**191.7**	**100**

PRODUCTS/OPERATIONS

2010 Sales

	$ mil.	% of total
Broadband DSL	115.7	60
Communication processors	45.1	24
Other	30.9	16
Total	**191.7**	**100**

Selected Products

Eight-port chipsets for network access concentrators (SmartLeap line)

Single-port chipsets for customer premise equipment (CleverConnect 150)

COMPETITORS

Aware, Inc.	Marvell Technology
Broadcom	Metalink
Cavium	PMC-Sierra
Freescale	STMicroelectronics
Semiconductor	Technicolor
Infineon Technologies	Teknovus
Intel	TranSwitch

HISTORICAL FINANCIALS

Company Type: Public

Income Statement

FYE: December 31

	REVENUE ($ mil.)	NET INCOME ($ mil.)	NET PROFIT MARGIN	EMPLOYEES
12/10	191.7	(49.8)	—	386
12/09	130.7	(37.1)	—	588
12/08	106.5	(41.1)	—	290
12/07	107.5	(33.3)	—	281
12/06	134.7	(23.4)	—	279
Annual Growth	9.2%	—	—	8.5%

2010 Year-End Financials

Debt ratio: —	No. of shares (mil.): 55.3
Return on equity: —	Dividends
Cash ($ mil.): 29.0	Yield: —
Current ratio: 3.13	Payout: —
Long-term debt ($ mil.): —	Market value ($ mil.): 74.1

	STOCK PRICE ($) FY Close	P/E High/Low		PER SHARE ($) Earnings	Dividends	Book Value
12/10	1.34	—	—	(0.88)	0.00	1.18
12/09	1.87	—	—	(0.97)	0.00	1.80
12/08	1.26	—	—	(1.41)	0.00	3.10
12/07	5.38	—	—	(1.16)	0.00	4.23
12/06	8.69	—	—	(0.86)	0.00	5.17
Annual Growth	(37.3%)	—	—	—	—	(30.8%)

Illumina

Illumina elucidates the human genome. The firm makes tools used by life sciences and drug researchers to isolate and analyze genes. Its systems include the machinery and the software used to sequence pieces of DNA and RNA, and the means to put them through large-scale testing of genetic variation and biological function. Its proprietary BeadArray technology uses microscopic glass beads which can carry samples through the genotyping process. The tests allow medical researchers to determine what genetic combinations are associated with various diseases, enabling faster diagnosis, better drugs, and individualized treatment. Customers include pharma and biotech companies, research centers, and academic institutions.

Illumina has steadily augmented its life sciences product lines, and has experienced rapidly climbing revenues as a result. Through acquisitions, the company is working to add DNA sequencing (determining the order of DNA codes) and gene expression analysis (studying when genes switch on or off) technologies to its existing expertise in genotyping (identifying the gene's nucleotide base, or code), making it a one-stop-shop for genetic researchers. To that end, Illumina paid nearly $26 million to acquire sequencing technology developer Avantome in 2008. Then in 2010 the company acquired Helexis, which added the Eco Real Time PCR genetic analysis system to its offerings, in a deal worth up to $105 million. It followed that buy up with Epicentre Biotechnologies in early 2011. Epicentre brought with it a range of nucleic acid sample preparation reagents and enzymes used in sequencing and microarrays. Epicentre's lead product is its Nextera technology used to prepare next-generation sequencing libraries from genomic DNA.

To further enhance its offerings, the company conducts research and development programs to create faster and more complex systems for genetic sequencing and analysis. One new product launched in 2010, the HiSeq 2000 instrument (based on technology gained through the 2007 acquisition of Solexa), allows for the sequencing of whole human genomes. Illumina is working to make its systems faster and more affordable, so that researchers, health care professionals, and individuals alike can further understand the genetic makeup of disease.

For customers who choose not to buy its systems, Illumina offers outsourced research services such as genome sequencing and genotyping array services. Customers for such services, which account for less than 10% of sales, include schools, biotech research firms, and drug development companies.

While most of the company's revenues come from its life sciences segment, Illumina is also working hard to enter the high-growth business of molecular diagnostics, which uses genetic biomarkers to diagnose clinical health conditions, through both acquisitions and R&D efforts. To that end, the company received FDA approval in 2010 for its BeadXpress Multiplex analysis system (based on the VeraCode technology acquired in 2006), and it is developing molecular diagnostic tests for conditions such as heart disease, viral infections, and cancers for use with the new system.

EXECUTIVES

Chairman, William H. (Bill) Rastetter, age 63
President, CEO, and Director, Jay T. Flatley, age 58, $5,695,858 total compensation
VP and Chief Scientist, David Bentley
VP Quality and Regulatory Affairs, B. Melina Cimler, age 53
VP Business Development, Jorge Velarde
VP Global Supply Chain, Elizabeth Brady
VP Worldwide Sales, Matthew L. (Matt) Posard
VP Diagnostics Development, Emily S. Winn-Deen
SVP and Chief Commercial Officer, Tristan B. Orpin, age 44, $1,882,258 total compensation
SVP Corporate Development, Nicholas J. (Nick) Naclerio
SVP and CTO, Mostafa Ronaghi, age 42
Senior Manager Product Marketing, Tanya Boyaniwsky
Senior Manager Public Relations, Wilson Grabill
SVP Operations, Bill Bonnar
SVP, CFO, and General Manager, Life Sciences, Christian O. Henry, age 43, $2,225,454 total compensation
SVP, General Counsel, and Secretary, Christian G. (Chris) Cabou, age 62, $1,863,229 total compensation
Senior Director Investor Relations, Peter J. Fromen
SVP and General Manager, Diagnostics, Gregory F. (Greg) Heath, age 53, $1,674,856 total compensation
Associate Director Corporate Marketing, Philomena Walsh
Auditors: Ernst & Young LLP

LOCATIONS

HQ: Illumina, Inc.
9885 Towne Centre Dr., San Diego, CA 92121-1975
Phone: 858-202-4500   **Fax:** 858-202-4545
Web: www.illumina.com

2009 Sales

	$ mil.	% of total
US	347.2	52
Europe		
UK	55.9	8
Other countries	140.9	21
Asia/Pacific	96.4	15
Other regions	25.9	4
Total	**666.3**	**100**

PRODUCTS/OPERATIONS

2009 Sales

	$ mil.	% of total
Products	627.2	94
Services & other	39.1	6
Total	**666.3**	**100**

Selected Products

BeadXpress Reader (VeraCode molecular diagnostics)
Genome Analyzer II (gene sequencing system)
GoldenGate Assay Method (high-throughput genotyping system)
GoldenGate Universal-32 Sample BeadChip (genotyping arrays)
HiSeq 2000 (high-throughput gene sequencing system)
iScan System (high-resolution imaging for BeadArray genotyping assays)
iSelect Genotyping BeadChips (custom genotyping arrays)
Paired-End Genomic DNA Sample Prep Kit (library preparation kit)

COMPETITORS

Affymetrix	Life Technologies
Agilent Technologies	Corporation
Beckman Coulter	Luminex
Fluidigm	Pacific Biosciences
GE Healthcare Medical	QIAGEN
Diagnostics	Roche Diagnostics
Helicos	Sequenom

Income Statement

FYE: December 31

	REVENUE ($ mil.)	NET INCOME ($ mil.)	NET PROFIT MARGIN	EMPLOYEES
12/10	902.7	124.9	13.8%	2,100
12/09	666.3	72.3	10.9%	1,781
12/08	573.2	50.5	8.8%	1,536
12/07	366.8	(278.4)	—	1,041
12/06	184.6	40.0	21.7%	596
Annual Growth	48.7%	32.9%	—	37.0%

2010 Year-End Financials

Debt ratio: —
Return on equity: 10.4%
Cash ($ mil.): 248.9
Current ratio: 2.35
Long-term debt ($ mil.): —

No. of shares (mil.): 125.0
Dividends
Yield: —
Payout: —
Market value ($ mil.): 7,920.3

	STOCK PRICE ($) FY Close	P/E High/Low		PER SHARE ($) Earnings	Dividends	Book Value
12/10	63.34	77	34	0.87	0.00	9.58
12/09	30.68	83	44	0.53	0.00	6.91
12/08	26.05	126	50	0.38	0.00	6.86
12/07	29.63	—	—	(2.57)	0.00	3.71
12/06	19.66	56	17	0.41	0.00	2.64
Annual Growth	34.0%	—	—	20.7%	—	38.0%

IMPAX Laboratories

Impax Laboratories is betting that its pharmaceuticals will make a positive impact its own financial health. The company makes specialty generic pharmaceuticals, which it markets through its Global Pharmaceuticals division and through marketing alliances with other firms, including Teva. It concentrates on controlled-release versions of various generic versions of branded and niche pharmaceuticals that require difficult-to-obtain raw materials or specialized expertise. Additionally, the company's branded pharmaceuticals business (Impax Pharmaceuticals) is developing and improving upon previously approved drugs that target Parkinson's disease, multiple sclerosis, and other central nervous system disorders.

Impax's Global Pharmaceuticals division sells its generic products to wholesalers, chain drug stores, and mail order pharmacies. Impax also works through strategic alliances; as part of its deal with Teva, for instance, Impax manufactures and supplies select generic products to Teva, including certain time-released versions of Teva's generic Prilosec, Zyban, and Ditropan products. Impax also receives a percentage of profits from the sale of some of Teva's generic Claritin products through the agreement.

Impax earns the vast majority of its overall revenue through its Global Pharmaceuticals division. Its Impax Pharmaceuticals division invests heavily in R&D costs and, with no products on the commercial market, has negative profit margins. However, Impax's Global Pharmaceuticals unit more than makes up for the deficit; in 2009, the company's overall profits were up 167% over the previous year, due to increased sales and lower expenses in the division. The company attributes a significant portion of the sales increase to revenue

earned from its mixed amphetamine salts products (used to treat attention-deficit hyperactivity disorder, or ADHD) and its fenofibrate products (cholesterol-lowering drugs). Overall, the company has been profitable in recent years.

Impax Pharmaceuticals currently has a few products in clinical stages of development, including treatments for multiple sclerosis and Parkinson's disease. The division also focuses its development efforts on other central nervous system disorders such as Alzheimer's disease, depression, epilepsy, and migraines. The company hopes to build its portfolio of branded products through internal development, acquisitions, and licensing agreements, with the ultimate goal of selling some products commercially.

EXECUTIVES

Chairman, Robert L. (Bob) Burr, age 60
President, CEO, and Director, Larry Hsu, age 62, $4,195,716 total compensation
President, Impax Pharmaceuticals Division, Michael J. Nestor, age 58, $1,171,436 total compensation
EVP Finance and CFO, Arthur A. Koch Jr., age 57, $1,858,009 total compensation
SVP Operations, Charles V. Hildenbrand, age 59, $1,314,524 total compensation
Senior Director Investor Relations and Corporate Communications, Mark Donohue
Auditors: Grant Thornton LLP

LOCATIONS

HQ: Impax Laboratories, Inc.
30831 Huntwood Ave., Hayward, CA 94544
Phone: 510-476-2000   **Fax:** 510-471-3200
Web: www.impaxlabs.com

PRODUCTS/OPERATIONS

2009 Sales

	$ mil.	% of total
Global pharmaceuticals	345.0	96
Impax pharmaceuticals	13.4	4
Total	**358.4**	**100**

Selected Generic Products

Bupropion hydrochloride (generic Wellbutrin SR, depression)
Colestipol hydrochloride (generic Colestid, high cholesterol)
Dantrolene sodium (generic Dantrium, spasticity)
Nadolol/Bendroflumethiazide (generic Corzide, hypertension)
Omeprazole (Prilosec ulcer treatment)
Oxybutynin chloride (generic Ditropan XL, urinary incontinence, with Teva)
Pilocarpine hydrochlorine (generic Salagen, dry mouth caused by radiation therapy)

COMPETITORS

Actavis	SkyePharma
Caraco Pharmaceutical	Synovics
Forest Labs	Teva
K-V Pharmaceutical	URL Pharma
Mylan	Valeant
Par Pharmaceutical	Pharmaceuticals
Companies	Watson Pharmaceuticals
Ranbaxy Laboratories	
Sandoz International GmbH	

Income Statement

FYE: December 31

	REVENUE ($ mil.)	NET INCOME ($ mil.)	NET PROFIT MARGIN	EMPLOYEES
12/10	879.5	250.4	28.5%	918
12/09	358.4	50.1	14.0%	801
12/08	210.1	18.7	8.9%	768
12/03	58.8	(14.2)	—	0
12/02	24.5	(20.0)	—	273
Annual Growth	56.5%	—	—	16.4%

2010 Year-End Financials

Debt ratio: —
Return on equity: 49.3%
Cash ($ mil.): 91.8
Current ratio: 4.12
Long-term debt ($ mil.): —

No. of shares (mil.): 64.5
Dividends
Yield: —
Payout: —
Market value ($ mil.): 1,296.6

	STOCK PRICE ($) FY Close	P/E High/Low		PER SHARE ($) Earnings	Dividends	Book Value
12/10	20.11	6	0	3.82	0.00	7.88
12/09	13.61	17	3	0.82	0.00	3.58
12/08	8.89	37	21	0.31	0.00	2.73
12/03	14.39	—	—	(0.28)	0.00	1.23
12/02	4.01	—	—	(0.42)	0.00	0.86
Annual Growth	49.6%	—	—	—	—	74.1%

Imperial Sugar

I'm going to sugar coat this for you: Imperial Sugar is one of the biggest producers and marketers of refined sugar in the US. Its white, brown, and powdered sugars are sold under name brands — Dixie Crystals, Holly, and Imperial — and private labels to retailers. Most refined sugar, which all told generates more than 95% of the company's sales, is sold domestically in bulk and liquid form to industrial markets (mainly food manufacturers of baked good, desserts, and beverages) and foodservice and industrial distributors, who sell the sugar to manufacturers, restaurants, and institutional foodservice customers. Imperial Sugar also sells organic sugar and a sugar/stevia sweetener blend through joint ventures.

Joint ventures open the door to new product development as well as markets in Mexico and Canada. In addition, Imperial Sugar capitalizes on joint ventures to extend its operating capacity as well as provide a modest boost to its troubled bottom line.

The company managed to post a dramatic increase in sales and earnings in 2010, buoyed in part by an insurance recovery related to an explosion at its plant in Port Wentworth, Georgia, early 2008. The event, which impacted approximately 60% of the company's refining capacity, drove earnings into the red in 2008 and 2009, on a year-over-year decline in sales of roughly 30% and 10%, respectively. It killed 13 workers, injured more than 40 others, and destroyed the plant's silos and packaging operations, but left refining and warehousing relatively intact. The explosion also spurred an investigation; the Occupational Safety and Health Administration (OSHA) fined Imperial Sugar $8.7 million for more than 200 safety violations at the plant. (The fine was the third-largest in OSHA history.) In 2009 Imperial Sugar completed the rebuilding of the Port Wentworth facility.

Meanwhile, as part of a venture formed in late 2009 the company put up its Gramercy, Louisiana refining facility and more than 200 acres of land in early 2011. The venture includes Cargill and Sugar Growers and Refiners, a cooperative representing eight sugar mills and more than 700 Louisiana sugar growers. Owned equally among the partners, Louisiana Sugar Refining (LSR) has broken ground on a new cane sugar refinery, next to the original facility, that will add 3,100 ton per day refining capacity. Imperial Sugar retains the Gramercy facility's small bag packaging operation and a long-term supply agreement for refined bulk sugar from LSR.

Imperial Sugar has also upped its control of Wholesome Sweeteners to a 50% interest. Formed in 2008, Wholesome is a joint venture held with a UK food and agriculture company, Edward Billington & Son. Wholesome drives the sale of organic cane sugar, agave syrup, honey and other specialty sweetwners to natural-food consumers in the US and Canada. Although the deal included an option to acquire Billlington's remaining 50% stake in mid-2011, Imperial Sugar allowed it to expire. The partners are exploring various options including selling off Wholesome.

Among other tie-ups, Imperial Sugar partners with PureCircle via Natural Sweet Ventures to manufacture and sell a reduced-calorie sweetener made from sugar and the stevia plant (a zero-calorie sugar alternative produced by PureCircle). The product is manufactured by Imperial Sugar and marketed and sold by both companies to food and beverage manufacturers in North America. In 2010 Imperial Sugar tested the blend in the retail market under the brand name Steviacane.

HISTORY

In 1843 Samuel May Williams' cane sugar crop and that of his neighbors were ample enough to start a commercial sugar mill. Thus was born the beginnings of a sugar giant. The company incorporated in 1924 as Imperial Sugar with its home base located in Sugar Land, Texas. It remained a Texas operation until the acquisition of Michigan Sugar in 1984 and Colonial Sugar Refinery in Louisiana in 1986. In 1988 Imperial acquired publicly held Holly Sugar, a beet processor in Colorado Springs. With that purchase Imperial doubled in size and began marketing both cane and beet sugar.

Acquisitions continued in the 1990s, with the purchase of Spreckels Sugar in California and Savannah Foods & Industries in Savannah, Georgia. These purchases again doubled Imperial's size. It had become the largest sugar producer in the US.

However, because of falling sugar prices, due in large part to soft-drink manufacturers switching from sugar to high-fructose corn syrup to sweeten its products, Imperial incurred unpayable debt and was forced to declare bankruptcy in 2001. It began selling parts of its businesses to reduce debt. In August 2001 Imperial emerged from bankruptcy.

In 2002 Imperial sold its Michigan Sugar and Great Lakes Sugar subsidiaries to the Michigan Sugar Beet Growers cooperative; its sugar beet factories in Hereford, Texas, to American Crystal Sugar; and its sugar, spice, and food-specialty unit, Diamond Crystal Brands, to Hormel Foods for an estimated $115 million. That year Imperial also sold off its foodservice business.

In 2003 Imperial discontinued sugar operations at its headquarters in Sugar Land, Texas; however, corporate activities continue there. Operations

were shifted to the company's Louisiana and Georgia, plants.

Imperial and Michigan Sugar updated a three-year old marketing agreement in 2005, giving Imperial responsibility for invoicing, collections, and other administrative tasks of the Michigan sugar cooperative.

The company sold its Holly Sugar subsidiary to Southern Minnesota Bee Sugar Cooperative for $51 million in 2005; Imperial Sugar retained its rights to the Holly brand, but it divested the Spreckels brand name. The company also sold its former refinery site in Sugar Land, Texas to Cherokee Sugar Land (a joint venture of W.C. Perry Land Development and Cherokee Investments) for $7 million. The deal did not include Imperial Sugar's corporate headquarters building.

As a result of the inclusion of sugar in the North American Free Trade Agreement, Imperial and Mexican sugar company, Ingenios Santos, entered into a distributing joint venture (Comercializadora Santos Imperial) 2007, bringing Imperial's products to Mexico and Santos products to the US.

EXECUTIVES

Chairman, James J. Gaffney, age 69
President, CEO, and Director, John C. Sheptor, age 51, $1,777,529 total compensation
VP Technology, Brian T. Harrison
VP and Treasurer, J. Eric Story, age 46
VP Sales, Paul J. Whitaker
VP Manufacturing and Engineering, Ralph D. Clements, age 61
VP Sales Planning, Supply Chain, and Information Technology, George Muller, age 55, $351,008 total compensation
SVP and CFO, Hal P. Mechler, age 56, $590,777 total compensation
SVP, General Counsel, and Secretary, Louis T. Bolognini, age 53, $507,689 total compensation
SVP Commodities Management and Sales, Patrick D. (Pat) Henneberry, age 55, $566,906 total compensation
Senior Director Environmental, Safety, Health, Quality and Food Safety, Ronald L. Allen
Auditors: Deloitte & Touche LLP

LOCATIONS

HQ: Imperial Sugar Company
1 Imperial Sq., 8016 Hwy. 90-A, Sugar Land, TX 77487
Phone: 281-491-9181   **Fax:** 281-490-9530
Web: www.imperialsugar.com

2010 Sales

	% of total
Domestic	95
International	5
Total	**100**

PRODUCTS/OPERATIONS

2010 Sales

	% of total
Sugar	98
Sugar by-products	2
Other products	-
Total	**100**

2010 Sales

	% of total
Industrial	52
Retail (consumer)	28
Distributor	20
Total	**100**

Selected Products and Brands

Granulated white, powdered, and brown sugar - Dixie Crystals, Holly, Imperial, Spreckels, Pioneer, and Savannah Gold (distributor and retail)
Organic cane sugar, agave syrup, honey, and other specialty sweeteners (Wholesome Sweeteners joint venture)
Refined sugar, molasses, and other ingredients (industrial)
Sugar/stevia sweetener blends - Steviacare (retail: Natural Sweet Ventures with PureCircle Limited)

COMPETITORS

ACH Food Companies
ADM
Ajinomoto U.S.A.
Amalgamated Sugar
American Crystal Sugar
Associated British Foods
B&G Foods
C&H Sugar
Cargill
Connell Company
Corn Products International
Cumberland Packing
Da
Sugar Cane Growers Cooperative of Florida
United Sugars

HISTORICAL FINANCIALS

Company Type: Public

Income Statement

FYE: September 30

	REVENUE ($ mil.)	NET INCOME ($ mil.)	NET PROFIT MARGIN	EMPLOYEES
09/10	992.7	136.9	13.8%	694
09/09	522.6	(23.2)	—	726
09/08	592.4	(20.9)	—	759
09/07	875.5	40.2	4.6%	839
09/06	946.8	50.1	5.3%	842
Annual Growth	1.2%	28.6%	—	(4.7%)

2010 Year-End Financials

Debt ratio: —
Return on equity: 62.6%
Cash ($ mil.): 22.8
Current ratio: 1.18
Long-term debt ($ mil.): —

No. of shares (mil.): 12.1
Dividends
 Yield: 0.6%
 Payout: 0.7%
Market value ($ mil.): 158.9

	STOCK PRICE ($) FY Close	P/E High/Low		PER SHARE ($) Earnings	Dividends	Book Value
09/10	13.08	2	1	11.33	0.08	18.01
09/09	12.68	—	—	(1.98)	0.18	7.19
09/08	13.54	—	—	(1.79)	0.28	12.10
09/07	26.13	10	6	3.43	0.27	16.96
09/06	31.12	8	3	4.45	0.23	16.45
Annual Growth	(19.5%)	—	—	26.3%	(23.2%)	2.3%

Imperva

Imperva aims to create an impervious barrier around corporate data centers. The company's data security platform, called SecureSphere, protects databases, files, and Web applications against threats from hackers and insiders and help its corporate customers maintain regulatory compliance. Subsidiary Incapsula provides cloud-based Web application security services for small and mid-sized companies. The company counts more than

1,300 customers in about 50 countries but generates two-thirds of sales in the US. Imperva was founded in 2002 by CEO Shlomo Kramer, one of the founders of competitor Check Point Software Technologies, and CTO Anichai Shulman. It filed a $75 million initial public offering in mid-2011.

As Imperva is focused on data security at the corporate level, not the consumer market, it isn't worried about whether a PC downloads a virus but whether a large company's IT assets get hacked and private information becomes compromised. SecureSphere is charged with protecting high-value, sensitive data, including financial information such as credit card numbers, intellectual property, and personal information such as Social Security numbers. Citing the actions of WikiLeaks and the 2011 infiltration of Google's corporate infrastructure, Imperva claims attacks are becoming more sophisticated and its clients, which include some 150 government agencies, must respond with increase security measures.

The company sells its products through a hybrid sales model that combines both channel sales and direct sales, although some 60% of sales in 2010 were originated via third-party channel sales. Imperva has a network of more than 350 channel partners worldwide, including both distributors and resellers such as IT service firms Accuvant, Carahsoft and FishNet Security in the US; Dimension Data of South Africa; Integralis AG of Germany; and Wipro Limited of India. Other channel partners include providers of managed security services, such as Rackspace, SAVVIS, and SecureWorks.

Imperva experienced significant growth for the first time in 2010, when sales increased 40% due to demand for software licenses, maintenance and support, professional services and training, and subscriptions. The company won almost 400 new customers that year and launched two new products, ThreatRadar and a file activity monitoring services for SecureSphere. However, Imperva has yet to become profitable as it puts more than half of its revenues into establishing itself through sales and marketing initiatives, hiring more salespeople, and awarding commissions. Incapsula has so far not generated any substantial income since its inception in 2009. Imperva has received funding from venture capital firms such as Accel Partners, Greylock, USVP, and Venrock. It plans to use the net proceeds from its IPO for working capital and general corporate purposes.

EXECUTIVES

Chairman, President, and CEO, Shlomo Kramer, age 45
CFO and Treasurer, Terrence J. Schmid, age 47
VP, Israel Site Manager, Udi Itzhayek
VP, General Counsel and Corporate Secretary, Scott Darling
VP Engineering, Yaniv Shaya, age 40
VP Worldwide Client Services, Prashant K. Karnik, age 55
VP Business Development, Farzad Tari
VP Finance, Aviv Shoham
VP Worldwide Marketing, Mark E. Kraynak, age 37
VP Worldwide Sales, Ralph Pisani, age 41
VP Business Operations, Jason Forget, age 37
VP, WW Channel, MSSP and SI Sales, Chris Cesio
CTO, Amichai Shulman, age 41
Investor Relations, Seth Potter
Auditors: Ernst & Young LLP

LOCATIONS

HQ: Imperva, Inc.
3400 Bridge Pkwy., Ste. 200, Redwood Shores, CA 94065
Phone: 650-345-9000   **Fax:** 650-345-9004
Web: www.imperva.com

2010 Sales

	$ mil.	% of total
Americas	36.6	66
Europe, Middle East & Africa	13.5	24
Asia/Pacific	5.3	10
Total	**55.4**	**100**

PRODUCTS/OPERATIONS

2010 Sales

	$ in mil.	% of total
Products & licenses	34.5	62
Services	20.9	38
Total	**55.4**	**100**

COMPETITORS

AVG Technologies	Kaspersky Lab
Check Point Software	McAfee
Citrix Systems	Oracle
CyberDefender	Sophos
Corporation	Sourcefire
EMC	Stonesoft
F-Secure	Symantec
F5 Networks	Trend Micro
Fortinet	Verint Systems
IBM Internet Security	
Systems	

HISTORICAL FINANCIALS

Company Type: Public

Income Statement				FYE: December 31
	REVENUE ($ mil.)	NET INCOME ($ mil.)	NET PROFIT MARGIN	EMPLOYEES
12/10	55.4	(12.4)	—	339
12/09	39.3	(12.3)	—	0
12/08	32.1	(7.7)	—	0
Annual Growth	31.4%	—	—	—

Debt ratio: —
Return on equity: 62.6%
Cash ($ mil.): 22.8
Current ratio: 1.18
Long-term debt ($ mil.): —
No. of shares (mil.): 12.1
Dividends
 Yield: 0.6%
 Payout: 0.7%
Market value ($ mil.): 158.9

Incyte

Incyte hopes its success with inhibitors is uninhibited. The biotechnology company is focused on discovering and developing drugs that inhibit specific enzymes associated with cancer, diabetes, blood disorders, and inflammatory diseases. The company's lead program is its JAK kinase inhibitor program, which covers treatments for inflammatory diseases and cancers, including rheumatoid arthritis, myelofibrosis, psoriasis, solid tumors, and breast cancer. Incyte's product candidates are in various stages of research and clinical trials, partially through partnerships with other drugmakers.

In 2009 the company partnered up on several of its JAK programs; it is working with Novartis on a lead candidate for myelofibrosis, and it has teamed with Eli Lilly on a rheumatoid arthritis candidate.

Incyte has also licensed out development and marketing rights to Pfizer for its CCR2 receptor antagonist program, including treatments for rheumatoid arthritis and insulin-resistant obese patients. Pfizer has rights to all future CCR2 products, excluding treatments for multiple sclerosis, lupus, and autoimmune diseases similar to lupus. Incyte is pursuing commercialization partnerships for other pipeline drugs.

However, like many drug developers, the company also drops programs that prove unpromising in clinical trials. In 2008 it halted development on a CCR5 antagonist designed to prevent the entry of HIV into target cells. Incyte is looking to license or sell the candidate.

Director Julian Baker and his brother Felix Baker, who together run investment firm Baker Bros. Advisors, own a 20% stake in the company.

HISTORY

British entrepreneur Roy Whitfield and researcher Randal Scott met in 1989 while working for Invitron, a biotech company that soon went under. They founded Incyte Pharmaceuticals in 1991 to design, develop, and market genomic database products, software tools, and related services.

The company went public in 1993, and in 1994 Pfizer became its first gene expression database subscriber. Two years later Incyte bought gene-mapping firms Genome Systems and Combion. The firm opened an office in Cambridge, UK, and formed joint venture diaDexus with SmithKline Beecham (now GlaxoSmithKline) to create and market diagnostic tests that use genetic data to develop effective drug reagents and services.

In 1998 the firm bought microarray maker Synteni. It made its own attempt to map the human genome using LifeSeq, buying British firm Hexagen for the mapping unit. Two years later, diaDexus filed an IPO, and the company changed its name to Incyte Genomics to reflect its focus. The name change, however, seemed shortsighted when, in 2001, the firm announced plans to become a drug developer. It even teamed with onetime rival Agilent to share DNA microarray technologies.

In 2003 the company made another name change — this time simply to "Incyte Corporation" — to represent its growing focus on drug development. As part of that focus, that year Incyte acquired the rights to Reverset in 2003 through a licensing agreement with Pharmasset.

In 2004, the company transitioned away from its former business — providing access to its genomic database and set of patents. In that year Incyte closed its Palo Alto, California, research facilities and headquarters. It also terminated further development of its information products, including LifeSeq — a library of information and expressed sequences that links biological information analysis with proprietary genetic information to aid drug discovery. In addition to closing the Palo Alto office, the company reduced its workforce by more than 50%.

Following the transition, a leading product candidate for the company was dexelvucitabine (also known as Reverset) to treat patients with HIV, but clinical trials were discontinued in 2006.

EXECUTIVES

Chairman, Richard U. (Dick) De Schutter, age 70
President, CEO and Director, Paul A. Friedman, age 68, $2,044,384 total compensation

EVP and Chief Drug Development and Medical
  Officer, Richard S. Levy, age 53
EVP and Chief Commercial Officer, Patricia S.
  Andrews, age 52
EVP and General Counsel, Patricia A. (Pat) Schreck,
  age 57, $919,186 total compensation
EVP Biology and Preclinical Development, Steven M.
  Friedman, age 65
EVP and CFO, David C. Hastings, age 49, $969,408
  total compensation
EVP Human Resources, Paula J. Swain, age 53,
  $962,388 total compensation
VP Investor Relations and Corporate
  Communications, Pamela M. (Pam) Murphy
Director Business Development, Dan Maravei
Auditors: Ernst & Young LLP

LOCATIONS

HQ: Incyte Corporation
  Experimental Station, Route 141 & Henry Clay
  Road, Bldg. E336, Wilmington, DE 19880
Phone: 302-498-6700   Fax: 302-425-2750
Web: www.incyte.com

PRODUCTS/OPERATIONS

2009 Sales

	$ mil.	% of total
Contract revenues	5.8	62
License and royalty revenues	3.5	38
Total	**9.3**	**100**

COMPETITORS

Abbott Labs	Human Genome Sciences
Amgen	Janssen Biotech
Array BioPharma	Lexicon
Biogen Idec	Pharmaceuticals
Bristol-Myers Squibb	Myriad Genetics
CuraGen	PDL BioPharma
Gilead Sciences	Roche Holding
GlaxoSmithKline	Xencor

HISTORICAL FINANCIALS
Company Type: Public

Income Statement   FYE: December 31

	REVENUE ($ mil.)	NET INCOME ($ mil.)	NET PROFIT MARGIN	EMPLOYEES
12/10	169.9	(31.8)	—	247
12/09	9.3	(211.9)	—	221
12/08	3.9	(178.9)	—	212
12/07	34.4	(86.9)	—	196
12/06	27.6	(74.2)	—	186
Annual Growth	**57.5%**	—	—	**7.3%**

2010 Year-End Financials

Debt ratio: —	No. of shares (mil.): 123.3
Return on equity: —	Dividends
Cash ($ mil.): 417.9	Yield: —
Current ratio: 4.01	Payout: —
Long-term debt ($ mil.): 293.4	Market value ($ mil.): 2,041.5

	STOCK PRICE ($) FY Close	P/E High/Low	Earnings	PER SHARE ($) Dividends	Book Value
12/10	16.56	— —	(0.26)	0.00	(0.72)
12/09	9.11	— —	(2.06)	0.00	(0.86)
12/08	3.79	— —	(1.99)	0.00	(2.27)
12/07	10.05	— —	(1.03)	0.00	(1.89)
12/06	5.98	— —	(0.89)	0.00	(1.01)
Annual Growth	**29.0%**	— —	—	—	—

Industrial Services of America

Industrial Services of America manages solid waste so its customers won't have to. Its Computerized Waste Systems (CWS) unit doesn't pick up trash but instead arranges waste disposal services for its commercial and industrial customers at 2,300 locations. CWS negotiates contracts with service providers and offers centralized billing and dispatching and invoice auditing services. Industrial Services of America's ISA Recycling unit handles ferrous and nonferrous metals and fiber products, and the company's Waste Equipment Sales & Service unit sells, leases, and services waste handling and recycling equipment. Chairman and CEO Harry Kletter and his family own about 35% of the company.

CWS offers its services throughout North America via a network of more than 6,500 vendors, including equipment manufacturing and maintenance companies, hauling companies, and recycling companies.

The company's revenues increased more than 89% in 2010, due mainly to increase volume in its recycling operations. Shipments of ferrous metals increased 97% while stainless steel shipments grew 34%. Business in its waste services segment was down about 10% for the year. Net income increased 52% on higher sales volumes and a significant gain on the sale of assets.

The company maintains its growth strategy by increasing efficiencies and productivity in its core operations. However, it is open to possible acquisitions, strategic partnerships, mergers, and/or joint ventures that promise to enhance its overall profitability.

EXECUTIVES

Chairman and CEO, Harry Kletter, age 84, $822,000
  total compensation
CFO and Treasurer, Alan L. Schroering, age 46
President, COO, and Director, Brian G. Donaghy, age
  35, $461,723 total compensation
EVP Recycling, Daniel C. Gascoyne
VP Recycling, James K. Wiseman III, age 57, $177,852
  total compensation
Chief Administration Officer, Donald (Don) Rodgers
Head, Alloys Division, Terry Hancock
Division Manager, WESSCO, Scott Necessary
General Manager, Alloys, Jeff Valentine
Auditors: Mountjoy & Bressler, LLP

LOCATIONS

HQ: Industrial Services of America, Inc.
  7100 Grade Ln., Louisville, KY 40232
Phone: 502-368-1661   Fax: 502-368-1440
Web: www.isa-inc.com/

PRODUCTS/OPERATIONS

2010 Sales

	$ mil.	% of total
Recycling	334.7	98
Waste Services	8.3	2
Total	**343.0**	**100**

COMPETITORS

Aleris Corp.
Avalon Holdings
Casella Waste Systems
Commercial Metals
David J. Joseph
OAKLEAF Waste Management
Philip Services
Republic Services
RockTenn CP
United Scrap Metal
Veolia Environmental Services North America
Waste Management
WM Recycle America

HISTORICAL FINANCIALS
Company Type: Public

Income Statement   FYE: December 31

	REVENUE ($ mil.)	NET INCOME ($ mil.)	NET PROFIT MARGIN	EMPLOYEES
12/10	343.0	8.1	2.4%	185
12/09	181.1	5.3	2.9%	165
12/08	100.0	1.5	1.5%	126
12/07	77.0	2.6	3.4%	139
12/06	62.1	2.2	3.5%	102
Annual Growth	**53.3%**	**38.5%**	—	**16.0%**

2010 Year-End Financials

Debt ratio: 106.7%	No. of shares (mil.): 6.8
Return on equity: 19.7%	Dividends
Cash ($ mil.): 2.5	Yield: 0.0%
Current ratio: 3.59	Payout: —
Long-term debt ($ mil.): 43.6	Market value ($ mil.): 83.5

	STOCK PRICE ($) FY Close	P/E High/Low	Earnings	PER SHARE ($) Dividends	Book Value
12/10	12.30	18 5	1.21	0.00	6.02
12/09	6.36	9 3	0.91	0.00	3.41
12/08	3.63	45 10	0.29	0.07	2.30
12/07	5.02	26 8	0.47	0.07	2.20
12/06	3.63	18 5	0.41	0.00	1.78
Annual Growth	**35.7%**	— —	**31.1%**	—	**35.5%**

Informatica

Thinking about data? Think Informatica. The company provides enterprise data integration software that enables companies to access, integrate, and consolidate their data across a variety of systems and users. Its PowerCenter platform consolidates, codes, and moves large data warehouses, and its PowerExchange software enables access to bulk or changed data. Other products include Fast Clone (data replication), Data Explorer (data quality), and a range of software-as-a-service (SaaS) offerings, which integrate data from other business applications into a single hosted platform. Informatica's customers have included British Airways, SAP, Avaya, and Rabobank.

Informatica continues to shift its focus from data warehousing to a broader enterprise data integration platform, which encompasses data migration, consolidation, management, and synchronization capabilities. The company has targeted the financial services industry by tailoring versions of its software for customers in banking and insurance. It also develops tools specifically for the retail, health care, and telecommunications industries among others.

In keeping with the broader IT industry trend toward cloud computing where software is hosted and made available to clients over the Web, while being supplemented with a range of managed IT services, Informatica makes many of its products available under the SaaS model. The company introduced its Informatica Cloud data integration service in 2010, and it continues to make more of its applications available on a hosted basis.

Informatica's sales continued along a decade long upward tractory in 2010, while profits also rose for the year. The company cited strong demand for its data integration applications, and to some degree sales from acquired businesses, as key contributing factors to revenue growth. It attributed increased sales of services to a growing customer base that is demanding more maintenance, consulting, and training.

The company supplements its organic growth with acquisitions. In 2010 Informatica purchased Siperian, a developer of master data management (MDM) infrastructure technology. Siperian's multidomain MDM software was used to help optimize business decisions across multiple entities, using many considerations. Master data refers to key information within an enterprise, such as citizens, customers, employees, locations, and products. Being able to analyze such data on a holistic basis helps businesses improve operational efficiency, manage customer relationships, and track regulatory compliance efforts.

Informatica also purchased 29West that year to gain its ultra-low latency messaging (ULLM) technology, allowing Informatica to enable faster data integration with its platform.

EXECUTIVES

Chairman, President, and CEO, Sohaib Abbasi, age 54, $2,778,900 total compensation
CEO, 29West, Mark G. Mahowald, age 51
EVP and CTO, James Markarian
EVP; President, Worldwide Field Operations, Paul J. Hoffman, age 60, $1,093,303 total compensation
EVP Data Quality Product, Ivan Chong, age 43
EVP Data Integration Product, Girish Pancha, age 46, $1,006,831 total compensation
EVP Global Customer Support, CFO, Chief Administration Officer, and Secretary, Earl E. Fry, age 52, $1,138,800 total compensation
VP Investor Relations, Stephanie Wakefield
VP Corporate Communications, Debbie O'Brien
Director Analyst Relations, Peggy O'Neill
SVP Global Customer Support, Ansa Sekharan
Senior Manager Analyst Relations, Misti Lusher
SVP and CIO, Tony Young
Director Corporate Communications, Deborah Wiltshire
Chief Marketing Officer, and SVP Education and Enablement, Chris Boorman
Senior Public Relations Manager, EMEA, Kristen Miller
Auditors: Ernst & Young LLP

LOCATIONS

HQ: Informatica Corporation
100 Cardinal Way, Redwood City, CA 94063
Phone: 650-385-5000   **Fax:** 650-385-5500
Web: www.informatica.com

2010 Sales

	$ mil.	% of total
North America	431.3	66
Europe	162.0	25
Other regions	56.8	9
Total	**650.1**	**100**

PRODUCTS/OPERATIONS

2010 Sales

	$ mil.	% of total
Software licenses	295.1	45
Maintenance services	255.4	39
Consulting, education & other services	99.6	16
Total	**650.1**	**100**

COMPETITORS

Embarcadero Technologies	Oracle
	SAP
IBM	SAS Institute
Microsoft	Sybase
MicroStrategy	Trillium

HISTORICAL FINANCIALS

Company Type: Public

Income Statement

FYE: December 31

	REVENUE ($ mil.)	NET INCOME ($ mil.)	NET PROFIT MARGIN	EMPLOYEES
12/10	650.1	86.3	13.3%	2,126
12/09	500.7	64.2	12.8%	1,755
12/08	455.7	56.0	12.3%	1,611
12/07	391.3	54.6	14.0%	1,365
12/06	324.6	36.2	11.2%	1,221
Annual Growth	**19.0%**	**24.3%**	**—**	**14.9%**

2010 Year-End Financials

Debt ratio: 2.0%	No. of shares (mil.): 94.5
Return on equity: 13.4%	Dividends
Cash ($ mil.): 208.9	Yield: —
Current ratio: 1.34	Payout: —
Long-term debt ($ mil.): 12.7	Market value ($ mil.): 4,159.1

	STOCK PRICE ($) FY Close	P/E High/Low		PER SHARE ($) Earnings	Dividends	Book Value
12/10	44.03	55	27	0.83	0.00	6.83
12/09	25.88	41	17	0.66	0.00	5.36
12/08	13.73	33	18	0.58	0.00	4.06
12/07	18.02	32	22	0.57	0.00	3.56
12/06	12.21	44	30	0.39	0.00	2.63
Annual Growth	**37.8%**	**—**	**—**	**20.8%**	**—**	**27.0%**

InfoSpace

Why crawl the Web when others can do it for you? InfoSpace operates online search services that rely on its metasearch search technology. The company's owned and operated consumer websites, which include Dogpile.com, WebFetch.com, MetaCrawler.com, and WebCrawler.com, query such leading search engines as Google, Yahoo!, MSN, and Ask, and then collate and rank those search results. InfoSpace also offers a private-label search product for businesses (which it calls distribution partners); it develops, hosts, and delivers search results for more than 100 distribution partners. In recent years the company disposed of its mobile, directory, and e-commerce assets in order to focus on its core online search business.

InfoSpace primarily generates revenue through paid search results and other online advertising. About 70% of its search services revenue is generated through its distribution partners. It has distribution and partnership agreements with search giants Google and Yahoo!, ensuring access to search results through at least part of 2013 (Google) and the entirety of 2013 (Yahoo!). The two search giants together account for more than 80% of sales.

The company continues to invest in its offerings in order to boost traffic on its owned and operated search engines and grow its distribution network. In 2011 InfoSpace expanded its offerings when it launched its new Content Experience Platform, an online news, weather, sports, and entertainment portal for search clients. The previous year it acquired Make The Web Better. Formerly one of InfoSpace's search distribution partners, Make The Web Better develops online products used on social networking sites.

InfoSpace reported positive earnings in fiscal year 2010, when both revenues and net income increased. These results were primarily due to growth in revenue from owned and operated properties, which account for about 10% of total sales. Specifically, InfoSpace's revenues from owned and operated properties received a boost from the Make The Web Better purchase, and from increased revenue from direct marketing initiatives. In addition, the company's net income was aided by a $19 million gain on a litigation settlement.

Despite its successful 2010, the company later admitted defeat with regards to one of its assets — selling Internet shopping service Mercantila at a loss in 2011, just a year after it acquired the company. It had bought Mercantila for about $8 million plus the assumption of up to $5.9 million in debt in order to diversify beyond Internet search. However, after the venture lost money, InfoSpace decided e-commerce no longer fit with its core strategy. It divested the business for a "nominal upfront payment" and the right to receive additional payments of up to $3 million.

Putting an end to a lengthy executive search, Bill Ruckelshaus was named InfoSpace's permanent CEO in 2011. He replaced Jim Voelker, who retired early in 2009. (Voelker had served as CEO since 2002.)

HISTORY

Indian immigrant Naveen Jain, a veteran of Microsoft's online services unit, set out to create an interactive "people and business finder" in 1996. Eschewing funding from venture capitalists (disdainfully calling them "vulture capitalists"), the outspoken Jain launched his new enterprise, dubbed InfoSpace, with $250,000 of his own money. Its online phone directory service debuted in May, and a few months later it unveiled an online e-mail directory. Unlike most Internet players, InfoSpace wasn't looking to lure users to its own website (though it did have one). Instead, the company focused on supplying information to other sites.

By the beginning of 1997 InfoSpace had added industry stalwarts Lycos (now owned by South Korea's Daum Communications) and Microsoft to its customer list. That year it signed up @Home Network, Playboy, Dow Jones' Wall Street Journal Online, and Go2Net. The company's content also found its way to cable TV that year by way of InfoSpace's alliance with Source Media's Interactive Channel. InfoSpace continued expanding beyond traditional Internet customers, inking deals to feed its content to Motorola and SkyTel pagers, the 3Com PalmPilot, and the AT&T PocketNet service.

The company secured two vital customers in 1998, signing America Online (AOL) and Netscape (later acquired by AOL) to content distribution deals. To get the agreements, however, InfoSpace had to pay AOL and Netscape to carry its content. Also in 1998 the company set up shop in the UK through a joint venture with Thomson Directories. It went public later that year as InfoSpace.com.

After going public, the company entered into e-commerce agreements with Cyberian Outpost and Multiple Zones (now known as just Zones). In 1999 it joined with Quote.com to create a financial content package. It later established a venture capital fund, launched its comparison shopping application ActiveShopper, and expanded into Canada and India. InfoSpace bolstered its wireless operations in 2000 through acquisitions of Saraide and Millet Software and signed agreements with GTE Wireless (now Cingular) and VeriSign. The company later dropped the ".com" from its name and Jain handed the CEO title to Arun Sarin.

In October 2000 InfoSpace expanded its infrastructure services and content offerings when it acquired online content company Go2Net for about $1.5 billion. The company's stock sank into the single digits, however, and a management shakeup led to the departures of its COO and CFO. Jain took back the CEO title from Sarin (who briefly served as vice chairman before resigning from the board) and realigned the company's focus on its core distribution products. The company later acquired Locus Dialogue, a developer of speech recognition technologies. In late 2002 one of the company's directors, Jim Voelker, replaced Jain as chairman and CEO.

InfoSpace cut about 115 jobs and sold its Silicon Investor site in 2003. It also purchased mobile media company Moviso for some $25 million from the now defunct Vivendi Universal Net USA Group. The company formed a Media Studios business unit in order to house its Moviso acquisition. Later that year, Jain resigned from the board of directors after the company filed a lawsuit against him claiming his new company, Intelius, violated non-compete clauses. (The suit was dismissed the following year.)

InfoSpace sold its payment solutions business to Lightbridge (later renamed Authorize.Net Holdings) in 2004 for $82 million and boosted its local directory offerings with the acquisition of Switchboard for $160 million. It also acquired mobile game creators Atlas Mobile and IOMO Limited.

In 2006 InfoSpace announced a restructuring plan as a response to revenue losses. The plan included 250 job cuts and the closing of its Hamburg, Germany, facility. Streamlining continued in 2007 with the company's sale of its online directory business, including Switchboard, to Idearc (now called SuperMedia) for $225 million. Also in 2007 InfoSpace sold Media Studios (including Moviso) to FunMobility Inc. of Pleasanton, California, for an undisclosed price and its mobile services business for $135 million to Motricity, a provider of mobile content.

In 2008 it closed its European facilities. Jim Voelker retired as CEO early in 2009. InfoSpace acquired Internet shopping service Mercantila in 2010, only to divest the business a year later. John Cunningham became chairman in early 2011, and Bill Ruckelshaus was named CEO later that year.

EXECUTIVES

Chairman, John E. Cunningham IV, age 53
President, CEO, and Director, William J. (Bill) Ruckelshaus, age 46
CFO, David B. Binder, age 41, $1,077,027 total compensation
CEO, Mercantila, Nikhil Behl
VP Corporate Development, Stephen P. Hawthornthwaite

VP Business Development, Michael J. (Mike) Glover, age 48, $1,053,252 total compensation
Chief Accounting Officer, Eric M. Emans, age 37, $755,067 total compensation
CTO, Leo Chang
General Manager Search, John Rodkin
General Counsel and Secretary, Alesia L. Pinney, age 46, $1,184,643 total compensation
Investor Relations and Corporate Communications, Stacy Ybarra
Auditors: Deloitte & Touche LLP

LOCATIONS

HQ: InfoSpace, Inc.
  601 108th Ave. NE, Ste. 1200, Bellevue, WA 98004
Phone: 425-201-6100   **Fax:** 425-201-6150
Web: www.infospaceinc.com

2010 Sales

	$ mil.	% of total
US	241.5	98
International	5.3	2
Total	**246.8**	**100**

PRODUCTS/OPERATIONS

2010 Sales

	$ mil.	% of total
Search Services		
Distribution partners	146.9	60
Owned & operated Web properties	22.1	9
Make The Web Better owned & operated	16.4	7
Make The Web Better distribution partner	9.4	4
Other search revenues	19.5	8
E-Commerce	32.5	13
Total	**246.8**	**100**

Owned & Operated Websites

Dogpile.com
InfoSpace.com
MetaCrawler.com
WebCrawler.com

COMPETITORS

Answers Corporation	LookSmart
AOL	Marchex
Ask.com	MSN
Daum Communications	ValueClick
Google	Vertro
Local.com	Yahoo!

HISTORICAL FINANCIALS

Company Type: Public

Income Statement

FYE: December 31

	REVENUE ($ mil.)	NET INCOME ($ mil.)	NET PROFIT MARGIN	EMPLOYEES
12/10	246.8	13.7	5.6%	174
12/09	207.6	7.4	3.6%	157
12/08	156.7	(18.7)	—	160
12/07	140.5	14.6	10.4%	170
12/06	371.7	(15.1)	—	530
Annual Growth	**(9.7%)**	**—**	**—**	**(24.3%)**

2010 Year-End Financials

Debt ratio: 0.3%
Return on equity: 4.4%
Cash ($ mil.): 155.6
Current ratio: 5.58
Long-term debt ($ mil.): 1.0
No. of shares (mil.): 36.1
Dividends
  Yield: —
  Payout: —
Market value ($ mil.): 299.5

STOCK PRICE ($) FY Close	P/E High/Low		PER SHARE ($) Earnings	Dividends	Book Value
12/10	8.30	33	18	0.37	0.00	8.61
12/09	8.57	43	24	0.21	0.00	7.91
12/08	7.55	—	—	(0.54)	0.00	7.59
12/07	18.80	62	28	0.45	0.00	7.74
12/06	20.51	—	—	(0.48)	0.00	21.64
Annual Growth	**(20.2%)**	—	—	—	—	**(20.6%)**

Inphi

Inphi wants to shift broadband networks into high gear. The fabless semiconductor company offers specialized logic devices, modulator drivers, and other components used in high-speed optical telecom networks. Key parts of Inphi's more than 170 products are made from indium phosphide (InP; hence the company name), which Inphi touts as running at much higher speeds — but with lower power consumption — than competing products made from other specialized materials, such as silicon germanium. Other elements of the company's designs are made from standard silicon to lower overall costs. The company gets around two-thirds of sales from customers in the Asia/Pacific region. Inphi went public in 2010.

The company plans to use proceeds from its IPO to fund future acquisitions, pay down debt, expand internationally, and fund increased product development. Inphi's strategy includes building up its sales, design, and technical support presence in Europe and Asia in order to extend its customer reach in those regions. The company set up an R&D center in the UK and established an international headquarters in Singapore in 2010. The same year, the company furthered its expansion in Asia with the purchase of Taiwan-based Winyatek Technology for about $2.5 million in cash, in addition to stock issued to Winyatek shareholders.

Inphi's products are sold directly and through distributors to manufacturers including Samsung Electronics (36% of sales), Micron, Agilent, Alcatel-Lucent, Cisco, and IBM. Its 10 largest customers accounted for about 80% of sales in 2009.

As a fabless semiconductor company, Inphi outsources its wafer fabrication to foundries and plants operated by GCS, Sumitomo, TSMC, Jazz Semiconductor, and United Monolithic Semiconductors. Its assembly and test operations are handled by companies including Kyocera, Natel Engineering, Orient Semiconductor, and STATS ChipPAC.

EXECUTIVES

Chairman, Diosdado P. (Dado) Banatao, age 65
President, CEO, and Director, Young K. Sohn, age 55
CFO and Chief Accounting Officer, John S. Edmunds, age 54
VP Engineering, Norman K. Yeung
VP Operations, Atul P. Shingal, age 50
VP Worldwide Sales, Ron Torten, age 44
VP Marketing, Networking, Communications, and Multi-Markets, Loi Nguyen
VP Human Resources, Diane Nott-Kilfoil
VP Engineering, New Business Initiatives, Lawrence Tse
VP Marketing, Computing and Storage, Paul Washkewicz
CTO, Gopal Raghavan, age 50
Auditors: PricewaterhouseCoopers LLP

LOCATIONS

HQ: Inphi Corporation
3945 Freedom Circle, Ste. 1100, Santa Clara, CA 95054
Phone: 408-217-7300
Web: www.inphi.com

2009 Sales

	$ mil.	% of total
South Korea	18.3	31
US	10.7	18
China	9.9	17
Japan	5.7	10
Taiwan	5.7	10
Other countries	8.5	14
Total	**58.8**	**100**

PRODUCTS/OPERATIONS

Selected Products

High-speed logic devices
Modulator drivers
Physical layer (PHY) components
Transimpedance amplifiers

COMPETITORS

Analog Devices
Applied Micro Circuits
Broadcom
CyOptics
Cypress Semiconductor
Gennum
Hittite Microwave
Infineon Technologies
Integrated Device Technology
LSI Corp.
NetLogic Microsystems
Texas Instruments
Thorlabs Quantum Electronics
Vitesse Semiconductor

HISTORICAL FINANCIALS

Company Type: Public

Income Statement

FYE: December 31

	REVENUE ($ mil.)	NET INCOME ($ mil.)	NET PROFIT MARGIN	EMPLOYEES
12/10	83.2	26.1	31.4%	166
12/09	58.9	7.3	12.4%	110
12/08	43.0	(3.4)	—	0
12/07	36.2	(5.3)	—	0
Annual Growth	**32.0%**	**—**	**—**	**50.9%**

2010 Year-End Financials

Debt ratio: —
Return on equity: 18.3%
Cash ($ mil.): 110.2
Current ratio: 9.55
Long-term debt ($ mil.): —
No. of shares (mil.): 25.1
Dividends
  Yield: —
  Payout: —
Market value ($ mil.): 504.0

	STOCK PRICE ($) FY Close	P/E High/Low		PER SHARE ($) Earnings	Dividends	Book Value
12/10	20.09	34	24	0.61	0.00	5.69
Annual Growth	**—**	**—**	**—**	**—**	**—**	**—**

Insulet Corporation

Insulet wants to isolate an insolent disease. The medical device company manufactures an insulin pump for people with insulin-dependent diabetes. Its disposable, waterproof product, called the OmniPod Insulin Management System, weighs a mere 1.2 ounces and adheres directly to the patient's skin, making it more discrete than most insulin in-fusion systems that typically clip to a belt or fit in a pocket. The company markets its products to physicians, academic centers, and clinics specializing in the treatment of diabetes treatments. It also sells directly to patients in the US and globally.

The company grows its business with an aggressive marketing campaign meant to introduce the product to potential users and by entering in to licensing deals with larger pharmaceutical and medical device companies. Insulet has a five-year agreement with Ypsomed Distribution to distribute and sell the OmniPod System in about a dozen countries including Germany, the UK, France, the Netherlands, Sweden, Norway, and Switzerland. Insulet also has an agreement with GlaxoSmithKline to distribute OmniPod in Canada.

Insulet targets markets, geographic and consumer, in which it can obtain the most lucrative third-party reimbursements. If patients are not reimbursed for the cost of using the OmniPod, it is much more difficult for the company to penetrate and sell in that market. Insulet continues to negotiate contracts establishing reimbursement for OmniPod with national and regional third-party payers, which are integral to the company's goal of reaching and maintaining profitability.

Insulet spent about half of its existence as a development-stage company before it began selling OmniPod, so it has yet to experience a profit. Since its inception in 2000, it has continued to accumulate losses, though in recent years its losses have been decreasing, going from about $100 million in 2008 to roughly $60 million in 2010. The company's objective is to obtain and maintain long-term profitability by gaining approval on a next generation version of the OmniPod, continuing to reduce its per-unit production costs on the existing OmniPod, and increasing sales in international markets.

The next-generation OmniPod will feature increased ease-of-use, functionality and an even smaller size. Insulet is also researching ways to combine the OmniPod with continuous glucose monitoring systems through partnerships with Abbott and DexCom.

Insulet also used the OmniPod system's technology for the delivery of other medications that are meant to be administered subcutaneously (under the skin) in precise and varied doses over an extended period of time. It developed such a product with Ferring Pharmaceuticals in Switzerland, which the company uses to deliver one of its own drugs. Under the terms of the agreement, Ferring funded development of a custom version of OmniPod's Personal Diabetes Manager; Insulet started selling the Ferring product in 2010, but income from the device has been minimal.

Insulet was founded in 2000 and went public through an IPO in 2007. Insulet management controls about 7% of the company. Investor Edward Johnson III holds another 8% of the company's shares.

EXECUTIVES

President, CEO, and Director, Duane M. DeSisto, age 56, $609,592 total compensation
CFO, Brian K. Roberts, age 40
VP Asian Operations, Jason Ng, age 45
VP International, Carsten Boess, age 44, $705,903 total compensation
VP Finance, Lars Boesgaard, age 41, $538,205 total compensation
VP Business Development, William D. (Bill) Arthur III, age 59
VP Clinical Services and Research, Robert Campbell, age 41
VP Human Resources, David Howe, age 44
VP Quality and Regulatory Affairs, Ruthann DePietro, age 51
VP Operations and Engineering, Kevin Schmid, age 52
COO and Director, Charles T. (Charlie) Liamos, age 51
Chief Commercial Officer, Peter J. Devlin
Co-Founder, John Garibotto, age 45
General Counsel and Secretary, R. Anthony Diehl, age 42
Auditors: Ernst & Young LLP

LOCATIONS

HQ: Insulet Corporation
9 Oak Park Dr., Bedford, MA 01730
Phone: 781-457-5000   **Fax:** 781-457-5011
Web: www.MyOmniPod.com

COMPETITORS

Abbott Diabetes Care
Animas
Eli Lilly
Fresenius Kabi
MannKind
Medtronic
Novo Nordisk
Roche Diagnostics
Smiths Medical
Takeda Pharmaceutical

HISTORICAL FINANCIALS

Company Type: Public

Income Statement

FYE: December 31

	REVENUE ($ mil.)	NET INCOME ($ mil.)	NET PROFIT MARGIN	EMPLOYEES
12/10	97.0	(61.2)	—	310
12/09	66.0	(79.5)	—	276
12/08	36.1	(92.8)	—	294
12/07	13.4	(53.5)	—	247
12/06	3.7	(36.0)	—	190
Annual Growth	**126.3%**	**—**	**—**	**13.0%**

2010 Year-End Financials

Debt ratio: 104.8%
Return on equity: —
Cash ($ mil.): 113.3
Current ratio: 7.52
Long-term debt ($ mil.): 69.4
No. of shares (mil.): 45.4
Dividends
  Yield: —
  Payout: —
Market value ($ mil.): 704.3

	STOCK PRICE ($) FY Close	P/E High/Low		PER SHARE ($) Earnings	Dividends	Book Value
12/10	15.50	—	—	(1.54)	0.00	1.46
12/09	14.28	—	—	(2.68)	0.00	1.40
12/08	7.72	—	—	(3.36)	0.00	0.15
12/07	23.48	—	—	(3.21)	0.00	3.49
Annual Growth	**(12.9%)**	**—**	**—**	**—**	**—**	**(25.3%)**

---

interclick

If there's an ad at the top of the page while you're reading this, it could have been placed by interclick. The online advertising firm sells space on third-party websites to it advertising agency clients. The company's customers include those serving the consumer goods, retail, electronics, software, travel, and entertainment industries. It says its Open Segment Manager (OSM) software allows its customers to learn more than from traditional ad campaigns. With offices in New York, Chicago, Los Angeles, and San Francisco, interclick lives where the big ad markets do. In late 2011, the company agreed to be acquired by Yahoo! in a deal valued at $270 million.

EXECUTIVES

CEO and Director, Michael Katz, age 31
CFO, Roger Clark, age 41
EVP Operations, Dave Myers, age 40
VP Business Development, Andrew Greenberg
VP Engineering, Brad Noe
Co-Chairman, Michael Brauser, age 54
Co-Chairman, Barry Honig, age 38
CTO, Andrew Katz, age 29
Chief Strategy Officer, Jason Lynn, age 37
Chief Software Architect, Gary Davidson
SVP Sales, National, Jay Freedman
SVP Sales, Mike Marvul
SVP Sales, West Coast, Kurt Munzinger
Auditors: J.H. Cohn LLP

LOCATIONS

HQ: interclick, inc.
 11 W. 19th St., 10th Fl., New York, NY 10011
Phone: 646-722-6260
Web: www.interclick.com

COMPETITORS

24/7 Real Media
AOL Advertising
Google
LinkShare
ValueClick

HISTORICAL FINANCIALS

Company Type: Public

Income Statement

	REVENUE ($ mil.)	NET INCOME ($ mil.)	NET PROFIT MARGIN	EMPLOYEES
12/10	101.2	4.1	4.1%	118
12/09	55.3	0.5	0.9%	91
12/08	22.5	(12.0)	—	37
12/07	6.7	(3.2)	—	24
Annual Growth	**147.2%**	**—**	**—**	**70.0%**

FYE: December 31

2010 Year-End Financials

Debt ratio: 2.5%
Return on equity: 10.9%
Cash ($ mil.): 12.5
Current ratio: 1.74
Long-term debt ($ mil.): 0.9

No. of shares (mil.): 24.1
Dividends
 Yield: —
 Payout: —
Market value ($ mil.): 129.2

	STOCK PRICE ($) FY Close	P/E High/Low		PER SHARE ($) Earnings	Dividends	Book Value
12/10	5.37	41	20	0.16	0.00	1.55
12/09	5.23	300	55	0.02	0.00	1.22
12/08	1.50	—	—	(0.64)	0.00	0.50
12/07	10.94	—	—	(0.24)	0.00	(0.00)
Annual Growth	**(21.1%)**	**—**	**—**	**—**	**—**	**—**

Intercontinental Exchange

If there were money to be made in ice futures, IntercontinentalExchange (ICE) would probably trade that as well. The company us a leading provider of online marketplaces for global commodity trading, primarily of electricity, natural gas, crude oil, refined petroleum products, precious metals, and weather and emission credits. It man-

ages two global OTC markets and a handful of regulated futures exchanges. The company owns the ICE Futures Europe, a leading European energy futures and options platform. ICE Data provides real-time, daily, and historical market data reports. ICE is based in Atlanta and has offices in Atlanta, Calgary, Chicago, Houston, London, New York, Singapore, Washington, DC, and Winnipeg.

In a major move, in 2011 ICE and NASDAQ OMX Group teamed up to make a joint $11.3 billion bid for NYSE Euronext.

As part of the deal ICE would buy NYSE Euronext's derivatives businesses, while NASDAQ OMXwould keep the remaining businesses, including the US-based business and NYSE Euronext stock exchanges in Amsterdam, Brussels, Lisbon, New York, and Paris. However, the bid, which countered Deutsche Börse's earlier offer to acquire NYSE EURONEXT, was initially rejected, prompting the two partners to reaffirm their bid.

The companies subsequently dropped the bid following discussions with the Antitrust Division of the US Department of Justice

ICE has built global market share (in 2010 it was serving customers in 70 countries).

In 2010 the company reported a major spike in revenues, driven by the recovering global economy and higher commodity prices. ICE Brent Crude and ICE Gas Oil futures contracts and OTC energy contracts led the improvement as well as an increase in credit default swaps (CDS) clearing revenues.

ICE has grown rapidly through a series of acquisitions and portfolio diversifications. It acquired the New York Board of Trade (renamed ICE Futures US) for $1 billion in 2007. Moving into a new asset area — credit default swaps (CDS) — in 2008 the company bought financial services firm Creditex from Internet Capital Group (which has expertise in CDS services) for slightly more than $500 million. In 2009 ICE launched CDS clearing services operations in the Europe and the US. Diversifying further, in 2010 it acquired Climate Exchange plc, a leader in the development of traded emissions markets.

Expanding its options market portfolio, in 2011 the company acquired broker/dealer Ballista, which offers an electronic options platform for the execution of large and complex multi-leg options transactions. That year it also agreed to buy 12% of Brazilian clearing-house operator Cetip SA for $512 million.

ICE was formed by a group of top financial and energy firms in 2000.

EXECUTIVES

Chairman and CEO, Jeffrey C. Sprecher, age 56, $6,795,519 total compensation
President, YellowJacket, Jacob E. Pechenik
President, Creditex, Grant Biggar
President and COO, Charles A. (Chuck) Vice, age 47, $3,205,363 total compensation
President and COO, ICE Futures Canada, E. Bradley (Brad) Vannan
President and COO, ICE Futures Europe, David J. Peniket, age 45
President and COO, ICE Clear Europe, Paul Swann
President and COO, ICE Clear U.S., Thomas J. (Tom) Hammond
President and COO, ICE Futures U.S., Thomas W. Farley, age 35
VP, ICE Data, Edward J. Fraim
VP Clearing Technology, Joseph W. Albert
VP Credit Derivatives Technology, Fred C. Doerr
VP Technology Development, Simon B. Shlyayfer
VP Administration, Douglas A. Foley

VP Information Security and Technology, Jerry Perullo
VP Oil Markets, Jeff A. Barbuto
VP Architecture, Mayur V. Kapani
VP North American Power and NGL Markets, James C. Kneale
VP and Chief Risk Officer, TCC, Stanislav Ivanov
VP North American Natural Gas Markets, Baldwin (Bud) Hum
VP and Corporate Controller, Dean S. Mathison
VP Investor Relations and Corporate Communications, Kelly L. Loeffler
VP Government Affairs, Peter S. Roberson
VP Product Development, Raymond J. Cummings
VP Government Affairs, Alex U. Albert
VP and Associate General Counsel, Andrew J. Surdykowski
VP Market Development, John Harding
VP Operations, Mark P. Wassersug
SVP, General Counsel, and Secretary, Johnathan H. Short, age 45
Director Investor and Public Relations, Melanie Shale
Head of Regulation, ICE Futures Europe, Deirdre Blake
Director Corporate Communications, Lee Underwood
COO, Creditex, Sophia Corona, age 47
Managing Director, ICE Data and European Sales, Martin Wadhwani
SVP and CTO, Edwin D. Marcial, age 43, $1,896,821 total compensation
SVP and Chief Strategic Officer, David S. Goone, age 50, $2,572,109 total compensation
SVP and CFO, Scott A. Hill, age 43, $2,542,882 total compensation
SVP and General Counsel, ICE Futures U.S., Audrey R. Hirschfeld
Auditors: Ernst & Young LLP

LOCATIONS

HQ: IntercontinentalExchange, Inc.
 2100 RiverEdge Pkwy., Ste. 500, Atlanta, GA 30328
Phone: 770-857-4700   **Fax:** 770-857-4755
Web: www.theice.com

2010 Sales

	$ mil.	% of total
US	609.4	53
EU & Canada	540.5	47
Total	**1,149.9**	**100**

PRODUCTS/OPERATIONS

2010 Sales

	$ mil.	% of total
Transaction & clearing fees	1,023.4	89
Market data fees	109.2	10
Other	17.3	1
Total	**1,149.9**	**100**

Founding Partners

BP p.l.c.
Deutsche Bank AG
The Goldman Sachs Group, Inc.
Morgan Stanley Dean Witter & Co.
Royal Dutch Shell plc
Société Générale
TOTAL S.A.

COMPETITORS

APX
BGC Partners
Bloomberg L.P.
CHOICE! Energy
CME
Enporion
GFI Group
ICAP
NYMEX Holdings
NYSE Euronext
Reuters
Unitil

HISTORICAL FINANCIALS

Company Type: Public

Income Statement

	REVENUE ($ mil.)	NET INCOME ($ mil.)	NET PROFIT MARGIN	EMPLOYEES
12/10	1,149.9	398.3	34.6%	933
12/09	994.8	316.0	31.8%	826
12/08	813.1	301.0	37.0%	795
12/07	574.3	240.6	41.9%	506
12/06	313.8	143.3	45.7%	226
Annual Growth	38.4%	29.1%	—	42.5%

FYE: December 31

2010 Year-End Financials

Debt ratio: 11.7%
Return on equity: 14.3%
Cash ($ mil.): 621.8
Current ratio: 1.02
Long-term debt ($ mil.): 325.8

No. of shares (mil.): 73.3
Dividends
  Yield: —
  Payout: —
Market value ($ mil.): 8,734.1

	STOCK PRICE ($) FY Close	P/E High/Low	PER SHARE ($) Earnings	Dividends	Book Value
12/10	119.15	24 17	5.35	0.00	37.89
12/09	112.30	29 12	4.27	0.00	32.65
12/08	82.44	42 12	4.17	0.00	27.77
12/07	192.50	57 35	3.39	0.00	21.23
12/06	107.90	47 15	2.40	0.00	7.91
Annual Growth	2.5%	— —	22.2%	—	47.9%

InterDigital

InterDigital is more than just interested in wireless digital telecommunications. The company develops and licenses circuitry designs, software, and other technology using CDMA (code-division multiple access) and other wireless communications standards. InterDigital is also developing semiconductors and software to enable voice and data transmissions in mobile phones and portable computing devices. Top customers LG Electronics and Samsung Electronics make up 40% of sales but its technology patents are also licensed to Acer, Apple, HTC, RIM, and to many other makers of chips, software, and telecom equipment. The company generates about 80% of its revenues from Asia, where cell phones are manufactured.

As a patent licensing firm, InterDigital must continually expand its pool of licensing customers to continue its growth, and the company has a limited number of licensees contributing most of its revenues. InterDigital must also spend money on developing patentable technologies — most of its patent portfolio in TDMA, or time-division multiple access, technology expired in 2006 — and it has had to litigate to defend the patents it holds, for years at a time in some cases. The company holds more than 1,300 US patents and nearly 7,500 patents issued by other countries. Some 150 patents were issued to the company in 2010, and it has about 8,500 patent applications pending around the world.

In 2009 InterDigital ceased product development of its SlimChip High Speed Packet Access (HSPA) technology and offered the HSPA intellectual property for licensing, resulting in the layoff of about 100 employees, a reduction in force of around 26%. The move marked a shift away from a strategy of developing silicon products, initiated

two years earlier, due to the cost of designing and fabricating products. This returned the company to technology development and licensing for cellular and non-cellular wireless protocols. In 2010 it signed its first license agreement for the SlimChip 2G and 3G modem technology to Inventec Appliances, a Chinese mobile chipset manufacturer and subsidiary of Taiwanese contract manufacturer Inventec.

The company has built its suite of technology and patent offerings through internal development, joint development projects with other companies, and acquisitions, although it hasn't made an acquisition in years. It generates revenues primarily from royalties for patent license agreements and by licensing technology solutions and providing related development support. Patent licensing accounts for about 95% of its total revenues. In 2010 InterDigital recognized revenue from more than half of all 3G mobile devices sold around the world.

InterDigital, which was founded in 1972 and has been a publicly traded company since 1981, was approached by Google in 2011 about a possible sale as the Internet giant seeks to expand its patent portfolio. In June InterDigital's board of directors announced its plan to explore a possible takeover, without naming Google as a potential bidder. Several other tech companies, including Apple, Nokia, and QUALCOMM, were reported to be interested too.

HISTORY

InterDigital was founded in 1972 as International Mobile Machines Corporation by Sherwin Seligsohn, who was its chairman until 1990. It began to develop technologies that held the potential to revolutionize radiotelephone communications, but as a small company unable to usher in the digital age on its own, the company patented its inventions. It went public in 1981, which allowed it to expand into product development.

The company expanded its technology portfolio by acquiring the assets of Tantivy Communications, a designer of CDMA-based and other wireless gear, in 2003 for $11.5 million.

Interdigital worked with Nokia at the turn of the century to develop Internet access technology for mobile phones. A legal dispute between the two companies over the amount of royalties Nokia owed was resolved in InterDigital's favor in 2005, when a US District Court judge upheld an international tribunal's verdict ordering Nokia to pay additional royalties to InterDigital. In 2006 Nokia agreed to pay $253 million in one lump sum to InterDigital, and the companies agreed to end their litigation against each other. Nokia and InterDigital immediately terminated their original license agreement and began negotiating a new pact.

Those talks apparently came to naught, as InterDigital in 2007 filed a complaint against Nokia with the US International Trade Commission (ITC), alleging that Nokia's handsets infringe on patents held by InterDigital. The company sought to ban sales in the US of the Nokia N75 model and any other handsets that infringe on InterDigital patents. InterDigital separately filed a patent infringement lawsuit against Nokia in US District Court, in Delaware. Nokia said it would vigorously defend against both actions.

LG Electronics signed a five-year patent licensing agreement with InterDigital in 2006. The pact calls for the Korean manufacturer of consumer electronics and home appliances to pay InterDigital a total of $285 million in the first three years of the agreement, in annual installments of $95 million. Even more checks should be coming from

the Korean peninsula: An international arbitration tribunal awarded InterDigital $134 million in past royalties, plus interest, from Samsung Electronics. The amount of royalties is tied to the company's patent licensing agreement with Nokia.

In 2007 the company shortened its name from InterDigital Communications Corporation to InterDigital, Inc. The change was made in connection with a reorganization that saw the company shift from a pure R&D and licensing venture to one selling application-specific integrated circuits (ASICs) and making strategic investments, in addition to wireless communications research and technology licensing.

In 2008 InterDigital and Nokia entered into settlement talks on the patent issues, after a US District Court ruling went against InterDigital and the company was ordered to enter arbitration with Nokia. InterDigital appealed the court ruling, but also said it made "substantial progress" in privately resolving the dispute with Nokia.

Unable to reach a patent licensing agreement with Samsung Electronics, InterDigital filed a complaint against the giant Korean manufacturer with the US International Trade Commission. It also filed a lawsuit, in US District Court in Delaware, alleging patent infringement by Samsung's Blackjack mobile phone and other models. The $134 million award against Samsung was upheld by the US District Court for the Southern District of New York in 2007.

In late 2008 InterDigital reported reaching terms of a possible settlement with Samsung, including a royalty-bearing license for Samsung that would be in effect through 2012. The companies in early 2009 signed a licensing agreement that calls for the Korean giant to pay $400 million in royalties to InterDigital.

EXECUTIVES

Chairman, Steven T. (Terry) Clontz, age 60
President, CEO, and Director, William J. Merritt, age 52, $1,572,653 total compensation
CFO, Scott A. McQuilkin, age 56, $921,080 total compensation
EVP Intellectual Property and Chief Intellectual Property Counsel; President, InterDigital Patent Ho, Lawrence F. Shay, age 52, $1,054,742 total compensation
EVP Communications and Investor Relations, Janet M. Point, age 52
EVP Corporate Development, Mark A. Lemmo, age 53, $743,428 total compensation
EVP, IP Sales and Services, William C. Miller, age 56, $746,340 total compensation
EVP Research and Development, James J. (Jim) Nolan, age 51, $719,555 total compensation
VP Standards, Brian G. Kiernan, age 64
VP, Chief Accounting Officer, and Controller, Richard J. Brezski, age 39
CTO, Naresh H. Soni, age 52
Chief Administrative Officer, Gary D. Isaacs, age 51
Director Corporate Marketing, Jack Indekeu
Associate General Counsel, Jannie K. Lau
General Counsel and Secretary, Steven W. Sprecher, age 55
Director, Gilbert F. (Gil) Amelio, age 68
Auditors: PricewaterhouseCoopers LLP

LOCATIONS

HQ: InterDigital, Inc.
781 3rd Ave., King of Prussia, PA 19406-1409
Phone: 610-878-7800   **Fax:** 610-992-7842
Web: www.interdigital.com

2010 Sales

	$ mil.	% of total
Asia		
Korea	175.6	44
Japan	121.1	31
Taiwan	21.5	5
China	6.3	2
Canada	38.8	10
US	19.0	5
Germany	10.3	3
Other Europe	1.9	-
Total	**394.5**	**100**

PRODUCTS/OPERATIONS

2010 Sales

	$ mil.	% of total
Fixed-fee royalties	195.8	50
Per-unit royalties	133.1	34
Past sales	41.3	10
Technology solutions	24.3	6
Total	**394.5**	**100**

COMPETITORS

Alcatel-Lucent	LSI Corp.
Broadcom	Marvell Technology
Conexant Systems	Nokia
Freescale	QUALCOMM
Semiconductor	Sonics
IBM Microelectronics	ST-Ericsson
Infineon Technologies	Texas Instruments
Intel	Xora

HISTORICAL FINANCIALS

Company Type: Public

Income Statement

FYE: December 31

	REVENUE ($ mil.)	NET INCOME ($ mil.)	NET PROFIT MARGIN	EMPLOYEES
12/10	394.5	153.6	38.9%	300
12/09	297.4	87.3	29.4%	299
12/08	228.5	26.2	11.5%	379
12/07	234.2	20.0	8.5%	380
12/06	480.5	225.2	46.9%	343
Annual Growth	**(4.8%)**	**(9.1%)**	**—**	**(3.3%)**

2010 Year-End Financials

Debt ratio: 0.1%
Return on equity: 43.5%
Cash ($ mil.): 215.5
Current ratio: 3.47
Long-term debt ($ mil.): 0.2

No. of shares (mil.): 45.0
Dividends
Yield: —
Payout: —
Market value ($ mil.): 1,875.1

	STOCK PRICE ($) FY Close	P/E High/Low		PER SHARE ($) Earnings	Dividends	Book Value
12/10	41.64	13	7	3.43	0.00	7.84
12/09	26.56	17	9	1.95	0.00	3.92
12/08	27.50	51	28	0.57	0.00	2.03
12/07	23.33	89	43	0.40	0.00	2.89
12/06	33.55	9	4	4.04	0.00	5.24
Annual Growth	**5.5%**	**—**	**—**	**(4.0%)**	**—**	**10.6%**

InterMune

InterMune has found a good thing in interferon gamma. The company's sole marketed product is Actimmune (interferon gamma-1b), an FDA-approved treatment for two rare congenital disorders: chronic granulomatous disease, an immune condition; and osteopetrosis, a disease causing abnormal bone growth. Most of Actimmune's sales, however, are for off-label use of the drug to treat the deterioration of lung function from scarring caused by idiopathic pulmonary fibrosis (IPF). InterMune is developing another potential IPF treatment called pirfenidone, and it is also researching hepatitis C therapies with Roche.

The company at one time had a larger stable of marketed products and a wider development focus that included infectious disease and oncology. Since 2005, however, it has divested some assets and limited its development efforts to two main therapeutic areas: pulmonology (lung disease) and hepatology (liver disease).

Among its divested products are Amphotec (which it sold to Three Rivers) and hepatitis drug Infergen, which Valeant Pharmaceuticals bought and later sold to Three Rivers. InterMune also sold an investigational antibiotic called oritavancin to Targanta Therapeutics.

The company makes virtually all of its money from sales of Actimmune for a disease (IPF) for which it is not approved. It had been working on getting FDA approval for the indication, so that it could actively promote the drug for IPF. However, InterMune halted those efforts after a disappointing clinical trial result in 2007. The previous year it had ceased development on Actimmune as a possible treatment for ovarian cancer. Actimmune is distributed primarily through specialty pharmacies and other distributors (including CuraScript, Caremark , and Medco) who deliver the drug directly to patients.

Intermune is hoping to launch a new drug treatment called Esbriet in Europe in 2011. The company received backing in late 2010 from a European advisory panel (generally drugs that receive a positive opinion from such advisory panels later receive approval to market the drug). Esbriet is being developed for the treatment of idiopathic pulmonary fibrosis (IPF) — a rare, fatal ailment in which lungs suffer scarring due to unknown causes. In 2010, the FDA rejected the company's bid to get the drug approved in the US requesting additional clinical trials.

Investment firm Warburg Pincus owns nearly 20% of InterMune.

EXECUTIVES

Chairman, President, and CEO, Daniel G. (Dan) Welch, age 53, $2,204,420 total compensation
VP Sales, Terri Shoemaker
VP Sales and Marketing, Europe, Manuela Maronati
VP Marketing, Erik Harris
VP Sales and Marketing, Barrett McGrath
SVP Clinical Affairs and Chief Medical Officer, Steven B. Porter, age 54, $1,105,728 total compensation
SVP and Chief Regulatory and Drug Safety Officer, Marianne T. Armstrong Porter, age 56, $1,085,418 total compensation
SVP Human Resources and Corporate Services. Chief Compliance Officer and Associate General Counsel, Howard A. Simon, age 52
SVP General Counsel and Secretary, Robin J. Steele, age 55
SVP Finance and CFO, John C. Hodgman, age 56, $1,144,777 total compensation
SVP Clinical Science and Biometrics, Williamson Z. Bradford, age 49
SVP Research and Technical Development, Scott Seiwert, age 44
SVP EU Medical and Global Medical Advisor, Frank Weber

SVP and General Manager, Germany, Markus L. Dieken
SVP and Managing Director, Europe, Giacomo Di Nepi, age 55
Auditors: Ernst & Young LLP

LOCATIONS

HQ: InterMune, Inc.
3280 Bayshore Blvd., Brisbane, CA 94005
Phone: 415-466-2200   **Fax:** 415-466-2300
Web: www.intermune.com

2009 Sales

	$ mil.	% of total
US	25.2	52
Other countries	23.5	48
Total	**48.7**	**100**

PRODUCTS/OPERATIONS

2009 Sales

	$ mil.	% of sales
Actimunne	25.4	52
Collaboration revenue	23.3	48
Total	**48.7**	**100**

Selected Products

Approved
Actimmune (chronic granulomatous disease, osteopetrosis)
In Development
ITMN-520 (pulmonary)
Pirfenidone (idiopathic pulmonary fibrosis)
RG7227/ITMN-121 (hepatitis C)

COMPETITORS

Actelion	Novartis
Gilead Sciences	Pfizer
GlaxoSmithKline	Vertex Pharmaceuticals
Merck	

HISTORICAL FINANCIALS

Company Type: Public

Income Statement

FYE: December 31

	REVENUE ($ mil.)	NET INCOME ($ mil.)	NET PROFIT MARGIN	EMPLOYEES
12/10	259.3	122.4	47.2%	105
12/09	48.7	(116.0)	—	121
12/08	48.2	(97.7)	—	130
12/07	66.7	(89.6)	—	132
12/06	90.8	(107.2)	—	195
Annual Growth	**30.0%**	**—**	**—**	**(14.3%)**

2010 Year-End Financials

Debt ratio: 56.9%
Return on equity: 82.0%
Cash ($ mil.): 110.6
Current ratio: 4.30
Long-term debt ($ mil.): 85.0

No. of shares (mil.): 56.6
Dividends
Yield: —
Payout: —
Market value ($ mil.): 2,060.0

	STOCK PRICE ($) FY Close	P/E High/Low		PER SHARE ($) Earnings	Dividends	Book Value
12/10	36.40	23	4	2.13	0.00	2.64
12/09	13.04	—	—	(2.62)	0.00	(2.27)
12/08	10.58	—	—	(2.51)	0.00	(3.17)
12/07	13.33	—	—	(2.52)	0.00	(0.79)
12/06	30.75	—	—	(3.22)	0.00	(1.17)
Annual Growth	**4.3%**	**—**	**—**	**—**	**—**	**—**

International Rectifier

In electronics as in politics, power tends to corrupt. International Rectifier (IR) doesn't apply itself to matters of statecraft, but it has plenty of ideas about the performance of power in electronic gear. IR is a top maker of power semiconductors, which refine the electricity flowing into a device from a battery or a power grid, enabling more efficient operation. Its products — including MOSFETs (metal oxide semiconductor field-effect transistors), diodes, relays, and rectifiers — are used in appliances, automobiles, computers, communication devices, lighting and displays, gaming consoles, industrial motors, and military equipment. Nearly 60% of the global company's sales come from Asian customers.

The applications for IR's products require continual improvements in energy-efficiency and reductions in energy usage, especially for those used in auto, display, lighting, and aerospace products. In the case of products such as enterprise servers, switches, and storage equipment, power density — increasing the amount of power that can be provided in a small space — along with efficiency drive the customer's purchasing decision. IR has technical sales teams that work with customers in the initial design phase in order to align IR product development and technologies with the customers' long-term product needs. This drives the strategic development of the company, which is focusing on developing technologies around energy conservation and on improvements in thermal management, high frequency, and high voltage applications.

After weathering one of the worst slumps in the global economy in decades, in 2010 IR reported sales were up by 21% on an annual basis, as demand for its products increased. Specifically, though all product lines reported increases in revenues, sales of power management devices and enterprise power products were each up around 47%. The company's bottom line improved in 2010 as well, due in part to higher sales, lower operating expenses, and a large benefit from provision for income taxes. IR reported net income of $80.8 million in 2010, compared to a net loss of $247 million in 2009.

To keep up with increased demand, the company has taken steps to boost its manufacturing capacity. It reopened the parts of its fabrication facility in Newport, Wales, that were closed as part of its restructuring efforts, and delayed the closure of its El Segundo plant. The company has also made capital investments in its remaining factory locations and increased its use of contract manufacturing facilities. To deal more efficiently with cyclical fluctuations in demand, IR plans to use contract manufacturers to assemble at least 60% of its products.

The company made its first acquisition in years with a $75 million cash purchase of CHiL Semiconductor. The addition of the private company, a fabless manufacturer of digital power management chips, expanded IR's presence in the high-performance computing and graphics segments. In time, the company plans for CHiL to expand its capabilities in the server, storage and notebook computer markets.

In 2009 IR responded to the global economic downturn by announcing cuts of about 850 jobs from its payroll, an 18% reduction in force. Around 80% of the planned reductions were made in 2009, but higher demand required that the company re-tain some of its manufacturing personnel. The company also set plans to close its wafer fabrication facilities in El Segundo, California, and in Newport, Wales. IR has delayed the closure of those facilities until at least the second half of 2011.

IR sells through distributors including Arrow Electronics and Avnet, as well as directly to OEMs and contract manufacturers. Top customers include Robert Bosch, Honda, Flextronics, Samsung Electronics, Delta Electronics, IBM, Lockheed Martin, Raytheon, and Sony, among others.

HISTORY

Lithuanian native Eric Lidow came to the US and in 1947 founded International Rectifier (IR) with his father. The company provided diodes, rectifiers, and transistors for the US market and became the first to introduce silicon technology to Japan.

Even though it held many pioneering high-tech patents, IR stagnated in the mid-1970s. In 1976 Lidow's son Alex developed the HEXFET, an advanced metal oxide semiconductor field-effect transistor (MOSFET) that broke electrical current into smaller, more usable units. Alex and his brother Derek joined IR in 1977.

The Lidow brothers argued constantly over corporate strategy. After a reorganization had devolved operations into autonomous realms controlled by each brother, IR was reconstituted in 1992. It moved away from selling commodity components, and instead focused on developing a low-cost electric power conversion chipset.

Alex and Derek became co-CEOs in 1995, succeeding their father. In 1998, to settle a patent squabble, Unitrode released its rights as the exclusive licensee for IR's power MOSFET technology in return for a percentage of licensing profits. Fuji Electric and Samsung Electronics later licensed the technology from IR.

Derek resigned in 1999 and Alex took over as CEO. In 2000 IR acquired rival Zing Technologies for about $29 million. Over the following two years it completed a string of small, complementary acquisitions to round out its product lines.

Booming markets, along with a strategic emphasis on higher-margin proprietary products, helped IR achieve record sales and earnings for fiscal 2001. However, business conditions quickly turned dire, and a precipitous decline in the global electronics industry led the company to cut 500 jobs — about 8% of its workforce.

After weathering a dismal 2001 — one of the worst years ever for electronics makers — IR announced a flurry of small acquisitions in 2002 to round out its product offerings and enhance its production capacity. The company expanded production capacity when it bought the assets of European Semiconductor Manufacturing, including a manufacturing plant in Wales, for $81 million in cash. It also broadened its product range by acquiring a line of high-reliability power MOSFETs (used for aviation and military applications) from Fairchild Semiconductor for about $30 million, and by acquiring Philips Electronics subsidiary TechnoFusion (power management components for automotive electronics systems) for $50 million in cash.

In 2003 the company joined SANYO Semiconductor in forming IR-SA Integrated Technologies; the joint venture made energy-efficient motor power modules for use in consumer appliances and industrial applications.

The following year IR acquired the specialty silicon epitaxial business of ATMI for more than $40 million. Also in 2004 the company spent $40 mil-lion to double the production capacity of the plant in Wales and to increase the Welsh workforce by 120 jobs. IR recorded its first billion-dollar year for revenues.

Alex Lidow resigned as CEO and left the board in 2007, several months after an internal investigation uncovered accounting irregularities at IR's Japanese subsidiary. EVP Donald Dancer was named acting CEO.

In 2007 IR sold its Power Control Systems (PCS) business to rival Vishay Intertechnology for nearly $340 million in cash. A year later Vishay made claims against IR related to the PCS transaction and said it wanted to unwind the deal. (In 2009 IR and Vishay reached a settlement, with IR refunding $30 million of the purchase price.)

In 2008 rival Vishay offered to buy IR, a bid the company rejected. The IR board evaluated the unsolicited acquisition bid and unanimously concluded that the offer (for about $1.6 billion in cash) significantly undervalued the company. Vishay responded by increasing its offer to around $1.7 billion, which was also rejected. Vishay also put up three nominees for the IR board at the company's annual meeting; Vishay's nominees were defeated and it later terminated its tender offer for IR.

The company recruited Oleg Khaykin from Amkor Technology in 2008 to take over as president and CEO. Founder Eric Lidow retired as chairman and left the board later that year.

EXECUTIVES

Chairman, Richard J. Dahl, age 59
President, CEO, and Director, Oleg Khaykin, age 46, $1,231,798 total compensation
EVP and CFO, Ilan Daskal, age 46, $685,511 total compensation
EVP and COO, Michael Barrow, age 57, $654,828 total compensation
VP, General Counsel, and Secretary, Timothy E. (Tim) Bixler, age 44, $523,994 total compensation
VP Operations and Engineering, HiRel, John Conley
VP and General Manager, Automotive Products Business Unit, Henning Hauenstein
VP Sales and Marketing, HiRel, Fred Farris
SVP Worldwide Sales, Adam White
Marketing Engineer, Power Management Devices, George Feng
Product Marketing Manager, Enterprise Power, Cecilia Contenti
Product Manager, Elk Kabaker
Product Manager, Automotive Products, Marzak Li
Executive Director Corporate and Product Marketing Communications, Sian Cummings
Product Manager, Automotive Products, Benjamin Jackson
Executive Director Investor Relations, Chris Toth
Auditors: PricewaterhouseCoopers LLP

LOCATIONS

HQ: International Rectifier Corporation
233 Kansas St., El Segundo, CA 90245
Phone: 310-726-8000   **Fax:** 310-252-7903
Web: www.irf.com

2010 Sales

	$ mil.	% of total
Asia/Pacific	517.0	58
US	204.5	23
Europe	164.4	18
Royalties	9.4	1
Total	**895.3**	**100**

PRODUCTS/OPERATIONS

2010 Sales

	$ mil.	% of total
Power management devices	345.6	39
Energy-savings products	185.4	21
HiRel	153.2	17
Enterprise power	128.7	14
Automotive products	72.9	8
Intellectual property	9.5	1
Total	**895.3**	**100**

Selected Products
Diodes
HEXFET Power MOSFETs (metal oxide semiconductor
  field-effect transistors)
  Discrete MOSFETs
  Dual MOSFETs
  Intelligent power switches
  Relays
High-reliability devices
  Control integrated circuits
  DC/DC converters
  EMI filters
  High voltage gate drivers
  Insulated gate bipolar transistors (IGBTs)
  Motor control modules
  Power MOSFETs
  Rad Hard solid-state relays
  Schottky diodes
  Solid state relays
  Ultrafast rectifiers
Integrated circuits (ICs)
  Analog motion ICs
  Audio Drivers
  DC-DC regulators
  Integrated regulator
  Intelligent power modules
  Lighting ballast controllers
  Motion control ICs
  Motor control ICs
  Sensorless motor control
  Switching controllers
  Voltage regulators
Relays
  Photovoltaic relays
  Photovoltaic isolators

COMPETITORS

Advanced Analogic	IXYS
Technologies	Linear Technology
Aeroflex	Maxim Integrated
Allegro MicroSystems	Products
Analog Devices	Microsemi
Fairchild	Mitsubishi Electric
Semiconductor	Nat
Infineon Technologies	STMicroelectronics
Intersil	Vishay Intertechnology

HISTORICAL FINANCIALS
Company Type: Public

Income Statement
FYE: June 30

	REVENUE ($ mil.)	NET INCOME ($ mil.)	NET PROFIT MARGIN	EMPLOYEES
06/11	1,176.6	166.5	14.2%	4,920
06/10	895.3	80.8	9.0%	4,534
06/09	740.4	(247.4)	—	3,939
06/08	984.8	(62.6)	—	5,100
06/07	1,202.5	77.7	6.5%	5,500
Annual Growth	**(0.5%)**	**21.0%**	**—**	**(2.7%)**

2011 Year-End Financials

Debt ratio: —	No. of shares (mil.): 69.9
Return on equity: 12.3%	Dividends
Cash ($ mil.): 298.7	Yield: —
Current ratio: 3.53	Payout: —
Long-term debt ($ mil.): —	Market value ($ mil.): 1,955.1

	STOCK PRICE ($) FY Close	P/E High/Low		PER SHARE ($) Earnings	Dividends	Book Value
06/11	27.97	15	8	2.33	0.00	19.43
06/10	18.61	22	12	1.13	0.00	16.94
06/09	14.81	—	—	(3.42)	0.00	15.95
06/08	19.20	—	—	(0.86)	0.00	20.01
06/07	37.71	41	30	1.07	0.00	21.14
Annual Growth	**(7.2%)**	**—**	**—**	**21.5%**	**—**	**(2.1%)**

Intevac

Intevac's sputtering doesn't stem from a speech impediment. The company's Equipment division manufactures sputtering systems that deposit alloy films onto hard-disk drives; the films magnetize the drives and thus enable them to record information. The Equipment division also makes disk lubrication systems and sputterers used to make flat-panel displays. Intevac's Photonics division develops sensitive electro-optical devices used in night vision equipment and handheld materials identification instruments. Top customers include Seagate, Fuji Electric, Hitachi Global Storage Technologies, which collectively account for nearly 80% of sales. Customers located in the Asia/Pacific region make up nearly 75% of sales.

Like many suppliers of capital equipment, Intevac saw lower sales during the global economic downturn. The electronics manufacturing equipment industry is highly cyclical, and a down cycle that started in 2007 continued throughout 2009, affecting Intevac's sales. The company also has a highly concentrated customer base, and the disk drive industry has seen extensive consolidation in recent years.

Intevac's business improved as spending on computers by businesses and consumers drove up demand for hard disk drives. In turn, equipment makers began spending on equipment to add capacity and enable production of next-generation products. The company expects sales in its Photonics division to continue to rise as technology development yields products for the government, medical, scientific, inspection, and security industries. In 2010 Intevac's sales were up by more than 150% over 2009, with a more than 225% increase in equipment sales. Its Photonics division saw sales rise by nearly 30%. The company returned to profitability, after two years in the red, on the higher sales volumes and higher gross margins in 2010.

Looking to reduce its dependence on disk drive makers, as well as jump on the solar bandwagon, Intevac launched a thin-film solar cell manufacturing system, LEAN SOLAR, in 2009. The following year, it bought Solar Implant Technologies, whose technology can run on the LEAN SOLAR platform. Intevac also developed an etching system for the semiconductor production equipment market, the Lean Etch, which was formally introduced in 2007. Intevac stopped offering the Lean Etch in 2010. Instead, it is focusing its efforts on developing linear wafer handling systems for the semiconductor market.

When equipment sales are down, services become a more important part of a company's operations. Intevac's Equipment division provides services such as applications support, installation, training, and repair services, as well as spare parts and consumables, for its sputtering systems. The

company's former Imaging business — renamed Intevac Photonics — collaborates with research institutions, such as Stanford University and The Charles Stark Draper Laboratory, to perform research for the US government.

Intevac was spun out of the old Varian Associates (later split into Varian, Varian Medical, and Varian Semiconductor) in a 1991 LBO.

EXECUTIVES
Chairman, Norman H. Pond, age 72
President, CEO, and Director, Kevin Fairbairn, age 57, $645,602 total compensation
EVP Emerging Markets, Christopher Smith, age 51
EVP and General Manager, Intevac Photonics, Joseph (Joe) Pietras, age 56, $318,687 total compensation
EVP Finance and Administration, CFO, Treasurer, and Secretary, Jeffrey (Jeff) Anderson, age 49, $323,882 total compensation
EVP and General Manager, Hard Disk Equipment Products, Michael Russak, age 64, $301,740 total compensation
VP and General Manager, Intevac Vision Systems, Jerry Carollo, age 58
VP Engineering, Intevac Vision Systems, Dave Kelly, age 48
VP Manufacturing and Customer Support, James (Jim) Birt, age 46
VP Operations, Intevac Photonics, Timothy E. Justyn, age 48
VP Human Resources, Kimberly Burk, age 45, $208,874 total compensation
VP Technology, Equipment Products, Terry Bluck, age 51
COO, Luke Marusiak, age 48
Investor Relations, Claire E. McAdams
CTO, Intevac Photonics, Verle W. Aebi, age 57
Auditors: Grant Thornton LLP

LOCATIONS
HQ: Intevac, Inc.
  3560 Bassett St., Santa Clara, CA 95054
Phone: 408-986-9888   **Fax:** 408-988-8145
Web: www.intevac.com

2010 Sales

	$ mil.	% of total
Asia/Pacific	149.5	74
US	47.5	23
Europe	5.0	3
Other regions	0.5	-
Total	**202.5**	**100**

PRODUCTS/OPERATIONS

2010 Sales

	$ mil.	% of total
Equipment	168.2	83
Intevac Photonics	34.3	17
Total	**202.5**	**100**

2010 Sales

	$ mil.	% of total
Systems & components	184.2	91
Technology development	18.3	9
Total	**202.5**	**100**

Selected Products
Equipment
  Deposition equipment (LithoPrime tool for nano-
    imprint lithography)
  Disk lubrication equipment (AccuLuber, DLS-100)
  Disk sputtering equipment (200 Lean series, legacy
    MDP-250 series)
  Flat-panel display sputtering systems (D-Star series)
  Wafer handling system (Continuum vacuum wafer
    handling system)
Intevac Photonics

Digital enhanced night vision goggle (ENVG-D)
Handheld Raman materials identification instruments
  (PHARMA-ID, RAPID-ID, ReporteR)
Laser-illuminated viewing and ranging (LIVAR)
  systems
Low-cost, low-light-level cameras (NightVista)
Near-eye display systems (I-Port)
Negative-electron-affinity (NEA) electron sources
Photoluminescence solar cell inspection system
  (NanoVista)
Raman microscopy system (ExamineR)
Thin-film solar cell processing (LEAN SOLAR)

COMPETITORS

Ahura	Hamamatsu Corp.
Applied Materials	HORIBA
Aviza Technology	ITT Corp.
Canon	Lam Research
centrotherm	Mitsui
CMC Electronics	Northrop Grumman
DRS Technologies	Raytheon
e2v	Renishaw
FLIR Systems	Roper Industries
Goodrich Corp.	Roth
Halma	Tokyo Electron

HISTORICAL FINANCIALS

Company Type: Public

Income Statement
FYE: December 31

	REVENUE ($ mil.)	NET INCOME ($ mil.)	NET PROFIT MARGIN	EMPLOYEES
12/10	202.5	28.0	13.8%	445
12/09	78.0	(10.1)	—	370
12/08	110.3	(15.3)	—	394
12/07	215.8	27.3	12.7%	480
12/06	259.9	46.7	18.0%	540
Annual Growth	(6.0%)	(12.0%)	—	(4.7%)

2010 Year-End Financials

Debt ratio: —
Return on equity: 13.5%
Cash ($ mil.): 109.5
Current ratio: 5.19
Long-term debt ($ mil.): —

No. of shares (mil.): 22.6
Dividends
Yield: —
Payout: —
Market value ($ mil.): 316.0

	STOCK PRICE ($) FY Close	P/E High/Low		PER SHARE ($) Earnings	Dividends	Book Value
12/10	14.01	14	7	1.22	0.00	9.19
12/09	11.47	—	—	(0.46)	0.00	7.76
12/08	5.07	—	—	(0.71)	0.00	7.94
12/07	14.54	25	10	1.23	0.00	8.58
12/06	25.95	15	6	2.13	0.00	6.82
Annual Growth	(14.3%)	—	—	(13.0%)	—	7.7%

Intuitive Surgical

Intuitive Surgical is haptic to meet you. Employing haptics (the science of computer-aided touch sensitivity), the firm developed the da Vinci Surgical System, a combination of software, hardware, and optics that allows doctors to perform robotically aided surgery from a remote console. The da Vinci system reproduces the doctor's hand movements in real time, with surgery performed by tiny electromechanical arms and instruments inserted in the patient's body through small incisions. The company also makes the instruments and accessories used with its system. Intuitive Surgical sells its products in the Americas, Asia, Australia, and Europe through both a direct sales force and independent distributors.

The leading maker of surgical robots, Intuitive Surgical has seen strong growth as demand for less traumatic, minimally invasive surgical procedures has increased. Along with reducing trauma to the patient related to large incisions, robotic systems are also said to increase precision and reduce the likelihood of hand tremors by employing "motion scaling," which, among other things, uses a filter to reduce tremors that are naturally inherent in a surgeon's hands.

The da Vinci systems (which cost in excess of $1 million) are primarily used in prostate-removal surgeries and for hysterectomies, though the company is expanding its efforts to include other gynecological specialties including the removal of uterine fibroids.

The company historically focused its marketing efforts within urology and gynecology, however as advances in the technology have allowed, Intuitive Surgical expanded those efforts to include cardiothoracic, general surgery, and transoral (head and neck) procedures.

Intuitive Surgical has strategic alliances with a number of medical device businesses in the areas of product development, training, and marketing. Some of its alliances include those with Covidien, Olympus Corporation, and Johns Hopkins University, among others.

Part of the company's growth strategy is to introduce next generation versions of the original da Vinci system. Newer models build on the robot's core technology adding enhancements that include increased visual acuity and ease of use. The da Vinci Si provides physicians with HD imaging that is comparable to that of 1080i HD used in commercial televisions. The Si-e System is a 3-arm robot designed to deliver core da Vinci functionality and the ability to be upgraded to the Si model by adding a fourth arm and other enhancements.

In 2010 the company introduced the da Vinci Skills Simulator that incorporates three-dimensional, physics-based computer simulation technology to help surgeons hone their surgical skills using the device. The user navigates through the environment and completes exercises by controlling virtual instruments from the surgeon console. The suite of exercises includes novice, intermediate, and advanced levels. Upon completion of a skills exercise, the simulator provides a quantitative assessment of user performance based on a variety of task-specific metrics.

Capital World Investors and BlackRock combined hold about 17% of the company. Intuitive Surgical got a new CEO in early 2010 with the appointment of Gary Guthart, formerly president and COO, to the company's helm. Guthart replaced Lonnie Smith who became chairman of the board (Smith also holds about 6% of the company's shares).

EXECUTIVES

Chairman, Lonnie M. Smith, age 67, $4,180,542 total compensation
President, CEO and Director, Gary S. Guthart, age 45, $3,988,842 total compensation
EVP Worldwide Sales and Marketing, Jerome J. (Jerry) McNamara, age 53, $3,823,971 total compensation
VP Training and Development, Gene Nagel
VP Sales, US, Jim Alecxih
VP Intellectual Property and Licensing, Frank D. Nguyen
VP Strategy, Aleks Cukic
VP Finance, Benjamin B. (Ben) Gong
VP Product Quality, William C. Nowlin
VP Clinical & Regulatory Affairs, Karen Uyesugi, age 55
VP Marketing and Business Development, Frank P. Grillo
SVP Customer Support Group, Colin Morales
SVP Product Development, Dave Rosa
SVP Engineering, Salvatore J. (Sal) Brogna
SVP and CFO, Marshall L. Mohr, age 55, $2,164,921 total compensation
SVP and General Counsel, Mark Meltzer, age 61, $2,143,671 total compensation
SVP Product Operations, Augusto V. Castello
Auditors: Ernst & Young LLP

LOCATIONS

HQ: Intuitive Surgical, Inc.
  1266 Kifer Rd., Bldg. 101, Sunnyvale, CA 94086-5304
Phone: 408-523-2100   **Fax:** 408-523-1390
Web: www.intuitivesurgical.com

2010 Sales

	$ mil.	% of total
US	1,126.0	80
Other countries	287.0	20
Total	**1,413.0**	**100**

PRODUCTS/OPERATIONS

2010 Sales

	$ mil.	% of total
Product	1,189.1	84
Service	223.9	16
Total	**1,413.0**	**100**

Selected Products

da Vinci Surgical System (surgeon's console, patient-side cart, and InSite 3-D visualization system)
da VinciSi System (next generation version of da Vinci system)
da VinciS System (uses 3D and HD endoscopy)
Electrosurgical accessories
EndoWrist surgical instruments (scalpels, scissors, graspers)
Sterilization trays
Skills simulator
Ultrasonic energy instruments
Vision equipment

COMPETITORS

Accuray	Maquet
Bard	Medtronic
Boston Scientific	MicroDexterity
Curexo Technology	Olympus
Hansen Medical	Prosurgics
Hitachi	Stereotaxis
Integrated Surgical Systems	Toshiba

HISTORICAL FINANCIALS

Company Type: Public

Income Statement
FYE: December 31

	REVENUE ($ mil.)	NET INCOME ($ mil.)	NET PROFIT MARGIN	EMPLOYEES
12/10	1,413.0	381.8	27.0%	1,660
12/09	1,052.2	232.6	22.1%	1,263
12/08	874.9	204.3	23.4%	1,049
12/07	600.8	144.5	24.1%	764
12/06	372.7	72.0	19.3%	563
Annual Growth	39.5%	51.7%	—	31.0%

2010 Year-End Financials

Debt ratio: —
Return on equity: 18.7%
Cash ($ mil.): 279.8
Current ratio: 4.66
Long-term debt ($ mil.): —

No. of shares (mil.): 38.9
Dividends
  Yield: —
  Payout: —
Market value ($ mil.): 10,026.5

	STOCK PRICE ($) FY Close	P/E High/Low		PER SHARE ($) Earnings	Dividends	Book Value
12/10	257.75	42	26	9.47	0.00	52.38
12/09	303.43	52	14	5.93	0.00	39.93
12/08	126.99	70	22	5.12	0.00	32.39
12/07	323.00	97	23	3.70	0.00	23.26
12/06	95.90	74	45	1.89	0.00	15.96
Annual Growth	28.0%	—	—	49.6%	—	34.6%

Investors Bancorp

Apostrophe? Investors Bancorp don't need no stinking apostrophe. The firm is the holding company for Investors Savings Bank, which serves New Jersey and New York from more than 80 branch offices. Founded in 1926, the bank offers such standard deposit products as savings and checking accounts, CDs, money market accounts, and IRAs. Over the past few years, Investors Savings Bank has increasingly focused on commercial lending; its portfolio of residential mortgages has gone from more than 90% to around 60% of the bank's loan portfolio. Other offerings include commercial mortgages, multifamily loans, and construction loans. Mutual holding company Investors Bancorp, MHC, owns a majority of Investors Bancorp's stock.

Investors Bancorp has been growing through acquisitions. Its latest deal is the proposed acquisition of Brooklyn Federal Bancorp, which will add five branches in Brooklyn and Long Island, New York. The company entered New York in 2010 through its purchase of Millennium Bank, which had 17 branches in New Jersey, New York, and Massachusetts. (It sold the four Massachusetts locations to Rhode Island-based Domestic Bank after the deal closed.)

Previous acquisitions include the 2009 purchases of the five-branch American Bancorp of New Jersey and six branches in New Jersey from Banco Popular North America. Investors acquired New Jersey-based Summit Federal Bankshares and its five Summit Federal Savings offices in 2008. The company also opens new branches and lending offices to expand its operations.

EXECUTIVES

Chairman, Robert M. Cashill, age 68
President, CEO, and Director, Kevin Cummings, age 56
EVP and Chief Lending Officer, Richard S. Spengler, age 49
SVP and CFO, Thomas F. Splaine Jr., age 46
SVP; Manager Lending Administration, Debra A. Richardson, age 54
SVP; Summit Market Manager, William V. Cosgrove
Chief Accounting Officer, Kelly Pecoraro, age 42
SVP Accounting Special Project, Susan B. Olson, age 57
SVP; Director Corporate Services, Diane C. Kraemer, age 52

SEVP, COO, and Director, Domenick A. Cama, age 55
Auditors: KPMG LLP

LOCATIONS

HQ: Investors Bancorp, Inc.
101 JFK Pkwy., Short Hills, NJ 07078-2716
Phone: 973-924-5100   **Fax:** 973-924-5192
Web: www.isbnj.com

PRODUCTS/OPERATIONS

2011 Sales

	$ mil.	% of total
Interest		
Loans receivable and held-for-sale	383.5	84
Mortgage-backed securities	35.9	8
Municipal bonds & other debt	4.5	1
Other	4.8	1
Noninterest		
Net gain on sales of mortgage loans	12.8	3
Fees & service charges	8.7	2
Other	5.0	1
Total	**455.2**	**100**

COMPETITORS

Bank of America
Bank of New York Mellon
Center Bancorp
Citigroup
Fulton Financial
M&T Bank
New York Community Bancorp
OceanFirst Financial
PNC Financial
Susquehanna Bancshares

HISTORICAL FINANCIALS

Company Type: Public

Income Statement

FYE: June 30

	ASSETS ($ mil.)	NET INCOME ($ mil.)	INCOME AS % OF ASSETS	EMPLOYEES
12/10*	9,602.1	62.0	0.6%	892
06/09	8,136.4	(64.9)	—	705
06/08	6,419.1	16.0	0.2%	571
06/07	5,601.1	22.3	0.4%	510
06/06	5,497.2	15.0	0.3%	502
Annual Growth	15.0%	42.6%	—	15.5%

*Fiscal year change

2010 Year-End Financials

Equity as % of assets: 9.39%
Return on assets: 0.6%
Return on equity: 6.9%
Long-term debt ($ mil.): 1,826.5
No. of shares (mil.): 112.9

Dividends
  Yield: —
  Payout: —
Market value ($ mil.): 1,480.6
Sales ($ mil.): 455.2

	STOCK PRICE ($) FY Close	P/E High/Low		PER SHARE ($) Earnings	Dividends	Book Value
12/10*	13.12	26	19	0.56	0.00	7.99
06/09	9.20	—	—	(0.62)	0.00	7.14
06/08	13.06	105	76	0.15	0.00	7.67
06/07	13.43	80	65	0.20	0.00	7.64
06/06	13.55	242	165	0.06	0.00	7.74
Annual Growth	(0.8%)	—	—	74.8%	—	0.8%

*Fiscal year change

INX Inc.

INX knows the IT sector. The company primarily offers Cisco-based IT infrastructure services and related hardware and software to customers in the educational, governmental, and private sectors. Its services include network design, systems integration, consulting, IP telephony implementation, network security auditing, and data center virtualization. The company also sells, installs, and integrates network storage systems from EMC and NetApp and provides virtualization products from VMWare; those three partners account for 90% of INX's product revenue.

INX operates from about ten US states (with Texas as its largest market) and has plans to expand into additonal US markets. As part of that strategy in 2009 the company acquired the operations of Marketware, expanding its reach in Northern California. The previous year it acquired Albuquerque, New Mexico-based Network Architects, a provider of services for Internet protocol telephony and network infrastructure services. That year INX also purchased AccessFlow, a specialist in delivering VMware-based virtualization services.

INX had operated other business lines in the past but began to pare down those operations in order to focus on its IT services. The company sold its Valerent unit — an outsourcer of IT staff for infrastructure management functions such as help desk support and network management. In addition to the Valerent sale, INX also sold its Stratasoft subsidiary (which offered computer telephony integration software) and wound down other operations.

The company appointed Mark Hilz as CEO replacing James Long who became chairman. Previously a company board member in 1999 and 2000, Hilz most recently served as the company's COO.

EXECUTIVES

Chairman, James H. Long, age 52, $400,697 total compensation
President, CEO, and COO, Mark T. Hilz, age 52, $381,873 total compensation
VP Federal, David Peoples
VP Operations, Paul Klotz, age 49
VP Business Development; VP NetSurant, David DeYoung
SVP and CFO, Philip (Phil) Rydzewski
Controller and Chief Accounting Officer, Larry I. Lawhorn, age 58
Secretary, Joseph E. Horzepa
Auditors: Grant Thornton LLP

LOCATIONS

HQ: INX Inc.
6401 Southwest Fwy., Houston, TX 77074
Phone: 713-795-2000   **Fax:** 713-795-2001
Web: www.inxi.com

PRODUCTS/OPERATIONS

Selected Services

Applications and systems development and integration
Customer relationship management (CRM) systems
Customer service and support applications
Data center design
Enterprise application integration
Information technology (IT) consulting
Network and systems security
Network design and implementation
Network management
Web and network consulting and development

COMPETITORS

AT&T
Avaya
Computer Sciences
IBM Global Services
Integrated Archive Systems

Corp.
eOn
Genesys
Telecommunications
HP Enterprise Services

Perot Systems
Red River Computer
Unisys
Verizon

HISTORICAL FINANCIALS
Company Type: Public

Income Statement
FYE: December 31

	REVENUE ($ mil.)	NET INCOME ($ mil.)	NET PROFIT MARGIN	EMPLOYEES
12/10	312.0	5.4	1.7%	470
12/08	259.2	(12.6)	—	433
12/07	208.0	3.7	1.8%	342
12/06	156.0	1.2	0.8%	287
12/05	121.6	(7.9)	—	225
Annual Growth	20.7%	—	—	15.9%

2010 Year-End Financials

Debt ratio: 0.1%
Return on equity: 13.1%
Cash ($ mil.): 12.1
Current ratio: 1.30
Long-term debt ($ mil.): 0.1

No. of shares (mil.): 9.5
Dividends
  Yield: —
  Payout: —
Market value ($ mil.): 60.9

	STOCK PRICE ($) FY Close	P/E High/Low		PER SHARE ($) Earnings	Dividends	Book Value
12/10	6.40	13	8	0.54	0.00	4.29
12/08	4.30	—	—	(1.55)	0.00	3.84
12/07	10.45	33	16	0.47	0.00	4.27
12/06	7.86	51	31	0.16	0.00	3.43
12/05	5.55	—	—	(1.38)	0.00	3.01
Annual Growth	3.6%	—	—	—	—	9.3%

IPC The Hospitalist Company

IPC The Hospitalist Company (IPC) is on the leading edge of a growing US trend toward hospitalist specialization. The staffing firm provides about 1,230 hospitalists to more than 345 hospitals and 440 other inpatient facilities in 22 states. Hospitalists, or health care providers (physicians, nurses, and physicians assistants), oversee all of a patient's treatment from the beginning to the end of their stay. They answer questions and coordinate treatment programs to improve the quality of care and reduce the length of a patient's hospital stay. In addition to providing staff, the company offers training, information management services, and risk management services for its medical professionals and clients.

In addition to its staff of affiliated hospitalists, IPC also utilizes another 470 physician and non-physician providers as needed and contracts through nearly 200 independent contractors. Private-pay patients make up only 5% of the company's revenue; the remainder is attributed to Medicare (45%), Medicaid (6%), and other third-party payors (44%).

IPC has used part of its 2008 IPO funds to help pay off debt and acquire smaller regional hospitalist practice groups. In 2009 the company expanded into a new state territory by acquiring two hospitalist groups in New Jersey. Later that year it ac-

quired practices that opened additional new areas including Connecticut and Rhode Island. Texas is IPC's largest territory and accounts for more than 20% of the company's revenues.

In 2010 the company acquired Hospital Internists of Bristol, a Connecticut-based practice, that fit with its strategy of growing its business in New England. IPC is also working to expand in the Southwest and Southeast regions of the country. Purchases in 2010 added more than a dozen practices that, combined, represented about 700,000 annualized patient encounters in states that included Arizona, Missouri, Nevada, Tennessee, and Texas.

Acquisitions made in 2011 added approximately 193,000 annual patient encounters. These included practices in new areas of operation such as Southern California (Inland Hospitalist Medical Group in Riverside, California) and Orlando, Florida (Coast To Coast Physicians Alliance). Other acquisitions in established areas included Mid-Michigan Hospitalist Group (Grand Blanc, Michigan), North Florida Acute Care Specialists (Jacksonville, Florida) and five smaller practices in Arizona, Florida, Michigan, and Nevada.

Besides acquiring existing practice groups in new markets, IPC's strategy for growth includes offering its services to new institutions in areas where it already operates. In 2011, for example, IPC partnered with Northeast Hospital Corporation to provide services to two of its hospitals in Massachusetts. The company also sees room for growth by recruiting and training additional hospitalists.

EXECUTIVES

President, COO, and Director, R. Jeffrey Taylor, age 62, $1,048,798 total compensation
CFO and Secretary, Devra G. Shapiro, age 64, $986,943 total compensation
Chairman, CEO, and Chief Medical Officer, Adam D. Singer, age 51, $1,670,840 total compensation
EVP and Chief Development Officer, Richard G. Russell, age 51, $845,326 total compensation
VP Information Systems, Mark C. Citron
VP Physician Staffing, Timothy Lary
VP Health Services, Kathleen Loya
VP Medical Affairs, Felix Aguirre
VP Legal Affairs, Perri Melnick
VP Central Business Office, Fred Torres
VP Finance and Corporate Controller, Fernando J. Sarria
VP Financial Analysis & Revenue Controls, Jamie S. Glazer
VP Technology, Patrick Holmes
VP Marketing and Development, Todd Kislak
Executive Director, San Antonio Region, John Geanes
Executive Director, Phoenix Region, Saul Blair
Director Medical Affairs, Greg Harlan
National Executive Director, Corporate Development, David Arpin
Executive Director, Corporate Development, Marcie Matthews
Auditors: Ernst & Young LLP

LOCATIONS

HQ: IPC The Hospitalist Company, Inc.
4605 Lankershim Blvd., Ste. 617, North Hollywood, CA 91602
Phone: 888-447-2362   **Fax:** 818-766-3999
Web: www.thehospitalistcompany.com

PRODUCTS/OPERATIONS

2010 Employees

	% of total
Employed physicians	48
Non-clinical employees	31
Independent contract physicians	11
Nurse practitioners & phycician assistants	10
Total	**100**

Selected Administrative and Professional Services

Billing and collections
Compliance
Financial reporting
Information management system
Recruiting
Regional management
Risk management
Training
Transition management

COMPETITORS

Cogent Healthcare
EmCare
Emergency Medical Services
Hospital Physician Partners

MEDNAX
Schumacher Group
Sheridan Healthcare
Team Health

HISTORICAL FINANCIALS
Company Type: Public

Income Statement
FYE: December 31

	REVENUE ($ mil.)	NET INCOME ($ mil.)	NET PROFIT MARGIN	EMPLOYEES
12/10	363.4	24.3	6.7%	1,792
12/09	310.5	18.6	6.0%	1,673
12/08	251.2	13.6	5.4%	1,028
12/07	190.0	(0.9)	—	856
12/06	148.1	1.8	1.2%	757
Annual Growth	25.2%	91.7%	—	24.0%

2010 Year-End Financials

Debt ratio: —
Return on equity: 13.9%
Cash ($ mil.): 18.9
Current ratio: 1.59
Long-term debt ($ mil.): —

No. of shares (mil.): 16.3
Dividends
  Yield: —
  Payout: —
Market value ($ mil.): 635.4

	STOCK PRICE ($) FY Close	P/E High/Low		PER SHARE ($) Earnings	Dividends	Book Value
12/10	39.01	27	15	1.46	0.00	10.71
12/09	33.25	30	12	1.14	0.00	8.98
12/08	16.83	33	15	0.87	0.00	7.66
Annual Growth	52.2%	—	—	29.5%	—	18.3%

Iridium

If you want to make a phone call from the North Pole, you want Iridium Communications (formerly Iridium Satellite). The company offers mobile voice, data, and Internet services worldwide, targeting companies that operate in remote areas. While Iridium focuses on such commercial industries as energy, defense, maritime, and mining, its main customer is the US Department of Defense. Boeing primarily operates and maintains the Iridium satellite system, which consists of 66 low-earth-orbit satellites linked to ground stations (the world's largest commercial satellite operation). The company has operations centers in Arizona and Virginia.

Looking to expand its service area, Iridium established service in Mexico during 2009, forming a joint venture there with Spacenet Communications Services de Mexico. Iridium-branded satellite service is sold in Mexico by Spacenet and other resellers. The company is also pursuing regulatory compliance so that it can operate in Russia.

Iridium has slated the launch of new satellites for 2014 in order to replace aging equipment and boost its transmission capacity so that it can offer more and better services. The company's next system will be known as Iridium NEXT.

Iridium in 2008 agreed to an infusion of $500 million by an affiliate of investment bank Greenhill & Co. in order to fund a new fleet of satellites. The deal, which included about $131 million of debt, gave Greenhill a stake in the company. The company filed a public stock offering later that year, and changed its name to Iridium Communications Inc. in 2009. Greenhill and Baralonco Limited each own approximately 16% of Iridium.

The company paid just $25 million for the $5 billion Iridium global satellite phone system after the Motorola-led Iridium consortium failed to meet subscriber goals set by creditors and went bankrupt amidst much media attention in 2000.

EXECUTIVES

Chairman, Robert H. (Bob) Niehaus, age 55
CEO and Director, Matthew J. (Matt) Desch, age 53
CFO, Thomas J. Fitzpatrick, age 53
EVP Global Operations and Product Development, Iridium Satellite, John M. Roddy, age 56
EVP, Iridium NEXT, S. Scott Smith, age 52
EVP Government Programs, Iridium Satellite, John H. Campbell, age 63
EVP Global Distribution Channels, Iridium Satellite, Gregory C. (Greg) Ewert, age 49
EVP Marketing, Iridium Satellite, Don L. Thoma, age 49
Executive Director, Investor Relations, Steve E. Kunszabo
Director Corporate Communications, Liz DeCastro
Auditors: Ernst & Young LLP

LOCATIONS

HQ: Iridium Communications Inc.
1750 Tysons Blvd., Ste. 400, McLean, VA 22102
Phone: 703-287-7400   **Fax:** 703-287-7450
Web: www.iridium.com

2009 Sales

	$ mil.	% of total
US	35.8	47
Canada	10.2	13
UK	8.7	11
Other countries	21.2	29
Total	**75.9**	**100**

PRODUCTS/OPERATIONS

Selected Services
Aviation
  Flight communications
  Flight training
  Helicopter systems
Land Mobile
  Prepaid phone services
Maritime
  Crew calling (ship to shore calls for crew members)
Fax
  In network (calls between ships via Iridium's network)
  Long range identification and tracking

Ship safety and alert system
Vessel monitoring

COMPETITORS

Globalstar	LightSquared
ICO Global	ORBCOMM
Communications	Stratos Global
Inmarsat	TerreStar

HISTORICAL FINANCIALS
Company Type: Public

Income Statement
FYE: December 31

	REVENUE ($ mil.)	NET INCOME ($ mil.)	NET PROFIT MARGIN	EMPLOYEES
12/10	348.2	22.7	6.5%	174
12/09	76.0	(44.2)	—	166
12/08	10.7	—	—	109
12/01	85.0	—	—	100
Annual Growth	**17.0%**	**—**	**—**	**6.3%**

2010 Year-End Financials

Debt ratio: —	No. of shares (mil.): 70.3
Return on equity: 3.5%	Dividends
Cash ($ mil.): 119.9	Yield: —
Current ratio: 1.57	Payout: —
Long-term debt ($ mil.): —	Market value ($ mil.): 579.6

	STOCK PRICE ($) FY Close	P/E High/Low		PER SHARE ($) Earnings	Dividends	Book Value
12/10	8.25	36	20	0.31	0.00	9.33
12/09	8.03	—	—	(0.82)	0.00	8.94
12/08	9.00	241	213	0.04	0.00	5.57
Annual Growth	**(4.3%)**	**—**	**—**	**178.4%**	**—**	**29.4%**

ISTA Pharmaceuticals

ISTA Pharmaceuticals has set its sights on treating eye diseases. The pharmaceutical company has products in development and on the market. ISTA's marketed products include Bepreve (for itchy eyes associated with allergic conjunctivitis), Istalol (a glaucoma treatment), and Bromday (used for pain and inflammation following cataract surgery) in the US. Its drug Vitrase is a spreading agent that promotes absorption of injected drugs. The drug candidates in the company's pipeline include treatments for dry eye syndrome, ocular pain, and inflammation. ISTA has additional ocular and allergy treatments in research and development stages.

As a commercial-stage pharmaceutical company, ISTA is focused on bringing new products through the last stages of development and ushering them to market. The company gained FDA approval for and launched Bromday in 2010. The drug was a next-generation version of its Xibrom offering, allowing for once-daily inflammation treatment (as opposed to Xibrom's twice-daily regimen). Upon Bromday's acceptance in the market, ISTA stopped selling Xibrom in mid-2011. Another recently launched drug is Bepreve, which received FDA approval in 2009.

ISTA built up its sales organization during 2009 and 2010 to support the launches of these new drugs in the US market. Its marketing operations are targeted towards ophthalmologists, op-

tometrists, and allergists. Products are distributed through drug wholesalers, including McKesson, Cardinal Health, and AmerisourceBergen.

Additionally, the firm is developing Remura, a new treatment for dry eye disease. It is also investigating the active ingredient in Bepreve for use as a nasal spray to treat allergy symptoms. Other R&D areas include additional inflammation, allergic conjunctivitis, and age-related macular degeneration treatments.

The company has obtained the bulk of its pipeline candidates and eventual products through licensing agreements with Japanese firm Senju Pharmaceuticals. Through the agreements, ISTA covers the costs of developing and marketing the products in the US, and pays Senju fees and milestone payments.

In addition, ISTA typically doesn't handle its own manufacturing functions, leaving most of the production of its marketed products (and the active pharmaceutical ingredients or APIs, for those products) to contract manufacturers. For instance Senju supplies ISTA with the API for Bepreve, and Regis Technologies makes the API for Bromday. Bausch & Lomb makes the finished pharmaceutical products Bromday, Bepreve, and Istalol, while Alliance Medical Products makes Vitrase. ISTA opened its first manufacturing plant in 2010 and subsequently started making the API for Vitrase at that facility.

Venture capital firm Sprout Group (an affiliate of Credit Suisse First Boston) owns about 25% of ISTA.

EXECUTIVES

Chairman, Richard C. Williams, age 68
President, CEO, and Director, Vicente Anido Jr., age 58, $1,246,434 total compensation
VP Corporate Development and CFO, Lauren P. Silvernail, age 53, $560,923 total compensation
VP Sales and Marketing, Thomas A. (Tom) Mitro, age 54, $559,001 total compensation
VP Regulatory Affairs, Quality, and Compliance, Marvin J. Garrett, age 60, $546,509 total compensation
VP Legal and Chief Compliance Officer, Glenn E. Davis
VP Clinical Research and Medical Affairs, Timothy R. McNamara, age 55, $510,933 total compensation
VP Human Resources and Corporate Services, Kathleen McGinley, age 62
VP Operations, Kirk McMullin, age 58
Auditors: Ernst & Young LLP

LOCATIONS

HQ: ISTA Pharmaceuticals, Inc.
15295 Alton Pkwy., Irvine, CA 92618
Phone: 949-788-6000   **Fax:** 949-788-6010
Web: www.istavision.com

PRODUCTS/OPERATIONS

Selected Products
Bepreve (allergic conjuntivitis)
Bromday (eye pain and inflammation following cataract surgery)
Istalol (glaucoma)
Vitrase (spreading agent)

COMPETITORS

Allergan	Johnson & Johnson
Bausch & Lomb	Novartis
Inspire	Pfizer
Pharmaceuticals	

HISTORICAL FINANCIALS

Company Type: Public

Income Statement

FYE: December 31

	REVENUE ($ mil.)	NET INCOME ($ mil.)	NET PROFIT MARGIN	EMPLOYEES
12/10	156.5	(5.3)	—	326
12/09	110.6	(57.8)	—	315
12/08	83.1	(30.7)	—	225
12/07	58.9	(38.2)	—	222
12/06	33.0	(38.4)	—	198
Annual Growth	47.6%	—	—	13.3%

2010 Year-End Financials

Debt ratio: —
Return on equity: —
Cash ($ mil.): 78.8
Current ratio: 1.15
Long-term debt ($ mil.): 0.1

No. of shares (mil.): 33.6
Dividends
Yield: —
Payout: —
Market value ($ mil.): 172.3

	STOCK PRICE ($) FY Close	P/E High/Low	PER SHARE ($) Earnings	Dividends	Book Value
12/10	5.13	— —	(0.16)	0.00	(2.35)
12/09	4.56	— —	(1.74)	0.00	(2.34)
12/08	0.72	— —	(0.93)	0.00	(0.52)
12/07	4.90	— —	(1.29)	0.00	(0.04)
12/06	7.11	— —	(1.48)	0.00	(0.18)
Annual Growth	(7.8%)	— —	—	—	—

ITT Educational

To get a mortarboard from ITT, you may need to know a little something about motherboards. One of the largest US providers of technical education, ITT Educational Services offers mainly associate and bachelor degree programs to nearly 85,000 students at about 135 ITT Technical Institutes in roughly 40 states. Although the company is known for its technology-focused degrees in such areas as computer-aided design, engineering technology, and information technology, it has expanded its offerings to include degrees in business, criminal justice, design, and health sciences. Programs are offered through a combination of classroom and online instruction.

ITT Educational Services has not suffered as other companies have during the economic downturn, in fact, the company has been steadily growing its operations thanks in part to funding cuts at state universities. The combination of rising tuition costs and class shortages at those institutions is making career colleges a more attractive option for postsecondary education. ITT Educational Services is also benefitting from the poor economy, with many people who have lost jobs signing up to train for a new career.

In response to increasing enrollment rates, the company is expanding both the number and types of programs it offers. ITT Educational Services opened nine new campuses in 2010 and intends to open another 10 in 2011 at both its ITT Technical Institute campuses and its Daniel Webster College campuses, which owned by ITT Educational Services and are four-year colleges known for their aviation offerings. ITT Educational Services also added more than 300 additional program offerings at 90 campuses. ITT Educational Serv-

ices offers one or more of its online programs to students in 48 states and the District of Columbia.

The school adds new programs based on forecasted job trends. As demand for certain industries grows, ITT Educational Services adds programs and markets them at job fairs and the like to potential students. For example, as demand for health care workers has increased (and is expected to continue to increase thanks to aging Baby Boomers) ITT Educational Services has augmented its health and allied services degree programs with nursing and health information technology degrees. The same goes for criminal justice, which has seen a surge in popularity thanks in part to the current prevalence of reality forensics television shows. ITT Educational Services grew that program by adding cyber security and paralegal studies to its roster.

A substantial majority of ITT Educational Services students work at least part-time during their programs of study. Most students pay a large portion of their tuition and expenses with funds received under various government-sponsored student financial aid programs, especially Title IV Programs (federal student aid programs). About 60% of its revenues come from Title IV Program funds.

Wellington Management holds about a 15% stake in the company. Blum Capital Partners has about 14% and Lazard Freres another 13%.

EXECUTIVES

Chairman and CEO, Kevin M. Modany, age 44, $7,629,170 total compensation
EVP and Chief Administrative and Legal Officer, Clark D. Elwood, age 50, $1,828,590 total compensation
EVP; President, Online Division, June M. McCormack, age 62, $1,512,783 total compensation
EVP and Chief Marketing Officer, Glenn E. Tanner, age 63, $693,416 total compensation
EVP and CFO, Daniel M. Fitzpatrick, age 51, $1,794,617 total compensation
EVP and CIO, Martin Van Buren, age 43
EVP; President, ITT Technical Institute, Eugene W. Feichtner, age 55, $1,601,380 total compensation
VP Curriculum Development, Carol M. Shaffer
VP Marketing, Jill M. Minnick
VP, Assistant General Counsel, and Director Real Estate, Phillip B. Frank
VP Regulatory Affairs, Shawn J. Crawford
VP Finance, Gregory C. Wallis
SVP and Chief Compliance Officer, Jeffrey R. Cooper, age 58
SVP Business Development, David E. Catalano, age 44
SVP and Chief Academic Officer, P. Michael Linzmaier
SVP Operations, Barry S. Simich
SVP Human Resources, Nina F. Esbin, age 53
SVP, General Counsel, and Secretary, Christine G. Long
SVP, Treasurer, and Controller, Angela K. Knowlton
Auditors: PricewaterhouseCoopers LLP

LOCATIONS

HQ: ITT Educational Services, Inc.
13000 N. Meridian St., Carmel, IN 46032-1404
Phone: 317-706-9200 **Fax:** 317-706-3040
Web: www.ittesi.com

PRODUCTS/OPERATIONS

Selected Schools

School of Business
School of Criminal Justice
School of Drafting and Design

School of Electronics Technology
School of Health Sciences
School of Information Technology

Selected Programs of Study

Business Accounting Technology
Business Administration
Construction Management
Criminal Justice
Criminal Justice - Cyber Security
Data Communication Systems Technology
Digital Entertainment and Game Design
Electronics and Communication Engineering Technology
Graphic Design
Industrial Automation Engineering Technology
Information Systems Security
Project Management
Software Engineering Technology
Software Applications Development
Technical Project Management

COMPETITORS

Apollo Group
Bridgepoint Education
Capella Education
Career Education
Corinthian Colleges
DeVry
Education Management

Kaplan
Laureate Education
Lincoln Educational Services
SkillSoft
Strayer Education
UTI

HISTORICAL FINANCIALS

Company Type: Public

Income Statement

FYE: December 31

	REVENUE ($ mil.)	NET INCOME ($ mil.)	NET PROFIT MARGIN	EMPLOYEES
12/10	1,596.5	374.2	23.4%	11,100
12/09	1,319.2	300.3	22.8%	9,800
12/08	1,015.3	203.0	20.0%	8,580
12/07	869.5	151.6	17.4%	7,200
12/06	757.8	118.5	15.6%	6,200
Annual Growth	20.5%	33.3%	—	15.7%

2010 Year-End Financials

Debt ratio: 117.1%
Return on equity: 292.2%
Cash ($ mil.): 163.8
Current ratio: 1.16
Long-term debt ($ mil.): 150.0

No. of shares (mil.): 30.0
Dividends
Yield: —
Payout: —
Market value ($ mil.): 1,910.3

	STOCK PRICE ($) FY Close	P/E High/Low		PER SHARE ($) Earnings	Dividends	Book Value
12/10	63.69	11	4	11.17	0.00	4.27
12/09	95.96	17	11	7.91	0.00	4.42
12/08	94.98	21	8	5.17	0.00	4.86
12/07	85.27	36	18	3.71	0.00	1.77
12/06	66.37	26	20	2.72	0.00	2.51
Annual Growth	(1.0%)	—	—	42.4%	—	14.2%

Ixia

Ixia nixes network glitches. The company designs interface cards that transmit and analyze signals over fiber-optic and copper-line networks. Its equipment evaluates the quantity and speed of transmission of data packets, how many packets are lost during transmission, and whether the packets are received intact and in order. Ixia also designs chassis to hold the interface cards, and software to operate them. The company primarily serves network equipment manufacturers, service providers, and communications chip makers. Customers include Alcatel-Lucent, AT&T, Broadcom, Cisco (15% of sales), Ericsson, Intel, NTT, and Time Warner Cable. Ixia generates more than half of its sales in the US.

Revenue-wise, Ixia had been stagnant for years until 2010. The turmoil and uncertainty of the economy in the US and around the world has affected Ixia's business, like many companies, as capital spending on network infrastructure usually decelerates during downturns. The credit crisis made life difficult for the company's customers, partners, suppliers, and employees. Approximately 10% of the latter were shed in mid-2009.

The company made two acquisitions in 2009 that helped it reach record revenues in 2010. Ixia purchased the assets of Agilent Technologies' N2X Data Networks product line for about $44 million in cash. The purchase brought an intuitive and powerful user interface, as well as a customer base to open further markets in the Middle East and Asia/Pacific regions. Earlier in 2009 Ixia bought Catapult Communications for about $105 million in cash. The company sees Catapult's 3G and 4G wireless networking test products as complementary to its Internet protocol performance test systems and service verification platforms. In 2011 Ixia bought VeriWave, a performance testing company for wireless LAN and Wi-Fi enabled smart devices, for an undisclosed amount. The acquisition will help carriers, multi-system operators (MSO), and network equipment manufacturers to support media-rich applications running on wireless smart devices.

Ixia outsources it manufacturing operations to a third party in Malaysia. The company invests heavily in research and development, spending about 30% of its annual revenue on R&D. Founder, Chairman and "Chief Innovation Officer" Errol Ginsberg heads Ixia Labs, an incubator to develop new technologies. Ixia maintains overseas R&D facilities in India and Romania.

Laurent Asscher, the grandson of Chairman Emeritus Jean-Claude Asscher, owns 20.5% of Ixia. (Jean-Claude Asscher founded testing equipment company Tekelec). Bahamas-based investment firm Addington Hills Ltd. owns about 19% of the company's stock. Ginsberg has an equity stake of around 8%. Other institutional investors own 21% of the company.

HISTORY

Chairman Errol Ginsberg founded Ixia in 1997 "in rather humble digs above a Mexican restaurant" in Calabasas, California, about a hour north of Los Angeles. The company went public in 2000 in a $57.5 million IPO, but sales failed to top $100 million for three more years.

In 2003 Ixia acquired G3 Nova Technology, a developer of VoIP test tools for enterprise call centers, communications networks, and network devices, for about $12 million in cash and stock. Two years later it bought Communication Machinery Corp. (CMC), a developer of Wi-Fi network testing tools, for $4 million in cash.

In 2006 Ixia acquired the video telephony test products of Dilithium Networks for around $5 million in cash. With the acquisition, the company introduced a product based on the Dilithium Network Analyzer (DNA). The IxMobile Video Telephony test tools are focused on mobile wireless conformance, interoperability, capacity, and performance testing.

Atul Bhatnagar succeeded Ginsberg as CEO in 2007. Bhatnagar came from Nortel.

EXECUTIVES

Chairman and Chief Innovation Officer, Errol Ginsberg, age 55, $753,956 total compensation
President, CEO, and Director, Atul Bhatnagar, age 53, $1,409,058 total compensation
CFO, Thomas B. (Tom) Miller, age 55, $325,932 total compensation
VP Operations, Raymond de Graaf, age 44
VP Carrier Sales, Maik Lankau
VP Human Resources, Chris Williams, age 50
VP Global Customer Delight, Walker H. Colston II, age 50
SVP Corporate Affairs and General Counsel, Ronald W. Buckly, age 59, $737,235 total compensation
SVP Product Development, Victor Alston, age 39, $483,548 total compensation
Director Public Relations, Kelly Maloit
SVP Worldwide Sales, Alan Grahame, age 58, $457,268 total compensation
Auditors: PricewaterhouseCoopers LLP

LOCATIONS

HQ: Ixia
26601 W. Agoura Rd., Calabasas, CA 91302
Phone: 818-871-1800   **Fax:** 818-871-1805
Web: www.ixiacom.com

2009 Sales

	$ mil.	% of total
US	101.7	57
Other countries	76.3	43
Total	**178**	**100**

PRODUCTS/OPERATIONS

2009 Sales

	$ mil.	% of total
Products	142.9	80
Services	35.1	20
Total	**178**	**100**

Selected Products

Electrical and optical interface cards
Multi-slot chassis (metal cases that contain a computer, a power supply, and interconnect components; used to house interface cards)
Software
   Application-specific test suites
   System management applications

COMPETITORS

Agilent Technologies	JDS Uniphase
Anritsu	RADCOM
Azimuth Systems	Rohde & Schwarz
Digital Lightwave	Spirent
EADS North America	Sunrise Telecom
Test and Services	Tektronix
Emrise	Tollgrade
EXFO	Communications
Fluke Networks	

HISTORICAL FINANCIALS

Company Type: Public

Income Statement

FYE: December 31

	REVENUE ($ mil.)	NET INCOME ($ mil.)	NET PROFIT MARGIN	EMPLOYEES
12/10	276.8	11.2	4.0%	1,100
12/09	178.0	(44.2)	—	1,073
12/08	175.9	(15.9)	—	769
12/07	174.1	7.0	4.0%	756
12/06	180.1	13.5	7.5%	750
Annual Growth	**11.3%**	**(4.6%)**	**—**	**10.0%**

HOOVER'S HANDBOOK OF EMERGING COMPANIES 2012

2010 Year-End Financials

Debt ratio: 68.6%	No. of shares (mil.): 67.6
Return on equity: 3.8%	Dividends
Cash ($ mil.): 76.1	Yield: —
Current ratio: 4.07	Payout: —
Long-term debt ($ mil.): 200.0	Market value ($ mil.): 1,134.5

	STOCK PRICE ($) FY Close	P/E High/Low		PER SHARE ($) Earnings	Dividends	Book Value
12/10	16.78	109	41	0.17	0.00	4.31
12/09	7.45	—	—	(0.70)	0.00	3.75
12/08	5.78	—	—	(0.24)	0.00	4.31
12/07	9.48	121	82	0.10	0.00	4.61
12/06	9.60	76	35	0.20	0.00	4.48
Annual Growth	**15.0%**	**—**	**—**	**(4.0%)**	**—**	**(1.0%)**

Jaguar Mining

Jaguar Mining is on the prowl for gold in Brazil. The company operates three gold mines in the mineral-rich state of Minas Gerais that have proved and provable reserves of almost 900,000 ounces. A fourth mining project is in development, also in Minas Gerais. Once in production, estimated to be in 2011, the Caeté mine by itself will double the company's reserves. Jaguar Mining is also exploring the northeastern state of Ceará through a partnership with Xstrata.

EXECUTIVES

Chairman, Gary E. German
CFO and Treasurer, James M. Roller
President, CEO, and Director, Daniel R. Titcomb
VP, Corporate Development and Investor Relations, Robert C. (Bob) Zwerneman
VP, Exploration and Engineering, Adriano Luiz do Nascimento
COO, Lúcio Cardoso
Director of Communication, Valéria Rezen DioDato
Corporate Secretary, Robert J. Lloyd
Auditors: KPMG LLP

LOCATIONS

HQ: Jaguar Mining Inc.
125 N. State St., Concord, NH 03301
Phone: 603-224-4800   **Fax:** 603-228-8045
Web: www.jaguarmining.com

COMPETITORS

Amarillo Gold	Solitario Exploration
Aura Minerals	& Royalty
Kinross Gold	Yamana Gold
Rio Tinto Limited	

HISTORICAL FINANCIALS

Company Type: Public

Income Statement

FYE: December 31

	REVENUE ($ mil.)	NET INCOME ($ mil.)	NET PROFIT MARGIN	EMPLOYEES
12/10	170.8	(23.8)	—	1,788
12/09	140.7	(8.0)	—	1,535
12/08	93.7	(4.3)	—	1,328
12/07	47.8	(27.7)	—	996
12/06	21.2	(12.7)	—	680
Annual Growth	**68.5%**	**—**	**—**	**27.3%**

2010 Year-End Financials

Debt ratio: 43.6%

Return on equity: —

Cash ($ mil.): 39.2

Current ratio: 1.26

Long-term debt ($ mil.): 141.8

No. of shares (mil.): 84.4

Dividends

Yield: —

Payout: —

Market value ($ mil.): 601.6

	STOCK PRICE ($) FY Close	P/E High/Low	PER SHARE ($) Earnings	Dividends	Book Value
12/10	7.13	— —	(0.28)	0.00	3.85
12/09	11.19	— —	(0.10)	0.00	4.13
12/08	5.23	— —	(0.07)	0.00	3.07
12/07	11.95	— —	(0.52)	0.00	1.82
12/06	5.78	— —	(0.30)	0.00	1.87
Annual Growth	5.4%	— —	—	—	19.9%

Jazz Pharmaceuticals

Jazz Pharmaceuticals is anything but free-form or improvisational in its development of drugs to treat psychiatric and neurological conditions. The company markets a treatment for narcolepsy under the name Xyrem and a treatment for social anxiety and obsessive compulsive disorder (OCD) under the name Luvox CR. Jazz Pharmaceuticals has license and supply agreements with Abbott Laboratories and Elan Pharmaceuticals for Luvox CR. The company's research and development pipeline includes a potential treatments for epileptic seizures, as well as next-generation versions of Xyrem. Jazz Pharmaceuticals is merging with private drugmaker Azur Pharma to form Jazz Pharmaceuticals plc.

In 2011 Jazz Pharmaceuticals agreed to acquire Ireland-based Azur Pharma in an all-stock reverse merger transaction. Through the deal, Jazz Pharmaceuticals will essentially relocate its headquarters to Ireland by merging into Azur, after which Azur will change its name to Jazz Pharmaceuticals plc and take over Jazz's public stock listing. Existing Jazz Pharmaceutical shareholder will control 80% of the combined entity, which will continue to have US operations in California (where Jazz is currently headquartered) and Pennsylvania (where Azur has a location).

Through the deal, the company will gain Azur Pharma's portfolio of about 10 central nervous system and women's health medications including chronic pain medication Prialt, schizophrenia drug FazaClo, and menopause therapy Elestrin. The new entity will be able to better compete through its broader financial resources and the combination of Jazz and Azur's compatible development programs and marketing networks.

Jazz Pharmaceuticals had been exploring strategic options prior to announcing the deal following the FDA's rejection of its most advanced R&D candidate, JZP-6, which was being studied for the treatment of fibromyalgia. The company cancelled studies of JZP-6 in 2011 after the FDA rejected its application in late 2010 saying it required additional clinical testing. Other candidates in the company's pipeline include a treatment for patients who suffer from repetitive epileptic seizures called JZP-8 and a solid oral dosage form of the active ingredient in Xyrem called sodium oxybate. The future of JZP-8 could also be in jeopardy as Jazz Pharmaceuticals is evaluating the estimated costs, development timeline, and competitive environ-

ment for epilepsy treatments to determine whether to proceed with its development.

Jazz Pharmaceuticals is likely looking for ways to maintain the profitability it finally reached in 2010 after losing money every year previous to 2010 since the company's inception in 2003. Jazz Pharmaceuticals' profit was primarily driven by sales of Xyrem, which the company promotes in the US through its own sales force to neurologists, psychiatrists, and other specialists. Jazz Pharmaceuticals is highly dependent upon sales of Xyrem for its overall success (the drug accounted for 85% of its sales in 2010); unfortunately for Jazz Pharmaceuticals, another pharmaceutical company is seeking to market a generic form of Xyrem. Though Jazz Pharmaceuticals has sued for patent infringement, if a generic form of Xyrem is introduced to the market it could impact Jazz's new-found profitability.

As part of its FDA approval, Xyrem may not be sold through retail pharmacies and can only be distributed by a single central pharmacy. To support that requirement, Jazz struck an exclusive distribution agreement with Express Scripts' specialty distribution unit, making Express Scripts the company's largest single customer. The company licensed out the international rights to Xyrem to UCB, which markets the drug in about a dozen other countries, and Valeant Pharmaceuticals, which markets it in Canada.

As Jazz Pharmaceuticals makes plans to merge with Azur Pharma and evaluates the future of its pipeline of drug candidates, it also plans to continue with its historical pattern of developing drug new candidates in-house and acquiring them from other sources. It is also focused on promoting sales of its marketed products.

Kholberg Kravis Roberts owns about a quarter of the company's shares. The company's executive officers and board of directors combined also represent about a quarter of Jazz Pharmaceuticals' shares. Of them, board member Patrick Enright has about a 10% stake.

EXECUTIVES

Chairman and CEO, Bruce C. Cozadd, age 47, $649,018 total compensation

VP and Deputy General Counsel, P.J Honerkamp

VP Development Operations, Joel M. Rothman

VP Clinical Development and Scientific Affairs, Diane R. Guinta

VP Intellectual Property, Felissa H. Cagan

VP Manufacturing and Supply Chain Operations, Nandan Oza

VP Human Resources, Heather McGaughey

VP Sales, Edwin W. (Ed) Luker

VP Clinical and Experimental Medicine and Chief Medical Officer, Annette L. Madrid

SVP Product Development, Michael DesJardin

SVP and CFO, Kathryn E. Falberg, age 50

SVP, General Counsel, and Corporate Secretary, Carol A. Gamble, age 58, $457,205 total compensation

SVP Research and Clinical Development, Mark G. Eller

Senior Director Financial Planning, Analysis and Strategy, Shawn Mindus

SVP Sales and Marketing, Russell J. Cox

SVP Chief Regulatory Officer and Chief Compliance Officer, Janne L. T. Wissel, age 55

Auditors: Ernst & Young LLP

LOCATIONS

HQ: Jazz Pharmaceuticals, Inc.
3180 Porter Dr., Palo Alto, CA 94304
Phone: 650-496-3777   **Fax:** 650-496-3781
Web: www.jazzpharmaceuticals.com

2010 Sales

	$ mil.	% of total
US	169.3	97
Europe	4.2	3
Other regions	0.3	-
Total	**173.8**	**100**

PRODUCTS/OPERATIONS

2010 Sales

	$ mil.	% of total
Product sales	170.0	98
Royalties	2.6	2
Contract revenues	1.2	-
Total	**173.8**	**100**

Selected Products

Approved
  Luvox CR (obsessive compulsive disorder)
  Xyrem (narcolepsy)
In development
  JZP-6 (fibromyalgia)
  JZP-8 (epilepsy)
  Sodium oxybate (Xyrem, solid oral dosage form)

COMPETITORS

Cephalon

Eli Lilly

Endo Pharmaceuticals

Forest Labs

Novartis Corporation

Pfizer

Shire

HISTORICAL FINANCIALS

Company Type: Public

Income Statement

FYE: December 31

	REVENUE ($ mil.)	NET INCOME ($ mil.)	NET PROFIT MARGIN	EMPLOYEES
12/10	173.8	32.8	18.9%	242
12/09	128.4	(6.8)	—	228
12/08	67.5	(184.3)	—	216
12/07	65.3	(138.8)	—	409
12/06	44.9	(59.4)	—	185
Annual Growth	40.3%	—	—	6.9%

2010 Year-End Financials

Debt ratio: 80.6%

Return on equity: 107.3%

Cash ($ mil.): 44.8

Current ratio: 1.24

Long-term debt ($ mil.): 24.6

No. of shares (mil.): 40.0

Dividends

Yield: —

Payout: —

Market value ($ mil.): 786.4

	STOCK PRICE ($) FY Close	P/E High/Low	PER SHARE ($) Earnings	Dividends	Book Value
12/10	19.68	24 8	0.83	0.00	0.76
12/09	7.88	— —	(0.23)	0.00	(2.33)
12/08	1.93	— —	(7.19)	0.00	(3.23)
12/07	14.70	— —	(10.04)	0.00	2.24
Annual Growth	10.2%	— —	—	—	(30.1%)

JDA Software

JDA Software Group supplies the links in the supply chain. The company's supply and demand optimization (SDO) software helps retailers and other businesses manage supply and demand chains, as well as business processes ranging from planning and forecasting to e-commerce and store operations. The company also offers point-of-sale applications to handle back-office functions, including inventory management, receipts, and returns. Other products include analytic applications for decision support and collaborative tools for maintaining product and catalog information with partners, distributors, and suppliers. JDA boasts more than 6,000 customers, including Dr Pepper Snapple Group, Kraft Foods and OfficeMax.

JDA's business is divided into three segments: Retail, Manufacturing and Distribution, and Services Industries. Its Retail segment provides software that enables large retail chains to manage merchandise, supply chains, and inventory across their organizations, as well as tools that help manage point-of-sale, scheduling, and back-office functions at the level of individual stores.

Manufacturing and Distribution serves auto makers, consumer goods manufacturers, oil and gas companies, technology providers, and aerospace and defense contractors.

Services Industries caters to businesses involved in the hospitality, media, telecommunications, transportation, and travel segments.

JDA has pursued acquisitions as a means of growing its business and staying competitive in a consolidating market. It acquired rival Manugistics Group for about $213 million in cash in 2006. The purchase moved JDA beyond retail, expanding its offerings for consumer goods manufacturers and wholesale distributors, and creating its Services Industries segment. In 2008 the company agreed to acquire competitor i2 Technologies for $346 million in cash. JDA later requested a renegotiation of the purchase price, but i2 terminated the merger agreement. In 2009 the two companies would once again return to the negotiating table, with i2 agreeing to be acquired for about $604 million in cash and stock. The transaction was completed in 2010.

In 2009 the company expanded its presence into Germany and Eastern Europe after acquiring a 49% equity interest in Strategix Enterprise Technology's businesses in Germany and Poland.

HISTORY

James Armstrong and Frederick Pakis founded JDA Software Group in 1985. The next year the company released MMS, a retail software package based on the IBM AS/400 platform.

In 1994 JDA acquired DSS, an in-store system from JDA Canada (a software development company formed by Armstrong in 1978 and sold in 1987), and began developing open-platform products.

Armstrong and Pakis, who had served since the company's founding as CEO and president, respectively, passed the helm to COO Brent Lippman in 1997 and became co-chairmen. That year the company released an in-store Windows-based system (Win/DSS) and a data warehouse system (Retail IDEAS). It gained a warehouse automation and management system that year when it acquired LIOCS Corporation.

JDA in 1998 acquired the Arthur Retail business unit, a maker of retail decision support software, from financial analysis software specialist Comshare. The purchase helped cause losses at JDA for the year, and prompted the return of Pakis and Armstrong to the co-CEO and chairman posts in 1999. The two closed unprofitable locations and cut more than 50 employees before Pakis turned over full CEO duties to Armstrong.

In 2000 JDA purchased Sweden-based space management specialist Intactix. Pakis retired as co-chairman later that year. Growth in sales of the company's software licenses, coupled with in-

creased international sales (especially in Asia) led the company back into the black for 2000. The next year JDA bought inventory management software maker E3 for about $50 million.

In 2003 Armstrong stepped down as CEO, but remained chairman. Hamish Brewer, who had served as the company's president since 2001, became CEO.

Also in 2003, the company acquired the assets of Engage, a provider of content management software for multi-channel marketing. The following year JDA bought the assets of integrated workforce management software maker Timera Retail Solutions for $13 million. The transaction adds Web-based labor management.capabilities — such as scheduling and budgeting, time and attendance, and demand forecasting — to the JDA portfolio. Plans to acquire e-commerce technology provider QRS for $100 million in 2004 were terminated after two other suitors got into the game with more attractive takeover offers. The company announced plans to cut staff and consolidate its product line in 2004, when it launched PortfolioEnabled.

EXECUTIVES

Chairman, James D. Armstrong, age 60
President, CEO, and Director, Hamish N. Brewer, age 48, $2,380,016 total compensation
EVP Prodct Development and Management, David R. (Dave) King, age 66
EVP and CFO, Peter S. (Pete) Hathaway, age 55, $1,561,848 total compensation
EVP Sales and Marketing, Thomas (Tom) Dziersk, age 47, $962,077 total compensation
SVP Marketing, Heather Loisel
SVP Manufacturing, Kelly Thomas
SVP Support, Kenneth Williams
SVP Retail, Wayne J. Usie, age 44
SVP, CSG, Duane A. Kotsen, age 47
SVP Human Resources, Brian P. Boylan, age 50
Regional VP Services Industries, Andy Archer
Group VP and CIO, Mark Geninatti
Regional VP Center of Excellence, Salil Joshi
Regional VP Asia Pacific, Stephen McNulty
GVP Treasury and Investor Relations, Mike Burnett
Director Corporate Communications, Beth Elkin
SVP, General Counsel, and Secretary, G. Michael Bridge, age 47
SVP and CTO, i2, Aditya Srivastava, age 53
SVP Supply Chain, David J. Johnston, age 48
Auditors: Deloitte & Touche LLP

LOCATIONS

HQ: JDA Software Group, Inc.
 14400 N. 87th St., Scottsdale, AZ 85260-3649
Phone: 480-308-3000   **Fax:** 480-308-3001
Web: www.jda.com

2009 Sales

	$ mil.	% of total
Americas	264.7	69
Europe	82.0	21
Asia/Pacific	39.1	10
Total	**385.8**	
100		

PRODUCTS/OPERATIONS

2009 Sales

	$ mil.	% of total
Retail	209.7	54
Manufacturing & Distribution	144.7	37
Services Industries	31.4	9
Total	**385.8**	**100**

COMPETITORS

Aldata	RedPrairie
Alphameric	Retail Pro
Kronos	Retalix
Manhattan Associates	SAP
Micro Strategies	SAS Institute
MICROS Systems	SymphonyIRI
Oracle	Tomax
Radiant Systems	VeriFone

HISTORICAL FINANCIALS

Company Type: Public

Income Statement

FYE: December 31

	REVENUE ($ mil.)	NET INCOME ($ mil.)	NET PROFIT MARGIN	EMPLOYEES
12/10	617.2	17.7	2.9%	3,000
12/09	385.8	26.3	6.8%	1,847
12/08	390.3	3.1	0.8%	1,718
12/07	373.6	26.5	7.1%	1,596
12/06	277.5	(0.4)	—	1,701
Annual Growth	**22.1%**	—	—	**15.2%**

2010 Year-End Financials

Debt ratio: 43.7%	No. of shares (mil.): 41.9
Return on equity: 2.8%	Dividends
Cash ($ mil.): 171.6	Yield: —
Current ratio: 1.97	Payout: —
Long-term debt ($ mil.): 272.7	Market value ($ mil.): 1,173.9

	STOCK PRICE ($) FY Close	P/E High/Low		PER SHARE ($) Earnings	Dividends	Book Value
12/10	28.00	76	49	0.42	0.00	14.89
12/09	25.47	53	18	0.50	0.00	11.91
12/08	13.13	233	112	0.09	0.00	10.99
12/07	20.46	34	18	0.76	0.00	11.13
12/06	13.77	—	—	(0.39)	0.00	9.90
Annual Growth	**19.4%**	—	—	—	—	**10.7%**

JDS Uniphase

JDS Uniphase (JDSU) is drawn to the warming glow of optical networks. Its Communications Test and Measurement division makes instruments and test tools used in optical and data networks, DSL services, cable networks, and digital video broadcast equipment. The Communications and Commercial Optical Communications unit produces optical transmission and transport products, lasers, and photovoltaic cells and receivers sold to makers of network and other equipment. Advanced Optical Technologies makes optical coating and holographic technologies to protect documents, transaction cards, and consumer electronics against counterfeiting. JDSU sells to the networking, communications, medical, aerospace, and defense markets.

The company's customers include some of the world's largest communications service providers, as well as OEMs, large corporate customers, and government organizations. Customers include AT&T, Alcatel-Lucent, Ciena, Cisco Systems, Ericsson, Hewlett-Packard, IBM, and TimeWarner. While its Communications Test and Measurement and Communications and Commercial Optical Communications businesses share many of the same customers, the company's Advanced Optical Technologies unit sells to a broader range of markets, with customers that include 3M, Lockheed Martin, MasterCard, and Dolby. Governments worldwide use JDSU's custom pigments and holograms to protect currency from counterfeiting.

Net revenue rose more than 32% in fiscal 2011 over the previous year thanks in part to strong demand for some specific products, including pluggables, high-powered lasers, modulators, tunables, reconfigurable optical add/drop multiplexers, commercial lasers, circuit packs, and gesture recognition and transaction card products.

Contracting out production, especially to facilities in Shenzhen, China, is key a part of JDSU's cost-cutting strategy. As part of another strategy, the acquisitive company continues to make select acquisitions that complement or add to its product lines and markets. For its international strategy, JDSU is developing products specific to regions it has identified as having the greatest growth potential: Asia/Pacific, Latin America, and Eastern Europe. As an example of that trend JDSU began making high-precision optical coatings at a Chinese factory in fiscal 2011.

JDSU plans to develop business for the Communications Test and Measurement division by targeting network operators with products that lower expenses and provide other services. JDSU's more general strategy for its Communications and Commercial Optical Products segment includes developing more business for optical communications by partnering with network equipment manufacturers, partnering with OEMs for its laser business, and targeting the solar-power market to drive up more sales of photonic power and photovoltaic products. Advanced Optical Technologies is specifically developing thin-film coating processes, as well as more generally focusing on its operations in optics, light management, and material technology to develop products.

In 2010 the company purchased the Network Solutions business of Agilent Technologies for $165 million in cash. The acquisition brings network protocol test and drive test products to the company and gives JDSU a market lead in wireless test instruments and systems. JDS Uniphase cites Network Solutions as an important factor in fiscal 2011's good sales results.

HISTORY

Engineer Dale Crane was already making helium neon lasers in his garage when he left laser developer Spectra-Physics in 1979 to start Uniphase. Initially the company developed and marketed gas laser subsystems to manufacturers of biomedical, industrial process control, and printing equipment. In 1992 Demax Software executive Kevin Kalkhoven became CEO, and Uniphase formed Ultrapointe, introducing the Ultrapointe laser imaging system for semiconductor production the following year. Expenses related to a gas laser subsystem patent-infringement suit filed by Spectra-Physics caused losses in 1993, the year Uniphase went public.

In the mid-1990s Uniphase began to use acquisitions to expand its market share and consolidate product lines. In 1995 the company bought optical components supplier United Technologies Photonics from United Technologies, entering the telecom market.

In 1997 it bought IBM's laser business and Australia-based Indx, a maker of reflection filters used to increase the carrying capacity of a fiber-optic strand. Uniphase's 1998 acquisitions included Philips Optoelectronics (semiconductor lasers) and Broadband Communications Products (fiber-optic transmitters and receivers). The company sold its

Ultrapointe unit to chip equipment maker KLA-Tencor late that year. The acquisition spree contributed to losses for fiscal 1997 and 1998.

In 1999 Uniphase merged with JDS FITEL, a Canada-based maker of fiber-optic communications gear, in a $7 billion deal. JDS FITEL, founded in 1981 by four Nortel engineers, focused on making so-called "passive" fiber-optic components that route and manipulate optical signals. It was a complementary fit to Uniphase's "active" gear that generates and transmits signals. The combined company named itself JDS Uniphase. Both JDS FITEL and Uniphase aggressively pursued acquisitions prior to the merger, and JDS Uniphase continued shopping.

In fiscal 2000, following a huge run-up in its share price, JDS Uniphase made 10 acquisitions, including EPITAXX (optical detectors and receivers) and Optical Coating Laboratory. Its largest acquisition was of rival E-Tek Dynamics (for $20.4 billion), which JDSU used to further increase its capacity to produce passive components such as amplifiers and better equip itself to offer customers complete optical systems. That year Kalkhoven retired, and co-chairman Jozef Straus (former CEO of JDS FITEL) was named as his replacement.

In 2001 JDSU bought rival SDL, a maker of equipment that lets customers send multiple light signals over a single fiber, in a $17 billion stock deal. The company sold a Zurich-based pump laser manufacturing plant to Nortel to gain regulatory approval for the SDL buy. JDS Uniphase faced a sharp drop in sales following the spending spree it used to build a presence in the optical telecommunications equipment market. In 2001 the company began a monumental restructuring program intended to offset massive losses of more than $56 billion brought on by a collapse of the global telecom market. JDSU subsequently cut its workforce by nearly three-quarters and shut down redundant operations and non-essential facilities. It closed more than 50 facilities worldwide, most of them in North America.

The company bought IBM's optical transceiver business in 2002; it also bought optical device startup Scion Photonics. Straus stepped down as CEO in 2003; director Kevin Kennedy took over as chief. Also that year, JDSU sold its MEMS (microelectromechanical systems) business, which made silicon chips with tiny movable mirrors used to direct light in fiber-optic networks, for about $4 million; JDSU paid 140 times that amount for the technology in 2000.

In 2004 JDSU bought datacom transceiver maker E2O Communications for about $60 million. Early the following year it acquired commercial laser provider Lightwave Electronics for $65 million in cash. Soon after it purchased network test and management systems provider Acterna for approximately $760 million in cash and stock. JDSU also acquired Photonic Power Systems, a developer of components used to transmit power over fiber optics, and laser component maker Agility Communications.

In 2007 the company acquired Picolight for about $115 million in stock, plus an earnout payment of up to $10 million in cash. Picolight, which makes optical pluggable transceivers, became part of the Optical Communications business.

Kevin Kennedy resigned as president and CEO in 2008, after the perennially unprofitable company reported yet another quarterly loss. While quitting his executive posts at the end of the year, following five years as chief executive, Kennedy remained on the JDSU board as vice chairman. He left to become president and CEO of Avaya.

Also in 2008 JDSU acquired American Bank Note Holographics (ABNH) for about $138 million in cash and stock. The purchase strengthened its position in security products for brand protection and expanded its position into security products for transaction card-based commerce. ABNH became part of JDSU's Advanced Optical Technologies business segment.

In 2009 JDSU bought the Network Tools business of archrival Finisar, a maker of fiber-optic subsystems, for about $40 million in cash; the business added storage area network test tools and software, and became the storage network test unit in JDSU's Communications Test and Measurement business.

Hurt in part by Nortel's bankruptcy protection filing, JDSU sold its factory in Shenzhen, China, to Sanmina-SCI in 2009. The transfer allowed the company to shed about 2,000 workers from its payroll. Sanmina-SCI was set to provide electronics manufacturing services to JDSU.

EXECUTIVES

Chairman, Martin A. (Marty) Kaplan, age 73
President, CEO, and Director, Thomas H. (Tom) Waechter, age 58, $2,317,662 total compensation
President, Communications Test and Measurement Business Segment, David W. Heard, age 40
EVP and CFO, David W. Vellequette, age 54, $1,050,526 total compensation
EVP; President, Communications and Commercial Optical Products, Alan S. Lowe, age 48, $1,998,261 total compensation
VP Global Services, Communications Test and Measurement Business, David Opsahl
VP and General Manager, Commercial Lasers, Ken Lo
VP and General Manager, Communications Test and Measurement Business, Lars Friedrich
Vice Chairman, Kevin J. Kennedy, age 55, $5,945,954 total compensation
Head of Executive Operations, Judith Kay
SVP Information Technology, John Rough
SVP Emerging Markets and Strategic Projects, David (Dave) Holly, age 45, $1,157,630 total compensation
SVP Communications Test and Measurement Business, Jerry Gentile
SVP Communcations Test and Measurement Business, Tom Smith
SVP Advanced Optical Technologies Products, Roy W. Bie, age 53, $886,565 total compensation
SVP Sales, Communications Test and Measurement Business, Bart Freedman
Media and Industry Analyst Relations, Noel Bilodeau
CTO, Optical Communications, Brandon Collings
Director Marketing, Authentication Solutions, Advanced Optical Technologies Business, Adam Scheer
Media Relations, Bernie Tylor
Senior Director Corporate Marketing and Communications, Jim Monroe
Director Marketing, Optical Components and Integrated Modules, CCOP, Toby Strite
Investor Relations, Michelle Levine
Human Resources, Brett Hooper, age 48
Product Manager, Custom Color Solutions, AOT, John Book
Industry Analyst Relations, Nick Rowan
Regional VP, Communications Test and Measurement Business, EMEA, Manuel Mato
General Manager, Communications Test and Management Business, Enzo di Luigi
Auditors: Ernst & Young LLP

LOCATIONS

HQ: JDS Uniphase Corporation
430 N. McCarthy Blvd., Milpitas, CA 95035
Phone: 408-546-5000   **Fax:** 408-546-4300
Web: www.jdsu.com

2010 Sales

	$ mil.	% of total
Americas	877.6	49
Europe	475.5	26
Asia/Pacific	451.4	25
Total	**1,804.5**	**100**

PRODUCTS/OPERATIONS

2011 Sales

	$ mil.	% of total
Communications Test & Measurement	803.0	44
Communications & Commercial Optical Products	770.8	43
Advanced Optical Technologies	230.7	13
Total	**1,804.5100**	**Selected**

Products
Optical Communications
  Components
    High-power pump lasers
    Modulators
    Switches and attenuators
    Wavelength division multiplexing couplers, filters, isolators, and circulators
  Modules and subsystems
    Agile optical amplifiers
    Agile optical switches
    Agile transmission modules
    Optical channel monitors
    Optical layer subsystems
    Transceivers and transponders
    Transmitters
Communications Test & Measurement
  Communications test and monitoring instruments
  Network test and management systems
Advanced Optical Technologies
  Custom optics
  Decorative products
  Document authentication and brand protection
Lasers
  Argon ion lasers
  Diode-pumped solid-state lasers
  Fiber lasers
  Helium-neon lasers
  Industrial diode lasers
  Photonic power products

COMPETITORS

Anritsu	FUJIFILM
Apogee Enterprises	Fujitsu
Asahi Glass	Furukawa Electric
Avago Technologies	IPG Photonics
BASF SE	Merck KGaA
Coherent, Inc.	Mitsubishi Electric
Cymer	MRV Communications
Deposition Sciences	Newport Corp.
EMCORE	Nikon
EXFO	Spirent
Finisar	

HISTORICAL FINANCIALS

Company Type: Public

Income Statement

FYE: June 30

	REVENUE ($ mil.)	NET INCOME ($ mil.)	NET PROFIT MARGIN	EMPLOYEES
06/11	1,804.5	71.6	4.0%	5,000
06/10	1,363.9	(61.8)	—	4,700
06/09	1,294.4	(866.4)	—	4,000
06/08	1,530.1	(21.7)	—	7,100
06/07	1,396.8	(26.3)	—	7,000
Annual Growth	**6.6%**	**—**	**—**	**(8.1%)**

2011 Year-End Financials

Debt ratio: 26.8%
Return on equity: 6.7%
Cash ($ mil.): 395.4
Current ratio: 3.12
Long-term debt ($ mil.): 285.8

No. of shares (mil.): 227.0
Dividends
  Yield: —
  Payout: —
Market value ($ mil.): 3,781.5

	STOCK PRICE ($) FY Close	P/E High/Low		PER SHARE ($) Earnings	Dividends	Book Value
06/11	16.66	94	29	0.31	0.00	4.69
06/10	9.84	—	—	(0.28)	0.00	4.21
06/09	5.72	—	—	(4.02)	0.00	4.05
06/08	11.36	—	—	(0.10)	0.00	8.09
06/07	13.43	—	—	(0.12)	0.00	8.14
Annual Growth	**5.5%**	**—**	**—**	**—**	**—**	**(12.9%)**

JMP Group

JMP Group wants to get the jump on the competition. Positioning itself as an alternative to bulge-bracket firms, the company provides investment banking services such as strategic advice, corporate finance, and equity underwriting, sales, trading, and research to small and midsized growth companies. It focuses on the technology, health care, consumer goods, financial services, and real estate sectors. Its research department covers more than 300 small- and mid-cap public companies. JMP Group's Heartland Capital Partners (HCP) subsidiary manages alternative investments such as equity hedge funds, middle-market corporate loans, and private equity for institutional and high-net-worth investors.

HCP's investment teams possess expertise in the technology, agriculture, financial services, small-cap equities, and secondary investments. The unit has more than $500 million of assets under management in six hedge funds, one hedge fund of funds, a private equity fund, and a real estate investment trust (REIT).

In an effort to diversify its asset management business, JMP Group acquired Altanta-based corporate credit manager Cratos Capital Partners (now JMP Credit Advisors) in 2009, and nearly $300 million worth of collateralized loan obligations (CLOs) from Princeton Advisory Group in 2010. The company now has some $750 million of CLOs under management.

JMP Group has enjoyed two consecutive years of profitability. Sales and income were down slightly in 2010, however, even though expenses and provisions in loan losses were lower as well. The difference in the results from the prior year could be traced in part to declines in the company's asset management and brokerage segments.

Founded in 2000, JMP Group once focused exclusively on specialty finance and real estate, but began to diversify even before the sectors began to tank in 2007 as a result of global economic turmoil. The company hopes that its experience has it poised to take advantage of opportunities in those industries as they rebound.

Chairman, CEO, and co-founder Joseph Jolson owns more than 15% of JMP Group. The company went public in 2007. It has offices in Boston, Chicago, New York, San Francisco, and the Atlanta area.

EXECUTIVES

CFO, Raymond S. Jackson, age 38
Chairman and CEO; CEO, Harvest Capital Strategies, Joseph A. Jolson, age 52, $1,598,933 total compensation
President and Director, Craig R. Johnson, age 56, $1,040,843 total compensation
VP and Senior Analyst, Data and Information Services, JMP Securities, Kevane A. Wong
VP Marketing, JMP Securities, Andrew Palmer
Managing Director and Chief Compliance Officer, Gil Mogavero, age 55
Managing Director; Chief Legal Officer, Janet L. Tarkoff, age 43
Director; Co-President and Director of Investment Banking, JMP Securities, Carter D. Mack, age 48, $947,844 total compensation
Director; Co-President and Director of Equities, JMP Securities, Mark L. Lehmann, age 46, $1,086,594 total compensation
Managing Director; Director of Institutional Sales, JMP Securities, Daniel A. Wychulis
Managing Director; Chief Operating Officer, Harvest Capital Strategies, K.C. Lynch
Managing Director; Director of Corporate Finance, JMP Securities, R. Kent Ledbetter
Managing Director; Director of Mergers and Acquisitions, JMP Securities, Peter A. Hunt
Director Financial Services Investment Banking Group, Alexander M. Alden
Co-Director of Technology Research and Senior Analyst, Enterprise and Application Software, JMP Secu, Patrick D. (Pat) Walravens
Managing Director; Director of Research, JMP Securities, James F. (Jim) Wilson, age 48
Managing Director, Director of Equity Capital Markets, JMP Securities, Stephen P. Ortiz
Managing Director; Director Product Management, Securities, Jeffrey H. (Jeff) Spurr, age 53
Auditors:

LOCATIONS

HQ: JMP Group Inc.
600 Montgomery St., Ste. 1100, San Francisco, CA 94111
Phone: 415-835-8900   **Fax:** 415-835-8910
Web: www.jmpg.com

PRODUCTS/OPERATIONS

2010 Sales

	$ mil.	% of total
Investment banking	45.5	25
Interest income	45.2	25
Gain on sale & payoff of loans	39.4	22
Brokerage	28.3	16
Asset management fees	12.2	7
Principal transactions	3.4	2
Net dividend income	2.2	1
Other	3.5	2
Total	**179.7**	**100**

COMPETITORS

Arlington Asset Investment	Moss Adams LLP
Burrill & Company	Nollenberger Capital Partners
Goldman Sachs	Piper Jaffray
Jefferies Group	Robert W. Baird & Co.
Merriman Holdings	Thomas Weisel Partners
Morgan Stanley	WR Hambrecht

HISTORICAL FINANCIALS
Company Type: Public

Income Statement
FYE: December 31

	REVENUE ($ mil.)	NET INCOME ($ mil.)	NET PROFIT MARGIN	EMPLOYEES
12/10	179.7	8.9	5.0%	215
12/09	181.2	10.8	6.0%	224
12/08	76.6	(10.6)	—	191
12/07	65.5	6.5	9.9%	202
Annual Growth	40.0%	11.0%	—	2.1%

2010 Year-End Financials
Debt ratio: 270.6%	No. of shares (mil.): 21.7
Return on equity: 6.8%	Dividends
Cash ($ mil.): 71.1	Yield: 0.7%
Current ratio: —	Payout: 13.8%
Long-term debt ($ mil.): 351.3	Market value ($ mil.): 165.9

	STOCK PRICE ($) FY Close	P/E High/Low		PER SHARE ($) Earnings	Dividends	Book Value
12/10	7.63	25	14	0.40	0.05	5.97
12/09	9.72	23	8	0.49	0.04	5.60
12/08	5.55	—	—	(0.53)	0.20	5.31
12/07	8.48	—	—	(4.80)	0.08	2.13
Annual Growth	(3.5%)	—	—	—	(14.5%)	41.0%

Joe's Jeans

Joe's Jeans has jettisoned just about everything but its jeans. Following its acquisition of the Joe's brand from JD Holdings in 2007, the private-label apparel maker changed its name from Innovo Group to Joe's Jeans and revised its business plan to focus on building the Joe's and Joe's Jeans brands of denim and denim-related products. Joe's Jeans sells its apparel online at the Joe's Jeans website, in the US and Europe through high-end retailers such as Saks and Macy's, and in specialty stores including Atrium and Fred Segal. Founded in 1987, the firm changed its name in October 2007, adopted a new ticker (JOEZ), and set out in 2010 to expand its business through non-denim items.

The company is making plans to boast a 50-50 product mix of denim and non-denim apparel by 2015. In 2008 non-denim items comprised 2% of Joe's Jean's revenue. It's looking to achieve its goal by scaling down its operations and improving its sourcing efforts. The company, which wrapped up 2009 with more than $80 million in sales, anticipated logging more than $100 million in revenue by the end of 2010.

Joe's Jeans is concentrating its expansion efforts in Europe — specifically France, Germany, and the UK — for its growth overseas as it grows its business in the US. The jeans maker planned to roll out about 10 outlets and a handful of full-price stores by the end of 2010.

During 2009 Joe's Jeans amended and restated some of its previously issued financial statements and other financial information associated with its October 2007 company restructuring.

Prior to its corporate transformation, the company developed private-label apparel for retail chains, such as Target and American Eagle Outfitters, until mid-2006, when it pared down its operations to focus on its Joe's Jeans unit. For sev-

eral years, Joe's Jeans had been clearing out its closet. The firm began to rid itself of noncore businesses in 2004, when it terminated its Fetish, Hot Wheel, and Shago branded apparel licenses, as well as discontinuing its Bongo and Fetish accessory licenses. In line with its plan to focus on denim wear, the company sold its craft and accessories businesses in 2005. That same year, it also terminated its licensing agreement with icon Betsey Johnson.

Most of the company's apparel is manufactured in Mexico, Morocco, China, and the US. Creative director and company director Joseph Dahan owns about 22% of the company.

EXECUTIVES
Chairman, Samuel J. (Sam) Furrow Sr., age 69
President, CEO, and Director, Marc B. Crossman, age 39, $1,238,000 total compensation
CFO, Hamish S. Sandhu, age 48, $300,000 total compensation
Creative Director and Director, Joseph M. (Joe) Dahan, age 43, $2,225,000 total compensation
Auditors: Ernst & Young LLP

LOCATIONS
HQ: Joe's Jeans Inc.
5901 S. Eastern Ave., Commerce, CA 90040
Phone: 323-837-3700   **Fax:** 323-837-3790
Web: joesjeans.com

PRODUCTS/OPERATIONS

Selected Fit Styles
Chelsea
Cigarette
Honey
Lover
Muse
Provocateur
Rocker
Socialite
Starlet
Twiggy

COMPETITORS
Abercrombie & Fitch	Kellwood
Armani	Levi Strauss
Calvin Klein	Phat Fashions
Diesel SpA	Polo Ralph Lauren
Guess?	Sean John
Jones Group	The Gap
Jordache Enterprises	True Religion Apparel
Juicy Couture	VF Corporation

HISTORICAL FINANCIALS
Company Type: Public

Income Statement
FYE: November 30

	REVENUE ($ mil.)	NET INCOME ($ mil.)	NET PROFIT MARGIN	EMPLOYEES
11/10	98.2	2.6	2.6%	281
11/09	80.1	24.5	30.6%	165
11/08	69.2	6.1	8.8%	109
11/07	62.8	2.3	3.7%	81
11/06	46.6	(9.3)	—	81
Annual Growth	20.5%	—	—	36.5%

2010 Year-End Financials
Debt ratio: —	No. of shares (mil.): 63.9
Return on equity: 4.0%	Dividends
Cash ($ mil.): 6.4	Yield: —
Current ratio: 2.77	Payout: —
Long-term debt ($ mil.): —	Market value ($ mil.): 101.5

	STOCK PRICE ($) FY Close	P/E High/Low		PER SHARE ($) Earnings	Dividends	Book Value
11/10	1.59	90	28	0.04	0.00	1.02
11/09	1.29	4	1	0.40	0.00	1.00
11/08	0.36	21	3	0.08	0.00	0.60
11/07	1.15	49	8	0.05	0.00	0.67
11/06	0.68	—	—	(0.27)	0.00	0.10
Annual Growth	23.7%	—	—	—	—	80.2%

JPS Industries

JPS Industries' glass and plastic products can be found surfing the waves and saving lives. Its JPS Composite Materials arm makes high-strength synthetic fabrics and fiberglass mesh for the aeronautics, military, electronics, construction, and other industries. The products are used in myriad applications, including body armor, insulation, plasma display screens, and even surfboards. JPS Industries also operates through JPS Elastomerics (doing business as Stevens Urethane), a maker of polyurethane film, sheet, tubing, and cords, used to make an array of goods, such as athletic shoes, medical devices, and auto parts. JPS Elastometrics' traces back to the 1863 founding of predecessor Easthampton Rubber Thread.

While demand in construction and auto-based markets has waned during the economic downturn, JPS has pursued growth in a range of niche sectors within aerospace, electronics, electrical, defense, and solar energy. Year-over-year sales in 2010 declined modestly; nonetheless, JPS Industries' focus has enabled the company to cut operating costs and reduce debt. The company managed to increase its earnings by more than five-fold in 2010 over 2009.

Reinventing itself in 2008, JPS narrowed its business operations and sold off Stevens Geomembranes and Stevens Roofing to Dow Building Solutions, a part of The Dow Chemical Company. Several of JPS Composite Materials' fiberglass and substrate businesses were acquired from rival Hexcel Corporation in 2007. The company has preserved four manufacturing plants, neighboring customers in South Carolina, North Carolina, and Massachusetts.

EXECUTIVES
Chairman, President, and CEO, Michael L. Fulbright, age 61
President, Stevens Roofing and Geomembrane Systems, Peter A. Kesser
EVP, CFO, Secretary, and Director; President, Stevens Urethane, Charles R. (Chuck) Tutterow, age 45
VP Sales, Eastern Region, JPS Elastomerics, Dow Roofing Systems, Paul Shepard
VP Sales, Western Region, JPS Elastomerics, Dow Roofing Systems, Tim Davis
VP Market and Product Development, Stevens Urethane, James P. (Jim) Galica
Chemical Engineer, JPS Elastomerics, Stevens Urethane, Gregor Prentice
Director Marketing, Dow Roofing Systems, Bill Lyon
Research and Development Leader, Stevens Urethane, Chau Chen
Product Specialist, JPS Elastomerics, Stevens Urethane, Kathy Bergeron

Manager International Customer Service, JPS Elastomerics, Dow Roofing Systems, Manuela Boisvert

Director International Sales, JPS Elastomerics, Dow Roofing Systems, Peter Bond

General Manager, Asia/Far East, JPS Elastomerics, Dow Roofing Systems, Yasuhisa Ueda

Manager Sales and Service, JPS Elastomerics, Stevens Urethane, Timothy Falcetti

Product Specialist, Stevens Urethane, Andrew Bigelow

Product and Marketing Manager, JPS Elastomerics, Stevens Urethane, Timothy (Tim) Graham

Auditors: PricewaterhouseCoopers LLP

LOCATIONS

HQ: JPS Industries, Inc.
55 Beattie Place, Ste. 1510, Greenville, SC 29601
Phone: 864-239-3900   **Fax:** 864-271-9939
Web: www.jpselastomerics.com

PRODUCTS/OPERATIONS

Selected Operations

JPS Composite Materials Corp. (formerly JPS Glass, Inc.)
JPS Elastomerics Corp.
Stevens Urethane

Selected Products

Aramid substrate materials (high performance yarns: Kevlar, Spectra, Twaron, S-2 Rovings)
Astroquartz fiber products
Ethylene vinyl acetates
Extruded urethanes (thermoplastic polyurethane film, sheet & tubing)
Fiberglass reinforcing mesh & substrates
Glass fabrics & needled insulation
Great WhiteTM surboard fabrics
Open-weave scrim products

Selected Applications

Advanced composite materials
Civilian & military aerospace components
Filtration & insulation products
High performance glass laminates for security & transportation applications
Medical, automotive & industrial components
Paint protection films
Photovoltaic solar modules
Plasma display screens;
Printed electronic circuit boards;
Specialty commercial construction substrates;
Soft body armor for civilian & military applications

COMPETITORS

Advanced Composites	Johns Manville
Alpha Associates	Johnston Textiles
Denali	OCV Fabrics US
Hexcel	

HISTORICAL FINANCIALS

Company Type: Public

Income Statement			FYE: Saturday nearest October 31	
	REVENUE ($ mil.)	NET INCOME ($ mil.)	NET PROFIT MARGIN	EMPLOYEES
10/07	219.7	18.0	8.2%	0
10/06	171.5	6.0	3.5%	0
10/04	155.0	15.0	9.7%	0
10/03	128.7	(0.1)	—	578
10/02	126.4	(0.4)	—	620
Annual Growth	11.7%	—	—	(6.8%)

Debt ratio: —
Return on equity: 4.0%
Cash ($ mil.): 6.4
Current ratio: 2.77
Long-term debt ($ mil.): —

No. of shares (mil.): 63.9
Dividends
  Yield: —
  Payout: —
Market value ($ mil.): 101.5

K12

K12 isn't a missing element from the periodic table, but it could help kids learn the periodic table. The company offers online educational programs to about 67,000 students in kindergarten through 12th grade through "virtual schools." It also offers online curriculum to public and private schools in more than two dozen states. It provides course material and product sales directly to parents and individualized supplemental programs offered through schools. Courses cover core subjects such as language arts, math, science, history, and art. K12 targets kids of all levels from struggling to advanced, as well as those who travel, have disabilities, or are athletes or performers. CEO Ron Packard founded K12 in 2000.

K12's virtual public schools are online programs that adhere to the programs and policies of public entities such as public school districts, independent, non-profit charter school boards, and state education agencies. It offers the same coursework and curriculum as most school districts' "brick and mortar" campuses. However, since virtual schools don't have the requirement of a physical classroom, they can accommodate a large dispersed student population. They also allow for more capital resources to be directed toward teaching, curriculum, and technology rather than keeping up a physical infrastructure. Students who attend virtual public schools receive assignments, complete lessons, and obtain instruction from certified teachers with whom they interact online, telephonically, in virtual classroom environments, and, at times, face-to-face.

This type of flexibility combined with its expanding curriculum has helped K12 increase its enrollment and, consequently, its income. Between 2009 and 2010, K12 upped its enrollment by about 22% and its revenue by the same about the same amount.

K12 started out offering programs for children in kindergarten through second grade. It gradually expanded and now instruction all the way up to a self-paced high school program. The company made a greater investment in its middle and high school products with its 2010 acquisition of KC Distance Learning (KCDL). The purchase brought in three brands targeting both public and private schools: Aventa Learning, The Keystone School, and iQ Academies. Also that year K12 formed a 60-40 joint venture with Middlebury College to create online foreign language classes.

In late 2010, K12 acquired American Education Corporation (AEC), a provider of research-based core curriculum instructional software for kindergarten through adult learners. The acquisition added to K12's portfolio of instructional and curriculum offerings and assessment tools. The following year, in mid-2011, K12 agreed to acquire the online high school business of Kaplan. The unit targets adults without high school diplomas and high school students who are looking to augment their brick-and-mortar education.

K12 also has a contract with the Delaware Department of Education to manage the Moyer Charter School. The agreement represented K12's first foray into bricks-and-mortar school management. Through the agreement K12 is authorized to serve up to 460 students in grades 6-12. K12 intends to expand its work with school districts and has established a dedicated sales team to further that effort. The services it provides to districts include teacher training programs, administrator support, and a student account management system.

K12 operates overseas through the K12 International Academy, a private school that enables K12 to deliver its learning system to students in other countries. In 2010 the company opened offices in Singapore and Switzerland and said it would consider a move into secondary education if the right opportunity came along.

EXECUTIVES

Chairman, Andrew H. Tisch, age 61
CEO and Director, Ronald J. (Ron) Packard, age 48, $1,731,530 total compensation
EVP Operations, John Olsen
EVP and Chief Marketing Officer, Celia Stokes, age 47, $532,604 total compensation
EVP and CFO, Harry T. Hawks, age 57
EVP Worldwide Business Development, Bruce J. Davis, age 48, $496,078 total compensation
EVP School Services, George B. (Chip) Hughes Jr., age 52, $528,558 total compensation
VP Public Relations, Jeff Kwitowski
SVP School Development, Peter G. Stewart, age 41
SVP Product Development, Maria A. Szalay, age 44
SVP Public Affairs, Bryan W. Flood, age 44
SVP Systems and Technology, Ray Williams, age 48
SVP Finance and Investor Relations, Keith T. Haas
SVP Human Resources, Howard Allentoff, age 48
SVP Content and Curriculum, John Holdren
SVP, General Counsel, and Secretary, Howard D. Polsky, age 58
Auditors: BDO Seidman, LLP

LOCATIONS

HQ: K12 Inc.
2300 Corporate Park Dr., Herndon, VA 20171
Phone: 703-483-7000   **Fax:** 703-483-7330
Web: www.k12.com

PRODUCTS/OPERATIONS

Selected Students Served/Services

Advanced and Enrichable Learners
Athletes and Performers
Credit Recovery (for missed classes, make-up credits)
Expat, Foreign Service, Overseas
Homebound
Homeschoolers
Military Families
Reading Program
Struggling Students
Summer School
Supplemental Education
World Languages

COMPETITORS

Apollo Group	Kaplan
DeVry	McGraw-Hill
Edison Learning	Nobel Learning
Florida Virtual School	Communities
Houghton Mifflin	Pearson plc
Harcourt	PLATO Learning

Income Statement

FYE: June 30

	REVENUE ($ mil.)	NET INCOME ($ mil.)	NET PROFIT MARGIN	EMPLOYEES
06/11	522.4	12.8	2.5%	2,500
06/10	384.5	21.5	5.6%	1,065
06/09	315.6	12.3	3.9%	993
06/08	226.2	33.8	14.9%	763
06/07	140.6	3.9	2.8%	636
Annual Growth	38.8%	34.6%	—	40.8%

2011 Year-End Financials

Debt ratio: 2.4%	No. of shares (mil.): 38.7
Return on equity: 2.9%	Dividends
Cash ($ mil.): 193.1	Yield: —
Current ratio: 4.16	Payout: —
Long-term debt ($ mil.): 10.9	Market value ($ mil.): 1,281.8

	STOCK PRICE ($) FY Close	P/E High/Low		PER SHARE ($) Earnings	Dividends	Book Value
06/11	33.14	107	57	0.37	0.00	11.60
06/10	22.18	36	22	0.71	0.00	7.57
06/09	21.55	70	28	0.42	0.00	6.22
06/08	21.51	28	15	1.10	0.00	5.42
Annual Growth	15.5%	—	—	(30.5%)	—	28.9%

Kapstone Paper and Packaging

Rock, paper, sissors? KapStone Paper and Packaging has the upper hand in the game of unbleached kraft. The company manufactures largely linerboard, a type of paperboard that is converted into laminated tier sheets and wrapping material. It also produces kraft paper (industry-speak for strong wrapping paper) for multiwall bags; saturating kraft (sold under the Durasorb brand) to produce mainly high pressure laminates for furniture, construction materials, and electronics; and unbleached folding carton board (Kraftpak), which is converted into packaging for consumer goods. KapStone counts 500-plus customers, including Graphic Packaging, Exopack, and other major converters. The US represents about 60% of sales.

Established in 2005, KapStone has evolved through a series of mergers, acquisitions, and other investments in the paper, packaging, and forest products industry. As of 2010, it is more than one-third of the way toward its goal of becoming a $2 billion revenue company by 2015.

In line with this strategy, KapStone announced in 2011 an agreement to acquire the stock of U.S. Corrugated, Inc. (USC) for $330 million in cash. USC operates a 240,000-ton recycled container-board paper mill in South Carolina and 20 converting facilities in the eastern and midwestern US, six of which will be disposed of by USC prior to the closing. The operations to be acquired from USC generated $423 million in net sales in 2010, and the deal is expected to increase KapStone's profitability.

Previous acquisitions have also helped to fuel KapStone's earnings. It acquired MeadWestvaco's North Charleston Kraft Division in 2008 for approximately $485 million. That deal added saturating kraft and unbleached kraft board to KapStone's offerings and significantly expanded its customer base outside of the US. It also gained a cogeneration facility, chip mills, and a lumber mill.

In 2007 KapStone pocketed the Kraft Papers Business of International Paper Company (IP) for $155 million. The business included an unbleached kraft paper manufacturing facility in North Carolina, and Ride Rite Converting, an inflatable dunnage bag manufacturer. The latter business was sold to Illinois Tool Works for $36 million in 2009 to help KapStone trim its debt and concentrate on its kraft operations. In early 2011 the company parlayed an early settlement with IP; it managed to pay IP the remaining purchase price for the papers business at a reduced amount.

The company has benefited recently from higher mill operating rates coupled with price increases in linerboard and kraft paper, driven by market demand from the recovering economy. Unbleached kraft sales have maintained a four-year positive trajectory, increasing by nearly 25% in 2010 over 2009. Nonetheless, year-over-year earnings in 2010 declined by almost 20% due, in large part, to expiring alternate fuel mixture tax credits, inflated input and freight costs, and fatter paychecks and employee benefits. Cash generated from operations dwindled, too, in 2010, diminished by capital expenditures for equipment upgrades and IT projects, and financing activities.

The kraft paper maker has also taken advantage of tax credits associated with the use of black liquor, a biofuel that is a by-product of the wood pulping process, to power its production facilities. As a result, it appreciably reduced its debt in 2009 and 2010, and effective tax rate in 2010, which helped position the company closer to its goals.

EXECUTIVES

Chairman and CEO, Roger W. Stone, age 76, $934,096 total compensation
President, Secretary, and Director, Matthew S. (Matt) Kaplan, age 54, $931,646 total compensation
VP and CFO, Andrea K. Tarbox, age 60, $275,000 total compensation
VP and General Manager, KapStone Charleston Kraft, Bruce Hoffman
VP and General Manager; President, Kraft Paper Business, Timothy P. Keneally, age 63, $501,497 total compensation
Manager Public Affairs and Communications, Kapstone Charleston, Larry Cobb
Communications Manager, Roanoke Rapids Mill, Kimberly (Kim) Bracy
Auditors: Ernst & Young LLP

LOCATIONS

HQ: KapStone Paper and Packaging Corporation
1101 Skokie Blvd., Ste. 300, Northbrook, IL 60062-4124
Phone: 847-239-8800   **Fax:** 847-205-7551
Web: www.kapstonepaper.com

2010 Sales

	$ mil.	% of total
US	482.4	62
Other countries	300.2	38
Total	782.6	100

PRODUCTS/OPERATIONS

2010 Sales

	$ mil.	% of total
Unbleached kraft	782.6	100
Other	-	-
Total	782.6	100

2010 Sales

	% of total
Linerboard	51
Kraft paper	21
Saturating kraft product (Durasorb)	21
Unbleached folding carton board (Kraftpak)	7
Total	100

COMPETITORS

Canfor	International Paper
Caraustar	Longview Fibre
Georgia-Pacific	Rock-Tenn
Graphic Packaging	Temple-Inland
Holding	West Fraser Timber

Income Statement

FYE: December 31

	REVENUE ($ mil.)	NET INCOME ($ mil.)	NET PROFIT MARGIN	EMPLOYEES
12/10	782.7	65.0	8.3%	1,600
12/09	632.5	80.3	12.7%	1,600
12/08	524.5	19.7	3.8%	1,750
12/07	256.8	27.0	10.5%	710
Annual Growth	45.0%	34.0%	—	31.1%

2010 Year-End Financials

Debt ratio: 22.2%	No. of shares (mil.): 46.1
Return on equity: 15.5%	Dividends
Cash ($ mil.): 67.4	Yield: —
Current ratio: 1.92	Payout: —
Long-term debt ($ mil.): 92.9	Market value ($ mil.): 705.1

	STOCK PRICE ($) FY Close	P/E High/Low		PER SHARE ($) Earnings	Dividends	Book Value
12/10	15.30	11	6	1.38	0.00	9.08
12/09	9.83	4	0	2.29	0.00	7.68
12/08	2.38	15	4	0.57	0.00	6.36
12/07	7.00	11	8	0.75	0.00	5.77
00/00	6.36	93	76	0.07	0.00	4.65
Annual Growth	24.5%	—	—	110.7%	—	18.2%

KBW

KBW is an investment bank for bankers. Clients of the firm include banks, insurance companies, broker/dealers, asset managers, and others in the financial services sector. The company provides investment banking, securities sales and trading, research, and asset management services, with a focus on small and midcap clients. Through subsidiary Keefe, Bruyette & Woods, KBW provides advisory services, securities underwriting, and structured finance products. KBW Asset Management offers investment advisory services to financial institutions and other institutional clients, as well as to wealthy individuals. The company has offices in the US, the UK, Hong Kong, and Japan.

KBW has been recovering from a rough turn in 2008, largely due to writedowns related to structured finance products. During the finacial crisis, mergers and acquisitions (M&A) and other corporate activities slowed down, which brought down investment banking fees. However, the need for strategic advisory services has grown as firms seek viable acquisition targets or consider capital-raising avenues. The recent wave of bank consolidations has also brought the company business.

The firm has also benefitted from its international push (although it doesn't report sales by geographic segments due to the interconnected nature of the financial world). KBW provides research on about 700 financial institutions, including more than 200 European and Asian entities.

Formerly headquartered at the World Trade Center, KBW lost a third of its staff on Sept. 11, 2001, including chairman Joseph Berry.

EXECUTIVES

Chairman and CEO, John G. Duffy, age 61, $2,692,477 total compensation

CEO and Director Equity Research, Keefe, Bruyette and Woods Limited, London; Global Business Coordin, Vasco Moreno, age 41

CEO, KBW Asset Management, Peter E. Roth, age 52

EVP, CFO, and Chief Administrative Officer, Robert (Bob) Giambrone, age 56, $1,706,265 total compensation

EVP, General Counsel, and Corporate Secretary, Mitchell B. Kleinman, age 56, $1,313,619 total compensation

VP and Credit Manager, Dan Frascone

Vice Chairman and COO, Thomas B. (Tom) Michaud, age 47, $2,692,477 total compensation

Vice Chairman and President, Andrew M. (Andy) Senchak, age 64, $2,692,477 total compensation

Managing Director, Diversified Finance, Chauncey Dewey

Co-Head Depository Investment Banking, Scott R. Anderson

Co-Head Depository Investment Banking, Joesph S. Berry Jr.

SVP and Head Convertible Securities, Rick Jeffrey, age 47

Global Head Investment Banking, Peter J. Wirth, age 54

Co-Head Fixed Income Sales, Joseph J. Spalluto

Director Global Capital Markets, Jeffrey D. Evans

Director Research, Keefe, Bruyette & Woods, Frederick Cannon

Director Equity Sales, Daryle A. Dilascia

Director Equity Sales, Keefe, Bruyette and Woods Limited, London, Julian L. Bird

SVP Loan Portfolio Sales Group, Michael MacDonald

Director Research, John N. Howard Jr., age 57

Co-Head Fixed Income Sales and Director Fixed Income Trading, Don Ullmann

Director Investment Banking, Keefe, Bruyette and Woods Limited, London, Stephen Howard

Senior Agency Pass-Through Trader, Mortgage Backed Securities Trading Team, Greg Hargraves

Auditors: KPMG LLP

LOCATIONS

HQ: KBW, Inc.
The Equitable Bldg., 787 7th Ave., 4th Fl., New York, NY 10019
Phone: 212-887-7777
Web: www.kbw.com

PRODUCTS/OPERATIONS

2010 Sales

	$ mil.	% of totals
Investment banking	208.9	49
Commissions	133.6	31
Principal transactions, net	54.0	13
Interest & dividends	13.1	3
Investment advisory fees	3.2	1
Other	13.1	3
Total	**425.9**	**100**

Selected Subsidiaries

KBW Asset Management, Inc.
KBW Ventures Inc.
Keefe, Bruyette & Woods Asia Limited (Hong Kong)
Keefe, Bruyette & Woods, Inc.
Keefe, Bruyette & Woods Limited (UK)

COMPETITORS

Credit Suisse (USA)	Morgan Keegan
FBR Capital Markets	Morgan Stanley
Goldman Sachs	National Bank
Jefferies Group	Financial
Legg Mason	Sandler O'Neill
Merrill Lynch	William Blair

HISTORICAL FINANCIALS

Company Type: Public

Income Statement

FYE: December 31

	REVENUE ($ mil.)	NET INCOME ($ mil.)	NET PROFIT MARGIN	EMPLOYEES
12/10	425.9	26.6	6.2%	585
12/09	387.2	23.6	6.1%	518
12/08	242.2	(62.3)	—	529
12/07	427.5	27.3	6.4%	529
12/06	406.6	53.3	13.1%	455
Annual Growth	1.2%	(15.9%)	—	6.5%

2010 Year-End Financials

Debt ratio: —	No. of shares (mil.): 35.4
Return on equity: 5.8%	Dividends
Cash ($ mil.): 162.3	Yield: 0.4%
Current ratio: —	Payout: 14.1%
Long-term debt ($ mil.): —	Market value ($ mil.): 988.9

	STOCK PRICE ($) FY Close	P/E High/Low	PER SHARE ($) Earnings	Dividends	Book Value
12/10	27.92	42 30	0.71	0.10	12.93
12/09	27.36	52 21	0.66	0.00	14.60
12/08	23.00	— —	(2.02)	0.00	10.74
12/07	25.59	45 26	0.86	0.00	15.31
12/06	29.39	16 13	1.93	0.00	13.58
Annual Growth	(1.3%)	— —	(22.1%)	—	(1.2%)

KEYW

If KEYW Holding had its way, the Pentagon would be based in Margaritaville. KEYW Holding (which stands for Key West - CEO Leonard Moodispaw is a Buffet fan) operates through KEYW Corporation, a government contractor and subcontractor involved in cyber security. The company builds computer networks and systems for federal agencies such as the National Security Agency and the Department of Defense. KEYW was founded in 2008 by former executives of Essex Corporation, a company that developed op-

tical hardware to monitor intelligence activity. About 15% of KEYW's revenue comes from this hardware, which is used to capture enemy intelligence in war zones. KEYW Holding went public in 2010.

Proceeds from its $100 million IPO were slated to pay off expenses incurred by KEYW as it acquired a string of companies after its founding in 2008.

The company has its origins in the acquisition of Essex Corporation by Northrop Grumman in 2007 for about $580 million. Moodispaw moved to Northrop Grumman to manage Essex as a subsidiary within its Mission Systems division for about a year, until he bought back some of the assets (along with 60 employees) and started up KEYW Corporation. (KEYW is the old NASDAQ trading symbol for Essex Corporation.)

Almost immediately, the company began buying smaller, competing businesses that also performed intelligence work for the US government. It spent almost $150 million buying seven businesses in two years, the largest being The Analysis Group for $62 million, and the most high-profile being certain assets of the Systems Engineering and Technical Assistance unit of General Dynamics' Advanced Information Systems. KEYW went on to pay $27 million in 2010 for Sycamore, a Maryland-based provider of IT services such as aerospace software engineering, cybersecurity, computer network systems engineering. The deal strengthened KEYW's data security business.

In 2011 it acquired government contractor and fellow Maryland native JKA Technologies for $13 million. KEYW was interested in JKA's complementary data security, software and systems engineering, and program and project management services. The company additionally purchased software development, integration, and support services provider Forbes Analytic Software for about $16.7 million to expand its intelligence and defense industry business. KEYW also acquired Flight Landata for about $30 million in cash. Flight Landata provided geospatial and imagery intelligence to the defense industry. The acquisition expanded KEYW's Quick Response Solutions division to include imagery and micro terrain intelligence capabilities.

EXECUTIVES

Chairman, President, and CEO, Leonard E. Moodispaw, age 68, $2,633,591 total compensation

CFO, John E. Krobath II, age 43, $1,068,799 total compensation

Chief Impact Officer, Mark A. Willard, $330,839 total compensation

Chief Administrative Officer and Secretary, Kimberly J. DeChello, age 50, $281,563 total compensation

Chief Strategy Officer, Edwin M. (Ed) Jaehne, age 58, $203,715 total compensation

Auditors: Grant Thornton LLP

LOCATIONS

HQ: The KEYW Holding Corporation
1334 Ashton Rd., Ste. A, Hanover, MD 21076
Phone: 443-270-5300   **Fax:** 443-270-5301
Web: www.keywcorp.com

COMPETITORS

Axsys	Northrop Grumman Info
Boeing	Systems
CACI International	Raytheon IIS
Lockheed Martin	SAIC
Information Systems	SRA International
ManTech	

HISTORICAL FINANCIALS

Company Type: Public

Income Statement

FYE: December 31

	REVENUE ($ mil.)	NET INCOME ($ mil.)	NET PROFIT MARGIN	EMPLOYEES
12/10	108.0	10.9	10.1%	722
12/09	39.0	(2.1)	—	408
12/08	23.6	(1.0)	—	0
12/07	15.4	2.3	14.9%	0
Annual Growth	91.4%	68.0%	—	77.0%

2010 Year-End Financials

Debt ratio: —
Return on equity: 6.2%
Cash ($ mil.): 5.8
Current ratio: 2.47
Long-term debt ($ mil.): —
No. of shares (mil.): 25.6
Dividends
Yield: —
Payout: —
Market value ($ mil.): 374.9

	STOCK PRICE ($) FY Close	P/E High/Low		PER SHARE ($) Earnings	Dividends	Book Value
12/10	14.67	31	20	0.51	0.00	6.85
Annual Growth	—	—	—	—	—	—

Kingstone Companies

Kingstone Companies (formerly DCAP Group) keeps things covered. While the company has transformed itself from a broker into an underwriter, its main business is still insurance. Its Kingstone Insurance Company (formerly Commercial Mutual Insurance Company) provides property/casualty insurance policies for individuals and businesses in New York State. Its products, including auto, business, and homeowners' policies, are sold through independent agents. The company has divested its former insurance brokerage business, which offered life and property/casualty policies through owned and franchised retail locations in New York and eastern Pennsylvania.

EXECUTIVES

CFO and Secretary, Victor Brodsky, age 53
Chairman, President, CEO, and Treasurer; Chairman and Chief Investment Officer, Kingstone Insurance, Barry B. Goldstein, age 58, $290,770 total compensation
Auditors: Holtz Rubenstein Reminick LLP

LOCATIONS

HQ: Kingstone Companies, Inc.
1158 Broadway, Hewlett, NY 11557
Phone: 516-374-7600   **Fax:** 516-295-7216
Web: kingstonecompanies.com

COMPETITORS

AIG	NYCM
Allstate	Progressive
GEICO	Corporation
GNY Mutual Insurance	The Hartford
New York Life	

HISTORICAL FINANCIALS

Company Type: Public

Income Statement

FYE: December 31

	ASSETS ($ mil.)	NET INCOME ($ mil.)	INCOME AS % OF ASSETS	EMPLOYEES
12/10	58.7	1.0	1.7%	43
12/09	52.6	4.8	9.1%	40
12/08	9.4	(1.0)	—	46
12/07	23.2	—	—	68
12/06	25.4	0.5	2.0%	87
Annual Growth	23.3%	18.9%	—	(16.2%)

2010 Year-End Financials

Equity as % of assets: 22.05%
Return on assets: 1.7%
Return on equity: 7.6%
Long-term debt ($ mil.): —
No. of shares (mil.): 3.8
Dividends
Yield: —
Payout: —
Market value ($ mil.): 13.4
Sales ($ mil.): 21.6

	STOCK PRICE ($) FY Close	P/E High/Low		PER SHARE ($) Earnings	Dividends	Book Value
12/10	3.50	13	8	0.29	0.00	3.37
12/09	2.49	2	0	1.62	0.00	3.47
12/08	0.48	—	—	(0.33)	0.00	1.77
12/07	1.67	—	—	(0.02)	0.00	2.07
12/06	3.06	20	6	0.17	0.00	2.07
Annual Growth	3.4%	—	—	14.3%	—	13.0%

KIT digital

A talking car won't help your company achieve its online goals, but maybe KIT digital can help. KIT digital operates an online platform that enables clients to publish, manage, and distribute Internet Protocol (IP)-based video content for marketing purposes. Its clients' video can be delivered through the Internet, set top boxes, and wireless devices. In its previous incarnation as ROO Group, the company was a syndicator of video-on-demand content for broadcast; in 2008 the firm refocused its operations on interactive marketing, and changed its name to KIT ("Knowledge, Imagination and Technology") digital.

After deciding to shift its emphasis to interactive marketing, KIT digital is now poised to grow through a large burst of acquisitions. In mid-2011, it acquired UK-based ioko365 Ltd, a provider of cloud-based digital media platforms used to deliver video content over Internet-connected devices. KIT digital paid roughly $90 million to acquire ioko, in a deal that enhanced its own core KIT Platform video asset management software (VAMS). ioko serves 50 clients, including such notable names as AT&T, Samsung, and Universal Music.

The company expanded its North American presence in 2010 when it purchased privately held US firm Multicast Media Technologies for some $18 million in cash and stock. Also that year it expanded in Asia when it bought Benchmark Broadcast Systems, a video asset management provider and broadcast video systems integrator based in Singapore.

Months later, KIT digital made two key acquisitions in Accela Communications and Megahertz Broadcast Systems. Based in Massachusetts, Accela provides software geared towards the production, delivery, and measurement of video communications; it caters to more than 150 customers in the health care, information technology, and financial services industries. Based in the UK, Megahertz Broadcast Systems has expertise in the integration of video broadcast systems. Both acquisitions contributed directly to KIT digital's core video broadcasting offerings. The previous year the company acquired online video distribution firm The FeedRoom for about $10 million in stock.

The company's reinvention was bolstered with 2008 acquisitions such as Sweden-based Kamera Content (Internet delivery of TV programming), Australia-based Morpheum (Web-based content management software), Sputnik Agency (online marketing services), and Czech Republic-based Visual Connection (technology for Internet delivery of TV programming). Also in 2008, KIT digital reduced its workforce by about 20% and consolidated its international businesses into a wholly-owned Dubai subsidiary, moving its operational headquarters and executives from New York and Australia to Dubai. The following year KIT digital moved that office to Prague.

EXECUTIVES

Chairman and CEO, Kaleil Isaza Tuzman, age 39, $289,652 total compensation
President and Director, Gavin Campion, age 38, $130,833 total compensation
CFO and Director, Robin Smyth, age 58
EVP Product Development and Director, Christopher Williams, age 52
COO, Alex Blum
Chief Administrative Officer, Barak Bar-Cohen
SVP Industry Solutions, Christopher W. Richardson
SVP Business Development and Global Faith Initiatives, Chance Mason
SVP Sales, EMEA, John Griffin
SVP Sales, Americas, Tricia Iboshi
SVP Sales, Latin America, Pablo Goldstein
General Manager and VP Software Solutions, APAC, Tristan Place
Managing Director Asia Pac, Steve W. Chung
Managing Director Global Sales and Strategic Accounts, Laura Kaatz
SVP Strategic Partnerships, EMEA, Tullio Pirovano
SVP Sales, Asia Pac, Ashish Mukherjee
Managing Director, Americas, Lou Schwartz
SVP Strategy and Innovation, Mark Christie
Managing Director Business Integration, Scott Sahadi
SVP Global Marketing, Gannon Hall
Managing Director EMEA, Frances Jarvis
Auditors: Grant Thornton LLP

LOCATIONS

HQ: KIT digital, Inc.
168 5th Ave., Ste. 302, New York, NY 10010
Phone: 212-661-4111   **Fax:** 646-619-4074
Web: www.kit-digital.com

2009 Sales

	$ mil.	% of total
EMEA	33.1	70
Asia/Pacific	10.5	22
Americas	3.7	8
Total	**47.3**	**100**

COMPETITORS

24/7 Real Media	Level 3 Communications
Acacia Technologies	Nokia
Akamai	RealNetworks
blinkx	YouTube
IBM Global Services	

Company Type: Public

Income Statement				FYE: December 31
	REVENUE ($ mil.)	NET INCOME ($ mil.)	NET PROFIT MARGIN	EMPLOYEES
12/10	106.6	(35.3)	—	842
12/09	47.3	(19.9)	—	325
12/08	23.4	(19.0)	—	188
12/07	13.9	(34.6)	—	135
12/06	9.8	(14.6)	—	140
Annual Growth	81.6%	—	—	56.6%

2010 Year-End Financials

Debt ratio: 1.8%	No. of shares (mil.): 33.2
Return on equity: —	Dividends
Cash ($ mil.): 141.2	Yield: —
Current ratio: 4.75	Payout: —
Long-term debt ($ mil.): 4.3	Market value ($ mil.): 532.5

	STOCK PRICE ($) FY Close	P/E High/Low	PER SHARE ($) Earnings	Dividends	Book Value
12/10	16.04	— —	(1.63)	0.00	7.40
12/09	11.00	— —	(3.03)	0.00	3.13
12/08	5.25	— —	(7.55)	0.00	5.59
12/07	5.95	— —	(34.65)	0.00	4,193.13
12/06	106.75	— —	(32.20)	0.00	5,830.87
Annual Growth	(37.7%)	— —	—	—	(81.1%)

KMG Chemicals

KMG Chemicals protects wood and helps make chips, though it has nothing to do with wood chips. Its electronic chemicals are used in the manufacture of semiconductors. KMG's largest customer is silicon chip kingpin Intel, which accounts for about 10% of sales. Its wood preservatives are pentachlorophenol (penta), sodium penta, and creosote. KMG sells penta and creosote in the US, primarily to the railroad, construction, and utility industries. Sodium penta is sold in Latin America. The company makes herbicides to kill weeds and pesticides to keep insects from livestock and poultry. Almost all of its sales are within the US. Chairman David Hatcher owns almost a third of KMG.

The company's strategy is to grow by discovering and exploiting opportunities that other companies overlook. It focuses on customer satisfaction, operational efficiencies, and optimizing its assets. It also seeks targeted acquisitions that mesh with and enhance existing business segments, and to effectively integrate acquisitions into ongoing operations.

KMG's revenues increase more than 9% in 2010, mainly due to a 30% increase in sales in its electronic chemicals segment, particularly in international markets. Net income was up 50% in 2010, due also to increased sales in the electronic chemicals unit, but partially offset by losses in KMG's other three reporting segments.

KMG acquired the electronic chemicals unit of General Chemical Performance Products in 2010 for $27 million. The unit manufactures wet process chemicals used primarily to clean and etch silicon wafers in the production of semiconductors. The deal not only increased KGM's electronic chemicals business but also expanding its reach into Asia markets.KGM's wood preserving chemicals, pen-

tachlorophenol, or penta, and creosote, are sold to industrial customers who use these preservatives primarily to extend the useful life of utility poles and railroad ties. The company is the sole distributor of penta for wood treatment purposes in the US and the principal supplier of creosote in the US to wood treaters who do not produce their own creosote.

EXECUTIVES

Chairman, David L. Hatcher, age 67
President, CEO, COO, and Director, J. Neal Butler, age 58, $601,924 total compensation
VP Operations, Ernest C. (Ernie) Kremling II, age 47, $329,054 total compensation
VP and CFO, John V. Sobchak, age 51, $304,553 total compensation
VP Sales, KMB-Bernuth, Thomas H. (Tom) Mitchell, age 67
VP, General Counsel and Secretary, Roger C. Jackson, age 59, $256,076 total compensation
Auditors: UHY LLP

LOCATIONS

HQ: KMG Chemicals, Inc.
9555 W. Sam Houston Pkwy. South, Ste. 600, Houston, TX 77099
Phone: 713-600-3800   Fax: 713-600-3850
Web: www.kmgb.com

2010 Sales

	$ mil.	% of total
US	175.1	84
Other countries	33.5	16
Total	**208.6**	**100**

PRODUCTS/OPERATIONS

2010 Sales

	$ mil.	% of total
Electronic chemicals	112.0	54
Creosote	63.2	30
Penta	22.8	11
Animal health	10.6	5
Total	**208.6**	**100**

Selected Products

Creosote (wood preservative)
Hydrochloric acid (for use in the steel and oil well service industries)
Monosodium and disodium methanearsonic acids (MSMA, herbicide)
Pentachlorophenol (aka "penta," wood preservative)
Sodium pentachlorophenol (aka "sodium penta," wood preservative)
Tetrachlorvinphos (insecticide)

COMPETITORS

American Vanguard	Merichem
Arch Chemicals	Monsanto Company
Cytec	Osmose
Innospec	Perstorp
Koppers Holdings	Rasa Industries

Company Type: Public

Income Statement				FYE: July 31
	REVENUE ($ mil.)	NET INCOME ($ mil.)	NET PROFIT MARGIN	EMPLOYEES
07/11	266.4	9.7	3.6%	336
07/10	208.6	15.3	7.3%	318
07/09	190.7	10.2	5.3%	272
07/08	154.4	5.7	3.7%	274
07/07	89.8	8.8	9.8%	118
Annual Growth	31.2%	2.5%	—	29.9%

2011 Year-End Financials

Debt ratio: 42.8%	No. of shares (mil.): 11.3
Return on equity: 10.1%	Dividends
Cash ($ mil.): 1.8	Yield: 0.5%
Current ratio: 2.08	Payout: 10.6%
Long-term debt ($ mil.): 41.3	Market value ($ mil.): 189.7

	STOCK PRICE ($) FY Close	P/E High/Low	PER SHARE ($) Earnings	Dividends	Book Value
07/11	16.76	24 15	0.85	0.09	8.53
07/10	15.17	16 5	1.34	0.08	7.55
07/09	7.32	13 2	0.91	0.08	6.39
07/08	11.18	56 20	0.48	0.08	5.78
07/07	20.75	35 9	0.80	0.08	5.17
Annual Growth	(5.2%)	— —	1.5%	3.0%	13.3%

Kodiak Oil & Gas

Kodiak Oil & Gas bears the responsibility for exploration, development, and production of oil and natural gas in the Rockies. The company, which focuses on assets in the Vermillion Basin of the Green River Basin and the Williston Basin (located in Montana and North Dakota), has proved reserves of 1.2 billion cu. ft. of natural gas and 344,000 barrels of oil. Kodiak Oil & Gas has 99,434 net acres of land holdings. In the Green River Basin it is exploring for unconventional gas through the exploitation of coalbed methane, overpressured shales, and tight-gas-sands. In recent years the company has increased its holdings in the Williston Basin to 110,000 acres through deals worth $345 million.

EXECUTIVES

President, CEO, and Director, Lynn A. Peterson, age 57, $1,310,917 total compensation
CFO, Treasurer, and Secretary, James P. Henderson, age 45
Land Manager, Michael N. Murray
Investor Relations, Sandra Oneil
Operations Manager, Russell A. Branting
COO, EVP, Chairman, and Secretary,, James E. (Jim) Catlin, age 64, $1,310,917 total compensation
Northern Rockies Exploration Manager, Russ D. Cunningham
Manager Southern Rockies Exploration, David G. Majewski, age 65
Auditors:

LOCATIONS

HQ: Kodiak Oil & Gas Corp.
1625 Broadway, Ste. 330, Denver, CO 80202
Phone: 303-592-8075   **Fax:** 303-592-8071
Web: www.kodiakog.com

PRODUCTS/OPERATIONS

2008 Sales

	$ mil.	% of total
Oil	5.4	77
Gas	1.4	20
Other	0.2	3
Total	**7.0**	**100**

2007 Sales

	$ mil.	% of total
Oil	6.8	73
Gas	1.0	11
Other	1.5	16
Total	**9.3**	**100**

2006 Sales

	$ mil.	% of total
Oil	3.5	70
Gas	0.7	14
Other	0.8	16
Total	**5.0**	**100**

COMPETITORS

Cabot Oil & Gas	Hugoton Royalty Trust
Double Eagle Petroleum	Marathon Oil
Gasco Energy	Samson Oil

HISTORICAL FINANCIALS
Company Type: Public

Income Statement
FYE: December 31

	REVENUE ($ mil.)	NET INCOME ($ mil.)	NET PROFIT MARGIN	EMPLOYEES
12/10	24.9	(2.4)	—	35
12/09	11.3	(2.6)	—	16
12/08	7.0	(56.5)	—	17
12/07	9.3	(38.2)	—	15
12/06	5.0	(2.8)	—	12
Annual Growth	**49.4%**	**—**	**—**	**30.7%**

2010 Year-End Financials
Debt ratio: 13.4%
Return on equity: —
Cash ($ mil.): 101.2
Current ratio: 5.32
Long-term debt ($ mil.): 40.0
No. of shares (mil.): 178.2
Dividends
  Yield: —
  Payout: —
Market value ($ mil.): 1,175.9

	STOCK PRICE ($) FY Close	P/E High/Low	PER SHARE ($) Earnings	Dividends	Book Value
12/10	6.60	— —	(0.02)	0.00	1.68
12/09	2.22	— —	(0.02)	0.00	0.59
12/08	0.31	— —	(0.62)	0.00	0.35
12/07	2.20	— —	(0.44)	0.00	0.78
12/06	3.96	— —	(0.04)	0.00	1.18
Annual Growth	**13.6%**	**— —**	**—**	**—**	**9.1%**

Kreisler Manufacturing

Your Chrysler might have a hemi under the hood, but this Kreisler focuses on bigger engines. Kreisler Manufacturing, through subsidiary Kreisler Industrial, makes precision metal components for commercial and military aircraft engines and industrial gas turbines. Tube assemblies — used to transfer fuel for combustion, hydraulic fluid for thrust reversers, and oil for lubrication — account for most of the company's sales. A second subsidiary, Kreisler Polska, supplies machined components to Kreisler Industrial from a manufacturing plant in Krakow, Poland.

The company has designs on using its operations in Poland as a potential magnet for growing its business in Europe. Kreisler Manufacturing has also used the Paris Air Show as a stage to demonstrate its abilities to prospective European clients.

Three industrial customers and the US government account for nearly 80% of Kreisler Manufacturing's sales. The company has benefited from increased demand for the engines used to power the F/A-22 Raptor aircraft used by the US military.

Chairman Wallace Kelly controls a 37% stake in Kreisler Manufacturing.

EXECUTIVES

Chairman, Wallace N. Kelly, age 70
Co-President, CEO, and Director, Michael D. Stern, age 44
Human Resources Manager, Lisa Sibrel
Co-President, CFO, Secretary, Treasurer,, Edward A. Stern, age 49
Auditors: Rothstein, Kass & Company, P.C.

LOCATIONS

HQ: Kreisler Manufacturing Corporation
180 Van Riper Ave., Elmwood Park, NJ 07407
Phone: 201-791-0700   **Fax:** 201-791-8015
Web: www.kreisler-ind.com

2008 Sales

	$ mil.	% of total
US	28.9	99
Poland	0.4	1
Total	**29.3**	**100**

PRODUCTS/OPERATIONS

2008 Sales

	$ Mil.
% of Total	
Military	14.6
50	
Commercial	10.7
36	
Industrial gas turbine	4.0
14	
Total	**29.3**
100	

Selected Products
Air ducting
Cooling baffles
De-icing lines
Environmental control lines
Fuel manifolds
Fuel tank and transfer lines
Hydraulic actuation systems

Selected Services
Bending
  CNC, hydraulic and manual bending
  End Prep (beading, flaring, swaging)
  SS, Ti, Inconel and Al alloys
  Tube forms, tube-inside-a-tube, 1 to 1 bend capable
Brazing
  Gold, silver, nickel, and copper braze alloys
  Induction and torch brazing
  Vacuum furnace brazing
Engineering
  AutoCAD software

Design, mechanical, method, and metallurgical engineers on staff
In house tool and die group
Pro Engineer CAD/CAM software
Forming
  Sheetmetal and tubular die forming
  500 ton hydraulic press
Heat treating
  Controlled atmosphere and vacuum furnace
  Precipitation hardening
  Solution heat treating and annealing
  Stress relieving (titanium and other alloys)
Welding
  Manual and machine welding (GTAW)
  Orbital Welding
  Vacuum chamber titanium welding

COMPETITORS

Argo-Tech	PCC Airfoils
Ducommun	Pratt & Whitney
GE Aviation	Rolls-Royce
Honeywell Aerospace	Corporation
Héroux-Devtek	Triumph Group
Magellan Aerospace	Volvo Aero
Pacific Aerospace	

HISTORICAL FINANCIALS
Company Type: Public

Income Statement
FYE: June 30

	REVENUE ($ mil.)	NET INCOME ($ mil.)	NET PROFIT MARGIN	EMPLOYEES
06/08	29.3	1.9	6.5%	247
06/07	23.9	2.0	8.4%	201
06/06	19.7	1.2	6.1%	155
06/05	14.4	0.2	1.4%	124
06/04	12.3	(0.7)	—	110
Annual Growth	**24.2%**	**—**	**—**	**22.4%**

2008 Year-End Financials
Debt ratio: 0.8%
Return on equity: 12.0%
Cash ($ mil.): 7.2
Current ratio: 4.16
Long-term debt ($ mil.): 0.1
No. of shares (mil.): 1.9
Dividends
  Yield: —
  Payout: —
Market value ($ mil.): 22.9

	STOCK PRICE ($) FY Close	P/E High/Low	PER SHARE ($) Earnings	Dividends	Book Value
06/08	12.25	20 11	0.99	0.00	8.32
06/07	15.52	27 9	1.04	0.00	7.04
06/06	13.37	26 8	0.63	0.00	5.86
06/05	5.30	102 46	0.10	0.00	5.23
06/04	7.20	— —	(0.37)	0.00	5.23
Annual Growth	**14.2%**	**— —**	**—**	**—**	**12.3%**

KS Bancorp

KS Bancorp is the holding company for KS Bank, which serves the eastern North Carolina counties of Johnston, Wake, Wayne, and Wilson, including portions of the Raleigh metro area. Through nearly 10 branches, it offers standard deposit products such as checking, savings, and money market accounts, as well as individual retirement accounts and certificates of deposit. The bank specializes in real estate lending, including one- to four-family residential mortgages, commercial mortgages, and construction and land development loans, which together account for more than 90% of its loan portfolio. It also offers investment services. KS Bank was chartered in 1924.

EXECUTIVES

President and CEO, KS Bancorp and KS Bank,
Harold T. Keen
CFO, KS Bancorp and KS Bank, Earl W. Worley Jr.
Smithfield City Executive, Ted G. Godwin
Branch Administrator, R. Walter Krentz Jr.
Mortgage Banking, William C. Clarke
Garner City Executive, Kevin J. Jorgenson
Auditors: Dixon Hughes PLLC

LOCATIONS

HQ: KS Bancorp, Inc.
207 W. Second St., Kenly, NC 27542
Phone: 919-938-3101   **Fax:** 919-938-2681
Web: www.ksbankinc.com

COMPETITORS

Bank of America
BB&T
Crescent Financial
First Citizens
BancShares

Four Oaks Fincorp
RBC Bank

HISTORICAL FINANCIALS

Company Type: Public

Income Statement

FYE: December 31

	ASSETS ($ mil.)	NET INCOME ($ mil.)	INCOME AS % OF ASSETS	EMPLOYEES
12/06	286.8	2.2	0.8%	86
12/05	261.4	1.7	0.7%	86
12/04	236.9	1.3	0.5%	76
12/03	201.5	1.4	0.7%	76
12/02	191.1	1.3	0.7%	62
Annual Growth	10.7%	14.1%	—	8.5%

2006 Year-End Financials

Equity as % of assets: 6.04%	Dividends
Return on assets: 0.8%	Yield: 2.0%
Return on equity: 12.6%	Payout: 31.1%
Long-term debt ($ mil.): 43.0	Market value ($ mil.): —
No. of shares (mil.): —	Sales ($ mil.): 20.6

	STOCK PRICE ($) FY Close	P/E High/Low		PER SHARE ($) Earnings	Dividends	Book Value
12/06	26.05	19	11	1.67	0.52	(0.00)
12/05	18.15	20	14	1.24	0.51	(0.00)
12/04	18.48	18	14	1.08	0.48	(0.00)
12/03	16.00	21	14	0.95	0.48	(0.00)
12/02	12.92	16	13	0.92	0.36	(0.00)
Annual Growth	19.2%	—	—	16.1%	9.6%	—

Kulicke and Soffa

Some assembly required is music to Kulicke and Soffa Industries' ears. Kulicke and Soffa (K&S) is one of the world's top suppliers of assembly equipment for the semiconductor industry. Its die bonders and wire bonders use fine wires to connect an integrated circuit to its package leads, thereby completing the chip's electrical circuit. K&S also makes consumables for its chip assembly equipment, such as dicing blades. The company sells its products to such contractors and chip makers as Advanced Semiconductor Engineering, Amkor, Intel, Micron Technology, STMicroelectronics, and Texas Instruments. Customers in Asia account for about three-quarters of the company's sales.

The worldwide recession of 2008 led to severely depressed conditions for the semiconductor industry, which hampered K&S's sales of equipment and expendable tools. The company reduced its headcount by about 11% during fiscal 2008. As the recession continued into 2009, K&S saw its sales keep falling as chip makers drastically cut their capital expenditures in the pronounced downturn. The company slashed its workforce by another 16% as a result. It went into the red for the first time in four years. Mirroring the semiconductor industry's ups and downs, K&S tends to lose money in bad years for the industry, and it carries an accumulated deficit of around $185 million.

In 2008 K&S acquired Orthodyne Electronics Corporation for $80 million in cash and about 7.1 million shares of common stock (worth around $45 million at the time the deal was struck). Orthodyne makes wedge bonders and wedges for the power management and hybrid module markets. The firm posted 2007 sales of $110 million. Its executive team and 280 employees joined K&S under the transaction.

At the same time, K&S sold its wire business to W.C. Heraeus GmbH, a unit of Heraeus Holding, for about $165 million in cash. While the wire business was strongly symbiotic with the company's core line of wire bonders, K&S noted the business had significant requirements for working capital that could better be handled by Heraeus.

Scott Kulicke retired as chairman and CEO in 2010. The son of a company co-founder, Kulicke became CEO in 1979 and chairman in 1984. He was replaced as CEO by Bruno Guilmart, former CEO of Lattice Semiconductor. Director MacDonell Roehm assumed the role of chairman.

Kulicke and Soffa Industries has facilities or offices in China, Germany, Hong Kong, Israel, Japan, Malaysia, the Philippines, Singapore, South Korea, Switzerland, Taiwan, Thailand, and the US.

HISTORY

Fred Kulicke and Albert Soffa formed a custom engineering business in 1951; five years later, they began developing transistor assembly equipment for Western Electric. The company went public in 1961. In 1970 it opened a manufacturing plant in Israel, but stumbled, and was forced to make drastic cuts. Kulicke's son Scott became product manager in 1975 and saved the firm by developing a computerized wire bonder. He became president and CEO in 1979.

After suffering through the industry's boom-and-bust cycles of the 1980s, Kulicke and Soffa (K&S) began making acquisitions in an attempt to insulate itself from market shifts. It acquired General Signal's Assembly Technologies division in 1994, American Fine Wire in 1995, and Semitec, a maker of blades for dicing saws, in 1996. Also in 1996 K&S formed a joint venture, Flip Chip Technologies, with GM's Delco Electronics unit to offer specialized "flip chip" packaging services and technology licensing.

In 1999 K&S acquired advanced packaging technology from MicroModule Systems and formed its Advanced Polymer Solutions joint venture with Polyset. The next year the company acquired two makers of test interconnect equipment, Cerprobe and privately held Probe Technology. In 2001 K&S made Flip Chip Technologies a wholly owned subsidiary when it bought out Delco's stake in the joint venture.

Also in 2001 the company laid off about 500 employees and shuttered a factory, moves brought on by a sharp downturn in global semiconductor markets. The next year K&S further retooled its organizational structure — a move tied to the loss of 200 more jobs — and moved some production lines to China and Singapore. In 2003 the company pared some product lines; it sold its sawing equipment and blades business to Israel-based Advanced Dicing Technologies.

In 2004 K&S sold off its flip chip operations to a newly formed company called FlipChip International. Albert Soffa, who retired from the management of K&S in 1986, died in 2005 at the age of 84.

In 2006 K&S sold its wafer test assets to SV Probe for $10 million and sold its package test assets to Investcorp Technology Ventures II, a unit of Investcorp Bank, for $17 million. The company divested those product lines to focus on the semiconductor assembly equipment market.

In 2006 the company acquired the Alphasem subsidiary of Dover Corp. for about $27 million in cash. Alphasem supplied die-bonding equipment for semiconductor manufacturing and packaging equipment for microelectromechanical systems (MEMS) devices. The die-bonding process in chip making precedes the wire-bonding process step, making Alphasem a complementary fit in the K&S product portfolio.

EXECUTIVES

Chairman, MacDonell Roehm Jr., age 71
President, CEO, and Director, Bruno Guilmart, age 50
VP, Ran Bareket, age 44
VP Worldwide Sales, Tek (TC) Chee Mak, age 56
VP and General Counsel, David J. Anderson
SVP, CFO and Principal Accounting Officer,
Jonathan H. Chou, age 46
SVP Legal Affairs and General Counsel, Lester A. Wong, age 44
SVP Business Operations, Christian Rheault, age 45, $342,311 total compensation
SVP Worldwide Operations, Shay Torton, age 49, $515,222 total compensation
Secretary, Susan Waters
SVP Engineering, Charles Salmons, age 55, $586,774 total compensation
Auditors: PricewaterhouseCoopers LLP

LOCATIONS

HQ: Kulicke and Soffa Industries, Inc.
1005 Virginia Dr., Fort Washington, PA 19034
Phone: 215-784-6000   **Fax:** 215-784-6001
Web: www.kns.com

2010 Sales

	$ mil.	% of total
Asia		
Taiwan	222.9	29
China	142.5	19
Korea	88.3	12
Hong Kong	83.7	11
Malaysia	43.2	6
Philippines	35.0	5
Japan	31.6	4
Thailand	24.8	3
Singapore	22.6	3
US	10.5	1
Other countries	57.7	7
Total	**762.8**	**100**

PRODUCTS/OPERATIONS

2010 Sales

	$ mil.	% of total
Equipment	692.0	91
Expendable tools	70.8	9
Total	**762.8**	**100**

Selected Products

Assembly Equipment
  Die bonders
  Solder sphere attachment systems
  Wire bonders (ball and wedge)
Expendable Tools
  Bonding wedges
  Capillaries
  Saw blades

COMPETITORS

Advanced Systems
  Automation
AEM Holdings
ASM International
BE Semiconductor
  Industries
CoorsTek

Disco Corp.
Palomar Technologies
Renesas Electronics
SHINKAWA
Suss MicroTec
Tokyo Seimitsu

HISTORICAL FINANCIALS

Company Type: Public

Income Statement

FYE: September 30

	REVENUE ($ mil.)	NET INCOME ($ mil.)	NET PROFIT MARGIN	EMPLOYEES
09/10	762.8	142.1	18.6%	2,950
09/09	225.2	(36.0)	—	2,167
09/08	328.0	3.8	1.2%	2,573
09/07	700.4	37.7	5.4%	2,903
09/06	696.3	52.2	7.5%	2,454
Annual Growth	**2.3%**	**28.4%**	**—**	**4.7%**

2010 Year-End Financials

Debt ratio: 30.5%
Return on equity: 44.1%
Cash ($ mil.): 178.1
Current ratio: 3.78
Long-term debt ($ mil.): 98.5

No. of shares (mil.): 70.4
Dividends
  Yield: 0.0%
  Payout: —
Market value ($ mil.): 436.0

	STOCK PRICE ($) FY Close	P/E High/Low		PER SHARE ($) Earnings	Dividends	Book Value
09/10	6.19	5	2	1.92	0.00	4.58
09/09	6.03	—	—	(0.58)	0.00	2.50
09/08	4.51	127	62	0.07	0.00	1.91
09/07	8.48	22	13	0.57	0.00	1.54
09/06	8.84	16	8	0.78	0.00	1.39
Annual Growth	**(8.5%)**	**—**	**—**	**25.3%**	**—**	**34.7%**

L & L Energy

You'll excuse L & L Energy (formerly L & L International) if it's a bit jet lagged. Incorporated in Nevada with headquarters in Seattle, the company mines coal in China. Granted a license by the government to extract a set amount of coal in exchange for up-front fees, L & L owns three mines in China's Yunnan and Guizhou provinces. The company currently extracts more than 630,000 tons of coal per year from the mines. It also processes coal to produce coke used in steel production, medium coal used for heating, and coal slurries used as a lower quality fuel. L & L's coking operation processes primarily purchased coal into metallurgical coke. The company also wholesales and brokers raw coal.

CompOn the heels of the Chinese government's mandate for coal industry consolidation, L & L Energy plans to expand its existing coal mines and purchase smaller operations that fail to meet the government's mandated production minimums. Inland China has begun to develop at a more rapid rate leading to an increased demand for energy, which is 70% coal fueled in that country.

As part of its plan to focus on inland coal operations, in 2009 L & L sold its 80% share in LEK air compressor operations back to the company for about $4.2 million. The following year it sold its 93% interest in Hon Shen Coal to Guangxi Liuzhou Lifu Machinery for $6 million. It had purchased the coal washing facility in late 2009 for $3.8 million. Also in 2010 the company purchased its Ping Yi mine, Hong Xing Coal Washing, and Zone Lin Coking.

President and CEO Dickson Lee holds about a quarter of the company's stock.

EXECUTIVES

Chairman and CEO, Dickson V. Lee, age 62, $232,899 total compensation
CEO, KMC Energy Operations, Tony Li
EVP US Operations, Clayton Fong, $129,865 total compensation
EVP Corporate Development, Connie Wong
VP Corporate Infrastructure, Edmund C. Moy
Vice Chairman, Norman Y. (Norm) Mineta, age 79
Acting CFO, Rosemary Wang, $205,702 total compensation
Chief Accounting Officer, Paul Cheng
Accounting Director, David Lin
General Manager, China Operations, Paul Lee
Operational Director, Sheng-Lin Chang
Auditors: Kabani & Company, Inc.

LOCATIONS

HQ: L & L Energy, Inc.
130 Andover Park East, Ste. 200, Seattle, WA 98188
Phone: 206-264-8065   **Fax:** 206-264-7971
Web: www.lnlinternational.com

PRODUCTS/OPERATIONS

2010 Sales

	$ mil.	% of total
Mining	64.5	59
Washing	18.3	17
Wholesale	13.2	12
Coking	13.2	12
Total	**109.2**	**100**

COMPETITORS

Anglo American
BHP Billiton
BHP Billiton Plc
China Coal Energy

Rio Tinto plc
Shenhua
Yanzhou Coal

HISTORICAL FINANCIALS

Company Type: Public

Income Statement

FYE: April 30

	REVENUE ($ mil.)	NET INCOME ($ mil.)	NET PROFIT MARGIN	EMPLOYEES
04/11	223.9	36.8	16.4%	1,600
04/10	109.2	32.9	30.1%	1,400
04/09	40.9	10.0	24.4%	1,200
04/08	32.1	1.4	4.4%	60
04/07	19.0	1.2	6.3%	300
Annual Growth	**85.3%**	**135.3%**	**—**	**52.0%**

2011 Year-End Financials

Debt ratio: 0.6%
Return on equity: 27.0%
Cash ($ mil.): 4.9
Current ratio: 1.14
Long-term debt ($ mil.): 0.8

No. of shares (mil.): 32.3
Dividends
  Yield: —
  Payout: —
Market value ($ mil.): 224.3

	STOCK PRICE ($) FY Close	P/E High/Low		PER SHARE ($) Earnings	Dividends	Book Value
04/11	6.95	11	4	1.21	0.00	4.23
04/10	10.80	12	1	1.28	0.00	2.76
04/09	1.80	5	1	0.46	0.00	1.07
Annual Growth	**96.5%**	**—**	**—**	**62.2%**	**—**	**99.2%**

Ladenburg Thalmann

Laden with cash? You might want to call Ladenburg Thalmann Financial Services. The company provides asset management, brokerage, and investment banking services to corporate, institutional, and individual clients throughout the US. Subsidiaries Triad Advisors, Investacorp, and Securities America are independent broker-dealers primarily serving retail clients; together they have some 2,700 registered representatives and manage more than $70 billion in assets. Subsidiary Ladenburg Thalmann & Co. is an investment bank providing capital raising and advisory services to middle-market companies. Ladenburg Thalmann Asset Management offers mutual funds, alternative investments, and investment counseling.

Ladenburg Thalmann bought retail brokerage Securities America from American Express for some $150 million in 2011. The deal more than doubled its network of registered representatives

Acquisitions are nothing new for Ladenburg Thalmann. The purchases of Triad Advisors and Investacorp built up the company's brokerage and investment management business, which now accounts for the majority of the company's sales. The segment's revenues have ballooned nearly tenfold since 2007. That growth has offset declining income from the firm's investment banking activities, which have slowed down over the years. Ladenburg Thalmann's wealth management business got another boost when the company acquired Premier Trust from Western Alliance Bancorporation in 2010.

Ladenburg Thalmann focuses its investment banking practice on underwriting IPOs for special purpose acquisition companies, also known as SPACs or blank check companies. Other offerings include advisory services, management fees, and private placements. Ladenburg Thalmann in 2008 also acquired New York-based Punk, Zeigel &

Company, a boutique investment bank serving the health care, biotechnology, and life sciences sectors.

Founded in 1876, Ladenburg Thalmann boasts of having had Albert Einstein as a client. Chairman Philip Frost (founder of drugmaker IVAX, sold to Teva Pharmaceutical Industries in 2006) owns about a third of the company.

EXECUTIVES

Chairman, Phillip Frost, age 74
President, CEO, and Director, Richard J. (Dick) Lampen, age 57, $547,437 total compensation
EVP and Director; President and CEO, Ladenburg Thalmann & Co., Mark Zeitchick, age 46, $1,253,673 total compensation
VP and Corporate Counsel, Brian Heller
VP and CFO, Brett H. Kaufman, $351,229 total compensation
Vice Chairman, Howard M. Lorber, age 62
Vice Chairman and Co-Head Investment Banking, James S. Cassel, age 55
Equity Research and Institutional Sales Coverage, Ladenburg Thalmann & Co., Ariel Schochet
Equity Research and Institutional Sales Coverage, Ladenburg Thalmann & Co., Edwin Groshans
Equity Research and Institutional Sales Coverage, Ladenburg Thalmann & Co., Bradley Ball
SVP Equity Research, Ladenburg Thalmann & Co., Aaron M. Schwartz
Auditors:

LOCATIONS

HQ: Ladenburg Thalmann Financial Services Inc.
4400 Biscayne Blvd., 12th Fl., Miami, FL 33137
Phone: 212-409-2000 **Fax:** 305-572-4199
Web: www.ladenburg.com

PRODUCTS/OPERATIONS

2010 Sales

	$ mil.	% of total
Commissions	108.4	56
Advisory fees	53.6	27
Investment banking	21.0	11
Interest & dividends	0.5	-
Principal transactions	0.1	-
Other	10.9	6
Total	**194.5**	**100**

2010 Sales by Segment

	$ mil.	% of total
Brokerage & Advisory Services	150.4	77
Ladenburg	41.2	21
Corporate	2.0	1
Premier	0.9	1
Total	**194.5**	**100**

COMPETITORS

Citigroup Global Markets	LPL Investment Holdings
Detwiler Fenton	Morgan Stanley
Gleacher & Company	National Holdings
Investors Capital Holdings	Sage Advisory Services
JPMorgan Chase	UBS Financial Services

HISTORICAL FINANCIALS

Company Type: Public

Income Statement

FYE: December 31

	REVENUE ($ mil.)	NET INCOME ($ mil.)	NET PROFIT MARGIN	EMPLOYEES
12/10	194.5	(11.0)	—	152
12/09	150.7	(18.7)	—	169
12/08	121.0	(20.3)	—	176
12/07	95.8	9.4	9.8%	173
12/06	46.9	4.7	10.0%	172
Annual Growth	**42.7%**	**—**	**—**	**(3.0%)**

2010 Year-End Financials

Debt ratio: 59.4%
Return on equity: —
Cash ($ mil.): 6.9
Current ratio: —
Long-term debt ($ mil.): 27.9

No. of shares (mil.): 183.5
Dividends
Yield: —
Payout: —
Market value ($ mil.): 214.7

	STOCK PRICE ($) FY Close	P/E High/Low		PER SHARE ($) Earnings	Dividends	Book Value
12/10	1.17	—	—	(0.06)	0.00	0.26
12/09	0.64	—	—	(0.11)	0.00	0.23
12/08	0.72	—	—	(0.12)	0.00	0.30
12/07	2.12	63	20	0.06	0.00	0.33
12/06	1.22	60	15	0.03	0.00	0.18
Annual Growth	**(1.0%)**	**—**	**—**	**—**	**—**	**8.7%**

Lafayette Community Bancorp

Lafayette Community Bancorp is the holding company for Lafayette Community Bank, which was founded in 2000 to serve consumers and businesses in its namesake Indiana city. Through about five branches, the bank offers such traditional retail products as checking and savings accounts, certificates of deposit, individual retirement accounts, and credit cards. Lafayette Community Bank uses funds from deposits mainly to originate one- to-four-family residential mortgages and commercial mortgages. It also issues business, construction, and land development loans.

EXECUTIVES

CFO, Bill Buchanan
VP and Operations Officer, Director; VP, Administration, Lafayette Community Bank, Cathy DeFord
VP and Controller, Lafayette Community Bank, Dennis R. Hardwick
Director; VP, Administration, Lafayette Community Bank, Richard D. Murray
Assistant VP and Branch Manager, Greenbush Branch, Lafayette Community Bank, Cathy Stachowicz
Assistant VP and Loan Officer, Lafayette Community Bank, Nancy Naville
Assistant VP and Mortgage Loan Officer, Lafayette Community Bank, Sharon K. Morrissey
Auditors:

LOCATIONS

HQ: Lafayette Community Bancorp
2 N. 4th St., Lafayette, IN 47901
Phone: 765-429-7200 **Fax:** 765-429-7100
Web: www.lafayettecommunitybank.com

COMPETITORS

Fifth Third	MainSource Financial
Huntington Bancshares	Old National Bancorp
JPMorgan Chase	PNC Financial
LSB Financial	

HISTORICAL FINANCIALS

Company Type: Public

Income Statement

FYE: December 31

	ASSETS ($ mil.)	NET INCOME ($ mil.)	INCOME AS % OF ASSETS	EMPLOYEES
12/06	165.2	5.3	3.2%	33
12/04	145.5	1.3	0.9%	34
12/03	98.8	0.8	0.8%	17
12/02	76.7	0.7	0.9%	17
12/01	43.9	(0.4)	—	16
Annual Growth	**30.3%**	**—**	**—**	**15.6%**

Equity as % of assets: 46.09%
Return on assets: 3.2%
Return on equity: —
Long-term debt ($ mil.): 27.9
No. of shares (mil.): 183.5
Dividends
Yield: —
Payout: —
Market value ($ mil.): 214.7
Sales ($ mil.): 194.5

LaPolla Industries

LaPolla Industries would hate for its customers to have leaky roofs over their heads or insufficiently protected exterior walls. The company makes foam products used to protect roofs and the "building envelope," which is the separation of the exterior and interior parts of a building. It also makes coatings for weatherproofing concrete and metal roofing and other materials. The company changed its name in 2005 when it absorbed subsidiary LaPolla Industries, a provider of roof coatings and polyurethane foam construction systems. The former IFT Corp., which had previously been called Urecoats, acquired LaPolla in 2005. Chairman Richard Kurtz owns 57% of LaPolla.

LaPolla established its first international branch in 2009, opening a Canadian headquarters in Toronto, Ontario. Later that year, the company received Canadian Product Approval, which allows it market Foam-LOK spray polyurethane foam insulation systems throughout Canada.

EXECUTIVES

Chairman, Richard J. Kurtz, age 71
President, CEO, and Director, Douglas J. Kramer, age 47, $1,032,361 total compensation
CFO and Treasurer, Charles Zajaczkowski
EVP, Chief Governance Officer, Secretary, and Director, Michael T. Adams, age 45, $182,814 total compensation
General Manager, Lapolla Canada., Marc Kast
Auditors:

LOCATIONS

HQ: LaPolla Industries, Inc.
15402 Vantage Pkwy. East, Ste. 322, Houston, TX
77032
Phone: 281-219-4100   **Fax:** 281-219-4102
Web: www.lapollaindustries.com

PRODUCTS/OPERATIONS

2009 Sales

	$ mil.	% of total
Foam	43.1	86
Coatings	6.9	14
Total	**50.0**	**100**

COMPETITORS

ADCO Products	Henkel
Ashland Performance	Henry Company
Materials	PPG Industries
Benjamin Moore	RPM International
Duro-Last Roofing	

HISTORICAL FINANCIALS

Company Type: Public

Income Statement   FYE: December 31

	REVENUE ($ mil.)	NET INCOME ($ mil.)	NET PROFIT MARGIN	EMPLOYEES
12/10	70.5	2.1	3.0%	79
12/09	50.0	(2.8)	—	59
12/08	47.6	(3.5)	—	66
12/07	31.8	(5.1)	—	41
12/06	30.3	(3.0)	—	48
Annual Growth	**23.5%**	**—**	**—**	**13.3%**

2010 Year-End Financials

Debt ratio: 1.1%	No. of shares (mil.): 83.7
Return on equity: 33.3%	Dividends
Cash ($ mil.): 0.0	Yield: —
Current ratio: 1.52	Payout: —
Long-term debt ($ mil.): 0.1	Market value ($ mil.): 50.2

	STOCK PRICE ($) FY Close	P/E High/Low	PER SHARE ($) Earnings	Dividends	Book Value
12/10	0.60	75 36	0.01	0.00	0.08
12/09	0.49	— —	(0.06)	0.00	0.06
12/08	0.51	— —	(0.07)	0.00	0.04
12/07	0.51	— —	(0.11)	0.00	0.03
12/06	0.56	— —	(0.06)	0.00	0.08
Annual Growth	**1.7%**	**— —**	**—**	**—**	**(1.5%)**

LHC Group

The injured and ailing in need of a little TLC need look no further than LHC. LHC Group administers post-acute health care services through home nursing agencies, hospices, and long-term acute care hospitals (LTAC). The company operates through two segments: home-based services and facility-based services in rural areas in about 20 US states. LHC's home health nursing agencies provide care to Medicare beneficiaries, offering such services as private duty nursing, physical therapy, and medically-oriented social services. Its hospices provide palliative care for terminal patients, while its LTACs serve patients who no longer need intensive care but still require complex care in a hospital setting.

LHC also operates a handful of rehabilitation, disease management, and other specialty health facilities. Its Telehealth Services segment delivers medical care remotely via telephone, Web-based applications, and e-mail. The use of telehealth expands access to care to more patients and rural locations, as well as provides for better monitoring of patients with chronic health problems.

LHC gets the majority of its revenue from its home-based health services, located primarily in the Southeast and Midwest regions of the country. Medicare payments account for more than 80% of its service income. Given that such a significant portion of the company's revenue is derived from federal payments, LHC is vulnerable to changes in reimbursement levels to Medicare.

The Patient Protection and Affordable Care Act first enacted in 2010 calls for a number of changes to the way Medicare is paid out; some benefit the company and some do not. LHC, like any other LTAC, hospice, and home care provider, is keeping close tabs on the various rules being set forth in the act and making changes to its operations accordingly. For example, the Affordable Care Act bases certain reimbursements for hospice providers on productivity and efficiency levels, meaning hospice providers will have to make the necessary adjustments to ensure they are complying with the new rules, which are being enacted between 2010 and 2015, in order to receive payments.

While Medicare will likely remain a thorn in the company's side for the next few years as it gets used to all the new rules, demand for services is an area that LHC is not expected to have problems with. Home health care, long-term care, and nursing services are expected to see a surge in demand with the aging US population. LHC's services were enough in demand in 2010 that the company was able to increase its net service revenue by about 20% compared to the prior year. To meet increased demand and to penetrate additional markets around the country, LHC in 2010 acquired a number of home nursing agencies, hospice agencies, an LTAC, and a private duty agency. It also opened a dozen home health agencies.

Along with expanding into new markets through development or acquisitions, LHC also partners with not-for-profit hospitals because such joint ventures tend to provide a more attractive return on investment for the company. It has such agreements with West Tennessee Healthcare, Southeast Alabama Medical Center, East Alabama Medical Center, Three Rivers Community Hospital (Oregon), Woods Memorial Hospital (Tennessee), and the continuing care arm of CHRISTUS Health in northeast Texas. In total, it has nearly 70 joint ventures across its home nursing, hospice, and LTAC agencies, mostly with hospitals.

LHC has also been focused on consolidating its old, disparate, legacy IT systems to just a couple of main systems to streamline and standardize its documentation and process requirements. By eliminating the many, many legacy systems it used to operate, LHC can easily add new acquisitions to the main IT platforms.

Chairman and CEO Keith Myers, who co-founded LHC Group in 1994, owns nearly 15% of the company.

EXECUTIVES

Chairman and CEO, Keith G. Myers, age 51, $836,708 total compensation
President and COO, Donald D. (Don) Stelly, age 42, $491,741 total compensation
VP and Chief Administrative Officer, Marcus Macip
VP Divisional Operations, Pat Derouen
VP Quality and Performance Improvement, Barbara Goodman
VP Investor Relations, Eric C. Elliott
VP Facility Based Services, Stuart Archer
VP Government Affairs, Harold Taylor
VP Marketing, Blaine C. Williams
VP and Associate General Counsel, Eden Ezell
VP and Business Development Project Manager, Michael Freeman
VP Procurement and Treasury Management, Albert Simien Jr.
VP Finance, John Whitlock
VP and Associate General Counsel, Josh Proffitt
VP Education and Risk Management, Kendra Case
VP Information Systems Operations, Morris Sanford
VP Clinical Leadership Training, Melanie Kuehn
VP Sales and Marketing, Stephen Lepley
VP Acquisition Transition, Pam Bridges
CIO, Rajesh (Raj) Shetye
SVP, Senior Counsel, Director Corporate Compliance, and Director Regulatory and Government Affairs, Richard A. MacMillan, age 58
SVP Corporate Development, Daryl J. Doise, age 53, $476,965 total compensation
SVP, General Counsel, and Director Mergers and Acquisitions, Peter C. November, age 41
Divisional VP, Home Based Services, Gateway Division, Chris Stagg
Divisional VP, Home Based Services, Coastal Division, Ammy Lee
Division VP, Home Based Services, Acadia, Angie Begnaud
Compliance Officer, Josh Profitt
Divisional VP, Eastern Division Sales, George Wyatt
Divisional VP, Western Division Sales, Scott Tobey
Special Advisor, CEO and Director, John L. Indest, age 59, $732,998 total compensation
SVP, CFO, and Treasurer, Peter J. (Pete) Roman, age 60, $356,841 total compensation
Director Human Resources, Lolanda B. Brown
Divisional VP, Home Based Services, Beltway Division, Susan Sylvester
Auditors: KPMG LLP

LOCATIONS

HQ: LHC Group, Inc.
420 W. Pinhook Rd., Ste. A, Lafayette, LA 70503
Phone: 337-233-1307   **Fax:** 337-235-8037
Web: www.lhcgroup.com

2010 Selected Locations

State	No.
Louisiana	64
Tennessee	35
Mississippi	30
Kentucky	30
Alabama	26
Arkansas	20
West Virginia	18
Idaho	16
Washington	14
Texas	12
Maryland	10
Missouri	9
Florida	6
Georgia	6
Oregon	4
Viriginia	4
North Carolina	2
Ohio	2
Oklahoma	2
Total	**310**

PRODUCTS/OPERATIONS

2010 Sales

	$ mil.	% of total
Home-based services	558.6	88
Facility-based services	76.4	12
Total	**635.0**	**100**

2010 Sales by Payer

	% of total
Medicare	80
Medicaid	3
Other	17
Total	**100**

COMPETITORS

Almost Family	Health First
Amedisys	Help at Home
American HomePatient	Home Instead
Apria Healthcare	Kindred Healthcare
Consulate Health Care	Manor Care
Critical Homecare	National Home Health
Solutions	NHC
Gentiva	Personal-Touch Home
Girling Health Care	Care
Guardian Home Care	Trinity HomeCare
Holdings	VITAS Healthcare

HISTORICAL FINANCIALS

Company Type: Public

Income Statement

FYE: December 31

	REVENUE ($ mil.)	NET INCOME ($ mil.)	NET PROFIT MARGIN	EMPLOYEES
12/10	635.0	48.8	7.7%	7,973
12/09	532.0	57.8	10.9%	6,998
12/08	383.3	30.2	7.9%	5,376
12/07	298.0	19.6	6.6%	4,498
12/06	215.2	20.6	9.6%	3,959
Annual Growth	31.1%	24.1%	—	19.1%

2010 Year-End Financials

Debt ratio: —
Return on equity: 17.8%
Cash ($ mil.): 0.3
Current ratio: 2.08
Long-term debt ($ mil.): —
No. of shares (mil.): 18.2
Dividends
 Yield: —
 Payout: —
Market value ($ mil.): 545.2

	STOCK PRICE ($) FY Close	P/E High/Low	PER SHARE ($) Earnings	Dividends	Book Value
12/10	30.00	14 7	2.68	0.00	15.06
12/09	33.61	15 7	2.43	0.00	12.29
12/08	36.00	22 8	1.69	0.00	9.71
12/07	24.98	30 17	1.11	0.00	7.96
12/06	28.51	23 11	1.27	0.00	6.84
Annual Growth	1.3%	— —	20.5%	—	21.8%

Life Partners Holdings

Life Partners Holdings, parent company of Life Partners, Inc., makes its bucks by helping its customers make a buck. The company facilitates viatical and life settlement transactions, in which an institution or wealthy investor purchases individual life insurance policies (at a discount) and becomes the beneficiary of those policies when they mature. Viatical settlements involve terminally ill policyholders with only a couple of years to live; life settlement transactions involve sellers with longer life expectancies. Life Partners makes its money from fees earned by facilitating viatical and life settlements. Nearly all of the company's business is done through life settlement brokers.

Life Partners has been stepping up marketing efforts to institutional investors, which the company sees as key to its future growth. It also serves as advisor and purchasing agent for a group of closed-end investment funds based in the Bahamas.

The majority of the company's clients are high net worth individuals who are referred to the company through a network of financial planners. Life Partners developed its network through referrals by forming long-standing relationships with its financial planners. Since its incorporation in 1991, Life Partners has completed over 117,000 transactions for its worldwide client base of about 30,000 clients in connection with the purchase of some 6,500 policies.

Chairman and CEO Brian Pardo owns just over 50% of the company.

EXECUTIVES

Chairman, President, and CEO; CEO, Life Partners, Inc., Brian D. Pardo, age 68, $1,022,398 total compensation
CFO and Principal Accounting Officer, David M. Martin, age 53, $145,164 total compensation
VP Administration, Life Partners, Inc., Deborah Carr, age 40, $463,702 total compensation
VP Policy Administration, Life Partners, Inc., Kurt D. Carr, age 41, $500,557 total compensation
Secretary, General Counsel, and Director; President, Life Partners, Inc., R. Scott Peden, age 47, $557,503 total compensation
COO and CIO, Life Partners, Inc., Mark Embry, age 55, $533,731 total compensation
Auditors:

LOCATIONS

HQ: Life Partners Holdings, Inc.
204 Woodhew, Waco, TX 76712
Phone: 254-751-7797 **Fax:** 254-751-1025
Web: www.lphi.net

COMPETITORS

Coventry First	Living Benefits
Forum National	National Financial
Investments	Partners
Life Equity	

HISTORICAL FINANCIALS

Company Type: Public

Income Statement

FYE: February 28

	ASSETS ($ mil.)	NET INCOME ($ mil.)	INCOME AS % OF ASSETS	EMPLOYEES
02/10	72.7	29.4	40.4%	62
02/09	52.4	27.2	51.9%	56
02/08	31.9	18.8	58.9%	40
02/07	16.6	3.4	20.5%	37
02/06	12.0	1.1	9.2%	37
Annual Growth	56.9%	127.4%	—	13.8%

2010 Year-End Financials

Equity as % of assets: 82.32%
Return on assets: 40.4%
Return on equity: 49.2%
Long-term debt ($ mil.): —
No. of shares (mil.): 18.8
Dividends
 Yield: 4.0%
 Payout: 41.4%
Market value ($ mil.): 309.2
Sales ($ mil.): 113.0

	STOCK PRICE ($) FY Close	P/E High/Low	PER SHARE ($) Earnings	Dividends	Book Value
02/10	16.46	11 7	1.58	0.66	3.19
02/09	13.69	20 5	1.46	0.19	2.37
02/08	9.63	27 5	1.00	0.15	1.22
02/07	5.35	31 10	0.20	0.11	0.41
02/06	2.94	55 27	0.06	0.10	0.28
Annual Growth	53.8%	— —	126.5%	60.3%	83.9%

Lighting Science Group

Going green turns on Lighting Science (LSGC). The company designs, manufactures, and markets eco-friendly, light-emitting diode (LED) technologies that conserve energy and eliminate the use of hazardous materials. It products use LED chips to integrate power sources with thermal management, optic, and control systems. The company sells optimized digital lighting (ODL) and LED replacement lamps, fixtures, and bulbs for streets, garages, stages, and retail displays. While most of its customers are in retail, commercial, industrial, and public sectors, LSGC also customizes ambiance and lighting systems for entertainment venues and nightclubs. Pegasus Capital Advisors and affiliates hold about a 90% stake in LSGC.

LSGC looks to benefit from the growing interest in energy efficient LED technologies. But cuts in discretionary spending by institutions and individuals impacted by the economic downturn, coupled with a slowdown by the general lighting market in adopting emerging, expensive technologies, threaten the company's future.

Another component of the company's success comes from continuing to release new products. LSCG introduced a retrofit LED lamp in 2010 and expects to introduce more in 2011. In addition to a spectrum of color-changing and white light systems, the company specializes in "architainment," which enhances interior and exterior architectural elements with stylish accents. Its marquee projects include Chanel's Ginza Tokyo store, Macy's San Francisco store, the Plaza Hotel in New York, and the 2009 Times Square New Year's Eve Ball. The strategy appears to be working — year-over-year sales in 2010 rose nearly 70%; sales in 2009 were more than 50% higher than 2008.

As it seeks to buoy sales, LSCG has initiated a restructuring effort to consolidate operations and lower operating expenses. In 2010 LSGC closed its offices in Japan and moved its California operations to its headquarters in Florida. In that same year it also opened a factory in Mexico to take advantage of cheaper wages. LSGC's earlier efforts included closing down its New Jersey facility and a Dallas office, streamlining R&D, expanding its lamp and infrastructure-related products, such as roadway luminaries, and leveraging supply activities.

The company's CEO and chairman, Zachary Gibler, passed away in early 2011. By spring, the board appointed James Haworth to succeed Mr. Gibler. Prior to joining LSCG, Haworth served as VP of marketing and strategy at Philips Professional Luminaires North America.

LSGC began as The Phoenix Group Corporation in 1988.

EXECUTIVES

Chairman and CEO, James F. (Jim) Haworth
CFO, Gregory T. (Greg) Kaiser, age 39
VP Strategic Accounts, John Bono
VP National Accounts, Travis Jones
VP Supply Chain, John (Jack) Becker
VP Professional Sales, Tom Benton
VP and General Manager, Custom Solutions, Gorm Teichert
Vice Chairman, Charles Darnell, age 72
Vice Chairman, Donald R. Harkleroad, age 66
Vice Chairman, Richard Weinberg, age 52
COO, John T. Stanley, age 43
CTO, Frederic S. (Fred) Maxik, age 49, $652,194 total compensation
Chief Development Officer, David Henderson
Managing Director, Lighting Science Group BV;
General Manager, Europe, Middle East, and Africa, Peter Harteveld
Chief Business Development Officer, Edward (Ted) Russ
Auditors: McGladrey & Pullen, LLP

LOCATIONS

HQ: Lighting Science Group Corporation
1227 S. Patrick Dr., Bldg. 2A, Satellite Beach, FL 32937-3969
Phone: 321-779-5520　　**Fax:** 321-779-5521
Web: www.lsgc.com

2010 Sales

	$ mil.	% of total
US	42.2	79
The Netherlands	8.9	17
Other countries	2.1	4
Total	**53.2**	**100**

COMPETITORS

Altman Lighting
Cree
El Products
Energy Focus
Nexxus Lighting
OSRAM SYLVANIA
Philips Lighting
Philips Solid-State Lighting Solutions, Inc.
Technical Consumer Products

HISTORICAL FINANCIALS

Company Type: Public

Income Statement

FYE: December 31

	REVENUE ($ mil.)	NET INCOME ($ mil.)	NET PROFIT MARGIN	EMPLOYEES
12/10	53.2	(295.1)	—	600
12/09	31.4	(48.1)	—	126
12/08	20.8	(95.0)	—	145
12/07	2.8	(13.1)	—	13
12/06	0.4	(9.8)	—	13
Annual Growth	**239.6%**	—	—	**160.6%**

2010 Year-End Financials

Debt ratio: 0.0%
Return on equity: —
Cash ($ mil.): 14.5
Current ratio: 1.23
Long-term debt ($ mil.): 0.0
No. of shares (mil.): 125.6
Dividends
　Yield: —
　Payout: —
Market value ($ mil.): 408.2

	STOCK PRICE ($) FY Close	P/E High/Low	PER SHARE ($) Earnings	Dividends	Book Value
12/10	3.25	— —	(6.69)	0.00	0.20
12/09	0.80	— —	(1.69)	0.00	(1.15)
12/08	0.37	— —	(3.55)	0.00	0.35
12/07	8.60	— —	(1.36)	0.00	1.63
12/06	8.40	— —	(4.00)	0.00	(1.56)
Annual Growth	**(21.1%)**	— —	—	—	—

Lime Energy

Being green is easy with help from Lime Energy. The company's Energy Services segment installs-energy efficient lighting upgrades for commercial and public customers in the US. Lime Energy also provides mechanical upgrades, as well as water conservation, weatherization, and renewable energy projects. It analyzes clients' energy use and develops a plan to reduce energy consumption and maintenance costs. The company works on all types of buildings including factories, high rises, retail, data centers, banks, government facilities, schools, and hospitals.

With its "Less is More Efficient" motto, Lime Energy often seeks out contracts from companies and utilities that are retrofitting their facilities. It helps its customers identify multiple energy-consuming points of a building and redesigns lighting systems to help them cost save and also reduce harmful emissions of carbon dioxide, sulfur dioxide, and nitric dioxide.

Demand for energy efficiency services is growing in the US. Businesses and governments are looking to save money on energy costs, while at the same time helping protect the environment. Lime Energy's revenues increased by 35% from 2009 to 2010. The jump was due mostly to the company being able to attract new clients in the utility and federal market.

In 2010 Lime Energy acquired the gas rights to a landfill in Florida with plans to develop a gas to electricity generating facility at the site. The deal helped establish the company in the asset development and management business. The landfill also will generate a steady stream of revenue for Lime Energy.

The company shuffled its management in 2011, a result of its rapid growth. Richard Kiphart (who controls some 40% of Lime Energy) stepped down as chairman, but remained lead director. Former CEO David Asplund became executive chairman and Daniel Parke stepped down as president (but remained president). COO John O'Rourke was promoted to president and CEO.

EXECUTIVES

Chairman, David R. Asplund, age 50, $1,387,624 total compensation
President and CEO, John O'Rourke
President, Public Sector and Regional Construction, James G. Smith
President, Energy Consulting and Technical Services, Adam Procell
EVP, CFO, Treasurer, and Assistant Secretary, Jeffrey R. Mistarz, age 50, $493,690 total compensation
Auditors: BDO Seidman, LLP

LOCATIONS

HQ: Lime Energy Co.
1280 Landmeier Rd., Elk Grove Village, IL 60007-2410
Phone: 847-437-1666　　**Fax:** 847-437-4969
Web: www.lime-energy.com

PRODUCTS/OPERATIONS

Selected Services

Asset management
Consulting
Energy engineering
Energy project development
Energy master planning
Lighting upgrade services
Mechanical and electrical conservation services
Renewable project development and implementation
Utility program management and implementation
Water conservation services
Weatherization services

COMPETITORS

Ameresco
E M C Engineers
EMCOR
Onsite Energy
Preferred Energy Services
Steiner Electric

HISTORICAL FINANCIALS

Company Type: Public

Income Statement

FYE: December 31

	REVENUE ($ mil.)	NET INCOME ($ mil.)	NET PROFIT MARGIN	EMPLOYEES
12/10	95.7	(5.2)	—	364
12/09	70.8	(18.0)	—	370
12/08	57.2	(13.0)	—	329
12/07	19.5	(15.6)	—	33
12/06	8.1	(16.4)	—	77
Annual Growth	**85.4%**	—	—	**47.5%**

2010 Year-End Financials

Debt ratio: 0.8%
Return on equity: —
Cash ($ mil.): 13.0
Current ratio: 1.87
Long-term debt ($ mil.): 0.4
No. of shares (mil.): 23.7
Dividends
　Yield: —
　Payout: —
Market value ($ mil.): 95.6

	STOCK PRICE ($) FY Close	P/E High/Low	PER SHARE ($) Earnings	Dividends	Book Value
12/10	4.04	— —	(0.22)	0.00	2.30
12/09	4.42	— —	(1.23)	0.00	2.48
12/08	4.65	— —	(1.59)	0.00	3.33
12/07	9.45	— —	(2.06)	0.00	1.80
12/06	6.30	— —	(10.64)	0.00	2.56
Annual Growth	**(10.5%)**	— —	—	—	**(2.6%)**

Limelight

Limelight Networks wants to be the center of attention for digital content providers. The company offers services for delivering media files such as video, music, games, software, and social media, via the Internet. Limelight Networks also provides on-demand and live streaming services for content in all major formats, including Adobe Flash, MP3 audio, QuickTime, RealNetworks RealPlayer, and Windows Media. Its more than 1,800 customers include social network site Myspace, video game company Electronic Arts, and software giant Microsoft. Limelight Networks' clients provide content through a variety of devices, including PCs, mobile phones, and digital video recorders.

Limelight is using acquisitions to build its online advertising and publishing capabilities. The company paid about $10 million in cash and stock in 2011 to buy San Francisco-based Clickability, provider of digital content management software. Clickability's Software-as-a-Service applications are used by clients in media, IT, financial services, and manufacturing to create, publish, and manage content related to marketing and social media among other areas. Its clients have included Amcor, BMC, and the Minneapolis Star Tribune.

Also that year Limelight acquired Tel Aviv-based Web site and application acceleration software maker AcceloWeb. With the deal, the company improved its ability to help clients speed up the delivery of online content and software as more business and data moves to the cloud. AcceloWeb's technology complemented Limelight's existing Portal and Commerce Accelerator services.

In 2010 Limelight acquired EyeWonder, a private firm that helped create and distribute rich media and interactive video advertising campaigns, for about $110 million in cash and stock. The company agreed to sell EyeWonder to Texas-based digital media distribution services provider DG FastChannel for $66 million in cash in 2011.

The company is also expanding its operations abroad in regions such as Europe and Asia, and in 2010 Limelight acquired a small German software company. About 30% of business comes from outside the US (a figure that grew from 20%, 16%, and 13% the previous three years, respectively). Limelight filed an IPO in 2007 and used the proceeds to buy network equipment, pay off debt, and make acquisitions.

The company has provided content delivery services for major live and on-demand online events such as Oprah Winfrey's interactive book club series, the US Open golf tournament, Microsoft and NBC's online coverage of the Beijing Olympic Summer Games, and the 2008 US presidential election results.

Private equity firm GS Capital Partners Entities owns more than 27% of the company.

EXECUTIVES

Chairman, President, and CEO, Jeffrey W. (Jeff) Lunsford, age 45, $3,788,811 total compensation
VP, Japan, Shinji Tsukamoto
VP, Asia/Pacific, Matthew H. Sturgess
VP Corporate Marketing and Communications, Paul Alfieri
VP Software Development, Jon Corley
VP Americas, Small, Medium, and Emerging Accounts, Dan Heydenfeldt
VP Network Operations, Joe DePalo
VP Marketing, Roxanne Ivory
VP Americas, Strategic Accounts and Government, Dan FitzSimons
VP and General Manager, IP Connect, Erik W. Gabler
VP, EMEA and Asia Pacific, George Fraser
VP Network Engineering, Denver Maddux
VP Product Management, Peter Coppola
VP Strategic Alliances, Channel, and Professional Services, Adam Wray
CTO and Director, Nathan F. Raciborski, age 44, $2,157,800 total compensation
SVP, Chief Legal Officer, and Secretary, Philip C. Maynard, age 56
SVP, CFO, and Treasurer, Douglas S. (Doug) Lindroth, age 44, $268,496 total compensation

SVP Software Engineering, Lonhyn Jasinskyj
SVP Worldwide Sales, Marketing, and Services, David M. Hatfield, age 42, $1,652,894 total compensation
Director; CEO, EyeWonder, John J. Vincent, age 40
Co-Founder, Michael M. Gordon, age 54, $1,341,630 total compensation
Auditors: Ernst & Young LLP

LOCATIONS

HQ: Limelight Networks, Inc.
2220 W. 14th St., Tempe, AZ 85281
Phone: 602-850-5000   **Fax:** 602-850-5001
Web: www.limelightnetworks.com

2010 Sales

	$ mil.	% of total
US	129.9	71
International	53.4	29
Total	**183.3**	**100**

PRODUCTS/OPERATIONS

Selected Customers

Amazon
Blue Cross
Deutche Bank
Electronic Arts
Microsoft
MySpace.com
Netflix
Nintendo Wii
Nissan
Oracle
Sony Playstation
Toyota of Japan
Yahoo!

Selected Format Delivery

Adobe Flash
MP3 audio
QuickTime
RealNetworks RealPlayer
Windows Media

Selected Offerings

LimelightDELIVER (media content delivery)
LimelightHD (high definition video content delivery)
LimelightSTREAM (audio and video streaming)

COMPETITORS

Akamai	GlobalSCAPE
Brilliant Digital Entertainment	Internap Network Services
CDNeworks Co.	Level 3 Communications
CrownPeak	Onstream Media
DG FastChannel	

HISTORICAL FINANCIALS

Company Type: Public

Income Statement

FYE: December 31

	REVENUE ($ mil.)	NET INCOME ($ mil.)	NET PROFIT MARGIN	EMPLOYEES
12/10	183.3	(20.4)	—	689
12/09	131.7	34.9	26.5%	328
12/08	129.5	(63.1)	—	294
12/07	103.1	(73.0)	—	239
12/06	64.3	(3.7)	—	158
Annual Growth	**29.9%**	**—**	**—**	**44.5%**

2010 Year-End Financials

Debt ratio: 0.7%	No. of shares (mil.): 100.1
Return on equity: —	Dividends
Cash ($ mil.): 56.7	Yield: —
Current ratio: 3.01	Payout: —
Long-term debt ($ mil.): 1.8	Market value ($ mil.): 581.4

	STOCK PRICE ($) FY Close	P/E High/Low	PER SHARE ($) Earnings	Dividends	Book Value
12/10	5.81	— —	(0.22)	0.00	2.56
12/09	3.92	14 5	0.40	0.00	2.39
12/08	2.45	— —	(0.77)	0.00	1.81
12/07	6.89	— —	(1.26)	0.00	2.36
Annual Growth	**(5.5%)**	**— —**	**—**	**—**	**2.7%**

Lincoln Educational Services

Lincoln hopes its graduates are better "Abe-l" to get a career. Lincoln Educational Services provides vocational programs from schools including Lincoln Technical Institute, Nashville Auto-Diesel College, and Euphoria Institute of Beauty Arts and Sciences. It offers programs in automotive technology, health sciences, skilled trades (including HVAC and electronics), hospitality services, and IT/business. Nearly 30,000 students are enrolled at 45 campuses about 20 states throughout the US. Lincoln tends to grow by buying smaller schools and by opening campuses in new markets. It also expands its campus facilities to accommodate higher enrollment numbers.

Lincoln Educational Services' most popular areas of study are health sciences, automotive, and the skilled trades, which combined account for about three-quarters of total enrollment. Business and information technology and hospitality services also see their fair share of student interest. Keeping student interest up (and therefore enrollment) is germane to Lincoln Educational Services' financial success. If enrollment drops, income drops, and the company suffers. In order to keep its curriculum fresh, the company assesses future job trends and adds degrees and classes accordingly. That strategy seems to be paying off; both enrollment and revenue increased by double digits at Lincoln Educational Services in 2010.

Acquisitions are key to Lincoln Educational Services' growth strategy, however the company has remained relatively quiet on the acquisition front since buying the seven schools that compose the Baran Institute of Technology (BAR) for about $25 million in 2009; the Baran schools were later given the Lincoln brand name. Previous to that, between 1999 and 2009, Lincoln Educational Services acquired more than two dozen schools, mostly in major metropolitan markets throughout the US. Along with acquisitions, Lincoln Educational Services expands by opening new schools. In 2010, the company entered into two leases for new schools in Ohio it plans to open in 2011.

All of Lincoln Educational Services schools offer diploma and certificate programs, 22 of its schools are approved to offer associate's degree programs, and three schools are approved to offer bachelor's degrees. The majority of its students pay for their educations with financial aid provided by the federal government.

These days if you offer vocational classes, it's practically unheard of not to offer at least some of them online. Much like with its physical campuses, Lincoln Educational Services bolsters its online offerings based on job trends and enrollment demographics. In 2010 the company launched its first regionally accredited online degree programs, students can obtain associates and bachelor's degrees online in a range of disciplines.

Formerly Lincoln's president and COO, Shaun McAlmont was named CEO in 2009. He succeeded the retiring David Carney, who became executive chairman for a transitional period.

EXECUTIVES

Chairman, Alexis P. Michas, age 53

President and CEO, Shaun E. McAlmont, $1,091,539 total compensation

President, Lincoln Education Group, Edward B. (Ed) Abrams

President, Lincoln Technical Group, Deborah (Debbie) Ramentol

SVP and Chief Compliance Officer, Thomas McHugh, age 63

SVP, CFO, and Treasurer, Cesar Ribeiro, age 47, $1,032,391 total compensation

SVP and Chief Academic Officer, John King

Chief Administrative Officer, Scott M. Shaw, age 48, $914,420 total compensation

Corporate Secretary, Kenneth M. Swisstack

SVP and Chief Marketing Officer, Piper Jameson

Auditors: Deloitte & Touche LLP

LOCATIONS

HQ: Lincoln Educational Services Corporation
200 Executive Dr., Ste. 340, West Orange, NJ 07052
Phone: 973-736-9340 **Fax:** 973-736-1750
Web: www.lincolnedu.com

PRODUCTS/OPERATIONS

2010 Enrollment

	% of total
Health science	40
Automotive technology	30
Skilled trades	11
Business & information technology	10
Hospitality	9
Total	**100**

Selected Brand Names

Euphoria Institute of Beauty Arts and Sciences
Lincoln College of New England
Lincoln College Onllne
Lincoln College of Technology
Lincoln Culinary Institute
Lincoln Technical Institute
Nashville Auto-Diesel College

COMPETITORS

Apollo Group	Grand Canyon Education
Capella Education	Heald College
Cardean Learning Group	ITT Educational
Career Education	Kaplan
Concorde Colleges	Laureate Education
Corinthian Colleges	Strayer Education
DeVry	UTI
Education Management	

HISTORICAL FINANCIALS

Company Type: Public

Income Statement

FYE: December 31

	REVENUE ($ mil.)	NET INCOME ($ mil.)	NET PROFIT MARGIN	EMPLOYEES
12/10	639.5	69.7	10.9%	4,500
12/09	552.5	49.2	8.9%	4,250
12/08	376.9	20.2	5.4%	3,206
12/07	327.8	8.3	2.5%	2,671
12/06	321.5	15.6	4.9%	2,862
Annual Growth	**18.8%**	**45.4%**	**—**	**12.0%**

2010 Year-End Financials

Debt ratio: 25.4%	No. of shares (mil.): 22.2
Return on equity: 31.3%	Dividends
Cash ($ mil.): 66.0	Yield: 1.6%
Current ratio: 0.97	Payout: 9.0%
Long-term debt ($ mil.): 56.5	Market value ($ mil.): 344.3

	STOCK PRICE ($) FY Close	P/E High/Low		PER SHARE ($) Earnings	Dividends	Book Value
12/10	15.51	10	3	2.79	0.25	10.02
12/09	21.66	14	6	1.82	0.00	8.46
12/08	13.25	20	13	0.78	0.00	6.87
12/07	14.72	51	35	0.32	0.00	6.28
12/06	13.49	31	20	0.60	0.00	5.97
Annual Growth	**3.6%**	**—**	**—**	**46.8%**	**—**	**13.8%**

Linear Technology

Linear Technology's chips keep real-world information in line. The company's high performance linear integrated circuits (ICs) transform analog signals — which convey information about real-world phenomena such as temperature, pressure, sound, or speed — into digital form, receivable by electronic devices. The company also makes linear devices that control power and regulate voltage in electronic systems. Its products are used in a myriad of equipment, including PCs and notebooks, cell phones, radar systems, automobiles, satellites, and industrial instrumentation. Customers located outside the US account for more than 70% of sales.

Linear Technology operates from a geographically diverse base, selling its products directly and through distributors to more than 15,000 manufacturers in a breadth of markets. The company caters largely to communications and industrial markets, as well as to the computer, consumer goods, space and military, and automotive markets. It fabricates most of its wafers at its own plants in California and Washington, though it outsources a small portion — around 5% — to silicon foundries.

The company makes some 7,500 devices, many of which are priced at $2 or less. Though minimal in price when compared with a top-of-the-line microprocessor, analog chips also cost a fraction of their price to make and use ancient (by semiconductor industry standards) wafer fabrication processes, giving the company one of the heftiest profit margins in the industry. In order to maintain its strong operating margin during the 2009 global economic downturn, when sales dropped by 18%, Linear instituted cost controls that included weekly plant closures, mandatory vacations, cuts in pay and profit-sharing, and nominal layoffs. The ag-

gressive cost cutting efforts paid off, as the company remained profitable throughout the recession. In fiscal 2010, the company reported sales and net income in line with 2008 levels.

The company's financial recovery was across all geographic regions and in most of its end markets. The breadth of Linear's product lineup and customer base helps the company from being too dependent on any one customer, or any particular type of end use. Linear Technology has worked to avoid competition from Asian rivals — which tend to focus on high-volume, low-margin chips — by offering semiconductor design and verification software lines, as well as IC manufacturing software products, to the high-end of the global electronics market.

HISTORY

In 1981 Robert Swanson (chairman) persuaded five of his fellow employees at National Semiconductor to join him in a new venture. (It soon had to defend itself in a series of lawsuits filed by National Semiconductor over trade secrets and patent infringement.) Linear Technology benefited from an analog integrated circuit (IC) shortage in the mid-1980s and used profits to develop proprietary products for laptop computers and data processing equipment. The company went public in 1986.

Linear Technology spent much of the 1990s expanding its design and production facilities, adding factories or design centers in Singapore (1994), Malaysia (1995), and Colorado and Washington (1997).

Despite a slump that bedeviled the chip industry, Linear Technology enjoyed record sales in fiscal 1998, during which it introduced 100 new products. Because of this rapid growth, the company reorganized in 1999 and again expanded its facilities. Company veteran Clive Davies became president, and Swanson remained CEO.

Davies retired in 2003, and another company veteran, David Bell, succeeded him as president. Company COO Lothar Maier succeeded Swanson as CEO early in 2005 (Swanson remained executive chairman).

Linear Technology opened its first European design center in early 2006, launching a facility in Munich, Germany.

Like many other Silicon Valley companies that generously gave out stock options to employees, executives, and directors, Linear Technology reviewed its past stock-option granting practices. The Internal Revenue Service, the SEC, and the US Department of Justice all initiated informal inquiries into the company's history of granting stock options. Linear Technology denied that it used backdating, a shady if generally legal practice in timing the issuing and sales of stock options, in granting its options, and concluded its review without finding any apparent fraud or misconduct, nor any need to restate its financial results from 1995 through 2006.

In late 2007 the SEC informed the company that it had concluded its investigation into Linear Technology's stock-option grants and didn't take any enforcement action.

EXECUTIVES

Chairman, Robert H. (Bob) Swanson Jr., age 72, $3,864,842 total compensation

CEO and Director, Lothar Maier, age 56, $5,143,823 total compensation

VP and General Manager, Mixed Signal Products, Robert Reay, age 50

VP and General Manager, D Power Products, Donald E. (Don) Paulus, age 54, $1,579,963 total compensation
VP and General Manager, S Power Products, Steve Pietkiewicz, age 51
VP and COO, Alexander R. (Alex) McCann, age 45
VP North American Sales, Richard Nickson, age 61
VP International Sales, David A. Quarles, age 45
VP Engineering and CTO, Robert C. Dobkin, age 67, $1,777,580 total compensation
VP and General Manager, Signal Conditioning Products, Erik M. Soule, age 47
VP Quality and Reliability, Paul Chantalat, age 61
VP Finance, CFO, and Secretary, Paul Coghlan, age 66, $3,267,715 total compensation
Director Marketing Communications, John Hamburger
Manager Media Relations, Doug Dickinson
Auditors: Ernst & Young LLP

LOCATIONS

HQ: Linear Technology Corporation
1630 McCarthy Blvd., Milpitas, CA 95035-7417
Phone: 408-432-1900   **Fax:** 408-434-0507
Web: www.linear.com

2010 Sales

	$ mil.	% of total
US	328.2	28
Europe	203.3	17
Japan	172.9	15
Other regions	465.6	40
Total	**1,170**	**100**

PRODUCTS/OPERATIONS

Selected Products

Amplifiers
Analog-to-digital and digital-to-analog converters
Battery monitors
Buffers
Comparators
Data converters
DC/DC power systems
Drivers
Filters
Hot swap circuits
Interface circuits
LED driver controllers
Line drivers
Line receivers
Lithium ion battery chargers
Monolithic filters
Motor controllers
Operational amplifiers
Power management devices
Power over Ethernet controllers
Radio-frequency (RF) circuits
Signal chain modules
Thermoelectric coolers
Timing devices
Transceivers
Voltage regulators
Voltage references

COMPETITORS

Allegro MicroSystems	Maxim Integrated
Analog Devices	Products
Analogic	Micrel
Cirrus Logic	Microchip Technology
Fairchild	Microsemi
Semiconductor	National Semiconductor
Freescale	O2Micro
Semiconductor	ON Semiconductor
Hittite Microwave	ROHM
International	Semtech
Rectifier	Siliconix
Intersil	STMicroelectronics
IXYS	Texas Instruments
Marvell Technology	Zetex

HISTORICAL FINANCIALS

Company Type: Public

Income Statement

FYE: Sunday nearest June 30

	REVENUE ($ mil.)	NET INCOME ($ mil.)	NET PROFIT MARGIN	EMPLOYEES
06/11	1,484.0	580.8	39.1%	4,505
06/10	1,170.0	361.3	30.9%	4,191
06/09	968.5	313.5	32.4%	3,821
06/08	1,175.2	387.6	33.0%	4,173
06/07	1,083.1	411.7	38.0%	3,837
Annual Growth	**8.2%**	**9.0%**	**—**	**4.1%**

2011 Year-End Financials

Debt ratio: 155.4%	No. of shares (mil.): 227.7
Return on equity: 114.9%	Dividends
Cash ($ mil.): 270.5	Yield: 2.8%
Current ratio: 6.82	Payout: 37.6%
Long-term debt ($ mil.): 785.7	Market value ($ mil.): 7,519.8

	STOCK PRICE ($) FY Close	P/E High/Low	Earnings	PER SHARE ($) Dividends	Book Value
06/11	33.02	14 11	2.50	0.94	2.22
06/10	27.81	20 14	1.58	0.90	0.18
06/09	23.35	24 13	1.41	0.86	(1.20)
06/08	32.57	22 15	1.71	0.78	(1.96)
06/07	36.18	28 20	1.39	0.66	(2.79)
Annual Growth	**(2.3%)**	**— —**	**15.8%**	**9.2%**	**—**

LinkedIn

Feeling a bit disconnected to the business world? LinkedIn wants to help. The firm operates an online professional network designed to help members find jobs, connect with other professoinals, and locate business opportunities. The site has grown to reach more than 100 million users in some 200 countries since its launch in 2003. LinkedIn is free to join; it offers a paid premium membership with additional tools, and sells advertising. It additionally earns revenue through its job listing service, which allows companies to post job openings and search for candidates on LinkedIn. Former CEO and current chairman Reid Hoffman co-founded the company, which filed to go public in 2011.

LinkedIn's public offering — significant in that it is the first major social networking company to file an IPO and the biggest US Internet IPO since Google — priced at $45 a share, raising more than $352 million. (It may raise more, should its underwriters decide to sell additional shares.) That figure was at the high end of underwriters' expectations, and values LinkedIn at about $4.25 billion. The company plans to use the proceeds for more investment — it expects to increase its product development efforts and expand its sales organization in the US and internationally.

The IPO comes after a period of rapid growth via the addition of new users. About 65 million unique users visit its site each month, and total members jumped from about 55 million in 2009 to its current figure of some 100 million. While this increase in membership caused revenue growth over the last three consecutive fiscal years, reaching revenues of $243.1 million in 2010, the company warned that it expects its revenue growth rate

to decline. It made made only $15.4 million in 2010.

Past investments LinkedIn enacted include making smaller, targeted acquisitions and product enhancements. To this end, in 2010 the company purchased mSpoke, a technology firm that provides users with more relevant Web content through recommendations, and ChoiceVender, a provider of content ratings and reviews. LinkedIn also made technology enhancements designed to make the site more relevant to members, including offering the ability to link users' status updates to Twitter feeds. In 2010 the company made more professional networking tools accessible on mobile devices such as the Android, Blackberry, iPad, iPhone, and Palm platforms.

LinkedIn is also focusing its efforts on international expansion, having experienced growth in India, Brazil, and China. More than half of its member base comes from outside the US, and its service is available in languages such as French, German, Italian, Portuguese, and Spanish. A reflection of its global focus, LinkedIn recently opened international offices in London, Mumbai, and Sydney. These operations add to its presence in Canada, Ireland, and the Netherlands.

At the close of 2008 Dan Nye resigned as CEO. He was replaced by Hoffman, who resumed the job he had for nearly four years when he started the business in 2003. In 2009 Jeff Weiner, a former EVP at Yahoo!, was appointed CEO. Hoffman remains with the company as executive chairman.

Hoffman and his wife Michelle Yee control more than 21% of LinkedIn's total votes. Hoffman, who was also a founding member of the board of directors at Paypal, is a partner at venture capital firm Greylock, which controls about 16%. Sequoia Capital, another venture capital firm, controls some 19%.

EXECUTIVES

Chairman, Reid Hoffman, age 43
CEO and Director, Jeffrey (Jeff) Weiner, age 40
VP, General Counsel, and Secretary, Erika Rottenberg, age 48
VP Marketing, Nick Besbeas
VP People Operations, Steve Cadigan
SVP and CFO, Steven J. (Steve) Sordello, age 41
SVP Operations and Engineering, David Henke, age 54
SVP Products and User Experience, Dipchand (Deep) Nishar, age 42
SVP Global Sales, Michael (Mike) Gamson, age 36
Head Corporate Development, Robby Kwok
Auditors: Deloitte & Touche LLP

LOCATIONS

HQ: LinkedIn Corporation
2029 Stierlin Ct., Mountain View, CA 94043
Phone: 650-687-3600   **Fax:** 650-687-0505
Web: www.linkedin.com

2009 Sales

	$ mil.	% of total
US	88.5	74
International	32.6	26
Total	**120.1**	**100**

International Locations

Australia
Canada
India
Ireland
The Netherlands
The UK

PRODUCTS/OPERATIONS

2009 Sales

	$ mil.	% of total
Premium subscriptions	45.7	38
Marketing solutions	38.3	32
Hiring solutions	36.1	30
Total	**120.1**	**100**

Selected Offerings

Premium Subscriptions
  Enhanced search results
  Enhanced communication capability
  Improved organizational functionality
  Priority customer support
Marketing Solutions
  Display ads
  Text ads
Hiring Solutions
  View candidates based on select criteria
    Industry
    Job function
    Geography
    Education

COMPETITORS

CareerBuilder	Socialtext
Classroom Connect	Spoke Software
Facebook	TheSquare
Gather Inc.	Tribe Networks
Harris Connect	Twitter
Jigsaw Data	Vault.com
Monster Worldwide	WhitePages
Plaxo	ZoomInfo

HISTORICAL FINANCIALS

Company Type: Public

Income Statement

FYE: December 31

	REVENUE ($ mil.)	NET INCOME ($ mil.)	NET PROFIT MARGIN	EMPLOYEES
12/10	243.1	15.4	6.3%	990
12/09	120.1	(4.0)	—	990
12/08	78.8	(4.5)	—	0
12/07	32.5	0.3	0.9%	0
Annual Growth	**95.6%**	**271.6%**	**—**	**0.0%**

2010 Year-End Financials

Debt ratio: —	No. of shares (mil.): —
Return on equity: 75.4%	Dividends
Cash ($ mil.): 93.0	Yield: —
Current ratio: 1.63	Payout: —
Long-term debt ($ mil.): —	Market value ($ mil.): —

Liquidmetal

It's not liquid, it's not metal — well, OK, it is metal. Still, Liquidmetal Technologies has built on research done at the California Institute of Technology by company officers William Johnson and Atakan Peker to sell amorphous metal alloys. Those products include an alloy that's lighter than titanium but twice as strong as conventional titanium alloys. The company's products are sold as bulk alloys, coatings, composites, and powders. Applications include casings for cell phones, defense products (armor-piercing ammunition), industrial coatings, and sporting goods (baseball bats, tennis rackets). Electronics giant Samsung is among the company's largest customers.

EXECUTIVES

CFO, Tony Chung, age 40, $21,527 total compensation
President, CEO, and Director, Thomas W. (Tom) Steipp, age 62
VP Finance, Won Chung, age 33
CTO, Neil Paton
Public Relations, Otis Buchanan
Auditors: Choi, Kim & Park, LLP

LOCATIONS

HQ: Liquidmetal Technologies, Inc.
30452 Esperanza, Rancho Santa Margarita, CA 92688
Phone: 949-635-2100   **Fax:** 949-635-2188
Web: www.liquidmetal.com

2008 Sales

	$ mil.	% of total
US	13.4	61
South Korea	1.1	5
Other countries	7.6	34
Total	**22.1**	**100**

PRODUCTS/OPERATIONS

2008 Sales

	$ mil.	% of total
Bulk alloys	12.5	57
Coatings	9.6	43
Total	**22.1**	**100**

COMPETITORS

Carpenter Technology	Titanium Metals
RTI International Metals	Wah Chang

HISTORICAL FINANCIALS

Company Type: Public

Income Statement

FYE: December 31

	REVENUE ($ mil.)	NET INCOME ($ mil.)	NET PROFIT MARGIN	EMPLOYEES
12/10	33.3	(1.9)	—	33
12/09	14.7	0.3	2.0%	54
12/08	22.1	(6.6)	—	73
12/07	29.0	(5.6)	—	176
12/06	27.7	(14.5)	—	690
Annual Growth	**4.7%**	**—**	**—**	**(53.2%)**

2010 Year-End Financials

Debt ratio: —	No. of shares (mil.): 93.7
Return on equity: —	Dividends
Cash ($ mil.): 5.0	Yield: —
Current ratio: 0.39	Payout: —
Long-term debt ($ mil.): 8.0	Market value ($ mil.): 43.6

	STOCK PRICE ($) FY Close	P/E High/Low		PER SHARE ($) Earnings	Dividends	Book Value
12/10	0.47	—	—	(0.03)	0.00	(0.19)
12/09	0.14	—	—	(0.00)	0.00	(0.40)
12/08	0.20	—	—	(0.15)	0.00	(0.47)
12/07	0.70	—	—	(0.12)	0.00	(0.33)
12/06	1.52	—	—	(0.33)	0.00	(0.23)
Annual Growth	**(25.4%)**	**—**	**—**	**—**	**—**	**—**

LivePerson

LivePerson wants to inject some life into your customer service. The company provides hosted software applications that help companies communicate with customers. Primarily serving retailers and other companies with an online presence, LivePerson's software enhances communications through multiple channels, including text-based chat, e-mail, and customer self-service tools. Clients install an icon on their websites that, when clicked, opens a dialogue window with a customer service representative. As part of its service, LivePerson keeps transcripts of customer interactions and offers the option of conducting user exit surveys. Customers in the US make up more than three-quarters of sales.

While monthly services fees for businesses make up the majority of sales, the company also gets revenues from online transactions between experts and users as part of its consumer segment, which rose from 5% of total revenues in 2007 to 14% in 2009. Its consumer business is an online marketplace where consumers pay a fee to chat live with experts who provide information in categories such as personal coaching, computers, health, education, shopping, spirituality and religion, finance, legal services, and the like.

In 2009 sales were up about 17% over 2008. The company credits a balance of new client acquisitions and service expansions for current clients for growth across all of its product lines. LivePerson reported net income of $7.8 million for 2009 compared to a net loss of $23.8 million in 2008, when it had a $23.5 million goodwill impairment charge related to an acquisition. The company was also able to reduce operating expenses by 23% in 2009.

LivePerson's strategy includes expanding its international operations, as well as focusing on its key target markets in industries such as financial services, retail, telecommunications, travel, and hospitality. It has identified new markets that are adjacent to its target markets, including health care, insurance, and energy and utilities. In 2009 the company added to its direct sales and services workforce to drive expansion within the financial services and telecom companies in the UK and Western Europe. The following year, LivePerson began looking at growth opportunities in the Asia/Pacific region.

In 2010 it bought Israeli start-up NuConomy for about $3 million. NuConomy's software monitors a website's traffic, targeting the user behaviors that companies should act on in real-time. LivePerson bought the company primarily for its Web analytics intellectual property.

LivePerson claims more than 8,500 customers, including Microsoft, Overstock.com, Discover, Patagonia, Verizon, and EarthLink.

Chairman and CEO Robert LoCascio owns about 10% of LivePerson.

EXECUTIVES

CFO, Daniel Murphy
Chairman and CEO, Robert P. LoCascio, age 42, $681,040 total compensation
EVP, Peter Phillips
EVP Marketing and Business Development, Stephen R. (Steve) Douty
EVP and General Manager Technology Operations, Tel Aviv, Eli Campo, age 45, $477,991 total compensation

VP Platform Technologies and Ecosystem, Mark Trang
VP Global Human Resource, Steven Schloss
SVP and Corporate Controller, Michael I. Kovach, age 42
SVP Business Affairs and General Counsel, Monica L. Greenberg, age 42, $397,903 total compensation
Auditors: BDO Seidman, LLP

LOCATIONS

HQ: LivePerson, Inc.
 462 7th Ave., 3rd Fl., New York, NY 10018
Phone: 212-609-4200   **Fax:** 212-609-4201
Web: www.liveperson.com

2009 Sales

	$ mil.	% of total
US	67.2	77
UK	9.7	11
Other countries	10.6	12
Total	**87.5**	**100**

PRODUCTS/OPERATIONS

2009 Sales

	$ mil.	% of total
Hosted services - Business	72.4	83
Hosted services - Consumer	11.9	14
Professional services	3.2	3
Total	**87.5**	**100**

Selected Software

LivePerson Contact Center
LivePerson Enterprise for Sales
LivePerson Enterprise for Service
LivePerson for Online Sales
LivePerson Premiere (for midsized businesses)
LivePerson Pro (for small businesses)

COMPETITORS

About.com	Oracle
eGain Communications	RightNow Technologies
Google	SAP
KANA	Talisma
Microsoft	Yahoo!

HISTORICAL FINANCIALS

Company Type: Public

Income Statement
FYE: December 31

	REVENUE ($ mil.)	NET INCOME ($ mil.)	NET PROFIT MARGIN	EMPLOYEES
12/10	109.9	9.3	8.5%	481
12/09	87.5	7.8	8.9%	416
12/08	74.7	(23.8)	—	349
12/07	52.2	5.8	11.1%	314
12/06	33.5	2.2	6.6%	178
Annual Growth	**34.6%**	**43.4%**	**—**	**28.2%**

2010 Year-End Financials

Debt ratio: —	No. of shares (mil.): 51.8
Return on equity: 8.8%	Dividends
Cash ($ mil.): 61.3	Yield: —
Current ratio: 3.56	Payout: —
Long-term debt ($ mil.): —	Market value ($ mil.): 584.8

	STOCK PRICE ($) FY Close	P/E High/Low		PER SHARE ($) Earnings	Dividends	Book Value
12/10	11.30	69	32	0.18	0.00	2.02
12/09	6.97	45	10	0.16	0.00	1.64
12/08	1.82	—	—	(0.50)	0.00	1.34
12/07	5.34	66	39	0.12	0.00	1.79
12/06	5.23	157	74	0.05	0.00	0.85
Annual Growth	**21.2%**	—	—	**37.7%**	—	**24.3%**

Local.com

Local.com traffics in keywords. Specializing in paid-search advertising, the company connects businesses to consumers online. Its Local.com search site draws about 20 million unique visitors per month. The company also operates a network of more than 750 local websites and one that distributes its advertising feeds to third-party sites; customers can also opt for banner ads. It makes money from direct advertisers who bid for placement (based on keywords) and pay per click, and from indirect advertising subscribers that gain inclusion on the network through paid-search firms including SuperMedia and Yahoo! Local.com also offers search engine optimization and other advertising support services.

The company has added custom content to its site, including local events listings, in hope of increasing its visitors and reducing its reliance on pay-per-click advertising, which currently accounts for about 80% of its revenue. Advertisers that deal directly with Local.com account for a large portion of its sales; Yahoo! alone represents more than half the total. In 2009 it purchased a total of nearly 45,000 local business listing subscribers from several sources. The acquisition boosted its small business products, further diversifying its revenue.

In early 2011, Local.com plunged into the growing group buying advertising arena through the purchase of iTwango LLC. The deal allowed it to make headway in the emerging local advertising segment and will allow it to roll out additional products throughout the course of the year.

Staying focused on this segment, Local.com snatched up Krillion, a product search provider connecting online shoppers with products available in local stores, a few months later. Krillion's search capabilities include more than 1,200 brands in 50,000 retail locations. Local.com is deploying Krillion's products across its business.

EXECUTIVES

Chairman and CEO, Heath B. Clarke, age 42, $738,859 total compensation
President and COO, Stanley B. (Bruce) Crair, age 55, $575,433 total compensation
CFO, Kenneth S. (Ken) Cragun, age 50
VP Product Management, Eileen Lictra
VP Human Resources, Heather A. Dilley, age 42
VP Operations, Ralph N. Kravitz, age 46
VP Marketing, Steven Schindler
VP Engineering, Peter (Pete) Mathews, age 43
VP Finance, Ken Cragun, age 50
CTO, Michael Plonski
SVP Corporate Development, Peter S. Hutto, age 52
SVP; General Manager, Private Label, Malcolm D. Lewis, age 45
General Manager, Owned & Operated, Rajan Mohan
Public Relations Contact, Cameron Triebwasser
General Counsel, Scott Reinke, age 37
General Manager, Network and Sales & Advertiser Services, Richard X. Szatkowski, age 55
Auditors: Haskell & White LLP

LOCATIONS

HQ: Local.com Corporation
 1 Technology Dr., Bldg. G, Irvine, CA 92618
Phone: 949-784-0800   **Fax:** 949-784-0880
Web: corporate.local.com

PRODUCTS/OPERATIONS

2009 Sales

	$ mil.	% of total
Pay-per-click	45.8	81
Subscription	7.5	13
Banner ads	2.9	6
License	0.1	-
Total	**56.3**	**100**

2009 Sales

	$ mil.	% of total
Owned and operated	36.7	65
Network	12.1	22
Sales and advertising services	7.5	13
Total	**56.3**	**100**

COMPETITORS

About.com	SuperMedia
Ask.com	Vertro
Google	Vibrant Media
InfoSpace	Yahoo!

HISTORICAL FINANCIALS

Company Type: Public

Income Statement
FYE: December 31

	REVENUE ($ mil.)	NET INCOME ($ mil.)	NET PROFIT MARGIN	EMPLOYEES
12/10	84.1	4.2	5.0%	116
12/09	56.3	(6.3)	—	86
12/08	38.3	(8.6)	—	74
12/07	21.5	(18.2)	—	68
12/06	14.2	(13.3)	—	58
Annual Growth	**56.0%**	**—**	**—**	**18.9%**

2010 Year-End Financials

Debt ratio: —	No. of shares (mil.): 16.6
Return on equity: 10.7%	Dividends
Cash ($ mil.): 13.1	Yield: —
Current ratio: 1.25	Payout: —
Long-term debt ($ mil.): —	Market value ($ mil.): 107.6

	STOCK PRICE ($) FY Close	P/E High/Low		PER SHARE ($) Earnings	Dividends	Book Value
12/10	6.49	35	13	0.25	0.00	2.38
12/09	5.81	—	—	(0.44)	0.00	1.58
12/08	1.55	—	—	(0.60)	0.00	1.89
12/07	4.81	—	—	(1.58)	0.00	2.32
12/06	4.05	—	—	(1.44)	0.00	2.22
Annual Growth	**12.5%**	—	—	—	—	**1.8%**

LogMeIn

LogMeIn helps you stay productive even on the go. The company provides remote access software and services to consumers, small and midsized businesses, and IT service providers. Consumers and remote workers can access their computers' desktops, files, applications, and network resources. Businesses and IT service providers use LogMeIn's technology to provide remote management and support. LogMeIn offers both free and subscription-based services. Its paid services add advanced features such as file transfer, remote printing, and drive mapping. Corporate customers include 3M, AMD, and IBM. LogMeIn's services come in a dozen different languages and are sold around the world. The company was founded in 2003.

The company's services have been used on more than 125 million devices worldwide, encompassing desktops, laptops, servers, kiosks, and mobile devices. More than 33 million users have registered an account with LogMeIn. The company offers three free services with limited remote access functionality; its nine premium services add more features and include capability for file transfer, remote printing, and desktop sharing. LogMeIn also offers other premium services such as Web-based remote technical support, disaster recovery, and data backup. About 95% of its premium subscriptions are sold as one-year deals.

All of its products are available as hosted services, which enables customers to quickly install, administer, and support remote access and file-sharing functionality without investing in expensive hardware or IT staff.

From 2006-2009 the company steadily grew its revenues while containing costs, but it was unprofitable. LogMeIn went public in 2009 and raised $106 million in its initial offering, about 20% more than it originally sought in 2008. The company achieved profitability for the first time in 2009 and experienced record revenue and growth in 2010. Overall sales jumped 36% and profit grew an astounding 140%. That year the company signed up more customers with premium accounts and launched new products, including join.me, a free application for online meetings, and it made its programs compatible with Apple products.

LogMeIn also made its first acquisition in 2011, buying UK-based Pachube for $15 million. Pachube (pronounced "patch bay") is a Web-based monitoring and management service for connected devices. The company sees the acquisition as an investment for its data sharing platforms.

EXECUTIVES

Chairman, President, and CEO, Michael K. Simon, age 46, $866,217 total compensation
CFO and Treasurer, James F. (Jim) Kelliher, age 51, $415,209 total compensation
VP Marketing Communications, Laura Pasquale
VP Customer Support, Andrew Thompson
VP Human Resources, Scott Chase
VP Ecommerce Sales, Alan DiPietro
VP Finance, Ed Herdiech
VP Business Development, Conan Reidy
VP Collaboration Technologies, Kevin Bardos
VP and General Counsel, Michael J. Donahue, age 37, $299,211 total compensation
VP Network Operations, Sandeep Bajaj
VP Sales and Marketing, EMEA, Seth Shaw
VP Creative, Paul Schauder
VP Corporate Business Development, Richard B. Redding
VP, Engineering, Kevin Farrell
VP Access and Management, Andrew Burton
CTO, Marton B. Anka, age 38, $537,826 total compensation
Director Corporate Communications, Craig E. VerColen
SVP, Sales and Marketing, Kevin K. Harrison, age 53, $404,836 total compensation
Auditors: Deloitte & Touche LLP

LOCATIONS

HQ: LogMeIn, Inc.
500 Unicorn Park Dr., Woburn, MA 01801
Phone: 781-638-9050   **Fax:** 781-998-7792
Web: https://secure.logmein.com

2010 Sales

	% of total
North America	70
International	30
Total	**100**

PRODUCTS/OPERATIONS

Selected Services

LogMeIn Backup (remote data backup)
LogMeIn Central (remote support and management services)
LogMeIn Free (free service for remote connectivity)
LogMeIn Hamachi (free service for hosted VPN)
LogMeIn Pro (remote access to computers, servers, and mobile devices)
LogMeIn Rescue (remote disaster recovery)

COMPETITORS

Apple Inc.	Microsoft
Cisco WebEx	Symantec
Citrix Systems	

HISTORICAL FINANCIALS

Company Type: Public

Income Statement

FYE: December 31

	REVENUE ($ mil.)	NET INCOME ($ mil.)	NET PROFIT MARGIN	EMPLOYEES
12/10	101.1	21.1	20.9%	415
12/09	74.4	8.8	11.8%	338
12/08	51.7	(5.4)	—	287
12/07	27.0	(9.1)	—	262
12/06	11.3	(6.7)	—	126
Annual Growth	**72.9%**	**—**	**—**	**34.7%**

2010 Year-End Financials

Debt ratio: —	No. of shares (mil.): 23.9
Return on equity: 16.2%	Dividends
Cash ($ mil.): 77.3	Yield: —
Current ratio: 3.22	Payout: —
Long-term debt ($ mil.): —	Market value ($ mil.): 1,057.9

	STOCK PRICE ($) FY Close	P/E High/Low		PER SHARE ($) Earnings	Dividends	Book Value
12/10	44.34	56	20	0.85	0.00	5.46
12/09	19.95	64	41	0.37	0.00	4.39
Annual Growth	**122.3%**	**—**	**—**	**129.7%**	**—**	**24.5%**

LRAD Corporation

High-tech sound may drive development for LRAD (formerly American Technology Corporation), but the firm is also banking on it to drive its bottom line. LRAD, whose past sales largely came from its portable radios, discontinued its portable consumer electronics division to make products that transmit sound over short and long distances. The company's Long Range Acoustic Devices generate the majority of revenues nowadays, and they have been deployed by the US military and used by public safety agencies worldwide. To strengthen its identity as a global provider of long-range acoustic technology systems, the company changed its name to LRAD in 2010.

LRAD primarily sells to government organizations and businesses in the US, but in recent years it has focused on expanding its international customer base. It intends to accelerate growth by increasing its direct sales to military and defense-related companies. In 2009 the company added sales teams in the Middle East and the Far East, a year after shipping its products to South America, Korea, and Japan.

Anchor Innovation was LRAD's largest customer in 2009, generating about 24% of revenue. In 2008 its two biggest buyers were ADS Inc. and Advanced Integrated Systems, which accounted for 17% and 10% of sales, respectively. Anchor Innovation is a representative to the US Navy while Advanced Integrated Systems is a reseller to several branches of the US military, including the US Department of Homeland Security, and international customers. For several years LRAD has generated nearly half of its sales (about 45% in 2009) by supplying the US government with its products.

Aside from equipping the armed forces with its innovations, LRAD made products that could be used by businesses. The company's Hyper Sonic Sound (HSS) technology could be installed in places like grocery stores, museums, zoos, and airports. HSS systems transmit messages and advertising to specific areas or groups of people, as well as reduce noise pollution in open and confined spaces. In late 2010 LRAD spun off its HSS business as a public company called Parametric Sound. As part of the spinoff, LRAD shareholders also own stock in Parametric Sound.

Chairman Elwood Norris owns about 15% of LRAD's shares. Austin Marxe and David Greenhouse, the controlling principals of New York-based AWM Investment, jointly hold about 10% of shares.

EXECUTIVES

Chairman, President, and CEO, Thomas R. (Tom) Brown, age 60, $977,796 total compensation
CFO and Secretary, Katherine H. (Kathy) McDermott, age 50, $335,786 total compensation
VP Business Development, United States and Europe, Scott Stuckey
Director Business Development, HSS Products, LRAD Regional Sales, David Pratt
Director Business Development, Asia, South and Central America, Ryk Williams
Auditors: Squar, Milner, Peterson, Miranda & Williamson, LLP

LOCATIONS

HQ: LRAD Corporation
15378 Avenue of Science, Ste. 100, San Diego, CA 92128
Phone: 858-676-1112   **Fax:** 858-676-1120
Web: www.lradx.com

2010 Sales

	$ mil.	% of total
US	11.4	68
Other	5.3	32
Total	**16.7**	**100**

PRODUCTS/OPERATIONS

2010 Sales

	$ mil.	% of total
LRAD	16.5	100
SoundSaber	0.1	-
Other	0.1	-
Total	**16.7**	**100**

Allegheny Technologies   HiWave
Bose   MartinLogan
Boston Acoustics   Sennheiser Electronic
Harman International

HISTORICAL FINANCIALS

Company Type: Public

Income Statement

FYE: September 30

	REVENUE ($ mil.)	NET INCOME ($ mil.)	NET PROFIT MARGIN	EMPLOYEES
09/10	16.7	3.0	18.0%	38
09/09	15.8	(1.0)	—	36
09/08	11.2	(6.4)	—	33
09/07	9.9	(5.6)	—	38
09/06	8.9	(7.7)	—	41
Annual Growth	17.0%	—	—	(1.9%)

2010 Year-End Financials

Debt ratio: —	No. of shares (mil.): 30.6
Return on equity: 28.9%	Dividends
Cash ($ mil.): 5.4	Yield: —
Current ratio: 4.49	Payout: —
Long-term debt ($ mil.): —	Market value ($ mil.): 48.1

	STOCK PRICE ($) FY Close	P/E High/Low		PER SHARE ($) Earnings	Dividends	Book Value
09/10	1.57	21	7	0.10	0.00	0.34
09/09	1.77	—	—	(0.03)	0.00	0.26
09/08	0.55	—	—	(0.21)	0.00	0.25
09/07	3.80	—	—	(0.18)	0.00	0.38
09/06	3.82	—	—	(0.31)	0.00	0.56
Annual Growth	(19.9%)	—	—	—	—	(11.7%)

LTX-Credence

LTX-Credence wasn't born on the bayou — the company was created from the 2008 merger of LTX Corp. and rival Credence Systems. LTX-Credence makes automated test equipment (ATE) used by chip makers to test semiconductors as they're being manufactured and as part of the final package test. The company consolidated its predecessors' product lines into four basic test equipment families — ASL, Sapphire, Diamond, and X-Series. Top customers include Taiwan's Spirox, Atmel, and Texas Instruments. More than three-quarters of sales come from outside the US.

The company's first full year (2009) after the LTX and Credence Systems merger was a rough one, as no one could have foreseen the coming global economic downturn. Sales remained flat and the company had to reduce headcount and operational expenses. It consolidated facilities, phased out older product lines, and reduced operating expenses by more than $110 million.

Business picked up during fiscal 2010, and revenues for the year increased almost 60%. LTX-Credence segments its revenue into products and services, with product sales almost doubling. The company also recorded a tidy net profit for the year.

LTX-Credence's X-Series product line (which evolved from LTX's earlier mixed-signal, discrete-device, and digital-device test systems) offers a single-platform system for testing digital, mixed-sig-

nal, and system-on-a-chip integrated circuits. The Credence side contributed the ASL, Diamond, and Sapphire product platforms. The company is phasing out and no longer developing upgrades to the Sapphire platform, though it continues to provide maintenance and support for the products. LTX-Credence has sold some 4,000 ASL systems and 500 Diamond systems. Like its competitors, LTX-Credence outsources the manufacturing of its products. Jabil Circuit, Plexus, and Benchmark Electronics make the company's products.

HISTORY

Graham Miller, Roger Blethen, and others formed LTX in 1976. The company unveiled a linear/mixed-signal test system in 1977 and began developing testers for digital chips via its 1984 acquisition of Trillium. The company launched its enVision programming software for digital testing in 1993 and introduced a digital test system the following year.

Miller served as chairman and CEO for 20 years; Blethen succeeded him as CEO in 1996. LTX restructured in 1996, integrating its West Coast digital and East Coast mixed-signal divisions to focus on Fusion testers (later known as the X-Series). An overall slowdown in the semiconductor industry caused LTX to implement another restructuring in 1998, including facilities consolidation and a 30% workforce reduction, and led to a loss for the year.

The company's first Fusion system was shipped to National Semiconductor in 1998. In 2000 the company sold its iPTest line of specialized semiconductor component testing systems in order to better focus on the Fusion product family. The next year LTX formed a manufacturing partnership with Jabil Circuit, a provider of electronic manufacturing services, for assembling and testing the Fusion systems.

Late in 2002 the company reduced its workforce by 27% in the face of dismal conditions across the semiconductor industry. The company expanded its offerings through its 2003 acquisition of privately held StepTech, a maker of chip testing instrumentation. In 2005 LTX cut headcount by another 28% as tester sales slumped again.

Roger Blethen stepped aside as CEO in late 2005; he remained as chairman of the board. Blethen was succeeded by David Tacelli, a 17-year veteran of LTX who had been the company's president and COO since 2002.

LTX merged with Credence Systems in 2008, creating LTX-Credence Corporation. The combined company made its headquarters in Milpitas, California, where Credence was based. The merger agreement called for Credence CEO Lavi Lev to become executive chairman of the combined company, while LTX CEO David Tacelli took over as president and CEO. Credence shareholders owned just a hair over half of the merged company's shares after the transaction closed, and LTX took five of the nine seats on the combined board of directors. The stock-swap deal was valued at about $177 million.

Lavi Lev resigned as chairman near the end of 2008, and was succeeded by Roger Blethen once again.

LTX's sales in fiscal 2008, which ended just before the merger was completed, were down by 8% from the year before, reflecting poor business conditions. Chip makers, especially those making memory devices, were further challenged by lower sales in the second half of calendar 2008, leading many to slash their capital expenditure budgets for 2008 and 2009, which didn't bode well for test equipment vendors.

EXECUTIVES

Chairman, Roger W. Blethen, age 59
President, CEO, and Director, David G. (Dave) Tacelli, age 51, $1,898,271 total compensation
VP Product Development and Operations, Peter S. Rood, age 54, $620,261 total compensation
VP Field Operations and Sales International, Michael Goldbach
VP, CFO, Treasurer, and Principal Accounting Officer, Mark J. Gallenberger, age 46, $1,089,694 total compensation
VP Operations, Thomas J. Young
VP Field Operations and Sales, NAM, Mark Yaeger
VP Marketing, Bruce R. MacDonald, age 48, $679,631 total compensation
VP Corporate Marketing and Investor Relations, Rich Yerganian
VP Worldwide Service, Daniel V. Wallace
Director Business Operations, Antoinette McKinley
Director Human Resources, Jill Barres
Director Quality, John Rae-Kelly
Auditors: Ernst & Young LLP

LOCATIONS

HQ: LTX-Credence Corporation
1355 California Cir., Milpitas, CA 95035
Phone: 408-635-4300   **Fax:** 408-635-4985
Web: www.ltx.com

2010 Sales

	$ mil.	% of total
Taiwan	70.1	32
US	51.7	24
Philippines	28.7	13
Singapore	26.3	12
Japan	1.4	-
Other countries	40.9	19
Total	**219.1**	**100**

PRODUCTS/OPERATIONS

2010 Sales

	$ mil.	% of total
Product sales	174.1	79
Services	45.0	21
Total	**219.1**	**100**

Selected Products

ASL Platform (tests linear, mixed-signal, and power management devices)
Diamond Platform (platform that uses high density packaging to test microcontrollers and digital consumer devices)
Sapphire Platform (CPU, graphics, and high-end digital testing)
X-Series Platform (testing of digital signal processor, power, automotive, mixed-signal, and radio-frequency applications)

COMPETITORS

Advantest   inTEST
Applied Materials   KLA-Tencor
Cascade Microtech   Roos Instruments
DFT MicroSystems   Teradyne
Fluke Corporation   Trio-Tech
FormFactor   Yokogawa Electric

HISTORICAL FINANCIALS
Company Type: Public

Income Statement
FYE: July 31

	REVENUE ($ mil.)	NET INCOME ($ mil.)	NET PROFIT MARGIN	EMPLOYEES
07/10	219.1	18.1	8.3%	643
07/09	137.4	(137.3)	—	627
07/08	135.8	(0.6)	—	482
07/07	147.6	(10.7)	—	454
07/06	216.5	12.2	5.6%	438
Annual Growth	0.3%	10.4%	—	10.1%

2010 Year-End Financials

Debt ratio: —   No. of shares (mil.): 49.1
Return on equity: 10.3%   Dividends
Cash ($ mil.): 75.0   Yield: —
Current ratio: 3.02   Payout: —
Long-term debt ($ mil.): —   Market value ($ mil.): 412.0

	STOCK PRICE ($) FY Close	P/E High/Low		PER SHARE ($) Earnings	Dividends	Book Value
07/10	8.40	29	6	0.39	0.00	3.60
07/09	2.70	—	—	(3.39)	0.00	2.48
07/08	6.54	—	—	(0.03)	0.00	5.60
07/07	13.77	—	—	(0.51)	0.00	5.43
07/06	16.17	40	16	0.60	0.00	5.70
Annual Growth	(15.1%)	—	—	(10.2%)	—	(10.8%)

Magnum Hunter Resources

The treasure this hunter seeks is gold, black gold. Magnum Hunter Resources (MHR) acquires producing oil and natural gas leases, conducts exploratory drilling, and produces crude oil and natural gas liquids. It has proved reserves of about 13.4 million barrels of oil equivalent, about half oil, on properties located primarily in Texas, Louisiana, West Virginia, and North Dakota. Most of the company's output comes from West Virginia, where it also owns a 182-mile natural gas pipeline through its Triad subsidiary. Other subsidiaries include an oilfield drilling business and a natural gas wastewater disposal facility; both are used by the company and third parties.

Magnum Hunter has been on acquisition spree, spending more than $600 million on companies, assets, and mineral leases. In 2010 it bought Triad Energy out of bankruptcy for about $81 million. Early the following year, the company purchased NuLoch Resources, a Canadian oil and gas producer, for $327 million in stock. The acquisition will bring about 6 million barrels of oil equivalent. Expanding its Appalachian assets, in 2011 the company acquired NGAS Resources for about $98 million in stock and liabilities, as well as the West Virginia assets of PostRock Energy for $44.6 million. Also in 2011 Magnum Hunter paid $57 million to buy a 95% stake in oil and gas mineral leases on 191 wells in the Williston Basin of North Dakota. The wells, sold by an unnamed private seller, have total proved reserves 2.6 million barrels.

Magnum Hunter's strategy going forward includes continued acquisitions of oil producing properties in North Dakota's Williston Basin and in Texas' Eagle Ford Shale region as well as the liquid gas Marcellus Shale area in West Virginia. It also plans to operate more of its wells and develop its Eureka Hunter Marcellus Shale gas and gas liquid pipeline. The company began work on a natural gas processing plant as part of the pipeline; completion is expected by late 2011.

Magnum Hunter was founded in 1997 and began oil and gas operations under the name Petro Resources Corporation in 2005. It changed its name to Magnum Hunter Resources Corporation in 2009 when Gary Evans, the former CEO of Magnum Hunter Resources, Inc., took over as Chairman and CEO.

EXECUTIVES

Chairman and CEO, Gary C. Evans, age 55
EVP, CFO, and Director, Ronald D. (Ron) Ormand, age 53
EVP Exploration, H.C. (Kip) Ferguson
VP Finance and Treasurer, Victor Ponce de León
VP Reservoir Engineering, Debbie Funderburg
VP Business Development and Legal, David Lipp
VP Land, Brian G. Burgher
COO, James W. (Jim) Denny III, age 63
SVP and General Counsel, Paul M. Johnston
SVP Capital Markets, M. Bradley Davis, age 51
SVP Equipment Services, Kirk Trosclair
SVP Business Development and Land, Richard S. Farrell, age 53
SVP and Chief Accounting Officer, David S. Krueger, age 61
SVP Administration and Product Marketing, Donald L. (Don) Kirkendall
Auditors:

LOCATIONS

HQ: Magnum Hunter Resources Corporation
777 Post Oak Blvd., Ste. 650, Houston, TX 77056
Phone: 832-369-6986   **Fax:** 832-369-6992
Web: www.magnumhunterresources.com

PRODUCTS/OPERATIONS

2010 Sales

	$ mil.	% of total
Oil and gas	27.7	85
Field operations	4.7	14
Sale of assets	.1	-
Other	.2	1
Total	**32.7**	**100**

COMPETITORS

Anadarko Petroleum	Hess Corporation
Apache	Huntsman International
Ashland Inc.	Marathon Oil
Belden & Blake	Miller Petroleum
BP	Murphy Oil
Cabot Oil & Gas	PDC Energy
Chevron	Range Resources
Delta Natural Gas	Royal Dutch Shell
Exxon Mobil	XTO Energy

HISTORICAL FINANCIALS
Company Type: Public

Income Statement
FYE: December 31

	REVENUE ($ mil.)	NET INCOME ($ mil.)	NET PROFIT MARGIN	EMPLOYEES
12/10	32.7	(13.8)	—	165
12/09	10.3	(15.1)	—	139
12/08	15.9	(6.9)	—	8
12/07	7.0	(5.5)	—	7
12/06	1.5	(3.9)	—	4
Annual Growth	116.1%	—	—	153.4%

2010 Year-End Financials

Debt ratio: 26.2%   No. of shares (mil.): 74.9
Return on equity: —   Dividends
Cash ($ mil.): 0.6   Yield: —
Current ratio: 0.30   Payout: —
Long-term debt ($ mil.): 26.7   Market value ($ mil.): 539.0

	STOCK PRICE ($) FY Close	P/E High/Low		PER SHARE ($) Earnings	Dividends	Book Value
12/10	7.20	—	—	(0.25)	0.00	1.36
12/09	1.55	—	—	(0.39)	0.00	0.75
12/08	0.33	—	—	(0.21)	0.00	0.92
12/07	1.98	—	—	(0.28)	0.00	1.13
12/06	2.82	—	—	(0.20)	0.00	0.54
Annual Growth	26.4%	—	—	—	—	25.8%

Main Street Capital

Main Street Capital doesn't care if its investments are on Main St., Manufacturing Blvd, or Professional Services Pkwy., just as long as they are not too big and are (preferably) located in the southwestern US. As an investment firm, Main Street provides long-term debt and equity capital to lower middle-market companies with annual revenues between $10 million and $100 million. Its portfolio includes more than 40 active investments in traditional and niche companies in the manufacturing, technology, restaurant, business services, and other sectors. Main Street tends to partner with business owners and management and provides capital to support buyouts, recapitalizations, growth financings, and acquisitions.

The firm typically offers debt capital in the form of single tranche debt and mezzanine loans; it often makes its equity investments in connection to its debt investments. Single tranche debt is a type of hybrid asset-backed security that combines low-risk secured debt and higher-risk subordinated debt into a single instrument. Main Street believes this type of debt capital is ideal for investments in lower middle-market companies, primarily because it lessens the risk associated with such companies, generates a somewhat predictable return on its investments, and is structured in way that reduces complexity and benefits creditors.

While 75% of the firm's investments are located in the western and southwestern US, Main Street does maintain some investments in the southeastern and central US.

EXECUTIVES

Chairman and CEO, Vincent D. Foster, age 53,
$879,287 total compensation

President, CFO, and Director, Todd A. Reppert, age 40, $624,432 total compensation
VP and Chief Accounting Officer, Michael S. Galvan, age 41
VP, General Counsel, and Secretary, Jason B. Beauvais, age 34
Chief Compliance Officer, SVP Finance and Administration, and Treasurer, Rodger A. Stout, age 58, $407,953 total compensation
SVP, David L. Magdol, age 39, $404,672 total compensation
SVP, Dwayne L Hyzak, age 37, $438,376 total compensation
SVP, Curtis L. Hartman, age 37, $438,376 total compensation
Analyst, Alejandro Capetillo
Analyst, Scott Gross
Analyst, George Taneff
Human Resources Manager, Susan Cannon
Senior Associate, Alejandro Palomo
Controller, Charles P. Rosenstein
Auditors: Grant Thornton LLP

LOCATIONS

HQ: Main Street Capital Corporation
1300 Post Oak Blvd., Ste. 800, Houston, TX 77056
Phone: 713-350-6000   Fax: 713-350-6042
Web: www.mainstcapital.com

COMPETITORS

American Capital	MCG Capital
Apollo Investment	Sentinel Capital
Ares Capital	Partners
Capital Southwest	WestView Capital
Castle Harlan	Partners

HISTORICAL FINANCIALS

Company Type: Public

Income Statement

FYE: December 31

	REVENUE ($ mil.)	NET INCOME ($ mil.)	NET PROFIT MARGIN	EMPLOYEES
12/10	36.5	38.7	106.0%	18
12/09	16.0	12.0	75.0%	16
12/08	17.3	10.9	63.0%	17
12/07	12.5	2.5	20.0%	12
12/06	9.8	15.8	161.2%	0
Annual Growth	38.9%	25.1%	—	14.5%

2010 Year-End Financials

Debt ratio: 63.4%
Return on equity: 15.8%
Cash ($ mil.): 22.3
Current ratio: 2.25
Long-term debt ($ mil.): 155.6

No. of shares (mil.): 18.8
Dividends
Yield: 8.2%
Payout: 63.0%
Market value ($ mil.): 341.9

	STOCK PRICE ($) FY Close	P/E High/Low		PER SHARE ($) Earnings	Dividends	Book Value
12/10	18.19	8	4	2.38	1.50	13.06
12/09	16.12	14	8	1.19	1.13	11.96
12/08	9.77	13	7	1.15	1.67	12.16
12/07	14.01	52	43	0.30	0.33	13.05
Annual Growth	9.1%	—	—	99.4%	65.7%	0.0%

MAKO Surgical

If osteoarthritis brings you to your knees, MAKO Surgical has a medical device that might help. The company developed and markets the MAKOplasty partial knee resurfacing system, a minimally invasive alternative to traditional knee replacement surgery for patients with early- to mid-stage osteoarthritis. Proprietary components of the system consist of patient-specific visualization technology and a robotic arm (RIO) that helps orthopedic surgeons prepare the knee joint for insertion of MAKO's resurfacing implants (RESTORIS) through a small incision. MAKO Surgical markets to hospitals and surgeons in the US and Europe via a direct sales force and independent orthopedic product agents and distributors.

After completing an initial public offering in 2008, MAKO gained FDA clearance for both its RIO (Robotic-Arm Interactive Orthopedic) and RESTORIS implants and commercially launched them in 2009. Since then, further enhancements to the platforms have also launched. MAKO isn't stopping at the knee, however. The company is directing research and development resources toward developing a hip MAKOplasty application, in which the RIO will be used to perform total hip arthroplasty. MAKO expects commercial release of the application and associated implant systems before the end of 2011.

Other R&D efforts include testing the viability of MAKOplasty on such areas of the body as the shoulder and spine. MAKO's research is based on its portfolio of owned or licensed US and foreign patents and patent applications.

Through Skyline Venture Partners, director John Freund controls about 10% of the company.

EXECUTIVES

Chairman, President, and CEO, Maurice R. Ferré, age 50, $2,708,184 total compensation
SVP Engineering, Richard Leparmentier, age 43
SVP Regulatory Affairs and Quality Assurance, James E. Keller, age 59
SVP Operations, Duncan H. Moffat, age 50, $399,046 total compensation
Director Marketing, Cynthia M. Kalb
SVP Sales and Marketing, Steven J. (Steve) Nunes, age 52, $633,150 total compensation
SVP Finance and Administration, CFO, and Treasurer, Fritz L. LaPorte, age 41, $662,907 total compensation
SVP, General Counsel, and Secretary, Menashe R. Frank, age 44, $399,046 total compensation
SVP Strategic Marketing and Business Development, Ivan Delevic, age 45, $640,753 total compensation
Auditors: Ernst & Young LLP

LOCATIONS

HQ: MAKO Surgical Corp.
2555 Davie Rd., Fort Lauderdale, FL 33317
Phone: 954-927-2044   Fax: 954-927-0446
Web: www.makosurgical.com

PRODUCTS/OPERATIONS

2010 Sales

	% of total
RIO systems	56
Procedures	40
Service & other	4
Total	100

COMPETITORS

Accellent	Johnson & Johnson
B. Braun Melsungen	Smith & Nephew
Biomet	Stryker
Curexo Technology	Tornier
DePuy Orthopaedics	Zimmer Holdings
Exactech	

HISTORICAL FINANCIALS

Company Type: Public

Income Statement

FYE: December 31

	REVENUE ($ mil.)	NET INCOME ($ mil.)	NET PROFIT MARGIN	EMPLOYEES
12/10	44.3	(38.7)	—	315
12/09	34.2	(34.0)	—	240
12/08	2.9	(37.1)	—	193
12/07	0.8	(20.7)	—	133
12/06	0.1	(10.6)	—	106
Annual Growth	358.8%	—	—	31.3%

2010 Year-End Financials

Debt ratio: —
Return on equity: —
Cash ($ mil.): 27.1
Current ratio: 6.37
Long-term debt ($ mil.): —

No. of shares (mil.): 39.9
Dividends
Yield: —
Payout: —
Market value ($ mil.): 608.0

	STOCK PRICE ($) FY Close	P/E High/Low		PER SHARE ($) Earnings	Dividends	Book Value
12/10	15.22	—	—	(1.13)	0.00	3.05
12/09	11.10	—	—	(1.22)	0.00	2.75
12/08	6.68	—	—	(2.20)	0.00	2.67
Annual Growth	50.9%	—	—	—	—	6.9%

MarketAxess

A little creative spelling never got in the way of a good bond trade. MarketAxess offers an electronic multi-dealer platform for institutional traders buying and selling US corporate, high-yield, and emerging market bonds, as well as Eurobonds. Participating broker-dealers include some of the world's largest, such as BNP Paribas, Citigroup, Deutsche Bank, Goldman Sachs, and Merrill Lynch. In all, MarketAxess serves more than 800 investment firms, mutual funds, insurance companies, pension funds, and other institutional investors. The company also provides real-time corporate bond price information through its Corporate BondTicker service.

MarketAxess is focusing on technology investments to expand its connectivity offerings for electronic transactions. In 2008 it acquired development firm Greenline Financial Technologies in a $43 million cash and stock deal. The purchase added Greenline's Financial Information Exchange (FIX)-related products and services and helped boost MarketAxess' revenues by more than 20% within one year.

In late 2010, the company began offering services to institutions based in the Asia/Pacific region. MarketAxess is targeting sovereign wealth funds, pension funds, asset managers, and central banks in the region.

EXECUTIVES

Chairman and CEO, Richard M. (Rick) McVey, age 51, $2,797,991 total compensation
CFO, Antonio L. (Tony) DeLise, age 49
President and Director, T. Kelley Millet, age 51, $1,728,286 total compensation
CIO, Nicholas Themelis, age 47, $1,153,942 total compensation
Head, MarketAxess Europe, Paul Ellis
Chief Operations, Credit, and Risk Officer, James N.B. (Jim) Rucker
Media Relations, Trey Gregory
Head Human Resources, Cordelia Boise, age 44
General Counsel and Corporate Secretary, Charles R. Hood, age 60
Head Business Development and Strategy, Richard J. Schiffman, age 43
Auditors: PricewaterhouseCoopers LLP

LOCATIONS

HQ: MarketAxess Holdings Inc.
299 Park Ave., 10th Fl., New York, NY 10171
Phone: 212-813-6000   **Fax:** 212-813-6390
Web: www.marketaxess.com

PRODUCTS/OPERATIONS

2009 Sales

	$ mil.	% of total
Commissions		
US high-grade bonds	62.6	55
European high-grade bonds	20.3	18
Other	13.2	11
Technology products & services	9.8	9
Information & user access fees	6.2	5
Interest & other income	2.3	2
Total	**114.4**	**100**

COMPETITORS

BGC Partners	Interactive Brokers
BondsOnline	
Cantor Fitzgerald	TRADEBOOK
GFI Group	Tradeweb
ICAP	Weeden

HISTORICAL FINANCIALS

Company Type: Public

Income Statement

FYE: December 31

	REVENUE ($ mil.)	NET INCOME ($ mil.)	NET PROFIT MARGIN	EMPLOYEES
12/10	146.2	31.4	21.5%	229
12/09	114.4	16.1	14.1%	212
12/08	93.1	7.9	8.5%	185
12/07	93.6	10.3	11.0%	182
12/06	83.3	5.4	6.5%	176
Annual Growth	**15.1%**	**55.3%**	**—**	**6.8%**

2010 Year-End Financials

Debt ratio: —	No. of shares (mil.): 33.7
Return on equity: 13.4%	Dividends
Cash ($ mil.): 125.0	Yield: 1.3%
Current ratio: 6.57	Payout: 35.0%
Long-term debt ($ mil.): —	Market value ($ mil.): 701.9

	STOCK PRICE ($) FY Close	P/E High/Low		PER SHARE ($) Earnings	Dividends	Book Value
12/10	20.81	27	15	0.80	0.28	6.95
12/09	13.90	34	14	0.42	0.07	6.30
12/08	8.16	56	18	0.22	0.00	5.78
12/07	12.83	66	39	0.30	0.00	5.22
12/06	13.57	101	58	0.15	0.00	5.74
Annual Growth	**11.3%**	**—**	**—**	**52.0%**	**—**	**4.9%**

MasTec

MasTec digs the trenches, lays the cable, and builds the towers that power communications. The contractor provides telecommunications and energy infrastructure construction to telecom vendors, wireless providers, cable TV operators, and utility companies. In addition to internal and external network construction — from erecting radio towers to installing wiring — MasTec designs communications infrastructure and builds cable TV networks. It offers engineering, installation, and maintenance of internal and external networks for clients such as Verizon and AT&T; however, its largest customer is DIRECTV. Nearly all sales come from customers in the US. The family of chairman Jorge Mas owns 27% of MasTec.

Communications services account for more than half of MasTec's revenue, but the company is seeing green in the alternative energy market. At least three of its top 10 customers, including Iberdrola Renewables, have wind energy operations. To expand its services for the sector, MasTec bought North Dakota-based Wanzek Construction for about $200 million in 2009. Wanzek derives most of its revenue from building wind farms.

Meanwhile, as utility companies move toward natural gas usage, MasTec has responded with acquisitions that boost its offerings for pipelines and plants. The company bought Canadian pipeline and facility construction services provider Fabcor in 2011 for about $30 million, adding access to the energy industry in Canada, primarily in Alberta and British Columbia. Fabcor specializes in pipeline construction, modification, and replacement; compressor and gas plant construction; and plant commissioning support. MasTec bought Precision Pipeline, a company that lays oil and gas pipeline, for $132 million in 2009.

In its move to expand, the company has not forgotten where it makes the most cash. In 2011 MasTec bought Halsted Communications, an install-to-the-home contractor whose primary customer is DIRECTV, for about $15 million. The tuck-in acquisition expands MasTec's business with DIRECTV and extends its existing install-to-the-home business to include parts of New York, Pennsylvania, and New England.

Sales rose 42% in 2010 over 2009; of this amount, 24% was attributable to organic growth while acquisitions contributed another 18%. The company benefited from strong demand in the wireless, pipeline, install-to-the-home, and renewable energy sectors. Net income increased 28% on higher revenues and lower expenses as a percentage of sales. The company can keep expenses down because it doesn't have a lot of overhead — it rents much of its equipment from fellow Florida company Neff Corp and its customers supply the necessary materials and supplies for its projects.

For 2011, MasTec is focusing on five markets with the most potential: natural gas pipelines, alternative and renewable energy projects, wireless and fiber communications network upgrades, electrical grid upgrades, and install-to-the-home. The latter is related to the increasing number of subscribers for DIRECTV, and a bundling agreement between the satellite service provider and AT&T. MasTec gets around a quarter of its sales from DIRECTV, and another 20% from AT&T. Other customers that were key to the company's growth in 2010 include El Paso Corporation, Tenaska, Edison Mission Energy, and Talisman Energy.

HISTORY

MasTec was formed by the merger of Burnup & Sims (B&S) and Church & Tower (C&T). B&S was founded in 1929 to provide construction and maintenance services to the phone and utilities industries. C&T began in 1968 building phone networks in Miami and Puerto Rico. Jorge Mas Canosa was brought on board in 1969 and given half of the company in exchange for managing it. By 1971 he had succeeded in turning C&T around and had bought the remainder.

In 1994 C&T and B&S merged; B&S became MasTec and C&T became a subsidiary. Mas was named chairman, and his son, who had been at C&T since 1980, was named president and CEO. The company began a program of acquisitions and started building a presence in Latin America.

MasTec doubled its size in 1996 by acquiring Sintel, a telecom infrastructure construction firm operating in South America and Spain, from Telefonica. MasTec continued to grow through acquisitions, buying 10 more companies the next year. Mas died in 1997 and his son, Jorge Jr., succeeded him. It sold a near-bankrupt Sintel and began to refocus on domestic operations.

In 2000 MasTec acquired GMR Telecom, a telecommunication systems engineering and design company. In 2004 the company exited Brazil and sold its Network Services division. Two years later it entered the market for the installation of residential and commercial satellite and security services with the acquisition of Digital Satellite Services, Inc. (DSSI), which operated as Ron's Digital Satellite and Ron's TV, for $18.5 million.

MasTec took the exit ramp for its highways business in 2007 after selling its Department of Transportation (DOT) Service Business, which provided specialty contracting services to state DOTs and local transportation authorities, to an investor group led by private equity firm LEÓN, MAYER & Co.

MasTec acquired oil and gas pipeline construction firm Pumpco and certain assets of wireless design and construction company Nsoro in 2008. One of its largest projects, was the construction of the Ruby Pipeline, a 680-mile natural gas line that stretches from Oregon to Wyoming.

The following year, MasTec bought Precision Pipeline, a company that lays oil and gas pipeline, for $132 million. It also bought North Dakota-based Wanzek Construction for about $200 million in 2009. Wanzek specialized in heavy and civil construction, as well as building wind farms.

EXECUTIVES

Chairman, Jorge Mas Jr., age 48
President, Ray E. Harris, age 54
CEO and Director, José R. Mas, age 39, $1,073,637 total compensation
EVP, General Counsel, and Secretary, Alberto de Cardenas, age 42, $499,439 total compensation
EVP and CFO, C. Robert (Bob) Campbell, age 66, $933,282 total compensation
EVP Mergers and Acquisitions, Pablo A. Alvarez
VP Investor Relations, J. Marc Lewis, age 49
VP Government Services, Larry Burch
VP Business Development, Electric Utility, Barry J. Batson
VP, Central Office, EF&I, John E. Brewer
COO, Robert E. (Bob) Apple, age 61, $720,412 total compensation
SVP Business Development, Oscar Primelles
Group President, Wireless, Darrell Mays
Group President, Satellite Services, Zach McGuire
Group President, Communications, Bryan Westerman

Director Human Resources, East Region, Ani de
Varona
**Director Human Resources, South and West
Regions,** Sandi Adler Cornelius
Director Compensation and Benefits, Cecilia Acevedo
Auditors: BDO USA, LLP

LOCATIONS

HQ: MasTec, Inc.
800 S. Douglas Rd., 12th Fl., Coral Gables, FL
33134
Phone: 305-599-1800   **Fax:** 305-406-1960
Web: www.mastec.com

PRODUCTS/OPERATIONS

2010 Sales

	$ mil.	% of total
Communications	1,222	53
Utilities	1,046	45
Government	40	2
Total	**2,308**	**100**

Selected Services

Broadband networks
  Aerial and underground construction
  Bonding/grounding
  Engineering and design
  FCC testing
  Modem installation
  Optical fiber splicing, activation, and testing
  Warehouse and inventory management
Telecommunications
  Aerial construction
  Copper/coaxial cable systems
  Directional drilling
  Engineering
  Fiber-optic cable systems
  Fiber-to-the-premises (FTTP) deployment
  Splicing and testing
  Underground construction
Utilities
  Design and engineering
  Gas distribution construction and maintenance
  Storm restoration
  Submarine cable installation
  Substation construction
  Transmission line construction
  Trench construction

COMPETITORS

Bechtel	MYR Group
Dycom	Pike Electric
Goldfield	Corporation
Henkels & McCoy	Quanta Services
M. A. Mortenson	Sirti
MDU Construction	
Services	

HISTORICAL FINANCIALS

Company Type: Public

Income Statement

FYE: December 31

	REVENUE ($ mil.)	NET INCOME ($ mil.)	NET PROFIT MARGIN	EMPLOYEES
12/10	2,308.0	90.5	3.9%	9,400
12/09	1,623.5	70.7	4.4%	8,600
12/08	1,378.7	65.8	4.8%	8,400
12/07	1,037.8	(7.3)	—	8,240
12/06	945.8	(50.3)	—	9,260
Annual Growth	**25.0%**	**—**	**—**	**0.4%**

2010 Year-End Financials

Debt ratio: 60.4%   No. of shares (mil.): 78.2
Return on equity: 13.9%   Dividends
Cash ($ mil.): 177.6   Yield: —
Current ratio: 1.48   Payout: —
Long-term debt ($ mil.): 394.2 Market value ($ mil.): 1,141.2

	STOCK PRICE ($) FY Close	P/E High/Low		PER SHARE ($) Earnings	Dividends	Book Value
12/10	14.59	15	9	1.05	0.00	8.35
12/09	12.50	16	10	0.90	0.00	6.95
12/08	11.58	16	6	0.96	0.00	6.52
12/07	10.17	—	—	(0.11)	0.00	4.71
12/06	11.54	—	—	(0.77)	0.00	4.68
Annual Growth	**6.0%**	**—**	**—**	**—**	**—**	**15.6%**

Materion

Materion (formerly Brush Engineered Materials) provides advanced engineered materials and services worldwide. Its products are sold to a number of markets, including consumer electronics, aerospace and defense, industrial components, telecommunications infrastructure, automotive electronics, and medical and appliance. It manufactures a variety of precious and specialty metal products, including frame lid assemblies and clad and plated metal systems. Other products include precision optics and thin film coatings; inorganic chemicals and powders; specialty coatings; beryllium, beryllium composites, and beryllium alloys. The company consolidated all of its divisions under the name Materion in 2011.

The names of all of the company's subsidiaries were changed as well, with each subsidiary having Materion as part of its name. The legal and ownership structure of the subsidiaries remained unchanged.

Each of Materion's divisions serves specialized markets. The largest group, advanced materials technologies, manufactures precious, non-precious, and specialty metal products, such as clad and precious metal pre-forms, high temperature brazing materials, ultra-fine wire, optics, performance coatings, and electronic packages. The advanced materials group is the company's primary breadwinner, accounting for more than two-thirds of annual sales.

Other groups have a different mission. For example, the beryllium and composites group is focused on the defense industry. It has a $90 million contract to construct a manufacturing facility for the US Department of Defense to provide the rare and toxic metal beryllium for use in weapons and aerospace applications.

Through subsidiary Materion Advanced Materials Technologies and Services, the company acquired EIS Optics in 2011. EIS Optics produces optical thin film filters and subassemblies, as well as glass processing and lithography products, that are used for various applications, including projectors, HDTV, hand-held cameras, and gaming systems. The acquisition widens Materion's footprint in Asia and gives it access to the fast-growing Chinese market, where EIS Optics operates a manufacturing site in Shanghai. The buy complements a number of recent acquisitions Materion has made to bolster its precision thin film optical filters and coatings operations.

In 2010 Materion's sales catapulted to a record high of $1.3 billion, 82% higher than sales of $715.2 million in 2009. Strong demand — following the steep slump in 2009 after the global economic crisis — contributed to each of the company's reportable segments growing at double digits in 2010. The company's net income was reported at $46.4 million in 2010, over a loss of $20.8 million in 2009.

The company had shown steady growth in the years prior to the global recession, but saw a significant dip in both revenues and net income in 2008 and 2009. Sales fell both years on lower demand from key markets, particularly defense and medical products. In response, the company moved to reduce manpower, freeze or cut compensation and benefits, and eliminate discretionary spending during that year.

Looking for other ways to improve its bottom line, the company made several acquisitions starting in 2008, beefing up its already large advanced materials division and entering some new markets. That group's Advanced Materials subsidiary acquired metallic-coated films maker Techni-Met for $90 million that year. Techni-Met's products, used in the medical and electronics field, include blood glucose test strips used to manage diabetes.

The company made two more acquisitions in the next two years, buying optical filter maker Barr Associates for $55 million, and precious metals refiner Academy Corporation for about $25 million. Barr manufactures thin film filters for the defense, aerospace, medical, energy, and astronomy markets, while Academy provides metals and refining for architectural glass, solar energy, electronics, and high-value jewelry.

EXECUTIVES

Chairman, President, and CEO, Richard J. (Dick)
Hipple, age 58, $3,424,083 total compensation
President, Performance Alloys, W. Glenn Maxwell, age
52
President, Beryllium Products, Michael D. Anderson,
age 59
**President, Brush International; Sales, Marketing,
and Technical Services, Alloy Products,** Richard L.
Trate
VP, Secretary, and Treasurer, Michael C. Hasychak
VP Corporate Communications, Patrick S. Carpenter
VP and Controller, James P. Marrotte
VP and General Counsel, Gregory R. Chemnitz
SVP Administration, Daniel A. Skoch, age 61,
$1,270,888 total compensation
SVP Finance, and CFO, John D. Grampa, age 63,
$1,233,176 total compensation
Assistant Treasurer and Assistant Secretary, Gary W.
Schiavoni
Auditors: Ernst & Young LLP

LOCATIONS

HQ: Materion Corporation
6070 Parkland Blvd., Mayfield Heights, OH 44124
Phone: 216-486-4200   **Fax:** 216-383-4091
Web: www.materion.com

2010 Sales

	$ mil.	% of total
Advanced Material Technologies	879.0	67
Performance Alloys	293.8	23
Technical Materials	67.5	5
Beryllium & Composites	61.9	5
Other	0.1	-
Total	**1,302.3**	**100**

2010 Sales

	$ mil.	% of total
US	933.2	72
Other countries	369.1	28
Total	**1302.3100Archive**	
This Chart		

COMPETITORS

Aeroflex
American Technical
  Ceramics
Anaren
BASF Catalysts
Cookson Group
Heraeus Holding
Honeywell
  International

Kyocera
NGK INSULATORS
Olin
Praxair
Sumitomo Metal
  Industries

HISTORICAL FINANCIALS

Company Type: Public

Income Statement

FYE: December 31

	REVENUE ($ mil.)	NET INCOME ($ mil.)	NET PROFIT MARGIN	EMPLOYEES
12/10	1,302.3	46.4	3.6%	2,484
12/09	715.2	(12.4)	—	2,196
12/08	909.7	18.4	2.0%	2,235
12/07	955.7	53.3	5.6%	2,201
12/06	763.1	49.6	6.5%	2,185
Annual Growth	**14.3%**	**(1.7%)**	**—**	**3.3%**

2010 Year-End Financials

Debt ratio: 10.0%
Return on equity: 12.1%
Cash ($ mil.): 16.1
Current ratio: 2.41
Long-term debt ($ mil.): 38.3

No. of shares (mil.): 20.3
Dividends
  Yield: 0.0%
  Payout: —
Market value ($ mil.): 785.2

	STOCK PRICE ($) FY Close	P/E High	P/E Low	PER SHARE ($) Earnings	Dividends	Book Value
12/10	38.64	18	7	2.25	0.00	18.92
12/09	18.54	—	—	(0.61)	0.00	16.80
12/08	12.72	40	8	0.89	0.00	17.11
12/07	37.02	24	12	2.59	0.00	17.34
12/06	33.77	15	6	2.45	0.00	14.45
Annual Growth	**3.4%**	**—**	**—**	**(2.1%)**	**—**	**7.0%**

Maxim Integrated Products

Maxim's maxim? Invent! Maxim Integrated Products makes more than 6,000 kinds of analog and mixed-signal integrated circuits (ICs); more than 80% were invented by the company. Maxim's chips — which include amplifiers, data converters, transceivers, and switching ICs — translate physical data such as temperature, pressure, and sound into digital signals for electronic processing. The company's ICs are used by thousands of electronics manufacturers in products that include computers and peripherals, appliances, telecommunications and networking gear, automobiles, medical devices, instruments, and utility meters. More than two-thirds of sales come from customers located in the Asia/Pacific region.

Net revenues for Maxim rose 24% — a company record — in fiscal 2011 compared with 2010 thanks mainly to strong sales of products in three segments: industrial (up 35%), consumer (up 28%), and communications (up 26%).

Maxim has manufacturing facilities in the Philippines, Thailand, and the US. Wafer assembly and testing is performed by subcontractors located in Asia. Maxim has about 50 technology centers and more than 20 sales offices throughout the world. While it continues to increase its manufacturing capacity, Maxim has been relying more on partner foundries, such as Seiko Epson, for wafer supply. The percentage of products made by these partners rose from 9% in fiscal 2009 to 32% in fiscal 2011.

Maxim's products are sold mostly as individual purchase orders through distribution channels as well as its own direct sales staff. Distributors such as Avnet are responsible for about 30% of revenue. Though not a direct customer, Avnet individually represented 14% of fiscal 2011 sales. One direct customer, Samsung, accounted for 12% of 2011 sales.

Even during the notorious roller-coaster ups and downs of the chip industry, Maxim backs up its emphasis on invention by reinvesting a substantial chunk of sales (typically between about 20%-30% a year) in R&D. The company's famously nononsense founder, Jack Gifford, fostered a work atmosphere built around total candor, high expectations, and high performance.

To a smaller extent Maxim grows through acquisitions. In 2011 it bought (for an undisclosed amount) Scotland-based Calvatec to boost its IP holdings of analog and mixed signal technology for consumer electronics and communications products. Next it bought SensorDynamics, an Austrian company that develops sensor technology for microelectromechanical (MEMS) systems for the automotive market. Maxim paid $130 million, plus $34 million in debt, for SensorDynamics.

More closely targeting the energy measurement and "smart meter" market, Maxim in 2010 acquired Teridian Semiconductor for about $315 million in cash. Teridian holds 50% of the system-on-a-chip energy measurement market, designing chips that combine the functions of an analog front end, a microcontroller, and a display driver on one device. A fabless semiconductor company, Teridian is a supplier to three of the top four utility meter manufacturers in the US and to more than 50 meter makers around the world.

In 2010 the company also purchased Phyworks for about $72.5 million. The deal expands Maxim's offerings for supplying chips for broadband communications and related applications. Phyworks provides optical transceiver chips that are used in high-speed optical networks and other broadband communications.

HISTORY

Jack Gifford, a former UCLA baseball star who began his career at Fairchild Semiconductor and later headed the Intersil subsidiary (later divested) of General Electric, founded Maxim in 1983. Gifford focused on analog chips, which were less vulnerable to Japanese competition than digital integrated circuits (ICs), had a longer product life, and cost less to make. Maxim went public in 1988.

From the beginning Maxim emphasized research and development: Gifford's 1983 business plan set the ambitious goal of developing at least 15 new products each quarter. The company developed 479 new products between 1993 and 1996.

In 1994 Maxim bought Tektronix's IC business, and the two companies formed the Maxtek joint venture, a maker of multichip modules and hybrid circuits. For the rest of the decade, Maxim focused on expanding and modernizing its manufacturing. It opened offices in Hong Kong, South Korea, and Singapore in 1996, and added factories in the Philippines and California in 1997.

Maxim released 250 new products in fiscal 1998, including breakthrough chips for portable computers, flat-panel displays, and paging. Maxim sold its half of Maxtek to Tektronix in 2000. That year it also introduced a record 383 products, and broke ground for a testing facility in Thailand.

In 2001 Maxim acquired specialty IC maker Dallas Semiconductor for about $2.5 billion. It also continued its "product proliferation" strategy as it topped itself once again by introducing 500 new products. Fiscal 2001 also saw the company expand its facilities in California, Thailand, and the Philippines.

Maxim bought a Texas chip fabrication plant from Philips Semiconductors (now NXP) in 2003.

In 2005 Maxim reorganized into two main product groups — Portable, Computing, and Instrumentation Electronics, with 10 business units, and Multimedia, Automotive, and Telecommunications Electronics, with seven business units. The company retained finance, manufacturing, and planning as central corporate functions.

For health reasons, Jack Gifford retired as CEO at the end of 2006 and also left the board of directors. He remained with the company on a part-time basis as a strategic advisor focusing on business direction and product planning. Tunc Doluca, a group president and 22-year veteran of Maxim, was named president and CEO effective at the beginning of 2007. Director Kipling Hagopian, a member of the board since 1997, was elected interim chairman to succeed Gifford.

Gifford's sudden departure came while the company was still investigating its past practices in granting stock options, a subject that came to dominate his last year with Maxim. Although he stepped down at the age of 65, many Silicon Valley observers were surprised to see Gifford go when he did, as many other founder CEOs kept running their companies well into their 70s. A shareholder derivative lawsuit challenging Maxim's practices in stock-option grants was filed in May 2006. While the company publicly dismissed the complaint as without merit, the SEC soon after opened an informal inquiry on the subject, and a month later Maxim received a subpoena from federal prosecutors for corporate records on stock options. The company's board also initiated a review of stock-option granting practices, with help from outside, independent legal counsel. Maxim delayed releasing its 10-K annual report for fiscal 2006 as a result of the investigations.

The board's special committee wrapped up its review in 2007, concluding that there were instances from 2000 to 2006 where the recorded price of certain stock-option grants did not reflect the fair market value of the shares on the actual measurement dates. As a result, Jack Gifford retired from his part-time advisory position and CFO Carl Jasper resigned from the company.

Near the end of 2007, Maxim reached a settlement with the SEC on options backdating, agreeing to a permanent injunction against violations of federal securities laws and anti-fraud statutes. The SEC didn't assess any fines, penalties, or money damages against the company under the settlement. The regulators brought civil charges against Gifford and Jasper for their roles in backdating options.

Gifford settled his case with the SEC, agreeing to return more than $650,000 in bonuses and to pay a penalty of $150,000. Jasper contested the charges, however.

Maxim also implemented a number of corporate reforms, such as new corporate governance guidelines, formal procedures for the granting of stock options and other equity awards, and a more comprehensive insider trading policy.

In 2007 Maxim bought a wafer fab in Irving, Texas, from competitor Atmel for about $38 million in cash. The 200mm wafer fab is idle while Maxim waits for market demand to recover. Later that year, looking to boost its storage product offerings, Maxim bought the Storage Products division of Vitesse Semiconductor for about $63 million in cash. The acquired business included serial attached storage ICs and related software and firmware.

The company also discontinued development of certain stand-alone, high-speed, high-resolution analog-to-digital converters. While Maxim concluded there was a limited market for these parts, it cut the converters in part to avoid an intellectual property dispute with rival Analog Devices over the devices. Jettisoning the products helped the company settle the case with ADI rather than going to trial.

In 2008 the company settled the shareholder derivative lawsuit over the misdated stock options for $28.5 million in cash to be paid to Maxim — $21 million from liability insurers, $6 million from Gifford, and $1.5 million from three directors. The plaintiffs received up to $15 million for legal fees and up to $500,000 for other expenses. Gifford cancelled vested and unexercised options for about 3.1 million shares of common stock.

Gifford died in 2009 at the age of 67.

In 2009 Maxim acquired two product lines from ZiLOG. The company purchased ZiLOG's Wireless Control business in concert with Universal Electronics. Maxim received the hardware portion of the business, microcontrollers and related intellectual property, and it combined those products with its ultra-low-power infrared microcontroller family. On its own, Maxim bought ZiLOG's Secure Transaction product line, with its Zatara line of 32-bit MCUs used in consumer payment terminals. The acquisition dovetailed with Maxim's earlier purchase of a French firm, Innova Card, in providing chips for the financial transaction terminal market.

Later that year Maxim spun out its radio-frequency (RF) division — consisting of designs, intellectual property, and an engineering team — to Intelleflex in exchange for equity ownership in that company and an agreement to partner on future product marketing.

EXECUTIVES

Chairman, B. Kipling (Kip) Hagopian, age 69
President, CEO, and Director, Tunc Doluca, age 53, $4,003,086 total compensation
VP and Senior Counsel, Edwin Medlin, age 54
VP and Principal Accounting Officer, Dave Caron, age 51
VP Human Resources, Steven T. (Steve) Yamasaki, age 56
VP Worldwide Sales, Matthew J. (Matt) Murphy, age 38
Group President, High Performance Analog Division, Pirooz Parvarandeh, age 51, $2,247,292 total compensation
Division VP, Conversion, Computing, and Secure Products Division, Christopher J. (Chris) Neil, age 45
Field Applications Engineer, India, Chandrashekara Atra

Inside Applications Engineer, Germany, Gerhard Winkler
Inside Applications Engineer, France and Spain, Javier Monsalve
Senior Field Applications Engineer, Italy, Massimo Caprioli
Inside Applications Engineer, United Kingdom, Andy Waller
Field Applications Engineer, Switzerland, Roland Sandfuchs
Corporate Field Applications Engineer, Russia, Anatoly Andrusevich
China MarCom and IAE Manager, Wei Zhi
Field Applications Engineer, Israel, Avi Zaccai
Senior Public Relations Specialist, Drew Ehrlich
SVP Manufacturing Operations, Vivek Jain, age 50, $2,415,604 total compensation
SVP Administration and General Counsel, Charles G. (Chuck) Rigg, age 67, $1,816,829 total compensation
Group President, Handheld Consumer Division, Vijay Ullal, age 52, $2,765,219 total compensation
SVP, CFO, and Principal Accounting Officer, Bruce E. Kiddoo, age 50, $1,948,437 total compensation
Manager Marketing Communications, Japan, Kohei Shimooka
Marketing Communications Specialist, Korea, Grace Kim
Investor Relations, Paresh Maniar
Auditors: Deloitte & Touche LLP

LOCATIONS

HQ: Maxim Integrated Products, Inc.
120 San Gabriel Dr., Sunnyvale, CA 94086
Phone: 408-737-7600   **Fax:** 408-737-7194
Web: www.maxim-ic.com

2010 Sales

	$ mil.	% of total
Asia		
China	915.6	37
Korea	294.0	12
Japan	163.1	7
Rest of Asia	283.1	11
US	360.3	15
Europe	379.2	15
Rest of World	77.0	3
Total	**2,472.3**	**100**

PRODUCTS/OPERATIONS

Selected Products

Amplifiers and comparators
  Audio amplifiers
  Operational amplifiers
Analog switches and multiplexers
Data converters, sample-and-hold devices, and voltage references
Digital potentiometers
Fiber and communications devices
  Circuits for fiber and cable data transmission
  Framers
  Transceivers
Filters
High-frequency application-specific integrated circuits (ASICs)
Hot-swap and power switching circuits
Interface and interconnect devices
LED lighting and LCD display devices
Memories
  Electrically erasable programmable read-only memories (EEPROMs)
  Erasable programmable read-only memories (EPROMs)
  Non-volatile static random-access memories (SRAMs)
  Non-volatile timekeeping RAMs
Microcontrollers
Microprocessor supervisors and non-volatile RAM controllers
Multiplexers
Optoelectronic devices
Power supplies and battery management devices

DC-to-DC power supplies
Low-dropout linear regulators
Power metal oxide semiconductor field-effect transistor (MOSFET) drivers
Protection and isolation circuits
Sensors, sensor conditioners, and thermal management devices
Storage products
Timing devices
  Counters and timers
  Oscillators and waveform generators
  Real-time clocks (RTCs)
Wireless and radio-frequency (RF) products
  Amplifiers
  Receivers
  Transmitters and transceivers
Video amplifiers, processors, and switches
Voltage monitors

COMPETITORS

Advanced Analogic Technologies
Altera
Analog Devices
Applied Micro Circuits
Atmel
Conexant Systems
Exar
Fairchild Semiconductor
Freescale Semiconductor
Fujitsu Microelectronics America
Infineon Technologies
Intel
International Rectifier
Intersil
Linear Technology
Marvell Technology
Micrel
Microchip Technology
Mindspeed
Mitsubishi Corp.
Mitsui
Monolithic Power Systems
National Semiconductor
NXP Semiconductors
O2Micro
ON Semiconductor
PMC-Sierra
QUALCOMM
RF Micro Devices
Ricoh Company
ROHM
Seiko
Semtech
Silicon Labs
Siliconix
Skyworks
STMicroelectronics
Texas Instruments
Vishay Intertechnology
Vitesse Semiconductor
Volterra Semiconductor

HISTORICAL FINANCIALS

Company Type: Public

Income Statement

FYE: Last Saturday in June

	REVENUE ($ mil.)	NET INCOME ($ mil.)	NET PROFIT MARGIN	EMPLOYEES
06/11	2,472.3	489.0	19.8%	9,370
06/10	1,997.6	125.1	6.3%	9,200
06/09	1,646.0	10.5	0.6%	8,765
06/08	2,052.8	317.7	15.5%	9,810
06/07	2,009.1	286.2	14.2%	10,136
Annual Growth	**5.3%**	**14.3%**	**—**	**(1.9%)**

2011 Year-End Financials

Debt ratio: 11.9%
No. of shares (mil.): 295.8
Return on equity: 19.5%
Dividends
Cash ($ mil.): 962.5
Yield: 3.3%
Current ratio: 4.17
Payout: 52.2%
Long-term debt ($ mil.): 300.0
Market value ($ mil.): 7,560.1

	STOCK PRICE ($) FY Close	P/E High/Low		PER SHARE ($) Earnings	Dividends	Book Value
06/11	25.56	18	10	1.61	0.84	8.49
06/10	16.73	53	37	0.40	0.80	7.82
06/09	15.69	757	357	0.03	0.80	8.48
06/08	21.15	36	17	0.98	0.75	9.82
06/07	33.41	39	30	0.87	0.62	9.77
Annual Growth	(6.5%)	—	—	16.6%	7.9%	(3.4%)

MaxLinear

MaxLinear could be considered a translator, but not in the linguistic world. A fabless semiconductor company, MaxLinear provides integrated radio-frequency (RF) and mixed-signal receivers used to receive and translate analog or digital radio, television, and other broadband signals into visual images. Its products, which are used in cable TV set-top boxes, digital TVs, and mobile phones, are sold to OEMs and original design manufacturers, including Panasonic (16% of revenue) and Toshiba (10% of revenue). Nearly all sales are to Asian customers. CEO Kishore Seendripu (who owns nearly 25% of the company's Class B common stock) and other executives founded MaxLinear in 2003. The company completed an IPO in 2010.

EXECUTIVES

Chairman, President, and CEO, Kishore Seendripu, age 42, $260,577 total compensation
CFO, Joe D. Campa, age 54, $202,437 total compensation
VP, Marketing, John M. Graham, age 49
VP, Sales, Michael C. Kastner, age 49
VP, IC and RF Systems Engineering, Madhukar Reddy, age 42, $206,107 total compensation
VP, Business Development, Brendan Walsh, age 38, $190,239 total compensation
VP, Operations and Semiconductor Technology, Kimihiko Imura, age 54, $190,239 total compensation
Regional Sales Manager, Korea, Dean Faith
Director Marketing, Patrick Tierney
Sales Director China, Taiwan, Singapore, Patrick Wu
Sales Director, EMEA, Safy Fishov
Country Manager, Japan, Takashi Izushi
Chief Accounting Officer and Controller, Patrick (Pat) McCready, age 53
CTO and Director, Curtis Ling, age 46, $195,245 total compensation
Auditors: Ernst & Young LLP

LOCATIONS

HQ: MaxLinear, Inc.
2051 Palomar Airport Rd., Ste. 100, Carlsbad, CA 92011
Phone: 760-692-0711 **Fax:** 760-692-0712
Web: www.maxlinear.com

COMPETITORS

Analog Devices
Broadcom
NXP Semiconductors
Silicon Labs

Entropic Communications
Maxim Integrated Products
Telegent

HISTORICAL FINANCIALS
Company Type: Public

Income Statement
FYE: December 31

	REVENUE ($ mil.)	NET INCOME ($ mil.)	NET PROFIT MARGIN	EMPLOYEES
12/10	68.7	10.1	14.7%	210
12/09	51.3	4.3	8.4%	166
12/08	31.3	(1.9)	—	146
12/07	9.7	(8.7)	—	0
12/06	0.6	(9.8)	—	0
Annual Growth	227.1%	—	—	19.9%

2010 Year-End Financials

Debt ratio: 0.0%
No. of shares (mil.): 31.9
Return on equity: 9.6%
Dividends
Cash ($ mil.): 21.6
Yield: —
Current ratio: 7.94
Payout: —
Long-term debt ($ mil.): 0.0
Market value ($ mil.): 343.1

	STOCK PRICE ($) FY Close	P/E High/Low		PER SHARE ($) Earnings	Dividends	Book Value
12/10	10.76	65	31	0.30	0.00	3.29
Annual Growth	—	—	—	—	—	—

Maxus Realty Trust

Maxus Realty Trust believes in the value of maximizing housing space. The real estate investment trust (REIT) invests in income-producing properties, primarily multifamily residential properties. It owns a portfolio of approximately 10 apartment communities in the Midwest US. Maxus Realty Trust was originally established to invest in office and light industrial facilities, but switched gears and began focusing on residential real estate in 2000. The REIT de-registered with the SEC and stopped trading on the NASDAQ in 2008.

EXECUTIVES

Chairman, President, and CEO, David L. Johnson, age 54
VP, Michael P. McRobert, age 52
Treasurer and Principal Financial Officer, John W. Alvey, age 52
Principal Accounting Officer and Corporate Secretary, DeAnn M. Trotta, age 45
Auditors: Moore Stephens Frost

LOCATIONS

HQ: Maxus Realty Trust, Inc.
104 Armour Rd., North Kansas City, MO 64116
Phone: 816-303-4500 **Fax:** 816-221-1829

PRODUCTS/OPERATIONS

COMPETITORS

AMLI Residential
Apartment Investment and Management
Equity Office
Equity Residential
Investors Real Estate

Camden Property Trust
CenterPoint Properties
Duke Realty
Paragon Real Estate Trust

HISTORICAL FINANCIALS
Company Type: Public

Income Statement
FYE: December 31

	REVENUE ($ mil.)	NET INCOME ($ mil.)	NET PROFIT MARGIN	EMPLOYEES
12/07	11.6	(1.6)	—	0
12/06	8.2	2.1	25.6%	0
12/05	7.9	(1.1)	—	0
12/04	6.0	1.5	25.0%	0
12/03	6.0	(0.2)	—	200
Annual Growth	17.9%	—	—	—

2007 Year-End Financials

Debt ratio: 629.8%
No. of shares (mil.): —
Return on equity: —
Dividends
Cash ($ mil.): 5.5
Yield: 7.6%
Current ratio: —
Payout: —
Long-term debt ($ mil.): 59.3
Market value ($ mil.): —

	STOCK PRICE ($) FY Close	P/E High/Low		PER SHARE ($) Earnings	Dividends	Book Value
12/07	10.49	—	—	(1.08)	0.80	(0.00)
12/06	13.25	12	6	1.53	0.00	(0.00)
12/05	13.93	—	—	(0.85)	0.75	(0.00)
12/04	13.91	14	8	1.18	1.00	(0.00)
12/03	10.55	—	—	(0.17)	1.00	(0.00)
Annual Growth	(0.1%)	—	—	—	(5.4%)	—

Maxwell Technologies

This Maxwell is using his silver hammer to pound energy storage into the 21st century. Maxwell Technologies makes ultracapacitors, postage stamp-sized cells that are able to store large amounts of energy for long periods of time. Its BOOSTCAP ultracapacitor cells and multi-cell modules are used to extend battery life in electronic devices in consumer electronics, hybrid vehicles, and renewable energy applications. The company also makes CONDIS-branded high-voltage capacitors for electrical grids and radiation-shielded microelectronics for aerospace applications, such as satellites and spacecraft. Customers outside the US (including ABB, with 10% of sales)account for three-quarters of revenues.

Founded in 1965, Maxwell is not a new company, but the market for ultracapacitors is. Maxwell is on the right track by marketing its BOOSTCAP ultracapacitors to the transportation industry, for use in braking energy recuperation and torque-augmentation systems for hybrid-electric vehicles and electric rail cars, as well as engine starting systems for regular gas-powered vehicles.

Top customer Continental AG uses BOOSTCAP ultracapacitors in its E-booster voltage stabilization systems, which are incorporated into Peugeot and Citroën vehicles. In 2009 three Chinese bus manufacturers paid $13.5 million for ultracapacitor modules to be used in hybrid buses. Hybrid vehicles require integrated modules consisting of hundreds of ultracapacitor cells, and Maxwell has sold more than 1 million BOOSTCAP ultracapacitors.

The renewable energy market is also boosting Maxwell's presence in the energy storage systems industry. Ultracapacitors are used in wind turbines, and the company estimates that more than 13,000 turbines in Asia, Europe, and North America are equipped with BOOSTCAP ultracapacitors. In addition, its ultracapacitors are used in flash memory solid-state drives (SSDs) to power enterprise-level storage products.

As such, ultracapacitors are the company's largest segment, accounting for 43% of sales in 2009. High-voltage capacitors, once the company's largest segment, accounted for 39% of revenues in 2009. Maxwell sells high-voltage capacitors to large systems integrators, including Areva and Siemens. Radiation-shielded microelectronics, such as include power modules, memory modules, and single-board computers, accounted for 18% of revenues.

Maxwell Technologies has seen its overall revenues grow 26% in 2009 and 42% in 2008 to meet market demand for ultracapacitors. 2010 revenues are projected to increase by about 20%, but the company has yet to become profitable. It has a history of losses and an accumulated deficit of $158 million.

Maxwell continues to seek opportunities in China, its third-largest market, where it has a contract manufacturing arrangement with Belton Technology Group. (Maxwell also has manufacturing plants in the US and Switzerland.) Maxwell collaborates with Chinese companies to expand its presence in that burgeoning market, supplying ultracapacitor electrode materials to Shanghai Sanjui Electric Equipment and Yeong-Long Technologies. In China, however, the company must carefully guard its intellectual property rights, where some manufacturers will illegally copy a company's product and then sell it for less in export markets.

EXECUTIVES

Chairman, Mark Rossi, age 54
President, CEO, and Director, David J. Schramm, age 61, $1,590,000 total compensation
VP Advanced Power, Energy Development, and CTO, Michael A. (Mike) Everett
VP Business Development, Market Intelligence, and Strategic Planning, Michael J. Liedtke, age 50
VP Operations, Everett E. (Earl) Wiggins III
VP and General Manager, Microelectronic Products, Larry Longden
VP Systems Applications and Integration, John M. Miller, age 61
VP Communications and Investor Relations, Michael W. (Mike) Sund
VP Ultracapacitor Engineering, Jeremy Cowperthwaite
SVP, CFO, Treasurer, and Secretary, Kevin S. Royal, age 46
SVP Sales and Marketing, Van M. Andrews
SVP and COO, George Kreigler III, age 58, $540,800 total compensation
General Manager, Maxwell, SA and VP High Tension, Sacha Jenny, age 42
Auditors: McGladrey & Pullen, LLP

LOCATIONS

HQ: Maxwell Technologies, Inc.
9244 Balboa Ave., San Diego, CA 92123
Phone: 858-503-3300   **Fax:** 858-503-3301
Web: www.maxwell.com

2009 Sales

	$ mil.	% of total
US	25.5	25
Germany	24.8	24
China	16.9	17
Hong Kong	7.4	7
France	4.3	4
Sweden	3.4	3
Switzerland	2.9	3
Korea	2.1	2
Italy	1.9	2
Spain	1.7	2
Canada	1.5	1
Russia	1.4	1
Netherlands	1.2	1
UK	.9	1
Other	5.4	5
Total	**101.3**	**100**

PRODUCTS/OPERATIONS

2009 Sales

	$ mil.	% of total
BOOSTCAP ultracapacitors	43.8	43
CONDIS high-voltage capacitors	39.8	39
Radiation-mitigated microelectronics	17.7	18
Total	**101.3**	**100**

COMPETITORS

Analog Devices	PMC Global
BAE SYSTEMS	Siemens AG
EPCOS	SION Power
Honeywell	Spectrum Control
International	Teledyne Technologies
KEMET	Vishay Intertechnology
Lockheed Martin	W.L. Gore
Murata Manufacturing	White Electronic
National Semiconductor	Designs
Panasonic Corp	

HISTORICAL FINANCIALS

Company Type: Public

Income Statement

FYE: December 31

	REVENUE ($ mil.)	NET INCOME ($ mil.)	NET PROFIT MARGIN	EMPLOYEES
12/10	121.9	(6.1)	—	368
12/09	101.3	(22.9)	—	361
12/08	82.2	(14.8)	—	346
12/07	57.4	(15.7)	—	302
12/06	53.9	(16.5)	—	377
Annual Growth	**22.6%**	**—**	**—**	**(0.6%)**

2010 Year-End Financials

Debt ratio: 14.3%
Return on equity: —
Cash ($ mil.): 39.8
Current ratio: 2.45
Long-term debt ($ mil.): 12.6

No. of shares (mil.): 27.2
Dividends
  Yield: 0.0%
  Payout: —
Market value ($ mil.): 513.5

	STOCK PRICE ($) FY Close	P/E High/Low	PER SHARE ($) Earnings	Dividends	Book Value
12/10	18.89	— —	(0.23)	0.00	3.24
12/09	17.84	— —	(0.94)	0.00	2.96
12/08	5.07	— —	(0.71)	0.00	2.81
12/07	8.27	— —	(0.86)	0.00	3.05
12/06	13.95	— —	(0.98)	0.00	2.66
Annual Growth	**7.9%**	**— —**	**—**	**—**	**5.1%**

Meadowbrook Insurance

Meadowbrook Insurance sounds pastoral, but there's very little nature involved in providing business insurance. Its Star, Savers, Williamsburg, and Ameritrust subsidiaries write a variety of specialty commercial property/casualty products including excess and surplus products for high-risk clients. With products tailored to fit small to midsize businesses, customers include self-insured companies, trade groups, and associations. Meadowbrook offers reinsurance brokering, risk management consulting, and insurance management services including claims handling and administrative services. It distributes its products through a network of independent agencies, brokers, and its own retail agency operations.

Meadowbrook's income is diversified geographically, with California bringing in the majority of its premium income (roughly 35%). After that come Florida and Texas, which together account for more than 15% of Meadowbrook's premiums.

The company's corporate strategy emphasizes a regional focus and diversification of revenues between underwriting premiums, fee-for-service revenue, and commissions. Meadowbrook's strategy allows the company to leverage its fixed costs over a larger revenue base, giving it the stability to take more risk when needed.

Of its different segments, the company's workers' compensation line of business is focused in California and New England; commercial auto and commercial multiple peril lines are clustered in the Southeast and California; the general liability line of business is primarily in Texas; and, the fee-for-service business is managed on a regional basis with an emphasis in the Midwest, New England, and southeastern regions of the United States.

Meadowbrook avoids becoming so concentrated in any one area that it becomes especially vulnerable to catastrophic events in that area (naturally occurring or intentional, such as terrorist attacks). When looking to add a program Meadowbrook seeks proven loss history, an established distribution system, and stability in past carrier relationships. It avoids start up programs, risk-sharing programs where the partner does not have adequate capital, and nursing home/assisted living facilities, among other factors.

The company's strategy of spreading around risk and being selective about adding new programs seems to be paying off. The company's total revenue has increased each year for several years, as have its gross and net written premiums.

EXECUTIVES

Chairman, Merton J. Segal, age 82
President, CEO, and Director, Robert S. Cubbin, age 53, $2,307,900 total compensation
EVP, Christopher J. Timm, age 54
VP Corporate Communications, Carol Ziecik
VP Human Resources, Sue Cubbin
VP, Southfield Branch, Laura Segal
SVP and Chief Actuary, Stephen A. Belden, age 55, $676,375 total compensation
SVP Field Operations, James M. Mahoney, age 60
SVP Business Operations and CIO, Robert Chris Spring, age 57
SVP Business Development, Archie S. McIntyre, age 45

SVP, General Counsel, and Secretary, Michael G. Costello, age 50, $900,458 total compensation
SVP and CFO, Karen M. Spaun, age 46, $892,257 total compensation
SVP; President, Meadowbrook Insurance Agency, Kenn R. Allen, age 62
Investor Relations, John P. Shallcross
SVP Insurance Operations, Joseph E. Mattingly, age 51
Auditors: Ernst & Young LLP

LOCATIONS

HQ: Meadowbrook Insurance Group, Inc.
26255 American Dr., Southfield, MI 48034-6112
Phone: 248-358-1100   **Fax:** 248-358-1614
Web: www.meadowbrookinsgrp.com

2010 Premium Distribution by State

	% of total
California	36
Florida	10
Texas	6
New Jersey	5
New York	3
Missouri	3
Michigan	3
Illinois	2
Louisiana	2
Pennsylvania	2
Other states	28
Total	

PRODUCTS/OPERATIONS

2010 Net Earned Premiums

	% of total
Workers' compensation	42
Commercial auto liability	14
Commercial multi-peril property	7
Commercial multi-peril liability	6
Other liability	19
All other lines	12
Total	**100**

Selected operations

Insurance Company Subsidiaries
  Ameritrust Insurance Corp.
  Century Surety Company
  Savers Property & Casualty Insurance Company
  Star Insurance Company
  Williamsburg National Insurance Company
Retail Agencies
  Commercial Carriers Insurance
  Insurance & Benefits Consultants
  Meadowbrook Insurance Agency
Wholesale Agencies
  Interline Insurance Agency
  Meadowbrook TPA Associates
  Preferred Comp
  US Specialty Underwriters

COMPETITORS

AIG
Alliant
American Financial Group
Delphi Financial Group
Markel
Sedgwick Claims Management Services
Specialty Underwriters' Alliance
Travelers Companies
W. R. Berkley
XL Group plc

HISTORICAL FINANCIALS

Company Type: Public

Income Statement

FYE: December 31

	ASSETS ($ mil.)	NET INCOME ($ mil.)	INCOME AS % OF ASSETS	EMPLOYEES
12/10	2,177.6	59.7	2.7%	967
12/09	1,989.8	52.7	2.6%	918
12/08	1,813.9	27.4	1.5%	921
12/07	1,114.0	28.0	2.5%	643
12/06	969.0	22.0	2.3%	660
Annual Growth	**22.4%**	**28.3%**	**—**	**10.0%**

2010 Year-End Financials

Equity as % of assets: 25.12%
Return on assets: 2.7%
Return on equity: 10.9%
Long-term debt ($ mil.): 118.7
No. of shares (mil.): 53.2
Dividends
  Yield: 1.3%
  Payout: 11.8%
Market value ($ mil.): 545.7
Sales ($ mil.): 750.1

	STOCK PRICE ($) FY Close	P/E High	P/E Low	PER SHARE ($) Earnings	PER SHARE ($) Dividends	PER SHARE ($) Book Value
12/10	10.25	10	5	1.10	0.13	10.28
12/09	7.40	9	5	0.92	0.09	9.06
12/08	6.44	16	6	0.61	0.08	7.60
12/07	9.41	15	9	0.85	0.00	8.16
12/06	9.89	17	8	0.75	0.00	6.94
Annual Growth	**0.9%**	**—**	**—**	**10.0%**	**—**	**10.3%**

MedAssets

MedAssets helps hospitals widen their profit margins — or at least not lose quite as much. The company's Spend Management segment operates a group purchasing organization (GPO) that negotiates prices for hospitals and health systems, which then get better deals on medical supplies and devices. Its Revenue Cycle Management segment provides software and consulting services that help track and analyze a hospital's revenue stream. Such services aim to increase collections and reduce account balances. MedAssets works from some 15 offices nationwide. Its customers include more than 125 big health systems, more than 3,300 hospitals, and some 40,000 non-acute health providers.

The company sells its products and services through an in-house sales team, and maintains a software development group for creating new software products. Rather than simply competing against other large group purchasing organizations, in some cases the company actually contracts with them to extend its range of products, and share marketing efforts.

While its overall strategy is focused on securing more new customers and selling those customers more products, the company also grows through acquisitions. In 2010 MedAssets acquired Broadlane, a leading GPO provider for the US health care industry, for some $850 million. The larger-than-usual transaction not only brought MedAssets to the forefront of the GPO market, but also added complementary operations in areas such as supply chain, process consulting, and workforce optimization, and allowed MedAssets to provide a full range of cost management services to its clients. Broadlane's operations were merged into the MedAssets organization, with the core GPO operations were combined with MedAssets' Spend Management division.

Other acquisitions in 2007 and 2008, including its $227-million purchase of revenue management provider Accuro Healthcare Solutions, also helped build up MedAssets' services.

Investment firm Galen Management owns 10% of the company's shares and holds a seat on its board of directors.

EXECUTIVES

Chairman, President, and CEO, John A. Bardis, age 55, $4,447,030 total compensation
President, Revenue Cycle Technology, L. Neil Hunn, age 38, $602,934 total compensation
President Client Management, Field Operations and Sales, Allen W. Hobbs, age 53
President, Spend Management, Maureen A. Gender
President, Spend Management Segment, Patrick T. Ryan, age 52
President, East Coast Customer Management Group, Sandra Green
President, West Coast Customer Management Group, Mark Hess
EVP and Chief Legal and Administrative Officer, Jonathan H. Glenn, age 60, $758,088 total compensation
EVP and Chief Financial Officer, Charles O. (Chuck) Garner
Vice Chairman, Bruce F. (Toby) Wesson, age 68
Vice Chairman, Terrence J. Mulligan, age 65
SVP and Chief Accounting Officer, Lance M. Culbreth, age 41
Chief Medical Officer, Nicholas J. (Nick) Sears
SEVP, COO, Chief Customer Officer, and Director, Rand A. Ballard, age 56, $3,243,347 total compensation
SVP Human Resources, R. Lynn Howard
SVP Investor Relations and Corporate Communications, Robert P. Borchert
Auditors: BDO Seidman, LLP

LOCATIONS

HQ: MedAssets, Inc.
100 North Point Center East, Ste. 200, Alpharetta, GA 30022
Phone: 678-323-2500   **Fax:** 678-323-2501
Web: www.medassets.com

PRODUCTS/OPERATIONS

2009 Revenues

	$ mil.	% of total
Revenue Cycle Management	205.9	60
Spend Management	135.4	40
Total	**341.3**	**100**

Selected Subsidiaries

Aspen Healthcare Metrics LLC
MedAssets Analytical Systems, LLC
MedAssets Net Revenue Systems, LLC
MedAssets Services LLC
MedAssets Supply Chain Systems, LLC
Dominic & Irvine, LLC

COMPETITORS

Accretive Health	Novation
Emdeon	OptumnInsight
HealthTrust	Premier, Inc.
McKesson	Siemens Healthcare
Navigant Consulting	SSI Group

Income Statement				FYE: December 31
	REVENUE ($ mil.)	NET INCOME ($ mil.)	NET PROFIT MARGIN	EMPLOYEES
12/10	391.3	(32.1)	—	3,100
12/09	341.3	19.9	5.8%	2,200
12/08	279.7	10.8	3.9%	1,700
12/07	188.5	6.3	3.3%	1,200
12/06	146.2	8.8	6.0%	1,100
Annual Growth	27.9%	—	—	29.6%

2010 Year-End Financials

Debt ratio: 221.1%	No. of shares (mil.): 58.4
Return on equity: —	Dividends
Cash ($ mil.): 46.8	Yield: —
Current ratio: 0.65	Payout: —
Long-term debt ($ mil.): 963.2	Market value ($ mil.): 1,179.3

	STOCK PRICE ($) FY Close	P/E High/Low		PER SHARE ($) Earnings	Dividends	Book Value
12/10	20.19	—	—	(0.57)	0.00	7.46
12/09	21.21	73	33	0.34	0.00	7.71
12/08	14.60	113	47	0.21	0.00	7.11
12/07	23.94	—	—	(0.75)	0.00	5.35
Annual Growth	(5.5%)	—	—	—	—	11.7%

Medidata Solutions

Medidata Solutions has remedies to help clinical trials run smoothly. Founded in 1999, the company offers cloud-based applications that help biotechnology, pharmaceutical, and other life sciences companies conduct clinical trials and related research. Its products include hosted software for administering and managing clinical trials, electronic data capture applications, study management applications, and patient diaries. The company also offers a variety of professional services, such as consulting, implementation, integration, and maintenance. Its customers include Johnson & Johnson, Roche (11% of sales each), and AstraZeneca (10% of sales). About two-thirds of sales come from the US.

Sales from its Professional Services segment fell significantly (21%) while its core business, Application Services, made up the difference, climbing 33%. That's in line with the company's strategy to make its customers more capable of using the applications on their own or through contract research organizations (CROs). Medidata expects that enablement to increase adoption of its application services. While the top and bottom line saw continuing improvements, its cash flow from operations took a hit from accounts receivable and deferred revenue.

Medidata has steadily grown its customer base from less than 100 at the beginning of 2008 to nearly 220 at the end of 2010, achieving retention rates between 87% and 93% during that period. Its top five customers, who are rounded out by Astellas Pharma and Takeda Pharmaceutical, account for more than 40% of sales. Among the rest of its customers are 22 of the top 25 global pharmaceutical companies, but it sees the small and mid-sized life sciences companies as a significant opportunity for expansion. The company also sees

room to increase sales to existing customers, primarily through adoption of its applications in new clinical trials and upgrades from single-study use to multi-study use.

Another key element in Medidata's strategy is to bolster its indirect sales channels through strategic partnerships with CROs and healthcare IT consultants. The company hopes to entrench its technology as the preferred platform for outsourced trial management.

In 2011 the company acquired Clinical Force, a developer of clinical trial management software, to add Software-as-a-Service delivery capabilities as more clients look for cloud-based application services.

EXECUTIVES

Chairman and CEO, Tarek Sherif, age 48, $866,136 total compensation
President and Director, Glen de Vries, age 38, $866,136 total compensation
CFO, Bruce D. Dalziel, age 52, $1,277,453 total compensation
EVP Global Sales and Alliances, Steven I. (Steve) Hirschfeld, age 48, $786,170 total compensation
EVP Product and Marketing, Lineene N. Krasnow, age 59, $472,347 total compensation
VP New Products, Richard J. Piazza, age 52
VP Corporate Strategy, Shih-Yin Ho
VP Development, Trial Planning, Peter Abramowitsch
VP Information Services, Trial Planning, David Gemzik
VP Integrations Development, Andrew Newbigging
VP Sales, Global, Alan Mateo
VP and Controller, Cory Douglas, age 44
VP Global CRO Partnerships, Graham Bunn
VP Operations, Trial Planning, Lori Shields
VP Global Information Security and Privacy and Corporate Security and Privacy Officer, Glenn Watt
VP Global Quality Assurance, Frances (Fran) Nolan
VP and Head, Europe, Middle East, Africa, and Australia, Steven (Steve) Heath
SVP Services, Vik Shah
SVP Human Resources, Arden Schneider
SVP Sales Operations and Knowledge Management, Joseph A. (Joe) Tyers
Investor Contact, Hulus Alpay
General Counsel and Secretary, Michael I. Otner
SVP Regulatory Compliance, Earl Hulihan
Senior Director Global Quality Assurance, EMEA, Tony Hewer
Auditors: Deloitte & Touche LLP

LOCATIONS

HQ: Medidata Solutions, Inc.
79 5th Ave., 8th Fl., New York, NY 10003
Phone: 212-918-1800 **Fax:** 212-918-1818
Web: www.mdsol.com

2010 Sales

	$ mil.	% of total
US	106.7	64
Japan	18.4	11
UK	14.0	9
Switzerland	8.9	5
Other countries	18.4	11
Total	**166.4**	**100**

PRODUCTS/OPERATIONS

2010 Sales

	$ mil.	% of total
Application services	136.4	82
Professional services	30.0	18
Total	**166.4**	**100**

Selected Customers

Pharmaceutical
 Abbott Laboratories
 Astellas Pharma
 AstraZeneca
 Baxter International
 Bayer HealthCare
 Daiichi Sankyo
 F. HoffmannLa Roche
 Johnson & Johnson
 H. Lundbeck
 Orion Corporation
 Pfizer
 Roche Holding
 Shionogi & Co.
 Takeda Pharmaceutical
Biotechnology
 Amgen
 Array BioPharma
 Elan Pharmaceuticals
 Genzyme Corporation
 Gilead Sciences
 Infinity Pharmaceuticals
 Seattle Genetics
Medical Devices and Diagnostics
 bioMérieux
 Boston Scientific
 DePuy International
 Edwards Lifesciences
Contract Research Organizations
 CMIC
 Covance
 EPS
 ICON Clinical Research
 INC Research
 Kendle International
 PRA International
 Quintiles Transnational
 Sumisho Computer Systems
Institutions
 Ludwig Institute for Cancer Research
 Northwestern University

COMPETITORS

Aptuit	M2S
BioClinica	MedNet Solutions
DATATRAK International	Microsoft
DRS Data & Research	OmniComm
DrugLogic	Oracle
eResearchTechnology	Patni Life Sciences
Liquent	Perceptive Informatics

HISTORICAL FINANCIALS

Company Type: Public

Income Statement				FYE: December 31
	REVENUE ($ mil.)	NET INCOME ($ mil.)	NET PROFIT MARGIN	EMPLOYEES
12/10	166.4	22.8	13.7%	598
12/09	140.4	5.2	3.7%	574
12/08	105.7	(18.3)	—	549
12/07	63.0	(23.7)	—	535
12/06	36.3	(19.0)	—	0
Annual Growth	46.3%	—	—	3.8%

2010 Year-End Financials

Debt ratio: 0.1%	No. of shares (mil.): 24.1
Return on equity: 44.6%	Dividends
Cash ($ mil.): 16.0	Yield: —
Current ratio: 1.61	Payout: —
Long-term debt ($ mil.): 0.1	Market value ($ mil.): 575.2

	STOCK PRICE ($) FY Close	P/E High/Low		PER SHARE ($) Earnings	Dividends	Book Value
12/10	23.88	26	14	0.95	0.00	2.12
12/09	15.62	79	58	0.25	0.00	0.88
Annual Growth	52.9%	—	—	280.0%	—	140.2%

Medifast

Medifast is helping people slim down and shape up... fast. The company develops and markets health and diet products under the Medifast brand name. The products, which are manufactured by subsidiary Jason Pharmaceuticals, include food and beverages (meal replacement shakes, bars), as well as disease management products for diabetics. Medifast operates through three channels: The Medifast Direct segment is the direct-to-consumer part of the business through which consumers order Medifast products online; Take Shape for Life is Medifast's personal coaching division composed of independent contractor health coaches; and, its Weight Control Centers are Medifast's bricks-and-mortar walk-in clinics.

Unlike other companies hawking weight loss, Medifast emphasizes the inclusion of medical practitioners in the development, sale, and use of their products. While the ranks of the overweight are growing, the company is also working to tailor its products to the rapidly growing population of diabetics. It maintains an in-house call center and support staff, with registered dieticians on hand to assist customers.

Medifast's promotion and distribution model has changed over time. When it was founded in 1993, the company primarily sold its products through doctor's offices. Customers received supervision from their family physician, who, in turn, received commissions on any products sold. However, as physicians had increasingly less time to spend with patients, the method grew less effective.

While some doctors still stock an inventory and resell the company's products, most of Medifast's sales are made through the its website, thus reducing the complexity of its product distribution. Even its Take Shape For Life coaches simply direct customers to the website or call centers and receive commissions for orders placed there. New doctors who wish to promote the products are signed on as coaches.

For customers who want more supervision, Medifast operates a chain of bricks-and mortar weight control centers (MWCC). Its MWCC division accounts for about 10% of Medifast's income and growing. The centers provide customers with weigh-ins and counselors and keep an inventory of products on hand. With centers already in Texas, Florida, Maryland, and Washington, DC, the company is growing this segment rapidly. It added about a dozen clinics in 2010 to bring its total to about 40; it intends to open up to 30 more in 2011. In addition to building more corporate-owned centers, Medifast has launched a franchise model to more rapidly expand the number of centers across the US. It has about two dozen franchises and intends to grow that model as well.

Despite the doom and gloom of the recession, Medifast saw its revenues jump in 2009 and 2010. How did the company manage that? Advertising, and plenty of it. Medifast participates in just about any type of advertising one can imagine including television and radio, but especially online by creating brand awareness through web-based weight loss support groups and seminars that direct users to the Medifast website. Once at the website, potential customers are given the chance to first become VIP members to receive discounts on products and enroll in a monthly automatic reordering and shipment program. Once they are established customers, they are eventually invited to become coaches and the process starts all over with coaches helping to recruit customers and so on.

Additionally, Medifast is in an industry that sees almost endless demand. It is partially seasonal (picking up after the holidays and before summer), but in general the weight loss industry is not wanting for customers.

Medifast expanded its product line in 2010 by introducing a line of desserts. The first product was the Medifast Brownie, a full meal replacement as part of the Medifast program. The company also added four flavors of soft serve ice cream meant to be made in an individual style blender such as the Medifast HealthMate Blender. Medifast also expanded its breakfast line to include pancakes.

EXECUTIVES

Chairman, Bradley T. (Brad) MacDonald, age 62, $794,600 total compensation
CFO, Brendan N. Connors, age 33, $412,900 total compensation
President, COO, and Director, Margaret MacDonald-Sheetz, age 34, $1,040,900 total compensation
CEO and Director, Michael S. McDevitt, age 33, $1,239,800 total compensation
EVP, Leo V. Willliams III, age 63, $224,600 total compensation
Auditors: Bagell, Josephs, Levine & Company, LLC

LOCATIONS

HQ: Medifast, Inc.
11445 Cronhill Dr., Owings Mills, MD 21117
Phone: 410-581-8042   **Fax:** 410-581-8070
Web: www.medifast.net

PRODUCTS/OPERATIONS

2010 Sales

	% of total
Medifast	89
Weight control centers and wholesale	11
Total	**100**

COMPETITORS

Atkins Nutritionals	Nutrisystem
Bazi	Reliv' International
eDiets.com	Slim-Fast
Herbalife Ltd.	USANA Health Sciences
Jenny Craig	Weight Watchers
NBTY	International
Nu Skin	

HISTORICAL FINANCIALS

Company Type: Public

Income Statement
FYE: December 31

	REVENUE ($ mil.)	NET INCOME ($ mil.)	NET PROFIT MARGIN	EMPLOYEES
12/10	257.6	19.6	7.6%	507
12/09	165.6	12.0	7.2%	365
12/08	105.4	5.4	5.1%	290
12/07	83.8	3.8	4.5%	245
12/06	74.1	5.1	6.9%	265
Annual Growth	**36.5%**	**40.0%**	**—**	**17.6%**

2010 Year-End Financials

Debt ratio: 6.7%	No. of shares (mil.): 15.4
Return on equity: 27.3%	Dividends
Cash ($ mil.): 17.2	Yield: —
Current ratio: 3.80	Payout: —
Long-term debt ($ mil.): 4.9	Market value ($ mil.): 445.7

	STOCK PRICE ($) FY Close	P/E High/Low		PER SHARE ($) Earnings	Dividends	Book Value
12/10	28.88	28	12	1.35	0.00	4.66
12/09	30.58	45	5	0.81	0.00	3.30
12/08	5.52	24	9	0.38	0.00	2.66
12/07	4.85	41	13	0.28	0.00	2.36
12/06	12.57	56	14	0.38	0.00	2.08
Annual Growth	**23.1%**	**—**	**—**	**37.3%**	**—**	**22.4%**

Medivation

Medivation motivates medicine makers. The company acquires, develops, and sells (or partners with companies working on) development stage biopharmaceuticals. Medivation initiates drug development programs, seeking out candidates that address unmet medical needs and have the potential to rapidly enter clinical development and marketing stages. Medivation typically develops its drug candidates through early stage clinical trials, and then determines whether to conduct further studies or to seek a partner or buyer to continue later-stage trials. Included in Medivation's current pipeline are therapies addressing Alzheimer's disease and prostate cancer.

The company has collaboration agreements for both of its lead development programs, and these affiliations provide most of the necessary funding for its R&D efforts. Medivation partners with Pfizer for its key drug candidate, Dimebon, which is in late-stage clinical trials for Alzheimer's. The collaboration is potentially worth up to $725 million to Medivation; however in 2010 Dimebon performed poorly in a late-stage trial. As a result, Medivation laid off about 20% of its workforce and downsized its facilities.

Trials of Dimebon for Alzheimer's disease are ongoing. The two companies were also investigating the drug as a treatment for Huntington's disease, but in 2011 the efforts were discontinued as trial results were not significant.

The company found another partner in 2009 when it teamed up with Astellas on its other drug candidate, small molecule MDV3100, which is in trials for the treatment of hormone-refractory prostate cancer. The companies are sharing the development costs of putting MDV3100 through late-stage trials. If approved, the drug will be marketed in the US by both firms, while efforts to commercialize MDV3100 will be handled by Astellas.

Medivation is looking for additional development candidates to acquire to expand and diversify its pipeline.

EXECUTIVES

Chairman, Kim D. Blickenstaff, age 58
President, CEO, and Director, David T. Hung, age 53, $5,981,189 total compensation
CFO, Chief Business Officer, and Corporate Secretary, C. Patrick Machado, age 47, $2,321,906 total compensation
VP Biometrics, Brian Selby
VP Medical Affairs, Hank Mansbach
VP Intellectual Property, Vandana Date
VP Chemistry and Manufacturing, Sue Wollowitz, age 57
VP Clinical Operations, Stewart Hallett
VP Translational Medicine, Joyce Mordenti

VP Clinical Development, Andria G. M. Langenberg, age 54

VP Preclinical Development, Andrew A. Protter, age 57

VP Medicinal Chemistry, Sarvajit Chakravarty

VP Regulatory and Quality, Michele D. Bronson

VP Clinical Development, Mohammad Hirmand

SVP and Chief Medical Officer, Lynn Seely, age 52, $3,095,213 total compensation

Regional Clinical Scientist, Janice King

Senior Director Clinical Development, Fong Wang

Chief Commercial Officer, Rohan Palekar, age 45, $2,575,242 total compensation

Auditors: PricewaterhouseCoopers LLP

LOCATIONS

HQ: Medivation, Inc.
   201 Spear St., 3rd Fl., San Francisco, CA 94105
Phone: 415-543-3470   **Fax:** 415-543-3411
Web: www.medivation.net

PRODUCTS/OPERATIONS

2010 Sales

	$ mil.	% of total
Pfizer collaboration	39.0	62
Astellas collaboration	23.5	38
Total	**62.5**	**100**

COMPETITORS

Abbott Labs	Novartis
Allon Therapeutics	Oncolytics Biotech
Dendreon	Pfizer
Forest Labs	Sanofi
Johnson & Johnson	

HISTORICAL FINANCIALS

Company Type: Public

Income Statement				FYE: December 31
	REVENUE ($ mil.)	NET INCOME ($ mil.)	NET PROFIT MARGIN	EMPLOYEES
12/10	62.5	(34.0)	—	92
12/09	69.3	(54.8)	—	98
12/08	12.6	(62.5)	—	59
12/03	0.0	—	—	0
12/02	0.0	(0.1)	—	0
Annual Growth	**—**	**—**	**—**	**24.9%**

2010 Year-End Financials

Debt ratio: —	No. of shares (mil.): 34.6
Return on equity: —	Dividends
Cash ($ mil.): 107.7	Yield: —
Current ratio: 2.66	Payout: —
Long-term debt ($ mil.): —	Market value ($ mil.): 524.5

	STOCK PRICE ($) FY Close	P/E High/Low		PER SHARE ($) Earnings	Dividends	Book Value
12/10	15.17	—	—	(0.99)	0.00	0.22
12/09	37.65	—	—	(1.71)	0.00	0.75
12/08	14.57	—	—	(2.12)	0.00	0.11
12/03	14.40	—	—	(1.14)	0.00	1.42
12/02	15.82	30	4	0.63	0.00	1.81
Annual Growth	**(1.0%)**	**—**	**—**	**—**	**—**	**(40.8%)**

MedQuist Holdings

MedQuist Holdings (formerly CBaySystems Holdings) helps transcribe and analyze doctors' spoken and written notes. The company is a leading provider of integrated clinical documentation products and outsourced medical transcription services to the US health care industry. Its offerings include mobile voice capture devices, speech recognition software, Web-based workflow platforms, and a global network of more than 4,000 medical transcriptionists and editors primarily in the US and India. Its customer base consists of more than 2,400 hospitals, clinics, and multifacility health care organizations, mostly in the US. In 2011 MedQuist Holdings completed a short-term merger with subsidiary MedQuist Inc.

As a result, MedQuist Inc. became an indirect wholly owned subsidiary of the company and its common stock ceased trading on the public market. The plan to integrate MedQuist Inc. was previously announced as a strategy to eliminate duplicate costs and inefficiencies associated with running two separate publicly traded companies.

Other recent M&A activity includes MedQuist Holdings' acquisition of M*Modal also in 2011 to further enhance its technology-based portfolio. The $48.4 million purchase specifically adds an advanced speech and natural language understanding technology. M*Modal's proprietary cloud-based software enables health care providers to easily convert a physician's spoken narrative into structured clinical information that can be integrated into electronic health records (EHRs). With many facilities transitioning from paper to electronic records, EHRs are a growing area within health care administration as they capture data that contribute to clinical and reimbursement decision making.

Among MedQuist Holdings' customers are The University of Texas M. D. Anderson Cancer Center, which uses the cloud-based speech and natural language understanding platform in its EHR systems, and the Los Angeles County Department of Health Services, which uses the SpeechQ front-end speech recognition technology for its radiology practices.

Earlier in 2011 MedQuist Holdings completed the integration of struggling competitor Spheris, which it had acquired in 2010. The acquisition added more than 2,000 transcriptionists and related services and technologies to its operations. At that time MedQuist Holdings also moved its corporate headquarters from Mt. Laurel, New Jersey, to Spheris' head office in Nashville, Tennessee, giving it closer access to several of its key hospital customers in that area. Spheris had previously filed for Chapter 11 bankruptcy protection.

EXECUTIVES

Chairman and CEO, Roger L. (Vern) Davenport
Vice Chairman, V. Raman Kumar
Co-COO, Michael F. Clark
Co-COO and CFO, Anthony D. James
Chief Information Officer, Kevin M. Piltz
General Counsel, Chief Compliance Officer, and Secretary, Mark R. Sullivan
Auditors: KPMG LLP

LOCATIONS

HQ: MedQuist Holdings Inc.
   9009 Carothers Pkwy., Franklin, TN 37067
Phone: 866-295-4600
Web: www.medquistholdings.com

2010 Sales

	% of total
US	98
Other countries	2
Total	**100**

PRODUCTS/OPERATIONS

2010 Sales

	% of total
Medical transcription	91
Other	9
Total	**100**

COMPETITORS

Acusis	Nuance Communications
Allscripts	Precyse Solutions
Cerner	QuadraMed
Epic Systems	Resourcing Edge
iSOFT Group	Sandata Technologies
Keystrokes	Sten-Tel
LanceSoft	Transcend Services
McKesson	

HISTORICAL FINANCIALS

Company Type: Public

Income Statement				FYE: December 31
	REVENUE ($ mil.)	NET INCOME ($ mil.)	NET PROFIT MARGIN	EMPLOYEES
12/10	417.3	17.7	4.2%	12,000
12/09	353.9	7.8	2.2%	0
12/08	171.4	(108.5)	—	0
Annual Growth	**56.0%**	**—**	**—**	**—**

Debt ratio: —	No. of shares (mil.): 34.6
Return on equity: —	Dividends
Cash ($ mil.): 107.7	Yield: —
Current ratio: 2.66	Payout: —
Long-term debt ($ mil.): —	Market value ($ mil.): 524.5

MEMSIC

It's all in the name. MEMSIC makes microelectromechanical systems (MEMS), integrated circuit (IC) products that allow a single chip to process signals from several sources. The company's specialized circuits are used as accelerometers (used to measure tilt and other motion) and sensors in automotive, consumer electronics, industrial, and mobile phone applications. The company partners with such companies as Sensata Technologies. Its customers include Autoliv (21% of sales), Mitsubishi Electric, Panasonic, Sony, and TomTom. MEMSIC gets around two-thirds of its sales in the Asia/Pacific region.

MEMSIC completed its acquisition in 2010 of the commercial catalog and distributor businesses of industrial sensor provider Crossbow Technology. Along with sales and engineering personnel, Crossbow products — accelerometer, tilt sensors, aviation products, and environmental monitoring product line, among others — transfers, as well. The acquisition will spur product growth and revenue for MEMSIC in commercial and industrial markets.

The global recession decreased sales in the automotive and consumer electronics industries, among others, and helped drive down MEMSIC's sales by about 21% in 2008. The credit crisis may affect the company's customers and suppliers, creating financial difficulties for those parties, which could affect MEMSIC, decreasing revenues and causing product delays, among other factors. The company does not have long-term purchase commitments from its customers. MEMSIC has a limited number of customers, with Autoliv and four distributors accounting for more than three-quarters of sales. The semiconductor industry in general is highly cyclical, and the company must manage its way through the current industry downturn.

The company contracts out some production to TSMC in Taiwan and Nantong-Fujitsu Microelectronics in China. It employs a CMOS process in manufacturing its devices, one of the most commonly used manufacturing technologies in semiconductor fabrication. MEMSIC has operations in China, buying land in Wuxi and opening a factory for MEMS fabrication.

Accelerometers are traditionally used in automotive airbags, sensing when the airbags should inflate. More recent applications include the remote controls on Nintendo's Wii game console and Apple's iPhone (to sense when the phone is tilted from one side to another).

MEMSIC was backed by capital from Still River Fund, InveStar Capital, Celtic House Venture Partners, and Elufar Limited, among others. The company was spun off from Analog Devices in 1999 and licenses MEMS technology from ADI.

EXECUTIVES

Chairman, President, and CEO, Yang Zhao, age 48, $266,571 total compensation
CFO, Patricia Niu, age 44, $186,303 total compensation
President, North American and European Operations, Paul M. Zavracky, age 61
VP Industrial Business, Julin Mao
VP Worldwide Sales Systems Business, Steve Tsui
VP, Technology, Albert M. Leung
VP Sales and Marketing, Mark S. Laich, $30,851 total compensation
Media Relations, Kerri Giard
Auditors: Ernst & Young LLP

LOCATIONS

HQ: MEMSIC, Inc.
1 Tech Dr., Ste. 325, Andover, MA 01810
Phone: 978-738-0900   **Fax:** 978-738-0196
Web: www.memsic.comMEMSIC has primary operations in China and the US, with sales offices in China, Japan, and Taiwan.

2008 Sales

	$ mil.	% of total
Asia/Pacific		
Japan	3.5	17
Other countries	9.6	48
North America	5.5	28
Europe	1.5	7
Total	**20.1**	**100**

PRODUCTS/OPERATIONS

2008 Sales

	$ mil.	% of total
Mobile phone	7.6	38
Automotive	5.6	28
Consumer	5.4	27
Industrial & other	1.5	7
Total	**20.1**	**100**

COMPETITORS

Akustica	Measurement
Analog Devices	Specialties
Apogee Technology	MEMSCAP
Axsys	Microfabrica
Custom Sensors &	Optek Technology
Technologies	STMicroelectronics
Freescale	Teledyne DALSA
Semiconductor	TT electronics
Honeywell	Ziptronix
International	

HISTORICAL FINANCIALS

Company Type: Public

Income Statement

FYE: December 31

	REVENUE ($ mil.)	NET INCOME ($ mil.)	NET PROFIT MARGIN	EMPLOYEES
12/10	38.7	(7.4)	—	0
12/09	28.4	—	—	0
12/08	20.1	(1.7)	—	0
12/07	25.3	6.1	24.1%	219
12/06	13.1	0.5	3.8%	219
Annual Growth	**31.1%**	**—**	**—**	**0.0%**

2010 Year-End Financials

Debt ratio: 20.2%
Return on equity: —
Cash ($ mil.): 55.7
Current ratio: 7.05
Long-term debt ($ mil.): 17.9

No. of shares (mil.): 23.8
Dividends
Yield: —
Payout: —
Market value ($ mil.): 81.0

	STOCK PRICE ($) FY Close	P/E High/Low		PER SHARE ($) Earnings	Dividends	Book Value
12/10	3.40	—	—	(0.31)	0.00	3.73
12/09	3.28	—	—	(0.00)	0.00	3.95
12/08	1.65	—	—	(0.07)	0.00	3.88
12/07	10.13	44	38	0.25	0.00	(0.00)
Annual Growth	**(30.5%)**	**—**	**—**	**—**	**—**	**—**

Merge Healthcare

Merge Healthcare wants your imaging department to share the health. The company develops imaging and information management software for radiology, cardiology, orthopedic, surgical, clinical, and other applications. Its Merge iConnect suite lets users create information exchanges that enable sharing of diagnostic images and results within a facility and with other entities. Other offerings include tools used to combine patient images into an electronic health record and picture archiving and communication systems (PACS) that integrate images with other systems. Merge also provides hosted software used to manage data in clinical trials. It makes more than 90% of sales in the US.

Merge has expanded from providing software primarily for radiology practices to offering information systems for a wide range of medical applications, such as clinical information systems that provide an electronic record of a medical procedure across a variety of specialties. Examples of specific applications include Merge OrthoEMR for orthopedics and Merge Anesthesia Information Management System for surgery. The company has also gotten into the business side of health care, offering revenue cycle management software and serv-

ices used by physician groups, radiology practices, imaging centers, and billing departments.

Merge pursues acquisitions as a way to expand its product offerings and enhance the capabilities of its imaging and radiology connectivity systems. It plans to buy other companies to build its portfolio of technology and supplement its own R&D. In 2011 Merge bought Ophthalmic Imaging Systems in a stock swap transaction, adding digital imaging and informatics systems for ophthalmology and other medical specialties. Ophthalmic Imaging Systems also sold image archival, medical records management, and practice management software.

In 2009 and 2010, the company made several acquisitions, significantly expanding the scope of its products and adding new markets and customers. In 2010 Merge acquired rival AMICAS in a deal valued at $248 million. The purchase expanded Merge's imaging and information management, revenue cycle management, and content management tools for electronic medical records. Also that year, Merge bought the clinical trials development assets of France-based KIKA Medical International, bolstering its clinical trials management capabilities and expanding its presence in Europe.

In 2009 the company acquired etrials Worldwide, a provider of clinical trial management software and services, and renamed the business Merge eClinical. That year Merge also bought computer-assisted detection software developer Confirma (renamed Merge CAD) to bolster its diagnostic imaging technologies.

In 2010 sales more than doubled over the previous year, primarily due to revenue contributed by acquisitions. Sales related to its maintenance and electronic data interchange (EDI) business were up 240% for the year. Professional services revenues — which includes its hosted clinical trial software, custom engineering, training, consulting, and project management — grew by more than 95%. In software, sales rose 28% on recurring revenue from licenses and new revenue from acquired software businesses. Profits for the year fell, due in part to expenses related to acquisitions. Merge reported a net loss of nearly $12 million in 2010 compared to a income of $285,000 in 2009 (its only profit in the past five years). Merge has sought to limit the financial impact of acquisitions through restructuring efforts that include employee layoffs, staff relocation, and abandonment of leases on some facilities.

EXECUTIVES

Chairman, Michael W. Ferro Jr., age 45
CEO and Director, Jeffrey A. Surges, age 44
President and Director, Justin C. Dearborn, age 41
CFO and Treasurer, Steven M. (Steve) Oreskovich, age 39
EVP Operations, Nancy J. Koenig, age 46
EVP Product Solutions, Steve Brewer
EVP Development, Antonia Wells, age 52
VP Operations, Nick Donofrio
VP Marketing, Julie Pekarek
SVP Customer Support, James M. Farrell
SVP Services, Jeff Schmidt
SVP Sales, Steve Martin
General Manager, Merge eClinical, Jon T. DeVries
General Counsel and Secretary, Ann Mayberry-French, age 50
Auditors: KPMG LLP

LOCATIONS

HQ: Merge Healthcare Incorporated
200 E. Randolph St., 24th Fl., Chicago, IL 60601-6436
Phone: 312-565-6868   **Fax:** 312-565-6870
Web: www.merge.com

2010 Sales

	$ mil.	% of total
US	126.0	90
Europe	7.7	5
Japan	2.8	2
South Korea	0.7	1
Canada	0.5	-
Other regions	2.6	2
Total	**140.3**	**100**

PRODUCTS/OPERATIONS

2010 Sales

	$ mil.	% of total
Maintenance & Electronic Data Interchange (EDI)	74.7	53
Software & other	42.4	30
Professional services	23.2	17
Total	**140.3**	**100**

COMPETITORS

Carestream Health	McKesson
Cerner	Medasys
FUJIFILM Medical Systems	Medidata Solutions
GE Healthcare	MedPlus
Hologic	Philips Healthcare
iCAD	Streamline Health Solutions

HISTORICAL FINANCIALS

Company Type: Public

Income Statement   FYE: December 31

	REVENUE ($ mil.)	NET INCOME ($ mil.)	NET PROFIT MARGIN	EMPLOYEES
12/10	140.3	(11.5)	—	750
12/09	66.8	0.3	0.4%	385
12/08	56.7	(23.7)	—	250
12/07	59.6	(171.6)	—	580
12/06	75.0	(258.5)	—	550
Annual Growth	**16.9%**	**—**	**—**	**8.1%**

2010 Year-End Financials

Debt ratio: —
Return on equity: —
Cash ($ mil.): 41.0
Current ratio: 1.34
Long-term debt ($ mil.): —

No. of shares (mil.): 83.3
Dividends
  Yield: —
  Payout: —
Market value ($ mil.): 310.6

	STOCK PRICE ($) FY Close	P/E High/Low	PER SHARE ($) Earnings	Dividends	Book Value
12/10	3.73	— —	(0.38)	0.00	1.26
12/09	3.36	— —	(0.00)	0.00	0.91
12/08	1.28	— —	(0.51)	0.00	0.16
12/07	1.19	— —	(5.06)	0.00	0.72
12/06	6.56	— —	(7.67)	0.00	6.55
Annual Growth	**(13.2%)**	**— —**	**—**	**—**	**(33.8%)**

Meridian Interstate

Contrary to its name, Meridian Interstate Bancorp pretty much keeps it to a single state. It is the holding company of East Boston Savings Bank, which provides standard deposit and lending services to individuals and businesses in the greater Boston area. The bank writes single-family, commercial, and multifamily mortgages, as well as construction and business loans and consumer loans. East Boston Savings operates about 20 branches in eastern Massachusetts. Mutual holding company Meridian Financial Services owns 55% of Meridian Interstate Bancorp.

EXECUTIVES

Chairman and CEO, Richard J. Gavegnano, age 63, $716,040 total compensation
EVP and Director, Philip F. Freehan, age 59, $684,815 total compensation
VP, Deposit Operations, Lynne Brown
SVP, Operations and IT, Paula M. Cotter
SVP, CFO, and Treasurer, Mark L. Abbate, age 55
Human Resources Officer, Anne Lyon
SVP, Consumer and Business Banking, Keith D. Armstrong
Auditors: Wolf & Company, P.C.

LOCATIONS

HQ: Meridian Interstate Bancorp, Inc.
10 Meridian St., East Boston, MA 02128
Phone: 617-567-1500
Web: www.ebsb.com

COMPETITORS

Bank of America	Middlesex Savings
Cambridge Financial	Peoples Federal
Citizens Financial Group	Bancshares, Inc.
Eastern Bank	Sovereign Bank
	TD Bank USA

HISTORICAL FINANCIALS

Company Type: Public

Income Statement   FYE: December 31

	ASSETS ($ mil.)	NET INCOME ($ mil.)	INCOME AS % OF ASSETS	EMPLOYEES
12/10	1,835.8	13.4	0.7%	360
12/09	1,211.4	3.8	0.3%	197
12/08	1,065.4	(2.1)	—	227
12/07	1,003.2	2.3	0.2%	194
12/06	899.6	3.3	0.4%	197
Annual Growth	**19.5%**	**42.0%**	**—**	**16.3%**

2010 Year-End Financials

Equity as % of assets: 11.74%
Return on assets: 0.7%
Return on equity: 6.2%
Long-term debt ($ mil.): 136.7
No. of shares (mil.): 22.8

Dividends
  Yield: —
  Payout: —
Market value ($ mil.): 268.9
Sales ($ mil.): 93.8

	STOCK PRICE ($) FY Close	P/E High/Low	PER SHARE ($) Earnings	Dividends	Book Value
12/10	11.79	20 14	0.61	0.00	9.45
12/09	8.70	57 37	0.17	0.00	8.91
12/08	9.25	— —	(0.00)	0.00	8.25
Annual Growth	**12.9%**	**— —**	**—**	**—**	**7.0%**

Meru Networks

Meru Networks believes wireless networking should be a seamless experience for customers who don't want to worry about technology. The company develops networking equipment and software used to build wireless LANs. Its products include access points, controllers, and network management applications. Meru's products allow for the transmission of video, voice, and data over Wi-Fi connections. It targets customers in the corporate enterprise, education, health care, hospitality, manufacturing, and retail sectors. Meru's some 4,400 customers have included CME Group and Hellmann Worldwide Logistics. The company gets about three-quarters of its sales in the Americas. Meru Networks completed an IPO in 2010.

The company plans to use proceeds from its public offering for working capital and general corporate purposes, including expansion of sales and marketing, investments in R&D, and capital expenditures. Meru may also use the money for acquisitions of other companies, technologies, and assets. It plans to hire additional personnel to support the growth of its business.

Meru Networks has yet to become profitable and carries an accumulated deficit of more than $195 million. It operates in a highly competitive market, facing off against Cisco Systems and Hewlett-Packard, among others. Cisco and HP are trying to dominate the enterprise data center market for computing and networking gear, and they are facing competition from Meru and other smaller companies that look to establish a technology advantage against the giants.

Distributors and value-added resellers account for the majority of Meru's sales. The company outsources production of its hardware to original design manufacturers and contract electronics manufacturers.

Meru's product development strategy has focused on extending the use of wireless networks beyond basic Internet access to advanced services, such as VoIP. The company claims that its product development efforts have resulted in a virtualized networking architecture that is different from other wireless networking products that are in wide use.

It has also used acquisitions to strengthen its network access offerings. In 2011, it bought Manchester, UK-based network guest access provisioning company Identity Networks. The purchase better enables the company to help enterprises manage their networks in an increasingly bring-your-own-device (BYOD) landscape populated by both employees and customers.

Meru is additionally expanding into new markets — including education, healthcare, hospitality, manufacturing, and retail — that are more and more understanding the strategic benefits of wireless networks. The company is also ready to tap more clients in the markets of finance, government, technology, telecommunications, transportation, and utilities.

Among its investors, Meru Networks counts Bluestream Ventures, Clearstone Venture Partners (which owns nearly 14% of Meru), D. E. Shaw, and NeoCarta Ventures (a stake of about 12%)

EXECUTIVES

CFO, Brett White, age 48, $422,249 total compensation
President, CEO, and Director, Ihab Abu-Hakima, age 55, $401,707 total compensation
VP Business Development, Sarosh Vesuna, age 51
VP Sales, International, David Kelly
VP and General Counsel, Richard (Rich) Mosher, age 41
VP Technical Sales, Srinath Sarang
VP Sales, Americas, Robert W. Bruce
VP Product Strategy, Rachna Ahlawat
VP International Sales, Anil Batra
VP Marketing, Steve Troyer
SVP Worldwide Operations, Keith Matasci, age 50
Director Product Management, Sri Juvvadi
SVP Corporate Development and Strategy, Kamal Anand, age 46
Director of Marketing, Joel Vincent
Press Contact, Lisa Schiltz
Auditors: Burr, Pilger & Mayer LLP

LOCATIONS

HQ: Meru Networks, Inc.
894 Ross Dr., Sunnyvale, CA 94089
Phone: 408-215-5300   **Fax:** 408-215-5301
Web: www.merunetworks.com

2010 Sales

	$ mil.	% of total
Americas	61.3	72
EMEA	18.4	22
Asia/Pacific	5.3	6
Total	**85**	**100**

PRODUCTS/OPERATIONS

2010 Sales

	$ mil.	% of total
Products	63.2	75
Ratable products & services	11.3	13
Support & services	10.5	12
Total	**85**	**100**

COMPETITORS

Aruba Networks	Hewlett-Packard
Avaya	InnerWireless
Bluesocket	Motorola Solutions
Cisco Systems	Proxim Wireless

HISTORICAL FINANCIALS

Company Type: Public

Income Statement

FYE: December 31

	REVENUE ($ mil.)	NET INCOME ($ mil.)	NET PROFIT MARGIN	EMPLOYEES
12/10	85.0	(36.6)	—	292
12/09	69.5	(17.4)	—	242
12/08	54.7	(26.8)	—	232
12/07	16.0	(41.2)	—	0
12/06	4.4	(29.4)	—	0
Annual Growth	109.6%	—	—	12.2%

2010 Year-End Financials

Debt ratio: —	No. of shares (mil.): 16.3
Return on equity: —	Dividends
Cash ($ mil.): 62.3	Yield: —
Current ratio: 2.72	Payout: —
Long-term debt ($ mil.): —	Market value ($ mil.): 251.9

	STOCK PRICE ($) FY Close	P/E High/Low	PER SHARE ($) Earnings	Dividends	Book Value
12/10	15.42	— —	(3.06)	0.00	3.06
Annual Growth	—	— —	—	—	—

Mesa Laboratories

Mesa Laboratories is reaching a plateau in the field of measurements. The company makes niche-market electronic measurement, testing, and recording instruments for medical, food processing, electronics, and aerospace applications. Mesa's products include sensors that record temperature, humidity, and pressure levels; flow meters for water treatment, polymerization, and chemical processing applications; and sonic concentration analyzers. The company also makes kidney hemodialysis treatment products, including metering equipment and machines that clean dialyzers (or filters) for reuse. It also provides repair, recalibration, and certification services. Customers in the US make up about three-quarters of sales.

The company's products are sold under various brand names — the DataTrace data loggers, biological indicators from Raven Labs, flow meters from Nusonics, and bottle cap test systems from Torqo. Its largest product segment, dialysis meters, are sold under the Mesa Medical banner. The company makes four models of dialysis meters that together accounted for about 35% of revenues in 2010.

Biological indicators from Raven Labs are used by dental offices and hospitals and by manufacturers of medical devices and pharmaceuticals for quality control testing in sterilization processes. Mesa Labs bought Raven Biological Laboratories in 2006 for nearly $7 million in cash and stock. The division now accounts for one-third of revenues. Mesa Labs made a further additions to its line of biological indicator products in 2010 with the purchase of Montana-based SGM Biotech for $12 million in cash and the purchase of North Carolina-based Apex Laboratories.

DataTrace data loggers measure temperature, humidity, and pressure for manufacturing, quality control, and transportation applications. DataTrace products account for about 25% of revenues. The Nusonics line of ultrasonic fluid measurement systems and the Torqo line of bottle cap test systems together account for 5% of revenues. In late 2009 Mesa Labs bought the bottle cap torque testing business of Vibrac LLC, a privately held maker of automated and manual precision test systems, for $2.7 million. The bottle cap testing products also expand DataTrace logging instruments; both product lines are used in the food and beverage and pharmaceutical industries for quality control applications.

Small-cap investor Royce & Associates owns 13% of Mesa Labs' stock.

EXECUTIVES

Chairman, Luke R. Schmieder, age 68, $111,315 total compensation
President, CEO, and Director, John J. Sullivan, age 58, $321,000 total compensation
VP Sales and Marketing, Glenn E. Adriance, age 56, $161,592 total compensation

VP Finance, CFO, Chief Accounting Officer, and Secretary, Steven W. Peterson, age 55, $158,406 total compensation
Auditors: Ehrhardt Keefe Steiner & Hottman PC

LOCATIONS

HQ: Mesa Laboratories, Inc.
12100 W. 6th Ave., Lakewood, CO 80228
Phone: 303-987-8000   **Fax:** 303-987-8989
Web: www.mesalabs.com

2010 Sales

	$ mil.	% of total
US	16.2	74
Other countries	5.7	26
Total	**21.9**	**100**

PRODUCTS/OPERATIONS

2010 Sales

	$ mil.	% of total
Product sales	18.4	84
Parts & service	3.5	16
Total	**21.9**	**100**

2010 Sales

	$ mil.	% of total
Dialysis meter & disposables	8	37
Raven biological indicators	7.2	33
DataTrace data loggers	5.8	26
Nusonics ultrasound meters	.6	3
Torqo bottle cap test systems	.3	1
Total	**21.9**	**100**

Selected Products

Biological and chemical indicators (Raven Biological Laboratories)
Electronic thermal sensors
  DATATRACE
  DATATRACE Micropack Tracers
  ELOGG
  Flatpack Tracers
  FRB Tracers
Hemodialysis products (Automata)
  Database management software (Reuse Data Management System)
  Dialyzer reprocessors (ECHO MM-1000)
  Meters (Western Meters)
Sonic fluid measurement products (NuSonics)
  Sonic concentration analyzers
  Sonic flowmeters

COMPETITORS

3M Health Care	Minntech
Badger Meter	Rockwell Medical
Cantel Medical	Siemens Corp.
Danaher	Siemens Water
Ellab	Technologies
Emerson Electric	STERIS
Euro Tech	Teledyne Isco
Gambro AB	Thermo Fisher
GE	Scientific
K-Tron	Velocys
Mikron Infrared	

HISTORICAL FINANCIALS

Company Type: Public

Income Statement

FYE: March 31

	REVENUE ($ mil.)	NET INCOME ($ mil.)	NET PROFIT MARGIN	EMPLOYEES
03/11	32.8	6.2	18.9%	177
03/10	21.9	4.8	21.9%	112
03/09	21.5	4.8	22.3%	111
03/08	19.6	4.6	23.5%	113
03/07	17.2	4.0	23.3%	100
Annual Growth	17.5%	11.6%	—	15.3%

Debt ratio: 4.1%	No. of shares (mil.): 3.3
Return on equity: 17.0%	Dividends
Cash ($ mil.): 3.5	Yield: 1.6%
Current ratio: 1.74	Payout: 24.7%
Long-term debt ($ mil.): 1.5	Market value ($ mil.): 93.6

	STOCK PRICE ($) FY Close	P/E High/Low		PER SHARE ($) Earnings	Dividends	Book Value
03/11	28.80	17	10	1.86	0.46	11.20
03/10	25.96	20	12	1.45	0.42	9.74
03/09	16.00	17	10	1.48	0.40	8.67
03/08	21.93	19	13	1.41	0.36	7.50
03/07	19.00	19	11	1.22	0.30	6.54
Annual Growth	**11.0%**	—	—	**11.1%**	**11.3%**	**14.4%**

Meta Financial Group

Don't worry, the money is real. Meta Financial Group is the holding company for MetaBank, a thrift with about a dozen branches in Iowa and South Dakota. MetaBank offers standard deposit products and services including checking and savings accounts. Its lending and investment activities are weighted towards real estate and real estate-related assets; commercial and multifamily residential mortgages comprise more than half of the bank's loan portfolio. It also writes single-family residential mortgages and business loans. Meta Financial's bread and butter, however, is the bank's Meta Payment Systems (MPS) division, which provides prepaid cards, consumer credit, and ATM sponsorship services nationwide.

The company has invested in MPS' growth by marketing new products and programs such as prepaid debit cards for tax refunds, eco-friendly recycled or recyclable cards, and lines of credit on prepaid cards. The initiatives have paid off, as MPS-related card fees account bring in the lion's share of Meta Financial's revenues and helped the company return to profitability in 2010.

In 2011 MetaBank received a cease and desist order from the Office of Thrift Supervision after the regulator determined that the bank engaged in unfair lending practices. It directed the company to discontinue its iAdvance subprime consumer lending program and suspend its tax loan and refund transfer operations.

Meta Financial sold trust services provider Meta Trust Company in 2010, and sold its MetaBank West Central commercial banking subsidiary to Anita Bancorporation in 2008. The moves allowed the company to focus on its stronger retail and payment services activities.

Directors and executive officers of Meta Financial own nearly 25% of the company's stock. Institutional investors own more than a quarter.

EXECUTIVES

Chairman, James S. Haahr, age 72
President, CEO and Director, Meta Financial Group and MetaBank, J. Tyler Haahr, age 47
EVP, Meta Payment Systems, Scott Galit, age 40
EVP and Director; EVP, MetaBank; Division President, Meta Payment Systems, Bradley C. (Brad) Hanson, age 46
EVP, Secretary, Treasurer and CFO, David W. Leedom, age 56

EVP and COO, Meta Financial Group and MetaBank, Troy Moore III, age 42
SVP, Product Development, Andrew Crowe
SVP and Director of Marketing, John Kenjar
SVP and Director Human Resources, Sandra K. Hegland
SVP, Meta Payment Systems Division, Michael Conlin
SVP and Chief Legal Officer, John D. Hagy
SVP and Chief of Staff, Meta Payment Systems, Ron Butterfield
SVP Operations, Meta Payment Systems, John DeLavis
SVP and Chief Risk Officer, Merid Eshete
Auditors: McGladrey & Pullen, LLP

LOCATIONS

HQ: Meta Financial Group, Inc.
121 E. 5th St., Storm Lake, IA 50588
Phone: 712-732-4117   **Fax:** 712-732-7105
Web: www.metacash.com

PRODUCTS/OPERATIONS

2010 Sales

	$ mil.	% of total
Noninterest		
Card fees	93.2	68
Gain on sale of securities	2.1	2
Other	2.1	2
Interest		
Loans receivable, including fees	24.9	18
Mortgage-backed securities	13.4	10
Other investments	0.8	-
Total	**136.5**	**100**

COMPETITORS

Bank of America	Green Dot
Blackhawk Network	HF Financial
Citi Prepaid Services	nFinanSe
First National of Nebraska	U.S. Bancorp
Great Western Bancorporation	West Bancorporation

HISTORICAL FINANCIALS

Company Type: Public

Income Statement

FYE: September 30

	REVENUE ($ mil.)	NET INCOME ($ mil.)	NET PROFIT MARGIN	EMPLOYEES
09/10	136.5	12.4	9.1%	415
09/09	116.7	(1.5)	—	468
09/08	75.1	0.1	0.1%	398
09/07	56.3	1.2	2.1%	323
09/06	54.0	3.9	7.2%	257
Annual Growth	**26.1%**	**33.5%**	—	**12.7%**

2010 Year-End Financials

Debt ratio: 44.8%	No. of shares (mil.): 3.1
Return on equity: 17.2%	Dividends
Cash ($ mil.): 87.5	Yield: 1.6%
Current ratio: —	Payout: 12.7%
Long-term debt ($ mil.): 32.3	Market value ($ mil.): 99.6

	STOCK PRICE ($) FY Close	P/E High/Low		PER SHARE ($) Earnings	Dividends	Book Value
09/10	32.00	9	4	4.11	0.52	23.15
09/09	23.86	—	—	(0.56)	0.52	17.97
09/08	17.00	2100	793	0.02	0.52	18.00
09/07	39.85	93	54	0.45	0.52	18.67
09/06	24.60	18	12	1.55	0.52	18.01
Annual Growth	**6.8%**	—	—	**27.6%**	**(0.0%)**	**6.5%**

Microchip Technology

While bigger semiconductor makers fight over your PC and mobile phone, Microchip Technology has probably chipped its way into your car, your office copier, and even your wallet. The semiconductor maker offers a variety of embedded devices, including eight-bit microcontrollers (it's one of the top makers of them worldwide); specialty memory products such as electrically erasable programmable read-only memories; and KEELOQ brand code-hopping devices used in keyless locks, garage door openers, and smart cards. Its chips are used by tens of thousands of customers in the automotive, computing, consumer, industrial, medical, and networking markets. Microchip gets about three-quarters of its sales outside the US.

The global economic meltdown, resulting in tight credit markets, victimized Microchip Technology by leaving the company with about $37 million in auction-rate securities in its portfolio. Microchip is unable to sell the securities and will have to hold them until they are divested in a successful auction. After selling $1.15 billion in debentures in 2007, the company holds more debt than it previously has, and could be subject to difficulties in refinancing those debentures. Microchip also is heavily dependent on distributors to sell its semiconductors, relying on them to provide around 61% of its sales.

Despite its challenging financial condition, Microchip is on a buying spree. The company in 2010 acquired flash memory maker Silicon Storage Technology (SST) for around $275 million in cash. The deal adds SST's flash technology, more than 360 patents, and more microcontrollers to Microchip's portfolio; SST also brings an entry to several new markets. Microchip plans to keep SST's best-performing business units and to divest the rest. It sold the NAND drives, NAND controllers, smart card integrated circuits, and other products to Greenliant Systems, a company formed by Bing Yeh, the former chairman and CEO of SST. About 100 employees transferred to to Greenliant as part of the transaction.

Earlier that year, Microchip Technology picked up ZeroG Wireless. The acquisition of Wi-Fi technology, which is being used more in embedded applications, was the crux of the purchase, enhancing its product line with Wi-Fi capability and related software. In 2009 the company purchased R&E International. R&E developed integrated circuits used in security and life safety equipment (smoke and carbon monoxide detectors). Also that year Microchip acquired Australia-based HI-TECH Software. The purchase added development tools for embedded systems and extended the company's market share in the compiler technology sector.

In 2008 Microchip made an unsolicited takeover offer for competitor Atmel, a supplier of microcontrollers and other chips. The company privately approached Atmel about a potential merger before going public with a cash offer to buy the company, valued at around $2.3 billion.

Microchip made the bid in concert with ON Semiconductor, which wanted to buy Atmel's automotive, nonvolatile memory, and radio-frequency (RF) product lines if Microchip succeeded in acquiring Atmel. Microchip also planned to divest Atmel's application-specific integrated circuit business, which provides customized chips to customers, to a third party.

Atmel's board of directors rejected the Microchip/ON Semi bid. Microchip then said it intended to nominate a slate of directors at Atmel's next annual meeting. The company reported that it received clearance from US antitrust regulators on acquiring Atmel.

In late 2008, however, ON Semi reported it was dropping out of the bid, citing "the unforeseen deterioration in the semiconductor market since we announced our proposal as well as the unprecedented weakness in the financial markets." Microchip withdrew its proposal as a result, while later nominating a dissident slate of nominees for Atmel's annual meeting. The company dropped the proxy battle in 2009, citing deteriorating conditions in Atmel's business, the semiconductor industry in general, and the global economy.

More than three-quarters of Microchip's sales come from microcontroller products; overall sales are balanced among Asia, Europe, and the Americas, with Asia predominating.

The company follows an "attach" strategy, under which it uses its strong position in microcontrollers as a springboard to sell complementary analog products to its microcontroller customers. Microchip has also used selective acquisitions to improve its fortunes: its purchase of California-based TelCom Semiconductor greatly expanded its analog chip product offerings, and its $180 million acquisition of a large chip factory in Oregon from Fujitsu significantly enhanced its production capacity.

The company promotes adoption of its dsPIC "digital signal controller," a part that combines the features of a digital signal processor with a microcontroller. With the dsPIC, Microchip targets applications such as motor control and power conversion, high-speed sensors, speech and audio, Internet and modem connectivity, telecommunications, encryption, and automotive engineering.

Microchip Technology has production facilities in Thailand and the US and sales offices throughout the world.

HISTORY

Investment firm Sequoia Capital acquired a washed-up semiconductor subsidiary from General Instrument in 1989. Sequoia executive Steve Sanghi, a veteran of Intel, was tapped to head the operation, Microchip Technology. Sanghi instituted a bare-bones operating budget and broadened the company's focus beyond low-cost memory products to include more profitable embedded microcontrollers. By 1992 Microchip turned a small profit.

In 1995 Microchip acquired the rights to KEELOQ secure data transmission products, developed by South Africa's Nanoteq Ltd. The following year the company introduced its own line of secure data transmission products and its first flash memory microcontrollers. In 1997 Microchip unveiled the world's smallest erasable read-only memory, to be used in devices such as keyless entries, dimmers, and thermostats. In 1998 Microchip settled litigation with ROHM, whose Exel Microelectronics unit was an original KEELOQ licensee; ROHM surrendered its licensing rights to the technology.

Streamlining around its more cost-effective manufacturing operations, Microchip in 1999 closed a wafer fabrication plant (or fab) and a test facility. In 2001 the company beefed up its analog product line by acquiring TelCom Semiconductor, a maker of chips for wireless phones.

In 2002 Microchip paid $54 million in cash for privately held PowerSmart, a Duracell spinoff that made embedded controllers and battery sensors.

Also that year the company acquired a large wafer fab from Fujitsu for about $180 million in cash. Microchip launched a new e-commerce Web site in 2003.

CEO Steve Sanghi and former HR VP Michael Jones wrote a book about the company's early years and how Microchip survived and prospered. Published in 2006 by John Wiley & Sons, *Driving Excellence: How the Aggregate System Turned Microchip Technology from a Failing Company to a Market Leader* recounted the hardscrabble measures taken in 1990 and following years to save the company from collapse, leading to its successful IPO in 1993. The "aggregate system" referred to in the title was a collection of 10 corporate precepts, including clear company values and having employees share in the company's prosperity.

Also in 2006 Microchip created a Medical Products Group, targeting the $100 billion medical devices market, especially those devices used by consumers.

EXECUTIVES

Chairman, President, and CEO; President and CEO, SST, Steve Sanghi, age 55, $5,053,479 total compensation
EVP and COO, Ganesh Moorthy, age 51, $1,566,949 total compensation
VP and CFO, J. Eric Bjornholt, age 40, $591,719 total compensation
VP Advanced Microcontroller Architecture Division, Mitchel Obolsky
VP Pacific Rim Finance, William Yang
VP Analog and Interface Products Division, Richard J. Simoncic, age 47
VP Information Services, Robert H. Owen
VP Development Tools Group, Derek P. Carlson
VP Fab 4 Operations, Kathy A. Clevenger
VP Human Resources, Lauren A. Carr
VP Global Sales Support and Electronic Manufacturing Systems, Paul R. Breault
VP Pacific Rim Manufacturing Operations, Mathew B. Bunker
VP Digital Signal Controller Division, Sumit K. Mitra
VP Asia Sales, Joseph R. Krawczyk
VP Vertical Markets Group, Dan L. Termer
VP Fab 2 Operations, Michael A. Finley
VP Analog and Interface Marketing, Bryan J. Liddiard
VP Worldwide Sales and Applications, Mitchell R. Little, age 59, $1,066,986 total compensation
VP Memory Products Division, Randall L. (Randy) Drwinga
VP Fab Operations, David S. Lambert, age 59, $689,851 total compensation
VP Business Development and Investor Relations, Gordon W. Parnell, age 61, $542,642 total compensation
VP European Sales, Gary P. Marsh
VP Security, Microcontroller, and Technology Division, Stephen V. (Steve) Drehobl, age 49
VP Worldwide Applications Engineering, Ken N. Pye
Editorial Contact, Michelle Ragsdale
Senior Product Marketing Manager, Analog and Interface Products Division, Art Eck
Product Marketing Engineer, Analog and Interface Products Division, Namrata Pandya
Director Applications, Security, Microcontroller, and Technology Development Division, Vivien Delport
Managing Counsel and Secretary, Kim van Herk
Public Relations Manager, Eric Lawson
Investor Relations, Deborah L. Wussler
Senior Worldwide Design Partner Program Manager, Cheri Keller
Auditors: Ernst & Young LLP

LOCATIONS

HQ: Microchip Technology Incorporated
2355 W. Chandler Blvd., Chandler, AZ 85224-6199
Phone: 480-792-7200   **Fax:** 480-792-7277
Web: www.microchip.com

2010 Sales

	$ mil.	% of total
Asia/Pacific	479.0	51
Europe	237.3	25
Americas	231.4	24
Total	**947.7**	**100**

PRODUCTS/OPERATIONS

2010 Sales

	$ mil.	% of total
Microcontrollers	767.7	81
Analog & interface products	99.8	11
Memory products	80.2	8
Total	**947.7**	**100**

Selected Products

Analog and Interface Integrated Circuits (ICs)
  Interface devices
    Controllers
    Infrared codecs
  Linear devices
    Audio amplifiers
    Comparators
    Operational amplifiers
  Mixed-signal devices
    Analog-to-digital (A/D) and digital-to-analog (D/A) converters
    Digital potentiometers
  Power management devices
    DC-to-DC converters
    Linear regulators
    Power MOSFET drivers
    Switching regulators
    System supervisors
    Voltage detectors
    Voltage references
  Thermal management devices
    Brushless DC fan controllers
    Temperature sensors
KEELOQ Security Devices
  Decoders
  Encoders
  Transcoders
Memory Chips
  Serial and parallel erasable programmable read-only memories (EPROMs)
  Serial electrically erasable programmable read-only memories (EEPROMs)
Microcontrollers
  Eight-bit microcontrollers (PICmicro and rfPIC lines)
  Mixed-signal controllers
Radio-frequency identification (RFID) ICs

COMPETITORS

Altera
Analog Devices
Atmel
Cypress Semiconductor
Dialog Semiconductor
Echelon Corporation
Fairchild Semiconductor
Freescale Semiconductor
Fujitsu Semiconductor
Intel
Intersil
Linear Technology
Macronix International
Maxim Integrated Products
Mitsubishi Electric
National Semiconductor
Oki Semiconductor
ON Semiconductor
RadiSys
Ramtron International
Renesas Electronics
ROHM
Silicon Labs
STMicroelectronics
Texas Instruments
Winbond Electronics
ZiLOG

HISTORICAL FINANCIALS

Company Type: Public

Income Statement
FYE: March 31

	REVENUE ($ mil.)	NET INCOME ($ mil.)	NET PROFIT MARGIN	EMPLOYEES
03/11	1,487.2	419.0	28.2%	6,970
03/10	947.7	217.0	22.9%	5,418
03/09	903.3	248.8	27.5%	4,895
03/08	1,035.7	297.7	28.7%	4,811
03/07	1,039.7	357.0	34.3%	4,582
Annual Growth	9.4%	4.1%	—	11.1%

2011 Year-End Financials

Debt ratio: 22.4%	No. of shares (mil.): 189.5
Return on equity: 23.1%	Dividends
Cash ($ mil.): 703.9	Yield: 3.6%
Current ratio: 5.22	Payout: 63.9%
Long-term debt ($ mil.): 405.5	Market value ($ mil.): 7,204.5

	STOCK PRICE ($) FY Close	P/E High/Low		PER SHARE ($) Earnings	Dividends	Book Value
03/11	38.01	18	12	2.15	1.37	9.56
03/10	28.16	25	17	1.16	1.36	8.27
03/09	21.19	29	12	1.33	1.35	5.44
03/08	32.73	30	19	1.40	1.21	5.49
03/07	35.53	24	19	1.62	0.96	9.18
Annual Growth	1.7%	—	—	7.3%	9.3%	1.0%

Millennium Bankshares

Millennium Bankshares is the holding company for Millennium Bank, which serves Northern Virginia through four branches. The bank, which opened in 1999, offers traditional retail and commercial products including checking and savings accounts, IRAs, CDs, and money market accounts. The bank has wound down its mortgage operations in an effort to focus on core banking activities. Millennium also dissolved its insurance services division. The relatively young bank ran into financial problems in 2007, when the Office of the Comptroller investigated Millennium and ordered it to become adequately capitalized. The Federal Reserve Bank of Richmond later issued a similar enforcement action.

EXECUTIVES

Chairman, Grayson P. Hanes, age 73
President and CEO, Millennium Bankshares and Millennium Bank, John F. (Jack) Novak, age 65
Chairman, Millennium Bank and Director, Joseph Paulini, age 56
EVP, Treasurer, and CFO, Millennium Bankshares; EVP, Treasurer, and CFO, Millennium Bank, Dale G. Phelps, age 55
EVP and Chief Credit Officer, Millennium Bank, William C. (Bill) O'Connor
EVP and Chief Lending Officer, Millennium Bank, Marcus J. Perry
SVP Lending, Millennium Bank, Edward W. (Ed) Lull Jr.
SVP Business Development, Millennium Bank, Ricardo Balcells
Auditors: Crowe Horwath LLP

LOCATIONS

HQ: Millennium Bankshares Corporation
21430 Cedar Dr., Ste. 200, Sterling, VA 20164
Phone: 703-464-0100
Web: www.millenniumbankshares.com

COMPETITORS

Access National	Comerica
Bank of America	PNC Financial
BB&T	SunTrust
Cardinal Financial	United Bankshares

HISTORICAL FINANCIALS

Company Type: Public

Income Statement
FYE: December 31

	ASSETS ($ mil.)	NET INCOME ($ mil.)	INCOME AS % OF ASSETS	EMPLOYEES
03/10*	171.1	(4.3)	—	0
12/09	240.0	(11.4)	—	49
03/09	32.3	(0.2)	—	0
12/08	313.7	(17.5)	—	58
03/08	123.0	9.1	7.4%	0
Annual Growth	17.9%	—	—	(15.5%)

*Fiscal year change

2010 Year-End Financials

Equity as % of assets: —	Dividends
Return on assets: 4.3	Yield: —
Return on equity: —	Payout: —
Long-term debt ($ mil.): 25.8	Market value ($ mil.): 0.4
No. of shares (mil.): 10.5	Sales ($ mil.): 59.6

	STOCK PRICE ($) FY Close	P/E High/Low		PER SHARE ($) Earnings	Dividends	Book Value
03/10*	0.04	—	—	(0.37)	0.00	8.58
12/09	0.02	—	—	(0.02)	0.00	1.48
03/09	0.00	—	—	(0.00)	0.00	(0.00)
Annual Growth	—	—	—	—	—	—

*Fiscal year change

Miller Petroleum

This Miller's tale is all about oil and gas in the Appalachian region. Miller Petroleum, which operates as Miller Energy Resources, has been exploring and producing in the southern Appalachian region since 1967. It operates oil and gas wells, organizes joint drilling ventures with partners, and rebuilds and sells oil field equipment (including compressors, oil field trailers, and drilling rigs). Active in drilling and production in eastern Tennessee, in 2008 Miller had total proved reserves of 1.8 billion cu. ft. of natural gas and 74,413 barrels of crude oil. It is developing more than 43,490 acres of oil and gas leases. Diversifying, in 2009 it acquired Alaskan oil explorer Cook Inlet Energy.

EXECUTIVES

Chairman, Deloy Miller, age 64
CFO, Paul W. Boyd, age 52
VP Geology, Gary G. Bible, age 61
VP Operations, Eugene D. Lockyear, age 65
Interim President, CEO, and Director, Scott M. Boruff, age 48
SVP Investor Relations, Robert L. Gaylor
Secretary and Treasurer, Teresa Cotton, age 48
Auditors: Rodefer Moss & Co, PLLC

LOCATIONS

HQ: Miller Petroleum, Inc.
3651 Baker Hwy., Huntsville, TN 37756
Phone: 423-663-9457   **Fax:** 423-663-9461
Web: www.millerpetroleum.com

PRODUCTS/OPERATIONS

COMPETITORS

Belden & Blake	EQT Corporation
Cabot Oil & Gas	Range Resources
CONSOL Energy	Talisman Energy
Dominion Resources	

HISTORICAL FINANCIALS

Company Type: Public

Income Statement
FYE: April 30

	REVENUE ($ mil.)	NET INCOME ($ mil.)	NET PROFIT MARGIN	EMPLOYEES
04/11	22.8	(4.4)	—	71
04/10	5.9	249.5	4228.8%	47
04/09	1.6	8.4	525.0%	19
04/08	0.8	(2.4)	—	20
04/07	1.3	(1.5)	—	8
Annual Growth	104.6%	—	—	72.6%

2011 Year-End Financials

Debt ratio: 0.0%	No. of shares (mil.): 39.9
Return on equity: —	Dividends
Cash ($ mil.): 1.6	Yield: —
Current ratio: 0.52	Payout: —
Long-term debt ($ mil.): 0.0	Market value ($ mil.): 230.1

	STOCK PRICE ($) FY Close	P/E High/Low		PER SHARE ($) Earnings	Dividends	Book Value
04/11	5.77	—	—	(0.12)	0.00	7.38
04/10	5.78	1	0	8.29	0.00	8.56
04/09	0.33	1	0	0.56	0.00	0.45
04/08	0.10	—	—	(0.17)	0.00	(0.19)
04/07	0.32	—	—	(0.11)	0.00	(0.06)
Annual Growth	106.1%	—	—	—	—	—

Mission Bancorp

Famous California missions include San Juan Capistrano, San Francisco de Asis, and San Luis Obispo de Tolosa. But there's another one: Mission Bancorp. It's the holding company for Mission Bank, a community bank with three locations in and near Bakersfield, California. Serving area consumers and small to midsized businesses, the bank offers checking and savings accounts; certificates of deposit; credit cards; and business, agricultural, commercial real estate, construction, residential, and consumer loans. It also provides credit card processing services to area merchants.

EXECUTIVES

President and CEO, Richard Fanucchi, age 61
VP and Manager, A.J. Antongiovanni
VP and Manager, Greenfield, Terry Redwine

VP and Administrative Operations Officer, Cindy Talley
SVP Commercial Lending, Stan Newman
SVP and Chief Credit Officer, Grady Buck
SVP and CFO, Craig Swenson
SVP Commercial Lending, Rob Hallum
Auditors: Brown Armstrong Paulden McCown Starbuck & Keeter

LOCATIONS

HQ: Mission Bancorp
 1330 Truxtun Ave., Bakersfield, CA 93301-4518
Phone: 661-859-2500   **Fax:** 661-321-4821
Web: www.missionbank.com

HISTORICAL FINANCIALS

Company Type: Public

Income Statement

FYE: December 31

	ASSETS ($ mil.)	NET INCOME ($ mil.)	INCOME AS % OF ASSETS	EMPLOYEES
12/06	142.3	3.2	2.2%	37
12/05	161.1	2.2	1.4%	32
12/04	120.7	1.1	0.9%	26
12/03	110.6	0.5	0.5%	27
12/02	73.8	0.4	0.5%	23
Annual Growth	17.8%	68.2%	—	12.6%

2006 Year-End Financials

Equity as % of assets: 10.24%   Dividends
Return on assets: 2.2%   Yield: —
Return on equity: 21.7%   Payout: —
Long-term debt ($ mil.): —   Market value ($ mil.): —
No. of shares (mil.): —   Sales ($ mil.): 11.0

	STOCK PRICE ($) FY Close	P/E High/Low		PER SHARE ($) Earnings	Dividends	Book Value
12/06	41.95	14	7	2.96	0.00	(0.00)
12/05	20.41	11	8	1.92	0.00	(0.00)
12/04	16.22	17	9	0.97	0.00	(0.00)
12/03	0.00	24	16	0.48	0.00	(0.00)
Annual Growth	—	—	—	83.4%	—	—

Mistras Group

Mistras could be all that stands between you and a massive oil refinery explosion, nuclear facility meltdown, or big bridge collapse. The engineering services company conducts non-destructive testing on critical equipment and processes used by petroleum, aerospace, infrastructure, power generation, and chemical manufacturing companies worldwide. It checks plant infrastructure for defects and problems without interrupting production; inspections take place during facility design, build, maintenance, and operation phases. Mistras works from nearly 70 offices in 15 nations to serve clients that include Alcan, Honeywell, Bechtel, BP, Dow Chemical, Airbus, and federal and state governments.

Mistras helps its customers beyond just avoiding catastrophic events. The company help clients comply with government safety standards, minimize repair costs, extend the useful life of assets, and increase productivity.

In addition to its on-site testing services, the company also offers testing equipment, instru-

ments, and software through its Software and Products division. Testing services include mechanical integrity and visual testing along with digital radiography, ground penetrating radar, and infrared and ultrasonic sensor testing. Mistras' software offerings include databases and enterprise software to store and analyze testing data, planning software, and on-line monitoring systems.

In the past, Mistras has grown through acquisitions. More recently though, the company has grown organically by about 18% a year. The company also wants to delve into newer markets seeing opportunities in alternative energy and public infrastructure. The company hopes to expand its services into such emerging markets as India and China. Mistras also wants to expand its services to existing clients, which includes providing multinational companies services in many of the countries they operate.

Asset heavy companies make up the bulk of Mistras' clients. Customers coming from the oil, gas, and chemical industries have historically comprised more than 50% of the company's international revenues, stemming primarily from contracts with major oil refineries in Brazil and Russia. Smaller pieces of the revenue pie come from testing other safety-critical industrial sites, infrastructure, manufacturing facilities, research centers, and universities.

Chairman, president, and CEO Sotirios Vahaviolos owns about 45% of the company.

EXECUTIVES

Chairman, President, and CEO, Sotirios J. Vahaviolos, age 65
EVP, CFO, and Treasurer, Francis T. (Frank) Joyce, age 58
EVP, General Counsel, and Secretary, Michael C. Keefe, age 54
Group EVP, Software and Products, Mark F. Carlos, age 60
Group EVP, Services and Director, Michael J. Lange, age 51
Group VP, Nuclear Products and Services, Fred Klorczyk
Director, Marketing and Communications, Nestor Makarigakis
Group EVP, International, Phillip T. Cole, age 58
Auditors: PricewaterhouseCoopers LLP

LOCATIONS

HQ: Mistras Group, Inc.
 195 Clarksville Rd., Princeton Junction, NJ 08550
Phone: 609-716-4000   **Fax:** 609-716-4145
Web: www.mistrasgroup.com

COMPETITORS

GE Inspection
 Technologies
Lloyd's Register
SGS

Siemens AG
Team
The Carlyle Group

HISTORICAL FINANCIALS

Company Type: Public

Income Statement

FYE: May 31

	REVENUE ($ mil.)	NET INCOME ($ mil.)	NET PROFIT MARGIN	EMPLOYEES
05/11	338.6	16.4	4.8%	2,700
05/10	272.1	10.4	3.8%	2,300
05/09	209.1	5.5	2.6%	2,000
05/08	152.3	7.4	4.9%	1,500
05/07	122.2	5.4	4.4%	1,500
Annual Growth	29.0%	32.0%	—	15.8%

2011 Year-End Financials

Debt ratio: 14.5%   No. of shares (mil.): 27.7
Return on equity: 9.8%   Dividends
Cash ($ mil.): 10.9   Yield: —
Current ratio: 2.11   Payout: —
Long-term debt ($ mil.): 24.2   Market value ($ mil.): 481.7

	STOCK PRICE ($) FY Close	P/E High/Low		PER SHARE ($) Earnings	Dividends	Book Value
05/11	17.41	30	15	0.61	0.00	6.04
05/10	11.94	36	23	0.43	0.00	4.89
Annual Growth	45.8%	—	—	41.9%	—	23.6%

Molycorp

Don't look for any mollycoddling of the earth here. Molycorp mines and produces lanthanide and molybdenum compounds, concentrates, and oxides using open-pit mining techniques. Lanthanides (which include cerium, lanthanum, and yttrium) are used in everything from cell phones and computers to X-ray film and television glass. The company, however, is staking its future on the production of rare earth oxides (REO). Molycorp went public in July 2010 with an initial public offering (IPO). The company plans to use funds from the IPO to modernize its California facility and expand into REO metals and alloys production. Later that year, Sumitomo Corp. invested $130 million for a guaranteed seven-year supply of REOs.

Molycorp is the only REO producer in the Western hemisphere and owns the world's largest rare earth project outside of China. Following a "mine-to-magnets" strategy, the company expects to be one of the world's top producers of rare earth products, including oxides, metals, alloys, and magnets. Rare earths are used in hybrid and electric vehicles, wind power turbines, fiber optics, lasers, disk drives, aviation guidance and control systems, global positioning systems, and advanced water treatment technology.

In 2011 Molycorp, through a subsidiary, acquired a controlling stake in AS Silmet, one of only two REO processing facilities in Europe, in a deal valued at about $89 million. The acquisition provides Molycorp with its first European base of operations as well as doubling the company's current annual production capacity to 6,000 tons. Molycorp will process the output from its Mountain Pass, California mine at the AS Silmet facility in Estonia, reducing that plant's dependence on REO materials sourced from China.

That same year, Molycorp acquired the rare-earth alloy and metal producer Santoku America for $17.5 million. Arizona-based Santoku America was a subsidiary of Japanese company Santoku Corp. The acquisition allows Molycorp to begin manufacturing and selling rare earth alloys for use in magnets found in electric and hybrid cars, wind turbines, electronics, and other applications.

Molycorp has an estimated total proven reserves of 88 million pounds and probable reserves of more than 2 billion pounds of REO. The company's Mountain Pass facility, when its upgrade is completed, will have the ability to mine, crush, mill, and separate rare earth ore to produce individual rare earth elements (REE). Global consumption of REEs is projected to steadily increase due to continuing growth in existing applications and increased innovation and development of new end uses.

Resource Capital Funds owns some 32% of Molycorp following its IPO.

EXECUTIVES

Chairman, Ross R. Bhappu, age 51
President, CEO, and Director, Mark A. Smith, age 52, $679,245 total compensation
CFO and Treasurer, James S. Allen, age 44, $12,256 total compensation
EVP and CTO, John L. Burba, age 59, $243,619 total compensation
EVP and General Counsel, John F. Ashburn Jr., age 56, $259,700 total compensation
General Manager, Mountain Pass Mine, Rocky Smith
Financial Reporting Manager, Jared M. Benedict
Sales Manager, Robert E. Noll
Corporate Controller, Ksenia A. Adams, age 29, $53,254 total compensation
Product Development Manager, Carl Hassler
Auditors: PricewaterhouseCoopers LLP

LOCATIONS

HQ: Molycorp, Inc.
5619 Denver Tech Center Pkwy., Ste. 1000, Greenwood Village, CO 80111
Phone: 303-843-8040   **Fax:** 303-843-8082
Web: www.molycorp.com

COMPETITORS

BHP Billiton Plc	Rio Tinto Limited
Freeport-McMoRan	Umicore
Norilsk Nickel	Xstrata

HISTORICAL FINANCIALS

Company Type: Public

Income Statement

FYE: December 31

	REVENUE ($ mil.)	NET INCOME ($ mil.)	NET PROFIT MARGIN	EMPLOYEES
12/10	35.2	(49.1)	—	150
12/09	7.1	(28.6)	—	120
12/08	2.1	(14.1)	—	0
Annual Growth	309.4%	—	—	25.0%

2010 Year-End Financials

Debt ratio: —
Return on equity: —
Cash ($ mil.): 316.4
Current ratio: 17.15
Long-term debt ($ mil.): —
No. of shares (mil.): 82.3
Dividends
  Yield: —
  Payout: —
Market value ($ mil.): 4,106.3

	STOCK PRICE ($) FY Close	P/E High/Low	PER SHARE ($) Earnings	Dividends	Book Value
12/10	49.90	— —	(0.79)	0.00	5.45
Annual Growth	—	— —	—	—	—

Momenta Pharmaceuticals

Momenta Pharmaceuticals isn't pausing in its development of new drugs. The biotech company specializes in unpacking and engineering complex molecules in order to copy existing biologic drugs, develop complex generic drugs, and discover new drugs. Momenta's primary product is M-Enoxaparin, a generic version of Sanofi's heparin drug Lovenox. It received FDA approval in 2010 and was developed under an agreement with Sandoz. It is used to treat patients with deep-vein thrombosis and acute coronary syndromes. The company is also developing a generic version of multiple sclerosis treatment Copaxone (marketed by Sanofi and Teva).

While regular generic drugs need to be reviewed and approved by the FDA, generic versions of biologic drugs (also known as "follow-on biologics") have to jump through additional hoops to prove that the facilities in which they are manufactured are fully up to the task.

Sandoz, the generic arm of Novartis, teamed with Momenta to develop and market M-Enoxaparin. During the development stage, this partnership was the source of all of Momenta's revenues. Now that the drug is being marketed, Momenta is eligible for 45% of profits from its sale as long as no other generic version of Lovenox hits the market. If that happens Momenta becomes eligible for a percentage of royalties. Sandoz is also working with Momenta on M356, the generic form of Copaxone.

Being in the business it is (developing generic forms of existing drugs) Momenta has to have a formidable legal team in place at all times to defend itself against other pharmaceutical manufacturers seeking to protect their territory. Shortly after it began marketing Lovenox, Momenta was sued by Sanofi in an attempt to limit or completely halt sales of M-Enoxaparin. Whatever the outcome of that lawsuit, Momenta can expect more of the same to come its way when and if it gets other generic versions of successful pharmaceuticals to market.

Along with M-Enoxaparin and Copaxone, Momenta is also developing a proprietary anticoagulant candidate to treat cardiovascular ailments including acute coronary syndromes. Another discovery stage program is exploring the role of complex sugars in cancer treatment.

Momenta Pharmaceuticals was founded in 2001. Novartis owns about a 10% stake in the company.

EXECUTIVES

Chairman, James R. (Jim) Sulat, age 60
President, CEO, and Director, Craig A. Wheeler, age 50, $2,690,494 total compensation
VP Regulatory Affairs, Gerard E. (Rod) Riedel
VP Corporate Development, Catharine Johnson
VP Business Development, Young T. Kwon
VP Biology, Kei Kishimoto
VP Development Operations, Ian D. Fier
VP Strategic Product Development, Barbara Rosengren
SVP Research and Chief Scientific Officer, Ganesh Venkataraman, age 44, $1,363,845 total compensation
SVP Human Resources, Jo-Ann Beltramello
SVP Development and Chief Medical Officer, James M. (Jim) Roach, age 51
SVP and CFO, Richard P. (Rick) Shea, age 59, $619,844 total compensation
Director Investor Relations, Beverly Holley
SVP Pharmaceutical Sciences, John E. Bishop, age 49, $1,010,023 total compensation
SVP Legal, General Counsel and Secretary, Bruce A. Leicher, age 55
Auditors: Ernst & Young LLP

LOCATIONS

HQ: Momenta Pharmaceuticals, Inc.
675 W. Kendall St., Cambridge, MA 02142
Phone: 617-491-9700   **Fax:** 617-621-0431
Web: www.momentapharma.com

COMPETITORS

Amphastar	Keryx
Bayer HealthCare	Biopharmaceuticals
Pharmaceuticals	Merck Serono
Biogen Idec	Optimer
Boehringer Ingelheim	Pfizer
Bristol-Myers Squibb	Sanofi
Genzyme	Teva
GlaxoSmithKline	The Medicines Company
Johnson & Johnson	

HISTORICAL FINANCIALS

Company Type: Public

Income Statement

FYE: December 31

	REVENUE ($ mil.)	NET INCOME ($ mil.)	NET PROFIT MARGIN	EMPLOYEES
12/10	116.8	37.3	31.9%	170
12/09	20.2	(64.0)	—	176
12/08	14.6	(62.6)	—	167
12/07	21.6	(68.9)	—	163
12/06	16.0	(51.9)	—	153
Annual Growth	64.4%	—	—	2.7%

2010 Year-End Financials

Debt ratio: —
Return on equity: 18.1%
Cash ($ mil.): 100.7
Current ratio: 11.52
Long-term debt ($ mil.): —
No. of shares (mil.): 49.7
Dividends
  Yield: —
  Payout: —
Market value ($ mil.): 744.7

	STOCK PRICE ($) FY Close	P/E High/Low	PER SHARE ($) Earnings	Dividends	Book Value
12/10	14.97	32 13	0.81	0.00	4.14
12/09	12.60	— —	(1.60)	0.00	2.11
12/08	11.60	— —	(1.74)	0.00	2.69
12/07	7.14	— —	(1.93)	0.00	3.50
12/06	15.73	— —	(1.62)	0.00	5.07
Annual Growth	(1.2%)	— —	—	—	(4.9%)

Monarch Financial Holdings inc

Money rules at Monarch Financial Holdings. The holding company serves the South Hampton Roads area of southeastern Virginia through Monarch Bank, Monarch Mortgage, Monarch Capital, Monarch Investment, and OBXBank. With about 10 offices, Monarch Bank offers standard services, including savings and checking accounts, IRAs, and CDS. Bank subsidiary Monarch Mortgage, formed in 2007, has about a dozen offices. Other divisions sell insurance, title, and investment products. Single-family mortgages make up the largest portion of the company's loan portfolio, which also includes commercial, construction, and land development loans. Monarch Bank division OBX Bank operates in North Carolina's Outer Banks area.

EXECUTIVES

Chairman, Jeffrey F. Benson, age 49, $13,715 total compensation
President, Real Estate and Construction, James R. (Jim) Ferber, age 54
President OBX Bank, David McGlaughon, age 53
President and CEO, Monarch Mortgage, Edward O. Yoder, age 45, $294,782 total compensation
President, Monarch Bank, Norfolk, Donald F. Price
President, Monarch Bank, Virginia Beach Region, W. Craig Reilly, age 35
President, Virginia Asset Group, Darin M. Ely, age 39
President, Chesapeake, Barry A. Mathias, age 61
President, CEO, and Director, William F. (Bill) Rountree Jr., age 67, $542,180 total compensation
President, Monarch Bank and Director, E. Neal Crawford, age 48
EVP, COO, CFO, Secretary, and Director; CEO, Monarch Bank, Brad E. Schwartz, age 48, $270,684 total compensation
EVP and Senior Operations Officer, Barbara N. Lane, age 61
EVP and COO, Monarch Mortgage, William T. Morrison, age 48
Vice Chairman, Lawton H. Baker, age 67, $9,775 total compensation
SVP and Chief Accounting Officer; SVP and CFO, Monarch Bank, Lynette P. Harris
SVP and Chief Credit Officer, Andrew N. Lock, age 47
SVP Marketing, Nancy B. Porter, age 42
SVP Monarch Bank, Virginia Beach and Director Monarch Capital, Norfolk, Charles M. (Chas) Wright
SVP Monarch Bank, Norfolk, Robert L. (Bob) White
SVP, Monarch Bank, R. Craig Baker
Auditors: Goodman & Company, L.L.P.

LOCATIONS

HQ: Monarch Financial Holdings, Inc.
1101 Executive Blvd., Chesapeake, VA 23320
Phone: 757-389-5159   **Fax:** 757-222-2101
Web: www.monarchbank.com

PRODUCTS/OPERATIONS

2009 Gross Revenues

	$ mil.	% of total
Interest		
Loans, including fees	32.2	47
Securities & other	0.3	-
Noninterest		
Mortgage banking	32.5	48
Service charges & fees	1.5	2
Other	1.7	3
Total	**68.2**	**100**

COMPETITORS

Bank of America	Hampton Roads
BB&T	Bankshares
Commonwealth	RBC Bank
Bankshares	SunTrust

HISTORICAL FINANCIALS

Company Type: Public

Income Statement

FYE: December 31

	ASSETS ($ mil.)	NET INCOME ($ mil.)	INCOME AS % OF ASSETS	EMPLOYEES
12/10	825.6	5.9	0.7%	527
12/09	689.6	4.9	0.7%	432
12/08	597.2	1.1	0.2%	295
12/07	503.2	3.2	0.6%	254
12/06	407.7	3.6	0.9%	126
Annual Growth	**19.3%**	**13.1%**	**—**	**43.0%**

2010 Year-End Financials

Equity as % of assets: 8.67%
Return on assets: 0.7%
Return on equity: 8.8%
Long-term debt ($ mil.): 30.3
No. of shares (mil.): 6.0

Dividends
Yield: 1.8%
Payout: 18.7%
Market value ($ mil.): 46.6
Sales ($ mil.): 92.8

	STOCK PRICE ($) FY Close	P/E High/Low		PER SHARE ($) Earnings	Dividends	Book Value
12/10	7.80	12	8	0.75	0.14	11.99
12/09	6.10	14	6	0.66	0.00	11.58
12/08	6.75	54	30	0.21	0.00	10.51
12/07	9.50	29	15	0.63	0.00	7.61
12/06	17.50	23	14	0.87	0.00	8.39
Annual Growth	**(18.3%)**	**—**	**—**	**(3.6%)**	**—**	**9.3%**

Moro

More is more for Moro Corporation. The industrial holding company owns a group of businesses that provide a range of materials and services for the commercial construction industry. Its J.M. Ahle, J&J Sheet Metal, and Whaling City Iron subsidiaries fabricate and distribute sheet metal products, and reinforcing and structural steel, in addition to other construction accessories. Titchener Iron Works specializes in architectural and ornamental metal. Its Rado Enterprises and Appolo Heating units provide plumbing and HVAC services, while Rondout Electric provides electrical contracting services. Chairman and CEO David Menard owns the majority of the company.

EXECUTIVES

Chairman, President, CEO, and CFO, David W. Menard, age 73
President, J.M. Ahle, John Ahle
President, Appolo Heating, Tom Drake
President, J and J Sheet Metal, Mike Azersky
VP and Director, Lawrence J. Corr, age 68
VP and General Manager, Rado, David Zeitler
General Manager, Whaling City Iron Co., Peterson Glenn
Auditors: McGladrey & Pullen, LLP

LOCATIONS

HQ: Moro Corporation
994 Old Eagle School Rd., Ste. 1000, Wayne, PA 19087
Phone: 484-367-0300   **Fax:** 484-367-0305
Web: www.morocorp.com

COMPETITORS

Canam Steel Corporation	Kreider Corporation
Gerdau Ameristeel	Metcam
Hirschfeld	United McGill

HISTORICAL FINANCIALS

Company Type: Public

Income Statement

FYE: December 31

	REVENUE ($ mil.)	NET INCOME ($ mil.)	NET PROFIT MARGIN	EMPLOYEES
12/03	23.1	0.4	1.7%	67
12/02	14.6	0.4	2.7%	68
12/01	10.9	0.5	4.6%	22
12/00	7.7	0.3	3.9%	17
Annual Growth	**44.2%**	**10.1%**	**—**	**58.0%**

2003 Year-End Financials

Debt ratio: 69.9%
Return on equity: 16.5%
Cash ($ mil.): 0.4
Current ratio: 1.72
Long-term debt ($ mil.): 1.6

No. of shares (mil.): —
Dividends
Yield: —
Payout: —
Market value ($ mil.): —

	STOCK PRICE ($) FY Close	P/E High/Low		PER SHARE ($) Earnings	Dividends	Book Value
12/03	0.44	13	4	0.06	0.00	(0.00)
12/02	0.41	15	5	0.07	0.00	(0.00)
12/01	0.40	10	3	0.09	0.00	(0.00)
12/00	0.35	1400	1	0.06	0.00	(0.00)
Annual Growth	**7.9%**	**—**	**—**	**(0.0%)**	**—**	**—**

MSCI

You ask your asset manager how your portfolio is doing, but who does he ask? Probably MSCI. The company, formerly Morgan Stanley Capital International, manages more than 145,000 daily equity, fixed income, and hedge fund indices for use by large asset management firms. MSCI is organized through two business segments. Its Performance and Risk business provides equity indices, portfolio risk and performance analytics, credit analytics, and environmental, social and governance (ESG) products under brands such as MSCI, RiskMetrics, and Barra. Its Governance business provides corporate governance and specialized financial research and analysis. All total, MSCI has about 5,800 clients across some 78 countries.

The company's indices act as benchmarks that measure the performance of global funds. Institutional investors use the indices as research tools, and as the basis for their various investment vehicles. MSCI makes the majority of its revenues (more than 80%) from annual, recurring subscriptions to its products. The company has consistantly achieved revenue growth and positive earnings by continually expanding its relationships with investment institutions and regularly developing and enhancing its products. It has also made key acquisitions in order to complement or expand its client base and offerings.

In 2010 MSCI made a significant purchase with the acquisition of rival RiskMetrics Group through a cash and stock transaction valued at approximately $1.5 billion. The deal united two risk management market leaders. The purchase enhanced MSCI's ability to provide investment decision support tools and widened its geographical reach. It also strengthened its customer base, adding RiskMetrics' 3,500 clients, including several of the largest asset managers, mutual funds, and hedge funds.

Nearly half of the company's revenues come from outside the Americas. All total, it has more than 30 offices in nearly 20 countries worldwide, including headquarters in New York, and sales offices in San Francisco, Chicago, and S o Paulo, Brazil. As part of its global expansion efforts, in the last few years MSCI has opened international offices in Budapest, Dubai, Monterrey, Mumbai, and Shanghai.

MSCI was formerly owned by financial services powerhouse Morgan Stanley, which began spinning off the business in 2007. MSCI became an independent, stand-alone public company 2009. Morgan Staley maintains an 8% share in the firm.

EXECUTIVES

Chairman, Michael H. Hoffman
CFO, David M. Obstler, age 50
President, CEO, and Director, Henry A. Fernandez, age 53, $12,069,762 total compensation
COO, David C. Brierwood
Head Strategy and Business Development and Chief Administrative Officer, Gary Retelny, $2,936,016 total compensation
Investor Relations, Lisa Monaco
Head Client Coverage, C.D. Baer Pettit, $3,746,385 total compensation
Auditors: Deloitte & Touche LLP

LOCATIONS

HQ: MSCI Inc.
One Chase Manhattan Plaza, 44th Fl., New York, NY 10005
Phone: 212-804-3900   **Fax:** 212-804-2919
Web: www.msci.com

2010 Sales

	$ mil.	% of total
Americas	353.3	57
Europe, Middle East & Africa	215.1	35
Asia & Australia	94.5	15
Total	**622.9**	**100**

PRODUCTS/OPERATIONS

2010 Sales

	$ mil.	% of total
Index and ESG	330.4	50
Risk management analytics	134.5	20
Portfolio management analytics	123.2	18
Governance	58.6	9
Energy & commodity analytics	16.2	2
Total	**662.9**	**100**

Selected Offerings

Barra (equity and multi-asset class portfolio analytics product)
CFRA (forensic accounting risk research, legal/regulatory risk assessment, due-diligence and educational services)
FEA (entergy and commodity asset valuation analytics)
ISS (governance research and outsourced proxy voting and reporting services)
MSCI Indices (flagship global equity indices)
RiskMetrics (risk and wealth management products)

COMPETITORS

Algorithmics	FTSE Group
Deutsche Börse	Nomura Securities
Dow Jones	Russell
FactSet	S&P

HISTORICAL FINANCIALS

Company Type: Public

Income Statement

FYE: December 31

	REVENUE ($ mil.)	NET INCOME ($ mil.)	NET PROFIT MARGIN	EMPLOYEES
11/10	662.9	92.2	13.9%	2,077
11/09	442.9	81.8	18.5%	878
11/08	431.0	68.3	15.8%	887
11/07	369.9	81.1	21.9%	681
11/06	310.7	71.4	23.0%	705
Annual Growth	**20.9%**	**6.6%**	**—**	**31.0%**

2010 Year-End Financials

Debt ratio: 111.8%   No. of shares (mil.): 119.5
Return on equity: 8.5%   Dividends
Cash ($ mil.): 226.6   Yield: —
Current ratio: 1.15   Payout: —
Long-term debt ($ mil.): 1,207.9 Market value ($ mil.): 4,070.9

	STOCK PRICE ($) FY Close	P/E High/Low		PER SHARE ($) Earnings	Dividends	Book Value
11/10	34.06	48	33	0.81	0.00	9.04
11/09	30.47	43	16	0.80	0.00	4.84
11/08	15.43	57	17	0.67	0.00	2.86
11/07	27.65	42	22	0.96	0.00	2.04
Annual Growth	**7.2%**	**—**	**—**	**(5.5%)**	**—**	**64.2%**

Multiband

Multiband Corporation (formerly Vicom) has found a singular purpose: providing satellite TV and telecom services to multidwelling units (MDUs) such as apartment complexes and time-share resorts. The company operates through two divisions. Its Minnesota Digital Universe unit is an exclusive DIRECTV Master System Operator providing direct broadcast satellite TV services to MDUs including apartments, lodging and hospitality facilities, and restaurants. The company's Multi-

band Consumer Services division offers voice, data, and video services to MDUs.

In 2011 Multiband bought WPCS International, which designs, engineers, and installs wireless and specialty communications systems. The acquisition expands Multiband's service offerings and add about $100 million in annual revenues. The deal is valued at around $22 million.

The company in 2009 acquired an 80% stake in DirecTECH Holding, a Kentucky-based provider of DIRECTV service in 32 cities, for $41 million. The deal expanded Multiband's service area and customer base. It bought the remaining 20% later that year.

EXECUTIVES

Chairman, Donald (Don) Miller, age 71
President, CFO, General Counsel, and Director, Steven M. (Steve) Bell, age 52, $231,537 total compensation
CEO and Director, James L. (Jim) Mandel, age 57, $438,713 total compensation
CIO, David (Dave) Ekman, age 48, $162,947 total compensation
Customer Service Director, Kevin Braaten
Auditors: Virchow, Krause & Company, LLP

LOCATIONS

HQ: Multiband Corporation
9449 Science Center Dr., New Hope, MN 55428
Phone: 763-504-3000   **Fax:** 763-504-3060
Web: https://www.multibandusa.com

COMPETITORS

AOL	Sprint Nextel
AT&T	Time Warner Cable
AT&T Mobility	tw telecom
Comcast	United Online
DISH Network	Verizon

HISTORICAL FINANCIALS

Company Type: Public

Income Statement

FYE: December 31

	REVENUE ($ mil.)	NET INCOME ($ mil.)	NET PROFIT MARGIN	EMPLOYEES
12/10	265.6	14.7	5.5%	3,202
12/09	269.0	(9.6)	—	2,849
12/08	43.0	0.9	2.1%	3,962
12/07	15.1	(6.1)	—	83
12/06	18.1	(10.2)	—	88
Annual Growth	**95.7%**	**—**		**145.6%**

2010 Year-End Financials

Debt ratio: 683.9%   No. of shares (mil.): 10.3
Return on equity: 289.3%   Dividends
Cash ($ mil.): 1.2   Yield: —
Current ratio: 0.77   Payout: —
Long-term debt ($ mil.): 34.7 Market value ($ mil.): 29.3

	STOCK PRICE ($) FY Close	P/E High/Low		PER SHARE ($) Earnings	Dividends	Book Value
12/10	2.84	3	1	0.92	0.00	1.96
12/09	2.00	—	—	(1.04)	0.00	0.52
12/08	1.19	—	—	(0.34)	0.00	19.30
12/07	2.71	—	—	(1.16)	0.00	0.09
12/06	2.85	—	—	(2.10)	0.00	0.81
Annual Growth	**(0.1%)**	**—**	**—**	**—**	**—**	**24.9%**

MV Oil Trust

Call it what you will, black gold, Texas tea, or the black blood of the earth, MV Oil Trust is wringing out the value from each drop and distributing it to shareholders. MV Oil Trust receives royalty interests from the mature oil and gas properties of MV Partners located in Kansas and Colorado. The properties have proved reserves of 9.5 million barrels of oil from 922 net wells. The trust receives royalties based on the amount of oil (and gas) produced and sold and then distributes virtually all of the proceeds to shareholders on a regular basis. MV Partners, a private company engaged in the exploration, production, gathering, aggregation, and sale of oil and natural gas, has the rights to 80% of net proceeds.

EXECUTIVES

VP and Trust Officer; The Bank of New York Trust Company, Trustee, Michael J. (Mike) Ulrich
Auditors: Grant Thornton LLP

LOCATIONS

HQ: MV Oil Trust
Global Corporate Trust, 919 Congress, Austin, TX 78701
Phone:

COMPETITORS

Cross Timbers Royalty Trust	Mesa Royalty Trust
	Panhandle Oil and Gas
Hugoton Royalty Trust	Sabine Royalty Trust
LL&E Royalty Trust	San Juan Basin

HISTORICAL FINANCIALS

Company Type: Public

Income Statement

FYE: December 31

	REVENUE ($ mil.)	NET INCOME ($ mil.)	NET PROFIT MARGIN	EMPLOYEES
12/10	32.5	31.7	97.5%	0
12/09	19.0	17.9	94.2%	0
12/08	21.4	20.8	97.2%	0
12/07	33.6	32.9	97.9%	0
12/05	36.0	17.2	47.8%	20
Annual Growth	(2.0%)	13.0%	—	—

2010 Year-End Financials

Debt ratio: —	No. of shares (mil.): 11.5
Return on equity: 87.7%	Dividends
Cash ($ mil.): 0.1	Yield: 6.9%
Current ratio: —	Payout: 100.0%
Long-term debt ($ mil.): —	Market value ($ mil.): 458.5

	STOCK PRICE ($) FY Close	P/E High/Low		PER SHARE ($) Earnings	Dividends	Book Value
12/10	39.87	15	7	2.76	2.76	3.14
12/09	20.20	13	5	1.56	1.56	3.43
12/08	7.85	16	4	1.81	1.81	(0.00)
12/07	24.64	10	7	2.86	2.86	(0.00)
Annual Growth	17.4%	—	—	(1.2%)	(1.2%)	—

MWI Veterinary Supply

It could stand for Mastiff, Weimaraner, and Irish Setter, but MWI Veterinary Supply is actually named after founder and veterinarian Millard Wallace Ickes. The veterinary products distributor supplies drugs, diagnostics, equipment, and other medical supplies for companion animals and livestock. It serves veterinary practices from about a dozen distribution centers across the US and in the UK. The firm offers 30,000 products from more than 500 vendors. In addition to medical supplies and equipment, MWI distributes pet food and nutritional products. The company, in business since 1976, offers customers online ordering, tools to manage inventory, consultation for equipment, and pet cremation services.

MWI publishes product catalogs and monthly magazines which are often used by customers as reference tools for ordering. While a robust sales force and roster of printed materials are vital to its marketing strategy, online ordering is becoming a significant sales channel, generating about 35% of MWI's product sales in 2010 (up from about 30% in 2009).

MWI has hundreds of sales and marketing representatives serving its clients. Its largest customers are Medical Management International (known as Banfield, the nation's largest private veterinary practice with about 750 vet hospitals), and Feeders' Advantage, a buying group formed by feedlot operators.

About 95% of MWI's product sales are from the sale of pharmaceuticals and supplies to veterinary practices (the rest from commissions and sales to parties other than veterinary practices). Pharmaceuticals account for 40% of its revenue and typically include anesthetics, analgesics, antibiotics, opthalmics, and hormones. Vaccines are MWI's second biggest earner, bringing in about 20% of its income, and are mostly composed of small animal, equine, and production animal biologicals. Its parasiticides (roughly 10% of annual sales) are used to get rid of fleas, ticks, flies, mosquitoes, and internal parasites.

MWI's other products range from capital equipment such as surgical monitors, dental machines, and x-ray machines to veterinary pet food and nutritional products that include premium pet foods, dietary supplements, vitamins, and specialty treats. The company does not manufacture the vast majority of its products, instead it relies on suppliers that include Pfizer, Boehringer Ingelheim, Merial, and Fort Dodge Animal Health. Products from its ten largest vendors account for about 70% of its sales. Pfizer is MWI's single biggest supplier, providing products that account for about one quarter of MWI's sales.

MWI grows, in part, by acquiring regional suppliers. Since the market for animal health products distribution is highly fragmented, there are plenty of national, regional, and local distributors that make attractive candidates for MWI to purchase and absorb into its own operations. For instance, in 2011 it acquired distributor Micro Beef Technologies, a distributor of production animal health products, for some $60 million. The purchase helped to expand MWI'S distribution network and management systems products.

Though the company makes the majority of its sales in the US, it is also looking to make acquisitions outside the country to increase its global footprint. It made one such acquisition in 2010

when it purchased Centaur Services, a UK-based supplier of animal health products.

In addition, MWI has widened its geographic presence by expanding or constructing new distribution centers; it operates about a dozen facilities in the US and one in the UK. Areas targeted for growth include the Northeastern, Midwestern, and Southeastern regions of the US.

The company also captures new customers by offering improved technology systems (its e-commerce platform, for example) and by increasing the numbers of sales and customer service representatives available to its potential and existing clients. Acquisitions also enhance the firm's technology offerings: Its purchase of Micro Beef Technologies adds computerized management systems for the production animal market.

MWI became an independent company in 2002 when venture capital firm Bruckmann, Rosser, Sherrill & Co. bought the firm from Agri Beef Co. Bruckmann, Rosser, Sherrill & Co. gradually sold off its shares in MWI, while Agri Beef retains a small minority (about 4%) stake of the publicly traded company. The majority shareholder in MWI is investment manager Neuberger Berman with about 12%. CEO James Cleary also serves on the board of directors and holds about 2% of MWI's shares.

EXECUTIVES

Chairman, John F. McNamara, age 75
President, CEO, and Director, James F. (Jim) Cleary Jr., age 47, $639,918 total compensation
VP Marketing, John R. Ryan, age 42
VP Operations, Bryan P. Mooney, age 43
VP and General Manager, Specialty Resource Group, John J. Francis, age 57, $300,710 total compensation
VP Sales, Jeffrey J. Danielson, age 51, $271,144 total compensation
VP and CIO, James S. Hay, age 68, $226,628 total compensation
VP Inventory Management, James W. Culpepper, age 57
Sales, Southeast Region, Bob Weinschenk
Sales, Great Lakes Region, Terry Walsh
Sales, Gulf States Region, Dianne Gallagher
Sales, Southwest Region, Jeff Hicks
Sales, Northeast Region, George White
Sales, Rocky Mountain Region, Steve Fitzjames
SVP Finance and Administration and CFO, Mary Patricia B. Thompson, age 48, $344,381 total compensation
Sales, Northwest Region, Jim Niple
Sales, California Region, Susan Donnelly
Sales, Central States Region, Eric Scott
Auditors: Deloitte & Touche LLP

LOCATIONS

HQ: MWI Veterinary Supply, Inc.
651 S. Stratford Dr., Ste. 100, Meridian, ID 83642
Phone: 208-955-8930   **Fax:** 208-955-8902
Web: www.mwivet.com

2010 Sales by Region

	$ mil.	% of total
US	1,074.2	87
UK	155.1	13
Total	**1,229.3**	**100**

PRODUCTS/OPERATIONS

2010 Sales

	$ mil.	% of total
Product sales	1,169.5	95
Related party product sales	43.0	4
Commissions	16.8	1
Total	**1,229.3**	**100**

2010 Product Sales

	% of total
Pharmaceuticals	40
Vaccines	18
Parasiticide	11
Diagnostic	8
Capital equipment	2
Other supplies	21
Total	**100**

Selected Products

Analgesics
Anesthesia machines
Anesthetics
Antibiotics
Bandages
Cages
Dental machines
Dietary supplements
Feline leukemia diagnostics
Grooming materials
Heartworm diagnostics
Hormones
Lyme diagnostics
Ophthalmics
Parasiticides
Parvovirus diagnostics
Premium pet foods
Specialty treats
Surgical monitors
Syringes
X-ray machines
Vaccines
Vitamins

COMPETITORS

A.C. Graham	Merck Animal Health
Central Garden & Pet	Patterson Companies
Darby Dental	PetMed
FarmVet	Professional
Henry Schein	Veterinary Product
IVESCO	The Harvard Drug Group
Lambriar Animal Health	TW Medical

HISTORICAL FINANCIALS

Company Type: Public

Income Statement

FYE: September 30

	REVENUE ($ mil.)	NET INCOME ($ mil.)	NET PROFIT MARGIN	EMPLOYEES
09/10	1,229.3	33.4	2.7%	1,179
09/09	941.3	24.9	2.6%	887
09/08	831.4	19.9	2.4%	881
09/07	710.1	16.9	2.4%	800
09/06	606.2	13.8	2.3%	719
Annual Growth	**19.3%**	**24.7%**	**—**	**13.2%**

2010 Year-End Financials

Debt ratio: 0.4%	No. of shares (mil.): 12.5
Return on equity: 13.6%	Dividends
Cash ($ mil.): 0.9	Yield: —
Current ratio: 1.77	Payout: —
Long-term debt ($ mil.): 1.0	Market value ($ mil.): 719.0

	STOCK PRICE ($) FY Close	P/E High/Low		PER SHARE ($) Earnings	Dividends	Book Value
09/10	57.72	22	13	2.70	0.00	19.81
09/09	39.95	21	10	2.02	0.00	17.05
09/08	39.29	28	20	1.62	0.00	15.02
09/07	37.75	31	21	1.40	0.00	13.32
09/06	33.53	31	16	1.25	0.00	11.24
Annual Growth	**14.5%**	**—**	**—**	**21.2%**	**—**	**15.2%**

Nanometrics

Makers of precision electronics that need their goods to measure up know that Nanometrics works on a nano scale. The company provides thin-film metrology and inspection systems used by makers of precision electronic gear. These stand-alone, integrated, and tabletop measurement devices gauge the thickness and consistency of film materials used in making semiconductors, magnetic recording heads, and flat-panel displays. Customers include Applied Materials, Hitachi, Hynix Semiconductor, Samsung Electronics, SMIC, and Toshiba Semiconductor. Nanometrics gets around two-thirds of its sales outside the US.

Metrology in the high-tech field is an expensive proposition, and Nanometrics regularly spends about 15% of annual sales on R&D. Having the most advanced and competitive equipment on the market doesn't do much good if customers aren't buying metrology systems, however. The weak global economy, tight credit markets, and continuing turmoil in the financial markets affect many of the company's customers. Nanometrics also is hampered by having a limited number of potential customers. Many of the company's competitors are larger and have greater financial resources, although almost all of those suppliers similarly are seeing lower sales and profits due to the prolonged semiconductor industry downturn. Many competitors are operating in the red, as well. Nanometrics hasn't made a profit on an annual basis since 2005, and it has an accumulated deficit of nearly $97 million as a result. The company reduced its headcount by about 11% during 2008.

Despite the difficulties of the past decade, through pronounced boom-and-bust periods in the semiconductor industry, Nanometrics remains active in acquisitions, although purchasing outside businesses and technologies always carries a multitude of risks. Expanding its portfolio of metrology products in 2008, the company acquired the assets of Tevet Process Control Technologies, a supplier of integrated metrology systems for manufacturing semiconductors and solar cells, for about $3.5 million.

In 2006 Nanometrics acquired Accent Optical Technologies, a supplier of semiconductor process control and metrology equipment, for around $81 million in stock and assumed debt. Following the merger, previous Nanometrics shareholders owned approximately 73% of the combined company and Accent Optical shareholders owned about 27%. Also that year the company acquired Soluris, a supplier of overlay and critical-dimension measurement equipment, for $7 million in cash.

The following year Nanometrics sold two product lines picked up in those two acquisitions. The DiVA instrument line, previously acquired by Accent Optical, was sold to Auriga Measurement Sys-

tems of the US. The Yosemite metrology system, previously developed by Soluris, was sold to SNU Precision of South Korea. Nanometrics decided those products were not core to its product strategy, concluding that DiVA was a mature product (posting annual sales of less than $1 million) with no technical synergy with the metrology equipment business, and development of Yosemite had ceased following the acquisition of Soluris, since the product serves a market outside of Nanometrics' product focus.

The company signed a merger agreement with August Technology, a supplier of semiconductor inspection equipment, in 2005. Rival Rudolph Technologies prevailed with a higher bid for August Technology, however. August Technology and Nanometrics later terminated their merger agreement. August paid Nanometrics a termination fee of $8.3 million, plus $2.6 million in reimbursed expenses, as a result. Also that year Nanometrics sold its flat-panel display equipment business unit to Toho Technology.

Nanometrics is mixing it up with competitors in the courtroom, as well as in the global market for metrology systems. The company was defending itself against patent infringement lawsuits by KLA-Tencor and Nova Measuring Instruments, and filed a countersuit against Nova. In 2007 Nanometrics and Nova reached a legal settlement of all patent claims, with the companies dismissing all three pending lawsuits between them and agreeing not to sue each other on any patent for one year.

Founder and vice chairman Vincent Coates owns about 18% of Nanometrics.

EXECUTIVES

Chairman, Bruce C. Rhine, age 53
President, CEO, and Director, Timothy J. (Tim) Stultz, age 63, $999,479 total compensation
CFO, Ronald W. (Ron) Kisling
VP Applications, Nagesh Avadhany
COO, Bruce A. Crawford, age 58, $673,451 total compensation
Press Contact, Kevin Heidrich
Auditors: BDO Seidman, LLP

LOCATIONS

HQ: Nanometrics Incorporated
1550 Buckeye Dr., Milpitas, CA 95035-7418
Phone: 408-435-9600   **Fax:** 408-232-5910
Web: www.nanometrics.com Nanometrics has operations in China, France, Italy, Japan, Singapore, South Korea, Taiwan, the UK, and the US.

2008 Sales

	$ mil.	% of total
US	30.1	29
Asia/Pacific		
Japan	28.6	28
South Korea	20.9	21
China	7.5	7
Taiwan	5.9	6
Europe	5.3	5
Other regions	3.8	4
Total	**102.1**	**100**

PRODUCTS/OPERATIONS

2008 Sales

	$ mil.	% of total
Products		
Automated metrology	40.6	40
Materials characterization	19.0	18
Integrated systems	16.0	16
Service	26.5	26
Total	**102.1**	**100**

Selected Products

Non-contact thin-film metrology systems (NanoSpec)
- Automated systems
- Integrated systems
- Tabletop systems

Overlay metrology and CD measurement systems (Metra and NanoOCS)

COMPETITORS

Applied Materials	Nova Measuring
ASM International	Qcept Technologies
Bio-Rad Labs	Rudolph Technologies
Dainippon Screen	Tokyo Electron
KLA-Tencor	Zygo
Metara	

HISTORICAL FINANCIALS

Company Type: Public

Income Statement

FYE: December 31

	REVENUE ($ mil.)	NET INCOME ($ mil.)	NET PROFIT MARGIN	EMPLOYEES
12/10	188.1	55.9	29.7%	456
12/09	76.7	(16.3)	—	399
12/08	102.1	(82.7)	—	465
12/07	146.3	(4.0)	—	523
12/06	96.4	(22.1)	—	522
Annual Growth	18.2%	—	—	(3.3%)

2010 Year-End Financials

Debt ratio: 5.5%
Return on equity: 32.7%
Cash ($ mil.): 66.5
Current ratio: 5.18
Long-term debt ($ mil.): 9.5
No. of shares (mil.): 22.2
Dividends
Yield: —
Payout: —
Market value ($ mil.): 285.1

	STOCK PRICE ($) FY Close	P/E High/Low		PER SHARE ($) Earnings	Dividends	Book Value
12/10	12.83	7	3	2.43	0.00	7.69
12/09	11.33	—	—	(0.87)	0.00	5.73
12/08	1.14	—	—	(4.46)	0.00	5.07
12/07	9.86	—	—	(0.22)	0.00	9.43
12/06	7.91	—	—	(1.47)	0.00	9.67
Annual Growth	12.9%	—	—	—	—	(5.6%)

National American University

National American University Holdings believes in the power of continuing education. Through subsidiary Dlorah, the for-profit company owns National American University (NAU), which has more than 20 campuses in eight states and offers classes online. Some locations are considered hybrids, offering both in-class and online courses. Targeting working adults and other non-traditional students, NAU offers associate's, bachelor's, and master's degrees, as well as certification in business, criminal justice, and health care disciplines. The university was founded in 1941 as the National School of Business, the holding company, which was formed in 2007 to acquire an education company, purchased Dlorah in 2009.

Though educating its nearly 9,000 students makes up the bulk of National American University Holdings' revenues, the company also operates in real estate. It owns apartment and condominium complexes in South Dakota.

NAU also offers its programs overseas through collaborations with foreign colleges and universities. Alumni include more than 1,400 graduates from Chile, Bolivia, the United Arab Emirates, and Greece. The company is pursuing similar opportunities in other countries, mostly in Eastern Europe, Asia, and the Middle East. Domestic targets for growth include expanded course offerings, additional hybrid centers, and acquisitions.

The Buckingham family, including chairman Robert Buckingham, owns more than 50% of the company.

EXECUTIVES

Chairman, Robert D. Buckingham
CEO and CFO, Ronald L. Shape, age 43
President of NAU, Distance Learning, Robert A. Paxton, age 54
President, Real Estate Operations, Michael Buckingham, age 52
CFO of NAU, Venessa D. Green, age 37
President and Director, Jerry L. Gallentine
VP, Institutional Support and Military Services, Scott E. Toothman, age 58
Regional President of NAU, Southwest, Lisa L. Knigge, age 48
Regional President of NAU, East and Southeast, Michaelle J. Holland, age 46
Provost, Secretary and General Counsel, Samuel D. Kerr, age 50
Auditors: Deloitte & Touche LLP

LOCATIONS

HQ: National American University Holdings, Inc.
5301 S. Hwy 16, Ste. 200, Rapid City, SD 57701
Phone: 605-721-5200   **Fax:** 605-721-5241
Web: www.national.edu

Selected Locations

Colorado
- Colorado Springs (2)
- Denver

Kansas
- Overland Park
- Wichita

Minnesota
- Bloomington
- Brooklyn Center
- Roseville
- Minnetonka

Missouri
- Independence
- Lee's Summit
- Zona Rosa

New Mexico
- Albuquerque
- Rio Rancho

South Dakota
- Ellsworth AFB
- Rapid City
- Sioux Falls
- Watertown

Texas
- Allen (online only)
- Austin

PRODUCTS/OPERATIONS

2010 Sales

	$ mil.	% of total
NAU		
Academic	82.5	92
Auxiliary (foodservice, bookstores, dorms)	5.5	6
Real estate		
Apartment rentals	.9	1
Condominium sales	.9	1
Total	**89.8**	**100**

COMPETITORS

Apollo Group	ITT Educational
Bridgepoint Education	Kaplan
Capella Education	Laureate Education
Career Education	Lincoln Educational
Corinthian Colleges	Services
DeVry	Strayer Education

HISTORICAL FINANCIALS

Company Type: Public

Income Statement

FYE: May 31

	REVENUE ($ mil.)	NET INCOME ($ mil.)	NET PROFIT MARGIN	EMPLOYEES
05/11	106.8	10.3	9.6%	1,200
05/10	89.8	10.0	11.1%	1,202
05/09*	62.6	3.1	5.0%	0
12/08	0.0	0.3	—	0
05/08	49.5	(0.4)	—	0
Annual Growth	29.2%	—	—	(0.2%)

*Fiscal year change

2011 Year-End Financials

Debt ratio: —
Return on equity: 17.5%
Cash ($ mil.): 25.7
Current ratio: 4.19
Long-term debt ($ mil.): —
No. of shares (mil.): 26.5
Dividends
Yield: 1.2%
Payout: 23.0%
Market value ($ mil.): 199.9

	STOCK PRICE ($) FY Close	P/E High/Low		PER SHARE ($) Earnings	Dividends	Book Value
05/11	7.53	28	12	0.38	0.09	2.21
05/10	9.00	4	2	3.23	0.03	0.99
Annual Growth	(16.3%)	—	—	(88.2%)	200.0%	123.1%

National Western

National Western Life Insurance sells life insurance and annuity products including individual, universal, whole, and term plans. The company operates throughout the US, except in New York, and internationally in Central and South America, the Caribbean, Eastern Europe, Asia, and the Pacific Rim. Annuities, sold by independent agents, make up most of its US sales. Some two-thirds of its life insurance premiums come from outside the US, where the company targets wealthy individuals. Investments, mainly in fixed income securities, account for 70% of revenues. CEO Robert Moody, (a member of the powerful Moody family of Galveston, Texas) owns one-third of the company and effectively controls its board of directors.

EXECUTIVES

Chairman and CEO, Robert L. Moody Sr., age 75, $3,136,353 total compensation
President, COO, and Director, Ross R. Moody, age 48
VP Information Technology, Allison G. Hasselmeier Jr.
VP Marketing, Charles S. Blundo
VP Valuation Actuary, Kitty S. Kennedy
VP International Life Underwriting, Carlos A. Martinez
VP Policy Benefits, Doris N. M. Kruse
VP Domestic life Underwritng, John Ptaszynski
VP Marketing, Gary L. Fischer
VP, Controller, and Assistant Treasurer, Thomas F. Kopetic, age 51

VP Policyowner Services, Larry D. White
VP Marketing, Paul T. Garofoli
VP Policyowner Services, Jo N. Morris
VP Human Resources, Linda G. Wishard
VP and Associate Actuary, Mark. D. Gulas
VP Actuarial Services, Sean L. Mcintosh
SVP and Chief Actuary, Paul D. Facey, age 59
SVP and Chief Investment Officer, Patricia L. Scheuer, age 59
SVP and Chief Marketing Officer, S. Christopher Johnson, age 42
SVP and Secretary, James P. Payne, age 66
SVP and CIO, Michael P. Hydanus, age 59
SVP, CFO, and Treasurer, Brian M. Pribyl, age 52, $351,223 total compensation
SVP Mortgage Loan and Real Estate, and Director, Charles D. Milos Jr., age 65
SVP, International Marketing, Scott E Arendale, age 66, $507,374 total compensation
Auditors: KPMG LLP

LOCATIONS

HQ: National Western Life Insurance Company
850 E. Anderson Ln., Austin, TX 78752-1602
Phone: 512-836-1010   **Fax:** 512-835-2729
Web: www.nationalwesternlife.com

2010 Premium Revenues & Deposits

	% of total
US	
Annuities	85
Life insurance	3
Other countries	
Life insurance	9
Annuities	3
Total	**100**

PRODUCTS/OPERATIONS

2010 Revenues

	$ mil.	% of total
Investment income	401.4	70
Universal life & annuity contract revenues	127.2	22
Life & annuity premiums	16.5	3
Other income	25.4	4
Gains on investments	5.5	1
Total	**576.0**	**100**

2010 Investment Income

	$ mil.	% of total
Debt securities	363.5	90
Derivative gains	16.6	4
Mortgage loans	9.2	2
Policy loans	5.4	2
Money market investments	0.6	-
Other & adjustment	8.5	2
Investment expenses	(2.4)	-
Total	**401.4**	**100**

COMPETITORS

Allstate	Lincoln Benefit Life
American Equity Life	Lincoln Life
American Fidelity	Old Mutual (US)
Assurance Company	Pan-American Life
Aviva	Presidential Life
BMI Financial Group	Sammons Financial
Citizens, Inc.	Securian Financial
FBL Financial	

HISTORICAL FINANCIALS

Income Statement

FYE: December 31

	ASSETS ($ mil.)	NET INCOME ($ mil.)	INCOME AS % OF ASSETS	EMPLOYEES
12/10	8,773.9	72.9	0.8%	292
12/09	7,518.7	45.5	0.6%	294
12/08	6,786.5	33.6	0.5%	296
12/07	6,835.3	85.4	1.2%	290
12/06	6,693.4	76.3	1.1%	273
Annual Growth	**7.0%**	**(1.1%)**	**—**	**1.7%**

2010 Year-End Financials

Equity as % of assets: 13.89%
Return on assets: 0.8%
Return on equity: 6.0%
Long-term debt ($ mil.): —
No. of shares (mil.): 3.6

Dividends
Yield: 0.2%
Payout: 1.8%
Market value ($ mil.): 605.1
Sales ($ mil.): 576.0

	STOCK PRICE ($) FY Close	P/E High/Low		PER SHARE ($) Earnings	Dividends	Book Value
12/10	166.72	10	6	20.09	0.36	335.83
12/09	173.62	15	4	12.87	0.36	307.24
12/08	169.17	29	11	9.48	0.36	271.99
12/07	207.37	11	8	23.95	0.36	279.29
12/06	230.14	12	10	20.88	0.00	257.67
Annual Growth	**(7.7%)**	**—**	**—**	**(1.0%)**	**—**	**6.8%**

NCI

NCI takes pride in information technology. The company, through its operating subsidiary NCI Information Systems, provides a variety of IT services primarily to US federal defense and intelligence agencies. Its services include enterprise systems management, systems integration, consulting, implementation, maintenance, network design, application development, and network engineering. Key clients include the US Army and the US Air Force. The company also serves federal civilian agencies including NASA and the Department of Energy. A very small portion of its work is done for commercial clients and state and local agencies. Chairman and CEO Charles Narang controls 87% of the company's voting power.

NCI uses periodic acquisitions to expanded its expertise and client base. In 2011 the company bought AdvanceMed, an affiliate of Computer Sciences Corporation. The deal gave NCI a boost in the area of fraud and waste prevention services for the health care industry. AdvanceMed provided investigative services to administrators of Medicare and Medicaid programs to identify cases of funds misappropriation.

In 2009 it acquired Reston, Virginia-based TRS Consulting, a provider of engineering and professional services to clients. The deal gave NCI's software development and database management capabilities a boost, and increased its access to the US intelligence agencies served by TRS, as well as the FAA.

The company's subsidiaries include Karta Technologies (medical-oriented IT services), Scientific & Engineering Solutions (technical services for intelligence agencies), and Operational Technologies Services (engineering and professional services for the FAA). NCI operates from eight US offices, as well as facilities in South Korea and Iraq.

EXECUTIVES

Chairman and CEO, Charles K. Narang, age 69, $934,798 total compensation
President and Director, Terry W. Glasgow, age 67, $801,037 total compensation
EVP, CFO, and Treasurer, Brian J. Clark, age 40
VP High Performance and Quality Management Office, Michael W. Donaldson
VP Investor Relations, Maureen Crystal
SVP and General Manager, Civilian Programs Group, Frederic A. (Fred) Zafran
SVP and CTO, Karl J. Leatham
SVP and General Manager, Air Force and Technology Services, Richard L. Riney III
SVP Human Resources and Administration, W. Norman (Norm) Pierce
SVP and General Manager, Army Programs Group, Clarence D. Johnson
SVP and General Manager National Security Group (NSG), T. Richard Stroupe Jr.
SVP Strategic Initiatives, John C. Woloski
SVP, General Counsel, and Secretary, Michele R. Cappello, age 60, $437,368 total compensation
SVP Business Development and Capture Management, Christopher M. (Chris) Bishop
Auditors: Ernst & Young LLP

LOCATIONS

HQ: NCI, Inc.
11730 Plaza America Dr., Reston, VA 20190
Phone: 703-707-6900   **Fax:** 703-707-6901
Web: www.nciinc.com

PRODUCTS/OPERATIONS

2009 Sales by Market

	$ mil.	% of total
Defense & intelligence agencies	411.6	87
Federal civilian agencies	55.8	12
Commercial, state & local entities	1.5	1
Total	**468.9**	**100**

COMPETITORS

BAE Systems Inc.
Booz Allen
CACI International
Computer Sciences Corp.
General Dynamics Information Technology
Harris Corp.
HP Enterprise Services
IBM
Lockheed Martin Information Systems
ManTech
Northrop Grumman Info Systems
Raytheon
SAIC
SRA International

HISTORICAL FINANCIALS

Company Type: Public

Income Statement

FYE: December 31

	REVENUE ($ mil.)	NET INCOME ($ mil.)	NET PROFIT MARGIN	EMPLOYEES
12/10	581.3	23.9	4.1%	2,600
12/09	468.9	22.2	4.7%	2,800
12/08	390.6	17.0	4.4%	2,500
12/07	304.4	12.6	4.1%	2,000
12/06	218.3	9.3	4.3%	1,400
Annual Growth	**27.7%**	**26.6%**	**—**	**16.7%**

HOOVER'S HANDBOOK OF EMERGING COMPANIES 2012   253

2010 Year-End Financials

Debt ratio: 13.1% No. of shares (mil.): 13.7
Return on equity: 15.6% Dividends
Cash ($ mil.): 2.8 Yield: —
Current ratio: 1.63 Payout: —
Long-term debt ($ mil.): 20.0 Market value ($ mil.): 314.3

	STOCK PRICE ($) FY Close	P/E High/Low		PER SHARE ($) Earnings	Dividends	Book Value
12/10	22.99	19	11	1.72	0.00	11.20
12/09	27.65	21	14	1.61	0.00	9.21
12/08	30.13	24	11	1.25	0.00	7.40
12/07	17.11	22	14	0.93	0.00	6.01
12/06	15.29	24	15	0.69	0.00	5.00
Annual Growth	10.7%	—	—	25.7%	—	22.4%

Nektar Therapeutics

Nektar Therapeutics has pegged its fortunes to making drugs more effective. The clinical-stage drug development firm uses its PEGylation technology, (based upon polyethylene glycol) to improve the delivery and efficacy of existing drugs. Nektar's pipeline is focused on anti-infectives and anti-virals, immunology, oncology, and pain treatments. Its lead candidate NKTR-118 (which it is developing in collaboration with AstraZeneca) is being tested as a treatment for opioid-induced constipation. It also maintains a handful of preclinical candidates. Nektar receives royalties on about a dozen marketed products which include its technology, and developed in collaboration with partners including Amgen and Pfizer.

Nektar's NKTR-102 candidate is in three separate clinical trials for breast, colorectal, and ovarian cancers. As the drug advances into late-stage clinical trials the company intends to find a collaborative partner to help shepherd it through regulatory filings and commercialization.

Such collaborations are a key part of Nektar's business strategy and it routinely enters into partnerships with major pharmaceutical companies to help finance the development of new products. The company's development deal with AstraZeneca, struck in 2009, netted it $125 million up-front and gives it the opportunity to earn an additional $1.5 billion in milestone payments. Another collaboration with Bayer Healthcare is working on development and commercialization of an inhaled antibiotic in clinical trials for the treatment of certain pneumonias.

Past deals (resulting in marketed PEGylated drugs) have included Roche's hepatitis C drug PEGASYS and OSI Pharmaceuticals' Macugen (for age-related macular degeneration). The technology was also used to develop UCB's anti-inflammatory drug Cimzia, which won FDA approval as a treatment for Crohn's disease in 2008 and rheumatoid arthritis in 2009.

In 2008 Nektar changed from focusing on drug delivery to drug development after Pfizer stopped selling Exubera (inhaled insulin), which used its technology. The failure of the drug — a much-hyped, first-of-its-kind product that flopped on the market — led Nektar to cut its workforce by nearly 20% and to recast itself as a drug developer, rather than a provider of drug delivery services to other pharma firms. The switch led to a significant drop in the company's cash flow that year, however, it rebounded quickly by selling some operations and jumping head-on into drug development.

Nektar's revenues dipped in 2008 when it sold its pulmonary delivery assets, including manufacturing facilities, personnel, and intellectual property, to Novartis for $115 million. The two companies had worked together on the development of Tobramycin inhalation powder (TIP), a potential treatment for cystic fibrosis. Nektar retained some drug programs involving pulmonary delivery, including its inhaled vancomycin candidate. Collaboration partners also had lower demand for Nektar's manufacturing services in 2008, which deepened the dip in its revenues that year.

EXECUTIVES

Chairman, Robert B. Chess, age 54
President, CEO, and Director, Howard W. Robin, age 58, $3,003,133 total compensation
SVP and Chief Business Officer, Rinko Ghosh
SVP and Chief Scientific Officer, Stephen K. Doberstein, age 51
SVP Finance and CFO, John Nicholson, age 59, $1,835,959 total compensation
SVP and Chief Medical Officer, Lorianne K. Masuoka, age 49
SVP Finance and Chief Accounting Officer, Jillian B. Thomsen, age 45
Senior Director Investor Relations and Corporate Affairs, Jennifer Ruddock
SVP, General Counsel, and Secretary, Gil M. Labrucherie, age 39, $1,175,975 total compensation
SVP Global Research, Timothy A. (Tim) Riley
SVP Human Resources and Facilities Operations, Dorian Rinella, age 53
Auditors: Ernst & Young LLP

LOCATIONS

HQ: Nektar Therapeutics
455 Mission Bay Blvd. South, San Francisco, CA 94158
Phone: 415-482-5300 **Fax:** 415-339-5300
Web: www.nektar.com

2010 Revenues

	$ mil.	% of total
Europe	129.4	81
US	29.6	19
Total	**159.0**	**100**

PRODUCTS/OPERATIONS

2010 Revenues

	$ mil.	% of total
License & collaboration	124.4	78
Product sales & royalties	34.6	22
Total	**159.0**	**100**

COMPETITORS

Agenus
Bristol-Myers Squibb
Cell Therapeutics
Dr. Reddy's
Enzon
GlaxoSmithKline
Neose Technologies
NOF
Novartis
Novo Nordisk
Pfizer
Progenics
 Pharmaceuticals
Roche Holding
Salix Pharmaceuticals
Sucampo
Takeda Pharmaceutical

HISTORICAL FINANCIALS

Company Type: Public

Income Statement

FYE: December 31

	REVENUE ($ mil.)	NET INCOME ($ mil.)	NET PROFIT MARGIN	EMPLOYEES
12/10	159.0	(37.9)	—	408
12/09	71.9	(102.5)	—	335
12/08	90.2	(34.3)	—	338
12/07	273.0	(32.8)	—	575
12/06	217.7	(154.8)	—	793
Annual Growth	(7.6%)	—	—	(15.3%)

2010 Year-End Financials

Debt ratio: 255.9% No. of shares (mil.): 94.5
Return on equity: — Dividends
Cash ($ mil.): 17.8 Yield: —
Current ratio: 5.52 Payout: —
Long-term debt ($ mil.): 232.0 Market value ($ mil.): 1,214.5

	STOCK PRICE ($) FY Close	P/E High/Low		PER SHARE ($) Earnings	Dividends	Book Value
12/10	12.85	—	—	(0.40)	0.00	0.96
12/09	9.32	—	—	(1.11)	0.00	1.10
12/08	5.56	—	—	(0.37)	0.00	2.06
12/07	6.71	—	—	(0.36)	0.00	2.33
12/06	15.21	—	—	(1.72)	0.00	2.51
Annual Growth	(4.1%)	—	—	—	—	(21.4%)

Neogen

Bacteriophobes have a friend in Neogen, a maker of products for the food safety and animal health markets. Its food safety testing products are used by the food industry to make sure our edibles are clean, unspoiled, and free of toxins, pathogens, and allergens. In Canada, the US, and Europe, Neogen reaches end users (including dairies, meat processors, and animal feed producers) through a direct sales force; it uses distributors elsewhere. On the animal health front, Neogen produces drugs, vaccines, diagnostics, and instruments for the veterinary market; it also makes rat poisons and disinfectants used in animal production plants and diagnostic products for research laboratories.

The firm's animal products are sold to distributors around the world, as well as through farm supply retailers in North America. International sales of all of its products account for about 40% of Neogen's sales.

Some of the company's best-selling food safety testing products include its Reveal and Alert tests used by meat, poultry, and seafood processors to detect food-borne bacteria. Others include its Veratox, Agre-Screen, and Reveal tests which are used by grain producers to detect mycotoxins (toxins produced by fungi).

When it comes to animals, lead products include PanaKare, a digestive aid; RenaKare, a supplement for potassium deficiency in cats and dogs; and the NeogenVet brand including Vita-15 and Liver 7, which are used for the treatment and prevention of nutritional deficiencies in horses.

The company sees its over-the-counter animal health products as being particularly ripe for growth, and because of that it seeks to increase its line of rodenticides, disinfectants, instruments, and horse care products.

Neogen grows its product lines in a number of ways, but a primary method is through acquisitions. It has, for instance, bought the dairy antibiotic testing operations of UCB and Eastman Chemical's former Centrus International unit, which added food-borne bacteria testing products. It also acquired a line of animal health products from DuPont Animal Health Solutions, a unit of chemicals giant DuPont, in 2009. That purchase gave Neogen about 15 new product formulations used in animal health and hygiene, including disinfectants and cleaners intended for farm production markets. During 2010 the company acquired GeneSeek, which operates an agricultural genetics laboratory that enhances Neogen's diagnostic test development operations. To enhance its aquaculture testing services, in 2011 it acquired Scotland-based VeroMara from GlycoMar. Neogen will support the operations, which provides seafood testing to the aquaculture industry, through its European headquarters, which are also based in Scotland.

Though the company has used its acquisitions to achieve relatively rapid growth, it is also looking for organic growth over the longer term through new product introductions, higher sales of existing products, and international expansion efforts. Neogen has ongoing development projects for new diagnostic tests and other complementary products for both the food safety and animal safety markets. The company plans to launch a range of new products between by 2012.

Based on the past few year's income, Neogen shouldn't have much trouble funding its development plans. The company has continued to post profits even during the most difficult economic times and in 2010 it experienced financial growth across all of its business lines except veterinary instruments and other, which fell 2% due to decreased demand. Neogen attributes its overall success to improving inventory control, product mix, and cost containment. Of its divisions, Food Safety saw a significant increase in sales of its rapid tests to detect toxins as weather conditions in some regions led a surge in demand for tests to determine the presence of certain toxins. Its Veterinary Biologics segment saw an increase in demand for vitamin injectibles for livestock. Life Sciences sales increased nearly 60% primarily due to the successful integration of acquisitions such as Gene-Seek.

EXECUTIVES

Chairman and CEO, James L. Herbert, age 71, $647,705 total compensation
President, COO, and Director, Lon M. Bohannon, age 58, $493,646 total compensation
VP Corporate Development, Anthony E. Maltese, age 68
VP Manufacturing, Kenneth V. Kodilla, age 54
VP Research and Development, Mark A. Mozola, age 54
VP Scientific Affairs, Joseph M. Madden, age 62
VP and CFO, Steven J. (Steve) Quinlan, age 47
VP Food Safety Operations, Edward L. Bradley, age 51, $293,167 total compensation
VP Animal Safety Operations, Terri A. Morrical, age 46, $283,310 total compensation
VP Basic and Exploratory Research, Paul S. Satoh, age 74
Director Industry Affairs and Hacco Operations, Keith Creagh
Senior Scientific Officer, Jennifer Rice
Auditors: Ernst & Young LLP

LOCATIONS

HQ: Neogen Corporation
620 Lesher Place, Lansing, MI 48912
Phone: 517-372-9200   **Fax:** 517-372-2006
Web: www.neogen.com

PRODUCTS/OPERATIONS

2010 Sales

	$ mil.	% of total
Food safety	76.4	54
Animal safety	64.1	46
Total	**140.5**	**100**

2010 Sales

	$ mil.	% of total
Food safety		
Natural toxins, allergans, drug residues	39.3	28
Bacterial and general sanitation	19.6	14
Dry culture media and other	17.6	13
Animal safety		
Veterinary instruments	28.6	20
Rodenticides and disinfectants	24.2	17
Life sciences	8.9	6
Vaccine	2.3	2
Total	**140.5**	**100**

Selected Products

Food safety
  AccuClean (detects proteins and sugars)
  AccuPoint (rapid sanitation test)
  AgriScreen (detects mycotoxins)
  Alert (detects food-borne bacteria, food allergens)
  Beta Star (detects antibiotics in milk)
  BioKits (detects allergens in food; also used for species identification)
  GeneQuence (detects food-borne bacteria)
  Reveal (detects food-borne bacteria, food allergens, ruminant by-products)
  Soleris (detects spoilage organisms)
  Veratox (detects mycotoxins, food allergens)
Animal safety
  AgTek (Kane) products (apparel, accessories, etc.)
  BioSentry (chemicals)
  CyKill (rodent control)
  Di-Kill (rodent control)
  ElectroJac (automated semen collection)
  Havoc (rodenticide)
  Ideal (animal health products and instruments)
  NeogenVet (animal health products)
  Prozap (rodenticide)
  Ramik (rodenticide)
  Rodex (rodenticide)
  Squire (animal health products)

Selected Subsidiaries

Acumedia Manufacturers, Inc.
Centrus International, Inc.
Hacco, Inc.
Hess & Clark, Inc.
Ideal Instruments, Inc.
International Diagnostic Systems Inc.
Neogen Europe Limited (UK)

COMPETITORS

American Animal Health	Merck
Bayer Animal Health	Merck Animal Health
Bioniche Life Sciences	Merial
Celldex Therapeutics	Novartis
Ecolab	Orchid Cellmark
Eurofins Scientific	Pfizer
Hartz Mountain	Phibro Animal Health
Heska	Silliker
IDEXX Labs	Strategic Diagnostics
Life Technologies	Virbac Corporation
Corporation	Warnex

HISTORICAL FINANCIALS

Company Type: Public

Income Statement

FYE: May 31

	REVENUE ($ mil.)	NET INCOME ($ mil.)	NET PROFIT MARGIN	EMPLOYEES
05/11	172.7	22.8	13.2%	654
05/10	140.5	17.5	12.5%	585
05/09	118.7	13.9	11.7%	515
05/08	102.4	12.1	11.8%	447
05/07	86.1	9.1	10.6%	427
Annual Growth	**19.0%**	**25.8%**	**—**	**11.2%**

2011 Year-End Financials

Debt ratio: —
Return on equity: 12.1%
Cash ($ mil.): 35.8
Current ratio: 6.88
Long-term debt ($ mil.): —

No. of shares (mil.): 23.3
Dividends
  Yield: —
  Payout: —
Market value ($ mil.): 1,044.4

	STOCK PRICE ($) FY Close	P/E High/Low		PER SHARE ($) Earnings	Dividends	Book Value
05/11	44.84	47	26	0.96	0.00	8.10
05/10	25.71	36	19	0.76	0.00	6.75
05/09	14.69	35	18	0.61	0.00	5.82
05/08	17.56	35	21	0.54	0.00	5.15
05/07	12.17	28	18	0.43	0.00	4.37
Annual Growth	**38.5%**	**—**	**—**	**22.2%**	**—**	**16.7%**

NeoGenomics

NeoGenomics is a fortune teller of sorts. The company offers genetic and molecular testing in four categories to determine a person's genetic predisposition to certain cancers and other diseases. Testing methods include cytogenetics, flourescence in-situ hybridization (FISH), flow cytometry, and molecular genetic testing. The company serves customers including community-based oncologists, pathologists, urologists, hospitals, and other health care facilities through its labs located across the US. Company director Steven Jones controls about 45% of the company through venture capital firm Aspen Select Healthcare.

The company expanded beyond its base operations in Florida by opening two new laboratories in California and Tennessee in 2006; it plans to continue to open additional facilities to provide localized services to its target market of community-based physicians.

NeoGenomics plans to broaden its services offerings into anatomic pathology testing; it also is expanding into the pharmaceutical Contract Research Organization (CRO) market.

EXECUTIVES

Chairman and CEO, Douglas M. Van Oort, age 55
CFO, George A. Cardoza, age 48
President, Chief Science Officer, and Director, Robert P. (Bob) Gasparini, age 56, $360,857 total compensation
EVP Finance, Director Investor Relations, and Director, Steven C. (Steve) Jones, age 47
VP Sales and Marketing, Mark Smits, age 53
VP Laboratory Operations, Jack G. Spitz, age 55
VP Information Technology, Marydawn Miller, age 50
VP Business Development, Grant D. Carlson, age 52
Auditors: Kingery & Crouse PA

LOCATIONS

HQ: NeoGenomics, Inc.
12701 Commonwealth Dr., Ste. 9, Fort Myers, FL 33913
Phone: 239-768-0600   **Fax:** 239-768-0711
Web: www.neogenomics.org

COMPETITORS

Advanced Cell Technology	Innogenetics
	LabCorp
Genzyme Oncology	Myriad Genetics
Human Genome Sciences	Orchid Cellmark
Incyte	

HISTORICAL FINANCIALS

Company Type: Public

Income Statement

FYE: December 31

	REVENUE ($ mil.)	NET INCOME ($ mil.)	NET PROFIT MARGIN	EMPLOYEES
12/10	34.4	(3.3)	—	185
12/09	29.5	(2.2)	—	166
12/08	20.0	(1.4)	—	114
12/07	11.5	(3.4)	—	92
12/06	6.5	(0.1)	—	48
Annual Growth	51.7%	—	—	40.1%

2010 Year-End Financials

Debt ratio: 43.0%	No. of shares (mil.): 37.4
Return on equity: —	Dividends
Cash ($ mil.): 1.1	Yield: —
Current ratio: 0.95	Payout: —
Long-term debt ($ mil.): 1.3	Market value ($ mil.): 48.7

	STOCK PRICE ($) FY Close	P/E High/Low		PER SHARE ($) Earnings	Dividends	Book Value
12/10	1.30	—	—	(0.09)	0.00	0.08
12/09	1.50	—	—	(0.06)	0.00	0.15
12/08	0.61	—	—	(0.04)	0.00	0.05
12/07	1.08	—	—	(0.11)	0.00	(0.00)
12/06	1.50	—	—	(0.00)	0.00	(0.00)
Annual Growth	(3.5%)	—	—	—	—	—

NeoStem

NeoStem has a vision, and it stems from life's building blocks. Operating in the US and China, the company collects and conducts research on, adult stem cells. It runs a dozen or so facilities that collect, process, and store bone marrow and umbilical cord specimens for individuals seeking to use stem cells to treat medical conditions that may occur later in life. NeoStem partners with scientists to discover and develop therapeutic uses of stem cells as well, including treatments for certain blood cancers and regenerative medicine. In addition to its stem cell business, NeoStem operates a pharmaceutical company that manufactures and distributes antibiotic products in China.

In early 2011 the company expanded its operations after acquiring Progenitor Cell Therapy, a provider of cellular therapy-based services that support the development and commercialization of stem cell therapies. The acquisition of Progenitor, which has its own client base and operates facilities in the US, serves to complement the company's existing US stem cell business and provide

an additional revenue stream for NeoStem. It followed that up by acquiring Amorcyte, a cell therapy company focused on developing treatments for cardiovascular diseases. Its lead candidate AMR-001 is a stem cell product for the treatment of damaged heart muscle following acute myocardial infarction. Amorcyte says the treatment works by increasing microvascular blood flow in the area.

Although NeoStem's operations a geared toward its stem cell-based operations, the bulk of the company's revenue actually comes from its pharmaceutical business. Based in China, Suzhou Erye has been around since the 1960s and has antibiotics on the market in China that generate income for the company. (NeoStem acquired a 51% stake in Erye in 2009.) The rest of its revenue came from the company's US stem cell business; its newer Chinese-based operations — established in 2009 — did not generate significant income that year.

Despite the revenue brought in by Erye and its US business, the company, like many biopharmaceutical companies, operates at a loss because it spends much more on research and development, sales and marketing, and administrative functions. A large part of the company's expenses comes from its development efforts, which include partnering with scientists and researchers from the University of Louisville.

Such partnerships are an important element of the company's long-term success, mainly because most stem cell therapies are still in development or are not yet approved for use by government regulators. For instance, in the US the only FDA-permitted uses of such therapies are limited to treating certain blood cancers. Regulations in China are not quite as restrictive and permit additional uses of the therapies, including regenerative medicine. As a result, the company is relying on the regenerative medicine business (mainly for orthopedic and cosmetic purposes) to gain traction in China and attract both Chinese and foreign customers. It is also hoping that the FDA will eventually approve additional therapeutic uses of adult stem cell therapies in the US. If progress is not made in these areas, the company would likely see a decline in demand for its collection and storage services, as there would be no use for stem cell storage if there were no therapies available in the future.

EXECUTIVES

Chairman and CEO, Robin L. Smith, age 45, $5,166,380 total compensation
President and Chief Scientific Officer, Progenitor Cell Therapy, Robert A. Preti
President of NeoStem China, Ian Zhang
VP and CFO, Larry A. May, age 60, $567,830 total compensation
VP Finance, Christopher C. (Chris) Duignan, age 34
VP Strategic Development and Academic Affairs, Anthony Salerno, age 56
VP Drug Development and Regulatory Affairs, Alan G. Harris, age 60
VP Administration, NeoStem, Daisy Dai
VP Strategic Business Development, Jason Kolbert, age 51
VP Business Development, Progenitor Cell Therapy, George S. Goldberger
VP Manufacturing Operations, Progenitor Cell Therapy, Daryl LeSueur
VP and General Counsel, Catherine M. Vaczy, age 48, $1,534,003 total compensation
VP Sales and Marketing, Teresa Lepore, age 50
General Manager, Erye, Jian Zhang, age 48

Chief Medical Officer, Progenitor Cell Therapy, Andrew L. Pecora
General Manager, NeoStem, Peter Sun, age 50
Auditors: Holtz Rubenstein Reminick LLP

LOCATIONS

HQ: NeoStem, Inc.
420 Lexington Ave., Ste. 450, New York, NY 10170
Phone: 212-584-4180   **Fax:** 646-514-7787
Web: www.neostem.com

COMPETITORS

Cbr Systems	Sinovac Biotech
China Biologic	Tianyin Pharmaceutical
Lifebank	ViaCord

HISTORICAL FINANCIALS

Company Type: Public

Income Statement

FYE: December 31

	REVENUE ($ mil.)	NET INCOME ($ mil.)	NET PROFIT MARGIN	EMPLOYEES
12/10	69.8	(23.3)	—	924
12/09	11.6	(25.3)	—	30
12/08	0.1	(9.2)	—	16
12/07	0.2	(10.4)	—	16
12/06	0.0	(6.1)	—	12
Annual Growth	—	—	—	196.2%

2010 Year-End Financials

Debt ratio: —	No. of shares (mil.): 63.8
Return on equity: —	Dividends
Cash ($ mil.): 15.6	Yield: —
Current ratio: 1.43	Payout: —
Long-term debt ($ mil.): —	Market value ($ mil.): 90.0

	STOCK PRICE ($) FY Close	P/E High/Low		PER SHARE ($) Earnings	Dividends	Book Value
12/10	1.41	—	—	(0.46)	0.00	0.76
12/09	1.55	—	—	(2.37)	0.00	0.67
12/08	0.47	—	—	(1.53)	0.00	0.12
12/07	1.34	—	—	(3.18)	0.00	0.70
12/06	7.50	—	—	(4.40)	0.00	0.15
Annual Growth	(34.2%)	—	—	—	—	50.5%

Netflix

Tapping technologies from multiple eras, Netflix steers couch potatoes away from the video store to the mailbox or PC. Its Netflix.com website offers DVD rentals to more than 20 million subscribers for a monthly fee. Movies are delivered via the US Postal Service from distribution centers located in major US cities or streamed to PCs or TVs. Netflix ships some 2 million discs daily in the US. It does not charge late fees or have due dates, and its service employs user ratings to predict preferences and make recommendations. An agreement with TiVo, which gives TiVo customers with certain DVR models access to a Netflix library of some 12,000 movies and TV shows, has spawned similar services with other devices.

The TiVo deal is an example of how movie rental is migrating from the mailbox to the set-top box or personal computer. By bypassing the post office, Netflix customers have instant access to movies and TV episodes for online viewing. Netflix was an early entrant in the evolving world of Internet video. Its streaming service, launched in 2007, allows customers to watch select movies and content through the Netflix website via their PCs.

It's one of Netflix's goals to eventually abandon its DVD-by-mail service altogether in favor of its streaming services. To that end, the company in mid-2011 proposed new menu of subscription options that separated its DVD-by-mail service from its streaming service. Instead of paying $10 for access to both DVD-by-mail operations as well as streaming video, Netflix broke up each delivery method into separate plans that cost $7.99 each, effectively raising prices by 60%. The move was widely unpopular with Netflix customers who began deserting the company in droves. Indeed, some 800,000 customers left the company in the quarter (ending September 30) following the announcement. Netflix has been in damage-control mode ever since and has scuttled its attempt to spin off its DVD-by-mail service.

To build its streaming service, the DVD rental company, in partnership with Roku, launched a set-top box that allows subscribers to stream videos from the Netflix website to their TVs. The Netflix box is the first of several devices to pipe Netflix's streaming service to TV sets. Netflix also is able to stream movies to LG Electronics' Blu-ray DVD players and VIZIO TVs. The company racked up similar content-delivery deals for TiVo digital video recorders, Microsoft Xbox 360 and Sony PlayStation 3 game consoles, Samsung Blu-ray players, and Sony's BRAVIA Internet Video-capable HDTVs.

Looking to expand its library of available selections to satisfy the growing appetites of its customers, Netflix has added content from CBS, Disney, MTV Networks, and Sony. In 2011 Netflix continues to explore agreements with pay TV channels and networks, such as HBO, as it plans to invest aggressively in streaming content. Also, Netflix is expanding its online streaming service internationally — one country at a time. What is fueling the company's subscriber growth in 2011 is its push to further separate subscriptions for DVDs and streaming capabilities, expansion into Canada with pure streaming, and the ability to tap into the now more than a couple hundred Netflix-ready devices on the market.

The recession in the US helped Netflix sign up many new subscribers as more Americans looked to movies for escapism and stayed at home to save money. As a result, Netflix enlisted more than 3 million new subscribers during 2010 while lowering its subscriber acquisition and service costs.

Since its founding in 1997 by its chairman and CEO Reed Hastings, Netflix has been battling rival Blockbuster, which started up its own online rental offerings in 2006. Netflix saw its growth slow in 2007, which it attributes in part to Blockbuster's aggressive expansion of its online rental business. While Blockbuster's 2010 Chapter 11 bankruptcy filing and potential 2011 purchase by DISH Network may ultimately be a plus for Netflix, the company is facing new competitors, including Apple, Amazon.com, and Google, as a result of the shift to online movie downloads.

In addition, Netflix must hurdle other potential rivals that offer DVD rentals in Europe and online downloads of movies. Competition from Redbox, which operates DVD-rental kiosks, began to heat up as long ago as 2009. Redbox's $1 DVD rentals and aggressive expansion has Netflix watching its back and proclaiming that kiosks will be its #1 competitor. In response, Netflix relaunched an ad campaign to offer $8.99 unlimited monthly DVD

rentals. Redbox places its vending-machine-like kiosks outside convenient locales, such as grocery stores, discount stores, and ubiquitous fast-food restaurants such as McDonald's. Indeed, Redbox is limited to 200 titles per kiosk and primarily only recent releases, making the company less threatening to Netflix. However, Redbox is busy behind the scenes preparing to launch a streaming service.

While one would think that Netflix generates more of its revenue from sales of recently released movies, the company uses its recommendation technology to keep the DVD shipments humming and a greater number of its older DVDs in circulation. Indeed, more than two-thirds of the DVDs shipped in 2009 were titles with release dates of greater than 13 weeks. Netflix is able to increase demand for older titles that are sitting in its distribution centers by recommending movies to users as they rate movies seen. Netflix also has leveraged its subscriber base by allowing companies to place ads in Netflix e-mails and on its signature red mailing envelopes.

EXECUTIVES

Chairman, President, and CEO, Reed Hastings, age 50, $2,756,268 total compensation
CFO, David Wells, age 39
CEO, Qwikster, Andrew (Andy) Rendich
VP and Controller, JC Berger
VP Personalization Technology, John Ciancutti
VP Corporate Communications, Steve Swasey
VP Finance and Investor Relations, Ellie Mertz
VP Global Corporate Communications, Jonathan Friedland
VP E-Commerce and Systems Engineering, Kevin McEntee
Chief Talent Officer, Patricia J. (Patty) McCord, age 57
Chief Product Officer, Neil Hunt, age 49, $1,510,006 total compensation
Chief Marketing Officer, Leslie J. Kilgore, age 45, $2,074,568 total compensation
Director Engineering, API, Daniel Jacobson
Chief Content Officer and VP Content, Ted Sarandos, age 46, $1,089,714 total compensation
Software Architect, Cloud Systems, Siddharth (Sid) Anand
General Counsel and Secretary, David Hyman, age 45
Director Content Delivery, Ken Florance
Director Engineering, Social Systems, Michael Hart
Cloud Architect, Adrian Cockcroft
Auditors: KPMG LLP

LOCATIONS

HQ: Netflix, Inc.
100 Winchester Cir., Los Gatos, CA 95032
Phone: 408-540-3700   **Fax:** 408-540-3737
Web: www.netflix.com

PRODUCTS/OPERATIONS

2010 Subscribers

	No.	% of total
Paid subscribers	18,268	91
Free subscribers	1,742	9
Total	**20,000**	**100**

COMPETITORS

Amazon.com	Hastings Entertainment
Apple Inc.	HBO
AT&T	Hulu
Best Buy	Kroger
Blockbuster	Redbox
Columbia House	Showtime Networks
Comcast	Starz

Cox Communications	Target Corporation
DIRECTV	Time Warner Cable
DISH Network	Verizon
EchoStar	Wal-Mart
Google	

HISTORICAL FINANCIALS

Company Type: Public

Income Statement

FYE: December 31

	REVENUE ($ mil.)	NET INCOME ($ mil.)	NET PROFIT MARGIN	EMPLOYEES
12/10	2,162.6	160.9	7.4%	4,329
12/09	1,670.3	115.9	6.9%	4,080
12/08	1,364.7	83.0	6.1%	1,644
12/07	1,205.3	67.0	5.6%	2,670
12/06	996.7	49.1	4.9%	1,300
Annual Growth	**21.4%**	**34.5%**	**—**	**35.1%**

2010 Year-End Financials

Debt ratio: 80.7%	No. of shares (mil.): 52.8
Return on equity: 55.4%	Dividends
Cash ($ mil.): 194.5	Yield: —
Current ratio: 1.65	Payout: —
Long-term debt ($ mil.): 234.1	Market value ($ mil.): 9,273.8

	STOCK PRICE ($) FY Close	P/E High/Low		PER SHARE ($) Earnings	Dividends	Book Value
12/10	175.70	71	16	2.96	0.00	5.50
12/09	55.09	31	15	1.98	0.00	3.73
12/08	29.89	31	14	1.32	0.00	5.92
12/07	26.62	30	16	0.97	0.00	6.55
12/06	25.86	47	26	0.71	0.00	6.05
Annual Growth	**61.4%**	**—**	**—**	**42.9%**	**—**	**(2.4%)**

NetLogic Microsystems

NetLogic Microsystems' chips try to bring logic to the content of the Internet. The company designs and sells knowledge-based processors, which are used in routers and other devices to optimize speed and search capabilities over the Internet, and integrated circuits used in data center, mobile wireless infrastructure, and enterprise networks. NetLogic's customers have included Alcatel-Lucent, Dell, Hewlett-Packard, and Juniper Networks. The company's semiconductors are principally produced by Taiwan Semiconductor Manufacturing and United Microelectronics. NetLogic Microsystems gets more than 80% of its sales outside the US. The company agreed to be acquired by Broadcom in 2011 for about $3.7 billion in cash.

Knowledge-based processors are the company's stock in trade and main line of business. They are chips used in processing packets in computer networks; they are said to operate faster and more securely than comparable processors. NetLogic's sales grew by 118% in 2010 over 2009, due to the acquisitions of a couple of product lines. The acquisitions were also to blame for the company going back into the red in 2009, after posting profits for four straight years; its net losses deepened in 2010. NetLogic has an accumulated deficit of $189 million.

In 2009 the company acquired assets from the network search engine product line of Integrated Device Technology (IDT). The acquisition included IDT's search accelerator, network search engine and route accelerator product families, and related patents and intellectual property. These products and technologies complement NetLogic's existing portfolio of knowledge-based processors, NETLite processors, and network search engines. NetLogic paid $100 million in cash for the IDT assets.

Also that year the company acquired RMI Corporation, a developer of low-power processors for Internet protocol networks, for about $175 million in cash and stock. The deal absorbed RMI's portfolio and trade names under the NetLogic product family, as well as opened a pipeline to RMI customers, including Alcatel-Lucent, Cisco, IBM, NEC, Samsung Electronics, and ZTE.

In 2011 NetLogic acquired California-based communications chip maker Optichron for $77 million in cash, with further payments of up to $108.5 million depending on future performance. The deal expanded the company's presence in the US.

Although the company has a limited number of customers, it is reducing its dependence on Cisco — its largest customer. In addition to the silicon foundries (contract semiconductor manufacturers) it uses to fabricate its devices, NetLogic also is dependent on other third-party contractors to assemble and test its devices in integrated circuit packaging, and for software tools from third-party vendors.

The fabless semiconductor company was founded by former CEO Norman Godinho (who owns about 13% of NetLogic) and CTO Varad Srinivasan.

EXECUTIVES

Chairman, Leonard C. (Len) Perham, age 67
President, CEO, and Director, Ronald S. (Ron) Jankov, age 52, $3,099,207 total compensation
EVP and General Manager, Behrooz Abdi, age 49, $13,658,771 total compensation
VP Worldwide Manufacturing, Mozafar (Mo) Maghsoudnia, age 44, $684,477 total compensation
VP and CFO, Michael T. (Mike) Tate, age 45, $1,112,047 total compensation
VP Marketing, Chris O'Reilly, age 37
VP, Secretary, and General Counsel, Roland Cortes, age 45
VP Engineering, Dimitrios Dimitrelis, age 53
VP Product Development and CTO, Varadarajan (Varad) Srinivasan, age 59, $967,948 total compensation
VP Corporate Development, Niall Bartlett
Media Relations, Alex Pantelis
SVP Worldwide Business Operations, Ibrahim (Abe) Korgav, age 62
SVP Worldwide Sales, Marcia Zander, age 47, $1,254,105 total compensation
Auditors: PricewaterhouseCoopers LLP

LOCATIONS

HQ: NetLogic Microsystems, Inc.
3975 Freedom Circle, Santa Clara, CA 95054
Phone: 408-454-3000 **Fax:** 408-454-3333
Web: www.netlogicmicro.com

2010 Sales

	% of total
China	38
Malaysia	26
US	18
Other countries	18
Total	**100**

PRODUCTS/OPERATIONS

Selected Products

Knowledge-based processors (classification, content, and forwarding processors)
Low-power embedded processors
Multi-core processors (XLP, XLR, and XLS Processor families)
Network search engines
Physical Layer (PHY) products
Software and hardware development kits

COMPETITORS

AMD	Intel
Applied Micro Circuits	LSI Corp.
Broadcom	Marvell Technology
Cavium	Mellanox
EZchip	PMC-Sierra
Freescale Semiconductor	Renesas Electronics
Integrated Device Technology	Vitesse Semiconductor

HISTORICAL FINANCIALS

Company Type: Public

Income Statement

FYE: December 31

	REVENUE ($ mil.)	NET INCOME ($ mil.)	NET PROFIT MARGIN	EMPLOYEES
12/10	381.7	(66.4)	—	645
12/09	174.7	(47.2)	—	550
12/08	139.9	3.6	2.6%	255
12/07	109.0	2.6	2.4%	225
12/06	96.8	0.6	0.6%	170
Annual Growth	**40.9%**	**—**	**—**	**39.6%**

2010 Year-End Financials

Debt ratio: —	No. of shares (mil.): 67.5
Return on equity: —	Dividends
Cash ($ mil.): 100.5	Yield: —
Current ratio: 6.17	Payout: —
Long-term debt ($ mil.): —	Market value ($ mil.): 2,120.5

	STOCK PRICE ($) FY Close	P/E High/Low		PER SHARE ($) Earnings	Dividends	Book Value
12/10	31.41	—	—	(1.10)	0.00	9.17
12/09	23.13	—	—	(1.02)	0.00	7.41
12/08	11.01	252	90	0.08	0.00	4.59
12/07	16.10	322	167	0.06	0.00	4.05
12/06	10.85	1501	585	0.01	0.00	3.49
Annual Growth	**30.4%**	**—**	**—**	**—**	**—**	**27.3%**

NetSpend

NetSpend offers prepaid debit cards to people who can't or don't want to deposit their money in a bank. The company offers pre-paid debit cards directly to consumers via the Internet or through major check cashers (such as ACE), convenience stores, and supermarkets. Clients can reload their cards for a fee at more than 100,000 locations. NetSpend's cards include features such as direct deposit, bill pay, savings accounts, and transfers. The company targets the more than 60 million underbanked consumers in the US and has more than 2 million active cards. NetSpend was founded in 1999 by Rogelio and Bertrand Sosa, brothers

who immigrated from Mexico in 1986. The company went public in October 2010.

NetSpend raised $204 million in its initial public offering (IPO). The company is using the proceeds to repay debt and fund working capital. NetSpend may also use funds raised to make acquisitions.

The IPO came three years after a deal for Capital One to acquire NetSpend fell through. After the soured deal, NetSpend moved forward with its strategy of increasing profitability as more cardholders load more money onto cards. NetSpend's main strategy for increasing deposits is to target clients who direct deposit their wages or other funds. The company is also looking to attract more underbanked consumers in the market by developing new distribution relationships and growing its network of locations where clients can reload their cards.

One of NetSpend's key moves to strengthen distribution was to acquire Skylight Financial, an Atlanta-based provider of prepaid debit and payroll cards, in 2008. Skylight was owned by JLL Partners, the parent of ACE Cash Express, one of NetSpend's largest distributors. As a result of the Skylight deal, JLL Partners acquired about a third of NetSpend.

Also in 2008 NetSpend announced the Emerging Markets Channel, a venture with Procesa International. The new channel offers NetSpend cards and other financial products to Hispanic customers both in the US and internationally. NetSpend then decided to focus its attention on its core reloadable prepaid debit cards, and stopped offering gift cards in August 2010.

NetSpend agreed to promote MetaBank as its preferred issuing bank, and in turn MetaBank promotes NetSpend as a preferred manager. As a part of the 2010 deal, NetSpend acquired a 5% stake in Meta Financial Group, MetaBank's parent.

The founding Sosa brothers no longer are involved with NetSpend's operations and have moved on to launch other businesses that also aim to serve underbanked clients. In 2008 NetSpend sued the Sosas for taking trade secrets and other proprietary information to competing companies. The suit was settled the following year.

Post-IPO, JLL Partners retained ownership of about 25% of NetSpend; Oak Investment Partners owns another 38%. The investment firms also have board representation, with two directors each.

EXECUTIVES

CEO and Director, Daniel R. (Dan) Henry, age 45
President, Charles J. (Chuck) Harris, age 49
CFO, George W. Gresham, age 44
EVP Information Technology, James DeVoglaer, age 50
EVP Online Business Development, Anh Hatzopoulos, age 39
EVP Sales and Distribution, Thomas A. (Tom) Cregan, age 40
EVP Card Operations, James P. (Jim) Jerome, age 53
Press Contact, Brad Russell
General Counsel and Secretary, Christopher T. Brown, age 47
Auditors: KPMG LLP

LOCATIONS

HQ: NetSpend Holdings, Inc.
701 Brazos St., Ste. 1300, Austin, TX 78701-2582
Phone: 512-532-8200 **Fax:** 512-857-0263
Web: www.netspend.com

COMPETITORS

Blackhawk Network	QC Holdings
Check Into Cash	Total System Services
DFC Global	Travelex United States
First Data	Wal-Mart
Green Dot	

HISTORICAL FINANCIALS

Company Type: Public

Income Statement

FYE: December 31

	REVENUE ($ mil.)	NET INCOME ($ mil.)	NET PROFIT MARGIN	EMPLOYEES
12/10	275.4	23.7	8.6%	507
12/09	225.0	18.2	8.1%	482
12/08	183.2	(11.6)	—	0
12/07	128.6	14.7	11.4%	300
Annual Growth	28.9%	17.3%	—	19.1%

2010 Year-End Financials

Debt ratio: 37.3%	No. of shares (mil.): 88.2
Return on equity: 15.1%	Dividends
Cash ($ mil.): 67.5	Yield: —
Current ratio: 2.29	Payout: —
Long-term debt ($ mil.): 58.5	Market value ($ mil.): 1,130.3

	STOCK PRICE ($) FY Close	P/E High/Low	PER SHARE ($) Earnings	Dividends	Book Value
12/10	12.82	60 41	0.27	0.00	1.78
Annual Growth	—	— —	—	—	—

NeuLion

NeuLion is poised for an attack on Internet television. The company offers technology and services that allow viewers to watch streaming video content over the Internet. It builds and manages private networks for content partners such as ESPN, the NFL, the Canadian hockey leagues, and about 170 NCAA schools to broadcast live and on-demand sports programming, viewed on personal computers, laptops, cell phones, and standard television sets through Internet-connected set-top boxes. NeuLion has offices in Canada, China, and the UK, as Internet Protocol television (IPTV) is popular outside the US. Chairman Charles Wang and CEO Nancy Li, who are married, together control more than half of the company.

EXECUTIVES

Chairman, Charles B. Wang, age 66
CFO, Arthur J. McCarthy, $47,380 total compensation
President, CEO, and Director; CEO, NeuLion USA, Nancy Li, $69,755 total compensation
EVP Research and Development, NeuLion and NeuLion USA, Michael H. Her, $511,217 total compensation
EVP Marketplace Strategy, NeuLion and NeuLion USA, J. Christopher (Chris) Wagner, $770,299 total compensation
EVP Marketing and Business Development, Marc Sokol
EVP Business Operations, NeuLion and NeuLion USA, Ronald M. E. (Ron) Nunn, $510,942 total compensation
Vice Chairman, G. Scott Paterson, age 47

General Counsel, Secretary, and Director, Roy E. Reichbach
Corporate Communications, Jennifer Powalski
Auditors: Ernst & Young LLP

LOCATIONS

HQ: NeuLion, Inc.
1600 Old Country Rd., Ste. 101, Plainview, NY 11803
Phone: 516-622-8300   **Fax:** 516-249-2922
Web: www.neulion.com

COMPETITORS

Alcatel-Lucent	Minerva Networks
Avid Technology	SeaChange
Cisco Systems	YouTube
Hulu	

HISTORICAL FINANCIALS

Company Type: Public

Income Statement

FYE: December 31

	REVENUE ($ mil.)	NET INCOME ($ mil.)	NET PROFIT MARGIN	EMPLOYEES
12/10	33.2	(17.2)	—	366
12/09	28.1	(19.6)	—	224
12/08	3.7	—	—	40
12/07	9.0	(30.6)	—	0
12/06	2.1	(25.6)	—	136
Annual Growth	99.4%	—	—	28.1%

2010 Year-End Financials

Debt ratio: —	No. of shares (mil.): 139.2
Return on equity: —	Dividends
Cash ($ mil.): 12.9	Yield: —
Current ratio: 1.08	Payout: —
Long-term debt ($ mil.): —	Market value ($ mil.): 75.2

	STOCK PRICE ($) FY Close	P/E High/Low	PER SHARE ($) Earnings	Dividends	Book Value
12/10	0.54	— —	(0.14)	0.00	0.11
12/09	0.70	— —	(0.18)	0.00	0.19
Annual Growth	(22.9%)	— —	—	—	(40.9%)

Neurocrine Biosciences

For Neurocrine Biosciences, drug development is all about body chemistry. The development-stage biotech develops treatments for neurological and endocrine hormone-related diseases, such as insomnia, depression, and menstrual pain. Lead drug candidate Elagolix is designed to treat endometriosis which causes pain and irregular menstrual bleeding in women. Neurocrine Biosciences works in additional therapeutic areas including anxiety, diabetes, and movement disorders. The company has about a dozen drug candidates in various stages of research and clinical development, through both internal progams and collaborative agreements with partnering drug firms.

While Neurocrine Biosciences develops a good number of its product candidates independently, the company also has development partnerships with the likes of GlaxosmithKline for the development of neurological and psychiatric diseases and disorders, and with Dainippon Sumitomo Pharma

to further the development of insomnia medication Indiplon in Japan.

In 2010, Abbott Laboratories agreed to pay as much as $605 million to help develop and commercialize Neurocrine Biosciences' clinical stage endometriosis treatment, Elagolix, as well as other preclinical candidates in the same hormone therapy product group. Terms of the agreement call for Abbott to fund all of the collaborative R&D programs and receive world-wide exclusive rights to commercialize the drugs. It will pay Neurocrine Biosciences $75 million up front and fund future development activities. The company is also eligible for eight additional milestone payments of about $530 million combined as well as royalties from any product sales.

Also in 2010 Neurocrine Biosciences gained a new development partner in German drugmaker Boehringer Ingelheim. The two companies are working together on a potential type II diabetes treatment, and the partnership could potentially extend to additional candidates.

Neurocrine Biosciences was founded in 1992. Like most development-stage biotech firms, the company has yet to turn a profit. Its efforts are focused on successfully bringing its candidates to market, as well as on acquiring or discovering new promising drug compounds to maintain a diverse pipeline. It also pursues additional partnerships to help fund its R&D programs and, upon market approval, to assist in commercialization efforts.

EXECUTIVES

Chairman, Joseph A. Mollica, age 70
President, CEO, and Director, Kevin C. Gorman, age 53, $1,519,487 total compensation
EVP, General Counsel, and Corporate Secretary, Margaret E. Valeur-Jensen, age 54, $1,350,780 total compensation
VP Research, Dimitri E. Grigoriadis, age 53, $874,949 total compensation
VP and CFO, Timothy P. Coughlin, age 44, $1,106,772 total compensation
VP Information Technology and Operations, Hernand W. (Bill) Wilson
SVP Clinical Development and Chief Medical Officer, Christopher F. (Chris) O'Brien, age 54, $926,837 total compensation
Manager Investor Relations, Claudia Woodworth
SVP Pharmaceutical and Preclinical Development, Haig P. Bozigian, age 53, $770,132 total compensation
Auditors: Ernst & Young LLP

LOCATIONS

HQ: Neurocrine Biosciences, Inc.
12780 El Camino Real, San Diego, CA 92130
Phone: 858-617-7600   **Fax:** 858-617-7601
Web: www.neurocrine.com

PRODUCTS/OPERATIONS

2010 Sales

	$ mil.	% of total
Milestones & license fees	22.6	67
Sponsored research & development	10.9	33
Total	**33.5**	**100**

Selected Drug Candidates

CRF 1 Antagonist (anxiety, depression, with GlaxoSmithKline)
CRF 2 Peptide Agonist (cardiovascular disease)
Elagolix (endometriosis and uterine fibroids, with Abbott)
GPR 119 (type II diabetes, with Boehringer Ingelheim)
GnRH Antagonist (oncology and men and women's health, with Abbott)

Indiplon (insomnia, with Dainippon Sumitomo Pharma)
VMAT2 Inhibitor (movement disorders, central nervous system)

COMPETITORS

Abbott Labs	Pfizer
AstraZeneca	Repros Therapeutics
Bayer HealthCare	Roche Holding
Pharmaceuticals Inc.	Sanofi
Bristol-Myers Squibb	Sunovion
Eli Lilly	Takeda Pharmaceutical
Forest Labs	Valeant
GlaxoSmithKline	Pharmaceuticals
H. Lundbeck	terna Zentaris

HISTORICAL FINANCIALS
Company Type: Public

Income Statement
FYE: December 31

	REVENUE ($ mil.)	NET INCOME ($ mil.)	NET PROFIT MARGIN	EMPLOYEES
12/10	33.5	(8.0)	—	66
12/09	3.0	(51.0)	—	65
12/08	4.0	(88.6)	—	125
12/07	1.2	(207.3)	—	135
12/06	39.2	(107.2)	—	267
Annual Growth	(3.9%)	—	—	(29.5%)

2010 Year-End Financials

Debt ratio: 34.0%	No. of shares (mil.): 54.9
Return on equity: —	Dividends
Cash ($ mil.): 54.1	Yield: —
Current ratio: 2.52	Payout: —
Long-term debt ($ mil.): 6.6	Market value ($ mil.): 419.3

	STOCK PRICE ($) FY Close	P/E High/Low		PER SHARE ($) Earnings	Dividends	Book Value
12/10	7.64	—	—	(0.15)	0.00	0.35
12/09	2.72	—	—	(1.30)	0.00	0.09
12/08	3.20	—	—	(2.30)	0.00	0.95
12/07	4.54	—	—	(5.45)	0.00	3.12
12/06	10.42	—	—	(2.84)	0.00	8.31
Annual Growth	(7.5%)	—	—	—	—	(54.6%)

Neutral Tandem

Neutral Tandem helps telecom providers stay in sync with customers. The company provides third-party interconnection services to competitive carriers via tandem switches, which allow wireline, wireless, and broadband phone providers to exchange traffic between networks without direct connections. Marketed as an alternative to incumbent local exchange carriers (ILECs), Neutral Tandem offers services for some 540 million number points in about 190 markets in the US. The company's largest customers are top US communications service providers AT&T (22% of business) and Sprint Nextel (18% of business).

In 2010 revenue rose more than 18% but net income fell about 21%.

That year Neutral Tandem expanded into a growing telecommunications market with the $95 million purchase of an Italy-based carrier, Tinet. Because Tinet operates a worldwide IP backbone system, the acquisition added IP Transit and Ethernet wholesale services to Neutral Tandem's core

business of interconnection services. Neutral Tandem now operates more than 100 Ethernet sites and maintains Internet Protocol and Ethernet service agreements with more than 650 customers in 70-plus countries.

EXECUTIVES

Chairman, James P. Hynes, age 63
CEO and Director, G. Edward (Ed) Evans, age 49
President and COO, Surendra Saboo, age 51, $3,440,487 total compensation
EVP and CFO, Robert M. (Rob) Junkroski, age 46, $2,675,635 total compensation
General Counsel, Secretary and SVP External Affairs, Richard Monto, age 46, $2,067,332 total compensation
Media Relations, Gerard Laurain
SVP Sales, David A. Lopez, age 46, $1,241,009 total compensation
Auditors: Deloitte & Touche LLP

LOCATIONS

HQ: Neutral Tandem, Inc.
550 W. Adams St., Ste. 900, Chicago, IL 60606
Phone: 312-384-8000   **Fax:** 312-346-3276
Web: www.neutraltandem.com

2010 Sales

	$ mil.	% of total
US	186.7	93
Italy	1.4	1
Rest of World	11.7	6
Total	**199.8**	**100**

COMPETITORS

AT&T	Level 3 Communications
Cogent Communications	TeliaSonera
Equinix	Telx Group
Global Crossing	Verizon
Hypercube	

HISTORICAL FINANCIALS
Company Type: Public

Income Statement
FYE: December 31

	REVENUE ($ mil.)	NET INCOME ($ mil.)	NET PROFIT MARGIN	EMPLOYEES
12/10	199.8	32.6	16.3%	230
12/09	168.9	41.3	24.5%	147
12/08	120.9	24.0	19.9%	137
12/07	85.6	6.3	7.4%	126
12/06	52.9	4.7	8.9%	110
Annual Growth	39.4%	62.3%	—	20.2%

2010 Year-End Financials

Debt ratio: —	No. of shares (mil.): 33.2
Return on equity: 12.0%	Dividends
Cash ($ mil.): 106.7	Yield: —
Current ratio: 4.70	Payout: —
Long-term debt ($ mil.): —	Market value ($ mil.): 478.9

	STOCK PRICE ($) FY Close	P/E High/Low		PER SHARE ($) Earnings	Dividends	Book Value
12/10	14.44	24	10	0.97	0.00	8.18
12/09	22.75	28	12	1.22	0.00	7.16
12/08	16.22	32	16	0.72	0.00	5.58
12/07	19.02	87	72	0.24	0.00	4.69
Annual Growth	(8.8%)	—	—	59.3%	—	20.4%

Nevada Gold & Casinos

Nevada Gold & Casinos knows there's gold in them thar casinos. The company owns the Colorado Grande Casino in Cripple Creek, Colorado, which has approximately 200 slot machines, four table games, seven guest rooms, and Maggie's Restaurant. The property attracts visitors from neighboring towns such as Colorado Springs and Denver. Nevada Gold also owns about 10 small casinos in Washington State. Three of these casinos — the Crazy Moose-Pasco, Crazy Moose-Mountlake Terrace, and Coyote Bob-Kennewick — are in close proximity to Seattle, while the remaining properties are located in western Washington. In 2011 the company announced plans to acquire AG Trucano, Son & Grandsons.

AG Trucano operates a slot machine route in Deadwood South Dakota, the only authorized commercialized gambling location in the state. The deal is estimated at $5.2 million and would add some 900 slots and 20 sites and open a new market for Nevada Gold.

The company had been seeking growth opportunities in the Pacific Northwest, specifically in the state of Washington. In 2009 it purchased three Washington casinos, and the following year it bought six more mini-casinos in that state: The Silver Dollar Seatac, The Silver Dollar Renton, The Silver Dollar Mill Creek, Club Hollywood, the Royal Casino, and The Golden Nugget Casino. In 2011 it purchased its 10th mini-casino in Washington, the Red Dragon in Mountlake Terrace, for $1.25 million.

These purchases follow the divestiture of several money-losing ventures. In 2008 the company sold its 43%-ownership stake in the Isle of Capri-Black Hawk. Isle of Capri-Black Hawk owned and operated two casinos in Black Hawk, Colorado — the Isle of Capri-Black Hawk Casino and Colorado Central Station Casino. And while Nevada Gold has historically operated gaming facilities on behalf of several Native American tribes, it has exited all of its North American casino projects.

EXECUTIVES

Chairman, William (Bill) Sherlock, age 61
President and General Manager, Horizon Casino Hotel, Gary L. Johnson
CEO and Director, Robert B. Sturges, age 64, $590,883 total compensation
VP Operations, Trevor A. Taylor
SVP, CFO, and Treasurer, James J. Kohn, age 61, $307,301 total compensation
SVP, General Counsel, and Secretary, Ernest E. (Ernie) East, age 68, $306,075 total compensation
Auditors: Pannell Kerr Forster of Texas, P.C.

LOCATIONS

HQ: Nevada Gold & Casinos, Inc.
3040 Post Oak Blvd., Ste. 675, Houston, TX 77056
Phone: 713-621-2245   **Fax:** 713-621-6919
Web: www.nevadagold.com

PRODUCTS/OPERATIONS

2009 Sales

	$ mil.	% of total
Casino	5.4	92
Food & beverage and other	1.9	8
Promotional allowances	(1.4)	-
Total	**5.9**	**100**

COMPETITORS

Ameristar Casinos	Hyatt
Caesars Entertainment	Penn National Gaming
Century Casinos	Riviera Holdings

HISTORICAL FINANCIALS

Company Type: Public

Income Statement

FYE: April 30

	REVENUE ($ mil.)	NET INCOME ($ mil.)	NET PROFIT MARGIN	EMPLOYEES
04/11	48.0	(0.5)	—	1,391
04/10	22.0	(4.7)	—	481
04/09	5.9	(4.2)	—	81
04/08	6.7	23.7	353.7%	89
04/07	12.3	(9.0)	—	104
Annual Growth	40.6%	—	—	91.2%

2011 Year-End Financials

Debt ratio: 49.7%	No. of shares (mil.): 12.8
Return on equity: —	Dividends
Cash ($ mil.): 5.7	Yield: —
Current ratio: 2.38	Payout: —
Long-term debt ($ mil.): 15.1	Market value ($ mil.): 21.6

	STOCK PRICE ($) FY Close	P/E High/Low		PER SHARE ($) Earnings	Dividends	Book Value
04/11	1.69	—	—	(0.04)	0.00	2.37
04/10	1.05	—	—	(0.37)	0.00	2.40
04/09	0.75	—	—	(0.32)	0.00	2.70
04/08	1.13	2	1	1.83	0.00	3.09
04/07	2.71	—	—	(0.69)	0.00	1.21
Annual Growth	(11.1%)	—	—	—	—	18.4%

New York Community Bancorp

It's big banking in the Big Apple and beyond. New York Community Bancorp is the holding company for flagship subsidiary New York Community Bank (one of the largest thrifts in the US), New York Commercial Bank, and seven other banking divisions. In its home state, New York Community Bank operates through Queens County Savings Bank, Richmond County Savings Bank, Roosevelt Savings Bank, and Roslyn Savings Bank. It serves customers in New Jersey through its Garden State Community Bank division. New York Community Bank also does business as Ohio Savings Bank and AmTrust Bank, which operates in Arizona and Florida. Altogether, New York Community Bancorp has about 275 bank branches in five states.

Serving both consumers and business customers, the banks provide standard services such as checking and savings accounts, CDs, IRAs, credit cards, mortgages, and loans. They offer life and long-term care insurance through an agreement with third-party provider LPL Financial. New York Community Bancorp also owns investment advisory firm Peter B. Cannell & Co.

Multifamily mortgage loans (with an emphasis on rent-regulated apartment buildings) are the company's key asset, making up approximately 70% of its loan book. New York Community Ban-corp prefers rent-regulated properties because they tend to have lower-than-average tenant turnover and can often be expected to bring in steady income during economic downturns. The company also focuses on loans secured by commercial real estate in New York and New Jersey.

It originates one- to four-family residential mortgages and home equity loans through brokers in all 50 states, but usually sells these loans to government-sponsored entities like Fannie Mae and Freddie Mac with servicing rights retained. After the economic downturn that began in 2007, New York Community Bancorp curtailed its business, construction, and real estate acquisition and development lending.

The company has been growing through acquisitions; it has made about ten since 2000. It acquired the failed AmTrust Bank through an FDIC-assisted transaction in 2009. The deal, which also brought in Ohio Savings, added about 65 branches in new markets and marked the company's first foray beyond the New York metropolitan area. In 2010 New York Community Bancorp expanded its presence in Arizona by acquiring the six branches of the failed Desert Hills Bank, also in an FDIC-assisted transaction. The acquired institution became part of AmTrust Bank.

New York Community Bancorp's previous transactions include the 2007 acquisitions of New Jersey banks PennFed Financial Services and Synergy Financial Group. The company established New York Commercial Bank after buying Long Island Financial in 2005. The following year it added to that division with the acquisition of Atlantic Bank of New York.

New York Community Bancorp typically does not open new stand-alone branches, but has been increasing its presence in its market areas by adding locations inside grocery stores and extending business hours. As the economy shows signs of stirring to life, the company has ramped up its loan production activities. An increase in interest income from loans, higher interest rate margins, and the addition of AmTrust, particularly its mortgage banking business, helped it to increase revenues and profits in 2010.

EXECUTIVES

Chairman, Dominick Ciampa, age 77
President, CEO, and Director, New York Community Bankcorp, New York Community Bank, and New York Com, Joseph R. Ficalora, age 64, $4,941,133 total compensation
EVP and Chief Accounting Officer; EVP, New York Community Bank and New York Commercial Bank, John J. Pinto, age 40, $1,017,118 total compensation
EVP, Chief Corporate Governance Officer, and Corporate Secretary, R. Patrick Quinn
EVP and Director Investor Relations and Corporate Communications, Ilene A. Angarola
SEVP and Chief Lending Officer, New York Community Bancorp and New York Community Bank; SEVP, New Yo, James J. Carpenter, age 50, $1,654,103 total compensation
SEVP and CFO, New York Community Bancorp and New York Community Bank, Thomas R. (Tom) Cangemi, age 42, $1,861,716 total compensation
Director; President and CEO, Atlantic Bank Division, New York Commercial Bank, Spiros J. Voutsinas, age 77
SEVP, COO, and Director; SEVP and COO, New York Community Bank; SEVP, New York Commercial Bank, Robert Wann, age 56, $2,485,264 total compensation
Auditors: KPMG LLP

LOCATIONS

HQ: New York Community Bancorp, Inc.
615 Merrick Ave., Westbury, NY 11590
Phone: 516-683-4100   **Fax:** 516-683-4424
Web: www.mynycb.com

2010 Locations

	No.
New York	157
New Jersey	52
Ohio	28
Florida	25
Arizona	14
Total	**276**

PRODUCTS/OPERATIONS

2010 Sales

	$ mil.	% of total
Interest		
Mortgage & other loans	1,669.9	74
Securities & money market investments	243.9	11
Noninterest		
Mortgage banking income	183.9	8
Fee income	54.6	3
Bank-owned life insurance	28.0	1
Net gains on sales of securities	22.4	1
Other	49.0	2
Total	**2,251.7**	**100**

COMPETITORS

Apple Bank for Savings	Provident Financial
Astoria Financial	Services
Bank of America	Ridgewood Savings Bank
Citigroup	Safra Bank
Emigrant Bank	TD Bank USA
Flushing Financial	Valley National
HSBC USA	Bancorp
Investors Bancorp	Wells Fargo
JPMorgan Chase	

HISTORICAL FINANCIALS

Company Type: Public

Income Statement

FYE: December 31

	ASSETS ($ mil.)	NET INCOME ($ mil.)	INCOME AS % OF ASSETS	EMPLOYEES
12/10	41,190.7	541.0	1.3%	3,883
12/09	42,153.9	398.6	0.9%	3,970
12/08	32,466.9	77.9	0.2%	2,699
12/07	30,579.8	279.1	0.9%	2,834
12/06	28,482.4	232.6	0.8%	2,431
Annual Growth	9.7%	23.5%	—	12.4%

2010 Year-End Financials

Equity as % of assets: 13.42%	Dividends
Return on assets: 1.3%	Yield: 5.3%
Return on equity: 9.8%	Payout: 80.6%
Long-term debt ($ mil.): 427.0	Market value ($ mil.): 8,211.9
No. of shares (mil.): 435.6	Sales ($ mil.): 2,251.7

	STOCK PRICE ($) FY Close	P/E High/Low		PER SHARE ($) Earnings	Dividends	Book Value
12/10	18.85	16	11	1.24	1.00	12.69
12/09	14.51	13	7	1.13	1.00	12.39
12/08	11.96	96	45	0.23	1.00	12.26
12/07	17.58	22	18	0.90	1.00	12.92
12/06	16.10	23	19	0.81	1.00	12.50
Annual Growth	4.0%	—	—	11.2%	(0.0%)	0.4%

NIC

So people can do business with government agencies, NIC helps government agencies plug in to the Internet. The company is a leading provider of outsourced Web portal services for state and local governments. It designs, implements, and operates websites under contracts with thousands of government entities in about 20 states. NIC generates much of its revenue from transaction fees for such services as online license renewals and for providing data on motor vehicle titles and business licenses to insurance companies, lenders, and other authorized organizations. Insurance information provider LexisNexis Risk Solutions (formerly ChoicePoint) accounts for about 33% of the company's sales.

To grow, NIC is striving to renew its existing contracts, which typically run for three- to five-year terms, and to win new business. In addition, the company hopes to develop new applications for government websites from which it can generate transaction fees, especially outside the realm of motor vehicle records.

Along with its Web portal outsourcing business, the company sells back-office software systems designed to help government agencies manage corporate filings and campaign finance reports.

Formerly National Information Consortium, the company was formed through the combination of five different Web services businesses in 1997. It went public during the heyday of the Internet boom in 1999 and was renamed NIC in 2002.

EXECUTIVES

Chairman and CEO, Harry H. Herington, age 51
CFO, Stephen M. (Steve) Kovzan, age 42
EVP Portal Operations, Robert Knapp, age 42
VP Marketing, Christopher (Chris) Neff
VP Sales, Elizabeth Proudfit
Director Partnerships and Alliances, Candy Irven
Chief Accounting Officer, Aimi M. Daughtery, age 40
COO, General Counsel, and Secretary, William F. (Brad) Bradley Jr., age 56
Director Communications and Investor Relations, Nancy S. Beaton
Auditors: PricewaterhouseCoopers LLP

LOCATIONS

HQ: NIC Inc.
25501 W. Valley Pkwy., Ste. 300, Olathe, KS 66061
Phone: 877-234-3468   **Fax:** 913-498-3472
Web: www.nicusa.com

PRODUCTS/OPERATIONS

2009 Sales

	$ mil.
% of total	
Outsourced portals 97	128.6
Software & services 3	4.3
Total **100**	**132.9**

COMPETITORS

Accenture	Manatron
Affiliated Computer Services	MAXIMUS
Agency.com	Microsoft
CGI Group	Official Payments
Computer Sciences	Oracle
	SAIC

Corp.
HP Enterprise Services
IBM Global Services
Idea Integration

Tyler Technologies
Unisys
USTI

HISTORICAL FINANCIALS

Company Type: Public

Income Statement   FYE: December 31

	REVENUE ($ mil.)	NET INCOME ($ mil.)	NET PROFIT MARGIN	EMPLOYEES
12/10	161.5	18.4	11.4%	596
12/09	132.9	13.9	10.5%	606
12/08	100.6	11.9	11.8%	473
12/07	85.8	12.0	14.0%	418
12/06	71.4	10.7	15.0%	339
Annual Growth	**22.6%**	**14.5%**	**—**	**15.1%**

2010 Year-End Financials

Debt ratio: —
Return on equity: 34.5%
Cash ($ mil.): 51.7
Current ratio: 1.77
Long-term debt ($ mil.): —

No. of shares (mil.): 63.7
Dividends
  Yield: —
  Payout: —
Market value ($ mil.): 618.6

	STOCK PRICE ($) FY Close	P/E High/Low	PER SHARE ($) Earnings	Dividends	Book Value
12/10	9.71	35 21	0.28	0.00	0.84
12/09	9.14	43 19	0.22	0.00	1.05
12/08	4.60	47 17	0.19	0.00	1.07
12/07	8.44	47 26	0.19	0.00	1.08
12/06	4.97	44 26	0.17	0.00	1.61
Annual Growth	**18.2%**	**— —**	**13.3%**	**—**	**(15.1%)**

Niska

Niska Gas Storage Partners provides natural gas storage in North America. The company is a large independent owner and operator of natural gas storage facilities in California, Oklahoma, and Alberta, Canada. It has total gas storage capacity of approximately 185.5 billion cu. ft. A small portion of that capacity is contracted from Natural Gas Pipeline Company of America, whose pipeline connects the Gulf Coast to certain midwestern US markets. Customers include natural gas producers and marketers, pipelines, power generators, financial institutions, and municipalities. Niska's revenues come from both multi-year long-term and fixed-fee short-term contracts. The company went public in 2010.

Niska also purchases, stores, and sells its own natural gas as a third source of revenue (which it refers to as optimization revenue). This revenue stream, while smaller, complements its multi-cycle gas contracts, which permit customers to inject and withdraw their natural gas multiple times in one year depending on the seasonal fluctuation of demand for natural gas.

With the $331 million proceeds from its May 2010 IPO, the company believes this flexibility, coupled with the size and strategic location of its storage facilities in major natural gas producing and consuming regions, may give it an upper hand over competitors. Those seeking to penetrate or add substantial storage capacity in these markets face serious challenges because of the scarcity of unexploited reserves that have the physical rock

formation characteristics and proximity to pipeline necessary to store gas economically.

In an effort to continue boosting its organic growth, Niska has near-term projects in progress to expand existing facilities by about 20% at its Alberta-based AECO Hub and California-based Wild Goose locations. A portion of the net proceeds from its offering will help fund the cost of those expansion projects. Other proceeds are expected to be used to repay borrowings under its revolving credit facility.

Funds affiliated with The Carlyle Group and Riverstone Holdings control the company.

EXECUTIVES

President, CEO, and Director, David F. Pope, age 54
CFO, Darin T. Olson, age 36
VP Business Development, Jason S. Kulsky, age 44
VP, General Counsel and Corporate Secretary, Jason A. Dubchak, age 38
COO, Simon Dupéré, age 48
SVP Commercial Operations, Rick J. Staples, age 48
Auditors: KPMG LLP

LOCATIONS

HQ: Niska Gas Storage Partners LLC
1001 Fannin St., Ste. 2500, Houston, TX 77002
Phone: 281-404-1890   **Fax:** 866-452-8832
Web: www.niskapartners.com

COMPETITORS

AEP	PG&E Corporation
ATCO	TransCanada
Buckeye Partners	U.S. Transmission
Enogex	

HISTORICAL FINANCIALS

Company Type: Public

Income Statement   FYE: December 31

	REVENUE ($ mil.)	NET INCOME ($ mil.)	NET PROFIT MARGIN	EMPLOYEES
03/11	230.1	57.5	25.0%	129
03/10*	270.5	53.2	19.7%	126
12/09	140.7	3.2	2.3%	126
03/09	252.2	108.8	43.1%	126
03/08	232.9	48.3	20.7%	0
Annual Growth	**(0.4%)**	**6.0%**	**—**	**1.2%**

*Fiscal year change

2011 Year-End Financials

Debt ratio: 87.2%
Return on equity: 6.3%
Cash ($ mil.): 117.7
Current ratio: 2.59
Long-term debt ($ mil.): 800.0

No. of shares (mil.): 67.6
Dividends
  Yield: 4.0%
  Payout: —
Market value ($ mil.): 1,478.6

	STOCK PRICE ($) FY Close	P/E High/Low	PER SHARE ($) Earnings	Dividends	Book Value
03/11	21.87	— —	(0.00)	0.87	13.56
Annual Growth	**—**	**— —**	**—**	**—**	**—**

North Bay Resources

North Bay Resources owns a number of gold, silver, and platinum properties in British Columbia.

Formerly called Enterayon — pronounced *en-TERRA-yon* — it owns more than 100 exploration properties throughout the Canadian province, none of which are in production. In 2008 the former Enterayon bought up North Bay Resources and took its new subsidiary's name. The next year it acquired a couple more properties, each Canadian prospects adjacent to productive mines owned by the likes of Barrick Gold. In 2011, North Bay acquired the Ruby Mine, a gold project in Northern California, in a deal valued at $7.5 million.

EXECUTIVES

President and CEO, Perry Leopold
Auditors:

LOCATIONS

HQ: North Bay Resources Inc.
 PO Box 162, Skippack, PA 19474
Phone: 215-661-1100
Web: www.northbayresources.com

HISTORICAL FINANCIALS

Company Type: Public

Income Statement
FYE: December 31

	REVENUE ($ mil.)	NET INCOME ($ mil.)	NET PROFIT MARGIN	EMPLOYEES
12/06	43.5	7.1	16.3%	181
12/05	37.8	6.6	17.5%	181
12/04	30.8	5.1	16.6%	172
12/03	26.1	4.4	16.9%	172
12/02	24.3	3.7	15.2%	158
Annual Growth	15.7%	17.7%	—	3.5%

2006 Year-End Financials

Debt ratio: 196.7%
Return on equity: 12.3%
Cash ($ mil.): 74.8
Current ratio: —
Long-term debt ($ mil.): 114.3

No. of shares (mil.): 4.2
Dividends
 Yield: 0.5%
 Payout: 8.6%
Market value ($ mil.): 118.0

	STOCK PRICE ($) FY Close	P/E High/Low		PER SHARE ($) Earnings	Dividends	Book Value
12/06	28.40	19	15	1.66	0.14	13.99
12/05	27.27	21	15	1.56	0.14	12.84
12/04	27.39	23	14	1.23	0.13	11.54
12/03	18.08	16	13	1.14	0.12	10.43
12/02	15.26	18	12	0.94	0.00	9.58
Annual Growth	16.8%	—	—	15.3%	—	9.9%

Northern Oil and Gas

It wouldn't be crude to say that living up north is a gas for this company. Northern Oil and Gas explores for and produces oil and natural gas on properties in the northern US. The company keeps overhead and risk down by purchasing minority, or non-operating, interests in producing oil and gas projects. With leaseholds on more than 151,000 acres in the Bakken and Three Forks oil and gas fields in North Dakota and Montana, the company has developed 15% of its property. That development has yielded proved and probable reserves of nearly 16 million barrels of oil equivalent (BOE),

almost all of it crude. Northern Oil and Gas was formed in 2007.

In 2010 the company drilled 170 exploratory wells and had a 100% success rate, increasing its proved reserves by nearly 160%. It also acquired nearly 57,000 acres across a handful of properties. Northern Oil and Gas looks for projects that are in the early stages of drilling or are about to start drilling.

EXECUTIVES

Chairman and CEO, Michael L. Reger, age 34
President and Director, Ryan R. Gilbertson, age 34
CFO, Chad D. Winter, age 34
VP Business Development, Erik Nerhus
Land Manager, Kruise Kemp
COO, General Counsel, and Secretary, James R. Sankovitz, age 35
Auditors: Mantyla McReynolds LLC

LOCATIONS

HQ: Northern Oil and Gas, Inc.
 315 Manitoba Ave., Ste. 200, Wayzata, MN 55391
Phone: 952-476-9800 **Fax:** 952-476-9801
Web: www.northernoil.com

COMPETITORS

Adams Resources	EOG
American Oil & Gas	Exxon Mobil
Anadarko Petroleum	Hunt Consolidated
Apache	Jones Energy
BP	Key Energy
Cabot Oil & Gas	National Fuel Gas
Chesapeake Energy	Noble Energy
Chevron	Pioneer Natural
Cimarex	Resources
ConocoPhillips	Royal Dutch Shell
Devon Energy	

HISTORICAL FINANCIALS

Company Type: Public

Income Statement
FYE: December 31

	REVENUE ($ mil.)	NET INCOME ($ mil.)	NET PROFIT MARGIN	EMPLOYEES
12/10	44.6	6.9	15.5%	11
12/09	14.2	2.8	19.7%	8
12/08	3.5	2.4	68.6%	4
12/02	0.0	—	—	0
12/01	0.0	—	—	0
Annual Growth	—	—	—	65.8%

2010 Year-End Financials

Debt ratio: —
Return on equity: 1.6%
Cash ($ mil.): 152.1
Current ratio: 3.91
Long-term debt ($ mil.): —

No. of shares (mil.): 62.1
Dividends
 Yield: —
 Payout: —
Market value ($ mil.): 1,690.5

	STOCK PRICE ($) FY Close	P/E High/Low		PER SHARE ($) Earnings	Dividends	Book Value
12/10	27.21	203	75	0.14	0.00	7.01
12/09	11.84	158	25	0.08	0.00	2.81
12/08	2.60	234	29	0.07	0.00	1.45
12/02	6.95	—	—	(0.18)	0.00	0.65
Annual Growth	57.6%	—	—	—	—	121.3%

NuVasive

When a back is seriously out of whack, NuVasive has some options. The company makes and markets medical devices for the surgical treatment of spinal disorders. NuVasive's products are primarily used in spinal fusion surgeries. Its minimally disruptive Maximum Access Surgery (MAS) platform enables surgeons to access the spine from the side of the body instead of from the front or back, and helps them avoid hitting nerves. NuVasive also offers the mesh, plates, screws, and biological implants (including allograft tissue) used with its MAS system. The company sells its FDA-approved products through a network of exclusive independent sales agencies, as well as NuVasive employees who target specific regions.

NuVasive's goal is to make its products part of the standard procedure for minimally invasive spinal surgery. The company's strategy for expanding its product line includes internal development as well as acquisition and licensing of new products and technologies.

To strengthen its presence in the bone grafting market, NuVasive has made a string of biologics acquisitions and investments. It paid $16 million to buy a bone grafting technology from Radius Medical in 2007, adding the FormaGraft bone void filler to its product line. It then acquired the Osteocel business of Osiris Therapeutics in 2008. Osteocel is an adult stem-cell bone graft used for bone regeneration in orthopedic procedures and at one point was the only commercially available stem-cell product in the US. NuVasive paid $35 million for the business, plus an additional $50 million in potential milestone payments, and a $52 million, 18-month product supply agreement with Osiris. In early 2009 the company acquired 40% of Netherlands-based Progentix to help fund its development of a synthetic bone substitute.

Cervical disc replacement technology — the holy grail for spinal device makers — is advancing rapidly. To keep pace, NuVasive acquired medical device developer Cervitech in 2009. The $47 million purchase gave NuVasive Cervitech's PCM cervical disc replacement system which is already in late-stage development.

In late 2011 the company acquired the Maryland-based Impulse Monitoring Inc. (IMI) for $80 million. IMI provides outsourcing of intraoperative monitioring services utilizing its team of neurophysiologists to hospitals and surgeons during spine, cardio, ENT, brain and orthopedic procedures.

NuVasive maintains a facility in California where it trains doctors in the use of its products. It ships its products directly to doctors overnight from a distribution facility in Tennessee. The company's revenues primarily come from the sale of disposable materials and implants. The full system of software and instruments are loaned to hospitals for free as long as they keep ordering disposables and implants. A small portion of the company's revenues are from the sale of instruments and systems.

The US accounts for the majority of NuVasive's sales, but it is working to establish its products in Europe and Asia. The first hurdle is obtaining regulatory approval for all of the components in its platform for each country it seeks to enter.

EXECUTIVES

Chairman and CEO, Alexis V. Lukianov, age 55, $6,347,034 total compensation
President and COO, Keith C. Valentine, age 43, $3,844,209 total compensation
President, Americas, Patrick S. (Pat) Miles, age 45, $2,917,074 total compensation
EVP and CFO, Michael J. Lambert, age 49, $589,617 total compensation
EVP, Americas, Sales, Jeffrey P. (Jeff) Rydin, age 44, $2,229,368 total compensation
EVP Biologics, Tyler P. Lipschultz
EVP, Europe, Stephan Siemers
EVP Corporate Development, General Counsel, and Secretary, Jason M. Hannon, age 39
EVP, Asia/Pacific, Takaaki Tanaka
VP and Chief Patent Counsel, Jonathan D. Spangler, age 43
VP Accounting, Quentin Blackford
VP Industry and Investor Relations, Patrick F. Williams
SVP Research and Clinical Resources, G. Bryan Cornwall, age 46
SVP Operations, William L. Reynolds
Auditors: Ernst & Young LLP

LOCATIONS

HQ: NuVasive, Inc.
7475 Lusk Blvd., San Diego, CA 92121
Phone: 858-909-1800   **Fax:** 858-909-2000
Web: www.nuvasive.com

PRODUCTS/OPERATIONS

Selected Products

Maximum Access Surgery (MAS) Platform
  Armada (pedicle screw system)
  CoRoent (implants, fixation systems)
  FormaGraft (biologic grafting material)
  MaXcess (retraction system for spine access)
  NeuroVision (software to avoid nerves)
  Osteocel (biologic grafting material)

COMPETITORS

Alphatec Spine	Orthofix
Biomet	Stryker
DePuy Spine	Synthes
Integra LifeSciences	Zimmer Holdings
Interpore	
Medtronic Sofamor	
Danek	

HISTORICAL FINANCIALS

Company Type: Public

Income Statement

FYE: December 31

	REVENUE ($ mil.)	NET INCOME ($ mil.)	NET PROFIT MARGIN	EMPLOYEES
12/10	478.2	78.3	16.4%	789
12/09	370.3	5.8	1.6%	665
12/08	250.1	(27.5)	—	444
12/07	154.3	(11.3)	—	345
12/06	98.1	(47.9)	—	233
Annual Growth	**48.6%**	**—**	**—**	**35.7%**

2010 Year-End Financials

Debt ratio: 53.0%	No. of shares (mil.): 39.5
Return on equity: 18.0%	Dividends
Cash ($ mil.): 92.6	Yield: —
Current ratio: 3.41	Payout: —
Long-term debt ($ mil.): 230.0	Market value ($ mil.): 1,013.9

	STOCK PRICE ($) FY Close	P/E High/Low	PER SHARE ($) Earnings	Dividends	Book Value
12/10	25.65	25 12	1.85	0.00	10.99
12/09	31.98	300 161	0.15	0.00	7.64
12/08	34.65	— —	(0.77)	0.00	5.19
12/07	39.52	— —	(0.32)	0.00	5.60
12/06	23.10	— —	(1.47)	0.00	5.21
Annual Growth	**2.7%**	**— —**	**—**	**—**	**20.5%**

NxStage

Patients suffering from end-stage renal disease can turn to NxStage Medical for help. The medical device company operates through two segments: System One and In-Center. The System One division features NxStage Medical's lead product, the System One portable hemodialysis machine, which can be used by patients at home or by professionals in a hospital setting. The device is also marketed to hospitals for critical care and to dialysis clinics that want to create or expand their services to home-based patients. The In-Center division sells NxStage Medical's blood tubing sets and needles to dialysis clinics primarily through distributor relationships.

Typically, customers rent the System One equipment, but NxStage Medical's two largest customers DaVita and Fresenius purchase the product. Together the two companies, which represent about 60% of the US dialysis market, account for more than half of NxStage Medical's System One division income.

Under an agreement that expires in 2013, NxStage Medical also serves as DaVita's primary supplier of safety needle equipment for its dialysis centers. Those products include the MasterGuard and ButtonHole safety needle sets sold through the In-Center segment.

The In-Center segment is highly concentrated with just a few major buyers. The division sells blood tubing sets and needles to customers in independent dialysis clinics as well as dialysis chains. NxStage Medical's two largest distributors in this segment are Henry Schein and Gambro . Revenues from those two companies account for 80% of the In-House segment's income.

NxStage is hoping agreements such as those it has with Henry Schein and Gambro Renal will help it finally reach profitability. Since its inception in 1998, NxStage has never recorded a profit; however in recent years it has improved its operating margins and cash flow, particularly in its Home and Critical Care segment. Its improved margins can be attributed to stronger sales and lower overall costs as a result of streamlining efforts and improvements made to its manufacturing infrastructure. For example, NxStage is not renewing a supplier agreement with Kawasumi Laboratories when it expires in 2012 for its needles and blood tubing. Instead NxStage will shift manufacturing in-house to one of its Mexican manufacturing facilities.

The company is also seeking to improve its profitability and increase sales by expanding internationally. Currently, substantially all of NxStage Medical's sales are generated in the US, however, it has formed several distribution agreements with international partners for the sale of the System One in Europe and the Middle East.

EXECUTIVES

Chairman, Philippe O. Chambon, age 53
President, CEO, and Director, Jeffrey H. (Jeff) Burbank, age 48, $578,155 total compensation
President North America, Joseph E. (Joe) Turk Jr., age 43, $354,160 total compensation
VP Manufacturing Operations, William (Bill) Weigel
VP, Research and Development, Dennis M. (Denny) Treu
VP Sales, Matt Pearman
VP Disposables Engineering, James Brugger
VP and General Manager, Critical Care, John C. Westman
VP Human Resources, Darren R. Scandone, age 57
VP Investor Relations, Kristen K. Sheppard
VP Human Resources, Elaine Palome
VP and General Manager, Home Market, Jeff Smith, age 51
VP and General Manager, In-Center Market, Mark Florence
VP and General Manager Critical Care Therapies, Elise A. Tordella
SVP Quality, Regulatory, and Clinical Affairs, Michael J. (Mike) Webb, age 44, $293,781 total compensation
SVP, General Counsel, and Secretary, Winifred L. (Winnie) Swan, age 46, $446,848 total compensation
Managing Director, EIR Medical, Martin Stillig
SVP Manufacturing Operations, Tom Shea, age 48
Chief Medical Advisor, Alan R. Hull
SVP, CFO, and Treasurer, Robert S. Brown, age 52, $344,160 total compensation
Auditors: Ernst & Young LLP

LOCATIONS

HQ: NxStage Medical, Inc.
439 S. Union St., 5th Fl., Lawrence, MA 01843
Phone: 978-687-4700   **Fax:** 978-687-4809
Web: www.nxstage.com

PRODUCTS/OPERATIONS

2010 Sales

	$ mil.	% of total
Home	85.7	48
In-center	65.4	36
Critical care	28.1	16
Total	**179.2**	**100**

COMPETITORS

B. Braun Medical (UK)	Fresenius
B. Braun Melsungen	Gambro AB
Baxter International	Renal Advantage
Cantel Medical	Rockwell Medical
Dialysis Clinic Inc	Terumo

HISTORICAL FINANCIALS

Company Type: Public

Income Statement

FYE: December 31

	REVENUE ($ mil.)	NET INCOME ($ mil.)	NET PROFIT MARGIN	EMPLOYEES
12/10	179.2	(31.7)	—	1,600
12/09	148.7	(43.5)	—	1,535
12/08	128.8	(51.2)	—	1,287
12/07	60.0	(58.4)	—	1,465
12/06	20.8	(39.6)	—	211
Annual Growth	**71.3%**	**—**	**—**	**65.9%**

2010 Year-End Financials

Debt ratio: 26.6%
Return on equity: —
Cash ($ mil.): 104.3
Current ratio: 4.27
Long-term debt ($ mil.): 40.5

No. of shares (mil.): 53.7
Dividends
  Yield: —
  Payout: —
Market value ($ mil.): 1,336.5

	STOCK PRICE ($) FY Close	P/E High/Low		PER SHARE ($) Earnings	Dividends	Book Value
12/10	24.88	—	—	(0.66)	0.00	2.83
12/09	8.35	—	—	(0.93)	0.00	1.91
12/08	2.67	—	—	(1.23)	0.00	2.63
12/07	15.17	—	—	(1.86)	0.00	3.54
12/06	8.38	—	—	(1.60)	0.00	3.00
Annual Growth	31.3%	—	—	—	—	(1.5%)

Oasis Petroleum

Oasis Petroleum is combing the northern US for a watering hole made of oil. The independent exploration and production company acquires and develops oil and gas resources in the Williston Basin of Montana and North Dakota, specifically in the Bakken and Three Forks formation. In 2009 Oasis Petroleum had estimated net proved reserves of 13.3 million barrels of oil equivalent from almost 300,000 net acres of land holdings. The company reports an average daily production of about 2,000 barrels of oil from 70 producing wells. (It sells most of its oil to marketing companies Tesoro and Texon.) Oasis Petroleum was formed in 2007 by former executives of Burlington Resources. The company filed to go public in 2010.

Oasis Petroleum plans to use the proceeds from its initial public offering to pay down debt and fund exploration activities. The company chose to focus on the Williston Basin because of its oil-rich reserves and the management's previous experience there. (With 3.65 billion barrels of recoverable oil reserves, the US Geological Survey called the basin the largest continuous oil accumulation ever assessed in the continental US.) The Williston Basin also maintains an established infrastructure and claims minimal regulatory delays. Oasis Petroleum plans to aggressively develop its leasehold there, aiming to operate five drilling rigs by 2011, which could drill as many as 60 wells per year.

The company has yet to turn a profit, since it began acquiring land leases and exploring for oil as soon as it was formed. Oasis Petroleum purchased its Williston Basin assets for a total of $137 million from Bill Barrett Corporation, Fidelity Exploration & Production Company (a subsidiary of MDU Resources), and Kerogen Resources, Inc. Most of its start-up financing was provided by private equity firm EnCap Investments, which was the majority shareholder of Oasis Petroleum. Now that the company has completed its acquisitions and plans to public, it expects revenues to increase.

Growing its asset base, in 2010 the company agreed to buy 10,000 acres of land, primarily in Richland County, Montana, for about $30 million.

EXECUTIVES

Chairman, President, and CEO, Thomas B. (Tommy) Nusz, age 51, $765,756 total compensation

---

EVP, COO, and Director, Taylor L. Reid, age 48, $540,907 total compensation
VP Development Geology, Dean A. Gilbert
VP and Assistant Controller, Steven C. Ellsberry, age 64
VP Operations Engineering, Robin E. Hesketh, age 52
VP Land and Contracts, Thomas F. Hawkins, age 57
VP Geophysics, Robert L. Stovall, age 53
SVP Finance, Michael H. Lou, age 36
SVP Land, Kent O. Beers, age 61, $418,632 total compensation
SVP and Chief Accounting Officer, Roy W. Mace, age 51, $259,215 total compensation
SVP Exploration, Robert J. Candito, age 56
SVP Asset Management, H. Brett Newton, age 44
SVP Operations, Walter S. Smithwick, age 51, $317,000 total compensation
Auditors: PricewaterhouseCoopers LLP

LOCATIONS

HQ: Oasis Petroleum LLC
1001 Fannin St., Ste. 1500, Houston, TX 77002
Phone: 281-404-9500

PRODUCTS/OPERATIONS

2009 Sales

	$ in mil.	% of total
Oil	36.4	96
Natural gas	1.4	4
Total	**37.8**	**100**

COMPETITORS

BP	Kodiak Oil & Gas
ConocoPhillips	Marathon Oil
Earthstone Energy	Royal Dutch Shell
Encore Energy	SM Energy
Exxon Mobil	Windsor Energy
GeoResources	Resources
Gulfport Energy	

HISTORICAL FINANCIALS

Company Type: Public

Income Statement

FYE: December 31

	REVENUE ($ mil.)	NET INCOME ($ mil.)	NET PROFIT MARGIN	EMPLOYEES
12/10	128.9	(29.7)	—	62
12/09	37.8	(15.2)	—	27
12/08	34.7	(34.4)	—	0
Annual Growth	92.7%	—	—	129.6%

2010 Year-End Financials

Debt ratio: —
Return on equity: —
Cash ($ mil.): 143.5
Current ratio: 2.50
Long-term debt ($ mil.): —

No. of shares (mil.): 92.2
Dividends
  Yield: —
  Payout: —
Market value ($ mil.): 2,501.6

	STOCK PRICE ($) FY Close	P/E High/Low		PER SHARE ($) Earnings	Dividends	Book Value
12/10	27.12	—	—	(0.61)	0.00	5.98
Annual Growth	—	—	—	—	—	—

Och-Ziff Capital Management

In the marvelous land of OZ, good investments are king. Och-Ziff Capital Management Group provides a variety of alternative asset management services for more than 600 fund investors through offices in New York and overseas in Mumbai, Beijing, Hong Kong, and London. Och-Ziff Capital Management Group's investment strategies include private equity, merger arbitrage, and equity restructuring, among others. With around $30 billion in assets under management, the majority of its equity holdings are invested in Europe and Asia. The hedge fund firm, which has some 125 investment professionals including around 20 partners, began operations in 1994.

The marketplace was not kind to Och-Ziff during the global financial crisis. Overall, US hedge funds lost massive amounts during the downturn. While Och-Ziff fared somewhat better than average, it still saw significant losses, primarily from negative investment performance and customer redemptions. Assets under management fell from $33 billion to $22 billion in 2008, and continued downward, hitting $20 billion in April 2009.

However, things began to look up again and its funds rebounded in 2010 and by the following year the firm's assets under management had climbed to more than $25 billion. Och-Ziff attributes its resiliency to its diverse multi-strategy model, which allows the firm to take advantage of a variety of opportunities in the market.

Och-Ziff is preparing for more growth spurred mostly by institutional investors. The firm is gaining new business from such investors who are attracted to its long-held policy of openness and transparency (it's the only US public hedge fund that reports fund performance and assets under management to the SEC every month). Institutional investors also are looking to hedge funds to further diversify their investments.

The company manages four main funds: its OZ Master Fund; OZ Europe Master Fund; OZ Asia Master Fund; and OZ Global Special Investments Master Fund. The OZ Global Special Investments fund invests in structured and distressed credit.

Daniel Och (a former Goldman Sachs trader) and the Ziff family founded the company. Och controls more than 70% of Och-Ziff Capital Management Group; Dubai-based sovereign wealth fund DIC Sahir owns around 10%.

EXECUTIVES

Chairman, CEO, and Executive Managing Director, Daniel S. Och, age 50, $9,479,458 total compensation
Executive Managing Director, COO, CFO, and Board Member, Joel M. Frank, age 55, $470,678 total compensation
Executive Managing Director and Head Global Convertible and Derivative Arbitrage, Harold Kelly, age 47
Executive Managing Director, Head US Investing, and Board Member, David Windreich, age 53, $2,234,452 total compensation
Executive Managing Director and Head Asian Investing; Director Och-Ziff Consulting (Beijing), Zoltan Varga, age 37, $76,925,680 total compensation
Executive Managing Director, Chief Legal Officer, Chief Compliance Officer, and Secretary, Jeffrey C. Blockinger, age 41, $11,289,271 total compensation

Executive Managing Director and Head European Investing, Michael Cohen, age 39, $1,423,249 total compensation

Auditors: Ernst & Young LLP

LOCATIONS

HQ: Och-Ziff Capital Management Group LLC
9 W. 57th St., 39th Fl., New York, NY 10019
Phone: 212-790-0041
Web: ozcap.com

PRODUCTS/OPERATIONS

2010 Sales

	$ mil.	% of total
Incentive income	446.2	48
Management fees	437.8	47
Och-Ziff funds income	38.5	5
Other	2.0	-
Total	**924.5**	**100**

2010 Assets Under Management

	% of total
OZ Master Fund	70
OZ Europe Master Fund	11
OZ Asia Master Fund	5
OZ Global Special Fund	4
Other	10
Total	**100**

COMPETITORS

AllianceBernstein
AXA Financial
Charles Schwab
Citigroup
Elliott Management

Greenlight Capital
Renaissance
 Technologies LLC
UBS Financial Services

HISTORICAL FINANCIALS

Company Type: Public

Income Statement

FYE: December 31

	REVENUE ($ mil.)	NET INCOME ($ mil.)	NET PROFIT MARGIN	EMPLOYEES
12/10	924.5	(294.4)	—	405
12/09	743.3	(297.4)	—	378
12/08	604.4	(510.6)	—	412
12/07	1,502.0	(915.0)	—	400
12/06	1,005.8	588.0	58.5%	300
Annual Growth	(2.1%)	—	—	7.8%

2010 Year-End Financials

Debt ratio: —
Return on equity: —
Cash ($ mil.): 117.6
Current ratio: 1.58
Long-term debt ($ mil.): 639.5

No. of shares (mil.): 369.4
Dividends
 Yield: 5.6%
 Payout: —
Market value ($ mil.): 5,755.4

	STOCK PRICE ($) FY Close	P/E High/Low	PER SHARE ($) Earnings	Dividends	Book Value
12/10	15.58	— —	(3.35)	0.88	(0.95)
12/09	13.74	— —	(3.79)	0.19	(1.04)
12/08	5.15	— —	(6.86)	0.22	(1.21)
12/07	26.28	— —	(0.00)	0.00	(0.00)
Annual Growth	(16.0%)	— —	—	—	—

Oclaro

And you thought splitting hairs was tedious. Oclaro (formerly Bookham) integrates the light-processing functions of optical networking components onto silicon chips, which it then puts into communications products such as transceivers, transponders, transmitters, receivers, and modulators. Typical devices for dividing wavelengths of light combine several components, such as tunable lasers, lenses, and filters. The global company gets around 80% of sales from outside the US. In early 2009 Bookham merged with rival Avanex in a stock-swap transaction and changed its name to Oclaro.

The combination of Avanex and Bookham continues a trend of consolidation among suppliers of optical components. The merger gives the company greater vertical integration, allowing it to control product development from chip and component design through subsystem manufacturing. It also makes Oclaro one of the top suppliers to the metro and long-haul networking market, and helps the company diversify into new growth markets such as biotechnology, medical instrumentation, and consumer electronics. The worldwide recession may be pushing more such companies into mergers in an industry historically prone to consolidation.

Another benefit of the merger is the expansion of in-house wafer manufacturing capacity, which lets the company respond more quickly to changes in customers' needs. It is often required to tailor new products to customer specifications, which can include new technologies. Oclaro's major customers include Alcatel-Lucent and Huawei Technologies. Huawei has named Oclaro a strategic supplier, which means the two will collaborate to develop new products. Other customers include Ciena, Cisco Systems, Tellabs, Nokia Siemens Networks, and Ericsson.

One of the drawbacks of the merger is the debt each of the companies contributed after years of losses. At the end of fiscal 2010, Oclaro had an accumulated deficit of about $1.1 billion. The company only recently achieved profitability, reporting net income of $12.4 million for 2010. Its sales for that year jumped by 86% over the prior period, primarily due to the combined companies' operations for a full year, along with a general improvement in market conditions in 2010 and gains in market share across most of its product lines. Its profits would have been higher had its operating expenses not also skyrocketed; the 73% increase was also primarily related to the merger with Avanex.

In addition to expanding its internal capabilities, Oclaro buys companies to spur growth. In 2010 it bought Mintera Corporation, a provider of optical transport subsystems products. The deal solidified Oclaro's position in the 40 Gbps regional and metro networks and enabled it to expand into the 40 Gbps LH and the 100 Gbps Coherent markets. Late in 2009 Oclaro expanded its optical networking business when it acquired Xtellus, adding ROADM (reconfigurable optical add/drop multiplexer) technology and optical modules for metro and long-haul networking applications. The purchase gave Oclaro the capability to provide complete wavelength selective switch systems for optical networks.

The company also selectively divests operations no longer considered strategic. In July 2009 Oclaro sold its New Focus subsidiary to competitor Newport in exchange for Newport's high-power laser diode manufacturing operations, located in Tucson, Arizona, and $3 million in cash. Oclaro became a supplier of high-power diodes to Newport, which uses the parts in lasers made by its Spectra-Physics subsidiary. The acquisition of Newport's laser diodes product line adds products for the biotechnology and medical industries and makes the company one of the top global suppliers of high power laser diodes. Oclaro is transferring the Arizona manufacturing operations to its European fabs, a move that it is counting on to reduce costs.

In response to changes in its business, Oclaro reorganized its business segments. Previously broken up into an optics unit and a research and industrial division (the latter representing the New Focus subsidiary), the company set up two new segments: telecom (optical transmission and regeneration components for the telecommunications, data communications, aerospace, and military industries) and advanced photonics solutions (optical and photonics products for biotechnology, medical, material processing, and other industrial applications). With the sale of New Focus, Oclaro no longer sells to semiconductor equipment manufacturers and research institutions.

Bookham president and CEO Alain Couder became president and CEO of the merged venture, which took its name — Oclaro — from combining the words "optical" and "clarity."

EXECUTIVES

Chairman, Bernard J. Couillaud, age 67
CFO, Jerry Turin, age 49, $473,138 total compensation
President, CEO, and Director, Alain Couder, age 65, $1,299,276 total compensation
EVP Human Resources, Kathy Zwickert
EVP and General Manager, Transmission Division, Adam Price, age 37
EVP and Division Manager, Richard Smart, age 45
EVP, General Counsel and Secretary, Kate H. Rundle, age 54, $430,774 total compensation
COO and Acting CTO, James (Jim) Haynes, age 49, $681,053 total compensation
Chief Commercial Officer, Yves LeMaitre, age 47, $375,233 total compensation
Auditors: Ernst & Young LLP

LOCATIONS

HQ: Oclaro, Inc.
2584 Junction Ave., San Jose, CA 95134
Phone: 408-383-1400   **Fax:** 408-919-6083
Web: oclaro.com

2010 Sales

	$ mil.	% of total
Asia/Pacific	176.5	45
Europe	96.4	25
US	75.9	19
Canada	14.8	4
Other regions	28.9	7
Total	**392.5**	**100**

PRODUCTS/OPERATIONS

2010 Sales

	$ mil.	% of total
Telecom	341.9	87
Advanced photonics solutions	50.6	13
Total	**392.5**	**100**

Selected Products

Amplifiers
Continuous wave lasers
Fixed wavelength laser transmitters
Modulators
Narrow tunable lasers

Passive filters
Pump laser diodes
Receivers
Software
Thin film filters
Transceivers
Transponder modules
Tunable laser transmitters
VCSEL products (low-power polarized products used in mouse and data communications applications)
Wideband optical modulator driver amplifiers

COMPETITORS

Avago Technologies	Opnext
CyOptics	Sumitomo Electric
Finisar	Thorlabs Quantum
IPG Photonics	Electronics
JDS Uniphase	WaveSplitter
Oplink Communications	

HISTORICAL FINANCIALS

Company Type: Public

Income Statement

FYE: Sunday closest to June 30

	REVENUE ($ mil.)	NET INCOME ($ mil.)	NET PROFIT MARGIN	EMPLOYEES
06/11	466.5	(46.4)	—	3,085
06/10	392.5	12.4	3.2%	2,865
06/09	210.9	(32.2)	—	2,585
06/08	235.5	(23.4)	—	2,393
06/07	202.8	(82.2)	—	1,985
Annual Growth	23.2%	—	—	11.7%

2011 Year-End Financials

Debt ratio: —	No. of shares (mil.): 50.5
Return on equity: —	Dividends
Cash ($ mil.): 62.8	Yield: —
Current ratio: 2.09	Payout: —
Long-term debt ($ mil.): —	Market value ($ mil.): 339.1

	STOCK PRICE ($) FY Close	P/E High/Low		PER SHARE ($) Earnings	Dividends	Book Value
06/11	6.72	—	—	(0.96)	0.00	4.54
06/10	11.09	55	9	0.29	0.00	5.94
06/09	3.18	—	—	(1.40)	0.00	3.77
06/08	8.45	—	—	(1.25)	0.00	7.40
06/07	11.25	—	—	(5.85)	0.00	7.22
Annual Growth	(12.1%)	—	—	—	—	(11.0%)

OCZ Technology

You down with OCZ? You should be, because OCZ Technology's solid-state drives (SSDs) and memory modules are found in PCs, servers, and industrial equipment. The company designs, manufactures, and sells high-performance SSDs, which use flash memory chips and are a smaller, faster, and more energy-efficient storage device than traditional hard disk drives. OCZ offers more than 450 products to about 375 customers in 69 countries, including retailers such as Amazon, original equipment manufacturers (OEMs), and computer distributors (Newegg accounted for almost 20% of sales in 2010). More than half of the company's sales come from outside the US. Co-founder and CEO Ryan Peterson owns almost 20% of its stock.

Besides SSDs and memory modules, OCZ designs, manufactures, and distributes other high-performance components for computing devices and systems, such as thermal management hardware (to keep electronics from overheating), AC/DC switching power supply units (PSUs), and Secure Digital (SD) memory cards used in portable consumer electronics. Memory products however, are the bulk of its business, accounting for 85% of sales in 2010; PSUs made up the remaining 15%. Samsung, Toshiba, and Intel are its key suppliers for integrated circuits (IC) used in flash memory products.

OCZ is focused on growing its SSD business and began discontinuing its unprofitable DRAM module products in 2010. Unlike flash memory, DRAM (dynamic random access memory) loses its data once it's unplugged; the technology is older than flash and its market is already saturated by major semiconductor companies such as Intel and Samsung. OCZ announced it was phasing out certain commodity-level DRAM module products (about 70% of its product portfolio) in August 2010, then decided to cut its losses and scrap the entire business in early 2011, citing continued weakness in the global market for DRAM.

The market for SSDs remains strong - OCZ reported unit sales were up almost 200% from 2009 to 2010, and the average price of an SSD was up by almost 15%. However, the DRAM legacy business took a toll on the company's earnings and overall revenue dropped about 8% in fiscal 2010. Including DRAM and PSU products, OCZ sold fewer products overall, down 25% from 3.4 million in 2009 to 2.6 million in 2010. In general, the decrease in unit sales resulted from constraints in working capital, which prevented OCZ from buying enough raw materials necessary to meet consumer demand. For fiscal 2011, DRAM will account for less than 20% of sales, and projections show revenues back up 25% for the year.

Like other electronics manufacturers, OCZ's products are made overseas. The company has one 40,000-sq.-ft. plant in Taiwan, and it opened a second one in October 2010. The new 20,000-sq.-ft. plant increases the company's manufacturing capacity for SSDs from 50,000 units a month to 140,000 units a month.

In March 2011 the company announced its plan one of its component suppliers. OCZ offered $32 million in stock for Indilinx, a South Korea-based fabless provider of flash controllers for SSDs. Indilinx's components have been used in OCZ's drives since 2008.

OCZ was founded in 2002 and made its first two acquisitions five years later, buying PC Power and Cooling, Inc. and Silicon Data Inc., doing business as Hypersonic PC Systems. PC Power and Cooling made power supply units (PSUs), and the company continues to sell both PC Power and Cooling and OCZ-branded PSUs to this day. Silicon Data was a boutique manufacturer of high-performance gaming PCs and laptops. OCZ stopped making Hypersonic PC products in 2010.

OCZ stands for "overclockers," a term used to describe someone who modifies their computer to run faster. By using SSDs to boost data storage, many of OCZ's customers are overclockers.

HISTORY

OCZ was founded in 2002 and listed on the London Stock Exchange's alternative investment market (AIM) in 2006. The next year it made its first two acquisitions, buying PC Power and Cooling, Inc. and Silicon Data Inc., doing business as Hypersonic PC Systems. PC Power and Cooling made power supply units (PSUs), and the company continues to sell both PC Power and Cooling and OCZ-branded PSUs to this day. Silicon Data was a boutique manufacturer of high-performance gaming PCs and laptops. OCZ stopped making Hypersonic PC products in 2010.

In April 2009 OCZ delisted from the London AIM. In the beginning of 2010 it listed on the OTC market in the US for two months, then moved up to the NASDAQ in April of that year.

EXECUTIVES

CEO and Director, Ryan M. Petersen, age 35
CFO and Director, Kerry T. Smith, age 48
EVP and Chief Marketing Officer, Alex Mei, age 34
VP Technology Development, Michael Schuette
VP Purchasing, Eugene Chang
VP Operations Power Management, Bob Roark
SVP Operations, John Apps
SVP Sales, Justin Shong, age 42
Auditors:

LOCATIONS

HQ: OCZ Technology Group, Inc.
6373 San Ignacio Ave., San Jose, CA 95119
Phone: 408-733-8400   **Fax:** 408-733-5200
Web: www.ocztechnology.com

2010 Sales

	$ mil.	% of total
US	62.5	43
Europe, Middle East & Africa	56.5	39
Rest of world	17.3	13
Canada	7.6	5
Total	**143.9**	**100**

PRODUCTS/OPERATIONS

2010 Sales

	$ mil.	% of total
Memory processing	72.8	51
Solid state drives & flash memory storage	49.6	34
Power supplies	21.5	15
Total	**143.9**	**100**

Selected Products

SSDs and Flash Products:
  MLC-based solid state disk drives
  SLC-based solid state disk drives
  USB key drives
  Normal and high-capacity SD and Micro SD Cards
Power Supply:
  High efficiency PSUs
  High wattage power supplies
  Low noise power supplies
  Modular PSUs
DRAM Modules (discontinued in 2010):
  High speed/low-latency DIMMs
  High speed/low-latency SODIMMs
  Industry standard SODIMMs
  Industry standard unbuffered DIMM
  Registered DIMMs

COMPETITORS

Centon Electronics	SMART Modular
Corsair	Technologies
Fusion-io	STEC
Intel	Unigen
Kingston Technology	Viking Modular
Micron Technology	Solutions
Samsung Electronics	Western Digital
SanDisk	

HISTORICAL FINANCIALS

Company Type: Public

Income Statement

FYE: February 28

	REVENUE ($ mil.)	NET INCOME ($ mil.)	NET PROFIT MARGIN	EMPLOYEES
02/11	190.1	(30.0)	—	422
02/10*	144.0	(13.5)	—	312
12/06	67.8	(1.8)	—	0
12/05	35.7	(0.6)	—	0
Annual Growth	32.1%	—	—	35.3%

*Fiscal year change

2011 Year-End Financials

Debt ratio: —
Return on equity: —
Cash ($ mil.): 17.5
Current ratio: 1.14
Long-term debt ($ mil.): —

No. of shares (mil.): 35.4
Dividends
  Yield: —
  Payout: —
Market value ($ mil.): 268.0

	STOCK PRICE ($) FY Close	P/E High/Low	PER SHARE ($) Earnings	Dividends	Book Value
02/11	7.57	— —	(1.05)	0.00	0.37
02/10*	5.25	— —	(0.64)	0.00	0.30
Annual Growth	44.2%	— —	—	—	24.8%

*Fiscal year change

Odyssey Marine Exploration

Gone are the days when one-eyed, peg-legged buccaneers counted their steps to where X marked the spot of lost treasure. Odyssey Marine Exploration, a new breed of treasure hunter, uses sonar, magnetometers, and remotely operated vehicles (ROVs) to locate and excavate shipwrecks. The company focuses on deepwater projects where the booty is less susceptible to damage and less likely to have been salvaged. Odyssey Marine Exploration surveys and maps seabeds too; its experience covers more than 10,000 sq. mi. The company sells artifacts salvaged from shipwrecks — most recently, thousands of silver and gold coins from an Atlantic Ocean site code-named Black Swan. Two coin dealers represent more than half of sales.

EXECUTIVES

Chairman Emeritus, John C. Morris, age 61, $1,411,416 total compensation
Chairman and CEO, Gregory P. (Greg) Stemm, age 53, $674,762 total compensation
President, COO, and Director, Mark D. Gordon, age 50, $343,163 total compensation
CFO, Michael J. (Mike) Holmes, age 61, $382,430 total compensation
VP and General Counsel, Melinda J. MacConnel
VP Communications, Laura L. Barton, age 48, $221,400 total compensation
Secretary and Treasurer, David A. Morris, age 60, $292,380 total compensation
Manager Corporate Communications, Natja Igney
Principal Accounting Officer, Jay A. Nudi, age 47
Auditors: Ferlita, Walsh & Gonzalez, PA

LOCATIONS

HQ: Odyssey Marine Exploration, Inc.
  5215 W. Laurel St., Tampa, FL 33607
Phone: 813-876-1776   **Fax:** 813-876-1777
Web: shipwreck.net

PRODUCTS/OPERATIONS

2007 Sales

	$ mil.
% of total	
Shipwreck exploration 93	5.7
Themed attractions 7	0.4
Total 100	**6.1**

COMPETITORS

A.P. Møller - Mærsk
Neptune Orient
RMS Titanic
Sovereign Exploration Associates

HISTORICAL FINANCIALS

Company Type: Public

Income Statement

FYE: December 31

	REVENUE ($ mil.)	NET INCOME ($ mil.)	NET PROFIT MARGIN	EMPLOYEES
12/10	21.0	(23.3)	—	42
12/09	4.3	(18.6)	—	43
12/08	4.1	(24.8)	—	47
12/07	6.1	(23.8)	—	50
12/06	5.1	(19.1)	—	57
Annual Growth	42.4%	—	—	(7.4%)

2010 Year-End Financials

Debt ratio: —
Return on equity: —
Cash ($ mil.): 0.2
Current ratio: 0.20
Long-term debt ($ mil.): 2.8

No. of shares (mil.): 67.1
Dividends
  Yield: —
  Payout: —
Market value ($ mil.): 186.5

	STOCK PRICE ($) FY Close	P/E High/Low	PER SHARE ($) Earnings	Dividends	Book Value
12/10	2.78	— —	(0.36)	0.00	(0.11)
12/09	1.41	— —	(0.33)	0.00	0.13
12/08	3.22	— —	(0.50)	0.00	0.35
12/07	6.19	— —	(0.51)	0.00	0.64
12/06	2.92	— —	(0.41)	0.00	0.38
Annual Growth	(1.2%)	— —	—	—	—

Oiltanking Partners

What do Germany and Houston have in common? Not much, besides Oiltanking Partners. The limited partnership formed in March 2011 by Oiltanking Holding Americas, a subsidiary of Oiltanking GmbH, the world's second-largest independent storage provider for crude oil, liquid chemicals, and gases. (Oiltanking GmbH is, in turn, owned by private German conglomerate Marquard & Bahls). Oiltanking Partners owns and operates pipeline terminals with about 135 tanks in Houston and Beaumont that have a storage capacity of about 18 million barrels. Customers include oil and companies, marketers, and distributors. At the time of its

formation, Oiltanking Partners filed a $200 million initial public offering.

Oiltanking GmbH spun off its Texas assets as Oiltanking Partners to combine two of its Gulf Coast businesses, Oiltanking Houston, L.P. and Oiltanking Beaumont Partners, L.P. (Oiltanking GmbH retained two other Texas assets in Port Neches and Texas City). Oiltanking GmbH intends for Oiltanking Partners to be its growth vehicle in the US to acquire, own, and operate terminals, oil storage, and pipeline assets. In the short term, it expects to expand storage capacity at its Houston and Beaumont terminals, and it the long term, the company has its eye on operations outside the Gulf Coast. Before it can do that, Oiltanking Partners needs to pay off some debt, and the company plans to use the proceeds from its IPO to repay its former parent and replenish working capital.

The company is banking its expansion plans to take advantage of pipeline construction by a number of oil & gas firms operating in Houston's Ship Channel. Enbridge, Enterprise Products Partners, Magellan Midstream, and TransCanada have all announced plans to expand their pipeline operations, and while these companies have their own terminal storage operations, Oiltanking Partners intends to be ready to offer additional storage capacity. It has options to buy land and build the necessary pipeline connections for another 7 million barrels of crude storage capacity. It also owns 24 acres located about six miles from the terminal and is allowed to build pipeline connections to link the two, and is permitted to locate more storage tanks on 63 acres also nearby the terminal.

EXECUTIVES

CFO, Kenneth F. Owen, age 37
President, CEO, and Director, Carlin G. Conner, age 43
VP Operations, Kevin L. Campbell, age 46
VP Corporate Affairs and Strategic Planning, Jan P. Vogel, age 41
VP Marketing and Sales, Robert J. (Bo) McCall, age 46
Auditors: BDO USA, LLP

LOCATIONS

HQ: Oiltanking Partners, L.P.
  15631 Jacintoport Blvd., Houston, TX 77015
Phone: 281-457-7900
Web: www.oiltankingpartners.com

COMPETITORS

Buckeye Partners
Cheniere Energy Partners
DCP Midstream Partners
Enbridge Energy
Enterprise Products
Kinder Morgan Energy Partners
Magellan Midstream
Martin Midstream Partners
TransCanada
Williams Partners

HISTORICAL FINANCIALS

Company Type: Public

Income Statement

FYE: December 31

	REVENUE ($ mil.)	NET INCOME ($ mil.)	NET PROFIT MARGIN	EMPLOYEES
12/10	116.4	37.8	32.5%	154
12/09	100.8	25.1	24.9%	0
12/08	79.1	12.6	15.9%	0
Annual Growth	21.3%	73.2%	—	—

Debt ratio: —
Return on equity: —
Cash ($ mil.): 8.7
Current ratio: 1.02
Long-term debt ($ mil.): 129.5

No. of shares (mil.): —
Dividends
Yield: —
Payout: —
Market value ($ mil.): —

OmniComm

Computers can't catch the kind of viruses that OmniComm Systems handles. The company's Web-based software helps pharmaceutical and biotechnology companies, clinical research organizations, and academic research institutions manage data collected during clinical trials. Its TrialMaster software enables researchers to collect, validate, and analyze data for clinical trials, to speed up the process of developing drugs and medical devices. The eClinical Suite combines a clinical data management system (CDMS) and a clinical trial management system (CTMS) to manage all phases of a clinical trial. OmniComm counts almost 100 customers, including Boston Scientific and Johnson & Johnson. The majority of its sales are in the US.

The company has expanded its electronic data capture (EDC) capabilities with two acquisitions. (TrialMaster uses EDC technology to collect clinical data). OmniComm bought hardware, software, and customer lists from UK-based Logos Technologies, Ltd. and rival eResearchTechnology in 2009. The Logos software, which helps screen volunteer for the human testing phase of a trial, was renamed TrialOne and launched in 2010.

EXECUTIVES

Chairman and CTO, Randall G. (Randy) Smith, age 53, $514,119 total compensation
President, Stephen E. (Steve) Johnson, age 45, $235,357 total compensation
President, CEO, and Director, Cornelis F. Wit, age 64, $579,929 total compensation
EVP and CFO, Ronald T. Linares, age 48, $312,208 total compensation
EVP Operations, Kenneth (Ken) Light
VP Engineering, Keith Howells
SVP Clinical Operations, Sondra Smyrnios
SVP Business Development, Beverly Hudson
SVP Technology, Thomas Wells
Director Marketing, Lizanne M. Kelley
Auditors: Greenberg & Company LLC

LOCATIONS

HQ: OmniComm Systems, Inc.
2101 W. Commercial Blvd., Ste. 4000, Fort Lauderdale, FL 33309
Phone: 954-473-1254   **Fax:** 954-473-1256
Web: www.omnicomm.com

PRODUCTS/OPERATIONS

2009 Sales

	$ mil.	% of total
Set-up fees	4.9	52
Maintenance	2.6	27
Hosting & subscriptions	.7	7
Licensing	.5	6
Change orders	.4	4
Professional services	.4	4
Total	**9.5**	**100**

COMPETITORS

DATATRAK International
DrugLogic
Encorium
eResearchTechnology
Kofax plc
Medidata Solutions
Oracle
Perceptive Informatics
Sparta Systems

HISTORICAL FINANCIALS

Company Type: Public

Income Statement

FYE: December 31

	REVENUE ($ mil.)	NET INCOME ($ mil.)	NET PROFIT MARGIN	EMPLOYEES
12/10	12.4	(3.1)	—	84
12/09	9.6	(8.1)	—	208
12/08	6.3	(10.6)	—	82
12/07	3.7	(5.3)	—	82
12/06	2.8	(4.2)	—	44
Annual Growth	**45.1%**	**—**	**—**	**17.5%**

2010 Year-End Financials

Debt ratio: —
Return on equity: —
Cash ($ mil.): 1.2
Current ratio: 0.20
Long-term debt ($ mil.): 9.5

No. of shares (mil.): 86.1
Dividends
Yield: —
Payout: —
Market value ($ mil.): 6.9

	STOCK PRICE ($) FY Close	P/E High/Low	PER SHARE ($) Earnings	Dividends	Book Value
12/10	0.08	— —	(0.04)	0.00	(0.21)
12/09	0.20	— —	(0.10)	0.00	(0.18)
12/08	0.32	— —	(0.15)	0.00	(0.14)
12/07	0.65	— —	(0.10)	0.00	(0.00)
12/06	0.48	— —	(0.14)	0.00	(0.00)
Annual Growth	**(36.1%)**	**— —**	**—**	**—**	**—**

OmniVision Technologies

OmniVision Technologies gets the big picture with a single chip. The fabless semiconductor company designs semiconductor image sensors that capture and convert images for cameras, mobile phones, notebooks, and webcams. Its CameraCube device combines the company's image sensors with wafer-level optics for a complete camera module. OmniVision sells to OEMs such as Creative Technology and Foxconn, as well as distributors such as Taiwan-based WPG Holdings. Manufacturers and value-added resellers account for more than half of sales, while distributors make up the rest. Most sales are outside the US, predominantly in China and other Asia/Pacific countries.

The global economic downturn dampened sales of consumer electronics, which in turn affected chip makers whose devices are incorporated into consumer products. OmniVision depends on sales to customers in the automotive, entertainment, mobile phone, notebook, and webcam markets, most of which experienced significantly reduced demand for their products. In addition, much of OmniVision's business is in mobile phones, a highly competitive market with a handful of leading manufacturers. The company must continually develop and introduce new products for the market to remain competitive with its industry rivals.

OmniVision is looking to expand in the medical and surveillance markets, which are less tied to consumer buying patterns. The company is making image sensors used in disposable medical ventilation tubes. Its automotive sensors are being used in driver assistance applications, including lane departure warning systems and 360 degree viewers, features that are growing in popularity on new cars.

In fiscal 2010 OmniVision's sales increased by 19% over 2009, though the company saw its sales fall nearly 37% in fiscal 2009. The company also returned to profitability in fiscal 2010, reporting net income of $6.7 million for the year, compared to a net loss of $37.3 million in 2009. The loss for 2009 was due in part to higher operating expenses and goodwill impairment, along with significantly lower sales. OmniVision cut its workforce by about 29% during 2009, which contributed to lower costs the following year.

Also in 2010 OmniVision expanded its product portfolio when it acquired Aurora Systems, a maker of LCoS (Liquid Crystal on Silicon) microdisplay panels used in high-definition home theater system and mobile projection applications, for about $5 million. The company hopes to take advantage of the popularity of image projection systems in consumer devices.

OmniVision bought 850 patents related to sensor imaging from Eastman Kodak for $65 million in cash in 2011. The deal doubled the size of the company's intellectual property holdings, adding many patents for CMOS technology used in the manufacture of integrated circuits.

OmniVision outsources manufacturing chores to silicon foundries (contract semiconductor manufacturers), primarily Taiwan Semiconductor Manufacturing Company (TSMC). The company formed a joint venture with TSMC, VisEra Technologies, for color filter processing of its semiconductor wafers and for assembly of its CameraCube imaging devices.

EXECUTIVES

Chairman, President, and CEO, Shaw Hong, age 74, $1,427,437 total compensation
VP Operations, Eugene Liaw
VP Finance and CFO, Anson H. Chan, age 42, $984,472 total compensation
VP Legal and General Counsel, Y. Vicky Chou, age 48, $917,480 total compensation
VP Quality and Reliability, John T. Yue, age 64
VP System Technologies, John Li
VP Worldwide Sales, Ray Cisneros
VP Process Engineering, Howard E. Rhodes
VP Engineering and Director, Henry Yang
COO and Director, Xinping (James) He, age 48, $1,059,993 total compensation
Medical Device Senior Marketing Manager, Zafer Zamboglu
Investor Relations, Chesha Gibbons
Senior Marketing Manager, Kelvin Chang
Global Automotive Senior Marketing Manager, Inayat Khajasha
Senior Product Marketing Manager, Nick Nam
Director Investor Relations, Steven Horwitz
Senior Marketing Manager, Scott Foster
Auditors: PricewaterhouseCoopers LLP

LOCATIONS

HQ: OmniVision Technologies, Inc.
4275 Burton Dr., Santa Clara, CA 95054
Phone: 408-542-3000   **Fax:** 408-542-3001
Web: www.ovt.com

2010 Sales

	$ mil.	% of total
China	504.9	84
Taiwan	51.1	8
Malaysia	21.9	4
Japan	8.0	1
South Korea	5.4	1
US	3.5	1
Other countries	8.2	1
Total	**603.0**	**100**

PRODUCTS/OPERATIONS

2010 Sales

	% of total
OEMs and value-added resellers	52
Distributors	48
Total	**100**

Selected Products

CameraCube (combines image sensors, chip scale packaging, and wafer-level optics)
Single-chip image sensors (CameraChip, OmniPixel)
Software drivers (for Linux, Mac, and Windows operating systems)

COMPETITORS

Aptina	Panasonic Corp
Avago Technologies	Pixelplus
Canon	Pixim
Eastman Kodak	Samsung Electronics
Foveon	SANYO Semiconductor
Freescale	Sharp Corp.
Semiconductor	Sony
FUJIFILM	STMicroelectronics
Hynix	Teledyne DALSA
Melexis	Tessera
Mitsubishi Electric	Texas Instruments
National Semiconductor	Toshiba Semiconductor
NXP Semiconductors	

HISTORICAL FINANCIALS

Company Type: Public

Income Statement

FYE: April 30

	REVENUE ($ mil.)	NET INCOME ($ mil.)	NET PROFIT MARGIN	EMPLOYEES
04/11	956.5	124.5	13.0%	1,465
04/10	603.0	6.7	1.1%	1,450
04/09	507.3	(37.3)	—	1,328
04/08	799.6	65.1	8.1%	1,882
04/07	528.1	24.0	4.5%	2,064
Annual Growth	**16.0%**	**50.9%**	**—**	**(8.2%)**

2011 Year-End Financials

Debt ratio: 5.6%
Return on equity: 16.6%
Cash ($ mil.): 379.4
Current ratio: 4.91
Long-term debt ($ mil.): 41.9
No. of shares (mil.): 58.0
Dividends
  Yield: —
  Payout: —
Market value ($ mil.): 1,947.4

	STOCK PRICE ($) FY Close	P/E High/Low		PER SHARE ($) Earnings	Dividends	Book Value
04/11	33.59	18	7	2.11	0.00	12.96
04/10	17.56	149	63	0.13	0.00	10.25
04/09	9.51	—	—	(0.74)	0.00	9.77
04/08	16.04	21	10	1.19	0.00	9.21
04/07	13.52	80	26	0.43	0.00	8.90
Annual Growth	**25.5%**	—	—	**48.8%**	—	**9.8%**

Onsite Energy

Onsite Energy says electricity efficiency is "outta sight." The energy services company identifies energy management measures that its mostly industrial and government clients can use to save on power and fuel-supply costs. It installs the recommended cost-effective systems, heat and power generation systems, central plant upgrades, lighting and refrigeration system upgrades, and air compressor and boiler retrofits. It also provides consulting services to help customers monitor energy usage and identify incentive programs. The company focuses on California, though its market extends throughout the western US and northern Mexico. Management bought control of Onsite in 2003.

EXECUTIVES

President and CEO, Richard T. Sperberg
CFO, Paul E. Blevins
EVP, David Bruder
VP, Gregory E. Maynard
VP, Elizabeth T. Lowe
Director Human Resources, Kimberly Boeck
Auditors: Swenson Advisors, LLP

LOCATIONS

HQ: Onsite Energy Corporation
2701 Loker Ave. West, Ste. 107, Carlsbad, CA 92010
Phone: 760-931-2400 **Fax:** 760-931-2405
Web: www.onsitenergy.com

PRODUCTS/OPERATIONS

Selected Services

Bill auditing
Distributed generation
Energy efficiency
Energy outsourcing
Energy purchasing
Financing
Transmission and generation

COMPETITORS

E M C Engineers	Preferred Energy
Edison International	Services
EMCOR	Public Service
FirstEnergy	Enterprise Group
Great Plains Energy	Southern Company

HISTORICAL FINANCIALS

Company Type: Public

Income Statement

FYE: June 30

	REVENUE ($ mil.)	NET INCOME ($ mil.)	NET PROFIT MARGIN	EMPLOYEES
06/96	22.7	0.8	3.5%	0
06/95	12.0	—	—	47
06/94	2.4	(2.2)	—	53
06/93	0.8	—	—	0
06/92	0.7	—	—	0
Annual Growth	**138.6%**	**—**	**—**	**(11.3%)**

Debt ratio: 5.6%
Return on equity: 16.6%
Cash ($ mil.): 379.4
Current ratio: 4.91
Long-term debt ($ mil.): 41.9
No. of shares (mil.): 58.0
Dividends
  Yield: —
  Payout: —
Market value ($ mil.): 1,947.4

Onyx Pharmaceuticals

Onyx Pharmaceuticals' cancer drug is a real gem. Working with health care behemoth Bayer, the biotechnology company developed Nexavar, an FDA-approved treatment for advanced kidney cancer and liver cancer. The partners are jointly promoting the drug in the US, while Bayer handles marketing duties in the European Union and elsewhere. Onyx and Bayer are also testing the drug as a possible treatment for other kinds of cancer, both alone and in combination with other therapies. The company has additional candidates in development for oncology and hematology applications.

The company's success is almost entirely dependent on the performance of Nexavar, both in the market and in further clinical trials. As such, the company is working to expand Nexavar indications for conditions including lung, thyroid, breast, colorectal, and ovarian cancers. But while sales of Nexavar are steadily increasing, Onyx is also looking to bring additional drugs to market to reduce its reliance on Nexavar royalty payments from Bayer.

The company is developing lead candidate carfilzomib, a potential treatment for multiple myeloma (a blood cancer). The candidate was added to the Onyx pipeline in 2009 through the acquisition of private biotech firm Proteolix for $275 million, plus another $535 million in potential milestone payments. Proteolix brought with it additional therapies under development for other types of cancer malignancies and tumors. Onyx also has an early stage clinical development program for solid tumor cancers licensed from drug technology firm BTG, and it has preclinical research programs for anti-inflammatory targets such as lupus and rheumatoid arthritis.

Onyx had acquired an option to license two additional development compounds with potential applications in cancer and autoimmune disease treatments from Singapore biotech firm S*BIO; however, it terminated the agreement in 2011.

Outside of its internal candidates and its Nexavar development work with Bayer, Onyx receives collaboration fees on an oncology candidate licensed out for development to Pfizer. In 2010 the company licensed Japanese development and marketing rights for carfilzomib and a similar oncology candidate to Ono Pharmaceutical. To further diversify its operations, Onyx is looking to form additional partnerships and licensing agreements.

EXECUTIVES

President, CEO, and Director, N. Anthony (Tony) Coles, age 50, $4,136,535 total compensation
EVP and CFO, Matthew K. (Matt) Fust, age 46, $2,910,742 total compensation
EVP Corporate Affairs, Laura A. Brege, age 53, $1,638,379 total compensation
EVP and Head Research and Development and Technical Operations, Ted W. Love, age 52
EVP Corporate Development and Strategy, Jürgen Lasowski, age 52, $1,740,972 total compensation
VP Public Affairs, Julianna R. (Julie) Wood, age 54
VP and Chief Legal Counsel, Gregory J. Giotta, age 64
SVP Commercial, Barry P. Flannelly
Chief Compliance Officer, Paul K. Ross
Director Corporate Communications and Investor Relations, Lori Murray
SVP and General Counsel, Suzanne M. Shema, age 53
Secretary, Robert L. Jones
Auditors: Ernst & Young LLP

LOCATIONS

HQ: Onyx Pharmaceuticals, Inc.
2100 Powell St., Emeryville, CA 94608
Phone: 510-597-6500   **Fax:** 510-597-6600
Web: www.onyx-pharm.com

PRODUCTS/OPERATIONS

2010 Sales

	$ mil.	% of total
Collaboration	265.3	82
License	59.2	18
Total	**324.5**	**100**

COMPETITORS

Amgen	Merck
ARIAD Pharmaceuticals	Novartis
AstraZeneca	OSI Pharmaceuticals
AVEO	Pfizer
Bristol-Myers Squibb	Progen Pharmaceuticals
Celgene	Regeneron
Genentech	Pharmaceuticals
GlaxoSmithKline	Takeda Pharmaceutical
ImClone	

HISTORICAL FINANCIALS

Company Type: Public

Income Statement   FYE: December 31

	REVENUE ($ mil.)	NET INCOME ($ mil.)	NET PROFIT MARGIN	EMPLOYEES
12/10	324.5	(84.8)	—	299
12/09	251.4	16.2	6.4%	271
12/08	194.3	1.9	1.0%	197
12/06	0.3	(92.7)	—	125
12/05	1.0	(95.2)	—	100
Annual Growth	**217.9%**	**—**	**—**	**24.5%**

2010 Year-End Financials

Debt ratio: 21.9%
Return on equity: —
Cash ($ mil.): 226.3
Current ratio: 8.86
Long-term debt ($ mil.): 152.7

No. of shares (mil.): 62.9
Dividends
  Yield: —
  Payout: —
Market value ($ mil.): 2,317.5

	STOCK PRICE ($) FY Close	P/E High/Low	PER SHARE ($) Earnings	Dividends	Book Value
12/10	36.87	— —	(1.35)	0.00	11.10
12/09	29.34	137 81	0.27	0.00	12.06
12/08	34.16	1945 722	0.03	0.00	8.42
12/06	55.62	— —	(0.67)	0.00	7.84
12/05	10.58	— —	(2.20)	0.00	5.10
Annual Growth	**36.6%**	**— —**	**—**	**—**	**21.4%**

OpenTable

Even if your favorite restaurant is closed for the day, you can still try to reserve a table through OpenTable. The firm provides online reservations at about 20,000 upscale restaurants in the US, Canada, and Mexico, as well as Germany, Japan, and the UK. The service is free to diners, but OpenTable charges participating restaurants an installation and monthly license fee for its Electronic Reservation Book (ERB), a computerized reservation system. It also provides training and support for ERB, and charges a fee for tables booked through Connect, a Web-based solution for reservations with less functionality than ERB. Since its founding in 1998, OpenTable has seated more than 200 million diners.

Restaurants pay between $200-$300 per month for an OpenTable subscription; they pay $2.50 for each reservation made through Connect, and $1 per diner booked directly through OpenTable.com. The company reported strong 2010 results thanks to an increase in participating restaurants and diner reservations. That year its revenues reached nearly $99 million, a more than 40% increase in revenues from the $68 million reported for 2009, and the company nearly tripled its net income from $5 million in 2009 to $14 million in 2010. The growth in restaurants and diners was mostly the result of OpenTable's 2010 acquisition of toptable.com, a UK-based restaurant reservation website, for about $55 million. The deal gave it access to toptable's more than 3,600 restaurant customers across Europe.

Before its acquisition of toptable, OpenTable opened its wallet in 2010 to purchase Table Maestro, a company that operates a telephone reservation management service for restaurants, for $1.5 million. The previous year it bought guest management solutions firm GuestBridge for some $3 million in cash. GuestBridge provides software for reservation, wait, and table management. On the technology front, OpenTable has been focusing its efforts on applications for smart phones. In 2010 the company reported that it had seated more than 700,000 diners cumulatively through its mobile applications. The firm is additionally working to introduce new marketing solutions; its Spotlight program, launched in 2010, is a Groupon-like service that sells coupons from local restaurants to OpenTable diners.

The company's decision to go public in 2009 surprised many given the dismal economy. (There had been no IPOs up to that point since 2008's Grand Canyon Education.) OpenTable owed at least part of its success to the fact that it doesn't rely on an advertising model for its revenue stream, maintaining restaurants as its only clients. The company used proceeds from its IPO for sales and marketing activities, general and administrative expenses, investing in technologies, and acquiring other businesses.

EXECUTIVES

Chairman, Jeffrey (Jeff) Jordan, age 52, $1,526,170 total compensation
CFO, Duncan Robertson, age 44
President, OpenTable Japan KK, Masao Tejima
President, CEO, and Director, Matthew (Matt) Roberts, age 42, $350,328 total compensation
SVP Operations, Joel Brown, age 49, $319,127 total compensation
SVP Sales, Michael Dodson, age 52, $472,592 total compensation
SVP and Managing Director, Europe, David Pritchard
SVP Product Management, Michael Xenakis
SVP Business Development, Douglas Boake
SVP Marketing, Ann Shepherd
SVP Engineering, Charles (Charlie) McCullough, age 59, $366,264 total compensation
Auditors: Deloitte & Touche LLP

LOCATIONS

HQ: OpenTable, Inc.
799 Market St., 4th Fl., San Francisco, CA 94103
Phone: 415-344-4200   **Fax:** 415-267-0944
Web: www.opentable.com

2010 Sales

	$ mil.	% of total
North America	90.1	91
International	8.9	9
Total	**99.0**	**100**

PRODUCTS/OPERATIONS

2010 Sales

	$ mil.	% of total
Reservations	47.5	48
Subscriptions	43.1	44
Installation & other	8.4	8
Total	**99.0**	**100**

Selected Offerings

Connect
ERB
Mobile applications
OpenTable website
Spotlight

COMPETITORS

CityGrid Media	SavvyDiner.com
Groupon	Time Out Group
LivingSocial	Yelp
Restaurant.com	Zagat

HISTORICAL FINANCIALS

Company Type: Public

Income Statement   FYE: December 31

	REVENUE ($ mil.)	NET INCOME ($ mil.)	NET PROFIT MARGIN	EMPLOYEES
12/10	99.0	14.1	14.2%	493
12/09	68.6	5.1	7.4%	329
12/08	55.8	(1.0)	—	304
12/07	41.1	9.2	22.4%	297
12/06	27.2	0.2	0.7%	0
Annual Growth	**38.1%**	**189.8%**	**—**	**18.4%**

2010 Year-End Financials

Debt ratio: —
Return on equity: 13.8%
Cash ($ mil.): 33.4
Current ratio: 2.29
Long-term debt ($ mil.): —

No. of shares (mil.): 23.3
Dividends
  Yield: —
  Payout: —
Market value ($ mil.): 1,642.0

	STOCK PRICE ($) FY Close	P/E High/Low	PER SHARE ($) Earnings	Dividends	Book Value
12/10	70.48	132 42	0.58	0.00	4.38
12/09	25.46	161 109	0.22	0.00	3.27
Annual Growth	**176.8%**	**— —**	**163.6%**	**—**	**34.0%**

Opko Health

Opko Health may have first found its calling in developing treatments for eye diseases, but it has expanded its scope to include a variety of therapeutics. In addition to research and development of its ophthalmic drug candidates, the company is working on pharmaceuticals for indications including oncology, neurology, and infectious diseases. It also has development programs for vaccines and diagnostic tests. To support its research programs, Opko Health sells a number of prescription pharmaceuticals and over-the-counter products in Latin American countries.

The company has been focused on strengthening and diversifying its pharmaceutical operations. In 2009 Opko moved into the vaccines market when it acquired a worldwide license to develop a vaccine that has the potential to protect people from all strains of the flu. If further testing proves successful in protecting against flu strains like swine and bird, the technology might be used to develop other vaccines.

Opko has also been acquiring development programs for a number of therapeutic pharma products, including potential cancer treatments. For instance, it purchased a promising drug candidate, rolapitant for the treatment of chemotherapy-induced vomiting and nausea, from Schering-Plough (now Merck) in 2009. In early 2011 Opko further expanded its pharma pipeline when it acquired Florida-based drug developer CURNA for $10 million. CURNA remained as a stand-alone facility devoted to development of its non-coding RNA AntagonNAT technology to combat diseases including cancers and cardiovascular conditions.

Its diagnostic programs, acquired in 2009 from the University of Texas Southwestern Medical Center, include potential molecular diagnostic tests that use protein-based technologies to detect ailments including cancers and neurological conditions such as Alzheimer's disease. To bolster its promising molecular diagnostics programs, Opko formed a partnership with Bristol-Myers Squibb to work on its Alzheimer's tests in 2010. In 2011 the company acquired Woburn Massachusetts-based Claros Diagnostics for an undisclosed sum. Claros has developed a novel blood test system for analysis of 20 separate tests necessary for urological and infectious disease screening complimenting Opko's portfolio of diagnostic products.

To further focus on its diagnostic, vaccine, and therapeutic drug development programs, in 2011 the firm agreed to sell its ophthalmic instrumentation division to medical technology firm Optos for some $18 million. The division makes diagnostic imaging systems used to diagnose and manage eye diseases.

To help provide funding for its R&D programs, as well as to gain a platform for commercial growth, the company has also established commercial pharmaceutical operations in South America. To gain entry into that market, the company acquired Chilean pharmaceutical maker Pharma Genexx (now known as OPKO Chile), which imports, markets, and distributes both prescription and over-the-counter pharmaceuticals and medical devices, in 2009.

The following year, Opko followed that buy with the acquisition of Pharmacos Exakta (now known as Exakta-OPKO), a Mexico-based pharmaceutical company that makes antibiotics, decongestants, ophthalmology products, and vitamins. Along with giving the company more products for eye care, the purchase fleshes out Opko's other non-ophthalmology products.

The firm, formerly named eXegenics, discontinued its former drug development operations in 2003 but revived itself in 2007 by merging with two privately held biotech companies: Froptix and Acuity Pharmaceuticals.

A private investment group led by the company's chairman and CEO Phillip Frost owns about 45% of Opko.

EXECUTIVES

Chairman and CEO, Phillip Frost, age 74
EVP Administration and Director, Steven D. (Steve) Rubin, age 50, $723,254 total compensation

SVP and CFO, Subbarao V. (Rao) Uppaluri, age 61, $618,174 total compensation
Vice Chairman and CTO, Jane H. Hsiao, age 63, $845,649 total compensation
Auditors: Ernst & Young LLP

LOCATIONS

HQ: Opko Health, Inc.
4400 Biscayne Blvd., Miami, FL 33137
Phone: 305-575-4100   **Fax:** 305-575-4140
Web: www.opko.com

2010

	% of total
Chile	60
Mexico	13
US	3
Other countries	24
Total	**100**

PRODUCTS/OPERATIONS

2010 Sales

	$ mil.	% of total
Products		
Pharmaceutical	21.8	59
Instrumentation	8.4	23
License	6.7	18
Total	**36.9**	**100**

COMPETITORS

Abbott Labs	Myriad Genetics
Alcon	Novartis
Allergan	Novo Nordisk
Alnylam	QIAGEN
Bausch & Lomb	QLT
Bio-Rad Labs	Regeneron
Gen-Probe	Pharmaceuticals
Genentech	Sanofi
GenVec	Siemens Healthcare
Merck	Diagnostics

HISTORICAL FINANCIALS

Company Type: Public

Income Statement

FYE: December 31

	REVENUE ($ mil.)	NET INCOME ($ mil.)	NET PROFIT MARGIN	EMPLOYEES
12/10	36.9	(18.9)	—	220
12/09	13.1	(30.1)	—	95
12/08	9.4	(39.8)	—	61
12/07	0.8	(268.4)	—	57
12/03	0.0	(5.8)	—	1
Annual Growth	—	—	—	**116.1%**

2010 Year-End Financials

Debt ratio: —
Return on equity: —
Cash ($ mil.): 18.0
Current ratio: 1.96
Long-term debt ($ mil.): —
No. of shares (mil.): 255.4
Dividends
  Yield: —
  Payout: —
Market value ($ mil.): 937.4

	STOCK PRICE ($) FY Close	P/E High/Low		PER SHARE ($) Earnings	Dividends	Book Value
12/10	3.67	—	—	(0.08)	0.00	0.09
12/09	1.83	—	—	(0.13)	0.00	0.23
12/08	1.62	—	—	(0.21)	0.00	0.00
12/07	2.85	—	—	(2.09)	0.00	0.10
12/03	0.85	—	—	(0.04)	0.00	0.48
Annual Growth	**44.1%**	—	—	—	—	**(34.0%)**

OPTi

OPTi has opted out of business — sort of. The semiconductor design company, which once derived most of its sales from its core logic chipsets (used to control key internal functions of PCs and embedded applications), more recently relied on peripheral products for the bulk of its sales. OPTi stopped developing new core logic products, then announced plans to wind down its business and liquidate all of its assets. It postponed those plans, however, to pursue a strategy of licensing its semiconductor intellectual property and pursuing related patent infringement claims. As part of this plan, it sold its semiconductor production operations to an unaffiliated company called OPTi Technologies, Inc.

EXECUTIVES

Chairman, President, and CEO, Bernard T. Marren, age 75, $338,750 total compensation
CFO and Secretary, Michael Mazzoni, age 48, $231,694 total compensation
Auditors: Ernst & Young LLP

LOCATIONS

HQ: OPTi Inc.
880 Maude Ave., Ste. A, Mountain View, CA 94043
Phone: 650-625-8787   **Fax:** 650-625-8781
Web: www.opti.com

HISTORICAL FINANCIALS

Company Type: Public

Income Statement

FYE: March 31

	REVENUE ($ mil.)	NET INCOME ($ mil.)	NET PROFIT MARGIN	EMPLOYEES
03/11	50.6	25.6	50.6%	3
03/10	0.6	7.0	1166.7%	3
03/09	3.8	(4.1)	—	3
03/07	11.0	7.0	63.6%	3
03/05	0.1	(1.2)	—	3
Annual Growth	**182.3%**	—	—	**0.0%**

2011 Year-End Financials

Debt ratio: —
Return on equity: 115.4%
Cash ($ mil.): 25.8
Current ratio: 28.52
Long-term debt ($ mil.): —
No. of shares (mil.): 11.6
Dividends
  Yield: 68.3%
  Payout: 63.6%
Market value ($ mil.): 23.9

	STOCK PRICE ($) FY Close	P/E High/Low		PER SHARE ($) Earnings	Dividends	Book Value
03/11	2.05	2	1	2.20	1.40	1.91
03/10	4.00	7	3	0.60	0.00	1.11
03/09	1.88	—	—	(0.36)	0.00	0.51
03/07	2.60	—	—	(0.30)	0.00	0.84
03/05	5.70	14	3	0.60	0.00	1.16
Annual Growth	**(22.6%)**	—	—	**38.4%**	—	**13.2%**

ORBIT/FR

ORBIT/FR tests how well your communications systems measure up. The company manufactures automated microwave test and measurement systems for evaluating cell phones, radio transmitters, Global Positioning System (GPS) receivers, and guided missiles. Other products include software, microwave receivers and antennas, and anechoic foam (a material that absorbs sound). ORBIT/FR designs systems for aerospace and defense, satellite, wireless communications, and automotive companies. Customers include BT Group, Nokia, Northrop Grumman, and the US government. In 2008 Israeli holding company Orbit-Alchut Technologies sold its 62% interest in ORBIT/FR to SATIMO, a French company, for about $17 million in cash.

SATIMO makes antenna measurement systems, electromagnetic field (EMF) exposure measurement instruments, and quality control systems for manufacturing of various materials.

ORBIT/FR has manufacturing facilities in California and its headquarters in Pennsylvania; it has engineering, sales, and technical support facilities in Israel and Germany.

EXECUTIVES

Chairman, Philippe Garreau
President, CEO, and Director, Per O. Iversen
CFO and Principal Accounting Officer, Relland Winand, age 56
President, Advanced ElectroMagnetics, Gabriel A. Sanchez
VP Business Development and CTO, John F. Aubin, age 57
VP Engineering and Program Management US, William Campbell, age 55
VP Software Development, US, Mark A. Bates, age 40
Director Human Resources, Office Manager, and Assistant to the CEO, Connie Dougherty
Regional Sales Manager, Frank Canonico
Regional Sales Manager, Anna Moyer
Managing Director, GmbH, Marcel Boumans, age 52
Managing Director, Engineering, Moshe Pinkasy, age 60
Regional Sales Manager, John Caserta
Managing Director, Advanced ElectroMagnetics, Scott Martin, age 47
Auditors: Hoberman, Miller, Goldstein & Lesser

LOCATIONS

HQ: ORBIT/FR, Inc.
506 Prudential Rd., Horsham, PA 19044-2309
Phone: 215-674-5100   **Fax:** 215-674-1102
Web: www.orbitfr.com

2009 Sales

	$ mil.	% of total
North America	16.1	52
Europe	8.2	26
Asia	6.9	22
Total	**31.2**	**100**

PRODUCTS/OPERATIONS

Selected Products

Anechoic chambers
Antennas and probes
Compact range products
  Corner-fed serrated reflectors
  Dual linear feed horns
  Feed carousel
  Side-fed serrated reflectors
  Single linear feed horns
  Specialty feed and AUT positioners
Controllers and PCUs
Linear positioners
Measurement software
Model towers
Near-field scanners

Radial power combiners
RCS products
RF absorbers
Rotary positioners

Subsidiaries and Affiliates
Advanced ElectroMagnetics
ORBIT/FR Engineering (Israel)
ORBIT/FR Europe (Germany)

COMPETITORS

Aeroflex	Micronetics
Agilent Technologies	National Instruments
Anaren	Nearfield Systems
ETS-Lindgren	Riken Corporation
Giga-tronics	Tektronix
Hubbell	Teledyne Technologies
MI Technologies	Wireless Telecom

HISTORICAL FINANCIALS
Company Type: Public

Income Statement
FYE: December 31

	REVENUE ($ mil.)	NET INCOME ($ mil.)	NET PROFIT MARGIN	EMPLOYEES
12/10	36.2	2.3	6.4%	138
12/09	31.2	1.5	4.8%	127
12/08	23.1	(3.5)	—	110
12/07	29.3	1.1	3.8%	103
12/06	29.4	1.2	4.1%	115
Annual Growth	**5.3%**	**17.7%**	**—**	**4.7%**

2010 Year-End Financials

Debt ratio: —
Return on equity: 21.8%
Cash ($ mil.): 2.4
Current ratio: 1.64
Long-term debt ($ mil.): —

No. of shares (mil.): 6.0
Dividends
  Yield: —
  Payout: —
Market value ($ mil.): 16.8

	STOCK PRICE ($) FY Close	P/E High/Low		PER SHARE ($) Earnings	Dividends	Book Value
12/10	2.80	10	3	0.38	0.00	1.76
12/09	1.19	6	2	0.24	0.00	1.38
12/08	0.94	—	—	(0.58)	0.00	1.12
12/07	2.05	15	9	0.18	0.00	1.49
12/06	2.08	16	8	0.19	0.00	1.29
Annual Growth	**7.7%**	**—**	**—**	**18.9%**	**—**	**7.9%**

Osiris Therapeutics

Unlike the Eygptian god, *this* Osiris seeks to keep people out of the afterlife. Osiris Therapeutics uses donated bone marrow stem cells to develop its drug candidates. Its lead candidate, Prochymal, is in clinical trials as a possible treatment for Crohn's disease and graft-vs.-host disease. The drug is also being investigated for use in prolonging insulin production in early onset diabetes patients and to restore cardiac functioning following a heart attack. Its second drug candidate, Chondrogen, is in clinical trials to treat osteoarthritis in the knee. Chairman Peter Friedli holds more than 40% of the company's stock.

The company's drugs are based upon human mesenchymal stem cells (MSCs). Harvested from adult donors, MSCs can be grafted onto various human tissue. They then can differentiate themselves to become bone, cartilage, fat, muscle, ten-

don, or other types of tissue. The company can produce up to 10,000 treatments from one bone marrow donation, and because the material is universally compatible, it does not have to be matched for individual patients. Osiris believes it is that availability and ease-of-use that will help the company achieve its goal of becoming the first company to receive FDA approval of a stem cell drug.

Osiris has a development agreement with Genzyme for Prochymal and Chondrogen under which Osiris retains the rights to commercialize the drugs in the North America, while Genzyme has been given the rights to market the drug in all other countries, except Japan, where Prochymal is already licensed to JCR Pharmaceuticals. The deal between Osiris and Genzyme is worth $130 million plus up to $1.25 billion in additional future milestone payments.

Osiris and Genzyme also have a collaboration worth about $220 million with the US Department of Defense for the development and stockpiling of Prochymal as a treatment for afflictions related to nuclear terrorism and other radiological emergencies. Aside from the one deal with the Department of Defense, Osiris doesn't intend to focus on anti-terrorism efforts.

The company previously manufactured and sold Osteocel, a stem-cell based therapy for regenerating bone in orthopedic surgical procedures, such as spinal fusions. However, it required a stronger sales force to take the drug further, so in 2008 Osiris sold the Osteocel business to NuVasive for $85 million. The success of Osteocel led Osiris to create a Biosurgery Division to develop additional biological products for use during surgery. Its first product was introduced in 2010. Grafix Prime, a wound care product based on human placenta, was later sold to NuVasive.

Along with getting Prochymal and Chondrogen to market, Osiris plans to expand its pipeline of biologic drug candidates; the company believes its development and eventual sale of Osteocel gave it the experience necessary to develop its next biologic drug candidate without the help of a partner, so it can self-commercialize all of its biologic drug candidates (and won't be required to split its profits).

Osiris' lead investor is director Peter Friedli who controls about nearly 60% of the company's shares through the investment firm he started in 1986, Friedli Corporate Finance.

EXECUTIVES

Chairman, Peter Friedli, age 57
CFO, Treasurer, and Secretary, Philip R. (Phil) Jacoby Jr., age 59, $204,106 total compensation
President, CEO, and Director, C. Randal (Charles) Mills, age 39, $1,215,917 total compensation
Chief Scientific Officer, Michelle LeRoux Williams, age 36, $370,019 total compensation
SVP Operations and Corporate Development, Stephen W. Potter, age 54
SVP Therapeutics, Lode Debrabandere, age 46, $388,664 total compensation
Public and Investor Relations Contact, Erica Elchin
Senior Director Business Development, Jesus Soriano
General Manager, Osteocel, Louis E. Barnes III, age 43
Executive Medical Director, Jeffry Lawrence
Senior Director, Prochymal, Rodney L. Monroy
Auditors: Stegman & Company

LOCATIONS

HQ: Osiris Therapeutics, Inc.
7015 Albert Einstein Dr., Columbia, MD 21046
Phone: 443-545-1800   **Fax:** 443-545-1701
Web: www.osiristx.com

COMPETITORS

Aastrom Biosciences	Cytori Therapeutics
Abbott Labs	Geron
Advanced Cell	Johnson & Johnson
Technology	MultiCell Technologies
Athersys	StemCells
Biogen Idec	UCB

HISTORICAL FINANCIALS

Company Type: Public

Income Statement   FYE: December 31

	REVENUE ($ mil.)	NET INCOME ($ mil.)	NET PROFIT MARGIN	EMPLOYEES
12/10	43.2	13.1	30.3%	59
12/09	44.5	14.6	32.8%	57
12/08	10.0	(33.5)	—	163
12/07	17.3	(53.9)	—	133
12/06	8.3	(45.0)	—	113
Annual Growth	51.0%	—	—	(15.0%)

2010 Year-End Financials

Debt ratio: —
Return on equity: 47.8%
Cash ($ mil.): 1.4
Current ratio: 1.59
Long-term debt ($ mil.): —

No. of shares (mil.): 32.8
Dividends
  Yield: —
  Payout: —
Market value ($ mil.): 255.5

	STOCK PRICE ($) FY Close	P/E High/Low		PER SHARE ($) Earnings	Dividends	Book Value
12/10	7.79	23	13	0.40	0.00	0.84
12/09	7.14	47	12	0.45	0.00	0.38
12/08	19.16	—	—	(1.05)	0.00	(0.16)
12/07	12.02	—	—	(1.89)	0.00	0.49
12/06	25.32	—	—	(2.70)	0.00	0.41
Annual Growth	(25.5%)	—	—	—	—	19.3%

Outdoor Channel

You might say this company brings the outdoors inside through the television. Outdoor Channel Holdings owns and operates the Outdoor Channel, a cable network that reaches more than 30 million homes in the US with programming focused on hunting, fishing, and other outdoor pursuits. Among the network's shows are *Jim Zumbo Outdoors, Addicted To The Outdoors,* and *Trev Gowdy's Monster Fish*. In addition to its cable network, the company owns television production subsidiary Winnercomm which specializes in creating sports programming and related entertainment shows. Chairman Perry Massie and his brother Thomas (director) together own about 25% of the company.

Like other cable networks, the Outdoor Channel generates revenue primarily through advertising and carriage fees paid by cable system operators. It focuses on boosting viewership with new programming in order to charge more to sponsors for air time and to demand higher fees from cable subscribers. The television sports entertainment

business has become crowded, though, with well-financed competitors such as VERSUS (now part of the NBCUniversal media empire) in addition to leaders including Walt Disney's ESPN and News Corporation's FOX Sports Net.

To separate itself from the rest of the pack, in early 2011 the Outdoor Channel acquired MyOutdoorTV.com, an online provider of more than 300 television shows and 8,400 online videos featuring outdoor lifestyle content. The deal significantly amplified its website network in addition to boosting the overall amount of hunting, fishing, and shooting content it owns.

In 2010 Outdoor Channel Holdings signed deals with partners to distribute programming in Asia, Europe, the Middle East, and Africa. The company moved to diversify its revenue early in 2009 when it acquired Tulsa, Oklahoma-based Winnercomm. The production company supplies outdoor-themed programming to a number of outlets including ESPN. It also owns the Skycam camera system used during live TV broadcasts of football games and other events.

EXECUTIVES

Chairman, Perry T. Massie, age 48, $124,523 total compensation
President, CEO, and Director; President and CEO, Outdoor Channel, Roger L. Werner Jr., age 61, $2,787,569 total compensation
EVP and CFO, Thomas D. (Tom) Allen, age 58
EVP, COO, and General Counsel; EVP and COO, Outdoor Channel, Thomas E. (Tom) Hornish, age 52, $1,175,463 total compensation
EVP Advertising Sales, Outdoor Channel, Gregory M. (Greg) Harrigan
VP Advertising Sales, Southeast Region, Brian Hughes
VP Human Resources, Vicki Windham
VP Digital Media Operations, Outdoor Channel, Arnel Ticsay
Chief Accounting Officer, Douglas Langston
SVP Advertising Sales, Central Region, Outdoor Channel, Jason Brist
SVP Operations and Engineering, Eugene A. (Gene) Brookhart
Senior Director Programming and Production, Michael Dorsey
Regional VP West, Affiliate Sales and Marketing, Michael Kim
SVP Advertising Sales, Eastern Region, Outdoor Channel, John Fabian
Regional Director, Affiliate Sales and Marketing, Midwest Region, Christy Benson
Regional VP, Northeast Region, Affiliate Sales and Marketing, Mark Romano
Director Research, Tamara Smith
Director Trade Marketing, Rebecca Nowlin
Regional VP, Central Region and Emerging Media, Affiliate Sales and Marketing, Daniel Soane
Director Business Development, Outdoor Channel, Jesi Steward
SVP Marketing and Research, Outdoor Channel, Denise Conroy-Galley
Vice Chairman, EVP, and Secretary, Thomas H. (Tom) Massie, age 46
National Account Manager, Southern Region, Outdoor Channel, Allison Hill
National Account Manager, Western Region, Outdoor Channel, Scott E. Fink
SVP Affiliate Sales and Marketing, Outdoor Channel, Randy Brown
National Account Manager, Central Region, Outdoor Channel, Teresa Chiniaeff
Director IT, Outdoor Channel, Steve Cheatham
Traffic Director, Kim Ransom
Auditors: Ernst & Young LLP

LOCATIONS

HQ: Outdoor Channel Holdings, Inc.
43445 Business Park Dr., Ste. 103, Temecula, CA 92590
Phone: 951-699-6991   **Fax:** 951-699-1849
Web: www.outdoorchannel.com

PRODUCTS/OPERATIONS

2009 Sales

	$ mil.	% of total
Advertising	34.3	39
Subscriptions	18.8	22
Production fees	33.7	39
Total	**86.8**	**100**

COMPETITORS

ABC, Inc.	FOX Sports
CBS	NBC
Discovery	Spike TV
Communications	The Golf Channel
ESPN	VERSUS

HISTORICAL FINANCIALS

Company Type: Public

Income Statement   FYE: December 31

	REVENUE ($ mil.)	NET INCOME ($ mil.)	NET PROFIT MARGIN	EMPLOYEES
12/10	83.3	1.2	1.4%	190
12/09	86.9	(0.3)	—	222
12/08	54.1	2.4	4.4%	121
12/07	46.9	(1.9)	—	118
12/06	48.5	(7.3)	—	138
Annual Growth	14.5%	—	—	8.3%

2010 Year-End Financials

Debt ratio: —
Return on equity: 0.9%
Cash ($ mil.): 32.6
Current ratio: 5.10
Long-term debt ($ mil.): —

No. of shares (mil.): 25.4
Dividends
  Yield: —
  Payout: —
Market value ($ mil.): 181.8

	STOCK PRICE ($) FY Close	P/E High/Low		PER SHARE ($) Earnings	Dividends	Book Value
12/10	7.17	146	86	0.05	0.00	5.35
12/09	5.80	—	—	(0.01)	0.00	5.44
12/08	7.49	101	42	0.09	0.00	5.39
12/07	6.90	—	—	(0.07)	0.00	5.62
12/06	12.83	—	—	(0.30)	0.00	5.67
Annual Growth	(13.5%)	—	—	—	—	(1.5%)

Oxford Resource Partners

Oxford Resource Partners strives to get its customers steamed. An operator and acquirer of surface coal mines, the company produces steam coal used by power plants and other energy producers to fire steam boilers. It owns and operates about 19 surface mines in the Northern Appalachia region and the Illinois Basin. In 2009 the company, which has assets that include more than 91 million tons of proved and probable reserves, produced 5.8 million tons of coal. It serves markets in Illinois, Indiana, Kentucky, Ohio, Pennsylvania, and

West Virginia and has counted AEP, Duke Energy, and East Kentucky Power as major customers. Formed in 2008, Oxford Resource Partners filed an initial public offering (IPO) in 2010.

The company intends to use the proceeds that it raises in its IPO ($250 million) to repay debt and replenish its capital base used for general corporate purposes. Some proceeds will also be distributed to C&T Coal and AIM Oxford, which each hold an interest in the company.

Prior to the IPO's filing, AIM Oxford and C&T Coal also held an ownership interest (66% and 34%, respectively) in the company's general partner, Oxford Resources GP. AIM Oxford and C&T Coal will continue to hold a similar ownership stake in Oxford Resources GP after the IPO closes.

Oxford Resource Partners is managed and operated by directors and executives at its general partner company. The general partner will continue to manage and operate the company after the IPO closes. Additionally, Oxford Resource Partners will operate through its primary operating subsidiary, Oxford Mining Company. The subsidiary will also own the company's mining assets.

In the future, Oxford Resource Partners intends to grow by expanding its customer base and acquiring mining assets. In 2009 the company took on a mining reserve in Kentucky after it bought Phoenix Coal, which controls the Gryphon Mining Complex. The acquisition expanded the company's mining production capabilities and bolstered its overall production numbers that year. The bump in production also helped fuel an increase in the company's 2009 coal sales, which in turn contributed to a rise in the company's profitability that year.

Oxford Resource Partners brings in most of its revenue from coal sold through long-term sales contracts with its customers. Its contracts serve to bring in a predictable flow of revenue and buffer the company from market-driven fluctuations in the price of coal.

EXECUTIVES

Chairman, George E. McCown, age 75
President, CEO, and Director, Charles C. Ungurean, age 61, $640,781 total compensation
SVP Operations, Gregory J. Honish, age 54, $224,983 total compensation
SVP, CFO, and Treasurer, Jeffrey M. Gutman, age 45, $402,236 total compensation
Senior Director Accounting, Denise M. Maksimoski, age 36
SVP Equipment, Procurement and Maintenance, Thomas T. Ungurean, age 59, $439,797 total compensation
Secretary and General Counsel, Michael B. Gardner, age 56, $241,210 total compensation
Auditors: Grant Thornton LLP

LOCATIONS

HQ: Oxford Resource Partners, LP
544 Chestnut St., Coshocton, OH 43812-1209
Phone: 740-622-6302
Web: www.oxfordresources.com

COMPETITORS

Alliance Resource	Patriot Coal
Alpha Natural Resources	Peabody Energy
Cline Mining	Rhino Resource Partners
CONSOL Energy	

HISTORICAL FINANCIALS

Company Type: Public

Income Statement

FYE: December 31

	REVENUE ($ mil.)	NET INCOME ($ mil.)	NET PROFIT MARGIN	EMPLOYEES
12/10	356.6	(7.4)	—	836
12/09	293.8	23.5	8.0%	800
12/08	230.5	(2.5)	—	0
12/07	191.1	(0.8)	—	0
Annual Growth	23.1%	—	—	4.5%

2010 Year-End Financials

Debt ratio: —
Return on equity: —
Cash ($ mil.): 0.9
Current ratio: 0.91
Long-term debt ($ mil.): 95.7

No. of shares (mil.): 20.6
Dividends
  Yield: 1.4%
  Payout: —
Market value ($ mil.): 502.1

	STOCK PRICE ($) FY Close	P/E High/Low	PER SHARE ($) Earnings	Dividends	Book Value
12/10	24.36	— —	(0.45)	0.35	(0.00)
Annual Growth	—	— —	—	—	—

PAA Natural Gas Storage

PAA Natural Gas Storage has much in store for its customers. The company operates and manages natural gas storage facilities in Louisiana, Michigan, and Mississippi. Its assets, together containing a storage capacity of 40 billion cu. ft., include its Bluewater facility located near Detroit and its Pine Prairie facility in Evangeline Parish, Louisiana. PAA Natural Gas Storage serves customers in the gas distribution, electric power generation and utilities, pipeline, and industrial sectors. It was established by oil transporter Plains All American Pipeline (PAA) and another investor in 2005. PAA Natural Gas Storage went public through an IPO in 2010. In 2011 it bought SG Resources Mississippi for $750 million.

EXECUTIVES

Chairman and CEO, PNGS GP LLC, Greg L. Armstrong, age 52
President and Director, PAA Natural Gas Storage and PNGS GP LLC, Dean Liollio, age 52
VP Optimization, W. Todd Brown
VP Operations, PNGS GP LLC, Dan Noack, age 40
VP Marketing, PNGS GP LLC, Richard Tomaski, age 39
VP Legal and Business Development and Secretary, PNGS GP LLC, Richard K. McGee, age 49
Vice Chairman, PNGS GP LLC, Harry N. Pefanis, age 53
SVP, CFO, and Director, PNGS GP LLC, Al Swanson, age 47
SVP Commercial, Benjamin J. (Ben) Reese, age 54
Chief Accounting Officer and Controller, PAA Natural Gas and PNGS GP LLC, Don O'Shea, age 40
Auditors: PricewaterhouseCoopers LLP

LOCATIONS

HQ: PAA Natural Gas Storage, LLC
333 Clay St., Ste. 1100, Houston, TX 77002
Phone: 713-646-4100

COMPETITORS

AGL Resources	Enterprise Products
ANR Pipeline	Sempra Energy
DTE	Spectra Energy

HISTORICAL FINANCIALS

Company Type: Public

Income Statement

FYE: December 31

	REVENUE ($ mil.)	NET INCOME ($ mil.)	NET PROFIT MARGIN	EMPLOYEES
12/10	100.3	29.8	29.7%	53
12/09	72.2	18.0	24.9%	0
12/08	49.2	19.6	39.8%	0
12/07	36.9	18.0	48.8%	0
Annual Growth	39.6%	18.3%	—	—

2010 Year-End Financials

Debt ratio: —
Return on equity: —
Cash ($ mil.): 0.3
Current ratio: 2.39
Long-term debt ($ mil.): 259.9

No. of shares (mil.): 57.0
Dividends
  Yield: 2.2%
  Payout: 101.6%
Market value ($ mil.): 1,421.5

	STOCK PRICE ($) FY Close	P/E High/Low	PER SHARE ($) Earnings	Dividends	Book Value
12/10	24.93	49 41	0.54	0.55	(0.00)
Annual Growth	—	— —	—	—	—

Pacific CMA

This company is banking on the fact that you can't spell "freight forwarding company" without AGI and CMA. Operating primarily through its AGI Logistics (HK) Ltd subsidiary, Pacific CMA offers logistics, supply chain management, and freight forwarding services. Serving mainly the Asia/Pacific region, CMA transports freight by air, ground, rail, river, and sea and offers warehousing services for exporting goods from China to other worldwide destinations. Its customers typically reside in the retail, distribution, and manufacturing and trading sectors. Based in Hong Kong, AGI Logistics also imports and exports cargo for several major cities in China.

EXECUTIVES

CFO, Anita Chan
CEO, Airgate International, Stanley Lee
President, Paradigm Global Logistics, Terence de Kretser, age 36
Chairman, CEO, and Treasurer, Alfred Lam, age 56
President and Director, Scott Turner, age 54
EVP and Director, Kaze Chan, age 43
EVP, Strategic Development, Ling Kwok, age 38
VP, Airgate International, Thomas Zambuto
Corporate Controller, Timmy Tse
Secretary, Rango Lam, age 38
Auditors: BKD, LLP

LOCATIONS

HQ: Pacific CMA, Inc.
153-04 Rockaway Blvd., Jamaica, NY 11434
Phone: 718-949-9700   **Fax:** 718-949-9740
Web: www.pacificcma.com

COMPETITORS

CEVA Logistics
DHL
Expeditors
UPS Supply Chain
Solutions
UTi Worldwide

HISTORICAL FINANCIALS

Company Type: Public

Income Statement   FYE: December 31

	REVENUE ($ mil.)	NET INCOME ($ mil.)	NET PROFIT MARGIN	EMPLOYEES
12/06	154.0	(2.5)	—	277
12/05	125.0	(0.4)	—	238
12/04	99.6	0.3	0.3%	193
12/03	73.1	—	—	115
12/02	52.9	1.1	2.1%	92
Annual Growth	30.6%	—	—	31.7%

2006 Year-End Financials

Debt ratio: 35.3%
Return on equity: —
Cash ($ mil.): 2.8
Current ratio: 1.28
Long-term debt ($ mil.): 3.6

No. of shares (mil.): —
Dividends
  Yield: —
  Payout: —
Market value ($ mil.): —

	STOCK PRICE ($) FY Close	P/E High/Low		Earnings	PER SHARE ($) Dividends	Book Value
12/06	0.29	—	—	(0.16)	0.00	(0.00)
12/05	0.66	—	—	(0.01)	0.00	(0.00)
12/04	0.86	207	49	0.01	0.00	(0.00)
12/03	1.97	—	—	(0.00)	0.00	(0.00)
12/02	0.45	39	7	0.05	0.00	(0.00)
Annual Growth	(10.4%)	—	—	—	—	—

Pacific WebWorks

Pacific WebWorks wants to ensure that you have the power of the Web working for you. Through its subsidiaries, the company targets small and midsized businesses with a number of Web page design applications and consulting and training services; it also provides Web site hosting for its customers, as well as hosted versions of its products. Customers use the company's products to build Web sites, manage e-commerce transactions, create online storefronts, and track Web site visitor behavior.

EXECUTIVES

Chairman, CEO, and Treasurer, Kenneth W. Bell, age 61, $218,291 total compensation
President, Secretary, and Director, Christian R. Larsen, age 36, $192,750 total compensation
Director, Business Development, Brad Kerr
Auditors:

LOCATIONS

HQ: Pacific WebWorks, Inc.
230 West 400 South, 1st Fl., Salt Lake City, UT 84111
Phone: 801-578-9020   **Fax:** 801-578-9019
Web: www.pacificwebworks.com

COMPETITORS

Authorize.Net
Digital River
Go Daddy
Microsoft
VeriSign
Yahoo!

HISTORICAL FINANCIALS

Company Type: Public

Income Statement   FYE: December 31

	REVENUE ($ mil.)	NET INCOME ($ mil.)	NET PROFIT MARGIN	EMPLOYEES
12/09	29.8	4.8	16.1%	24
12/08	9.2	0.5	5.4%	21
12/07	10.7	0.9	8.4%	25
12/06	5.0	(1.0)	—	19
12/05	5.9	(0.3)	—	54
Annual Growth	49.9%	—	—	(18.4%)

2009 Year-End Financials

Debt ratio: —
Return on equity: 50.7%
Cash ($ mil.): 1.5
Current ratio: 9.34
Long-term debt ($ mil.): —

No. of shares (mil.): 45.1
Dividends
  Yield: —
  Payout: —
Market value ($ mil.): 3.2

	STOCK PRICE ($) FY Close	P/E High/Low		Earnings	PER SHARE ($) Dividends	Book Value
12/09	0.07	4	0	0.11	0.00	0.21
12/08	0.03	7	1	0.02	0.00	0.10
12/07	0.13	8	2	0.02	0.00	0.09
12/06	0.05	—	—	(0.03)	0.00	0.06
12/05	0.12	—	—	(0.01)	0.00	0.09
Annual Growth	(12.6%)	—	—	—	—	23.9%

Pandora Media

This Pandora's box is filled with music. The Internet radio station generates playlists based on a user's favorite artist or song. As part of the company's Music Genome Project, songs are analyzed according to musical features — including details of instrumentation, harmony, lyrics, melody, rhythm, and vocals. Users enter the name of a song, and Pandora creates a playlist of songs with similar characteristics. Pandora's service, free to its more than 90 million registered users and available only in the US, is supported by local and national advertising. Chief strategy officer Tim Westergren founded the company in 2000; Pandora went public in 2011.

Pandora raised about $235 million through its initial public offering. Even though the company has always been unprofitable, the Internet radio service took advantage of the momentum in the capital markets for digital media and online networking websites. The trend is embodied by recent IPOs from LinkedIn and online coupon service Groupon, along with speculation that Twitter could fetch $8 billion or more if it files. Meanwhile, the mighty social networking site Facebook is expected to file an eye-popping IPO later in 2011 or sometime in 2012.

Although Pandora offers a subscription service that allow customers to skip ads and skip through more songs per hour, the company will use the bulk of the IPO proceeds to invest in improving the user experience of its free service. Like the traditional radio station model, Pandora gets the ma-

jority of its revenue from advertising and the number of loyal listeners it claims translates directly to the advertising rates it can charge. Even in a struggling economy, Pandora's ad revenue has been growing as companies look for ways to save money by targeting specific groups of users and the company expects mobile advertising to continue to grow.

In addition to its traditional Internet service, Pandora's reach has broadened through applications for users of mobile devices including Apple's iPhone and iPad, Research in Motion's BlackBerry, and Google's Android operating software. Pandora uses display ads on its landing pages, and launched a program that lets advertisers sponsor free streaming of new albums before they are released — with custom landing pages, banner ads, and an advertiser-branded radio station. The company is constantly updating its advertising platforms to keep pace with the dynamic online and mobile advertising market. So more and more car radios will be equipped to access Pandora, the company has also developed partnerships with automotive manufacturers such as Ford and Mercedes-Benz and after-market radio developers, such as Alpine, Pioneer, Samsung, and Sony.

Pandora has not been immune to the same headaches that have affected all new music distribution technologies. The company has been involved in a protracted battle over how much Internet radio services pay in royalties and continues to negotiate with artists and record companies. Because of this licensing dispute and the even more complex foreign royalty system, Pandora is actively blocking users from outside the US or Canada.

Prior to the IPO, major shareholders included venture capital firms Crosslink Capital (23%), Walden Venture Capital (18%), and Greylock Partners (14%). Joe Kennedy, a former E-LOAN executive, has been Pandora's CEO since 2005.

EXECUTIVES

Chairman, President, and CEO, Joseph J. (Joe) Kennedy, age 51
CFO, Steven M. (Steve) Cakebread, age 59
EVP Business and Corporate Development, Jessica Steel, age 36
EVP, Product and CTO, Thomas (Tom) Conrad, age 41
VP Sales, Brian Mikalis
VP Human Resources, Peter Ekman, age 45
General Counsel and Secretary, Delida Costin, age 41
Chief Revenue Officer, John Trimble, age 47
Chief Strategy Officer and Director, Tim Westergren, age 45
Auditors: Ernst & Young LLP

LOCATIONS

HQ: Pandora Media, Inc.
2101 Webster St., Ste. 1650, Oakland, CA 94612
Phone: 510-451-4100   **Fax:** 510-451-4286
Web: www.pandora.com

PRODUCTS/OPERATIONS

2011 Sales

	$ mil.	% of total
Advertising	119.3	87
Subscription services & other	18.4	13
Total	**137.7**	**100**

COMPETITORS

AOL	Myspace
Apple Inc.	Napster
Atrinsic	RealNetworks
CBS Radio	SIRIUS XM
Clear Channel	Yahoo!
Facebook	YouTube
MSN	

HISTORICAL FINANCIALS

Company Type: Public

Income Statement

FYE: January 31

	REVENUE ($ mil.)	NET INCOME ($ mil.)	NET PROFIT MARGIN	EMPLOYEES
01/11	137.8	(1.8)	—	295
01/10	55.2	(16.8)	—	295
01/09	19.3	(28.2)	—	200
01/08	14.3	(14.0)	—	102
Annual Growth	112.8%	—	—	42.5%

2011 Year-End Financials

Debt ratio: —	No. of shares (mil.): —
Return on equity: —	Dividends
Cash ($ mil.): 43.0	Yield: —
Current ratio: 1.71	Payout: —
Long-term debt ($ mil.): 0.8	Market value ($ mil.): —

Par Pharmaceutical Companies

Generic drugs are par for the course for Par Pharmaceutical Companies (Par). The company markets about 50 generic drugs in some 175 dosages; its generic product line focuses on central nervous system, cardiovascular, and anti-inflammatory medications, as well as infectious disease. The generic division manufactures some of its own products, but it also distributes drugs manufactured by strategic partners. The company is moving into the branded pharmaceutical market as well by developing updated versions of off-patent drugs through its Strativa division. Par markets product through its internal sales force, mainly to wholesalers, retail pharmacy chains, and managed care organizations across the US.

In addition to its own portfolio of off-patent generics, Par Pharmaceutical sells some authorized generics, which are off-brand versions of drugs that are sanctioned by the patent holders (and hence gain rights to a period of market exclusivity). Par has sold an authorized generic version of diabetes drug Glucophage, under contract with Bristol Myers Squibb; it has had other authorized generic contracts with GlaxoSmithKline for Flonase and Zantac and with AstraZeneca for Toprol XL. This strategy paid off for Par Pharmaceutical in 2009 when sales of Toprol XL skyrocketed; though the company's version of Toprol XL was no longer an exclusive product, Par benefited from a reduction in competition for generic versions of the drug that year.

In 2009 the company announced that it would pursue additional market exclusivity opportunities by focusing on its traditional generics business, which operates as Par Pharmaceutical, on "first-to-file" opportunities (which are gained through

patent-challenge litigation) and "first-to-market" opportunities (which involve drugs that are difficult to formulate or manufacture). At the same time the company downsized the internal R&D organization of the generics division, announcing plans to instead focus on gaining new development candidates through partnerships, licensing agreements, or acquisitions.

One such acquisition will be India-based generics maker Edict Pharmaceuticals. Par announced plans in 2011 to acquire the company for some $38 million to obtain its research pipeline fat with first-to-file candidates and its solid oral dosage manufacturing capacity. The two companies have previously collaborated on existing Par products. It also agreed mid-year to acquire Anchen Pharmaceuticals, a private maker of niche and extended-release generic drugs, for some $410 million.

The company expanded its generic offerings later in 2011 through the purchase of several drug rights from Teva Pharmaceuticals for an undisclosed price. The sale was part of requirements made by the FTC to ensure fair competition following Teva's acquisition of Cephalon. Par gained a generic equivalent of Cephalon's Actiq drug (fentanyl lozenges for pain), as well as rights to launch future versions of Cephalon's Provigil narcolepsy and Amrix muscle relaxant offerings.

To further diversify, and to reduce reliance on its generics business, the company has been working to expand branded products division Strativa Pharmaceuticals. Par's first brand-name product, Megace ES, was launched in 2005 to treat anorexia and severe weight loss associated with AIDS; the drug is a version of a compound owned by Bristol-Myers Squibb. Strativa is widening its offerings by entering additional licensing agreements with drugmakers; to that end it acquired the US marketing rights to Nascobal, a vitamin B-12 nasal spray, from drugmaker QOL Medical in 2009. Another branded product, Oravig (licensed from drug development firm BioAlliance), was approved by the FDA in 2010 for the treatment of certain fungal infections.

However, during 2011 Par announced that it was restructuring the Strativa division to focus on the marketing of two core products: Megace ES and Nascobal. (Efforts to market Oravig were reduced.) The plan included layoffs of about 100 employees (primarily Strativa sales representatives), or about 15% of Par's total workforce.

Strativa had previously entered a partnership with MonoSol in 2009 to market MonoSol's chemotherapy-induced nausea candidate Zuplenz, but the rights to Zuplenz were returned to MonoSol as part of the 2011 restructuring initiatives. Strativa's co-marketing relationship with Solvay's for its testosterone replacement product Androgel had already been terminated at the end of 2010.

EXECUTIVES

Chairman, President, and CEO, Patrick G. (Pat) LePore, age 56, $3,667,258 total compensation
EVP and CFO, Michael A. Tropiano, age 54
EVP; President, Generic Products Division, Paul V. Campanelli, age 49, $1,326,844 total compensation
EVP, Chief Administration Officer, General Counsel, and Secretary, Thomas J. Haughey, age 47, $1,364,703 total compensation
VP Investor Relations and Corporate Affairs, Allison Wey
VP Business Development and Licensing, Chad Gassert
VP Formulation Development, Suketu Sanghvi

VP Materials Management, Anthony Guacci
VP Marketing, Michael Altamuro
VP Corporate Development; VP Business Development, Strativa, John A. Neczesny
VP Marketing and Business Analytics, John Ameres
VP Managed Markets, Strativa, Melissa Masterson
VP Regulatory Affairs, Michelle Bonomi-Huvala
SVP Human Resources, Stephen Montalto
SVP Manufacturing and Technical Operations, Robert Polke
Chief Medical Officer, Strativa, Jim Jones
Director Branded Regulatory Affairs, Strativa, Casilda Barnes
Senior Director Alliance Management, Strativa, Rob Campanelli
SVP Sales, Strativa, Rick Painter
SVP Quality and Compliance, Joseph Barbarite
Director Business Development and Valuation, David Saber
SVP Sales, Renee Kenney
Auditors: Deloitte & Touche LLP

LOCATIONS

HQ: Par Pharmaceutical Companies, Inc.
300 Tice Blvd., Woodcliff Lake, NJ 07677
Phone: 201-802-4000   **Fax:** 201-802-4600
Web: www.parpharm.com

PRODUCTS/OPERATIONS

2009 Sales

	$ mil.	% of total
Generic products		
Metoprolol succinate ER (Toprol XL)	742.7	62
Sumatriptan succinate injection (Imitrex)	72.3	6
Meclizine Hydrochloride (Antivert)	38.9	3
Clonidine TDS (Catapres TTS)	33.7	3
Dronabinol (Marinol)	25.0	2
Cabergoline (Dostinex)	12.9	1
Propranolol HCl ER (Inderal LA)	12.5	1
Cholestyramine powder (Questran)	10.3	1
Methimazole (Tapazole)	10.1	1
Megestrol oral suspension (Megace)	9.1	1
Tramadol HCl and acetaminophen tablets (Ultracet)	8.6	1
Fluticasone (Flonase)	5.9	-
Ibuprofen Rx (Advil, Motrin, Nuprin)	5.7	-
Various amoxicillin products (Amoxil)	2.3	-
Other generic	114.3	10
Strativa (branded products)		
Megace ES	68.7	6
Nascobal nasal spray	10.2	1
Other	10.0	1
Total	**1,193.2**	**100**

COMPETITORS

Actavis	Perrigo
Apotex	Pfizer
Bayer AG	Ranbaxy Laboratories
Bristol-Myers Squibb	Roche Holding
Caraco Pharmaceutical	Roxane Laboratories
Forest Labs	Sandoz International
GlaxoSmithKline	GmbH
IMPAX Laboratories	Sanofi
Johnson & Johnson	Teva
Merck	Watson Pharmaceuticals
Mylan	

HISTORICAL FINANCIALS

Company Type: Public

Income Statement
FYE: December 31

	REVENUE ($ mil.)	NET INCOME ($ mil.)	NET PROFIT MARGIN	EMPLOYEES
12/10	1,008.9	92.7	9.2%	686
12/09	1,193.2	76.9	6.4%	616
12/08	578.1	(47.8)	—	654
12/07	769.7	49.9	6.5%	716
12/06	725.2	6.7	0.9%	794
Annual Growth	8.6%	92.9%	—	(3.6%)

2010 Year-End Financials

Debt ratio: —
Return on equity: 14.8%
Cash ($ mil.): 218.7
Current ratio: 4.28
Long-term debt ($ mil.): —

No. of shares (mil.): 35.9
Dividends
  Yield: 0.0%
  Payout: —
Market value ($ mil.): 1,382.6

	STOCK PRICE ($) FY Close	P/E High/Low		PER SHARE ($) Earnings	Dividends	Book Value
12/10	38.51	15	9	2.60	0.00	17.50
12/09	27.06	12	4	2.25	0.00	14.31
12/08	13.41	—	—	(1.43)	0.00	11.73
12/07	24.00	21	12	1.43	0.00	12.94
12/06	22.37	204	67	0.19	0.00	11.87
Annual Growth	14.5%	—	—	92.3%	—	10.2%

Park City Group

Park City Group understands that managing complex retail operations is no picnic. The company supplies retailers with operation management software used to optimize supply chains. Park City sells to supermarkets, convenience stores, and specialty retailers. Its software packages include Fresh Market Manager, Supply Chain Profit Link, and ActionManager. The company counts Circle K, The Home Depot, Williams-Sonoma, and Limited Brands among its customers. Park City was founded by chairman and CEO Randy Fields, who also co-founded Mrs. Fields Cookies. Fields controls almost half of Park City Group's stock.

In 2007 Park City changed its business strategy, opting to transition from a software licensing-based system to a subscription model. In early 2009 the company acquired Prescient Applied Intelligence.

EXECUTIVES

Chairman and CEO, Randall K. (Randy) Fields, age 65, $411,040 total compensation
VP and CFO, David Colbert
VP Business Services, Steve Lewis
VP Development, Shaun Broadhead
SVP, Mark Deuschle
Auditors: HJ & Associates, LLC

LOCATIONS

HQ: Park City Group, Inc.
3160 Pinebrook Rd., Park City, UT 84098
Phone: 435-645-2000   **Fax:** 435-645-2010
Web: www.parkcitygroup.com

PRODUCTS/OPERATIONS

2010 Sales

	$ mil.	% of total
Subscription	6.0	56
Maintenance	2.5	23
Professional services	1.2	11
License	1.2	10
Total	**10.9**	**100**

COMPETITORS

Capgemini	Kronos
HP Enterprise Services	Radiant Systems
Infor Global	Tomax

HISTORICAL FINANCIALS

Company Type: Public

Income Statement
FYE: June 30

	REVENUE ($ mil.)	NET INCOME ($ mil.)	NET PROFIT MARGIN	EMPLOYEES
06/11	10.8	(0.2)	—	53
06/10	10.9	0.2	1.8%	52
06/09	6.0	(4.0)	—	52
06/08	3.3	(2.9)	—	36
06/07	2.6	(3.0)	—	32
Annual Growth	42.8%	—	—	13.4%

2011 Year-End Financials

Debt ratio: 24.7%
Return on equity: —
Cash ($ mil.): 2.6
Current ratio: 0.67
Long-term debt ($ mil.): 1.3

No. of shares (mil.): 11.6
Dividends
  Yield: —
  Payout: —
Market value ($ mil.): 55.2

	STOCK PRICE ($) FY Close	P/E High/Low		PER SHARE ($) Earnings	Dividends	Book Value
06/11	4.75	—	—	(0.09)	0.00	0.46
06/10	3.80	—	—	(0.01)	0.00	0.39
06/09	1.50	—	—	(0.48)	0.00	(0.05)
06/08	3.15	—	—	(0.35)	0.00	0.17
06/07	2.76	—	—	(0.34)	0.00	0.49
Annual Growth	14.5%	—	—	—	—	(1.5%)

Patient Safety Technologies

Patient Safety Technologies wants to give you one less thing to worry about on your next trip to the operating room. Its SurgiCount Medical subsidiary develops and markets the Safety-Sponge System which uses hand-held barcode scanning technology to help keep track of sponges and towels used during surgeries so that they don't go home *inside* patients. Hospitals and surgical centers first invest in the system and then must keep ordering the coded products. Cardinal Health is the exclusive distributor of SurgiCount Medical products. China-based A Plus International is the exclusive supplier of its bar-coded surgical dressings.

EXECUTIVES

President, CEO, and Director, Brian E. Stewart, age 38
CEO, Automotive Services Group, Darrell W. Grimsley, age 44
VP and COO, John A. (Jack) Hamilton, age 52
VP and CFO, David C. Dreyer, age 54
Director Manufacturing, SurgiCount Medical, James Schafer, age 63
Auditors: Squar, Milner, Peterson, Miranda & Williamson, LLP

LOCATIONS

HQ: Patient Safety Technologies, Inc.
27555 Ynez Rd., Ste. 330, Temecula, CA 92591
Phone: 951-587-6201   **Fax:** 310-895-7751
Web: www.patientsafetytechnologies.com

HISTORICAL FINANCIALS

Company Type: Public

Income Statement
FYE: December 31

	REVENUE ($ mil.)	NET INCOME ($ mil.)	NET PROFIT MARGIN	EMPLOYEES
12/10	14.8	2.0	13.5%	13
12/09	4.5	(17.5)	—	16
12/08	2.8	(4.4)	—	3
12/07	1.1	(7.0)	—	13
12/06	0.2	(12.0)	—	13
Annual Growth	193.3%	—	—	0.0%

2010 Year-End Financials

Debt ratio: —
Return on equity: 54.7%
Cash ($ mil.): 1.9
Current ratio: 0.68
Long-term debt ($ mil.): —

No. of shares (mil.): 24.0
Dividends
  Yield: —
  Payout: —
Market value ($ mil.): 22.5

	STOCK PRICE ($) FY Close	P/E High/Low		PER SHARE ($) Earnings	Dividends	Book Value
12/10	0.94	32	8	0.06	0.00	0.16
12/09	1.90	—	—	(0.90)	0.00	(0.25)
12/08	0.75	—	—	(0.33)	0.00	0.00
12/07	1.39	—	—	(0.70)	0.00	0.15
12/06	1.74	—	—	(2.15)	0.00	0.16
Annual Growth	(14.3%)	—	—	—	—	0.1%

Peapack-Gladstone Financial

Peapack-Gladstone Financial hopes its customers are happy as peas in a pod. The company is the parent of Peapack-Gladstone Bank, which operates more than 20 branches serving New Jersey's Hunterdon, Morris, Somerset, and Union counties. Founded in 1921, the bank serves area individuals and small businesses by providing such traditional services as checking, savings, and money market accounts; CDs; IRAs; and credit cards. It offers trust and investment management services through its PGB Trust and Investments unit. Mortgages secured by residential properties represent about half of the company's loan portfolio. The bank also originates commercial real estate, construction, consumer, and business loans

EXECUTIVES

Chairman and CEO, Peapack-Gladstone Financial and Peapack-Gladstone Bank, Frank A. Kissel, age 60, $446,732 total compensation

President, COO, and Director; President and COO, Peapack-Gladstone Bank, Robert M. Rogers, age 52, $268,302 total compensation

EVP and CFO, Peapack-Gladstone Financial and Peapack-Gladstone Bank, Jeffrey J. Carfora, age 52

EVP and Director; President, PBG Trust and Investments, Peapack-Gladstone Bank, Craig C. Spengeman, age 55, $294,900 total compensation

EVP and Chief Lending Officer, Peapack-Gladstone Bank, Vincent A. Spero

EVP and General Counsel, Peapack-Gladstone Bank, Finn M.W. Casperson Jr., age 41

VP and Director Tax, PGB Trust and Investments, James R. Housman

VP and Director Facilities, Peapack-Gladstone Bank, Rene Merghart

VP and Mortgage Officer, Peapack-Gladstone Bank, Margaret O. Volk

VP and Auditor, Peapack-Gladstone Bank, Karen M. Chiarello

VP and Business Development Officer, Peapack-Gladstone Bank, Veronica V. Valentine

VP and Director Sales, Paula L. Palermo

VP and Security Officer, Peapack-Gladstone Bank, Lynda A. Cross

VP and Risk Management Administrator, Peapack-Gladstone Bank, Katherine M. Kremins

VP and Bank Secrecy Act Compliance Officer, Peapack-Gladstone Bank, Todd T. Brungard

VP and Comptroller, Peapack-Gladstone Bank, Mary M. Russell

VP and Director Marketing, Peapack-Gladstone Bank, Denise M. Pace

VP and Business Development Officer, Peapack-Gladstone Bank, Denise L. Parella

VP and Trust Officer, PGB Trust and Investments, Michael E. Herrmann

VP and Trust Officer, PGB Trust and Investments, Michael T. Tormey

VP and Trust Officer, PGB Trust and Investments, George P. Kurtz Jr.

VP and Trust Officer, PGB Trust and Investments, Catherine M. Denning

VP and Trust Officer, PGB Trust and Investments, Glenn C. Guerin

VP and Trust Officer, PGB Trust and Investments, Scott A. Marshman

VP and Trust Officer, PGB Trust and Investments, MJ Sully

VP and Trust Officer, PGB Trust and Investments, John Tarver

VP and Trust Officer, PGB Trust and Investments, John J. Lee

VP and Trust Officer, PGB Trust and Investments, Anne M. Smith

VP and Trust Officer, PGB Trust and Investments, Liza Rosenzweig

VP and Trust Officer, PGB Trust and Investments, John Markovich

VP and Trust Officer, PGB Trust and Investments, Edward P. Nicolicchia

VP and Trust Officer, PGB Trust and Investments, Peter T. Lillard

VP, Peapack-Gladstone Bank, Susan K. Smith
VP, Peapack-Gladstone Bank, Elaine Muldowney
VP, Peapack-Gladstone Bank, Christopher P. Pocquat
VP, Peapack-Gladstone Bank, Scott Searle
VP, Peapack-Gladstone Bank, Stephen S. Miller
VP, Peapack-Gladstone Bank, Valerie L. Kodan
VP, Peapack-Gladstone Bank, Karen M. Ferraro
VP, Peapack-Gladstone Bank, Dirk H. Graham
VP, Peapack-Gladstone Bank, James S. Stadtmueller
VP, Peapack-Gladstone Bank, Jesse D. Williams

VP, Peapack-Gladstone Bank, Frank C. Waldron
VP, Peapack-Gladstone Bank, Marc R. Magliaro
VP, Peapack-Gladstone Bank, John A. Scerbo
VP, Peapack-Gladstone Bank, Diane M. Ridolfi
VP, Peapack-Gladstone Bank, V. Sherri Licata
VP, Peapack-Gladstone Bank, Randall J. Williams
VP, Peapack-Gladstone Bank, Thomas N. Kasper

SVP and CIO, Peapack-Gladstone Bank, Hubert P. Clarke

SVP and Branch Administrator, Peapack-Gladstone Bank, Robert A. Buckley

First VP and Director Business Development, PGB Trust and Investments, John M. Bonk

SVP and Construction Lender, Peapack-Gladstone Bank, Charles T. Kirk

First VP and Senior Investment Officer, PGB Trust and Investments, John C. Kautz

First VP and Senior Trust Operations Officer, PGB Trust and Investments, Michael Pylypyshyn

Assistant Corporate Secretary; Secretary and Trust Officer, PGB Trust and Investments, Catherine A. McCatharn

Corporate Secretary, Antoinette Rosell

SVP and Director Human Resources, Peapack-Gladstone Bank, Bridget J. Walsh

Vice President and Corporate Trainer, Peapack-Gladstone Bank, Doreen A. Macchiarola

First VP and Senior Trust Officer, PGB Trust and Investments, Kurt G. Talke

First VP and Senior Portfolio Manager, PGB Trust and Investments, John E. Creamer

SVP and Retail Delivery, Peapack-Gladstone Bank, Michael J. Giacobello

First VP and Trust Officer, PGB Trust and Investments, Bryant K. Alford

Auditors: Crowe Horwath LLP

LOCATIONS

HQ: Peapack-Gladstone Financial Corporation
158 Rte. 206 North, Gladstone, NJ 07934
Phone: 908-234-0700   **Fax:** 908-234-0795
Web: www.pgbank.com

PRODUCTS/OPERATIONS

2007 Sales

	$ mil.	% of total
Interest		
Loans, including fees	55.9	65
Securities	15.7	18
Other	0.7	1
Noninterest		
Trust fees	9.6	11
Service charges & fees	2.4	3
Other	2.1	2
Total	**86.4**	**100**

COMPETITORS

Bank of America	PNC Financial
Hudson City Bancorp	TD Bank USA
JPMorgan Chase	Valley National
MSB Financial	Bancorp

HISTORICAL FINANCIALS

Company Type: Public

Income Statement

FYE: December 31

	ASSETS ($ mil.)	NET INCOME ($ mil.)	INCOME AS % OF ASSETS	EMPLOYEES
12/10	1,505.4	7.7	0.5%	284
12/09	1,512.4	7.1	0.5%	281
12/08	1,385.4	(22.1)	—	278
12/07	1,347.0	11.9	0.9%	254
12/06	1,288.4	10.2	0.8%	232
Annual Growth	**4.0%**	**(6.8%)**	**—**	**5.2%**

2010 Year-End Financials

Equity as % of assets: 7.82%	Dividends
Return on assets: 0.5%	Yield: 1.5%
Return on equity: 7.9%	Payout: 29.4%
Long-term debt ($ mil.): 30.4	Market value ($ mil.): 114.7
No. of shares (mil.): 8.8	Sales ($ mil.): 75.0

	STOCK PRICE ($) FY Close	P/E High/Low		PER SHARE ($) Earnings	Dividends	Book Value
12/10	13.05	24	15	0.68	0.20	13.39
12/09	12.68	40	17	0.64	0.25	13.70
12/08	25.37	—	—	(2.53)	0.58	9.64
12/07	23.40	23	17	1.35	0.56	12.33
12/06	26.76	24	19	1.16	0.53	11.96
Annual Growth	**(16.4%)**	**—**	**—**	**(12.5%)**	**(21.6%)**	**2.9%**

Pegasystems

Pegasystems helps companies soar through business changes without being tied down by their old processes. The company provides rules-driven business process management software designed to help clients in the financial services, insurance, and health care industries update their operations and systems to reflect changes to business goals and strategies. Established in 1983, Pegasystems offers tools for analyzing and simulating processes, integrating enterprise applications and portals, managing content integration, and managing processes for customer service, claims resolution, and transaction processing. The company's customers include Aetna, WellPoint, Bank of America, and Credit Suisse.

Financial services and health care companies are Pegasystems' primary markets, but the company also sells to clients in the manufacturing, government, travel and hospitality, retail, consumer packaged goods, and telecommunications industries. Pegasystems sells its products through its direct sales force, as well as through distributors and resellers.

In 2010 Pegasystems acquired competitor Chordiant Software for about $161 million in cash. The company's business process management offerings complemented Chordiant's predictive decision management software.

Founder and CEO Alan Trefler owns more than 55% of Pegasystems.

EXECUTIVES

Chairman and CEO, Alan Trefler, age 55, $526,298 total compensation

VP Finance and Chief Accounting Officer, Efstathios A. (Stathis) Kouninis, age 49

VP, General Counsel, and Secretary, Shawn S. Hoyt

VP Industry Solutions, Willy Fox

Vice Chairman, Richard H. (Rick) Jones, age 59

SVP Engineering and Product Development, Michael R. (Mike) Pyle, age 56, $491,314 total compensation

SVP Global Services, Douglas I. (Doug) Kra, age 48, $508,825 total compensation

SVP Corporate Development, Max Mayer, $495,019 total compensation

SVP and CFO, Craig A. Dynes, age 55, $558,924 total compensation

Senior Director, Product Marketing, Amy Bethke

SVP Sales, Leon Trefler

Manager Public Relations, Frank Tutalo

Director Corporate Communications, Brian Callahan

Product Manager, Care Management, Mary Tamir
Chief Marketing Officer, Grant E. Johnson
SVP Human Capital, Jeff Yanagi
Manager Public Relations and Communications, Europe, Middle East, and Africa, Joanna Richardson
Senior Director Corporate Marketing, Russell Keziere
Auditors: Deloitte & Touche LLP

LOCATIONS

HQ: Pegasystems Inc.
101 Main St., Cambridge, MA 02142-1590
Phone: 617-374-9600   Fax: 617-374-9620
Web: www.pega.com

2009 Sales

	$ mil.	% of total
US	175.0	66
Europe		
UK	46.4	18
Other countries	27.1	10
Other regions	15.5	6
Total	**264.0**	**100**

PRODUCTS/OPERATIONS

2009 Sales

	$ mil.	% of total
Software licenses	115.9	44
Professional services	98.0	37
Maintenance	50.1	19
Total	**264.0**	**100**

Selected Software

PegaRULES (business rule development)
Pegasystems SmartBPM Suite (rules-driven business process management)

COMPETITORS

Appian	Progress Software
EMC	salesforce.com
Fair Isaac	SAP
Global 360	Software AG
IBM	SunGard
Metastorm	TIBCO Software
Microsoft Dynamics	Trintech
Oracle	TriZetto

HISTORICAL FINANCIALS

Company Type: Public

Income Statement

FYE: December 31

	REVENUE ($ mil.)	NET INCOME ($ mil.)	NET PROFIT MARGIN	EMPLOYEES
12/10	336.6	(5.9)	—	1,509
12/09	264.0	32.2	12.2%	1,076
12/08	211.6	11.0	5.2%	825
12/07	161.9	6.6	4.1%	657
12/06	126.0	1.8	1.4%	547
Annual Growth	**27.8%**	**—**	**—**	**28.9%**

2010 Year-End Financials

Debt ratio: —
Return on equity: —
Cash ($ mil.): 71.1
Current ratio: 1.63
Long-term debt ($ mil.): —
No. of shares (mil.): 37.3
Dividends
Yield: 0.3%
Payout: —
Market value ($ mil.): 1,364.5

	STOCK PRICE ($) FY Close	P/E High/Low	PER SHARE ($) Earnings	Dividends	Book Value
12/10	36.63	— —	(0.16)	0.12	5.25
12/09	34.00	42 14	0.85	0.12	5.57
12/08	12.36	52 30	0.29	0.12	4.80
12/07	11.93	73 45	0.18	0.15	4.79
12/06	9.87	212 124	0.05	0.06	4.70
Annual Growth	**38.8%**	**— —**	**—**	**18.9%**	**2.8%**

Piper Jaffray

Piper Jaffray provides a range of investment banking services, including mergers and acquisitions (M&A) advice, financing, industry research, and equity and debt underwriting, sales, and trading for corporate clients, institutional investors, government entities, private equity groups, and not-for-profits. The company targets middle-market companies in the consumer, financial services, health care, media, telecommunications, technology, alternative energy, business services, and industrial sectors. It operates nearly 30 US offices, plus locations in Hong Kong, London, and Zurich. Piper Jaffray also offers financial advisory and asset management services and has approximately $12 billion under management.

Piper Jaffray sold its Private Client business to UBS Financial Services in 2006 and began focusing on asset management with the 2007 purchases of St. Louis-based Fiduciary Asset Management (FAMCO), which brought in some $6 billion of assets under management, and Hong Kong-based Goldbond Capital. Three years later it acquired Chicago-based Advisory Research, Inc. (ARI), which has more than $6 billion in assets under management in equity strategies.

The company hopes the acquisition of ARI will provide a steady stream of revenue to help offset lower trading volumes in its institutional brokerage business. Though the economy has shown signs of stabilizing, Piper Jaffray said it expected market volatility, which it cites as the reason for decreased trading activity, to continue through 2011.

The company spun off its private capital operations to that unit's management in 2010. Renamed North Sky Capital, the business continues to manage the existing capital commitments (some $700 million) it held. In another restructuring move, Piper Jaffray streamlined its European operations to focus on M&A advice and the distribution of US and Asian securities to institutional investors in Europe. The company is reallocating capital to China, which it believes has better prospects for growth. Piper Jaffray's revenues were up slightly in 2010, but net income was down, as higher compensation costs and expenses related to the firm's European restructuring weighed on its bottom line.

Financial services giant U.S. Bancorp acquired Piper Jaffray in 1998 (renaming it U.S. Bancorp Piper Jaffray), but spun it off to U.S. Bancorp shareholders five years later.

HISTORY

In 1913 Harry Piper and Palmer Jaffray founded a commercial paper brokerage that helped finance companies like Pillsbury and Archer-Daniels-Midland. It soon moved into public finance and underwriting. It gained a seat on the NYSE with its purchase of Hopwood & Co., which was hard hit by the 1929 crash. Piper Jaffray & Hopwood grew over the next 40 years, going public in 1971. Three years later it became Piper Jaffray.

During the 1980s boom Piper Jaffray, still managed by the Piper family, expanded into asset management and mutual funds. It was relatively unscathed by the 1987 crash.

Real trouble hit in 1994 when a derivatives-heavy bond mutual fund foundered. Investors, claiming they were uninformed of the risk, brought a class-action suit against the firm, which paid out more than $100 million in settlements beginning in 1995.

In 1997 Piper Jaffray began offering new classes of shares of its mutual funds to provide more fee options for investors. The SEC sued the company for fraud related to the 1994 mutual fund debacle in 1998.

That year U. S. Bancorp, looking to expand its securities business, bought the company and bundled its own investment operations into U. S. Bancorp Piper Jaffray. In 1999 the unit expanded with the purchase of investment banker Libra Investments. The firm also entered an alliance with Tel Aviv-based investment bank Nessuah Zannex to back technology and health care ventures in Israel.

Piper Jaffray traditionally has taken pride in its investment research, yet it was one of several investment banks scrutinized for alleged conflicts-of-interest between research and I-banking operations. In 2003 the firm was fined $25 million, and required to pay an additional $7.5 million to provide independent research for investors. As part of the settlement, the company combined its research functions into a single group, and implemented firewalls between its analysts and investment bankers. Losing money, Piper Jaffray was spun off from U.S. Bancorp and returned to the publicly traded arena that same year.

In 2004 the firm was fined again, this time to the tune of $2.4 million for alleged IPO "spinning" (trading hot IPO shares for investment banking business).

Piper Jaffray sold its Private Client business, which offered mutual funds, securities, and annuities to individual investors, to Swiss bank UBS AG in 2006. Piper Jaffray used proceeds from the sale of the unit, which included some 90 branches mainly west of the Mississippi, to expand its industry focus.

EXECUTIVES

Chairman and CEO, Andrew S. Duff, age 53, $1,611,691 total compensation
President and COO, Thomas P. (Tom) Schnettler, age 54, $1,482,750 total compensation
CFO, Debbra L. Schoneman, age 42, $546,963 total compensation
President and CEO, Fiduciary Asset Management, LLC (FAMCO), Wiley D. Angell
CEO, Piper Jaffray Ltd., David I. Wilson, age 47
CEO, Piper Jaffray Asia, Alex P.M. Ko, age 52
Chairman, Financial Institutions Group Corporate Investment Banking, Robert (Bob) Rinek
VP Public Finance Investment Banking, Everado (Lalo) Trujillo
VP Public Finance Investment Banking, Steven Gortler
VP Municipal Derivatives and Reinvestment Products, Mark Kaplan
VP Public Finance Investment Banking, John Peterson
VP Public Finance Investment Banking, Greg Swartz

VP Public Finance Investment Banking, Helen Cregger

VP Public Finance Investment Banking, Ivory Li

VP Public Finance Investment Banking, Matthew (Matt) Gillaspie

VP Public Finance Investment Banking, Gordon Hoven

VP Public Finance Investment Banking, Michael Lund

VP Corporate Investment Banking, Kevin Jakuc

Chief Administrative Officer, R. Todd Firebaugh, age 48

SVP Public Finance Investment Banking, Dustin Avey

SVP Corporate Investment Banking, Clean Technology and Renewables, Christopher (Chris) Flannery

SVP Public Finance Investment Banking, Real Estate and Housing, Patrick O'Leary

SVP Public Finance Investment Banking, Matthew Challis

SVP Sacramento Public Finance Investment Banking, Dennis McGuire

SVP Public Finance Investment Banking, Mark Farrell

SVP Public Finance Investment Banking, Todd Van Deventer

SVP Public Finance Investment Banking, James (Jim) Sult

SVP Public Finance Investment Banking, Real Estate and Housing and State and Local Government Groups, Michael (Mike) Sorth

SVP Public Finance Investment Banking, Tina Neal

SVP Public Finance Investment Banking, Jay Hromatka

SVP Public Finance Investment Banking, Hospitality, Lisa Sexton

SVP Public Finance Investment Banking, Health Care, Matthew Weaver

SVP Public Finance Investment Banking, Mark Piscatelli

Global Co-Head Health Care Corporate Investment Banking, Stuart M. Duty, age 46

Head Fixed Income Services, M. Brad Winges, age 43, $1,856,626 total compensation

Managing Director and Global Co-Head, Consumer Corporate Investment Banking Group, Murray Huneke

Head Health Care Public Finance Investment Banking, Steven (Steve) Proeschel

Head and Managing Director Public Finance Investment Banking, Hospitality, Peter Phillippi

Managing Director and Global Co-Head, Technology, Media and Telecommunications Corporate Investment, Mark Leavitt

Global Co-Head Health Care Corporate Investment Banking, Robert (Bob) DeSutter

Head Financial Institutions Corporate Investment Banking, Thomas (Tom) Chen

Head Asset Management; CEO, Advisory Research, Inc., Brien M. O'Brien

Co-Head Investment Banking and Capital Markets, Scott LaRue

Managing Director, Corporate Investment Banking, John Lonnquist

Head and Managing Director, Industrial Growth and Financial Sponsor Coverage Investment Banking, Larry Zimmerman

Co-Head Investment Banking and Capital Markets, Chad R. Abraham

Managing Director and Group Head Restructuring, Peter Schwab

Principal and Senior Research Analyst, Solar and Clean Technologies, Ahmar Zaman

Assistant General Counsel and Assistant Secretary, John W. Geelan

Principal, European Health Care Investment Banking, Piper Jaffray Ltd., Stuart Rankine

Director Investor Relations, Jennifer A. Olson-Goude

Head Public Finance Services, Francis E. (Frank) Fairman, age 53

Head Global Equities, Robert W. (Bob) Peterson, age 43, $626,444 total compensation

Managing Director and Global Co-Head, Technology, Media and Telecommunications Investment Banking, David Castagna

General Counsel and Secretary, James L. Chosy, age 47

Head, Asian Distribution, Michael Chan

Managing Director and Global Head Clean Technology and Renewables, Corporate Investment Banking, Chris McCabe

Treasurer, Timothy L. Carter, age 43

Managing Director, Public Finance Investment Banking, Todd Goffoy

Senior Research Analyst, Semiconductor and Enabling Tehnologies, Auguste (Gus) Richard

Auditors: Ernst & Young LLP

LOCATIONS

HQ: Piper Jaffray Companies
800 Nicollet Mall, Ste. 800, Minneapolis, MN 55402-7020
Phone: 612-303-6000   Fax: 612-303-8199
Web: www.piperjaffray.com

Selected Locations
Aliso Viejo, CA
Boston
Charlotte, NC
Chicago
Clayton, MO
Dallas
Denver
Des Moines, IA
East Palo Alto, CA
El Suegundo, CA
Gastonbury, CT
Hong Kong
Houston
Jacksonville, FL
Leawood, KS
London
Milwaukee
Minneapolis
New York
Philadelphia
Phoenix
Pittsburgh
Portland, OR
Sacramento, CA
San Antonio
San Francisco
Seattle
Westlake, OH
Zurich

PRODUCTS/OPERATIONS

2010 Sales

	$ mil.	% of total
Investment banking	266.4	47
Institutional brokerage	168.0	30
Asset management	66.8	12
Interest	51.9	9
Other	12.0	2
Total	**565.1**	**100**

COMPETITORS

CIBC World Markets	Jefferies Group
Citigroup Global Markets	JPMorgan Chase
Cowen Group	Morgan Stanley
Credit Suisse (USA)	Raymond James Financial
Deutsche Bank Alex. Brown	Robert W. Baird & Co.
	Thomas Weisel Partners
Goldman Sachs	UBS Financial Services
Houlihan Lokey	

HISTORICAL FINANCIALS
Company Type: Public

Income Statement
FYE: December 31

	REVENUE ($ mil.)	NET INCOME ($ mil.)	NET PROFIT MARGIN	EMPLOYEES
12/10	565.1	24.4	4.3%	1,053
12/09	460.9	30.4	6.6%	1,054
12/08	345.1	(183.0)	—	1,045
12/07	522.6	42.2	8.1%	1,239
12/06	535.2	235.3	44.0%	1,104
Annual Growth	**1.4%**	**(43.3%)**	**—**	**(1.2%)**

2010 Year-End Financials
Debt ratio: 15.4%
Return on equity: 3.0%
Cash ($ mil.): 50.6
Current ratio: —
Long-term debt ($ mil.): 125.0
No. of shares (mil.): 14.7
Dividends
Yield: —
Payout: —
Market value ($ mil.): 513.0

	STOCK PRICE ($) FY Close	P/E High/Low		PER SHARE ($) Earnings	Dividends	Book Value
12/10	35.01	43	22	1.23	0.00	55.51
12/09	50.61	37	12	1.55	0.00	49.80
12/08	39.76	—	—	(11.55)	0.00	39.61
12/07	46.32	31	17	2.43	0.00	52.16
12/06	65.15	6	3	12.40	0.00	49.75
Annual Growth	**(14.4%)**	**—**	**—**	**(43.9%)**	**—**	**2.8%**

PLX Technology

PLX Technology's devices handle complex traffic inside electronic gear. PLX makes input/output accelerators and other chips that are used to manage data transfer between the microprocessor, memory, and peripheral chips within an embedded system. It also sells hardware and software development kits used to design subsystems that employ its chips. Its chips are compatible with communications processors made by industry leaders, such as Broadcom. Electronics manufacturers use the company's industry-standard Peripheral Component Interconnect (PCI) chips in products such as medical instruments, printers, servers, and video equipment. PLX Technology gets more than three-quarters of its sales outside the US.

Distributors generate nearly 90% of PLX's sales. Customers include Cisco, General Electric, IBM, and Siemens. The company has more than 1,000 OEMs using its chips.

While 2009 sales weren't hurt by the lingering global recession and credit crisis, PLX Technology has struggled with profitability in the past decade. Business conditions improved in the second half of 2009 and early 2010, yet the company may still be affected by the highly cyclical nature of the semiconductor industry, which is driven by sales of computers, consumer electronics, and other electronic products.

In 2010 the company agreed to acquire Teranetics, a fabless provider of high-performance mixed-signal semiconductors. The deal will expand PLX's offerings in 10 Gigabit Ethernet over copper physical layer (10GBase-T PHY) applications, which Teranetics is a key supplier for.

In 2009 PLX acquired competitor Oxford Semiconductor for 5.6 million shares of PLX's common stock. Oxford Semi designed chips for data storage products in the small office/home office market. At PLX's stock price when the deal was closed, the transaction was valued at about $16 million.

As a fabless semiconductor company, PLX relies on MagnaChip Semiconductor, Samsung Electronics, and Taiwan Semiconductor Manufacturing, among others, to fabricate its microchips. Other contractors assemble, package, and test the company's parts from wafers supplied by the silicon foundries (contract semiconductor manufacturers).

PLX Technology has offices in China, Japan, South Korea, Taiwan, the UK, and the US.

EXECUTIVES

Chairman, D. James Guzy Sr., age 75
President, CEO, and Director, Ralph A. Schmitt, age 50, $375,553 total compensation
VP Operations, Michael Grubisich, age 52
VP Engineering, Switching, Vijay Meduri, age 40
VP Human Resources, Kenneth A. (Ken) Murray, age 60, $343,102 total compensation
VP Worldwide Sales, Gene Schaeffer, age 47, $344,340 total compensation
VP Engineering, Storage, James Tout
VP Finance, CFO, and Secretary, Arthur O. (Art) Whipple, age 63, $431,426 total compensation
VP Engineering, Architecture and Applications, PHY, John Dring
VP Marketing and Business Development, David K. Raun, age 49, $512,971 total compensation
COO, Lawrence (Larry) Chisvin, age 56, $486,410 total compensation
Public Relations, Jerry Steach
Auditors: BDO Seidman, LLP

LOCATIONS

HQ: PLX Technology, Inc.
870 W. Maude Ave., Sunnyvale, CA 94085
Phone: 408-774-9060   **Fax:** 408-774-2169
Web: www.plxtech.com

2009 Sales

	$ mil.	% of total
Asia/Pacific		
China	29.1	35
Singapore	11.8	14
Taiwan	10.7	13
Other countries	8.3	10
Americas		
US	13.0	16
Other countries	1.9	2
Europe	8.0	10
Total	**82.8**	**100**

PRODUCTS/OPERATIONS

2009 Sales

	$ mil.	% of total
Connectivity products	32.0	39
PCI Express products	31.8	38
Storage products	19.0	23
Total	**82.8**	**100**

Semiconductor Products

Peripheral component interconnect (PCI) input/output accelerators
PCI Express (PCI-X) bridge chips
Universal Serial Bus (USB) controllers

COMPETITORS

Altera	Intel
AMD	Lattice Semiconductor
Applied Micro Circuits	LSI Corp.

Atmel	Marvell Technology
Cavium	Microsemi SoC
Cypress Semiconductor	NXP Semiconductors
Epson	Pericom Semiconductor
Exar	QuickLogic
Fujitsu Semiconductor	Renesas Electronics
Gennum	Standard Microsystems
IBM Microelectronics	Texas Instruments
Integrated Device Technology	Toshiba Semiconductor
	Xilinx

HISTORICAL FINANCIALS

Company Type: Public

Income Statement

FYE: December 31

	REVENUE ($ mil.)	NET INCOME ($ mil.)	NET PROFIT MARGIN	EMPLOYEES
12/10	116.6	(3.3)	—	260
12/09	82.8	(18.8)	—	197
12/08	81.1	(56.5)	—	158
12/07	81.7	1.2	1.5%	157
12/06	81.4	3.0	3.7%	150
Annual Growth	**9.4%**	**—**	**—**	**14.7%**

2010 Year-End Financials

Debt ratio: 1.8%
Return on equity: —
Cash ($ mil.): 5.8
Current ratio: 2.11
Long-term debt ($ mil.): 1.7
No. of shares (mil.): 44.5
Dividends
  Yield: —
  Payout: —
Market value ($ mil.): 160.7

	STOCK PRICE ($) FY Close	P/E High/Low		PER SHARE ($) Earnings	Dividends	Book Value
12/10	3.61	—	—	(0.08)	0.00	2.20
12/09	3.23	—	—	(0.53)	0.00	1.95
12/08	1.72	—	—	(2.00)	0.00	2.47
12/07	9.30	343	221	0.04	0.00	4.44
12/06	13.04	152	81	0.10	0.00	4.26
Annual Growth	**(27.5%)**	**—**	**—**	**—**	**—**	**(15.2%)**

Portfolio Recovery

When times are tough, some businesses find the going a little easier with Portfolio Recovery Associates (PRA). The firm makes its way in the world by collecting on defaulted consumer debt. Its primary business is collections on behalf of clients (including banks, credit unions, consumer and auto finance companies, and retail merchants). PRA also buys charged-off and bankrupt consumer debt portfolios and then collects the debts on its own behalf. The company's subsidiaries are dedicated to skip-tracing and asset location for auto finance companies (IGS) and government accounts receivable management (Revenue Discovery Systems).

PRA added to its services in 2010 when it acquired more than 60% of Claims Compensation Bureau (CCB), which specializes in recovering and processing class action lawsuit claims and settlements. As part of the deal, PRA has the right to buy the remaining stake in CCB.

The company has focused on diversifying its business by expanding services through acquisitions of other companies and through the acquisition of debt portfolios. In 2008 PRA acquired MuniServices and the assets of Louisiana's tax audit services provider Broussard Partners. Both

---

acquisitions augmented the company's capabilities in the government sector. They also were in line with its strategy of diversifying its fee-based business.

PRA's revenues increased despite the weakened state of the economy during the recession. The company attributes its growth to several long-term strategies such as strengthening operational efficiencies, as well as expanding its internal legal collections business, and bankruptcy business.

PRA was formed in 1996 by veterans of the consumer receivables unit of the former Household International (now HSBC Finance). It has locations in Birmingham, Alabama; Fresno, California; Hampton and Norfolk, Virginia; Houston; Hutchinson, Kansas; Jackson, Tennessee; and Las Vegas.

EXECUTIVES

Chairman, President, and CEO, Steven D. (Steve) Fredrickson, age 51, $2,118,279 total compensation
President, Government Services, Mike Pelone
President, Revenue Enhancement Services and Business Development, Kent McCammon, $961,087 total compensation
EVP, CFO, Chief Administrative Officer, Treasurer, and Assistant Secretary, Kevin P. Stevenson, age 46, $1,104,995 total compensation
EVP, General Counsel, and Secretary, Judith S. (Judy) Scott, age 65, $581,568 total compensation
EVP Portfolio Acquisitions, Craig A. Grube, age 50, $846,288 total compensation
VP Bankruptcy Services, Naomi Muellner
VP Business Development, Elizabeth Shumadine
VP Audit and Business Development, Andrea Hunter
VP Portfolio Acquisitions, Tom Choi
VP Portfolio Acquisitions, Claire Arndt
VP Bankruptcy Underwriting, Luanne Ormsbee
VP Corporate Communications, Tanya M. Madison
VP Utility Acquisitions, Joel Lewis
SVP Operations, Vivian Coffey
SVP and COO, Owned Portfolios, Neal Stern
Corporate Counsel, Jeffrey A. Sanborn
SVP Core Operations, Tara Privette
SVP Finance, Neal A. Petrovich, age 49
SVP Bankruptcy Acquisitions, Michael J. Petit, $1,141,995 total compensation
SVP Portfolio Acquisitions, Chris Graves
Auditors: KPMG LLP

LOCATIONS

HQ: Portfolio Recovery Associates, Inc.
120 Corporate Blvd., Norfolk, VA 23502
Phone: 757-519-9300   **Fax:** 757-518-0901
Web: www.portfoliorecovery.com

2009 Accounts by State

	% of total
Texas	16
California	10
Florida	8
New York	6
Illinois	4
Pennsylvania	3
North Carolina	3
Ohio	3
Georgia	3
Michigan	3
Virginia	3
Massachusetts	2
New Jersey	2
Tennessee	2
South Carolina	2
Arizona	2
Other states	28
Total	**100**

PRODUCTS/OPERATIONS

2009 Sales

	$ mil.	% of total
Finance receivables	215.6	77
Commissions	65.5	23
Total	**281.1**	**100**

2009 Portfolio Composition

	% of total
Major credit cards	61
Consumer finance	23
Private-label credit cards	14
Auto deficiency	2
Total	**100**

COMPETITORS

Asset Acceptance Capital	iQor
Asta Funding	Nationwide Recovery Systems
Encore Capital Group	NCO Group
FirstCity Financial	Rampart Capital
GC Services	

HISTORICAL FINANCIALS

Company Type: Public

Income Statement   FYE: December 31

	REVENUE ($ mil.)	NET INCOME ($ mil.)	NET PROFIT MARGIN	EMPLOYEES
12/10	372.7	73.5	19.7%	2,473
12/09	281.1	44.3	15.8%	2,213
12/08	263.3	45.4	17.2%	2,032
12/07	220.7	48.2	21.8%	1,240
12/06	188.3	44.5	23.6%	1,291
Annual Growth	**18.6%**	**13.4%**	**—**	**17.6%**

2010 Year-End Financials

Debt ratio: 0.5%	No. of shares (mil.): 17.1
Return on equity: 15.0%	Dividends
Cash ($ mil.): 41.1	Yield: —
Current ratio: 1.81	Payout: —
Long-term debt ($ mil.): 2.4	Market value ($ mil.): 1,283.2

	STOCK PRICE ($) FY Close	P/E High/Low		PER SHARE ($) Earnings	Dividends	Book Value
12/10	75.20	18	10	4.35	0.00	28.75
12/09	44.85	18	7	2.87	0.00	21.62
12/08	33.84	18	8	2.97	0.00	18.58
12/07	39.67	21	12	3.06	0.00	15.57
12/06	46.69	19	14	2.77	0.00	15.53
Annual Growth	**12.7%**	**—**	**—**	**11.9%**	**—**	**16.6%**

PostRock Energy

PostRock Energy (formerly Quest Resource) is looking to create a rock solid energy company specializing in oil and gas exploration and production and the transportation of natural gas. Its exploration and drilling efforts are focused in the Cherokee Basin of southeastern Kansas and northeastern Oklahoma, and the Appalachian Basin, where it is accumulating leasehold acreage. PostRock Energy has net proved reserves of 192.2 billion cu. ft. of net proved reserves (the bulk of which is coal bed methane gas) and operates more than 2,200 miles of gas gathering pipeline in Kansas and Oklahoma. It also operates more than 1,100 miles of interstate natural gas transmission pipelines in the region.

To simplify its business and free up cash, in 2010 Quest Resource merged its three business units (Quest Resource, Quest Energy Partners, and Quest Midstream Partners) into one entity, PostRock Energy. Following the reorganization the company was 44% owned by former Quest Midstream Partners shareholders, 33% by former Quest Energy Partners unitholders, and 23% by former Quest Resource stockholders.

As a result of the reorganization PostRock Energy operates and controls PostRock Energy Services (formerly Quest Resource Corporation), PostRock MidContinent Production, LLC (formerly Quest Energy Partners) and PostRock Midstream, LLC (formerly Quest Midstream Partners).

To raise cash, in 2011 the company sold its West Virginia assets to Magnum Hunter Resources for $44.6 million. That year the company also boosted its assets in the Cherokee Basin, buying a 15% stake in Constellation Energy Partners from Constellation Energy for $6.6 million in cash and 1 million shares of stock. PostRock Energy had initially planned to buy Constellation Energy's entire stake for about $22.5 million. Constellation Energy Partners owns more than 2,200 producing wells in the Cherokee Basin.

In 2009 the company reported a slump in revenues and income, primarily due to the impact of the global recession in lowering commodity prices and demand for oil and gas. Impairment of oil and natural gas properties also hurt income.

It has also had to clean up some of its finances. Following the exposure of some financial irregularities, in 2008 Quest Resource fired CFO David Grose. Eddie LeBlanc was appointed to that slot in early 2009. In 2010, company veteran Duke Ligon was appointed as chairman of PostRock Energy, replacing Gary Pittman. In 2011 the company appointed Terry Carter as Interim President and CEO.

EXECUTIVES

Chairman, Jon H. Rateau, age 55
CFO, Eddie M. LeBlanc III, age 62
EVP Exploration and Resource Development, Steven L. (Steve) Hochstein, age 53
EVP Quest Eastern Resource, Thomas A. (Tom) Lopus, age 51
EVP Land, David W. (Dave) Bolton, age 42
EVP Engineering, Richard Marlin, age 58
EVP Midstream Assets, Richard A. (Randy) Hoover, age 52
EVP Exploration and Geoscience, Douglas K. Strickland
EVP Finance and Corporate Development, Jack T. Collins, age 35
EVP Acquisitions and Divestures, Bryan T. Simmons, age 54
VP Commercial Activity, Quest Midstream, Mike Forbau
Interim President and CEO, Terry W. Carter, age 58
Chief Compliance Officer and General Counsel, Stephen L. (Steve) DeGiusti
Auditors:

LOCATIONS

HQ: PostRock Energy Corporation
210 Park Ave., Ste. 2750, Oklahoma City, OK 73102
Phone: 405-600-7704   **Fax:** 405-600-7722
Web: www.pstr.com

PRODUCTS/OPERATIONS

2009 Sales

	% of total
Oil & gas	75
Gas pipeline	25
Total	**100**

2008 Sales

	% of total
Oil & gas	85
Gas pipeline	15
Total	**100**

2007 Sales

	% of total
Oil & gas	91
Gas pipeline	9
Total	**100**

COMPETITORS

Belden & Blake	Range Resources
Cabot Oil & Gas	Sharpe Resources
Dorchester Minerals	Unit Corporation
PDC Energy	

HISTORICAL FINANCIALS

Company Type: Public

Income Statement   FYE: December 31

	REVENUE ($ mil.)	NET INCOME ($ mil.)	NET PROFIT MARGIN	EMPLOYEES
12/08	176.1	(167.4)	—	310
12/07	122.9	(30.4)	—	309
12/06	60.3	(48.5)	—	312
12/05	48.5	(31.9)	—	359
12/04	26.2	(4.9)	—	192
Annual Growth	**61.0%**	**—**	**—**	**12.7%**

2008 Year-End Financials

Debt ratio: —	No. of shares (mil.): 32.0
Return on equity: —	Dividends
Cash ($ mil.): 13.8	Yield: —
Current ratio: 1.02	Payout: —
Long-term debt ($ mil.): 343.1	Market value ($ mil.): 14.1

	STOCK PRICE ($) FY Close	P/E High/Low		PER SHARE ($) Earnings	Dividends	Book Value
12/08	0.44	—	—	(6.20)	0.00	(0.12)
12/07	7.17	—	—	(1.37)	0.00	4.09
12/06	10.10	—	—	(2.19)	0.00	3.66
12/05	13.20	—	—	(3.81)	0.00	17.02
12/04	15.00	—	—	(0.85)	0.00	(0.08)
Annual Growth	**(58.6%)**	**—**	**—**	**—**	**—**	**—**

Power Integrations

Power Integrations has an integrated approach to power conversion. The company makes high-voltage analog integrated circuits (ICs) that convert alternating current (AC) to lower-voltage direct current (DC). Power Integrations' high-voltage analog semiconductors, which account for virtually all of the company's sales, are used in PCs, cell phones, cable boxes, and other consumer and industrial electronics. The TOPSwitch line features products made with its environmentally friendly EcoSmart technology, which reduces energy waste. The fabless company sells its chips to electronics manufacturers such as Dell, Nokia, and Samsung Electronics. Power Integrations earns nearly all of its sales overseas.

The fabless manufacturing model allows Power Integrations to focus on engineering and design and still have access to high-volume manufacturing capacity, while not having to maintain a silicon foundry. Power Integrations relies on three contract manufacturers to fabricate its chips: Oki Semiconductor and Seiko Epson in Japan and X-FAB Silicon Foundries in Germany. Its products are then assembled and packaged by independent subcontractors in China, Malaysia, Thailand and the Philippines.Energy-efficiency is the driving factor in developing new power management chips, and Power Integrations has sold nearly 4 billion EcoSmart chips since they were introduced in 1998. The company has since introduced three more product lines that interrupt the power supply when electronics are turned off: CAPZero, LinkZero, and SENZero. In 2010 Power Integrations invested $30 million in SemiSouth Laboratories to accelerate the development of silicon-carbide energy-efficient power devices. SemiSouth Laboratories' silicon-carbide semiconductors, used in solar and wind inverters and hybrid-electric vehicles, are produced at its 10,000-sq.-ft. clean room in Mississippi.

Power Integrations doesn't have any long-term contracts with its customers, and is subject to market conditions and customers' whims on orders. The semiconductor industry remains highly cyclical, and lower sales of consumer electronics due to the global recession is generally driving down sales for chip makers. (However, company sales continue to inch upward). The high-voltage power supply industry is subject to intense competition and characterized by significant price sensitivity, and Power Integrations may see lower average selling prices and sales volume as a result.

The company's chips are sold to original equipment manufacturers and merchant power supply manufacturers around the world. Electronics distributors handle nearly two-thirds of the company's sales. (US distributor Avnet and ATM Electronic Corp. of Taiwan together account for 15% of sales). Power Integrations has offices in 10 countries — China, Germany, India, Italy, Japan, Singapore, South Korea, Taiwan, the UK, and the US.

EXECUTIVES

Chairman, E. Floyd Kvamme, age 73
President, CEO, and Director, Balu Balakrishnan, age 56, $3,663,598 total compensation
VP Finance and CFO, Sandeep Nayyar, age 51
VP Corporate Development and Information Technology, Clifford J. Walker, age 59
VP Marketing, Douglas (Doug) Bailey, age 43
VP Operations, John Tomlin, age 63, $1,370,205 total compensation
VP Engineering, Derek Bell, age 67, $975,887 total compensation
Acting VP Sales, Ben Sutherland
Product Marketing Manager, Andrew Smith
Director, Investor Relations and Corporate Communications, Joe Shiffler
Auditors: Deloitte & Touche LLP

LOCATIONS

HQ: Power Integrations, Inc.
5245 Hellyer Ave., San Jose, CA 95138-1002
Phone: 408-414-9200   **Fax:** 408-414-9201
Web: www.powerint.com

2009 Sales

	% of total
Asia/Pacific	
Taiwan	30
China & Hong Kong	26
South Korea	22
Japan	4
Singapore	2
Europe	
Germany	2
Other countries	8
Americas	5
Other regions	1
Total	**100**

PRODUCTS/OPERATIONS

2009 Sales

	% of total
TinySwitch	43
LinkSwitch	33
TOPSwitch	23
Other	1
Total	**100**

2009 Sales by Market

	% of total
Consumer	35
Communications	34
Industrial electronics	17
Computer	14
Total	**100**

Selected Products

AC-to-DC power conversion products (LinkSwitch)
DC-to-DC power conversion products (DPA-Switch)
Capacitor discharge ICs (CAPZero)
High-voltage analog ICs for power conversion (TOPSwitch, TinySwitch, Hiper, SENZero)
Off-line switcher ICs (PeakSwitch)

COMPETITORS

Allegro MicroSystems	Monolithic Power
BCD Semiconductor	Systems
Fairchild	NXP Semiconductors
Semiconductor	ON Semiconductor
Infineon Technologies	Samsung Electronics
iWatt	Sanken Electric
Maxim Integrated	Semtech
Products	STMicroelectronics
Micrel	Vishay Intertechnology

HISTORICAL FINANCIALS

Company Type: Public

Income Statement

FYE: December 31

	REVENUE ($ mil.)	NET INCOME ($ mil.)	NET PROFIT MARGIN	EMPLOYEES
12/10	299.8	49.5	16.5%	444
12/09	215.7	23.3	10.8%	400
12/08	201.7	1.8	0.9%	402
12/07	191.0	26.6	13.9%	385
12/06	162.4	9.4	5.8%	354
Annual Growth	**16.6%**	**51.5%**	**—**	**5.8%**

2010 Year-End Financials

Debt ratio: —	No. of shares (mil.): 28.4
Return on equity: 14.0%	Dividends
Cash ($ mil.): 155.7	Yield: 0.5%
Current ratio: 5.29	Payout: 12.0%
Long-term debt ($ mil.): —	Market value ($ mil.): 1,139.6

	STOCK PRICE ($) FY Close	P/E High/Low		PER SHARE ($) Earnings	Dividends	Book Value
12/10	40.16	28	16	1.67	0.20	12.48
12/09	36.36	45	20	0.82	0.10	10.44
12/08	19.88	583	243	0.06	0.03	8.86
12/07	34.43	41	24	0.85	0.00	9.77
12/06	23.45	91	44	0.31	0.00	7.70
Annual Growth	**14.4%**	**—**	**—**	**52.3%**	**—**	**12.8%**

Power-One

One may be the loneliest number, but it can be a powerful one. Power-One makes power supplies that include inverters, AC/DC converters, and voltage power switchers. Its Renewable Energy unit makes Aurora-brand inverters for use in wind and solar plants, along with related infrastructure products. Its Power Solutions business unit offers the company's traditional power conversion, network power, and digital power products, which are used in wireless communications, optical networking, data storage, industrial, and other gear. The company sells more than 2,500 types of power supplies, mostly to original equipment manufacturers. More than half of sales come from Europe; North America accounts for another 25%.

The renewable energy products market is providing an increasing amount of sales for the company. Power-One got into the business of making power inverters for solar panels and small wind turbines when it acquired the Power Electronics Group of competitor Magnetek in 2006. Inverters convert energy from DC to AC in order to feed it back in to the utility grid. The company has continued to build on the acquisition by developing wind inverters for higher power commercial and turbine farm applications. In early 2010 Power-One launched a 2.5MW inverter for an offshore wind farm development. The company expects sales from its renewable products unit to grow significantly over the next few years.

In October 2010, Power-One acquired Fat Spaniel, a developer of hosted software for the renewable energy sector. By integrating Fat Spaniel's remote monitoring and asset management software with its inverters, Power-One extends the features of its power conversion systems to include greater customer control and management of their energy assets. The acquisition also brings a strong global customer base and, by adding software engineering expertise, meets the company's goal of strengthening its R&D capabilities.

Another area of growth for Power-One is smart motor controls, which are board-level products embedded by manufacturers into high-end appliances and air-conditioners to increase energy efficiency. In addition, the company is getting into the market for intelligent monitoring and control, which connects infrastructure devices by communicating over power lines. This allows systems such as streetlights and electrical distribution transformers to be remotely operated for greater efficiency.

Power-One is perennially unprofitable and has an accumulated deficit of more than $500 million. The company's net loss rose to around $63 million in 2009 from $17 million in 2008. Its results were impacted by goodwill impairment and restructuring costs.

In response to the financially challenging economic environment, in 2009 Power-One cut its workforce by about 1,300 people, a 29% reduction in headcount. In addition to the general problems associated with the global recession, Power-One has experienced manufacturing and supply chain management problems. Aligning its demand forecasts with factory loading, materials procurement, and manpower utilization has been difficult at times, leading to delayed, missed, or rescheduled deliveries.

Looking to squeeze cost savings out of its worldwide manufacturing footprint, Power-One closed its factory in the Dominican Republic, transferring the plant's production to its plant in China, to a Chinese joint venture, and to contract manufacturers.

Power-One's customers have included Agilent, Cisco Systems, Nokia, and Siemens. The company also sells its products through electrical component distributors.

EXECUTIVES

Chairman, Jay Walters, age 63
President, CEO, and Director, Richard J. (Rich) Thompson, age 61, $1,731,543 total compensation
President, Renewable Energy Solutions, Alexander Levran, age 60, $453,953 total compensation
President, Power Solutions, Steven (Steve) Hogge, age 54
VP Sales, North America, Kent Sheldon
VP Finance and Investor Relations, Kevin Trosian
SVP Operations, Neil Dial, age 60, $252,392 total compensation
SVP Finance and CFO, Gary R. Larsen, age 47
Secretary and General Counsel, Tina D. McKnight, age 53
Auditors: Deloitte & Touche LLP

LOCATIONS

HQ: Power-One, Inc.
740 Calle Plano, Camarillo, CA 93012
Phone: 805-987-8741   **Fax:** 805-388-0476
Web: www.power-one.com

2009 Sales

	$ mil.	% of total
Europe		
Italy	84.7	20
Other countries	151.7	35
North America	101.4	24
Asia/Pacific	83.2	19
Other regions	10.6	2
Total	**431.6**	**100**

PRODUCTS/OPERATIONS

2009 Sales

	$ mil.	% of total
Power systems	275.0	64
Embedded products	156.6	36
Total	**431.6**	**100**

2009 Sales by Industry

	% of total
Renewable energy	30
Network telecom equipment	28
Computer & office equipment	18
Industrial equipment	17
Other	7
Total	**100**

Selected Products

High-power AC/DC switchers
Linear power supplies
Low-power AC/DC switchers
Low-power DC/DC converters
Mid-power AC/DC switchers
Web-based lifecycle management software

COMPETITORS

Acme Electric	Phihong
C&D Technologies	Shindengen Electric
Century Electronics	Manufacturing
Delta Electronics	SL Industries
Digital Power	SMA Solar Technology
Elec & Eltek	TDK
Emerson Electric	Transistor Devices
Emrise	Trippe Manufacturing
Lineage Power	Vicor Corp.
Lite-On Technology	

HISTORICAL FINANCIALS

Company Type: Public

Income Statement

FYE: Sunday nearest December 31

	REVENUE ($ mil.)	NET INCOME ($ mil.)	NET PROFIT MARGIN	EMPLOYEES
12/10	1,047.1	147.9	14.1%	3,470
12/09	431.6	(63.3)	—	3,342
12/08	537.5	(17.5)	—	4,541
12/07	511.6	(36.4)	—	4,159
12/06	338.0	(14.6)	—	4,167
Annual Growth	**32.7%**	**—**	**—**	**(4.5%)**

2010 Year-End Financials

Debt ratio: 12.7%	No. of shares (mil.): 106.7
Return on equity: 52.4%	Dividends
Cash ($ mil.): 227.9	Yield: —
Current ratio: 1.75	Payout: —
Long-term debt ($ mil.): 35.9	Market value ($ mil.): 1,088.1

	STOCK PRICE ($) FY Close	P/E High/Low		PER SHARE ($) Earnings	Dividends	Book Value
12/10	10.20	14	3	0.96	0.00	2.64
12/09	4.35	—	—	(0.74)	0.00	1.39
12/08	1.19	—	—	(0.20)	0.00	2.10
12/07	3.99	—	—	(0.42)	0.00	2.28
12/06	7.44	—	—	(0.17)	0.00	2.58
Annual Growth	**8.2%**	**—**	**—**	**—**	**—**	**0.6%**

Premier Alliance Group

First and foremost, Premier Alliance Group looks to be a business and technology ally to its customers. Premier Alliance provides technology consulting and professional services to organizations in the education, financial, health care, utility, and other sectors. Its core consulting services include systems implementation and architecture, information management, business intelligence, and analysis. Other offerings include expertise in key professional areas such as risk management, compliance, and finance. Tracing its roots back to 1995, Premier Alliance has counted Duke Energy, Bank of America, and a handful of other large companies as among its key customers.

EXECUTIVES

President and Director, Mark S. Elliott
EVP, Robert Yearwood
EVP, Mike Rose
EVP, Kevin Hasenfus
EVP Professional Services, Graeme Booth
Director Business Performance and Technology, Mark Delane

Director Enterprise Risk Management Services, Troy Snyder
Auditors: Scharf Pera & Co., PLLC

LOCATIONS

HQ: Premier Alliance Group, Inc.
4521 Sharon Rd., Ste. 300, Charlotte, NC 28211
Phone: 704-521-8077   **Fax:** 704-521-8078
Web: www.premieralliance.com

COMPETITORS

Accenture	Deloitte LLP
CIBER	North Highland

HISTORICAL FINANCIALS

Company Type: Public

Income Statement

FYE: December 31

	REVENUE ($ mil.)	NET INCOME ($ mil.)	NET PROFIT MARGIN	EMPLOYEES
12/10	17.1	0.1	0.6%	0
12/09	9.3	0.3	3.2%	0
12/08	9.0	(1.3)	—	0
12/07	7.6	0.1	1.3%	0
12/06	8.4	0.1	1.2%	0
Annual Growth	**19.4%**	**0.0%**	**—**	**—**

2010 Year-End Financials

Debt ratio: 0.5%	No. of shares (mil.): 8.0
Return on equity: 3.2%	Dividends
Cash ($ mil.): 0.4	Yield: —
Current ratio: 1.29	Payout: —
Long-term debt ($ mil.): 0.0	Market value ($ mil.): 5.8

	STOCK PRICE ($) FY Close	P/E High/Low		PER SHARE ($) Earnings	Dividends	Book Value
12/10	0.73	—	—	(0.02)	0.00	0.58
12/09	0.99	34	5	0.03	0.00	0.37
12/08	0.46	—	—	(0.23)	0.00	0.32
12/07	0.60	—	—	(0.00)	0.00	(0.00)
Annual Growth	**6.8%**	**—**	**—**	**—**	**—**	**—**

Premier Financial Bancorp

Premier Financial Bancorp is the holding company for a handful of rural and small-town banks in Kentucky, Virginia, Ohio, Maryland, West Virginia, and the District of Columbia. Its holdings include Citizens Deposit Bank, Farmers Deposit Bank, Ohio River Bank, and Premier Bank. The firm entered the DC area in 2009 with the purchase of Adams National Bank, which became its largest affiliate bank. Altogether, Premier's banks have about 40 branches that offer standard deposit, trust, and lending services. Premier's loan portfolio is mainly made up of commercial real estate and mortgage loans. In 2011 the company merged five of its banks, including Adams National Bank, to create Premier Bank.

EXECUTIVES

President, CEO, and Director, Robert W. Walker, age 64, $286,396 total compensation
VP Credit Administration, Scot A. Kelley, age 54
VP Human Resources, Katrina Whitt, age 36
SVP; CEO, First Central Bank, Dennis Klingensmith, age 57, $152,408 total compensation
SVP and CFO, Brien M. Chase, age 46, $135,128 total compensation
Auditors: Crowe Horwath LLP

LOCATIONS

HQ: Premier Financial Bancorp, Inc.
2883 5th Ave., Huntington, WV 25702
Phone: 304-525-1600　　**Fax:** 304-525-9701

COMPETITORS

ASB Financial	Huntington Bancshares
BB&T	Ohio Valley Banc
Camco Financial	PNC Financial
City Holding	Porter Bancorp
Community Trust	S.Y. Bancorp
Farmers Capital Bank	United Bancorp
Fifth Third	United Bankshares

HISTORICAL FINANCIALS

Company Type: Public

Income Statement
FYE: December 31

	ASSETS ($ mil.)	NET INCOME ($ mil.)	INCOME AS % OF ASSETS	EMPLOYEES
12/10	1,183.3	9.2	0.8%	354
12/09	1,101.8	9.1	0.8%	369
12/08	724.5	7.5	1.0%	270
12/07	549.3	7.1	1.3%	226
12/06	535.5	6.5	1.2%	225
Annual Growth	**21.9%**	**9.1%**	**—**	**12.0%**

2010 Year-End Financials

Equity as % of assets: 11.10%	Dividends
Return on assets: 0.8%	Yield: 3.4%
Return on equity: 8.4%	Payout: 22.4%
Long-term debt ($ mil.): 33.1	Market value ($ mil.): 50.8
No. of shares (mil.): 7.9	Sales ($ mil.): 60.3

	STOCK PRICE ($) FY Close	P/E High/Low		PER SHARE ($) Earnings	Dividends	Book Value
12/10	6.40	10	6	0.98	0.22	16.55
12/09	6.70	6	3	1.32	0.44	16.20
12/08	7.03	11	5	1.25	0.43	13.99
12/07	12.78	12	9	1.35	0.40	12.87
12/06	14.07	13	11	1.24	0.10	11.65
Annual Growth	**(17.9%)**	**—**	**—**	**(5.7%)**	**21.8%**	**9.2%**

Primoris

Since the beginning of time, or at least since the 20th century, Primoris has played a part in the evolution of the utility and infrastructure landscape. Through subsidiaries, the company provides construction, engineering, and maintenance services such as replacing and repairing underground pipelines, upgrading and maintaining industrial plants, designing and building concrete structures, and managing the construction of water and wastewater facilities. It also engineers industrial machinery used in oil refineries, petrochemical plants, and other facilities. Primoris' clients have included Duke Energy, Chevron, Sempra, and Kinder Morgan, as well as public sector entities.

The company's roots go back to 1946, and it has historically operated in California and other western states. Primoris took itself public in 2008, which helped it grow rapidly through acquisitions. In 2009, it purchased Louisiana-based James Construction Group, a heavy civil construction firm with a presence in the Gulf Coast region. The following year, Primoris acquired Oregon-based Rockford Corporation, a specialist in natural gas and liquid pipeline projects active in the Pacific Northwest.

With a focus on diversification, Primoris is able to expand its service offerings and attract new clients. Another recent addition is Cravens Partners (renamed Cravens Services), a Texas-based utilities and telecommunications contractor, furthering its Gulf Coast operations. In 2009 the company created subsidiary Juniper Rock Corporation after buying the 88-acre Juniper Flats rock quarry in Southern California. The unit adds a new revenue source in the production and sale of aggregates and other construction materials. In 2010, Primoris bought a 50% stake in WesPac Energy, a general energy infrastructure developer, which broadens its exposure to pipeline and energy-related work throughout the US.

As a result of the poor economic conditions, especially in California and Florida, Primoris reported a 20% decline in revenue in 2009. The company quickly rebounded, thanks to the acquisitions of James Construction and Rockport, and revenues doubled the following year. Additionally, Primoris exited its operations in Ecuador, which were costing the company money.

Looking ahead, Primoris is seeking more opportunities in the infrastructure and renewable energy sectors. It expects demand to rise as the need for electric power grows — a need that it could help deliver through solar power or other energy-efficient sources.

Chairman, president, and CEO Brian Pratt controls some 40% of Primoris.

EXECUTIVES

Chairman, President, and CEO, Brian Pratt, age 59, $640,848 total compensation
President, Cardinal Contractors, William J. McDevitt
President, James Construction Group, Danny L. Hester
President, ARB Industrial, Timothy R. Healy
President, ARB Structures, Mark A. Thurman
President, ARB Underground, Scott E. Summers, $471,675 total compensation
EVP, CFO and Director, Peter J. Moerbeek, age 63
EVP, Corporate Development and Director, John P. Schauerman, age 54, $365,333 total compensation
EVP and Director Construction Services, Michael D. (Mike) Killgore
SVP Government Contracting Services, R. Steve Lewis
SVP, Finance and Accounting, Alfons Theeuwes, $482,804 total compensation
SVP and General Counsel, John M. Perisich
Auditors: Moss Adams, LLP

LOCATIONS

HQ: Primoris Services Corporation
2100 McKinney Ave., Ste. 1500, Dallas, TX 75201
Phone: 214-740-5600
Web: www.primoriscorp.com

2010 Sales

	$ in mil.	% of total
US	920.1	98
Other countries	21.7	2
Total	**941.8**	**100**

PRODUCTS/OPERATIONS

2010 Sales by Segment

	$ mil.	% of total
East Construction Services	480.5	51
West Construction Services	402.3	43
Engineering	59.0	6
Total	**941.8**	**100**

Selected Subsidiaries

ARB, Inc.
Arb Chile, Ltda
ARB Structures, Inc.
Born Heaters Canada, ULC
Cardinal Contractors, Inc.
Cardinal Mechanical, Inc.
Cravens Services, Inc.
GML Coatings, LLC
James Construction Group, LLC
Juniper Rock Corporation
Onquest, Inc.
Rockford Corporation
Stellaris, LLC

COMPETITORS

AMEC	Fluor
Balfour Beatty	Jacobs Engineering
Infrastructure	KBR
Bechtel	Parsons Corporation
EMS USA	Skanska
FCI Constructors	

HISTORICAL FINANCIALS

Company Type: Public

Income Statement
FYE: December 31

	REVENUE ($ mil.)	NET INCOME ($ mil.)	NET PROFIT MARGIN	EMPLOYEES
12/10	941.8	33.6	3.6%	4,034
12/09	467.0	25.9	5.5%	2,648
12/08	609.1	36.4	6.0%	1,651
Annual Growth	**24.3%**	**(3.9%)**	**—**	**56.3%**

2010 Year-End Financials

Debt ratio: 35.1%	No. of shares (mil.): 49.4
Return on equity: 16.1%	Dividends
Cash ($ mil.): 115.4	Yield: 1.0%
Current ratio: 1.12	Payout: 13.9%
Long-term debt ($ mil.): 73.2	Market value ($ mil.): 470.9

	STOCK PRICE ($) FY Close	P/E High/Low		PER SHARE ($) Earnings	Dividends	Book Value
12/10	9.54	13	8	0.72	0.10	4.22
12/09	7.97	11	4	0.75	0.10	4.40
12/08	7.90	200	182	0.04	0.00	5.13
00/00	5.17	7	3	1.29	0.05	1.85
00/00	7.33	108	101	0.07	0.00	5.09
Annual Growth	**6.8%**	**—**	**—**	**79.1%**	**—**	**(4.6%)**

Princeton Review

Sharp minds with sharpened pencils descend annually on The Princeton Review to hone their test-taking skills. The company is one of the country's lead providers of prep courses for the Scholastic Aptitude Test (SAT) as well as a leading provider of courses for other admissions tests (including ACT, AP subjects, GMAT, LSAT, GRE, and TOEFL preparation). The courses serve hundreds of thousands of students from company-owned and franchised locations worldwide. The Princeton Review also produces about 165 educational books published by Random House as well as software titles; it also offers online classes. The company has more than 100 offices throughout the US and in Canada.

Along with its owned offices, Princeton Review operates about 20 franchises outside the US in Asia, Mexico, and the Middle East. Within the US, the company does not operate any independent franchises, choosing to run its own operations domestically.

Princeton Review operates through three divisions. The Higher Education Readiness division brings in the majority of the company's income and houses its test preparation services and its more than 165 print and software titles. The Penn Foster segment accounts for about 45% of Princeton Review's annual sales and provides about 100 accredited, career-oriented online degrees and 2,000 vocational programs in the US, Canada, and 150 other countries worldwide. The Career Education Partnerships division brings in a nominal amount of income and is the segment responsible for forming strategic relationships with universities and colleges to help them develop and administer online courses and programs. In 2010 it formed two such deals with the National Labor College (NLC) and Bristol Community College (BCC).

The deal with the NLC offers the AFL-CIO's 11.5 million members an expanded online degree program. Called the College for Working Families, the program is meant to enhance the NLC's existing curriculum to suit the needs and interests of union members and their families. Together the two companies formed a new subsidiary called NLC-TPR Services (49% owned by Princeton Review and 51% by NLC) to support the development and launch of new programs.

The collaboration with BCC calls for Princeton Review to provide capital, facilities and other assistance to BCC to enable the school to create and sustain an allied health care program to educate aspiring health care workers.

Princeton Review operated a fourth division called Supplemental Educational Services until 2010 when it decided to exit the business, which offered tutoring and supplemental educational services under the No Child Left Behind Act of 2001. Prior to exiting that business, Princeton Review decided to sell its K-12 Services Division in 2009 to CORE Education and Consulting Solutions, an India-based education technology company for about $9.5 million. The transaction allowed Princeton Review to narrow its focus on college and graduate school admissions test preparation.

The Penn Foster division brings in nearly as much income as the Higher Education Readiness division and offers a wide variety of services to Princeton Review's client base. Examples of Penn Foster programs include bridal consultant, electrician, medical billing, and veterinary assistant. Penn Foster also operates one of the largest virtual high schools in the US, with more than 40,000 active students and about 140 courses that include algebra, chemistry, history, and a range of advanced placement classes.

Princeton Review also partners with corporations to offer employees courses to help them prepare for business, graduate, or law school admissions. Programs include online tools, information about standardized testing, financial aid, and on-site instructors.

Bain Capital Venture Fund holds about a 20% stake in Princeton Review, followed by Alta Colleges which holds about a 14% share of the company.

EXECUTIVES

Chairman, David Lowenstein, age 49
President, Penn Foster, Thomas G. (Tom) O'Keefe, age 57
President, Test Preparation Services, H. Scott Kirkpatrick Jr., age 38, $1,485,978 total compensation
EVP and CFO, Christian G. (Chris) Kasper, age 40
EVP, Secretary, and General Counsel, Neal S. Winneg, age 51, $901,213 total compensation
VP Operations, Joel Rubin
VP and Publisher, Robert Franek
Interim President and CEO, John M. Connolly
Director Public Relations, Harriet Brand
Auditors: PricewaterhouseCoopers LLP

LOCATIONS

HQ: The Princeton Review, Inc.
111 Speen St., Framingham, MA 01701
Phone: 508-663-5050
Web: www.princetonreview.com

PRODUCTS/OPERATIONS

2010 Sales

	$ Mil.
% of Total	
Higher Education Readiness	102.8
48	
Penn Foster	96.3
45	
Supplemental Education Services	14.7
7	
Career Education Partnerships	0.6
—	
Total	**214.4**
100	

Selected Book Titles and Software

Anatomy Coloring Book
Cracking the AP Calculus
Cracking the AP Chemistry
Cracking the AP European History
Cracking the AP US History
Cracking the ASVAB
Cracking the GED
Cracking the GMAT
Cracking the GRE
Cracking the Praxis
Cracking the SAT
Cracking the LSAT
Crash Course for the GRE
Crash Course for the SAT
GrammarSmart
Essential SAT Vocabulary Flashcards
Essential TOEFL Vocabulary Flashcards
MathSmart
Math Workout for the GMAT
MCAT Biology Review
MCAT General Chemistry Review
MCAT Organic Chemistry Review
MCAT Physics and Math Review
MCAT Verbal Reasoning & Review
Verbal Workout for the GMAT
WordSmart

Test Reviews

ACT (American College Test)
GMAT (Graduate Management Admissions Test)
GRE (Graduate Record Examination)
MCAT (Medical College Admissions Test)
PSAT (Preliminary SAT)
SAT LSAT (Law School Admissions Test)

SAT Subject Tests
TOEFL (Test of English as a Foreign Language)
USMLE (United States Medical Licensing Examination)

COMPETITORS

ACT, Inc.	Laureate Education
College Board	McGraw-Hill
College Coach	Multi-Media Tutorial
Courier Corporation	New Oriental
Edison Learning	Noah Education
Educate	Holdings Ltd.
ETS	Paradigm Learning
Kaplan	Peoples Educational
KnowledgePoints	Holdings

HISTORICAL FINANCIALS

Company Type: Public

Income Statement

FYE: December 31

	REVENUE ($ mil.)	NET INCOME ($ mil.)	NET PROFIT MARGIN	EMPLOYEES
12/10	214.4	(51.7)	—	5,866
12/09	143.5	(12.4)	—	11,183
12/08	138.8	(8.7)	—	10,985
12/07	146.6	(28.7)	—	3,511
12/06	140.7	(9.5)	—	3,465
Annual Growth	**11.1%**	**—**	**—**	**14.1%**

2010 Year-End Financials

Debt ratio: 379.6%	No. of shares (mil.): 53.5
Return on equity: —	Dividends
Cash ($ mil.): 14.8	Yield: —
Current ratio: 0.70	Payout: —
Long-term debt ($ mil.): 124.5	Market value ($ mil.): 63.1

	STOCK PRICE ($) FY Close	P/E High/Low	PER SHARE ($) Earnings	Dividends	Book Value
12/10	1.18	— —	(1.29)	0.00	0.61
12/09	4.06	— —	(0.13)	0.00	1.34
12/08	4.93	— —	(0.41)	0.00	1.38
12/07	8.33	— —	(1.11)	0.00	0.46
12/06	5.28	— —	(0.36)	0.00	1.49
Annual Growth	**(31.2%)**	**— —**	**—**	**—**	**(19.9%)**

Procera Networks

Procera Networks makes it easier for broadband and mobile service providers to run a tight ship. The company's deep packet inspection (DPI) devices are sold under the brand name PacketLogic. As network management equipment, it monitors network traffic, optimizes bandwidth, identifies security threats, and manages application usage. Customers also PacketLogic to differentiate service levels. Procera sells directly and through resellers, distributors, and systems integrators worldwide. Its customers include cable, phone, and Internet service providers, as well as businesses and schools that manage their own networks. Procera counts more than 500 customers who have installed more than 1,300 PacketLogic systems.

EXECUTIVES

Chairman, Scott McClendon, age 72
President, CEO, and Board Member, James F. Brear, age 46, $787,296 total compensation
VP Product Management, Cam Cullen

VP Global Operations, Michael Marken
VP Sales Asia-Pacific, Benjamin Teh
VP, CFO, Principal Accounting Officer, Treasurer,
 and Secretary, Charles Constanti, age 48
VP Sales, Americas, David (Dave) Ahee, age 44
VP Sales EMEA, Paul Gracie
VP Global Marketing, Jon Lindén, age 36
CTO, Alexander Havång, age 32
Auditors: PMB Helin Donovan, LLP

LOCATIONS

HQ: Procera Networks, Inc.
 100 Cooper Ct., Los Gatos, CA 95032
Phone: 408-354-7200   Fax: 408-354-7211
Web: www.proceranetworks.com

2009 Sales

	$ mil.	% of total
US	12.5	62
Europe	3.8	19
Asia	3	15
Australia	.7	3
Latin America	.1	1
Total	**20.1**	**100**

PRODUCTS/OPERATIONS

2009 Sales

	$ mil.	% of total
Products	17	84
Support services	3.1	16
Total	**20.1**	**100**

COMPETITORS

Allot Communications	Cisco Systems
Arbor Networks	Ericsson
Bivio Networks	Juniper Networks
Blue Coat	SAIC
Brocade Communications	Sandvine

HISTORICAL FINANCIALS

Company Type: Public

Income Statement

FYE: Last Sunday in December

	REVENUE ($ mil.)	NET INCOME ($ mil.)	NET PROFIT MARGIN	EMPLOYEES
12/10	20.3	(2.9)	—	70
12/09	20.1	(7.4)	—	46
12/08	11.5	(13.9)	—	50
12/07	6.7	(12.5)	—	60
12/06	1.9	(7.5)	—	41
Annual Growth	**80.8%**	**—**	**—**	**14.3%**

2010 Year-End Financials

Debt ratio: —	No. of shares (mil.): 11.3
Return on equity: —	Dividends
Cash ($ mil.): 7.9	Yield: —
Current ratio: 2.25	Payout: —
Long-term debt ($ mil.): —	Market value ($ mil.): 70.2

	STOCK PRICE ($) FY Close	P/E High/Low	PER SHARE ($) Earnings	Dividends	Book Value
12/10	6.20	— —	(0.27)	0.00	1.22
12/09	4.40	— —	(0.80)	0.00	0.91
12/08	9.10	— —	(1.80)	0.00	1.08
12/07	14.00	— —	(1.70)	0.00	1.60
12/06	22.00	— —	(1.50)	0.00	1.96
Annual Growth	**(27.1%)**	**— —**	**—**	**—**	**(11.3%)**

Promise Technology

Promise Technology keeps data storage under control. The company makes storage controller cards and redundant array of independent disk (RAID) subsystems, interfacing through the Parallel Advanced Technology Attachment standard and the newer Serial ATA. Its controllers are designed for use with computers ranging from desktop PCs to midrange enterprise systems, and its storage systems include direct attached storage (DAS) and storage area network (SAN) configurations. Promise partners include hard-disk drive makers, such as Seagate, as well as computer manufacturers, including Dell, Gateway, and Fujitsu. Founded in 1988, the company went public in Taiwan in 2002.

Promise Technology is a leader in the development of products utilizing the Serial Advanced Technology Attachment (or SATA) interface standard and Serial Attached SCSI (SAS) drives, although it still offers products based on the older Parallel ATA (PATA) standard.

EXECUTIVES

President and CEO, James Lee
VP Sales and Marketing Americas, Ray Bahar
SVP; General Manager Network Server and Storage,
 Chi-Chen Wu
Auditors: Deloitte & Touche

LOCATIONS

HQ: Promise Technology, Inc.
 580 Cottonwood Dr., Milpitas, CA 95035
Phone: 408-228-1400   Fax: 408-228-0730
Web: www.promise.com

COMPETITORS

Broadcom	Nexsan
Intel	Silicon Image
LSI Corp.	Sonnet Technologies
Marvell Technology	VIA Technologies

HISTORICAL FINANCIALS

Company Type: Public

Income Statement

FYE: December 31

	REVENUE ($ mil.)	NET INCOME ($ mil.)	NET PROFIT MARGIN	EMPLOYEES
12/09	79.3	4.5	5.7%	450
12/08	74.9	5.0	6.7%	450
12/07	50.3	1.8	3.6%	450
12/06	43.5	0.3	0.7%	400
12/03	53.2	11.2	21.1%	300
Annual Growth	**6.9%**	**(14.1%)**	**—**	**7.0%**

2009 Year-End Financials

Debt ratio: —	No. of shares (mil.): 147.3
Return on equity: 8.2%	Dividends
Cash ($ mil.): 23.3	Yield: 2.1%
Current ratio: 4.41	Payout: 55.7%
Long-term debt ($ mil.): —	Market value ($ mil.): 121.6

	STOCK PRICE ($) FY Close	P/E High/Low	PER SHARE ($) Earnings	Dividends	Book Value
12/09	0.83	28 10	0.03	0.02	0.38
12/08	0.32	27 8	0.03	0.00	0.35
12/07	0.51	101 34	0.01	0.00	0.34
12/06	0.80	371 133	(0.00)	0.00	0.29
Annual Growth	**1.2%**	**— —**	**—**	**—**	**8.7%**

ProPhotonix

ProPhotonix (formerly StockerYale) lights the way with lasers and LEDs. The company makes light-emitting diode (LED) modules used in semiconductor manufacturing, machine vision, biomedical, and other applications. It also makes custom LED modules for OEMs, systems integrators, and end users with unique lighting needs. Its Photonic Products, Ltd. (PPL) subsidiary makes custom laser modules and other electro-optical subassemblies and optoelectronic components based on semiconductor laser diode technology. It also distributes precision optical lenses from Panasonic to OEMs in the industrial, medical, scientific, and defense markets. ProPhotonix has operations in Ireland, the UK, and the US.

After expanding its offerings to add optical components, including specialty optical fiber, diffraction gratings, phase masks, and optical subcomponents for telecommunications applications, ProPhotonix began to reorganize in order to reduce its debt. In 2009 the company sold its North American operations — including the Lasiris laser, fluorescent lighting, specialty optical fiber systems, and phase mask product lines — to Coherent for about $15 million in cash. The company is focusing its resources on its LED and custom manufacturing operations, which are located in Ireland and the UK. Customers in Europe make up about 49% of ProPhotonix's sales, while those located in the US account for another 43%.

In 2008 ProPhotonix made an unsolicited offer to acquire Canadian laser manufacturer Virtek Vision International. Virtek rejected the offer, saying it was not in the best interests of the company's shareholders and was made with too many conditions. A tender offer by ProPhotonix was unsuccessful, and Virtek was acquired later that year by Gerber Scientific.

EXECUTIVES

Chairman, President, and CEO, Mark W. Blodgett, age
 54, $592,979 total compensation
COO and CFO, Timothy P. (Tim) Losik, age 52,
 $217,325 total compensation
SVP Human Resources, Marianne Molleur, age 62,
 $197,424 total compensation
Managing Director, Photonic Products, Ltd., Jeremy
 Lane
Managing Director, Specialty Optical Fiber, Stephen
 L. Abbey
General Manager Canada, Nicolas Cadieux
Auditors: Vitale, Caturano & Company PC

LOCATIONS

HQ: ProPhotonix Limited
 32 Hampshire Rd., Salem, NH 03079
Phone: 603-893-8778
Web: www.prophotonix.com

2009 Sales

	% of total
Europe	49
North America	43
Other regions	8
Total	**100**

PRODUCTS/OPERATIONS

2009 Sales by Market

	% of total
Industrial	80
Defense	12
Medical	8
Total	**100**

COMPETITORS

Cree
Electrocomponents
Philips Solid-State Lighting Solutions, Inc.
Solid State

HISTORICAL FINANCIALS

Company Type: Public

Income Statement   FYE: December 31

	REVENUE ($ mil.)	NET INCOME ($ mil.)	NET PROFIT MARGIN	EMPLOYEES
12/08	32.1	(10.3)	—	183
12/07	29.9	(8.5)	—	219
12/06	19.4	(5.2)	—	203
12/05	16.2	(11.9)	—	147
12/04	17.7	(12.7)	—	175
Annual Growth	**16.0%**	**—**	**—**	**1.1%**

2008 Year-End Financials

Debt ratio: 427.6%	No. of shares (mil.): —
Return on equity: —	Dividends
Cash ($ mil.): 1.6	Yield: —
Current ratio: 0.65	Payout: —
Long-term debt ($ mil.): 9.7	Market value ($ mil.): —

	STOCK PRICE ($) FY Close	P/E High/Low	PER SHARE ($) Earnings	Dividends	Book Value
12/08	0.15	— —	(0.27)	0.00	(0.00)
12/07	0.98	— —	(0.24)	0.00	(0.00)
12/06	1.28	— —	(0.17)	0.00	(0.00)
12/05	0.96	— —	(0.46)	0.00	(0.00)
12/04	1.31	— —	(0.62)	0.00	(0.00)
Annual Growth	**(41.8%)**	**— —**	**—**	**—**	**—**

Prospect Capital

Prospect Capital (formerly Prospect Energy) is a closed-end investment company focused on prospecting for riches. The company was founded by former senior managers of Merrill Lynch with an interest in underperforming energy-related businesses. However, it changed its name from Prospect Energy in 2007 to reflect a broadening interest beyond the energy industry; it has since invested in the consumer, food, health care, and manufacturing sectors, among others. Prospect targets middle-market firms with annual revenues of less than $500 million and typically invests from $5 million to $50 million per transaction. It prefers private or thinly traded public companies, and also makes investments in distressed firms.

Propect's portfolio consists of interests in more than 60 companies. To protect its assets, the firm avoids directly investing in any energy companies exclusively engaged in oil and gas exploration, or in speculative development and trading in oil, gas, and/or other commodities.

In 2009, the company acquired middle-market investment firm Patriot Capital Funding for nearly $200 million. The deal is part of Prospect's plan to pursue new portfolio acquisitions and investment opportunities. The company said it would even consider a "hostile offer" for a potential target. In 2010, Prospect made a bid to acquire Allied Capital (which already had announced that it was selling itself to Ares Capital). Prospect's first offer was rejected by Allied, and the company later withdrew a second offer.

EXECUTIVES

Chairman and CEO, John F. Barry III, age 59
CFO, Chief Compliance Officer, Treasurer, and Secretary, Brian H. Oswald, age 50
President, COO, and Board Member, M. Grier Eliasek, age 38
Auditors: BDO USA, LLP

LOCATIONS

HQ: Prospect Capital Corporation
10 E. 40th St., 44th Fl., New York, NY 10016
Phone: 212-448-0702   **Fax:** 212-448-9652
Web: www.prospectstreet.com

PRODUCTS/OPERATIONS

2010 Sales

	$ mil.	% of total
Interest	86.5	76
Dividends	15.4	14
Other	11.7	10
Total	**113.6**	**100**

Selected Portfolio Investments

Advanced Rig Services, LLC (oilfield services)
Aircraft Fasteners International, LLC
AIRMALL USA, Inc.
Ajax Rolled Ring & Machine, Inc. (manufacturing)
American Gilsonite Company (mineral mining and processing)
Arrowhead General Insurance Agency, Inc.
Biotronic NeuroNetwork (neurophysiological monitoring services)
Borga, Inc. (manufacturing)
Boxercraft, Inc. (specialty apparel)
C&J Cladding LLC (metals services and minerals)
Castro Cheese Company, Inc.
Clean Change Energy Holdings, Inc. (biomass power)
Conquest Cherokee, LLC (oil and gas production)
Custom Direct, Inc. (printed checks and accessories)
Deb Shops (apparel retailer)
EXL Acquisition Corp. (lab testing supplies)
Fischbein, LLC (machinery)
Freedom Marine Services LLC (shipping vessels)
Gas Solutions Holdings, Inc. (gas gathering and processing)
H&M Oil & Gas, LLC
Hoffmaster, Inc. (paper-based tableware)
Impact Products, LLC (commercial cleaning and maintenance products)
Integrated Contract Services, Inc.
Iron Horse Coiled Tubing, Inc.
LHC Holdings (home health care)
Mac & Massey, LLC (food ingredients)
Manx Energy, Inc. (oil and gas production)
Maverick Healthcare, Inc. (dba Preferred Homecare)
Miller Petroleum, Inc.
Northwestern Management Services (dba Gentle Dental, dental practice management)
NRG Manufacturing, Inc. (drilling rig components)

Nupla Corporation (striking and digging tools)
Prince Mineral Company (specialty minerals)
Qualitest Pharmaceuticals
R-V Industries, Inc. (metal fabrication)
Regional Management Corp. (consumer finance)
Resco Products, Inc. (refractory materials)
ROM Corporation (roll-up doors)
Royal Adhesives & Sealants
Seaton Corp. (staffing services)
Shearer's Foods, Inc. (snack foods)
Stryker Energy, LLC (oil and gas)
TriZetto Group (health care information technology)
Unitek (telecom services)
Wind River Resources Corp. (oil and gas production)
Yatesville Coal Holdings, Inc.

COMPETITORS

ACI Capital	NGPC
First Reserve	Stephens Group
GFI Energy Ventures	TPG
Katalyst	Venrock

HISTORICAL FINANCIALS

Company Type: Public

Income Statement   FYE: June 30

	REVENUE ($ mil.)	NET INCOME ($ mil.)	NET PROFIT MARGIN	EMPLOYEES
06/11	169.5	118.2	69.7%	0
06/10	113.6	18.9	16.6%	29
06/09	100.5	35.1	34.9%	22
06/08	79.4	27.6	34.8%	19
06/07	40.7	16.7	41.0%	19
Annual Growth	**42.9%**	**63.1%**	**—**	**15.1%**

2011 Year-End Financials

Debt ratio: —	No. of shares (mil.): 107.6
Return on equity: 10.6%	Dividends
Cash ($ mil.): 1.5	Yield: 12.0%
Current ratio: 0.16	Payout: 87.8%
Long-term debt ($ mil.): —	Market value ($ mil.): 1,087.9

	STOCK PRICE ($) FY Close	P/E High/Low	PER SHARE ($) Earnings	Dividends	Book Value
06/11	10.11	9 7	1.38	1.21	10.36
06/10	9.65	41 27	0.32	1.33	10.29
06/09	9.20	13 5	1.11	1.62	12.40
06/08	13.18	16 10	1.17	1.59	16.35
06/07	17.47	18 14	1.06	1.54	14.99
Annual Growth	**(12.8%)**	**— —**	**6.8%**	**(5.9%)**	**(8.8%)**

ProtoSource

ProtoSource is a source of change. Through Malaysia-based subsidiary P2i, ProtoSource is engaged in the business of converting print advertisements into Web-based advertising products for newspapers, magazines, and mail-order businesses. Its primary facility is located in Kuala Lumpur where the company receives and processes electronic files sent by its clients (largely from the US). Customers include such publishers as Tribune, McClatchy, and Gannett. P2i also serves other content publishers, technology companies, retailers, and government entities. While most of ProtoSource's business is done in the US, it also has customers in the UK, Spain, and Canada.

EXECUTIVES

CEO, Peter A. Wardle, age 56
VP Sales and Marketing, P2i Newspapers, James Zito
Controller, ProtoSource and P2i Newspapers, Kenneth DiStefano
Senior Account Manager and European Sales, Cheryl Burow
SVP Product Development, Thomas C. Butera, age 44
Auditors: Margolis & Company P.C.

LOCATIONS

HQ: ProtoSource Corporation
1236 Main St., Ste. C, Hellertown, PA 18055
Phone: 610-814-0550   **Fax:** 610-838-2031
Web: p2ionline.com

PRODUCTS/OPERATIONS

2007 Sales

	$ mil.	% of total
Media & data conversion technologies	2.7	87
Technical support & hosting services	0.4	13
Total	**3.1**	**100**

HISTORICAL FINANCIALS

Company Type: Public

Income Statement

FYE: December 31

	REVENUE ($ mil.)	NET INCOME ($ mil.)	NET PROFIT MARGIN	EMPLOYEES
12/08	35.4	(0.6)	—	150
12/07	3.1	(0.9)	—	133
12/06	2.6	(0.3)	—	143
12/05	1.9	(0.5)	—	113
12/04	1.6	(1.2)	—	24
Annual Growth	**116.9%**	**—**	**—**	**58.1%**

2008 Year-End Financials

Debt ratio: —	No. of shares (mil.): 9.9
Return on equity: —	Dividends
Cash ($ mil.): 0.0	Yield: —
Current ratio: 0.09	Payout: —
Long-term debt ($ mil.): 0.0	Market value ($ mil.): 0.3

	STOCK PRICE ($) FY Close	P/E High/Low	PER SHARE ($) Earnings	Dividends	Book Value
12/08	0.03	— —	(0.02)	0.00	(0.51)
12/07	0.06	— —	(0.03)	0.00	(0.45)
12/06	0.04	— —	(0.01)	0.00	(0.37)
12/05	0.04	— —	(0.02)	0.00	(0.28)
12/04	0.04	— —	(0.04)	0.00	(0.23)
Annual Growth	**(6.9%)**	**— —**	**—**	**—**	**—**

PSB Holdings, Inc.

PSB Holdings thinks it offers Pretty Smart Banking for the businesses and individuals of Connecticut's Windham and New London counties. The holding company owns Putnam Savings Bank, a thrift with about 10 bank branches and lending offices. Putnam Savings Bank offers standard deposit products and services, including checking and savings accounts, merchant and check cards, CDs, and IRAs. It largely uses funds from deposits to write real estate loans: Residential and commercial mortgages together account for about 95% of the bank's loan portfolio. Mutual holding company Putnam Bancorp owns a majority stake in PSB Holdings.

EXECUTIVES

Chairman and CEO; Chairman and CEO, Putnam Bank, Thomas A. Borner, age 57, $387,604 total compensation
President and CFO, Putnam Bank, Robert J. (Bob) Halloran Jr., age 56, $237,196 total compensation
VP and Loan Officer, Putnam Savings Bank, LeeAnn C. Kieltyka
VP and Compliance Officer, Putnam Bank, Lori Lagace
VP and Controller, Putnam Bank, Sandra J. (Sandy) Maciag
SVP and Branch Administrator, Putnam Bank, Lynn K. Brodeur
SVP and Senior Retail Loan Officer, Putnam Bank, John F. LaFountain
Auditors: Wolf & Company, P.C.

LOCATIONS

HQ: PSB Holdings, Inc.
40 Main St., Putnam, CT 06260
Phone: 860-928-6501   **Fax:** 860-928-2147
Web: www.putnamsavings.com

COMPETITORS

Bank of America	People's United Financial
Citizens Financial Group	Rockville Financial
Liberty Bank	SI Financial
New England Bancshares	Webster Financial

HISTORICAL FINANCIALS

Company Type: Public

Income Statement

FYE: June 30

	ASSETS ($ mil.)	NET INCOME ($ mil.)	INCOME AS % OF ASSETS	EMPLOYEES
06/11	472.5	1.1	0.2%	120
06/10	489.4	1.3	0.3%	121
06/09	477.3	(7.1)	—	116
06/08	494.5	3.1	0.6%	116
06/07	491.2	1.9	0.4%	117
Annual Growth	**(1.0%)**	**(12.8%)**	**—**	**0.6%**

2011 Year-End Financials

Equity as % of assets: 9.89%	Dividends
Return on assets: 0.2%	Yield: 0.0%
Return on equity: 2.3%	Payout: —
Long-term debt ($ mil.): 83.5	Market value ($ mil.): 33.9
No. of shares (mil.): 6.5	Sales ($ mil.): 22.2

	STOCK PRICE ($) FY Close	P/E High/Low	PER SHARE ($) Earnings	Dividends	Book Value
06/11	5.19	35 15	0.17	0.00	7.16
06/10	4.82	27 13	0.20	0.04	6.72
06/09	4.85	— —	(1.14)	0.29	6.11
06/08	8.99	22 16	0.48	0.31	7.57
06/07	10.89	41 36	0.28	0.30	7.68
Annual Growth	**(16.9%)**	**— —**	**(11.7%)**	**—**	**(1.7%)**

Purple Communications

Purple Communications (formerly GoAmerica) provides a colorful alternative to traditional phone services for the hearing impaired. It offers telecommunications relay services such as text relay, video relay, and Internet Protocol text relay, whereby hard of hearing subscribers can video chat, send and receive text telephone messages, faxes, and e-mail over computers or wireless devices. Purple Communications maintains 15 call centers in the US to facilitate the calls. The company also offers on-site live interpreting services in a dozen US cities, and via video across the country. Clearlake Capital Group owns nearly all of the company's stock.

Some 90% of Purple Communications' revenues come from services reimbursed by the Telecommunications Relay Services (TRS) Fund, created by the Federal Communications Commission under the Americans with Disabilities Act. The not-for-profit National Exchange Carriers Association (NECA) administers the TRS Fund.

The company boosted its services in 2008 when it made four acquisitions — Verizon's relay services division, Hands On Video Relay Services (HOVRS), Sign Language Associates, and Visual Language Interpreting. That year sales jumped about 600% and surpassed the $100 million mark for the first time. (However, the company has never recorded a profit and carries a substantial amount of debt). It changed its name from GoAmerica to Purple Communications in 2009 as part of a re-branding strategy intended to bring its various products and services under a single, more recognizable banner.

Purple Communications has struggled to keep up with SEC reporting requirements and restated its 2008 revenues from $130 million to $119 million. In 2010 it delisted from the NASDAQ and deregistered with the SEC. The company now trades on the OTC market.

EXECUTIVES

Chairman, Behdad Eghbali, age 34
CEO and Director, Daniel R. (Dan) Luis, age 44, $912,754 total compensation
VP Enterprise Outreach, Jerry Nelson
VP Professional Services, Jana Owen
VP Technical Program Management, Mark L. Stern
VP VRS and Community Operations, Fran Cummings
VP Product Design and Development, Russ Albright
VP Marketing, Jeff Stone
VP Regulatory and Strategic Policy, Kelby Brick
VP Finance, Edward Reginelli
VP Enterprise Information Technology, Tony LaRosa
VP Product Strategy, George Sutcliffe
VP Marketing Communications, Brandon Arthur
VP Sales Operations, Ron Montgomery
Vice Chairman, Ronald E. Obray
COO and CFO, John R. Ferron, age 46, $406,257 total compensation
SVP Community Interpreting, Janet L. Bailey
SVP Operations, Gordon Ellis
Senior Director Spanish, Mark Bella
Senior Consultant, Damien Kelly
General Counsel and Secretary, Michael J. Pendergast, age 47, $179,816 total compensation
Senior Director Outreach, Amir Rassouli
Auditors: WithumSmith+Brown

LOCATIONS

HQ: Purple Communications, Inc.
773 San Marin Dr., Ste. 2210, Novato, CA 94945
Phone: 415-408-2300　　**Fax:** 415-408-2301
Web: www.purple.us

COMPETITORS

AT&T　　　　　　　　Sprint Nextel
Skype　　　　　　　　Verizon
Sorenson

HISTORICAL FINANCIALS

Company Type: Public

Income Statement

FYE: December 31

	REVENUE ($ mil.)	NET INCOME ($ mil.)	NET PROFIT MARGIN	EMPLOYEES
12/09	109.2	(128.7)	—	428
12/08	130.1	(5.0)	—	570
12/07	18.6	(3.7)	—	393
12/06	12.8	(2.0)	—	34
12/05	8.1	(4.4)	—	33
Annual Growth	91.6%	—	—	89.8%

2009 Year-End Financials

Debt ratio: —　　　　　　No. of shares (mil.): 9.2
Return on equity: —　　　Dividends
Cash ($ mil.): 2.4　　　　　Yield: —
Current ratio: 0.21　　　　Payout: —
Long-term debt ($ mil.): —　Market value ($ mil.): 3.1

	STOCK PRICE ($) FY Close	P/E High/Low		PER SHARE ($) Earnings	Dividends	Book Value
12/09	0.34	—	—	(14.67)	0.00	(10.77)
12/08	4.61	—	—	(0.92)	0.00	8.30
12/07	5.50	—	—	(1.68)	0.00	1.04
12/06	8.16	—	—	(0.93)	0.00	1.20
12/05	3.86	—	—	(2.05)	0.00	1.36
Annual Growth	(45.5%)	—	—	—	—	—

Qlik

Qlik Technologies puts important business data just a click away. The company provides its QlikView business intelligence software that gives clients the tools to search and query business data in a variety of ways; reports are displayed in a visual format that can be explored and analyzed further. Qlik serves midsized and large enterprises throughout the world; its 21,000-plus customers have included Campbell Soup Company, Colonial Life, Dannon, and Kraft Foods. The company was originally founded in Sweden in 1993, and about 75% of its sales come from clients outside the US. Qlik went public in July 2010.

The company had stated that it would use proceeds from its IPO to fuel expansion into new geographic areas, acquire other companies, and to expand its product offerings, as well as for general corporate purposes.

While its principal executive offices are located in the US, the bulk of the company's business comes from Nordic and Western European markets, as Qlik was founded in Sweden and operated locally for much of its early history. The company is now eyeing expansion in other targeted markets, including Australia, Brazil, China, Japan, Russia,

and the US. It has more than 1,100 channel partners that sell and distribute Qlik's software to 100-plus countries.

Qlik differentiates itself in a competitive, crowded field for business intelligence software by eschewing the normal sales model. Instead of pushing potential clients, the company's "land-and-expand" strategy calls for introducing QlikView to a company for one purpose and then nurturing its spread and growth throughout the organization for other uses. Qlik's confidence in the superiority of its software — claiming that it takes days or weeks to accomplish tasks that require months or years from rival products — drives this viral approach.

Unlike some technology companies that file for IPOs to raise desperately needed funds to offset losses, Qlik has been solidly profitable since fiscal 2008.

EXECUTIVES

Chairman, Bruce Golden, age 52
CFO, Treasurer, and Secretary, William G. (Bill) Sorenson, age 55, $436,910 total compensation
President, CEO, and Director, Lars Björk, age 48, $538,050 total compensation
VP Marketing, Douglas C. (Doug) Laird, age 49, $271,258 total compensation
COO, Leslie (Les) Bonney, age 52, $725,948 total compensation
CTO, Jonas Nachmanson, age 47
SVP Products, Anthony Deighton, age 37, $520,610 total compensation
Auditors: Ernst & Young LLP

LOCATIONS

HQ: Qlik Technologies, Inc.
150 N. Radnor Chester Rd., Ste. E220, Radnor, PA 19087
Phone: 888-828-9768　　**Fax:** 610-975-5987
Web: www.qlikview.com

2010 Sales

	$ mil.	% of total
Europe	138.4	61
Americas	70.9	31
Rest of World	17.2	8
Total	**226.5**	**100**

PRODUCTS/OPERATIONS

2010 Sales

	$ mil.	% of total
License revenue	145.2	64
Maintenance revenue	59.8	26
Professional services	21.5	10
Total	**226.5**	**100**

COMPETITORS

Actuate　　　　　　　MicroStrategy
IBM　　　　　　　　　Oracle
Information Builders　　SAP
JasperSoft　　　　　　SAS Institute
Microsoft　　　　　　TIBCO Software

HISTORICAL FINANCIALS

Company Type: Public

Income Statement

FYE: December 31

	REVENUE ($ mil.)	NET INCOME ($ mil.)	NET PROFIT MARGIN	EMPLOYEES
12/10	226.5	13.5	6.0%	780
12/09	157.4	6.9	4.4%	574
12/08	118.3	3.0	2.5%	481
12/07	80.6	(0.4)	—	440
Annual Growth	41.1%	—	—	21.0%

2010 Year-End Financials

Debt ratio: —　　　　　　No. of shares (mil.): 78.8
Return on equity: 8.5%　　Dividends
Cash ($ mil.): 158.7　　　　Yield: —
Current ratio: 2.45　　　　Payout: —
Long-term debt ($ mil.): —　Market value ($ mil.): 2,037.3

	STOCK PRICE ($) FY Close	P/E High/Low		PER SHARE ($) Earnings	Dividends	Book Value
12/10	25.87	139	57	0.21	0.00	2.02
Annual Growth	—	—	—	—	—	—

Quality Systems

Quality Systems can't help doctors' with the legibility of their signatures, but it knows how to insure the integrity of their digital records. The company develops data management software for medical and dental practices, and a variety of other health care businesses. Its NextGen subsidiary (75% of sales) makes electronic records and practice management software tailored for patient data, scheduling, billing, and claims handling. Its practice management unit focuses on electronic claims submission, remittance, and payments services. The company's QSI Dental division makes practice management software for dentists. Its inpatient unit focuses on clinical and financial software for rural hospitals.

Quality Systems' NextGen medical practice software business represents three quarters of total sales. In 2010 the company expanded its product line with the acquisitions of Opus Healthcare Solutions and Sphere Health Systems. The Opus deal helped Quality Systems to target rural and community health care markets, in keeping with a broader strategy of focusing on health care organizations and hospitals with 100 or fewer beds as works to diversify its market beyond products for larger institutions. The former Opus operations comprise the company's inpatient division.

The next year Quality Systems established an outsourcing operation in India known as QSIH to perform in-house application development and business processing services. Also in 2011 the company agreed to acquire Texas-based CQI Solutions. The company provides software implementation and other IT services, as well as the Care Tracker line of scheduling and surgical data management software, for about 100 hospitals nationwide. CQI products and services will be sold independently, and will also be sold as integrated components with NextGen products.

Quality Systems enjoyed increased revenue and profit for 2011 despite higher costs related to selling expenses, which rose due to higher sales headcount, and higher research and development costs. The company cited robust sales of recurring software maintenance service revenue, as well as sales of tools for dental practices and small medical practice revenue cycle management as key drivers of growth.

While nearly all of Quality Systems' sales come from a traditional software licensing model, the company has embraced the Software-as-a-Service (SaaS) delivery model, which it offers as a way for smaller practices to quickly start using the select NextGen products. The company primarily makes sales directly, with less than 10% of sales made through resellers.

Chairman Sheldon Razin and director Ahmed Hussein own 17% and 15% respectively of Quality Systems.

EXECUTIVES

Chairman, Sheldon Razin, age 73
CEO and Director, Steven T. Plochocki, age 59, $388,355 total compensation
President, NextGen Healthcare Information Systems, Scott Decker
President and Chief Strategy Officer, Patrick B. Cline, age 50, $1,036,428 total compensation
EVP and CFO, Paul A. Holt, age 45, $426,772 total compensation
EVP, General Counsel, and Secretary, James J. (Jim) Sullivan, age 53
EVP and General Manager, QSI Dental Division, Donn E. Neufeld, age 54, $265,810 total compensation
VP, QSI Dental Division, Kathleen Noll
Auditors: Grant Thornton LLP

LOCATIONS

HQ: Quality Systems, Inc.
18111 Von Karman Ave., Ste. 600, Irvine, CA 92612
Phone: 949-255-2600   **Fax:** 949-255-2605
Web: www.qsii.com

PRODUCTS/OPERATIONS

2011 Sales

	$ mil.	% of total
NextGen	266.5	75
Practice solutions	49.0	14
QSI Dental	19.9	6
Inpatient solutions	17.9	5
Total	**353.4**	**100**

Selected Products

Clinical data management software
Dental charting software
Dental practice management systems
Internet-based consumer health portal
Medical records storage software
Medical practice management systems

COMPETITORS

Allscripts	GE Healthcare
CareCentric	Global Med
Cerner	McKesson
CPSI	MEDITECH
Epic Systems	QuadraMed

HISTORICAL FINANCIALS

Company Type: Public

Income Statement

FYE: March 31

	REVENUE ($ mil.)	NET INCOME ($ mil.)	NET PROFIT MARGIN	EMPLOYEES
03/11	353.4	61.6	17.4%	1,579
03/10	291.8	48.4	16.6%	1,502
03/09	245.5	46.1	18.8%	1,263
03/08	186.5	40.1	21.5%	704
03/07	157.2	33.2	21.1%	661
Annual Growth	**22.4%**	**16.7%**	**—**	**24.3%**

2011 Year-End Financials

Debt ratio: —
Return on equity: 27.4%
Cash ($ mil.): 116.6
Current ratio: 2.07
Long-term debt ($ mil.): —

No. of shares (mil.): 58.1
Dividends
  Yield: 1.5%
  Payout: 59.0%
Market value ($ mil.): 2,419.7

	STOCK PRICE ($) FY Close	P/E High/Low		PER SHARE ($) Earnings	Dividends	Book Value
03/11	41.67	39	25	1.06	0.63	3.87
03/10	30.72	41	26	0.84	0.60	3.26
03/09	22.63	30	16	0.81	0.57	2.73
03/08	14.94	31	18	0.72	0.50	2.08
03/07	20.00	38	23	0.61	0.00	1.68
Annual Growth	**20.1%**	**—**	**—**	**14.8%**	**—**	**23.2%**

QuinStreet

QuinStreet connects companies with potential customers through the information superhighway. The online direct marketing company uses proprietary technologies to provide leads to companies. These clients, which have included DeVry and ADT, then use the leads as the targets of direct marketing campaigns. As a sign of its confidence in its quality, QuinStreet has adopted a pay-for-performance model of pricing in which customers are charged based on lead performance. QuinStreet was founded in 1999. It has five offices in the US, one in India, and one in the UK. Catering mainly to the education and financial services sectors, the company went public in 2010.

As an overall strategy, QuinStreet aims to grow over time by increasing the number of verticals it serves while also entering new verticals either organically or through acquisitions. (Education and financial services remain the company's largest vertical markets, bringing in about 88% of its total revenue each year). In 2009, for-profit education company DeVry accounted for 19% of the company's total revenue. During 2010, however, QuinStreet was able to attract a broader client base, and no one client represented more than 10% of its revenue.

In the latter part of 2011 the company added the B2B media and marketing company IT Business Edge, formed in 2002. In 2010 QuinStreet acquired online insurance businesses Insurance.com for about $33 million and CarInsurance.com (almost $50 million) in order to increase traffic in its lucrative financial services vertical. In late 2009 it acquired the Internet.com division of online network operator WebMediaBrands for about $18 million. The unit comprised five content channels: Developer, Internet News, IT, Personal Technology,

and Small Business. A month earlier QuinStreet bought the Insure.com brand and media asset from Life Quotes for $16 million. QuinStreet also made a pair of acquisitions in 2008: online business-to-business company VendorSeek.com, and credit card information firm CardRatings.com. Overall, the company purchased 53 online publishing businesses in 2008 and 2009.

QuinStreet raised some $150 million from its February 2010 IPO (it filed in November 2009). It used about $26 million to repay the outstanding balance it owes on a five-year term loan. It also used the proceeds to whittle down additional debt and to fund its 2010 acquisitions.

Chairman and CEO Douglas Valenti owns about 14% of QuinStreet. Investment vehicles Split Rock Partners and Sutter Hill Ventures collectively own about 21% and are represented on the company's board of directors by James Simons and Gregory Sands.

EXECUTIVES

Chairman and CEO, Douglas (Doug) Valenti, age 51, $1,137,342 total compensation
CFO, Kenneth R. (Ken) Hahn, age 44, $566,972 total compensation
President, COO, and Director, Bronwyn Syiek, age 46, $982,865 total compensation
EVP, Scott Mackley, age 37, $759,713 total compensation
EVP, Tom Cheli, age 39, $703,553 total compensation
CTO, Nina Bhanap, age 37
SVP, Timothy J. (Tim) Stevens, age 44
SVP, Patrick Quigley, age 35
SVP, Christopher Mancini, age 38
General Counsel, Daniel Caul, age 44
Editor-in-Chief and Director, Compliance, Katrina Boydon
Auditors: PricewaterhouseCoopers LLP

LOCATIONS

HQ: QuinStreet, Inc.
950 Tower Ln., 6th Fl., Foster City, CA 94404
Phone: 650-578-7700   **Fax:** 650-578-7604
Web: www.quinstreet.com

PRODUCTS/OPERATIONS

2010 Sales

	$ mil.	% of total
DMS (Direct Marketing Services)	333.1	99
DSS (Direct Selling Services)	1.7	1
Total	**334.8**	**100**

COMPETITORS

24/7 Real Media	Monster Worldwide
Agency.com	Proven Direct
Aptimus	ValueClick
Digitas	

HISTORICAL FINANCIALS

Company Type: Public

Income Statement

FYE: June 30

	REVENUE ($ mil.)	NET INCOME ($ mil.)	NET PROFIT MARGIN	EMPLOYEES
06/11	403.0	27.2	6.7%	675
06/10	334.8	20.6	6.2%	637
06/09	260.5	17.3	6.6%	505
06/08	192.0	12.9	6.7%	495
06/07	167.4	15.6	9.3%	461
Annual Growth	**24.6%**	**14.9%**	**—**	**10.0%**

Debt ratio: 27.0% No. of shares (mil.): 47.4
Return on equity: 7.7% Dividends
Cash ($ mil.): 132.3 Yield: —
Current ratio: 3.35 Payout: —
Long-term debt ($ mil.): 96.0 Market value ($ mil.): 615.1

	STOCK PRICE ($) FY Close	P/E High/Low		PER SHARE ($) Earnings	Dividends	Book Value
06/11	12.98	45	18	0.55	0.00	7.50
06/10	11.51	40	25	0.46	0.00	6.43
Annual Growth	12.8%	—	—	19.6%	—	16.5%

Rackspace

Rackspace Hosting may be fanatically focused on hosting services, but sometimes it has its head in the clouds. The company provides a range of Web hosting and managed network services for businesses. It primarily offers traditional hosting services with dedicated servers, but it is expanding into cloud hosting, which lets customers utilize pooled server resources on an on-demand basis. Rackspace also provides hosted collaboration, e-mail, and file backup applications. The company markets its services under the Fanatical Support brand. It has more than 90,000 enterprise customers and operates nine data centers in Hong Kong, the UK, and the US. Rackspace gets about three-quarters of its sales in the US.

The company generates most of its revenues from hosting subscription fees, but a small portion is derived from professional services and other nonrecurring charges.

Rackspace has invested in internal development and acquisitions to build its cloud hosting business, which accounted for about 9% of its revenues in 2009. The company bought San Francisco-based cloud data server management software startup Cloudkick in late 2010 to add tools for automating tasks for systems admistrators. It purchased cloud storage specialist Jungle Disk and cloud hosting service provider Slicehost in 2008. Rackspace also offers a suite of combined dedicated and cloud computing services called Hybrid Hosting.

Employees of Rackspace are known as "Rackers" and the company's highest accolade is the "Straightjacket Award," given to employees for exemplifying Fanatical Support in action. *FORTUNE* magazine includes Rackspace in its annual ranking of the "100 Best Companies to Work For."

Through various entities, chairman Graham Weston controls nearly 17% of Rackspace Hosting's outstanding shares.

EXECUTIVES

Chairman, Graham M. Weston, age 47
President, CEO, and Director, A. Lanham Napier, age 40, $6,729,520 total compensation
VP Corporate Development, Jim Curry
VP and General Manager, Enterprise Services, Taylor Rhodes
VP Sales and Marketing, Cloud Division, Frederick Mendler
VP Information Technology, Kiprian (Kip) Miles, age 49
VP Corporate Development US, Brian Thompson, age 37
VP Enterprise Sales, Pat Cathey

VP Finance, Jason Luce
VP Enterprise Strategy, Andy Schroepfer
COO, Mark Roenigk, age 50, $2,192,289 total compensation
Acting Chief Financial Officer, Principal Financial Officer, and Treasurer, Karl Pichler
CIO, Steve Mills, age 52
CTO, John Engates
SVP and Co-General Manager, Hybrid, Wayne Roberts, age 48
SVP, General Counsel, and Secretary, Alan Schoenbaum, age 53
SVP Customer Care, John Lionato, age 48, $1,085,029 total compensation
SVP Marketing and Product Development, Klee Kleber, age 43
SVP Cloud, Pat Matthews, age 34
Managing Director and SVP International, David Kelly, age 46
Chief Strategy Officer; President, The Rackspace Cloud, Lew Moorman, age 40, $2,477,226 total compensation
Director Human Resources, EMEA, Alison Grace
Director Product, Cloud Applications, Kirk Averett
Media Contact, Rachel Ferry
Director Media Services, Wes Laird
Investor Relations, Krisana Puccio
SVP Worldwide Sales and Co-General Manager, Hybrid, Jim Lewandowski, age 50
Corporate Counsel, EMEA, Tiffany Lathe
Director Marketing, EMEA, Fabio Torlini
Director Real Estate, Randy Smith
Director Software Development, Troy Toman, age 44
Director Sales, EMEA, Jairo Romero
Auditors: KPMG LLP

LOCATIONS

HQ: Rackspace Hosting, Inc.
5000 Walzem Rd., San Antonio, TX 78218
Phone: 210-312-4000 **Fax:** 210-447-4300
Web: www.rackspace.com

2009 Sales

	$ mil.	% of total
US	467.9	74
Other countries	161.1	26
Total	**629.0**	**100**

PRODUCTS/OPERATIONS

2009 Sales

	$ mil.	% of total
Managed hosting	572.6	91
Cloud	56.4	9
Total	**629.0**	**100**

COMPETITORS

Amazon.com	NaviSite
AT&T	NetNation
BT	Communications
Cable & Wireless	salesforce.com
Computer Sciences	SAVVIS
Corp.	SoftLayer
Critical Path	Switch and Data
CyrusOne	Facilities
DuPont Fabros	Terremark Worldwide
Equinix	USinternetworking
Google	Verio
HP Enterprise Services	Verizon
IBM	XO Holdings
Microsoft	

HISTORICAL FINANCIALS

Company Type: Public

Income Statement

FYE: December 31

	REVENUE ($ mil.)	NET INCOME ($ mil.)	NET PROFIT MARGIN	EMPLOYEES
12/10	780.6	46.4	5.9%	3,262
12/09	629.0	30.2	4.8%	2,774
12/08	531.9	21.7	4.1%	2,611
12/07	362.0	17.8	4.9%	2,021
12/06	224.0	19.8	8.8%	1,300
Annual Growth	**36.6%**	**23.7%**	**—**	**25.9%**

2010 Year-End Financials

Debt ratio: 16.0% No. of shares (mil.): 123.8
Return on equity: 10.6% Dividends
Cash ($ mil.): 104.9 Yield: —
Current ratio: 0.98 Payout: —
Long-term debt ($ mil.): 70.1 Market value ($ mil.): 3,887.7

	STOCK PRICE ($) FY Close	P/E High/Low		PER SHARE ($) Earnings	Dividends	Book Value
12/10	31.41	93	43	0.35	0.00	3.55
12/09	20.85	98	17	0.24	0.00	2.98
12/08	5.38	63	24	0.19	0.00	2.31
Annual Growth	**141.6%**	**—**	**—**	**35.7%**	**—**	**23.9%**

Radiant Logistics

When companies need someone to transport their freight, Radiant Logistics delivers. Operating through its Airgroup and Adcom Worldwide subsidiaries, the company offers logistics services such as domestic and international air, ocean, and ground freight forwarding (Radiant purchases transportation capacity from carriers and resells to its customers). In addition, Radiant provides supply chain management services such as warehousing, order fulfillment, and inventory management. Government and automotive sectors (e.g., US Transportation Command, Ford, and General Motors) make up the company's customer base. Radiant operates through about 65 offices located throughout North America.

Since its inception in 2001, the company has been actively expanding its operations through acquisitions. In spring 2011 Radiant Logistics purchased DBA Distribution Services (dba Distribution By Air or "DBA"), a New Jersey-based company that provides domestic and international transportation and logistics services in North America. The deal is valued at $12 million and will expand Radiant's markets in Newark, New Jersey, and Los Angeles.

Radiant expects that its future growth will come from additional acquisitions, as well as through organic growth. In addition, it hopes to expand its global operations; currently, the company operates primarily within the North American market.

EXECUTIVES

Chairman and CEO, Bohn H. Crain, age 46, $266,418 total compensation
CFO, Todd Macomber
President, Adcom Express, Robert F. Friedman, age 66

VP and COO, Airgroup, Daniel Stegemoller, age 55, $261,057 total compensation
Auditors: Peterson Sullivan P.L.L.C.

LOCATIONS

HQ: Radiant Logistics, Inc.
1227 120th Ave. NE, Bellevue, WA 98005
Phone: 425-943-4599   Fax: 425-943-4598
Web: www.radiant-logistics.com

COMPETITORS

AIT Worldwide
  Logistics
APL Logistics
CEVA Logistics
DHL

Landstar System
UPS Supply Chain
  Solutions
UTi Worldwide

HISTORICAL FINANCIALS

Company Type: Public

Income Statement

FYE: June 30

	REVENUE ($ mil.)	NET INCOME ($ mil.)	NET PROFIT MARGIN	EMPLOYEES
06/11	203.8	2.9	1.4%	151
06/10	146.7	2.0	1.4%	82
06/09	137.0	(9.7)	—	82
06/08	100.2	1.4	1.4%	120
06/07	75.5	0.2	0.3%	74
Annual Growth	28.2%	95.1%	—	19.5%

2011 Year-End Financials

Debt ratio: 196.0%
Return on equity: 47.1%
Cash ($ mil.): 0.4
Current ratio: 1.21
Long-term debt ($ mil.): 11.9

No. of shares (mil.): 31.7
Dividends
  Yield: —
  Payout: —
Market value ($ mil.): 76.0

	STOCK PRICE ($) FY Close	P/E High/Low		PER SHARE ($) Earnings	Dividends	Book Value
06/11	2.40	28	3	0.09	0.00	0.19
06/10	0.27	5	3	0.06	0.00	0.02
06/09	0.30	—	—	(0.28)	0.00	(0.02)
06/08	0.21	21	3	0.04	0.00	0.26
06/07	0.60	—	—	(0.00)	0.00	(0.00)
Annual Growth	41.4%	—	—	—	—	—

RAIT Financial Trust

RAIT Financial Trust was not founded by an '80s hair-rock band, but it is just as commercially minded. The real estate investment trust (REIT) specializes in providing commercial mezzanine and short-term bridge financing, mostly first mortgages that are refinanced with other lenders. It also acquires real estate loans from lenders or investors, typically loans under default or forbearance. Most loans (between $250,000 and $75 million) are secured by multifamily residences and other commercial properties. RAIT also invests in apartment buildings in its key markets. Subsidiary Taberna Realty Finance provides long-term real estate capital.

Betsy Cohen, chairman of RAIT, is also the chairman of The Bancorp Bank and the CEO and director of its parent company, The Bancorp, Inc.

EXECUTIVES

Chairman, President, and CEO, Scott F. Schaeffer, age 49, $1,310,605 total compensation
CFO and Treasurer, Jack E. Salmon, age 56, $1,124,362 total compensation
EVP and Director, Originations, Samuel J. Greenblatt
EVP Asset Management, Plamen M. Mitrikov, age 37, $2,523,136 total compensation
EVP Risk Management, Kenneth R. (Ken) Frappier, age 58
COO and Secretary, Raphael Licht, age 42
SVP Finance and Chief Accounting Officer, James J. Sebra, age 35
Managing Director, RAIT Securities, LLC, Kenneth Kates
Managing Director, RAIT Securities, LLC, Michael Gaffney
Auditors: Grant Thornton LLP

LOCATIONS

HQ: RAIT Financial Trust
2929 Arch St., 17th Fl., Philadelphia, PA 19104
Phone: 215-243-9000   Fax: 215-243-9039
Web: www.raitft.com

COMPETITORS

Ares Commercial Real
  Estate
AvalonBay
Brandywine Realty
BRT Realty

Capital Trust
iStar Financial Inc
Newcastle Investment
Pacific Premier
Vestin

HISTORICAL FINANCIALS

Company Type: Public

Income Statement

FYE: December 31

	REVENUE ($ mil.)	NET INCOME ($ mil.)	NET PROFIT MARGIN	EMPLOYEES
12/10	244.6	111.8	45.7%	405
12/09	208.5	(427.6)	—	329
12/08	147.1	(429.2)	—	61
12/07	939.2	(367.5)	—	76
12/06	170.5	77.9	45.7%	70
Annual Growth	9.4%	9.5%	—	55.1%

2010 Year-End Financials

Debt ratio: 200.2%
Return on equity: 12.2%
Cash ($ mil.): 27.2
Current ratio: —
Long-term debt ($ mil.): 1,838.2

No. of shares (mil.): 35.3
Dividends
  Yield: 0.0%
  Payout: —
Market value ($ mil.): 231.9

	STOCK PRICE ($) FY Close	P/E High/Low		PER SHARE ($) Earnings	Dividends	Book Value
12/10	6.57	4	1	3.33	0.00	26.01
12/09	3.93	—	—	(20.31)	0.00	30.92
12/08	7.80	—	—	(21.09)	3.81	49.90
12/07	25.86	—	—	(18.78)	7.68	28.48
12/06	103.44	15	11	6.90	7.80	56.38
Annual Growth	(49.8%)	—	—	(16.7%)	—	(17.6%)

Rambus

Looking for faster memory chips, lawsuits, or both? Get on the bus — Rambus. Rambus licenses an innovative computer memory design — called Rambus DRAM, or RDRAM — that speeds the exchange of signals between a computer's memory and logic chips. RDRAM chips are used in PCs, video game consoles, and other electronic systems. Rambus' leading licensees include AMD, Fujitsu, NEC, Panasonic, and Toshiba. It also sells LCD lighting products. The company holds more than 950 patents. Rambus has been involved in sometimes bitter litigation with several of the world's largest memory chip makers over the validity of its patent claims. The company gets most of its revenues in Japan.

Unprofitable on an annual basis since 2005, Rambus cut its workforce by 21% in 2008, laying off about 90 people. The company estimated it would save around $17 million a year in expenses following the cutbacks, principally in employee compensation. It trimmed another 130 positions in 2009, a reduction of nearly 40%.

Like many other chip makers, Rambus was vulnerable to the global recession and the resulting dramatic downturn in sales for the semiconductor industry. Since the company depends on royalties from its licensees for most of its revenues, lower sales for its customers means lower royalty payments to Rambus.

In 2009 Rambus bought a portfolio of advanced lighting and optoelectronics patents from Global Lighting Technologies for about $26 million. The acquisition gave Rambus a greater range of technology for the computer and consumer electronics markets, specifically for light-emitting diode (LED) backlighting applications. The company bolstered its lighting and display business in early 2011 when it acquired patents and technology related to general lighting, LCD backlighting, and microelectromechanical (MEMS) displays from Imagine Designs. The purchase added a customer base in the architecture, entertainment, and street lighting markets.

In an attempt to extend its technology licensing portfolio into the chip security arena, Rambus acquired Cryptography Research (CRI), an R&D and licensing company that focuses on developing data security technologies to prevent fraud, piracy, and counterfeiting. The $342 million cash and stock deal is part of Rambus' strategy to improve lagging revenue numbers by offering a broad range of complementary technologies for the mobile computing market. Infineon, Microsoft, Atmel, Raytheon, STMicro, and Visa are among CRI's licensees. Terms of the transaction consist of $167 million in cash, about 6.4 million shares of newly issued Rambus stock, and $50 million paid in cash or stock to Cryptography employees over three years.

In 2010 Samsung Electronics agreed to pay Rambus up to $900 million over five years to settle its memory chip patent infringement suit. Samsung will also buy $200 million of Rambus stock and the two companies will collaborate on next-generation memory technology development. As part of the settlement, Samsung will no longer face the antitrust charges Rambus had filed, claiming that Samsung, Micron Technology, and Hynix conspired to boycott Rambus technology. The Korean chip giant took an equity stake of about 8% in Rambus.

Samsung is expected to represent a significant portion of licensing revenue for Rambus over the next five years. Rambus has traditionally depended on a small number of licensees, with its top five accounting for about three-quarters of revenues.

Rambus reached a legal settlement in 2009 with Hynix after eight years of litigation. Hynix will take out a license for certain memory parts and pay royalties on sales of the devices. The Korean chip maker also committed to paying $397 million in damages and interest to Rambus.

Chip kingpin Intel originally championed the costly Rambus technology as an industry standard, but later switched gears and began outfitting many of its microprocessors to work with competing double-data-rate (DDR) DRAM memory chip designs. Rambus, meanwhile, broadened its technology suite beyond memory chips by debuting designs for chips used in high-speed networking devices, and by developing a new high-speed chip interconnect technology.

Some Rambus detractors allege that it also "broadened its technology suite" in another way with its assertion of patent claims on crucial design elements of synchronous DRAM (SDRAM) and DDR DRAM technology. In asserting its claims, Rambus became embroiled in a series of intellectual-property lawsuits with major memory makers around the world. Some of its licensees, in fact, signed on with Rambus to avoid facing it in court.

Rambus has design centers and offices in Germany, India, Japan, Taiwan, and the US.

HISTORY

Rambus was founded in 1990 by Michael Farmwald and Mark Horowitz. Farmwald, whose business cards sported the title "visionary," previously built supercomputers at Lawrence Livermore National Laboratory. Horowitz was a Stanford electrical engineering professor.

In 1991 AMD chip expert Geoff Tate was named CEO. The next year Rambus began licensing its technology. Farmwald left in 1993 to start media processor company Chromatic Research (later part of ATI Technologies, which was acquired by AMD in 2006).

Rambus's big break came in 1995, when Nintendo used Rambus dynamic random-access memories (RDRAMs) to speed up its Nintendo 64 video game system. In 1997 (the year it went public) Rambus and Intel began developing a chipset to support the use of RDRAM with Intel's PC microprocessors.

Concern over implementation of RDRAM technology grew among PC makers in 1999 when Intel delayed its Rambus-based Camino chipset. Camino was finally unveiled later that year, but the delay spooked PC makers, several of whom opted for cheaper, more familiar memory technologies. Nonetheless, Dell and Hewlett-Packard were among PC makers to release systems with RDRAM chips in 1999.

In 2000 Intel announced a move away from exclusive use of RDRAMs. Meanwhile, Rambus filed suit against numerous chip companies for patent infringement; it avoided going to court by reaching licensing agreements with Hitachi, Mitsubishi Electric, NEC, Oki, Samsung Electronics, and Toshiba, but was itself sued by Hyundai Electronics (now Hynix Semiconductor) and Micron Technology.

In 2001 the US Federal Trade Commission (FTC) opened a preliminary investigation into antitrust claims against Rambus; the investigation led to an FTC antitrust suit against the company in 2002, but the suit was dismissed in 2004. Some Rambus opponents suggested that it improperly concealed key patent filings while it was involved in an industry standards-setting body (called JEDEC) in the early and mid-1990s; these claims alleged that Rambus was therefore able to incorporate elements of the standards for what would become advanced DRAMs into its own patents — giving it a potential royalties claim on every DRAM maker in the world.

Later in 2001, Rambus suffered a legal setback in the first round of its US federal court case against Infineon; the jury found Rambus guilty of fraud in connection with its participation in the JEDEC group. (The punitive damage award in the case was far below what Infineon requested). A federal judge later cleared Rambus of some alleged misconduct, while upholding other parts of the fraud verdict. An appeals court later overturned the verdict in the Infineon case; in 2003 the US Supreme Court refused to hear Infineon's appeal of the appellate court's decision. The appeals court later ordered a retrial on Rambus's patent claims against the German chip maker.

Rambus expanded its offerings by acquiring high-speed signaling technology from Velio Communications in 2003. The following year Rambus sued Hynix, Infineon, Micron, and Siemens (Infineon's former parent company and still a significant shareholder in the chip maker at the time) in state court in San Francisco, accusing the companies of collusion in the memory market. Later that year, Infineon pleaded guilty to federal charges of criminal price fixing and agreed to pay a fine of $160 million. Rambus and Infineon reached a legal settlement of all patent claims in 2005, with Infineon agreeing to pay nearly $47 million to Rambus over two years.

Geoff Tate stepped aside as CEO in 2005, becoming chairman of the board. He was succeeded as CEO by Harold Hughes, a Rambus director and a former Intel executive who was CEO of Pandesic, a joint venture between Intel and SAP.

Just weeks before their patent licensing agreement was due to expire in 2005, Rambus and Samsung Electronics exchanged patent infringement lawsuits. Rambus claimed that the world's largest manufacturer of memory chips should pay Rambus royalties for DDR2 chips, while Samsung asserted that Rambus's patents and its licensing deal with Rambus didn't apply to DDR2 technology. Samsung lodged its complaint in the same federal district court in Virginia where Infineon once litigated against Rambus with some success.

Later that year, the federal court in Virginia granted a motion by Rambus to dismiss Samsung's claims for declaratory judgment, but denied a motion by the company regarding Samsung's claim for attorneys' fees. Rambus then signed a five-year patent licensing deal with AMD that would be worth $75 million to the company over the life of the agreement.

Micron Technology again sued Rambus in 2006, claiming that Rambus violated the federal Racketeer Influenced and Corrupt Organizations act and Virginia conspiracy laws through its business practices. Micron also sued Rambus in Italy over a patent infringement case in that country.

IBM and Rambus inked a licensing agreement that allowed IBM to make Cell Broadband Engine processors and related chips using the Rambus FlexIO processor bus and XDR memory interface technologies. The Cell processor was jointly developed by IBM, Sony, and Toshiba. Sony designed the processor into its PlayStation 3 game console. The Cell processor was also designed into computer servers, HDTVs, and high-performance computers.

In 2006 a US District Court jury awarded Rambus nearly $307 million in damages in the patent infringement case with Hynix Semiconductor. However, the federal judge hearing the case later reduced the award to nearly $134 million; Rambus decided to accept that amount, as the judge threatened to grant Hynix a new trial in the case. In addition to Micron and Samsung, Rambus had left a patent case pending against Nanya Technology,

and the antitrust case pending against Hynix, Micron, and Samsung. (Samsung was later excused from the antitrust case after the Korean company agreed to separate litigation of its claims against Rambus.)

The JEDEC case came back to haunt Rambus in 2006, as the FTC ruled that the company deceived the industry standards body and was therefore liable for damages due to its monopolistic practices. In 2007 the commission ordered a financial remedy, imposing maximum royalty rates on JEDEC-compliant memory devices for three years. Rambus appealed the FTC decision and the commission's remedy order.

Geoff Tate resigned from the board of directors in 2006, after an inquiry by the board into past stock-option granting practices concluded that the actual dates for certain option grants did not match up with the official granting dates. Also in 2006 the federal district court in eastern Virginia issued several orders in the cases between Rambus and Samsung, most of which were favorable to the Samsung side. Rambus appealed the decision.

In 2008 Rambus prevailed in a jury trial over antitrust issues in the JEDEC case, with the jury rejecting claims by Hynix, Micron, and Nanya after a two-month trial. Later that year the US Court of Appeals for the District of Columbia overturned the FTC's orders, saying the commission failed to show that Rambus had harmed competition in the market for memory devices. The appellate court sent the case back to the FTC for further proceedings; the commission appealed the ruling, asking the court to reconsider its action. The appeals court later refused to rehear the case en banc, leaving the FTC with appealing the decision to the US Supreme Court — traditionally reluctant to hear patent-related cases — as its only remaining option. The Supreme Court declined to hear the case in 2009, and the FTC then dismissed the remainder of its case against Rambus.

The company won another decision on appeal in 2008, as the US Court of Appeals for the Federal Circuit vacated the 2006 orders by the district court in Virginia and instructed the lower court to dismiss Samsung's remaining claims against Rambus. The two companies previously resolved certain patent claims on their own.

EXECUTIVES

Chairman, Bruce W. Dunlevie, age 54
President, CEO, and Director, Harold E. Hughes Jr., age 65, $1,761,145 total compensation
VP Marketing, Tim Messegee
VP Engineering, David Nguyen
VP Engineering, John T. C. Ho
VP Corporate Development, Joseph J. Curry
VP and Managing Director, Japan, Eric Ries
VP Human Resources, Michael Schroeder, age 51
SVP and General Counsel, Thomas R. (Tom) Lavelle, age 60, $770,666 total compensation
SVP Licensing, Christopher Pickett
SVP Finance and CFO, Satish Rishi, age 51, $764,966 total compensation
SVP Research and Technology Development, Martin Scott, age 56, $759,644 total compensation
SVP Lighting and Display Technology, Jeffrey (Jeff) Parker
SVP IP Strategy, Kevin S. Donnelly, age 49
SVP Corporate Development, Laura S. Stark, age 42
Director Corporate Communications, Linda Ashmore
Director Business Development, Europe, Udo Muerle
SVP and General Manager, Semiconductor Business, Sharon E. Holt, age 46, $762,193 total compensation
Investor Relations, Nicole Noutsious
Auditors: PricewaterhouseCoopers LLP

LOCATIONS

HQ: Rambus Inc.
4440 El Camino Real, Los Altos, CA 94022
Phone: 650-947-5000 **Fax:** 650-947-5001
Web: www.rambus.com

2009 Sales

	$ mil.	% of total
Asia/Pacific		
Japan	92.0	82
South Korea	1.3	1
Other countries	0.1	-
North America	19.4	17
Europe	0.2	-
Total	**113.0**	**100**

PRODUCTS/OPERATIONS

2009 Sales

	$ mil.	% of total
Royalties	108.0	96
Contract revenues	5.0	4
Total	**113.0**	**100**

Selected Products

Rambus application-specific integrated circuit (ASIC) design
Rambus-based dynamic random-access memory (RDRAM) design
Rambus Channel (interconnect circuitry) design
RaSer (serial link technology for fast communications and networking applications)
Yellowstone (chip connection technology with high-speed data transfer rates)

COMPETITORS

ARM Holdings	Ramtron International
Elpida Memory	Samsung Electronics
Fujitsu Semiconductor	Sonics
Hynix	Spansion
Micron Technology	Synopsys
MOSAID Technologies	T-RAM
MoSys	Toshiba Semiconductor
Nanya	Winbond Electronics
NVIDIA	
Powerchip Semiconductor	

HISTORICAL FINANCIALS

Company Type: Public

Income Statement

FYE: December 31

	REVENUE ($ mil.)	NET INCOME ($ mil.)	NET PROFIT MARGIN	EMPLOYEES
12/10	323.4	150.9	46.7%	390
12/09	113.0	(92.2)	—	350
12/08	142.5	(195.9)	—	330
12/07	179.9	(27.7)	—	430
12/06	195.3	(13.8)	—	415
Annual Growth	**13.4%**	**—**	**—**	**(1.5%)**

2010 Year-End Financials

Debt ratio: 46.0%
Return on equity: 45.1%
Cash ($ mil.): 215.3
Current ratio: 9.46
Long-term debt ($ mil.): 154.0
No. of shares (mil.): 102.7
Dividends
  Yield: —
  Payout: —
Market value ($ mil.): 2,102.8

	STOCK PRICE ($) FY Close	P/E High/Low	PER SHARE ($) Earnings	Dividends	Book Value
12/10	20.48	20 12	1.30	0.00	3.26
12/09	24.40	— —	(0.88)	0.00	2.41
12/08	15.92	— —	(1.87)	0.00	2.13
12/07	20.94	— —	(0.27)	0.00	3.92
12/06	18.93	— —	(0.13)	0.00	3.68
Annual Growth	**2.0%**	**— —**	**—**	**—**	**(3.0%)**

ReachLocal

When looking to broaden their online presence, local business owners can get a hand from ReachLocal. Targeting small to midsized businesses, ReachLocal offers Internet-based advertising and marketing services, including search engine marketing (for preferred placement of a company's listing on Yahoo! or Google's search results pages), marketing analytics, and display advertising. The company serves mostly US businesses through a network of locally based marketing consultants that use, among other tools, the company's proprietary technology platform to create advertising and marketing campaigns. ReachLocal was founded in 2003 and has 45 offices worldwide; it launched an initial public offering in mid-2010.

The company used the proceeds raised from its IPO (around $35 million after deducting underwriting fees and other expenses) to fund its general operations, buy out the remaining shares of its Australian operations, and invest in complementary businesses and technologies. Although ReachLocal's revenues increased by almost 44% from 2009 to 2010 ($203.1 million to $291.7 million), the company suffered a net los of $11 million for 2010, after earning $10 million in profits the year before. It cites the expenses involved in ramping up its ReachLocal Australia operations as one of the chief reasons for the loss.

ReachLocal's long-term strategy includes expanding its network of marketing consultants and offices and bolstering its offerings, primarily through expansion of its advertising capabilities and by offering its customers advertising and marketing capabilities on video and mobile formats. Along those lines, in early 2011 ReachLocal bought DealOn for around $10 million. DealOn is a local deals provider catering to 18 markets in the US, and ReachLocal plans to integrate DealOn's technology platform with its own infrastructure. A year earlier, it obtained Virginia-based SMB:LIVE, a company specializing in image management on social media and directory sites, such as Twitter and Facebook.

ReachLocal also has been moving into international markets; it recently began offering services in Australia and the United Kingdom. In early 2011, it launched an office in Berlin to cater to the German market, one of the largest concentrations of Internet users in the world.

Prior to its IPO, ReachLocal was owned by private equity firms and private investors. Since it began trading, VantagePoint Venture Partners owns about 44% of the company. Chairman Alan Salzman is affiliated with VantagePoint Venture Partners.

EXECUTIVES

Chairman, Alan E. Salzman, age 57
President, CEO, and Director, Zorik Gordon, age 38
CFO, Ross G. Landsbaum, age 48
CEO, ReachLocal UK Limited, John Mazur, age 40
EVP Global Sales Operations, Steven Power, age 37
EVP and General Manager, ReachLocal Xchange, Robert (Rob) Wright, age 33
COO and Chief Product Officer, Michael Kline, age 44
CTO, Jeffrey Hagins
Chief Distribution Officer, Nathan Hanks, age 37
SVP, Advanced Product Development, Gadi Shamia, age 42
SVP, Corporate Controller, and Chief Accounting Officer, Chris Powell, age 39
General Manager, Digital Presence, Alex Hawkinson
Auditors: Grant Thornton LLP

LOCATIONS

HQ: ReachLocal, Inc.
21700 Oxnard St., Ste. 1600, Woodland Hills, CA 91367
Phone: 818-274-0260
Web: www.reachlocal.com

2010 Sales

	$ mil.	% of total
North America	241.7	83
International	50.0	17
Total	**291.7**	**100**

PRODUCTS/OPERATIONS

2010 Sales

	$ mil.	% of total
Direct local	217.9	75
National brands, agencies & resellers	73.8	25
Total	**291.7**	**100**

COMPETITORS

Dex One	QuinStreet
Google	SuperMedia
Local Insight Regatta Holdings	ValueClick
Microsoft	Yahoo!
	Yellowbook

HISTORICAL FINANCIALS

Company Type: Public

Income Statement

FYE: December 31

	REVENUE ($ mil.)	NET INCOME ($ mil.)	NET PROFIT MARGIN	EMPLOYEES
12/10	291.7	(11.1)	—	1,381
12/09	203.1	10.0	4.9%	940
12/08	146.7	(7.0)	—	909
12/07	68.4	(2.6)	—	0
12/06	25.6	(1.1)	—	0
Annual Growth	**83.7%**	**—**	**—**	**23.3%**

2010 Year-End Financials

Debt ratio: —
Return on equity: —
Cash ($ mil.): 79.9
Current ratio: 1.40
Long-term debt ($ mil.): —
No. of shares (mil.): 28.2
Dividends
  Yield: —
  Payout: —
Market value ($ mil.): 560.8

	STOCK PRICE ($) FY Close	P/E High/Low	PER SHARE ($) Earnings	Dividends	Book Value
12/10	19.91	— —	(0.42)	0.00	2.91
Annual Growth	**—**	**— —**	**—**	**—**	**—**

Real Goods Solar

Things are heating up nicely at Real Goods Solar. The company, which got its start as a small seller of solar panels in 1978, specializes in designing, procuring, and installing renewable energy systems for homes and small businesses. Real Goods offers solar parts from such manufacturers as Sharp, SunPower, Sanyo, and Kyocera Solar. In addition to its solar panel business, Real Good also sells renewable energy and sustainable living products through its website and catalog. Products range from apparel and camping gear to solar batteries, water heating pumps, and biodiesel processors. Majority owned by green lifestyle company Gaiam, Real Goods Solar is buying Earth Friendly Energy Group.

The combination will bring together two leaders in the solar industry. Earth Friendly Grou, known as Alteris Renewables, is one of the largest design/build solar integration companies, with a strong presence in the Northeast. Together, the company will have operations covering both coasts and national capabilities in the design/build sector.

Headquartered in Colorado, Real Goods Solar has distribution operations in Ohio, as well as a flagship retail store and a 12-acre solar living center in California, where it features interactive demonstrations of renewable energy technologies for visitors.

Real Goods Solar was formerly a wholly-owned subsidiary of Gaiam, which still controls about two-thirds of the company.

EXECUTIVES

Chairman, Jirka Rysavy, age 56, $326,342 total compensation
President and Director, John Schaeffer, age 61, $249,386 total compensation
CFO, Erik Zech, age 39, $272,969 total compensation
EVP Operations, Scott Carlson
VP Sales, Kent Halliburton
VP Marketing and Business Development, Joel Kauffman
Secretary, John Jackson
Auditors: Ehrhardt Keefe Steiner & Hottman PC

LOCATIONS

HQ: Real Goods Solar, Inc.
833 W. South Boulder Rd., Louisville, CO 80027
Phone:
Web: www.realgoods.com

PRODUCTS/OPERATIONS

Selected Products and Services
Solar energy products
  Batteries and controllers
    Electrical supply (adapters, boxes, breakers, and cables)
    Inverters (grid-tie and off-grid)
    Power centers (pre-assembled and pre-wired)
    Solar photovoltaic modules
    System monitoring (digital meters, monitors, and diagnostic tools)
  Water, heating, and pumping
    Pumps
    Solar hot water parts
    Tankless water heaters (gas, propane, and electric)
    Water pumps (submersible, surface, and booster)
  Wind, hydro, and transportation
    Biodiesel processors
    Electric bicycles
    Hydro turbines
    Vegetable oil conversion system
  Wind turbines and towers
Retail
  Books and videos
  Camping, gifts, and apparel
  Home and outdoor
Solar energy residential services
  Design
  Grid connection
  Installation
  Maintenance
  Procurement

COMPETITORS

AEE Solar	SolarCraft Services
BP Solar	SunPower Systems
Entech Solar	Sunvalley Solar
REC Solar	Westinghouse Solar
SCHOTT Solar	

HISTORICAL FINANCIALS

Company Type: Public

Income Statement

FYE: December 31

	REVENUE ($ mil.)	NET INCOME ($ mil.)	NET PROFIT MARGIN	EMPLOYEES
12/10	77.3	1.2	1.6%	270
12/09	64.3	(1.6)	—	200
12/08	39.2	(28.0)	—	177
12/07	18.9	0.1	0.5%	83
12/06	16.8	0.3	1.8%	0
Annual Growth	46.5%	41.4%	—	48.2%

2010 Year-End Financials

Debt ratio: —
Return on equity: 3.9%
Cash ($ mil.): 11.1
Current ratio: 2.47
Long-term debt ($ mil.): —
No. of shares (mil.): 18.3
Dividends
  Yield: —
  Payout: —
Market value ($ mil.): 46.7

	STOCK PRICE ($) FY Close	P/E High/Low	PER SHARE ($) Earnings	Dividends	Book Value
12/10	2.55	69 32	0.07	0.00	1.74
12/09	3.23	— —	(0.09)	0.00	1.66
12/08	3.65	— —	(1.86)	0.00	1.73
Annual Growth	(16.4%)	— —	—	—	0.5%

RealD

Thanks to RealD, a new era of 3-D movies is upon us. The new crop of feature films projected by RealD's three-dimensional digital projection equipment is dispelling the schlocky image of such 1950s fare as *It Came from Outer Space*. Recent films that have used RealD's 3-D technology include *Kung Fu Panda 2, Toy Story 3*, and *Despicable Me*. The firm has outfitted more than 15,000 movie screens in some 60 countries with its 3-D systems. Its products are also used by engineers, industrial designers, and scientific researchers for applications such as consumer electronics, education, aerospace, defense, and health care. (RealD has even helped pilot the Mars Rover.) The company filed an IPO in 2010.

RealD technology can be found in more than 700 motion picture exhibitors. License revenue from leading theater chains AMC Entertainment, Cinemark Holdings, and Regal Entertainment together comprised nearly 25% of the company's gross license revenue in fiscal year 2011. While its licensees are an important revenue stream, a greater source of revenue comes from the distribution of 3-D eyewear to exhibitors.

RealD raised about $200 million through its IPO, and used the proceeds from the offering to repay debt. It also funded growth initiatives, such as deploying its technology on approximately 1,000 additional screens by the close of fiscal year 2011. In addition, RealD is working with consumer electronics manufacturers such as JVC, Panasonic, Samsung, and Sony Electronics to grow its consumer electronics business. It plans to incorporate its technology in plasma and LCD televisions, DVRs, gaming consoles, and laptop and desktop computers.

The rapidly growing company has the leading global market share of 3-D-enabled theater screens, which represented more than 80% of total domestic 3-D box office in 2011. RealD has reported significant increases in revenue for the past three consecutive fiscal years (from $39.7 million in 2009 to $149.8 million in 2010, to $246.1 million in 2011). Its net loss also declined considerably in 2011 (to $6.8 million, down from $39.7 million in 2010). The positive earnings were primarily due to an increase in the number of RealD-enabled screens, combined with an increase in the number of 3D movies released.

Although the company has helped the movie industry get viewers out of the living room and into the theater in an era of increasingly fancy home theater systems, RealD has yet to turn a profit since its founding in 2003. Among the overall industry challenges the company faces is that much of its potential success is dependent on forces outside its control, such as the quality of output from Hollywood. And while the movie-going public is currently embracing 3-D movies, fickle audiences may tire of the technology, and the studios may produce less films as a result. In addition, the company is counting on the growth of its nascent consumer products business, the success of which has yet to be seen.

Company co-founders Michael Lewis (chairman and CEO) and Joshua Greer (board member and former president) each own about 10% of RealD.

EXECUTIVES

Chairman and CEO, Michael V. Lewis, age 47
President and Director, Joshua Greer, age 41
President, Worldwide Cinema, Joseph Peixoto, age 58
President, Consumer Electronics, Robert Mayson, age 55
EVP and General Counsel, Craig S. Gatarz, age 49
COO and CFO, Andrew A. (Drew) Skarupa, age 45
Auditors: Ernst & Young LLP

LOCATIONS

HQ: RealD Inc.
100 N. Crescent Dr., Ste. 120, Beverly Hills, CA 90210
Phone: 310-385-4000   **Fax:** 310-385-4001
Web: www.reald.com

2011 Sales

	$ mil.	% of total
US and Canada	91.2	37
Other regions	154.9	63
Total	**246.1**	**100**

PRODUCTS/OPERATIONS

2011 Sales

	$ mil.	% of total
Product & other	144.6	59
License	101.5	41
Total	**246.1**	**100**

Selected ReaID-Enabled Movies

Alice in Wonderland
Avatar
A Christmas Carol
Cloudy with a Chance of Meatballs
Coraline
G-Force
How to Train Your Dragon
Ice Age 3
Kung Fu Panda 2
Monsters vs. Aliens
Toy Story 3
Up

COMPETITORS

Dolby	Panasonic Corp
IMAX	Sony Electronics
NVIDIA	

HISTORICAL FINANCIALS

Company Type: Public

Income Statement

FYE: March 31

	REVENUE ($ mil.)	NET INCOME ($ mil.)	NET PROFIT MARGIN	EMPLOYEES
03/11	246.1	(7.4)	—	114
03/10	149.8	(38.9)	—	74
03/09	39.7	(15.6)	—	74
03/08	23.4	(29.7)	—	0
03/07	15.9	(12.7)	—	0
Annual Growth	**98.3%**	**—**	**—**	**24.1%**

2011 Year-End Financials

Debt ratio: 0.0%	No. of shares (mil.): 53.6
Return on equity: —	Dividends
Cash ($ mil.) 16.9	Yield: —
Current ratio: 1.09	Payout: —
Long-term debt ($ mil.): 0.0	Market value ($ mil.): 1,465.7

	STOCK PRICE ($) FY Close	P/E High/Low	PER SHARE ($) Earnings	Dividends	Book Value
03/11	27.36	— —	(0.29)	0.00	2.68
Annual Growth	**—**	**— —**	**—**	**—**	**—**

RealPage

RealPage touts its software as a real asset to real estate managers. The company's on-demand software platform is designed to make the property management process more efficient, enabling owners and managers of single- and multifamily rental properties to oversee their accounting, leasing, marketing, pricing, and screening operations from a single, shared database. The centralized system helps with managing incoming and outgoing residents and overseeing property functions, from hiring plumbers to training staff. Its customers include most of the top 10 largest multifamily property management companies in the US. RealPage went public in 2010.

RealPage filed its IPO on the heels of a few years of rapid growth in terms of employees, customers, and products. It has also been using acquisitions to fuel expansion, purchasing the assets of Domin-8 Enterprise Solutions, an on-premise property management system company, in early 2010. (It is migrating customers that use its on-premise software to the Domin-8 on-demand platform). Late that year RealPage bought Level One, a provider of apartment leasing services, for $54 million in cash and a deferred payment of $8 million. The company combined the acquired assets with its CrossFire apartment sales and marketing software product line to form a package that includes software as well as leasing support services.

In 2011 RealPage bought Compliance Depot, a provider of risk management and compliance services for the real estate industry. The deal continued the company's strategy of expanding its portfolio of products and services for the rental housing market. That year, it also paid $4.5 million in cash for SeniorLiving.net, a Web-based lead generation and placement service for the senior housing market. In a related move in 2011 RealPage agreed to acquire Multifamily Technology Solutions, which operates the MyNewPlace website, for more than $74 million. Both the SeniorLiving.net and MyNewPlace acquisitions boost RealPlace's origination and syndication operations.

Its on-demand software is its primary revenue segment and consists of an integrated software platform that provides a single point of access containing data on residents, prospects, and properties. The software is generally licensed under one-year customer subscription agreements. A smaller portion of the company's revenue is generated from professional services, which include consulting, training, and implementation services.

The company's expansion has been both a boon and a bane, however, as the cost of the resources needed to support the increasing size, complexity, and diversity of its business has resulted in a history of operating losses. That likely won't stop RealPage from continuing to invest in developing and enhancing its products, but it may at some point turn to equity or debt refinancings to secure additional funds. It intends to use certain net proceeds from its IPO to pay unpaid dividends and pay down debt.

Meanwhile, its in-house sales organization is focused on renewing existing customers and attracting new ones. As it jockeys for retention, RealPage competes primarily against traditional software vendors, application service providers (ASPs), and software-as-a-service (SaaS) providers. It also competes with newer market entrants as technologies are developed. Key competitors offer enterprise resource planning products and services that include both software and ASP delivery platforms targeted at the multi-family real estate market. Other rivals offer products and services in specific niches, such as applicant screening, customer relationship management, payment processing, renter's insurance, revenue management, and utility billing. Web portals and searchable databases, such as Apartments24-7.com and Spherexx.com, which offer apartment marketing and leasing services, pose additional competition.

RealPage was formed in 1998 to acquire Rent Roll, Inc., which marketed and sold on-premise property management systems for certain multifamily housing markets. Three years later it released OneSite, its first on-demand property management system.

EXECUTIVES

Chairman and CEO, Stephen T. (Steve) Winn, age 64, $650,440 total compensation
President, Dirk D. Wakeham, age 45, $729,943 total compensation
CFO and Treasurer, Timothy J. Barker, age 48, $788,546 total compensation
President, Velocity, William Chaney
President, OneSite, Leslie Turner
President, CrossFire and Learning, Tony Pusateri
President, YieldStar, Janine Steiner Jovanovic
President, EverGreen Solutions, Georgianna Oliver
President, LeasingDesk, David Carner
President, Propertyware, Sina Shekou
President, OpsTechnology, Sukhi Singh
EVP Multifamily Solutions, Ashley Chaffin Glover, age 39, $670,515 total compensation
COO, Jason D. Lindwall
CTO, Norman Denler
SVP Cloud Technologies, Nagi Prabhu
SVP Sales, John Yager
SVP Mergers and Acquisitions, Michael Britti
Chief Product Officer, Dean Schmidt
Chief Legal Officer and Secretary, William E. Van Valkenberg, age 64, $583,557 total compensation
Chief Sales Officer, Mark Case
SVP Marketing, Andrea Massey
Principal Scientist and Chief Product Officer, YieldStar, Jeffrey Roper
Director, Richard M. Berkeley, age 58
Auditors: Ernst & Young LLP

LOCATIONS

HQ: RealPage, Inc.
4000 International Pkwy., Carrollton, TX 75007-1913
Phone: 972-820-3000   **Fax:** 972-820-3036
Web: www.realpage.com

PRODUCTS/OPERATIONS

2009 Sales

	$ mil.	% of total
On-demand	128.4	91
Professional & other	8.6	6
On-premise	3.9	3
Total	**140.9**	**100**

COMPETITORS

Archibus	Infor Global
Assurant	MoneyGram
Chase Paymentech	International
Solutions	PROS Holdings
Communities Group	SiteStuff
First Advantage	TransUnion
First Data	Who's Calling
Fiserv	Yardi Systems

HISTORICAL FINANCIALS

Company Type: Public

Income Statement

FYE: December 31

	REVENUE ($ mil.)	NET INCOME ($ mil.)	NET PROFIT MARGIN	EMPLOYEES
12/10	188.3	0.1	0.1%	1,759
12/09	140.9	28.4	20.2%	1,141
12/08	112.6	(3.2)	—	0
12/07	83.6	(3.1)	—	0
Annual Growth	**31.1%**	**—**	**—**	**54.2%**

2010 Year-End Financials

Debt ratio: 32.0%
Return on equity: 0.0%
Cash ($ mil.): 118.0
Current ratio: 1.81
Long-term debt ($ mil.): 55.3

No. of shares (mil.): 68.5
Dividends
Yield: —
Payout: —
Market value ($ mil.): 2,118.4

	STOCK PRICE ($) FY Close	P/E High/Low	PER SHARE ($) Earnings	Dividends	Book Value
12/10	30.93	— —	(0.07)	0.00	2.52
Annual Growth	—	— —	—	—	—

2008 Year-End Financials

Debt ratio: 463.6%
Return on equity: —
Cash ($ mil.): 23.1
Current ratio: —
Long-term debt ($ mil.): 1,012.6

No. of shares (mil.): 30.9
Dividends
Yield: 83.3%
Payout: —
Market value ($ mil.): 5.6

	STOCK PRICE ($) FY Close	P/E High/Low	PER SHARE ($) Earnings	Dividends	Book Value
12/08	0.18	— —	(5.14)	0.15	7.06
12/07	5.34	— —	(2.33)	0.80	6.88
12/06	15.71	31 24	0.60	0.19	13.31
Annual Growth	(89.3%)	— —	—	(11.1%)	(27.2%)

Realty Finance Corporation

Realty Finance Corporation (formerly CBRE Realty Finance) invests in, finances, and manages loans and securities related to commercial real estate. The company's portfolio consists of whole loans, interests in whole loans, mezzanine loans, and collateralized mortgage-backed securities (CMBS). Nearly half of its portfolio is secured by office properties; investments in hotel, multifamily, and industrial real estate help to round out its activities. Realty Finance was managed and advised by an indirect subsidiary of CB Richard Ellis, until the real estate services giant cut its ties with the firm in 2008. Realty Finance changed its name and is now internally managed.

EXECUTIVES

Chairman, Douglas C. Eby, age 52
President, CEO, and Director, Kenneth J. Witkin, age 61
CFO, Daniel Farr, age 37
SVP and General Counsel, Susan M. Orr
Auditors: Ernst & Young LLP

LOCATIONS

HQ: Realty Finance Corporation
2080 Silas Deane Hwy., Rocky Hill, CT 06067
Phone: 860-275-6200   **Fax:** 860-275-6225
Web: www.realtyfinancecorp.com

COMPETITORS

Clarion Partners
Cypress Sharpridge Investments
Jones Lang LaSalle
LNR Property
RREEF Funds

HISTORICAL FINANCIALS

Company Type: Public

Income Statement

FYE: December 5/

	REVENUE ($ mil.)	NET INCOME ($ mil.)	NET PROFIT MARGIN	EMPLOYEES
12/08	105.9	(157.0)	—	0
12/07	141.0	(70.9)	—	29,300
12/06	74.1	13.7	18.5%	24,000
12/05	12.4	1.1	8.9%	14,500
Annual Growth	104.4%	—	—	42.2%

Red Hat

Red Hat hopes that businesses are ready to try open-source operating systems on for size. The company dominates the market for Linux, the open-source computer operating system (OS) that is the chief rival to Microsoft's Windows operating systems. In addition to its Red Hat Enterprise Linux OS, the company's product line includes database, content, and collaboration management applications; server and embedded operating systems; and software development tools. Red Hat also provides consulting, custom software development, support, and training services. The company's business model is a mix of providing free, open-source software paired with subscription-based support, training, and integration services.

Although Red Hat originally offered support for consumer-oriented Linux products, the company has shifted its focus entirely to supporting and servicing Linux technologies in enterprise environments. While Linux has failed to gain any traction versus Microsoft's Windows operating system in the consumer space, Linux has been much more successful in corporate environments, especially for managing data center operations such as virtualization, server management, and enterprise application integration.

In October 2011 Red Hat announced its plans to expand into the storage market through the purchase of California-based Gluster, Inc. for $136 million in cash. Gluster's open-source file system offers cloud-based storage services deployed as a virtual appliance. Customers such as Brightcove and Pandora Media use its software-based GlusterFS to store large amounts of unstructured data (pictures, audio, video, etc.) without needing to buy conventional hardware-based storage systems. Gluster's technology on the Linux operating system will allow IT organizations to have an on-premise storage service, an all-cloud deployment, or a combination of the two in a hybrid cloud.

The company bought data services deployment and management software developer Makara in late 2010. The deal was intended to speed Red Hat's internal development of tools for moving and managing enterprise applications from the networks of corporate clients to hosted facilities, enabling cloud computing.

Red Hat's $350 million acquisition in 2006 of JBoss added middleware tools to its product line, which are used to develop and deploy applications throughout an enterprise that are accessible via the Internet, intranets, extranets, and virtual private networks. JBoss (which operates as a division of Red Hat) specializes in open-source middleware software, including application servers and messaging systems.

HISTORY

Finnish graduate student Linus Torvalds created the Linux operating system in 1991 as a hobby. When Torvalds released its programming code free over the Internet for anyone to revise, Linux quickly attracted a core base of devoted programmers — including Marc Ewing. A programmer for IBM by day, Ewing developed improvements to Linux in his spare bedroom. Soon he began selling the improved operating system as Red Hat — named after a red and white Cornell lacrosse cap Ewing's grandfather had given him.

In 1994 Ewing was contacted by Robert Young, who after selling typewriters and running a computer leasing company had started a UNIX newsletter. But Young saw better profit margins in catalog sales. Young's ACC Corp. bought the rights to Ewing's creation and the two went into business together. ACC Corp. was renamed Red Hat Software, Inc.

The company compiled Linux's most significant improvements and distributed them on a CD-ROM and through the budding Internet. Their revenues actually came from manuals and technical support sold to new users and businesses who were challenged by the software's ever-changing source code.

By 1997 Linux — and Red Hat's package — were known only among the most militant programmers who sought alternatives to Microsoft's Windows. Hundreds of developers had continually doctored Linux online to create an operating system known for its speed and reliability.

Red Hat exploded in popularity in 1998 after Intel and Netscape both made minor investments in the company. In 1999 Compaq, IBM, Novell, Oracle, and SAP invested in Red Hat. The company went public later that year.

In 2000 Red Hat used its soaring stock as currency to acquire embedded programming specialist Cygnus Solutions for $674 million and Hell's Kitchen Systems (HKS), a maker of payment processing software. President Matthew Szulik replaced Young as CEO and Ewing stepped down as CTO.

Red Hat expanded its software products in 2001 to include database applications and an e-commerce software suite designed for midsized businesses. The following year Szulik assumed the additional role of chairman.

In late 2003 Red Hat acquired Sistina Software, a supplier of data storage infrastructure software for Linux operating systems, for about $31 million in stock.

The company established a government business unit in 2005; Red Hat's US government customers include the Department of Energy and the Federal Aviation Administration. In 2006 it acquired open-source middleware developer JBoss for about $350 million.

Red Hat expanded its middleware offerings in 2007 through the acquisition of MetaMatrix. Jim Whitehurst took over as president and CEO that year. In 2008 the company purchased Qumranet, an Israel-based virtualization software provider, for $107 million.

In mid-2010 director Hugh Shelton, a retired general, replaced Szulik as chairman.

EXECUTIVES

Chairman, Henry H. (Hugh) Shelton, age 69
President, CEO, and Director, James M. (Jim) Whitehurst, age 43, $8,974,936 total compensation
EVP and CFO, Charles E. (Charlie) Peters Jr., age 59, $4,517,527 total compensation
EVP and General Counsel, Michael R. Cunningham, age 50, $2,981,498 total compensation
EVP Engineering and President, Products and Technologies, Paul J. Cormier, age 54, $3,075,664 total compensation
EVP and President, Global Sales, Services, and Field Marketing, Alex Pinchev, age 61, $3,089,389 total compensation
EVP Corporate Affairs, Tom Rabon
VP Global Support Services, Marco Bill-Peter
VP and General Manager, Government Sales Operations, Paul Smith
VP Corporate Development, Michael (Mike) Evans
VP Open Source Affairs, Michael (Mike) Tiemann, age 46
VP, Platform Business Unit, Scott Crenshaw
VP, Management Solutions Business Unit, Katrinka B. McCallum, age 36
VP and Assistant General Counsel, Rob Tiller
VP Corporate Affairs and Global Public Policy, Mark Bohannon
VP Worldwide Engineering and CTO, Brian Stevens
VP, Middleware Business Unit, Craig Muzilla
CIO, Lee Congdon
Senior Director Virtualization Business, Navin Thadani
SVP People and Brand, DeLisa Alexander
Auditors: PricewaterhouseCoopers

LOCATIONS

HQ: Red Hat, Inc.
1801 Varsity Dr., Raleigh, NC 27606
Phone: 919-754-3700   **Fax:** 919-754-3701
Web: www.redhat.com

2010 Sales

	$ mil.	% of total
Americas	474.6	63
Europe, Middle East & Africa	168.1	23
Asia/Pacific	105.5	14
Total	**748.2**	**100**

PRODUCTS/OPERATIONS

Selected Software

Red Hat Applications
  Red Hat Cluster Suite
  Red Hat Content Management System
  Red Hat Developer Suite
  Red Hat Portal Server
Red Hat Enterprise
Red Hat Network

Selected Services

Consulting
Custom development
Technical support
Training

COMPETITORS

Apple Inc.	Microsoft
BMC Software	Novell
CA, Inc.	Oracle
Hewlett-Packard	Unisys
IBM	Xandros
Mandriva	

HISTORICAL FINANCIALS

Company Type: Public

Income Statement

FYE: Last day of February

	REVENUE ($ mil.)	NET INCOME ($ mil.)	NET PROFIT MARGIN	EMPLOYEES
02/11	909.3	107.3	11.8%	3,700
02/10	748.2	87.3	11.7%	3,200
02/09	652.6	78.7	12.1%	2,800
02/08	523.0	76.7	14.7%	2,200
02/07	400.6	59.9	15.0%	1,800
Annual Growth	**22.7%**	**15.7%**	**—**	**19.7%**

2011 Year-End Financials

Debt ratio: —	No. of shares (mil.): 193.0
Return on equity: 8.3%	Dividends
Cash ($ mil.): 642.6	Yield: —
Current ratio: 1.74	Payout: —
Long-term debt ($ mil.): —	Market value ($ mil.): 7,969.0

	STOCK PRICE ($) FY Close	P/E High/Low		PER SHARE ($) Earnings	Dividends	Book Value
02/11	41.28	89	49	0.55	0.00	6.69
02/10	28.05	71	29	0.45	0.00	5.93
02/09	13.69	64	19	0.39	0.00	5.78
02/08	17.83	70	47	0.36	0.00	4.89
02/07	22.45	112	47	0.29	0.00	4.25
Annual Growth	**16.4%**	**—**	**—**	**17.4%**	**—**	**12.0%**

Redwood Trust

Redwood Trust, a real estate investment trust (REIT), is growing a forest of real estate mortgage assets harvested in the form of real estate mortgage loans and mortgage-backed securities. The REIT trades mainly in jumbo residential mortgages (loans with balances above the conventional limit, which in 2010 was $417,000). Historically, Redwood also has invested in commercial real estate loans. Redwood acquires assets throughout the US and had an emphasis on California and Florida. However, the continued housing market downturn has forced Redwood to branch out more to the Midwest.

Although Redwood Trust's exposure to the subprime mortgage crisis was minimal, as the company generally targeted prime or near-prime loans for securitization, it suffered from the general downturn nonetheless. In mid 2008 Redwood halted all investing activity in order to asses the impact of the recession from the sidelines. The company picked back up with its investments at the end of 2008 with a focus on long-term-residential-mortgage-related investments. Redwood has conservative plans to invest in commercial mortgage-backed securities as the commercial real estate market endures difficult times.

EXECUTIVES

Chairman, George E. Bull III, age 62, $3,895,457 total compensation
CFO and Managing Director, Diane L. Merdian, age 52
President, CEO, and Director, Martin S. Hughes, age 53, $2,213,446 total compensation
EVP, COO and Chief Investment Officer, Brett D. Nicholas, age 42, $2,309,904 total compensation

Managing Director, Commercial Mortgage Debt Investment, Scott Chisholm, age 45
Controller, Christopher J. Abate
General Counsel and Secretary, Andrew P. Stone, age 40
Investor Relations, Lauren Morgensen
Chief Risk Officer and Managing Director, Harold F Zagunis, age 53, $1,476,080 total compensation
Director Human Resources, Rosalyn Chan
Auditors: Grant Thornton LLP

LOCATIONS

HQ: Redwood Trust, Inc.
1 Belvedere Place, Ste. 300, Mill Valley, CA 94941
Phone: 415-389-7373   **Fax:** 415-381-1773
Web: www.redwoodtrust.com

COMPETITORS

Annaly Capital Management	iStar Financial Inc
	MFA Financial
Bank of America	Residential Capital
Capstead Mortgage	Starwood Property
Dynex Capital	

HISTORICAL FINANCIALS

Company Type: Public

Income Statement

FYE: December 31

	REVENUE ($ mil.)	NET INCOME ($ mil.)	NET PROFIT MARGIN	EMPLOYEES
12/10	293.5	110.1	37.5%	67
12/09	263.4	39.2	14.9%	68
12/08	88.5	(444.4)	—	79
12/07	868.3	(1,108.6)	—	99
12/06	907.7	127.5	14.0%	91
Annual Growth	**(24.6%)**	**(3.6%)**	**—**	**(7.4%)**

2010 Year-End Financials

Debt ratio: 366.4%	No. of shares (mil.): 78.1
Return on equity: 10.3%	Dividends
Cash ($ mil.): 46.9	Yield: 6.7%
Current ratio: —	Payout: 73.5%
Long-term debt ($ mil.): 3,901.1	Market value ($ mil.): 1,166.4

	STOCK PRICE ($) FY Close	P/E High/Low		PER SHARE ($) Earnings	Dividends	Book Value
12/10	14.93	13	10	1.36	1.00	13.63
12/09	14.46	35	18	0.55	1.00	12.50
12/08	14.91	—	—	(13.46)	3.00	9.03
12/07	34.24	—	—	(39.70)	3.00	(25.59)
12/06	58.08	12	8	4.85	2.80	38.34
Annual Growth	**(28.8%)**	**—**	**—**	**(27.2%)**	**(22.7%)**	**(22.8%)**

Regeneron Pharmaceuticals

Regeneron isn't the Pentagon, but the company is fighting some serious enemies. Regeneron Pharmaceuticals develops protein-based drugs used to battle a variety of diseases and conditions, including cancer, inflammatory ailments, and eye diseases. The biotechnology company's first commercialized product is ARCALYST, a treatment for rare inflammatory diseases including Muckle-Wells Syndrome. Regeneron is also collaborating with

Sanofi to develop candidate Aflibercept (VEGF Trap) as a possible treatment for cancerous tumors, and it is developing VEGF Trap Eye with Bayer Healthcare for treatment of eye diseases using intraocular delivery.

ARCALYST (rilonacept) was approved by the FDA in 2008 and subsequently became the company's first market-stage product. Regeneron has built up a small marketing force to promote the product in the US; ARCALYST is manufactured at the company's plant in New York and is distributed through third parties. ARCALYST targets Cryopyrin-Associated Periodic Syndromes (CAPS), a series of diseases caused by genetic mutations including Muckle-Wells Syndrome and Familial Cold Auto-inflammatory Syndrome. The drug is also being tested for the treatment of gout.

The company has expanded the applications of its protein-based technology to include the creation of human monoclonal antibodies (laboratory produced cloned proteins). Outside of their partnership on Aflibercept, Regeneron has an antibody development agreement with Sanofi that includes $475 in potential milestone payments and covers potential treatments for ailments including cancer, rheumatoid arthritis, pain, cholesterol, and allergic conditions.

As its largest partner, Sanofi (which also owns a 19% stake in Regeneron), accounts for about 65% of sales. The company's other large partner, Bayer, accounts for more than 15% of sales; the two firms are working together to treat ophthalmic diseases including diabetic macular edema and wet age-related macular degeneration.

The company also licenses its human antibody technology out to drug developers, which then use Regeneron's technology in researching their own antibody drugs. Licensing partners include AstraZeneca and Astellas Pharma. Astellas extended its agreement in 2010, licensing the technology for a longer period of time in a deal worth up to $295 million.

EXECUTIVES

Chairman, P. Roy Vagelos, age 81
President, CEO, and Director, Leonard S. Schleifer, age 58, $6,349,308 total compensation
EVP, Chief Scientific Officer, and Director; President Regeneron Research Laboratories, George D. Yancopoulos, age 51, $5,108,375 total compensation
VP Corporate Communications, Peter G. Dworkin, age 58
VP, Controller, and Assistant Treasurer, Douglas S. McCorkle, age 54
VP Strategy and Investor Relations, Michael Aberman, age 40
VP Regulatory Development and Medical Safety, William G. Roberts, age 53
SVP Commercial, Robert J. Terifay, age 51, $1,305,496 total compensation
SVP Clinical Development, Peter Powchik, age 54
SVP Finance and Administration, CFO, Assistant Secretary, and Treasurer, Murray A. Goldberg, age 66, $2,014,849 total compensation
SVP Research and Development Sciences, Neil Stahl, age 54, $2,867,458 total compensation
SVP and General Manager, Industrial Operations and Product Supply, Daniel P. Van Plew, age 38, $1,551,280 total compensation
Auditors: PricewaterhouseCoopers LLP

LOCATIONS

HQ: Regeneron Pharmaceuticals, Inc.
777 Old Saw Mill River Rd., Tarrytown, NY 10591-6707
Phone: 914-345-7400   **Fax:** 914-347-2113
Web: www.regeneron.com

PRODUCTS/OPERATIONS

2009 Sales

	$ mil.	% of total
Collaboration		
Sanofi-Aventis	247.2	65
Other collaboration	67.3	18
Technology licensing	40.0	10
Product sales	18.4	5
Contract research & other	6.4	2
Total	**379.3**	**100**

COMPETITORS

Abbott Labs	Merck
Amgen	Novartis
AstraZeneca	Onyx Pharmaceuticals
Bayer AG	Pfizer
Bristol-Myers Squibb	Roche Holding
Eli Lilly	Sanofi
GlaxoSmithKline	XOMA
Johnson & Johnson	

HISTORICAL FINANCIALS

Company Type: Public

Income Statement

FYE: December 31

	REVENUE ($ mil.)	NET INCOME ($ mil.)	NET PROFIT MARGIN	EMPLOYEES
12/10	459.1	(104.5)	—	1,395
12/09	379.3	(67.8)	—	1,029
12/08	238.5	(82.7)	—	919
12/07	125.0	(105.6)	—	682
12/06	63.4	(102.3)	—	573
Annual Growth	**64.0%**	**—**	**—**	**24.9%**

2010 Year-End Financials

Debt ratio: 30.2%
Return on equity: —
Cash ($ mil.): 112.6
Current ratio: 3.28
Long-term debt ($ mil.): 159.4
No. of shares (mil.): 89.4
Dividends
  Yield: —
  Payout: —
Market value ($ mil.): 2,935.7

	STOCK PRICE ($) FY Close	P/E High/Low	PER SHARE ($) Earnings	Dividends	Book Value
12/10	32.83	— —	(1.26)	0.00	5.90
12/09	24.18	— —	(0.85)	0.00	4.89
12/08	18.36	— —	(1.05)	0.00	5.26
12/07	24.15	— —	(1.59)	0.00	6.96
12/06	20.07	— —	(1.77)	0.00	3.77
Annual Growth	**13.1%**	**— —**	**—**	**—**	**11.9%**

Response Genetics

For Response Genetics, the answer to cancer is in the genes. The life sciences company develops clinical diagnostic tests for cancer based on genetic analysis of tumor tissues. Results of these tests can predict a patient's response to chemotherapy, as well as the potential for cancer recurrence, and can help doctors determine the best course of treatment. Its two commercial ResponseDx prod-

ucts are sold to select medical institutions and test lung and colorectal cancer. Response Genetics makes most of its revenue by providing laboratory testing services on clinical trial specimens for the pharmaceutical industry in the US, Europe, and Japan. Customers include GlaxoSmithKline and Taiho Pharmaceutical.

The company has also licensed rights to Roche Diagnostics to use its pre-diagnostic assays to develop diagnostic kits that can then be sold to pharmaceutical companies.

Response Genetics is following through with a geographic expansion plan that takes its gene testing technology far east. Through partnerships with companies in Japan and China, it is increasing its exposure to clients in the Asia/Pacific region by providing pharmacogenomic testing services there.

Director Michael Serruya and his family own about 51% of the company. Vice chairman David Smith and family own another 38%.

EXECUTIVES

Chairman, Kirk K. Calhoun, age 67
Chairman, Tom R. Demeester, age 73
President, Christine Meda, age 62
VP Finance and Administration, Eric Alcorn
VP Regulatory Affairs, Janine Cooc
Vice Chairman, David M. Smith, age 44
Interim CEO, VP, General Counsel and Secretary, Denise McNairn, age 43, $350,075 total compensation
Founder and Executive Scientific and Technology Officer, Kathleen (Kathy) Danenberg, age 64, $806,703 total compensation
Auditors: Singer Lewak Greenbaum & Goldstein LLP

LOCATIONS

HQ: Response Genetics Inc.
1640 Marengo St., 6th Fl., Los Angeles, CA 90033
Phone: 323-224-3900   **Fax:** 323-224-3096
Web: www.responsegenetics.com

2007 Sales

	$ mil.	% of total
US	4.0	51
Europe	0.9	12
Japan	2.9	37
Total	**7.8**	**100**

COMPETITORS

Clarient	Precision Therapeutics
Genomic Health	Quest Diagnostics
Med BioGene	

HISTORICAL FINANCIALS

Company Type: Public

Income Statement

FYE: December 31

	REVENUE ($ mil.)	NET INCOME ($ mil.)	NET PROFIT MARGIN	EMPLOYEES
12/10	21.3	(4.7)	—	95
12/09	9.1	(9.3)	—	56
12/08	7.1	(9.5)	—	47
12/07	7.8	(5.1)	—	43
12/06	6.0	(1.4)	—	41
Annual Growth	**37.3%**	**—**	**—**	**23.4%**

2010 Year-End Financials

Debt ratio: —
Return on equity: —
Cash ($ mil.): 4.1
Current ratio: 1.65
Long-term debt ($ mil.): —
No. of shares (mil.): 18.4
Dividends
  Yield: —
  Payout: —
Market value ($ mil.): 45.5

	STOCK PRICE ($) FY Close	P/E High/Low	PER SHARE ($) Earnings	Dividends	Book Value
12/10	2.48	— —	(0.26)	0.00	(0.18)
12/09	1.26	— —	(0.70)	0.00	0.04
12/08	1.18	— —	(0.93)	0.00	0.67
12/07	4.65	— —	(0.78)	0.00	1.48
Annual Growth	(18.9%)	— —	—	—	—

Responsys

Responsys is responsive to the changing needs of marketing programs. The company provides hosted marketing software and services to clients that use direct mail, e-mail, mobile devices, social media, the Web, and other marketing channels to reach their customer base. Its Interact Suite of software and related services helps clients assesses their potential customers and then plan and implement marketing campaigns. Responsys serves customers from a variety of industries, and targets enterprise and larger mid-market companies. It has international offices in Australia, Denmark, India, and the UK. Customers have included Carlson Hotels Worldwide, Lands' End, and Petco. Responsys went public in April 2011.

Spending on interactive marketing is expected to grow as marketers shift resources away from traditional media. The company capitalized on this trend through its public offering, which raised about $79.2 million. Responsys intends to use the proceeds for general corporate purposes, including working capital and potential acquisitions.

The company's IPO comes on the heels of a relatively successful 2010. During the first nine months of that year, Responsys posted a 36% increase in revenues, though its profit was slightly less when compared to the same period in 2009. This revenue growth was the result of an increased number of enterprise customers and higher subscription fees. Positive revenues were offset by higher operating expenses due to a need to increase bandwidth and other resources to support a bigger business.

Any future acquisitions made with IPO money will add to the purchases Responsys made in recent years. Looking to expand in the Asia/Pacific market, in 2010 the company acquired a non-controlling, 50% stake in Eservices Group, an e-mail and cross-channel marketing services provider based in Australia. The move came about one year after Responsys launched its first office in that country. (Eservices Group has since been renamed Eservices Responsys.) In 2009, Responsys strengthened its strategic planning, creative design, and cross-channel marketing services by acquiring Smith-Harmon, a Seattle-based digital marketing company.

The company has raised $62 million in venture capital funding since its founding in 1998, with investors such as Foundation Capital and Sigma Partners holding significant pre-IPO stakes. Responsys chairman and CEO Daniel Springer owns about 10% of the company. Board member Michael Schuh owns 20% through his position at Foundation Capital, while member Greg Gretsch owns 19% through his association with Sigma Partners.

EXECUTIVES

Chairman and CEO, Daniel D. (Dan) Springer, age 48
CFO, Christian A. (Chris) Paul, age 50
VP, General Counsel, and Secretary, Julian K. Ong, age 44
VP Products, John Berkley
CIO, Donald E. (Don) Smith, age 51
CTO, Antonio Casacuberta, age 50
Chief Customer Officer, Andrew W. (Andy) Priest, age 48
SVP Professional and Strategic Services, Edward (Ed) Henrich
Media Contact, Kimberly Canedo
Chief Marketing and Sales Officer, Scott V. Olrich, age 39
Auditors: Deloitte & Touche LLP

LOCATIONS

HQ: Responsys, Inc.
900 Cherry Ave., 5th Fl., San Bruno, CA 94066
Phone: 650-745-1700 **Fax:** 650-745-1701
Web: www.responsys.com

2009 Sales

	$ mil.	% of total
Americas	59.5	89
Europe	6.7	10
Asia/Pacific	0.4	1
Total	**66.6**	**100**

PRODUCTS/OPERATIONS

2009 Sales

	$ mil.	% of total
Subscription	53.0	80
Professional services	13.6	20
Total	**66.6**	**100**

Selected Offerings

Subscription
  Interact Suite software
Professional services
  Campaign services
  Creative and strategic marketing services
  Education services
  Technical services

COMPETITORS

Acxiom	PGi
Digital River	PointRoll
e-Dialog	Return Path
Eloqua	Teradata
Epsilon Data	ValueClick
MediaMind	yesmail

HISTORICAL FINANCIALS

Company Type: Public

Income Statement

FYE: December 31

	REVENUE ($ mil.)	NET INCOME ($ mil.)	NET PROFIT MARGIN	EMPLOYEES
12/10	94.1	8.6	9.1%	488
12/09	66.6	5.9	8.9%	414
12/08	50.1	20.4	40.7%	0
12/07	37.6	5.4	14.4%	0
Annual Growth	**35.8%**	**16.8%**	**—**	**17.9%**

2010 Year-End Financials

Debt ratio: —
Return on equity: 16.2%
Cash ($ mil.): 13.9
Current ratio: 2.54
Long-term debt ($ mil.): —
No. of shares (mil.): —
Dividends
  Yield: —
  Payout: —
Market value ($ mil.): —

Rigel Pharmaceuticals

When immune systems attack, Rigel Pharmaceuticals wants to be there. The drug discovery and development firm focuses its research and development efforts on inflammatory/autoimmune, muscle, and metabolic diseases. Drugs in development include candidates for treating rheumatoid arthritis, psoriasis, muscle wasting, multiple sclerosis, and transplant rejection. Rigel prefers to collaborate with larger pharmaceutical companies in the development of its drug candidates. It is working with Astra Zeneca on developing FosD, an oral syk inhibitor in clinical trials for the treatment of rheumatoid arthritis.

Rigel is also collaborating with Pfizer on a early stage candidate to treat asthma. Such partnerships are structured so that Rigel takes compounds through the early stages of discovery and development, and then hands them over to the larger collaborator to fund and conduct the later stages of development, approval, and commercialization. Along the way, its collaborators make milestone payments and, ultimately, royalties on product sales. However, none of Rigel's candidates have ever made it through later stages to market.

Earlier research of possible drugs to address viral infection and cancer were ended in 2009. At the same time, the company reduced its staff by 20%.

EXECUTIVES

Chairman, President, and CEO, James M. Gower, age 62, $4,169,303 total compensation
President and COO, Raul R. Rodriguez, age 50, $2,973,399 total compensation
EVP and CFO, Ryan D. Maynard, age 41, $2,003,198 total compensation
EVP and Chief Medical Officer, Elliott B. Grossbard, age 63, $3,090,390 total compensation
EVP, President, Discovery and Research, and Director, Donald G. Payan, age 62, $3,346,174 total compensation
EVP Corporate Affairs, General Counsel, and Corporate Secretary, Dolly A. Vance, age 46
VP Clinical Research, Daniel B. Magilavy
Corporate Communications, Mari Avila
Auditors: Ernst & Young LLP

LOCATIONS

HQ: Rigel Pharmaceuticals, Inc.
1180 Veterans Blvd., South San Francisco, CA 94080
Phone: 650-624-1100 **Fax:** 650-624-1101
Web: www.rigel.com

HISTORICAL FINANCIALS

Company Type: Public

Income Statement

FYE: December 31

	REVENUE ($ mil.)	NET INCOME ($ mil.)	NET PROFIT MARGIN	EMPLOYEES
12/10	125.0	37.9	30.3%	145
12/09	0.8	(111.5)	—	142
12/07	12.6	(74.3)	—	159
12/06	33.5	(37.6)	—	152
12/05	16.5	(45.3)	—	151
Annual Growth	**49.9%**	**—**	**—**	**(0.8%)**

2010 Year-End Financials

Debt ratio: 0.0%
Return on equity: 22.8%
Cash ($ mil.): 8.9
Current ratio: 15.89
Long-term debt ($ mil.): 0.0

No. of shares (mil.): 52.3
Dividends
  Yield: —
  Payout: —
Market value ($ mil.): 393.6

	STOCK PRICE ($) FY Close	P/E High/Low	PER SHARE ($) Earnings	Dividends	Book Value
12/10	7.53	14 8	0.72	0.00	3.18
12/09	9.51	— —	(2.73)	0.00	2.11
12/07	8.00	— —	(3.67)	0.00	2.85
12/06	25.39	— —	(2.57)	0.00	2.65
12/05	11.87	— —	(1.51)	0.00	3.48
Annual Growth	(10.8%)	— —	—	—	(2.2%)

Riverbed Technology

Riverbed Technology keeps data flowing through the network. The company develops hardware and software that improves the performance of applications shared over networks. Its Steelhead network appliances are designed for small businesses and global enterprises. Riverbed's Steelhead Central Management Console software keeps track of Steelhead appliances across wide area networks (WANs). Its Steelhead Mobile application enables mobile access to business software and data. Customers have included Carhartt, OMV, and Tatts Group. The company markets directly, but most of its sales are made through resellers, distributors, and systems integrators. The company gets more than half of its sales in the US.

Riverbed's revenue rose again in 2010, as it has every year since 2003, due to strong demand for WAN optimization products. Sales made via indirect channels grew for the year and the company expects that trend to continue as it seeks out additional distribution partners. Profits jumped dramatically for the year, rising to nearly five times the level of 2009, despite increased operational expenses associated with higher sales volume, particularly in the area of sales and marketing expenses.

Riverbed acquired UK-based Zeus Technology and New Zealand-based Aptimize in 2011 to further extend its ability to help clients manage their network resources. Zeus specializes in software used to balance data traffic in virtual and cloud computing systems, while Aptimize offers tools for optimizing Web content that complement Riverbed's Steelhead product. The previous year, the company bought CACE Technologies, a specialist in data packet capture and analysis products for wired and wireless networks. The deal included CACE Technologies' open source Wireshark application. In 2009 Riverbed acquired network analysis and reporting software developer Mazu Networks for about $25 million.

In addition to enhancing and extending its product line, Riverbed plans to grow sales through adding more third-party applications on its Riverbed Services Platform. It also intends to build indirect sales channels by forming additional reseller agreements to extend its geographic reach and market penetration. Support and services, which accounts for an increasing amount of the company's revenues, are also targeted to help drive global growth.

Riverbed's key rivals are Blue Coat Systems and Cisco Systems. It also faces a large potential competitor in Microsoft, which is improving the performance of its software for users in remote offices.

EXECUTIVES

Chairman, President, and CEO, Jerry M. Kennelly, age 60, $3,875,651 total compensation
VP Sales, Central Europe, Klaus Seidl
VP Cloud Storage Acceleration Products, Edward J. (Ed) Chapman
VP Product Management, John Martin
VP Corporate Development and Strategy, Paul O'Farrell
VP Technical Operations, Stephen R. Smoot, age 43
VP Global Employee Services, Mike Guerchon
VP Worldwide Channel Sales, Randy Schirman, age 49
VP Worldwide Marketing, Carolyn Crandall
VP Alliances, Venugopal Pai
VP Product Marketing, Apurva Davé
VP Sales Europe, Middle East, and Africa, Marcus Chambers
VP Engineering, Gordon Chaffee, age 41
VP Software Engineering, David Wu
VP Corporate and Legal Affairs, General Counsel, and Secretary, Brett A. Nissenberg, age 37
VP Business Services Operations, Lisa Grant
CIO, Thomas Bakewell
Chief Scientist, Mark S. Day
SVP Marketing and Business Development, Eric Wolford, age 44, $1,568,053 total compensation
Media Relations, Kristalle Ward
Head Purchasing, Dave Olson
Technical Director, Josh Tseng
Director Product Marketing, Nik Rouda
SVP Worldwide Sales, David M. (Dave) Peranich, age 49, $1,662,124 total compensation
SVP Business Services and CFO, Randy S. Gottfried, age 45, $1,503,241 total compensation
General Manager, Cloud Storage Acceleration, Ray Villeneuve
Investor Relations, Renee Lyall
Sales Director, Latin America, Andres Hurtado
Controller, Michael Palu
CTO and Director, Steven (Steve) McCanne, age 42, $2,545,393 total compensation
Auditors: Ernst & Young LLP

LOCATIONS

HQ: Riverbed Technology, Inc.
199 Fremont St., San Francisco, CA 94105
Phone: 415-247-8800   **Fax:** 415-247-8801
Web: www.riverbed.com

2010 Sales

	$ mil.	% of total
US	294.6	53
Europe, Middle East & Africa	149.7	27
Other regions	107.6	20
Total	**551.9**	**100**

PRODUCTS/OPERATIONS

2010 Sales

	$ mil.	% of total
Product	380.2	69
Support & services	171.7	31
Total	**551.9**	**100**

COMPETITORS

Arbor Networks
Blue Coat
Certeon
Cisco Systems
Citrix Systems
Expand Networks
F5 Networks
Internap Network Services
Juniper Networks
Lancope

HISTORICAL FINANCIALS

Company Type: Public

Income Statement

FYE: December 31

	REVENUE ($ mil.)	NET INCOME ($ mil.)	NET PROFIT MARGIN	EMPLOYEES
12/10	551.9	34.2	6.2%	1,244
12/09	394.1	7.1	1.8%	1,013
12/08	333.3	10.6	3.2%	857
12/07	236.4	14.8	6.3%	623
12/06	90.2	(15.8)	—	325
Annual Growth	57.3%	—	—	39.9%

2010 Year-End Financials

Debt ratio: —
Return on equity: 6.4%
Cash ($ mil.): 165.7
Current ratio: 3.23
Long-term debt ($ mil.): —

No. of shares (mil.): 150.9
Dividends
  Yield: —
  Payout: —
Market value ($ mil.): 5,306.0

	STOCK PRICE ($) FY Close	P/E High/Low	PER SHARE ($) Earnings	Dividends	Book Value
12/10	35.17	172 50	0.22	0.00	3.56
12/09	11.48	260 89	0.05	0.00	2.51
12/08	5.70	184 51	0.07	0.00	2.06
12/07	13.37	264 114	0.10	0.00	1.84
12/06	15.35	— —	(0.29)	0.00	0.82
Annual Growth	23.0%	— —	—	—	44.2%

Rodman & Renshaw

For investment bank Rodman & Renshaw, biotech is where it's at. The company provides private placements, underwriting, mergers & acquisitions support, equity research, and alternative financing techniques for its clients, with a special focus on emerging companies in the life sciences (biotech) sector. It is also the market maker for many companies in that industry. Rodman & Renshaw has also performed investment banking services for the environmental, technology, security, oil and gas, retail and logistics industries. Former presidential candidate and retired general Wesley Clark is chairman of Rodman & Renshaw.

As part of a specialization strategy, the investment bank in 2006 launched its Acumen BioFin unit, specializing in serving clients in the biotechnology, medical device, and specialty pharmaceutical industries.

In 2010 Rodman & Renshaw announced plans to acquire assets of the Over the Counter Bulletin Board (OTCBB) electronic quotation system from the Financial Industry Regulatory Authority (FINRA). The deal, which includes the rights to the OTCBB trademark and website, will diversify Rodman & Renshaw's business beyond its traditional investment banking activities.

The company then arranged to buy small cap market maker Hudson Holding in a $7 million transaction. That deal boosted Rodman & Renshaw's sales and trading business and expanded its research coverage to industries including transportation, gaming, and industrials.

The firm began as a Chicago-based partnership in the early 1950s, went public, was sold to Mexico's Abaco Casa de Bolsa, and ultimately was liquidated. A group of executives relaunched the firm, and in 2007 the company completed a reverse merger with Enthrust Financial Services, allowing the company to be listed as a public company without the entanglements of an IPO.

The following year it acquired Miller Mathis, a mergers & acquisitions advisor focused on the steel industry. Miller Mathis, which continues to operate as a subsidiary of Rodman & Renshaw, has an international presence (in Asia, Russia, and Mexico, for example) and so added to the group's client base geographically as well as by industry. It followed that purchase with the acquisition of COSCO Capital Management, which specializes in the oil and gas sectors in the US and Canada.

In 2008 Rodman & Renshaw made an unsolicited bid for the troubled Cowen Group, which has a similar focus on the life sciences and health care industries. Cowen Group management rejected the offer.

EXECUTIVES

Chairman, Wesley K. Clark
President, CEO, and Director, Edward Rubin, age 43, $150,000 total compensation
CFO, David Horin, $728,424 total compensation
Vice Chairman and Senior Managing Director, Michael Vasinkevich, age 43, $150,000 total compensation
Executive Officer, Thomas Pinou, age 51, $299,646 total compensation
Senior Managing Director, Co-Head Investment Banking, and Director, John J. Borer III, age 53, $150,000 total compensation
Auditors: Marcum & Kliegman LLP

LOCATIONS

HQ: Rodman & Renshaw Capital Group, Inc.
1251 Avenue of the Americas, 20th Fl., New York, NY 10020
Phone: 212-356-0500   **Fax:** 212-581-5690
Web: www.rodmanandrenshaw.com

COMPETITORS

Arlington Asset Investment	Houlihan Lokey
	Jefferies Group
Burrill & Company	Piper Jaffray
Canaccord Genuity	Sandler O'Neill
Cowen Group	

HISTORICAL FINANCIALS

Company Type: Public

Income Statement

FYE: December 31

	REVENUE ($ mil.)	NET INCOME ($ mil.)	NET PROFIT MARGIN	EMPLOYEES
12/10	83.6	(5.6)	—	131
12/09	132.2	27.3	20.7%	114
12/08	49.2	(37.4)	—	130
12/07	71.4	4.8	6.7%	108
12/06	0.0	(0.1)	—	105
Annual Growth	—	—	—	5.7%

2010 Year-End Financials

Debt ratio: —	No. of shares (mil.): 33.4
Return on equity: —	Dividends
Cash ($ mil.): 14.8	Yield: —
Current ratio: 2.67	Payout: —
Long-term debt ($ mil.): —	Market value ($ mil.): 89.5

	STOCK PRICE ($) FY Close	P/E High/Low		PER SHARE ($) Earnings	Dividends	Book Value
12/10	2.68	—	—	(0.15)	0.00	1.57
12/09	4.07	9	0	0.73	0.00	1.79
12/08	0.86	—	—	(1.12)	0.00	0.84
12/07	3.25	50	3	0.20	0.00	1.80
12/06	0.51	—	—	(0.03)	0.00	(0.00)
Annual Growth	51.4%	—	—	—	—	—

Roma Financial

Roma Financial Corporation may have Italian roots, but its branches are in good ol' American capitalism. The holding company owns Roma Bank, which was founded in 1920 by Italian immigrants in New Jersey and now operates about two dozen branches in that state's Burlington, Mercer, and Ocean counties. It offers the usual personal and commercial services, such as checking and savings accounts, CDs, business and consumer loans, and credit and debit cards. The company established RomAsia bank in 2008. Two years later, it added 10 branches to Roma Bank's network through its $14.7 million acquisition of Sterling Banks. Mutual holding company Roma Financial Corporation, MHC, owns some 70% of Roma Financial.

EXECUTIVES

CFO, Sharon L. Lamont, age 63, $266,205 total compensation
Chairman and EVP, Maurice T. Perilli, age 92, $390,687 total compensation
President, CEO, and Director; President and CEO, Roma Bank, Peter A. Inverso, age 72, $634,634 total compensation
COO, C. Keith Pericoloso, age 47, $230,319 total compensation
SVP Information Technology, Roma Bank, Robert W. Sumner, age 57
SVP Compliance, Barry J. Zadworny, age 66, $296,043 total compensation
SVP Investments and Treasurer, Roma Bank, Madhusudhan Kotta, age 60
SVP Lending, Roma Bank, Peter Villa, age 61
Auditors: Beard Miller Company LLP

LOCATIONS

HQ: Roma Financial Corporation
2300 Rte. 33, Robbinsville, NJ 08691
Phone: 609-223-8300
Web: www.romabank.com

COMPETITORS

1st Constitution Bancorp	Ocean Shore
	OceanFirst Financial
Amboy Bancorp	PNC Financial
Bank of America	Sovereign Bank
JPMorgan Chase	TD Bank USA

HISTORICAL FINANCIALS

Company Type: Public

Income Statement

FYE: December 31

	ASSETS ($ mil.)	NET INCOME ($ mil.)	INCOME AS % OF ASSETS	EMPLOYEES
12/10	1,819.2	5.1	0.3%	377
12/09	1,312.0	2.6	0.2%	248
12/08	1,077.1	4.7	0.4%	218
12/07	907.1	7.2	0.8%	192
12/06	876.1	5.2	0.6%	173
Annual Growth	20.0%	(0.5%)	—	21.5%

2010 Year-End Financials

Equity as % of assets: 11.58%	Dividends
Return on assets: 0.3%	Yield: 3.0%
Return on equity: 2.4%	Payout: 188.2%
Long-term debt ($ mil.): 36.9	Market value ($ mil.): 321.0
No. of shares (mil.): 30.3	Sales ($ mil.): 73.8

	STOCK PRICE ($) FY Close	P/E High/Low		PER SHARE ($) Earnings	Dividends	Book Value
12/10	10.60	76	55	0.17	0.32	6.96
12/09	12.36	156	108	0.09	0.40	6.94
12/08	12.59	117	79	0.15	0.24	6.84
12/07	15.69	78	59	0.23	0.24	6.67
12/06	16.56	89	68	0.19	0.00	7.17
Annual Growth	(10.6%)	—	—	(2.7%)	—	(0.7%)

Rovi

Rovi wants to help media junkies find their ideal fix - as long as they are willing to pay for it. The company develops and licenses copyright protection technology; middleware applications; metadata on music, movies, and television programming; and interactive programming guides. Telecom service providers, cable companies, movie studios, and makers of consumer electronics such as set-top boxes and DVD players use its technology to manage and protect digital content and track customer usage patterns. Rovi has expanded beyond video content protection into recorded music protection services in response to digital piracy. Clients have included Universal Studios, HBO, and Universal Music Group.

While Rovi increased its sales in 2008 and 2009, the company lost money in both years. Its sales did rise in 2009, but Rovi cited increased expenses, including integration costs associated with the 2008 purchase of Gemstar-TV Guide International for $2.8 billion, as a key contributor to losses. (Rovi subsequently sold the TV Guide Magazine business to private equity firm OpenGate Capital and it sold the TV Guide Network assets to movie studio Lions Gate Entertainment.) Rovi's loss in 2009 was caused income tax expenses related to the sale of TV Guide assets, as well as by expenses related to the purchase that year of online digital content search and shopping specialist Muze.

Meanwhile, the company's most significant sales growth during 2009 came from its service provider business segment which benefitted from a full year of sales of interactive program guide products and patents acquired in the Gemstar-TV Guide purchase.

Just over half of the Rovi's sales are made outside of the US, and the company is expanding in growing markets and industry niches through licensing deals. Its presence in Latin America received a boost in 2010 from agreements with Cable & Wireless in Panamá, Cooperativa de Telecomunicaciones de Santa Cruz in Bolivia, and Supercanal in Argentina. These cable operators signed multi-year licensing agreements to offer the Rovi Passport Guide and related applications to their subscribers. Cable & Wireless Panamá also licenses Rovi TV information. Rovi also licensed its interactive program guide patents to Telstra. in Australia that year.

Rovi is also looking to grow again through acquisitions. In 2011 the company bought digital entertainment software maker Sonic Solutions in a deal valued at around $720 million in cash and stock. With its RoxioNow software — including a catalog of more than 10,000 movies and TV shows that consumers can access through connected entertainment devices — and its DivX Internet-based video player software, Sonic Solutions offered a product portfolio that, combined with Rovi's interactive program guide and premium content licensing deals, provides a complete consumer entertainment product. The purchase broadened Rovi's offerings for content owners, device makers, and retailers, as well as expanded its advertising-supported distribution. All of Sonic Solutions' brands were integrated into Rovi. The company also acquired DigiForge that year, boosting its interactive program guide capabilities for cable operators.

Rovi has sold some of its noncore operations including its games business, its eMeta division, and its FLEXnet suite of electronic license management tools. The company has also exited the GuideWorks joint venture it started with Comcast in 2004, giving Comcast full ownership of the service that provides interactive programming guides. Rovi and Comcast will still work closely, with Comcast distributing Rovi's enhanced entertainment products and licensing certain Rovi patents across its distribution platforms.

Formerly known as Macrovision, the company changed its name to Rovi in 2009.

EXECUTIVES

Chairman, Andrew K. (Andy) Ludwick, age 65
CFO, James W. Budge, age 44, $1,917,497 total compensation
President, CEO, and Director, Alfred J. (Fred) Amoroso, age 61, $6,089,976 total compensation
EVP Corporate Development, Jim Wickett, age 58
EVP Products, Corey Ferengul
EVP, General Counsel, and Corporate Secretary, Stephen Yu, age 45, $1,346,196 total compensation
EVP Worldwide Sales and Services, Thomas (Tom) Carson, age 52, $1,216,885 total compensation
EVP Data Services, John Moakley
EVP Human Resources, Eileen Schloss
VP Corporate Finance and Investor Relations, Lauren Landfield
VP Worldwide Data Sales, Al Miyashita
SVP Licensing, Samir Armaly
SVP, Asia Pacific, Akitaka Nishimura
SVP Worldwide Sales, Service Providers, Bob Shallow
Auditors: KPMG LLP

LOCATIONS

HQ: Rovi Corporation
2830 De La Cruz Blvd., Santa Clara, CA 95050
Phone: 408-562-8400   **Fax:** 408-567-1800
Web: www.rovicorp.com

2009 Sales

	$ mil.	% of total
US	239.4	49
Other countries	244.5	51
Total	**283.9**	**100**

PRODUCTS/OPERATIONS

2009 Sales by Market

	$ mil.	% of total
Service providers	230.7	48
Consumer electronics manufacturers	199.9	41
Other	53.3	11
Total	**483.9**	**100**

Selected Products and Services

Digital content protection
Interactive program guides
Media recognition services

COMPETITORS

ContentGuard	Microsoft
Google	NEC
Hitachi	Pioneer Corporation
IBM	RealNetworks
Intel	Sony
Intertrust Technologies	Yahoo!

HISTORICAL FINANCIALS

Company Type: Public

Income Statement

FYE: December 31

	REVENUE ($ mil.)	NET INCOME ($ mil.)	NET PROFIT MARGIN	EMPLOYEES
12/10	541.5	212.9	39.3%	1,200
12/09	483.9	(53.0)	—	1,200
12/08	330.0	(108.9)	—	1,186
12/07	155.7	31.5	20.2%	450
12/06	247.6	33.0	13.3%	784
Annual Growth	**21.6%**	**59.4%**		**11.2%**

2010 Year-End Financials

Debt ratio: 21.6%
Return on equity: 12.2%
Cash ($ mil.): 200.2
Current ratio: 2.76
Long-term debt ($ mil.): 378.1

No. of shares (mil.): 106.1
Dividends
  Yield: —
  Payout: —
Market value ($ mil.): 6,578.1

	STOCK PRICE ($) FY Close	P/E High/Low	PER SHARE ($) Earnings	Dividends	Book Value
12/10	62.01	32 14	1.94	0.00	16.48
12/09	31.87	— —	(0.52)	0.00	14.69
12/08	12.65	— —	(1.26)	0.00	14.56
12/07	18.33	53 31	0.58	0.00	10.28
12/06	28.26	46 25	0.63	0.00	9.10
Annual Growth	**21.7%**	**— —**	**32.5%**	**—**	**16.0%**

Royal Gold

Royal Gold deals only with royalty. Rather than operating gold mines, the company buys the right to collect royalties from mine operators. This strategy allows Royal Gold to minimize its exposure to the costs of mineral exploration and development. More than one-third of the company's revenue comes from its royalty interests related to the Cortez Pipeline Mining Complex, a project in Nevada, operated by Barrick; the Robinson mine operated by Quadra accounts for 24%. Royal Gold holds royalty stakes in other producing properties elsewhere in the Americas, as well as in Africa. The company also owns interests in exploration- and development-stage projects in the US and in Argentina, Finland, and Russia.

Royal Gold revenues increased 85% in 2010 due to the rising market price of gold, copper and other metals. Despite the increase in royalty payments, net income was down for the year by 44% due to increased operating costs and expenses related to severance payments and acquisitions.

The company is expanding its portfolio. It has invested $35 million in the construction and development of High River Gold Mines' Taparko open pit gold project in Burkina Faso, in West Africa. Royal Gold has acquired royalty stakes in projects operated by Kennecott Minerals (in projects in Nevada and Mexico), Nevada Star Resource Corp. (a smelter return royalty), Minefinders (a smelter return royalty interest on a Mexican property), Kennecott Exploration (Mexico), and Barrick.

In 2010 Royal Gold acquired the rights to 25% of the payable gold produced from the Mt. Milligan copper-gold project in British Columbia from Thompson Creek Metals Company. Royal Gold paid some $311 million for the rights.

It added another acquisition in 2009 when it paid Teck $100 million for a percentage of a Chilean gold mine's output. Early the next year it bought International Royalty for about $700 million. International Royalty owns percentage stakes in mines in Australia, Canada, and Chile.

EXECUTIVES

Chairman, Stanley Dempsey, age 72, $637,104 total compensation
President, CEO, and Director, Tony Jensen, age 49, $991,641 total compensation
CFO and Treasurer, Stefan L. Wenger, age 38, $545,471 total compensation
VP Operations, William M. Zisch, age 53
VP Corporate Development, William Heissenbuttel, age 46, $412,321 total compensation
VP and General Counsel, Bruce C. Kirchhoff, age 52, $406,037 total compensation
VP and Secretary, Karen P. Gross, age 57, $539,468 total compensation
Auditors: Ernst & Young LLP

LOCATIONS

HQ: Royal Gold, Inc.
1660 Wynkoop St., Ste. 1000, Denver, CO 80202-1132
Phone: 303-573-1660   **Fax:** 303-595-9385
Web: www.royalgold.com

2011 Royalty Revenue

	% of total
US	24
Chile	21
Canada	19
Mexico	18
Africa	9
Other regions	9
Total	**100**

COMPETITORS

Anglo American	Franco-Nevada
BHP Billiton	Rio Tinto Limited

HISTORICAL FINANCIALS

Company Type: Public

Income Statement
FYE: June 30

	REVENUE ($ mil.)	NET INCOME ($ mil.)	NET PROFIT MARGIN	EMPLOYEES
06/11	216.5	71.4	33.0%	21
06/10	136.6	21.5	15.7%	20
06/09	73.8	38.3	51.9%	17
06/08	69.4	26.1	37.6%	16
06/07	48.4	19.7	40.7%	15
Annual Growth	45.4%	38.0%	—	8.8%

2011 Year-End Financials

Debt ratio: 14.4%
Return on equity: 4.9%
Cash ($ mil.): 114.2
Current ratio: 5.87
Long-term debt ($ mil.): 210.5

No. of shares (mil.): 54.2
Dividends
  Yield: 0.7%
  Payout: 32.6%
Market value ($ mil.): 3,176.4

	STOCK PRICE ($) FY Close	P/E High/Low	PER SHARE ($) Earnings	Dividends	Book Value
06/11	58.57	48 33	1.29	0.42	26.92
06/10	48.00	114 76	0.49	0.35	26.32
06/09	41.69	47 21	1.07	0.31	18.51
06/08	31.36	52 36	0.68	0.28	14.31
06/07	23.77	47 29	0.79	0.25	11.13
Annual Growth	25.3%	— —	13.0%	13.8%	24.7%

RPX

In our litigious society, RPX Corporation helps keep technology companies out of the courtroom. RPX owns a portfolio of more than 1,500 intellectual property patents that it licenses to customers in order to prevent patent infringement lawsuits. (So one company can't sue another over a patent, since it's RPX that owns the patent). Its patent portfolio spans six industries — consumer electronics, software, media content, mobile communications and devices, networking, and semiconductors. RPX counts more than 70 customers, including Cisco, Google, Nokia, Sharp, Sony, and Verizon, and earns one-third of its revenues from Asian firms. Founded in 2008, RPX launched an IPO in 2011.

Patent litigation is an emerging, multi-billion dollar industry that even has its own insults - companies that make big business of suing others over alleged patent infringement are called non-practicing entities (NPEs) but are known derogatively as patent trolls or patent pirates. Tech companies of all sizes have had their business operations disrupted by major verdicts and high settlement costs. Many patents can overlap; for example, there are more than 6,200 patents for the semiconductor technology known as DRAM (dynamic random access memory). Potential infringement can happen for any company that makes, uses, or sells a device with DRAM technology.

RPX operates as a legal middleman; so far it has spent about $250 million acquiring patents to help customers mitigate litigation risks. Its customers pay between $40,000 to more than $5 million a year to license its intellectual property. RPX's separates itself from competitors (such as Acacia) by charging its subscription fees based on a company's revenues, not the perceived value of the patent.

RPX is experiencing significant growth as its revenues doubled from 2009, its first full year of operations, to the first nine months of 2010. Continuing this impressive trajectory, the company saw its revenues increase from $32 million in 2009 to almost $95 million in 2010 — a staggering increase of 189%. In May 2011, the company raised almost $160 million by going public. It wants to use the proceeds to acquire additional patents in 2011, as well as hire more personnel for client relations, patent research and analysis, and to develop reporting systems. PRX also plans to offer complementary services, such as facilitating joint defense agreements and cross-licensing arrangements for its clients. Finally, it aims to recruit more clients that are consistently faced with IP-related lawsuits.

Several investment vehicles own major stakes in the company. Index Ventures Growth; Charles River Partnership; and Kleiner Perkins Caufield & Byers each own about 18%. They are represented on the company's board by Giuseppe Zocco, Izhar Armony, and Randy Komisar, respectively.

EXECUTIVES

CEO and Director, John A. Amster, age 42
President and Director, Eran Zur, age 42
EVP, Mallun Yen
VP Memberships and Legal, Eric Olsen
VP Marketing, Lily Loh
VP Client Relations, Steve Swank
VP Memberships, France Szeto
VP and Head of Acquisitions, Kevin Barhydt
VP RPX Corp and President, RPX Asia Corp, Hisao Yamasaki
VP Structured Acquisitions, Thomas Westerlund
VP Memberships, Anderson R. Scott
VP and Corporate Controller, Paul Chopra
VP Corporate Development, David Ruder
COO and Director, Geoffrey T. Barker, age 49
CTO, Steve Waterhouse
Chief Intellectual Property Officer, Paul M. Saraceni
SVP Memberships and General Manager, Henri Linde, age 52
Vice President Memberships and General Manager, David Potts
Chief Knowledge Officer, Mike MacKay
General Counsel, Marty Roberts
Director Client Relations, Francois Thuiliere
Director Acquisitions, Reza Mashouf
SVP Finance, CFO, and Treasurer, Adam C. Spiegel, age 47
Senior Director Client Relations, Shoichi Endo
SVP Memberships, Paul Reidy, age 50
Director Corporate Development, David Anderson
Auditors: PricewaterhouseCoopers LLP

LOCATIONS

HQ: RPX Corporation
  1 Market Plaza, Ste. 700, San Francisco, CA 94105
Phone: 866-779-7641
Web: www.rpxcorp.com

2010 Sales

	$ mil.	% of total
Americas	53.1	56
Asia	31.8	33
Europe	10.0	11
Total	**94.9**	**100**

COMPETITORS

Acacia Research	Howrey
Alston & Bird	Jones Day
Baker & McKenzie	Kirkland & Ellis
Convex Group	Walker Digital
Duane Morris	White & Case

HISTORICAL FINANCIALS

Company Type: Public

Income Statement
FYE: December 31

	REVENUE ($ mil.)	NET INCOME ($ mil.)	NET PROFIT MARGIN	EMPLOYEES
12/10	94.9	13.9	14.6%	66
12/09	32.8	1.9	5.8%	66
12/08	0.8	(5.2)	—	0
Annual Growth	989.2%	—	—	0.0%

2010 Year-End Financials

Debt ratio: 6.9%
Return on equity: 18.9%
Cash ($ mil.): 46.7
Current ratio: 0.66
Long-term debt ($ mil.): 5.1

No. of shares (mil.): —
Dividends
  Yield: —
  Payout: —
Market value ($ mil.): —

	STOCK PRICE ($) FY Close	P/E High/Low	PER SHARE ($) Earnings	Dividends	Book Value
Annual Growth	—	— —	—	—	—

Rubicon Technology

Rubicon Technology says *Alea iacta est* (The die is cast) and crosses over into the empire of advanced technology. Using proprietary crystal growth technology, Rubicon makes sapphire materials, wafers, and components for a variety of products. In the the field of optoelectronics, Rubicon makes sapphire components for light-emitting diodes (LEDs) used in cell phones, video screens, and other items. Rubicon's sapphire materials also are used for compound semiconductor manufacturing and laser imaging. In the telecom sector, the company's silicon materials are in demand for the silicon-on-sapphire (SOS) components of cellular and fiber-optics products. Asian customers account for about 90% of Rubicon's sales.

Rubicon is counting on industry's seeing more value in LED-based lighting. In 2010 90% of the company's sales were of products used for the making of LED products. The world's factories have been rising to the occasion and adding LED to new products, such as backlit LCD TVs. And around the end of 2009 more consumers have been doing their part by buying them as well as other LED-loaded products. After weathering a net loss of $9.6 million in 2009, Rubicon made a net income of $29.1 million in 2010. But the same year the company had an accumulated deficit of about $130 million.

The LEDs made with Rubicon's sapphire provide colored lighting for mobile phone display screens. LEDs made with sapphire also equip the backlighting units of notebook computers, desktop monitors, and LCD TVs. LEDs are additionally being used more for automobile headlights, taillights, and even interior lighting. Another growing market for LEDs — and Rubicon's sapphire — is large and outdoor commercial signage.

Radio-frequency integrated circuits (RFICs) that need sapphire to be manufactured offer more opportunities for Rubicon's materials. Among the products that use RFICs needing Rubicon's sapphire are mobile phones, broadband television set-top boxes, and satellites.

Rubicon has additionally discovered a window of opportunity in the transportation and military sectors. Its sapphire and fluoride materials are in demand for transparent armor in military vehicles and for special windows used for steering aircraft in conditions of low visibility.

Another application of sapphire materials is for blue laser diodes, which are increasingly being used in Blu-ray DVD players and advanced video game systems.

To grow with its market, Rubicon is developing larger sapphire wafers that will be needed for producing next-generation LEDs and RFICs. Rubicon also projects more demand as the electronics and optical industries create new products that require sapphire and other single-crystal products for manufacturing. Additionally Rubicon sees more market opportunities in the aerospace, petroleum, and laser industries, which are replacing glass and quartz with sapphire for high-performance and harsh-environment uses.

Through Cross Atlantic Capital Partners, director Donald Caldwell controls about 25% of Rubicon Technology.

EXECUTIVES

Chairman, Don N. Aquilano, age 44
President, CEO, and Director, Raja M. Parvez, age 53, $2,652,453 total compensation
CFO, Secretary, and Treasurer, William F. (Bill) Weissman, age 52, $1,230,550 total compensation
VP Operations, Faisal Nabulsi
VP Quality and Supply Line Management, Akhtar Zaman
Chief Scientist, Elena Dobrovinskaya
SVP Sales and Marketing, Sunil B. Phatak
Auditors: Grant Thornton LLP

LOCATIONS

HQ: Rubicon Technology, Inc.
9931 Franklin Ave., Franklin Park, IL 60131
Phone: 847-295-7000   **Fax:** 847-295-7555
Web: www.rubicon-es2.com

2010 Sales

	$ mil.	% of total
Asia	69.4	90
North America	6.5	8
Europe	1.5	2
Total	**77.4**	**100**

HISTORICAL FINANCIALS

Company Type: Public

Income Statement

FYE: December 31

	REVENUE ($ mil.)	NET INCOME ($ mil.)	NET PROFIT MARGIN	EMPLOYEES
12/10	77.4	29.1	37.6%	250
12/09	19.8	(9.6)	—	138
12/08	37.8	4.4	11.6%	99
12/07	34.1	(2.9)	—	144
12/06	20.8	(7.4)	—	122
Annual Growth	**38.9%**	**—**	**—**	**19.6%**

2010 Year-End Financials

Debt ratio: —	No. of shares (mil.): 23.0
Return on equity: 15.2%	Dividends
Cash ($ mil.): 16.1	Yield: —
Current ratio: 8.34	Payout: —
Long-term debt ($ mil.): —	Market value ($ mil.): 484.0

	STOCK PRICE ($) FY Close	P/E High/Low		PER SHARE ($) Earnings	Dividends	Book Value
12/10	21.08	28	11	1.28	0.00	8.37
12/09	20.31	—	—	(0.48)	0.00	4.82
12/08	4.26	184	13	0.19	0.00	5.09
12/07	23.75	—	—	(27.22)	0.00	5.49
Annual Growth	**(3.9%)**	**—**	**—**	**—**	**—**	**15.1%**

Rudolph Technologies

Rudolph Technologies' inspection and metrology systems lead the way to better yields for chip makers. To create semiconductors, manufacturers deposit precise layers of conducting and insulating materials on silicon wafers. Rudolph makes process control metrology equipment that monitors these layers to ensure that the material doesn't get too thick or too thin. Its inspection equipment (around half of sales) looks for defects not obvious to the human eye, such as tiny scratches or gouges in the surface of a silicon wafer. The company sells to some 90 semiconductor manufacturers worldwide; Intel accounts for about 11% of sales. Rudolph gets around three-quarters of sales outside the US, primarily in Asia.

Rudolph Technologies has a limited number of customers, some of whom may be experiencing financial difficulties due to the global economic environment and turmoil in the credit markets. The company operates in a highly competitive market, with Camtek and KLA-Tencor as its principal rivals. While Camtek is about the size of Rudolph, KLA-Tencor dwarfs both companies in terms of annual sales, employees, and financial resources. Rudolph's equipment is complex and has a history of containing design defects and software bugs when introduced; the company carries product liability insurance which covers up to $14 million per claim, but financial damages to semiconductor manufacturers whose manufacturing operations are disrupted by Rudolph products could run substantially higher than that if the disruption is not quickly resolved by the company and its customers.

In 2009 the company acquired Adventa Control Technologies in Plano, Texas. Adventa offers advanced process control technologies to semiconductor manufacturers, especially for tool automation and fault detection. Rudolph Technologies is looking to expand its process control software with Adventa's complementary products. In August 2010 Rudolph acquired the Yield Dynamics software business of MKS Instruments, further expanding its process control software portfolio.

In 2006 Rudolph acquired August Technology, a supplier of semiconductor inspection and metrology tools, for about $193 million in cash and stock, beating out competing bids from KLA-Tencor and Nanometrics. The August Technology acquisition saga played out for more than a year, from Nanometrics' agreement to acquire August to Rudolph's winning bid in 2005. August then restated its financial results for fiscal 2004 and the first half of fiscal 2005, which delayed the consummation of Rudolph's acquisition offer until 2006. August became Rudolph's Advanced Macro Defect Inspection business unit.

In 2007 Rudolph bought the semiconductor division of Applied Precision for nearly $58 million in cash and 1.3 million shares of the company's common stock. The division became Rudolph's Probe Card Test and Analysis division. The following year the company bought the assets and intellectual property of RVSI Inspection, LLC, which became the Wafer Scanner Product Group. Later in 2008 Rudolph sold the lead scanner assets and related IP acquired from RVSI Inspection to BKM Technology Partners, LLC. Rudolph also expanded its offerings with its 2002 purchase of ISOA, a privately held maker of defect control equipment.

EXECUTIVES

Chairman and CEO, Paul F. McLaughlin, age 65, $1,976,283 total compensation
EVP; General Manager, Inspection Business Unit, Nathan H. Little, age 59, $705,361 total compensation
VP Engineering, Inspection Business Unit, Scott R. Danciak, age 41
VP; General Manager, Metrology, Avishai Kepten
VP Corporate Marketing, Ardelle R. Johnson, age 55
VP Business Development and Director Back-end Product Management, Rajiv Roy, age 52
VP Manufacturing, Jeffrey T. (Jeff) Nelson, age 55
VP and General Counsel, Robert A. Koch, age 49
VP Global Customer Support, Robert DiCrosta, age 63
VP Operations, Metrology Business Unit, Christopher J. Morath, age 42
VP; General Manager, Data Analysis and Review, Michael P. Plisinski, age 41, $365,715 total compensation
SVP Finance and Administration, CFO, and Secretary, Steven R. Roth, age 50, $671,507 total compensation
SVP Worldwide Sales and Field Operations, D. Mayson Brooks, age 52, $412,041 total compensation
General Manager, Europe, Martin Molan
Auditors: Ernst & Young LLP

LOCATIONS

HQ: Rudolph Technologies, Inc.
1 Rudolph Rd., Flanders, NJ 07836
Phone: 973-691-1300   **Fax:** 973-691-4863
Web: www.rudolphtech.com Rudolph Technologies has facilities in China, Japan, Singapore, South Korea, Taiwan, the UK, and the US.

2008 Sales

	$ mil.	% of total
Asia/Pacific	74.7	57
US	30.7	23
Europe	25.6	20
Total	**131.0**	**100**

PRODUCTS/OPERATIONS

2008 Sales

	$ mil.	% of total
Systems		
Inspection	71.3	55
Metrology	21.1	16
Parts	19.3	15
Services	14.9	11
Software licensing	4.4	3
Total	**131.0**	**100**

Selected Products

3Di Inspection System (inspection for bumped devices)
AutoEL Series (ellipsometers for measuring film thickness, refractive index, and absorption)
AXi Series (defect inspection for various process steps)
Genesis Enterprise (fabwide yield management software platform with data mining and workflow development capabilities)
MetaPULSE Systems (optical acoustic-based systems for opaque thin-film layers)
NSX Series (macro-defect inspection)
S3000 and S2000 Systems (transparent thin-film measurement systems)

WaferView (automated macro-defect lithography
inspection systems)
YieldView (yield management and process control
software)

COMPETITORS

Applied Materials	KLA-Tencor
Camtek	Metara
Carl Zeiss	Nanometrics
Dainippon Screen	Nikon
FEI	Nova Measuring
Hexagon AB	PANalytical
Hitachi	PDF Solutions
High-Technologies	Qcept Technologies

HISTORICAL FINANCIALS

Company Type: Public

Income Statement
FYE: December 31

	REVENUE ($ mil.)	NET INCOME ($ mil.)	NET PROFIT MARGIN	EMPLOYEES
12/10	195.3	27.0	13.8%	550
12/09	78.7	(29.6)	—	497
12/08	131.0	(249.7)	—	536
12/07	160.1	11.9	7.4%	648
12/06	201.2	12.7	6.3%	620
Annual Growth	(0.7%)	20.8%	—	(3.0%)

2010 Year-End Financials

Debt ratio: —	No. of shares (mil.): 31.4
Return on equity: 14.6%	Dividends
Cash ($ mil.): 71.1	Yield: —
Current ratio: 6.96	Payout: —
Long-term debt ($ mil.): —	Market value ($ mil.): 258.6

	STOCK PRICE ($) FY Close	P/E High	P/E Low	PER SHARE ($) Earnings	PER SHARE ($) Dividends	PER SHARE ($) Book Value
12/10	8.23	13	7	0.86	0.00	5.89
12/09	6.72	—	—	(0.96)	0.00	4.88
12/08	3.53	—	—	(8.16)	0.00	5.74
12/07	11.32	46	25	0.40	0.00	14.55
12/06	15.92	44	28	0.46	0.00	13.57
Annual Growth	(15.2%)	—	—	16.9%	—	(18.8%)

rue21

It's rue21's sincere hope that people, young and old, long to be 21 (again or for the first time). The fast-growing chain sells value-priced apparel and accessories, including jewelry and fragrances, for girls and guys through more than 600 stores in malls and strip centers in about 45 US states. Daily deliveries ensure that the company's stores stock the latest fashion trends and encourage frequent visits by customers. rue21 caters to 11- to 17-year-olds and stocks its own rue21 etc!, Carbon, tarea, and rueKicks brands of apparel and footwear. Founded in 1976, rue21 was formerly known as Pennsylvania Fashions. Apax Partners, owner of the teen apparel chain, took rue21 public in 2009.

The youth retailer, which opened its 600th store in August 2010 (up from just about 195 stores in 2005), plans to add 100 new stores in fiscal 2011 (ends January) and could have more than 1,000 shops by 2015. rue21's value-priced, fast-fashion strategy appears well suited to the recent retail slump as its sales continued to grow despite the weak economy. Indeed, in fiscal 2010 sales rose about 34% vs. fiscal 2009, with same-store sales up nearly 8%. Profits soared, with net income rising 74% in fiscal 2010. Value-priced fast-fashion, pioneered by rivals H&M and Forever 21, is proving to be a hot retail concept as shoppers are reluctant to spend much money on clothes that will quickly go out of style.

About 400 of the shops conform to the retailer's etc! format (launched in 2006), which features higher-margin accessory product categories, such as shoes, jewelry, and handbags. The chain is also stocking mores bras, underwear, and pajama-style apparel, under its tarea private label, in response to the success of such intimates lines as Victoria Secret's Pink and American Eagle's aerie.

The company uses social media marketing (Facebook, Myspace, and Twitter) to stay close to its young clientele. Surprisingly, rue21 does not yet offer online shopping, but says it has plans to offer it in the future.

Following the November 2009 IPO, which raised about $129 million (including some $29 million for the company), Apax still controls about 30% of rue21's shares. rue21 used its portion of the proceeds to retire debt.

EXECUTIVES

Chairman, President, and CEO, Robert N. (Bob) Fisch, age 61, $2,288,097 total compensation
VP and General Counsel, Stacy B. Siegal, age 44
VP and Director Strategic Merchandising, Judy M. Kucinski, age 49
SVP Information Technology, Michael A. Holland, age 47, $316,386 total compensation
SVP and General Merchandising Manager, Kim A. Reynolds, age 53, $961,106 total compensation
SVP and Director of Stores, John P. Bugnar, age 62, $504,506 total compensation
SVP and CFO, Keith A. McDonough, age 52, $559,160 total compensation
SVP Real Estate, Robert R. Thomson, age 52
SVP Planning and Allocation, Mark K. J. Chrystal, age 38, $489,722 total compensation
Auditors: Ernst & Young LLP

LOCATIONS

HQ: rue21, inc.
800 Commonwealth Dr., Ste. 100, Warrendale, PA 15086-7527
Phone: 724-776-9780   **Fax:** 724-776-4111
Web: www.rue21.com

2010 Stores

	No.
Alabama	27
Arizona	13
Arkansas	8
California	17
Colorado	7
Connecticut	1
Delaware	1
Florida	21
Georgia	37
Illinois	16
Indiana	14
Iowa	7
Kansas	4
Kentucky	8
Louisiana	22
Maine	1
Maryland	6
Massachusetts	3
Michigan	14
Minnesota	4
Mississippi	19
Missouri	14
Nebraska	2
Nevada	4
New Hampshire	2
New Jersey	3
New Mexico	7
New York	13
North Carolina	34
Ohio	14
Oklahoma	14
Oregon	4
Pennsylvania	24
South Carolina	16
Tennessee	23
Texas	69
Utah	10
Vermont	1
Virginia	11
Washington	4
West Virginia	7
Wisconsin	8
Wyoming	1
Total	**535**

PRODUCTS/OPERATIONS

2010 Sales

	% of total
Girls' apparel	57
Girls' accessories	24
Guys' apparel & accessories	19
Total	**100**

COMPETITORS

American Apparel	J. Crew
American Eagle Outfitters	Pacific Sunwear
	Target Corporation
Aéropostale	The Buckle
Charlotte Russe	The Gap
dELiA*s	Urban Outfitters
Forever 21	Wal-Mart
H&M	Wet Seal

HISTORICAL FINANCIALS

Company Type: Public

Income Statement
FYE: Saturday nearest January 31

	REVENUE ($ mil.)	NET INCOME ($ mil.)	NET PROFIT MARGIN	EMPLOYEES
01/11	634.7	30.2	4.8%	7,243
01/10	525.6	22.0	4.2%	5,765
01/09	391.4	12.6	3.2%	5,927
01/08	296.9	9.1	3.1%	0
01/07	225.6	7.8	3.5%	0
Annual Growth	29.5%	40.3%	—	10.5%

2011 Year-End Financials

Debt ratio: —	No. of shares (mil.): 24.4
Return on equity: 29.6%	Dividends
Cash ($ mil.): 50.1	Yield: —
Current ratio: 1.42	Payout: —
Long-term debt ($ mil.): —	Market value ($ mil.): 719.2

	STOCK PRICE ($) FY Close	P/E High	P/E Low	PER SHARE ($) Earnings	PER SHARE ($) Dividends	PER SHARE ($) Book Value
01/11	29.50	31	17	1.21	0.00	4.19
01/10	28.03	34	23	0.96	0.00	2.78
Annual Growth	5.2%	—	—	26.0%	—	50.5%

Ruger

Whether you like to shoot birdies or bogeys, Sturm, Ruger & Company can accommodate you. The company, also called Ruger, is one of the nation's biggest gun makers and the only one that produces all four categories of firearms: pistols, revolvers, rifles, and shotguns. Models include hunting and target rifles, single- and double-action revolvers, muzzleloading guns, and double-barreled shotguns. Its guns are sold by independent wholesale distributors to independent firearms retailers and chains, including Academy Sports and Cabelas. Ruger also makes metal products — known as castings — for the commercial and military markets. Sturm, Ruger & Company was founded in 1949 by William Ruger and Alexander Sturm.

The company's firearm sales have doubled from about $133 million in 2005 to more than $266 million in 2009. Indeed, sales increased by more than 50% in 2009 vs. 2008 driven by extraordinary retail demand beginning in late 2008. The company said the unusually high demand is likely driven by politics and the economy. Sales of handguns — purchased with self defense in mind — were particularly strong. To keep pace, Ruger increased production in 2009 by 56% from 2008 and 101% from 2007.

Firearms account for more than 95% of Ruger's net sales, with its Pine Tree Castings (PTC) division comprising the balance. PTC supplies the architectural hardware, sporting goods, marine hardware, firearms, precision machinery, pneumatic and hand tools industries, among others. The company stopped manufacturing titanium castings in 2007 and consolidated its Arizona casting operations into its New Hampshire facilities. Following the move, Ruger produces only castings made from steel alloys.

The company's top four distributors contribute to about half of its total firearms sales. Foreign sales (primarily to law enforcement and government agencies) account for less than 5% of the total.

The firm is among a number of gun makers being sued by municipalities alleging gun companies knowingly distribute guns to disreputable dealers, which then sell them to criminals. (As with tobacco suits, the cities hope to regain some of the costs related to gun crime.) The vast majority of these cases have now been dismissed or withdrawn.

An investment group led by Allianz Global Investors Management Partners owns about 10% of the company's shares.

HISTORY

Sturm, Ruger & Company was founded in 1949 by William Ruger, who designed a notable machine gun used by the military during WWII, and Alexander Sturm, who backed the production of a new Ruger design by investing $50,000. Sturm died of hepatitis in 1951 at age 28 and after a battle with Sturm's family, Ruger took control of the company.

The gun maker's growth during the 1960s and 1970s was driven by demand for single-action revolvers and .22-caliber autoloading pistols produced at its original plant in Southport, Connecticut. Ruger went public in 1969, still the only American gun company to do so.

In 1986 the company forced its distributors to choose between it and archrival Smith & Wesson; about half chose to stay with Ruger. By streamlining its distribution channels, the manufacturer made its products more difficult to find, thus increasing their prestige.

Decreasing firearms sales prompted the company to expand its castings operations. Ruger bought Callaway Golf's share in their joint foundry to become its sole owner in 1997. In 1998 Ruger unveiled its first muzzleloader, the Ruger 77/50, to capitalize on the growing popularity of muzzleloading rifles. Later that year New Orleans became the first municipality to sue gun makers, including Ruger, in an effort to recover the cost of gun violence. Other local governments followed suit.

In 2000 the company sent letters to gun distributors asking that its guns be sold at regular places of business, not trade shows. In 2001, the Louisiana Supreme Court threw out New Orleans' suit, but remained a defendant in some 37 lawsuits at the end of 2001.

Co-founder William Ruger died in July 2002. In early 2003, after 2 years of pretrial discovery, the consolidated California cities suit against almost all firearms manufacturers (including Ruger) was dismissed.

EXECUTIVES

Chairman, C. Michael Jacobi, age 69
Chairman Emeritus, James E. Service, age 80
President, CEO, and Director, Michael O. Fifer, age 53, $1,530,001 total compensation
VP Newport Operations, Thomas P. (Tom) Sullivan, age 50, $681,594 total compensation
VP Sales and Marketing, Christopher J. Killoy, age 52, $686,060 total compensation
VP Lean Business Development, Steven M. (Steve) Maynard, $865,851 total compensation
VP and General Counsel, Kevin B. Reid Sr.
VP, CFO, and Treasurer, Thomas A. Dineen, age 42, $658,437 total compensation
Group VP, Prescott Firearms, Mark T. Lang, age 54, $347,149 total compensation
Corporate Secretary, Leslie M. Gasper, age 57
Auditors: McGladrey & Pullen, LLP

LOCATIONS

HQ: Sturm, Ruger & Company, Inc.
Lacey Place, Southport, CT 06890
Phone: 203-259-7843   **Fax:** 203-256-3367
Web: www.ruger-firearms.com

PRODUCTS/OPERATIONS

2009 Sales

	$ mil.	% of total
Firearms	266.6	98
Castings	4.4	2
Total	**271.0**	**100**

Selected Products

Firearms
  Pistols
    P-Series (centerfire)
    Ruger 22/45 (rimfire)
    Ruger Mark II (rimfire)
  Revolvers
    Single-action
      Birds Head Vaquero
      Bisley Hunter
      New Bearcat
      New Model Blackhawk
      New Model Single Six
      New Model .32 Magnum Super Single-Six
      New Model Super Blackhawk
      Old Army Cap & Ball
      Ruger Bisley
      Single-Six
      Super Blackhawk
      Vaquero
    Double-action
      GP100
      SP101
      Redhawk
      Super Redhawk
  Rifles
    10/22
    77/17
    77/22
    77/44
    77/50 Muzzle Loader
    96/17
    96/22
    96/44
    Deerfield Carbine
    M-77 Mark II
    M-77 Mark II Magnum
    Mini-14
    Mini Thirty
    Model 96 Rimfire
    No.1 Single Shot
    Ruger Carbine
  Shotguns
    Gold Label (side-by-side, 12 gauge)
    Red Label (12, 20, 28 gauge)
    Woodside (12 gauge)
Castings
  Aluminum
  Chrome-molybdenum
  Cobalt
  Nickel
  Stainless steel

COMPETITORS

A. Finkl & Sons	GKN Sinter Metals
Beretta USA	Glock
Browning Arms	Marlin Firearms
Colt Defense	Mossberg
Colt's	Remington Arms
Fabbrica D'Armi Pietro	Savage Arms
Beretta	SIG SAUER
Freedom Group	Smith & Wesson Holding
Gibbs Die Casting	Springfield Armory

HISTORICAL FINANCIALS

Company Type: Public

Income Statement

FYE: December 31

	REVENUE ($ mil.)	NET INCOME ($ mil.)	NET PROFIT MARGIN	EMPLOYEES
12/10	255.2	28.3	11.1%	1,160
12/09	271.0	27.5	10.1%	1,150
12/08	181.5	8.7	4.8%	1,150
12/07	156.5	10.3	6.6%	1,100
12/06	167.6	1.1	0.7%	1,100
Annual Growth	**11.1%**	**125.2%**	**—**	**1.3%**

2010 Year-End Financials

Debt ratio: —	No. of shares (mil.): 18.8
Return on equity: 24.7%	Dividends
Cash ($ mil.): 5.1	Yield: 2.2%
Current ratio: 3.16	Payout: 22.7%
Long-term debt ($ mil.): —	Market value ($ mil.): 288.0

	STOCK PRICE ($) FY Close	P/E High/Low		PER SHARE ($) Earnings	Dividends	Book Value
12/10	15.29	12	7	1.46	0.33	6.08
12/09	9.70	11	4	1.42	0.31	5.01
12/08	5.97	22	10	0.43	0.00	3.44
12/07	8.28	49	16	0.46	0.00	3.66
12/06	9.60	272	138	0.04	0.00	3.86
Annual Growth	**12.3%**	**—**	**—**	**145.8%**	**—**	**12.0%**

Sagent Pharmaceuticals

Sagent Pharmaceuticals (formerly Sagent Holding) is imbued with a restorative spirit. Through its subsidiaries, Sagent develops, markets, and sells a range of generic injectable products used by US hospitals, dialysis centers, and other health care organizations. Its products — which include anti-infection drugs, chemotherapy drugs, and critical care treatments used to stabilize cardiac conditions like blood clotting and arrhythmia — consist of more than 20 ready-to-use pre-filled syringes, single and multiple-dose vials, and pre-mix bags. Sagent develops its products using finished drugs supplied by partner pharmaceutical companies in Asia, Europe, and the US. Founded in 2006, Sagent went public through an IPO in 2011.

Sagent filed its public offering in mid-2010 and began trading in April 2011. It changed its name from Sagent Holding to Sagent Pharmaceuticals and reincorporated from the Cayman Islands to the US shortly after its stock began trading. The company intends to use the IPO proceeds (about $92 million) for general corporate purposes, such as funding its working capital, product development, and operating expenses, as well as to potentially expand its collaborations and its commercial infrastructure.

Sagent's attempt to raise public funds is, at its core, driven by its ongoing effort to achieve profitability. The company has enjoyed a healthy rise in its revenues since its inception, but like many relatively young pharmaceutical companies, it has also experienced deep operating losses. High sales and marketing and product development expenses have adversely impacted its bottom line, as have the high costs of the products it sells. Such costs come from Sagent's relationships with its partner companies, mainly because it sources the generic drugs in its products to other drugmakers. This model leaves the company with only a small portion of the revenue it earns.

The company's growth strategy (and effort to obtain profitability) includes ramping up its revenues by growing its partner network and product portfolio. The company recently bolstered its portfolio after launching its Heparin product line with drug partner Gland. Used by surgeons and at dialysis centers to treat blood clots, Heparin — together with Sagent's more established anti-infection drug cefepime — accounted for about half of the company's 2010 revenue. Going forward, the company has plans in the works to add launch 45 additional products in the near future.

Other aspects of its growth strategy include identifying new channels through which to generate income, such as leveraging its sales staff to offer sales and marketing services to pharmaceutical manufacturers. Currently the company provides such services to pharmaceutical manufacturer Actavis and hopes to expand its relationship with the company in the future.

To take some manufacturing operations into its own hands, Sagent has a joint venture with Chinese pharmaceutical company CKT to construct and operate a manufacturing plant in China. The plant is expected to be fully operational by 2012.

Sagent uses a third-party logistics manager to administer the warehousing and shipping of its products from two facilities in California and Tennessee. Sales to wholesale drug distributors Cardinal Health, AmerisourceBergen, and McKesson account for about 85% of revenues.

Prior to the 2011 IPO, the company was owned by a group of institutional investors, several of which still hold stakes in Sagent following the offering. For instance Vivo Ventures Funds holds a 33% stake (down from 42%) and Morgan Stanley & Affiliates owns 16% (down from 20%).

EXECUTIVES

Chairman, President, and CEO, Jeffrey M. Yordon, age 62, $940,650 total compensation
CFO, Ronald E. (Ron) Pauli, age 49, $328,026 total compensation
VP, Project Management, Ravi Malhotra, age 68
VP, Sales and Marketing, Lorin Drake, age 57, $313,146 total compensation
VP, Corporate Development, Anthony Gulczynski, age 53
VP, Secretary and Chief Legal Officer, Michael Logerfo, age 46, $402,792 total compensation
VP, Finance, Dave Hebeda, age 43
VP, Quality, Sheila Moran, age 44
VP, Regulatory Affairs, Tom Moutvic, age 48
SVP, Operations, Albert Patterson, age 67
Auditors: Ernst & Young LLP

LOCATIONS

HQ: Sagent Pharmaceuticals, Inc.
1901 N. Roselle Rd., Ste. 700, Schaumburg, IL 60195
Phone: 847-908-1600   **Fax:** 847-908-1601
Web: www.sagentpharma.com

COMPETITORS

Baxter International
Boehringer Ingelheim
Fresenius
Hikma
Hospira
Pfizer
Sandoz International GmbH

HISTORICAL FINANCIALS

Company Type: Public

Income Statement

FYE: December 31

	REVENUE ($ mil.)	NET INCOME ($ mil.)	NET PROFIT MARGIN	EMPLOYEES
12/10	74.1	(24.5)	—	85
12/09	29.2	(30.5)	—	84
12/08	12.0	(30.5)	—	0
12/07	0.1	(13.2)	—	0
Annual Growth	804.9%	—	—	1.2%

2010 Year-End Financials

Debt ratio: —	No. of shares (mil.): —
Return on equity: —	Dividends
Cash ($ mil.): 34.4	Yield: —
Current ratio: 1.57	Payout: —
Long-term debt ($ mil.): —	Market value ($ mil.): —

salesforce.com

salesforce.com knows the power of good customer relations. The company offers hosted applications that manage customer information for sales, marketing, and customer support, providing clients with a rapidly deployable alternative to buying and maintaining enterprise software. salesforce.com's applications are used by more than 85,000 clients for generating sales leads, maintaining customer information, and tracking customer interactions. The company's applications can be accessed from PCs and mobile devices. salesforce.com's customers come from a variety of industries, including financial services, telecommunications, manufacturing, and entertainment.

salesforce.com continues to bolster its enterprise offerings as part of a push to expand past its core market of small and midsized businesses. The company has also begun to encourage third parties (including customers and independent software vendors) to develop applications that run on salesforce.com's technology platform but are sold separately as modules or add-ons in its AppExchange marketplace.

salesforce.com is embracing and developing products for new technologies such as cloud computing, and it was a pioneer in establishing that the Software-as-a-Service (SaaS) business model could be both profitable and scalable. It also offers clients access to application development code on its Force.com platform, which independent software vendors, IT departments, and software developers use to build custom business applications. The company's revenues and net income have grown substantially each year since fiscal 2007.

In 2011 the company acquired San Francisco-based Heroku for about $212 million in cash. Heroku operated a cloud application platform for Ruby, a programming language for building and deploying Web applications. Also that year the company acquired business contact data provider Jigsaw for about $142 million. The deal expanded salesforce.com's cloud computing offerings and extended its reach into the business-to-business data service market, where Jigsaw has existing partnerships with providers such as D&B and LexisNexis.

The company is also expanding its social networking and collaboration capabilities through the launch of its Chatter product, which enables sharing updates and data within organizations on people, projects, groups, and documents. In 2011 it bolstered its Chatter product with the acquisition of Dimdim, which has created a real-time communication platform used to participate in online meetings, demos, and webinars using a Web browser. salesforce.com plans to combine Dimdim's cloud-based communication capabilities with its Chatter collaboration product in order to provide an integrated social networking product, similar to Facebook, for the enterprise market. Also that year the paid $267 million in cash and $50 million in stock to buy Radian6, a developer of software used by corporate clients to manage and monitor social networking efforts for customer service and sales purposes.

Previous acquisitions include the 2008 purchase of InStranet, a provider of call center software; salesforce.com integrated InStranet's software into its SaaS platform. The deal was part of a broader strategic move by salesforce.com to extend its product set past core CRM applications to encompass areas such as call center management, partner relationship management, and more.

EXECUTIVES

Chairman and CEO, Marc Benioff, age 46, $9,102,420 total compensation
President, Asia-Pacific, Stephen (Steve) McWhirter
President, Latin America, Enrique Perezyera
President and CEO, Japan, Eiji Uda
Chairman and President, EMEA, Stephen Garnett
EVP Customers for Life, Maria Martinez

EVP and CFO, Graham V. Smith, age 51, $2,800,063 total compensation
EVP and General Counsel, David Schellhase, age 47, $1,173,927 total compensation
EVP International Enterprise Sales, Lindsey Armstrong
EVP Global Corporate Sales, Hilarie Koplow-McAdams
EVP Marketing and Alliances, George Hu, age 36, $2,549,684 total compensation
EVP Technology, Parker Harris, age 44, $2,800,063 total compensation
VP Investor Relations, David Havlek
VP Global Corporate Communications, Jane Hynes
VP Worldwide Training and Certifications, Eric Kelleher
VP Platform Development, Chris Fry
CTO, David (Dave) Moellenhoff, age 40
Chief Sales Officer; President, Worldwide Sales and Services, Frank R. Van Veenendaal, age 51, $2,539,184 total compensation
SVP Service Delivery and CIO, Jim Cavalieri, age 40
SVP Corporate Development, John Somorjai
SVP Global Public Policy, Daniel (Dan) Burton
Director Global Recruiting Programs, Scott Morrison
Senior Director Tools and Agile Development, Steve Greene
Chief Customer Officer, Jim Steele, age 55, $1,804,381 total compensation
Chief Adoption Officer, Polly A. Sumner, age 56, $2,196,756 total compensation
SVP Media Sales, Geoffrey A. Dodge, age 51
Chief Marketing Officer, Kendall Collins
Auditors: Ernst & Young LLP

LOCATIONS

HQ: salesforce.com, inc.
1 Market St., Ste. 300, The Landmark, San Francisco, CA 94105
Phone: 415-901-7000   Fax: 415-901-7040
Web: www.salesforce.com

2010 Sales

	$ mil.	% of total
Americas	924	71
Europe	232	18
Asia/Pacific	150	11
Total	**1,306**	**100**

PRODUCTS/OPERATIONS

2010 Sales

	$ mil.	% of total
Subscription & support	1,210	93
Professional service & other	96	7
Total	**1,306**	**100**

Selected Software and Services

Chatter (social networking collaboration tool for business)
Force.com (application development platform)
Salesforce CRM (customer relationship management)

COMPETITORS

CDC Software	NetSuite
Consona CRM	Oracle
FrontRange Solutions	RightNow Technologies
IBM	Sage Software
Infor Global	SAP
KANA	SugarCRM
Microsoft Dynamics	

HISTORICAL FINANCIALS

Company Type: Public

Income Statement

FYE: January 31

	REVENUE ($ mil.)	NET INCOME ($ mil.)	NET PROFIT MARGIN	EMPLOYEES
01/11	1,657.1	64.5	3.9%	5,306
01/10	1,305.6	80.7	6.2%	3,969
01/09	1,076.8	43.4	4.0%	3,566
01/08	748.7	18.4	2.5%	2,606
01/07	497.1	0.5	0.1%	2,070
Annual Growth	**35.1%**	**237.0%**	**—**	**26.5%**

2011 Year-End Financials

Debt ratio: 39.0%
Return on equity: 5.1%
Cash ($ mil.): 424.3
Current ratio: 0.84
Long-term debt ($ mil.): 498.0
No. of shares (mil.): 132.9
Dividends
Yield: —
Payout: —
Market value ($ mil.): 17,162.7

	STOCK PRICE ($) FY Close	P/E High/Low	PER SHARE ($) Earnings	Dividends	Book Value
01/11	129.14	322 130	0.47	0.00	9.60
01/10	63.55	120 40	0.63	0.00	8.21
01/09	26.61	215 59	0.35	0.00	5.47
01/08	51.91	437 248	0.15	0.00	3.79
01/07	43.83	— —	(0.00)	0.00	2.48
Annual Growth	**31.0%**	**— —**	**—**	**—**	**40.2%**

Salix Pharmaceuticals

Salix Pharmaceuticals is a finishing school for drugs. With a focus on treating gastrointestinal ailments, the company prefers to acquire drug candidates nearing commercial viability. It then takes them through the final development stages and brings them to market. The company's marketed products include Apriso and Colazal (for ulcerative colitis), Pepcid (gastric ulcers and acid reflux), and Xifaxan (an antibiotic for travelers' diarrhea and liver troubles). Other products include colonoscopy preparatory bowel purgatives MoviPrep, Osmo-Prep, and Visicol. Its late-stage candidates include both new drugs and new uses for existing drugs. Salix's sales and marketing team primarily targets US gastroenterologists.

Salix avoids the riskier, capital intensive process of early-stage research by sticking strictly to late stage commercialization and marketing. It also sidesteps the expense of maintaining manufacturing facilities and relies on third-party manufacturers to produce its materials.

The company's biggest seller is Xifaxan, and the firm is investing heavily in researching and marketing the antibiotic for additional uses. Salix also struck a collaborative agreement with Lupin in 2009 to help develop and commercialize that company's bioadhesive formulation of gastrointestinal antibiotic rifaximin. Xifaxan is a version of rifaximin and Salix is testing it for use in a variety of conditions; the company hopes the newer formulation will offer better absorption rates. In 2010 Xifaxan's use was extended (beyond its first travelers' diarrhea indication) when it was approved by the FDA for treatment of hepatic encephalopathy, a disorder caused by chronic liver failure. It's still being tested for the treatment of irritable bowel syndrome. Salix's former bestseller, Colazal, lost

patent protection and began facing generic competition in 2008.

To keep its operations nimble in the face of future additional patent expirations, Salix depends on regular shopping trips to keep its pipeline well stocked. For instance, in 2010 Salix paid $4 million to acquire the rights to develop Lumacan, a fluorescent agent that it hopes will make colon cancer lesions easier to see during colonoscopy screenings.

The company started 2011 with a bang by licensing the worldwide rights (except in Japan) to constipation treatment Relistor from Progenics Pharmaceuticals in a deal worth up to $350 million. Under terms of the agreement, Salix paid $60 million upfront and agreed to sales-related milestone payments of up to $200 million and development-related milestone payments of some $90 million for the drug, which is used to treat constipation related to opioid pain killers. Salix will also pay Progenics royalties on US product sales and 60% of revenue received from non-US sales, except in Japan where Relistor is already licensed by Ono Pharmaceutical.

Later in 2011 Salix made another bold acquisition move when it agreed to purchase private US drugmaker Oceana Therapeutics for some $300 million. The purchase will add gastroenterology and urology therapeutics, including fecal incontinence medication Solesta and Deflux, a treatment for vesicoureteral reflux (a malformation of the bladder in children).

Felix and Julian Baker represent about 10% of Salix's shares through Baker Bros. Investments, Baker Brothers Life Sciences, and Baker/Tisch Investments.

EXECUTIVES

Chairman, Thomas W. (Tom) D'Alonzo, age 67
President, CEO, and Director, Carolyn J. Logan, age 62, $2,335,579 total compensation
EVP Finance and Administration and CFO, Adam C. Derbyshire, age 45, $963,504 total compensation
EVP Research and Development and Chief Development Officer, William P. (Bill) Forbes, age 49, $793,192 total compensation
Associate VP Investor Relations and Corporate Communications, G. Michael Freeman
Auditors: PricewaterhouseCoopers LLP

LOCATIONS

HQ: Salix Pharmaceuticals, Ltd.
1700 Perimeter Park Dr., Morrisville, NC 27560-8404
Phone: 919-862-1000   Fax: 919-862-1095
Web: www.salix.com

PRODUCTS/OPERATIONS

2009 Sales

	$ mil.	% of total
Xifaxan	117.9	51
Purgatives	76.3	33
Inflammatory bowel disease	5.8	2
Other	32.8	14
Total	**232.8**	**100**

COMPETITORS

Abbott Labs	Prometheus Labs
Aptalis Pharma	Ranbaxy
Bayer AG	Pharmaceuticals
Ferndale Laboratories	Shire
GlaxoSmithKline	Warner Chilcott
Pfizer	

HISTORICAL FINANCIALS
Company Type: Public

Income Statement
FYE: December 31

	REVENUE ($ mil.)	NET INCOME ($ mil.)	NET PROFIT MARGIN	EMPLOYEES
12/10	337.0	(27.1)	—	390
12/09	232.9	(43.6)	—	395
12/08	178.8	(47.0)	—	280
12/07	235.8	8.2	3.5%	270
12/06	208.5	31.5	15.1%	240
Annual Growth	12.8%	—	—	12.9%

2010 Year-End Financials

Debt ratio: 80.7%
Return on equity: —
Cash ($ mil.): 518.0
Current ratio: 5.47
Long-term debt ($ mil.): 324.5

No. of shares (mil.): 58.1
Dividends
  Yield: —
  Payout: —
Market value ($ mil.): 2,730.3

	STOCK PRICE ($) FY Close	P/E High/Low		PER SHARE ($) Earnings	Dividends	Book Value
12/10	46.96	—	—	(0.47)	0.00	6.91
12/09	25.39	—	—	(0.88)	0.00	6.58
12/08	8.83	—	—	(0.98)	0.00	5.22
12/07	7.88	96	44	0.17	0.00	6.15
12/06	12.17	29	15	0.65	0.00	5.92
Annual Growth	40.2%	—	—	—	—	4.0%

Satcon Technology

Satcon Technology moved from motion control to clean technology. The company makes power inverters for photovoltaic solar energy systems and fuel cells, which are typically used by alternative energy-producing electric utilities and industrial manufacturers. Satcon also makes power converters that are used in electric ships and for military applications. In addition, the company offers its customers services such as systems design, management, and monitoring. Customers include Akeena Solar, BP Solar, EDF Energies Nouvelles, Honeywell, IBERDROLA, Johnson Controls, NASA, Samsung, the US Department of Defense, and the US Department of Energy. The company gets about three-quarters of its sales in the US.

Satcon sold its Applied Technology business unit at the outset of 2010 for about $1 million in cash. With the sale, the company completed its transformation from a diversified manufacturer to one focused on utility-scale power products for the renewable energy market.

In 2008 Satcon sold the assets of its SatCon Electronics subsidiary, its semiconductors and motors divisions, to Spectrum Control for nearly $6 million in cash. The high-performance motors and electric drivetrains are used in applications such as industrial automation and machine tool motors. Satcon sold the product lines to focus on its power conditioning offerings in the fuel cell and photovoltaic power markets.

As part of its growth strategy, the company plans to develop new products and technologies, as well as form new marketing, distribution, and manufacturing partnerships. Satcon sells its products and services in the US and abroad through its direct sales force and independent distributors.

Despite all the changes in its product focus and lines of business, Satcon has been unprofitable for the past decade and has an accumulated deficit of nearly $232 million.

Satcon Technology has facilities in Canada, China, the Czech Republic, and the US.

HISTORY

David Eisenhaure and fellow MIT engineers founded Satcon Technology in 1985. The company originally developed products for NASA, including satellite control systems (the "sat" and "con" in "Satcon"), and expanded into defense projects. However, as the end of the Cold War brought military budget cuts in the late 1980s, Satcon began to market its technology commercially.

Satcon sought government and commercial contracts to develop cutting-edge technology for commercial uses. The company relied heavily on an electric car project with Chrysler (later DaimlerChrysler and now Chrysler again), but ran into delays in 1995 and posted its first loss of the 1990s (preceding a string of losses that continued throughout the rest of the decade). Chrysler canceled the project in 1996, costing Satcon almost $4 million.

In 1997 Satcon bought K&D MagMotor (motors for factory automation) and veered toward semiconductor manufacturing technology with its purchase of Film Microelectronics (thin-film substrates and hybrid integrated circuits). Satcon unveiled a line of brushless motors designed for remote-control deep-sea vehicles in 1998.

The US Department of Energy awarded a $10 million contract to Satcon in 1999 to develop components for electric vehicles. That year the company broadened its product line by acquiring Ling Electronics (shaker vibration test equipment and power converters) from Mechanical Technology, the power electronics division of Northrop Grumman, and Lighthouse Software (industrial machine automation software). In 2000 Satcon spun off its Beacon Power Corporation subsidiary, but retained 30% of Beacon Power. The following year Satcon made a 5-million-share distribution of its Beacon Power stock to its stockholders.

In 2002 the company acquired Sipex's hybrid assembly operations. Satcon sold its 11% interest in Beacon Power in 2003.

In 2004 and again in 2005, the company sold shares to raise capital. In late 2005 Satcon sold its shaker and amplifier product lines to QualMark for around $2 million.

Founder David Eisenhaure stepped aside as president and CEO in 2008; he remained on the board as a director and received the honorary title of chairman emeritus. Steve Rhoades, the COO of Advanced Energy Industries, succeeded Eisenhaure as president and CEO.

EXECUTIVES

Chairman, John M. Carroll, age 64
President, CEO, and Director, Charles S. (Steve) Rhoades, age 50, $1,522,844 total compensation
CFO, Donald R. (Don) Peck
EVP, CFO, and Treasurer, Aaron Gomolak
EVP Worldwide Sales and Marketing, Peter (Pete) DeGraff, age 41
VP Sales, Darryl Parker
VP Engineering and CTO, Leo F. Casey, $366,526 total compensation
VP Administration and Human Resources and Secretary, Daniel E. (Dan) Gladkowski, age 61, $263,646 total compensation
Chief Accounting Officer and Controller, John W. Peacock
Senior Director Product Management, Steven Klosterman
Investor Relations, Leah Gibson
Senior Director Field Marketing, Michael Levi
Auditors: Vitale, Caturano & Company, Ltd.

LOCATIONS

HQ: Satcon Technology Corporation
27 Drydock Ave., Boston, MA 02210
Phone: 617-897-2400   **Fax:** 617-897-2401
Web: www.satcon.com

2009 Sales

	$ mil.	% of total
US	39.7	76
China	4.3	8
Czech Republic	3.3	6
Belgium	2.4	5
Other countries	2.8	5
Total	**52.5**	**100**

PRODUCTS/OPERATIONS

COMPETITORS

ABB	C&D Technologies
Advanced Energy Industries	Powell Industries
ALSTOM	Power-One
American Superconductor	Schneider Electric
Beacon Power	Siemens Corp.
	SMA Solar Technology

HISTORICAL FINANCIALS
Company Type: Public

Income Statement
FYE: December 31

	REVENUE ($ mil.)	NET INCOME ($ mil.)	NET PROFIT MARGIN	EMPLOYEES
12/10	173.3	(11.8)	—	430
12/09	52.5	(29.9)	—	268
12/08	62.5	(13.2)	—	278
12/07	56.6	(17.8)	—	333
12/06	33.8	(19.8)	—	251
Annual Growth	50.5%	—	—	14.4%

2010 Year-End Financials

Debt ratio: —
Return on equity: —
Cash ($ mil.): 30.1
Current ratio: 1.82
Long-term debt ($ mil.): —

No. of shares (mil.): 117.9
Dividends
  Yield: —
  Payout: —
Market value ($ mil.): 530.6

	STOCK PRICE ($) FY Close	P/E High/Low		PER SHARE ($) Earnings	Dividends	Book Value
12/10	4.50	—	—	(0.25)	0.00	0.41
12/09	2.82	—	—	(0.57)	0.00	(0.20)
12/08	1.55	—	—	(0.34)	0.00	(0.18)
12/07	1.65	—	—	(0.66)	0.00	0.09
12/06	1.14	—	—	(0.50)	0.00	(0.06)
Annual Growth	41.0%	—	—	—	—	—

SCBT Financial

SCBT Financial is the holding company for South Carolina Bank and Trust and South Carolina Bank and Trust of the Piedmont (both banks are also known as SCBT), which operate about 80 branches throughout the Palmetto state. The company also owns North Carolina Bank and Trust, or NCBT, which has three locations in the Charlotte area. Serving retail and business customers, the banks provide deposit accounts, loans, and mortgages, as well as trust and investment services. Approximately half of the company's loan portfolio is devoted to commercial mortgages; consumer real estate loans are almost one quarter.

SCBT Financial entered northern Georgia in 2010 when it acquired the failed Community Bank & Trust; the deal added more than 30 locations, most of them inside supermarkets. SCBT acquired another failed bank the following year, Habersham Bank, bringing another eight locations in Georgia. Both transactions were made with assistance from the FDIC. The acquisitions, particularly that of Community Bank & Trust, helped SCBT achieve record net income in 2010, though its number of nonperforming assets continues to rise. The company acquired another failed bank, South Carolina-based BankMeridian, in 2011.

In addition to the FDIC-assisted deals, SCBT Financial is growing by opening new branches and loan production offices. It is also seeking out other whole bank acquisitions.

EXECUTIVES

Chairman, SCBT Financial and South Carolina Bank and Trust, Robert R. Horger, age 60
President, CEO, and Director; CEO, South Carolina Bank and Trust, Robert R. Hill Jr., age 44, $718,125 total compensation
President, Wealth Management Group, Todd Harward
President, South Carolina Bank and Trust, John F. Windley, age 58, $326,432 total compensation
President, Northern Banking Group, Thomas S. Camp, age 59, $340,637 total compensation
President, Western Banking Group, Greg A. Lapointe
EVP and CFO, Donald E. (Donnie) Pickett
EVP and Treasurer, Richard C. Mathis, age 60, $354,714 total compensation
Vice Chairman, SCBT Financial and South Carolina Bank and Trust, Dwight W. Frierson, age 54
SEVP and COO, John C. Pollok, age 45, $440,950 total compensation
SEVP, Manager Retail Banking, and Division Head, Lowcountry and Orangeburg Regions, Dane H. Murray, age 61
SEVP and Chief Risk Officer, Joe E. Burns, age 56
Secretary, Renee R. Brooks
Auditors: Dixon Hughes PLLC

LOCATIONS

HQ: SCBT Financial Corporation
520 Gervais St., Columbia, SC 29201
Phone: 803-771-2265   **Fax:** 803-531-0524
Web: www.scbandt.com

PRODUCTS/OPERATIONS

2010 Sales

	$ mil.	% of total
Interest		
Loans, including fees	143.5	49
Taxable investment securities	10.0	3
Other	1.9	1
Noninterest		
Gain on acquisition	98.1	34
Service charges on deposit accounts	21.3	7
Bankcard services	9.0	3
Mortgage banking	6.6	2
Other	2.7	1
Total	**293.1**	**100**

COMPETITORS

Bank of America	First Financial
Bank of South Carolina	Holdings
BB&T	Regions Financial
First Citizens	Security Federal
Bancorporation	

HISTORICAL FINANCIALS

Company Type: Public

Income Statement

FYE: December 31

	ASSETS ($ mil.)	NET INCOME ($ mil.)	INCOME AS % OF ASSETS	EMPLOYEES
12/10	3,594.8	51.9	1.4%	1,015
12/09	2,702.2	13.6	0.5%	700
12/08	2,766.7	15.8	0.6%	692
12/07	2,597.2	21.6	0.8%	701
12/06	2,178.4	19.8	0.9%	634
Annual Growth	**13.3%**	**27.2%**	**—**	**12.5%**

2010 Year-End Financials

Equity as % of assets: 9.18%	Dividends
Return on assets: 1.4%	Yield: 2.1%
Return on equity: 15.7%	Payout: 16.7%
Long-term debt ($ mil.): 47.0	Market value ($ mil.): 419.0
No. of shares (mil.): 12.8	Sales ($ mil.): 293.1

	STOCK PRICE ($) FY Close	P/E High/Low		PER SHARE ($) Earnings	Dividends	Book Value
12/10	32.75	10	7	4.08	0.68	25.79
12/09	27.69	46	22	0.74	0.68	22.20
12/08	34.50	30	17	1.52	0.51	21.79
12/07	31.67	17	12	2.32	0.67	23.35
12/06	39.74	20	15	2.05	0.65	17.69
Annual Growth	**(4.7%)**	**—**	**—**	**18.8%**	**1.1%**	**9.9%**

SciClone

This SciClone won't take you to Oz, but it has taken its drugs to China. The drug firm's flagship product Zadaxin is approved to treat hepatitis B in some 30 countries, including China, its primary market. Zadaxin also has uses in additional viral vaccines and cancer treatments. The drug has yet to receive the regulatory green light, however, in the world's two largest drug markets — the US and the European Union (EU). SciClone is working with development partner Sigma-Tau to gain marketing approval in the US and EU; the company also wants to expand the use of the drug to include additional conditions. In the meantime, SciClone is seeking to commercialize additional products in the core Chinese market.

In 2011 the company made progress on its expansion goals by acquiring China-based NovaMed Pharmaceuticals in a $62 million cash and stock transaction (plus potential future milestone payments of up to $43 million). The purchase added 18 commercial products in the Chinese market, including cancer, cardiovascular, neurology, and urology medicines, and broadened SciClone's existing sales force in the country.

Zadaxin is approved in China as a treatment for hepatitis B and as a vaccine adjuvant. SciClone's own sales force markets the drug to doctors and hospitals there. The drug also has marketing approval in numerous other countries for hepatitis B and C and as a vaccine and chemotherapy adju-

vant, primarily in Asia, Eastern Europe, Latin America, and the Middle East, where distributors handle sales and marketing activities.

In addition to earning FDA and European approval for Zadaxin, the company aims to develop its product pipeline. Lead drug candidate SCV-07 is a potential treatment for viral infectious diseases including hepatitis C, as well as oral mucositis in cancer patients. Another candidate, DC Bead, is under development to treat liver cancer and is under regulatory review in the Chinese market. SciClone intends to further expand on its presence in China by in-licensing or acquiring new products to market there.

The company was also developing investigational cancer drug RP101, until phase II clinical trials of that drug were discontinued in late 2009. The suspension of the trials was a major blow to the company and led to a 17% reduction in its workforce, primarily in research and development. SciClone stopped the trial of RP101, which was being tested to treat mid-stage pancreatic cancer, upon the recommendation of a safety panel.

Development partner Sigma-Tau Finanziaria owns about 20% of the company.

EXECUTIVES

Chairman, Jon S. Saxe, age 74
President, CEO, and Director, Friedhelm Blobel, age 62, $1,380,572 total compensation
President and Managing Director, SciClone Pharmaceuticals International, Hans P. Schmid, age 59, $581,292 total compensation
VP Business Development, Jeffery Lange
VP Legal Affairs, Eric J. Hoechstetter
VP Regulatory Affairs and Quality Assurance, Craig Halverson
SVP Scientific Affairs and Chief Scientific Officer, Cynthia W. Tuthill
SVP Medical Affairs and Chief Medical Officer, Israel Rios, age 64, $513,114 total compensation
SVP and CFO, Gary S. Titus, age 51, $43,390 total compensation
Assistant VP Finance, Ivan B. Hui, age 48, $318,736 total compensation
Auditors: Ernst & Young LLP

LOCATIONS

HQ: SciClone Pharmaceuticals, Inc.
950 Tower Lane, Ste. 900, Foster City, CA 94404-2125
Phone: 650-358-3456   **Fax:** 650-358-3469
Web: www.sciclone.com

2009 Sales

	$ mil.	% of total
China	69.7	96
Other countries	2.7	4
Total	**72.4**	**100**

COMPETITORS

Amgen	Immtech
Bristol-Myers Squibb	Intarcia Therapeutics
Enzon	Merck
Gilead Sciences	Roche Holding
GlaxoSmithKline	Three Rivers
Hemispherx BioPharma	Pharmaceuticals
Idenix Pharmaceuticals	

HISTORICAL FINANCIALS

Company Type: Public

Income Statement

FYE: December 31

	REVENUE ($ mil.)	NET INCOME ($ mil.)	NET PROFIT MARGIN	EMPLOYEES
12/10	85.1	21.1	24.8%	261
12/09	72.4	11.9	16.4%	223
12/08	54.1	(8.3)	—	227
12/07	37.1	(9.9)	—	200
12/06	32.7	0.7	2.1%	166
Annual Growth	27.0%	134.3%	—	12.0%

2010 Year-End Financials

Debt ratio: 3.0%
Return on equity: 25.7%
Cash ($ mil.): 53.0
Current ratio: 7.91
Long-term debt ($ mil.): 2.5

No. of shares (mil.): 48.0
Dividends
Yield: —
Payout: —
Market value ($ mil.): 200.7

	STOCK PRICE ($) FY Close	P/E High	P/E Low	PER SHARE ($) Earnings	Dividends	Book Value
12/10	4.18	10	5	0.43	0.00	1.71
12/09	2.33	21	3	0.25	0.00	1.22
12/08	0.74	—	—	(0.18)	0.00	0.88
12/07	2.22	—	—	(0.22)	0.00	1.02
12/06	3.22	208	99	0.02	0.00	1.19
Annual Growth	6.7%	—	—	115.3%	—	9.5%

SciQuest

SciQuest helps organizations get closer to their suppliers. The company's on-demand procurement software helps customers reduce costs and more closely monitor their spending. Its SciQuest Supplier Network enables clients to tap into a marketplace of more than 30,000 different suppliers and includes tools for negotiating discounts, automating orders, and managing contracts. The company serves customers in a broad range of industries such as life sciences, pharmaceuticals, consumer goods, energy and utilities, food and beverage, health care, and education. SciQuest was acquired in 2004 by investment firm Trinity Ventures, changing the public company's status to private. SciQuest went public again in 2010.

The company plans to use the proceeds from its IPO to fund potential acquisitions, international expansion, and product development in the future. It also plans to redeem about $35.5 million worth of outstanding shares of preferred stock. SciQuest has steadily grown its revenues while controlling costs over the last three years, with fiscal 2009 becoming its first profitable year since 2005.

In late 2010 SciQuest bought supplier management and sourcing software maker AECsoft USA for about $13 million. The deal was intended to improve the functionality of SciQuest's electronic procurement tools.

SciQuest's hosted software is available in tailored versions for specific industries, including the vertical markets it has strategically targeted: life sciences, higher education, health care, and government agencies. Its more than 150 clients include Biogen, GlaxoSmithKline, and Merck. Focused on building its presence in the academic market, SciQuest has inked deals with The University of Michigan, The University of Notre Dame, The University of Pennsylvania, and Yale University.

SciQuest clients subscribe to its offerings (and pay initial implementation service fees) under multi-year contracts that are typically three to five years. The company boasts a customer renewal rate of 94% and has had success in upgrading clients to higher-priced offerings when they renew. SciQuest's products can be integrated with other existing enterprise software so that data can easily be shared when procurement, accounting, and settlement functions are managed.

EXECUTIVES

Chairman, Noel J. Fenton, age 72
CFO, Rudy C. Howard, age 53
President, CEO, and Director, Stephen J. Wiehe, age 47, $620,543 total compensation
VP Global Professional Services and Supplier Enablement, Ralph Mazza
VP Marketing and Strategy, C. Gamble Heffernan, age 49, $387,511 total compensation
VP Finance, Jennifer G. Kaelin, age 39, $294,964 total compensation
VP Business Development, Suzanne Miglucci
VP Human Resources, Ann Thomas
COO, James B. (Jamie) Duke, age 47, $451,507 total compensation
SVP Worldwide Sales, Jeffrey A. (Jeff) Martini, age 52, $456,569 total compensation
Director Practice, Tony Im
Director Procurement Strategies, Judith C. Smith
Sales Director, Germany and France, Melanie Kalms
Sales Director, EMEA, David Rimmington
Auditors: Ernst & Young LLP

LOCATIONS

HQ: SciQuest, Inc.
6501 Weston Pkwy., Ste. 200, Cary, NC 27513
Phone: 919-659-2100 **Fax:** 919-659-2199
Web: www.sciquest.com

PRODUCTS/OPERATIONS

Selected Products

SciQuest Supplier Network (hosted network for procurement management)

COMPETITORS

Ariba	Omnicell
AspenTech	Oracle
BravoSolution US	Perfect Commerce
ePlus	SAP
Global Healthcare Exchange	SupplyCore

HISTORICAL FINANCIALS

Company Type: Public

Income Statement

FYE: December 31

	REVENUE ($ mil.)	NET INCOME ($ mil.)	NET PROFIT MARGIN	EMPLOYEES
12/10	42.5	1.7	4.0%	192
12/09	36.2	19.4	53.6%	158
12/08	29.8	1.1	3.7%	0
12/07	20.1	(5.0)	—	0
12/03	6.6	(16.6)	—	89
Annual Growth	30.5%	—	—	11.6%

2010 Year-End Financials

Debt ratio: —
Return on equity: 5.1%
Cash ($ mil.): 17.5
Current ratio: 1.39
Long-term debt ($ mil.): —

No. of shares (mil.): 20.5
Dividends
Yield: —
Payout: —
Market value ($ mil.): 267.1

	STOCK PRICE ($) FY Close	P/E High	P/E Low	PER SHARE ($) Earnings	Dividends	Book Value
12/10	13.01	—	—	(0.02)	0.00	1.67
Annual Growth	—	—	—	—	—	—

Seattle Genetics

To heck with verbs, Seattle Genetics is conjugating antibodies and drugs to fight cancer. The company's technologies use genetically engineered monoclonal antibodies (MAbs, or single source proteins) to trigger cell death in some cancers, but when they can't do it alone, Seattle Genetics pairs them up with drugs using its Antibody-Drug Conjugate (ADC) technology for a one-two punch. Its first product, Adcetris, gained FDA approval in 2011 for treatment of lymphoma in specific patient categories. With partner Millennium Pharmaceuticals, the company is working to expand Adcetris' indications. Additionally, Seattle Genetics licenses its ADC technology to larger drugmakers to develop their own new cancer therapies.

The approval of Adcetris (brentuximab) in mid-2011 was limited to very specific patient categories — Hodgkin lymphoma patients that have failed to respond to cell transplants or multiple chemotherapy regimens, and patients with anaplastic large cell lymphoma (ALCL) after at least one unsuccessful round of chemotherapy. However, Seattle Genetics is working diligently to expand the drug's approved uses; Adcetris is also in clinical trials for conditions including certain types of residual Hodgkin lymphoma and relapsed or refractory non-Hodgkin lymphomas. It teamed up with Millennium in 2009 to help fund the advancement of Adcetris through clinical trial and commercialization stages.

Other candidates under development include ASG-5ME, which is being researched and developed with Astellas Pharma subsidiary Agensys for pancreatic and prostate cancer, and SGN-75, which is in trials for metastatic renal cell carcinoma and non-Hodgkin lymphoma. In addition to its clinical candidates, the firm has several preclinical products in its pipeline. In 2010 the company ended a collaboration with Genentech that was focused on developing its SGN-40 candidate, dacetuzumab, and the program has since been halted. However, Seattle Genetics regularly looks to partner with other biotech firms to carry its candidates further.

Seattle Genetics' ADC technology involves attaching a highly potent drug to a MAb, which delivers and releases the drug inside the tumor cell. The technology is believed to reduce some of the side-effects related to chemotherapy treatments. The company's other development platform is its Sugar Enhanced Antibody (SEA) technology. Using SEA, researchers use modified sugar to create antibodies that may be potent enough to fight cancer on their own.

Outlicensing deals for the ADC technology are germane to Seattle Genetics' marketing strategy and have netted the company most of its annual revenue figures to date. Licensees have included Bayer, Celldex, Daiichi Sankyo, and GlaxoSmithKline. In early 2011 the firm additionally licensed rights to use its ADC technology to Pfizer for about $8 million, plus the opportunity to earn more than $200 million in additional milestone payments.

EXECUTIVES

Chairman, President, and CEO, Clay B. Siegall, age 50, $2,073,634 total compensation
CFO, Todd E. Simpson, age 50, $933,716 total compensation
EVP Process Sciences, Morris Z. Rosenberg, age 51, $830,172 total compensation
EVP Commercial, Bruce J. Seeley, age 47
EVP Technical Operations, Vaughn B. Himes, age 50
VP Managed Markets, Darren Cline
VP Legal Affairs and Compliance and General Counsel, Kirk D. Schumacher
VP Marketing, Chris Boerner
VP Preclinical Therapeutics, Iqbal S. Grewal
VP Chemistry and Distinguished Fellow, Peter D. Senter
VP Sales, Charles R. (Chip) Romp
VP Clinical Affairs, Eric Sievers
COO, Eric L. Dobmeier, age 42, $1,144,505 total compensation
Chief Medical Officer, Thomas C. (Tom) Reynolds, age 52, $1,359,661 total compensation
SVP Regulatory Affairs, Elaine Waller, age 59
SVP Human Resources, Christopher (Chris) Pawlowicz
SVP Research and Translational Medicine, Jonathan Drachman
Director Corporate Communications, Peggy Pinkston
Auditors: PricewaterhouseCoopers LLP

LOCATIONS

HQ: Seattle Genetics, Inc.
21823 30th Dr. SE, Bothell, WA 98021
Phone: 425-527-4000 **Fax:** 425-527-4001
Web: www.seattlegenetics.com

COMPETITORS

Allos Therapeutics	ImmunoGen
Amgen	Micromet
Bayer AG	Millennium: The Takeda
Biogen Idec	Oncology Company
Bristol-Myers Squibb	Novartis Corporation
Celgene	Onyx Pharmaceuticals
Cephalon	Pfizer
Eisai	Sanofi
Genentech	Xencor

HISTORICAL FINANCIALS

Company Type: Public

Income Statement

FYE: December 31

	REVENUE ($ mil.)	NET INCOME ($ mil.)	NET PROFIT MARGIN	EMPLOYEES
12/10	107.5	(66.3)	—	348
12/09	52.0	(81.7)	—	289
12/08	35.2	(85.5)	—	261
12/07	22.4	(48.9)	—	189
12/06	10.0	(36.0)	—	151
Annual Growth	**81.1%**	**—**	**—**	**23.2%**

2010 Year-End Financials

Debt ratio: —	No. of shares (mil.): 101.6
Return on equity: —	Dividends
Cash ($ mil.): 21.1	Yield: —
Current ratio: 5.55	Payout: —
Long-term debt ($ mil.): —	Market value ($ mil.): 1,519.0

	STOCK PRICE ($) FY Close	P/E High/Low	PER SHARE ($) Earnings	Dividends	Book Value
12/10	14.95	— —	(0.66)	0.00	1.59
12/09	10.16	— —	(0.90)	0.00	2.05
12/08	8.94	— —	(1.09)	0.00	0.92
12/07	11.40	— —	(0.80)	0.00	0.80
12/06	5.33	— —	(0.74)	0.00	1.73
Annual Growth	**29.4%**	**— —**	**—**	**—**	**(2.1%)**

Semtech

If Semtech's products seem highly technical, it's because they are. Not to be confused with semiconductor research consortium SEMATECH, Semtech makes analog and mixed-signal semiconductors used by manufacturers of computer, communications, and industrial electronics. The company's chips are used for power management, circuit protection, transmission, and other functions in a variety of devices, including cellular phones and base stations, notebook and desktop PCs, network transmission equipment, and automated test equipment. It counts Apple, HP, Intel, LG Electronics, Samsung, and Sony among its customers. Semtech generates more than half of its sales in the Asia/Pacific region.

The semiconductor industry is highly cyclical, and thanks to the global recession, it's in a prolonged downturn due to lower sales of consumer electronics. Semtech competes with many larger semiconductor manufacturers, and must contend with a small number of customers. Most of its sales go into big end-use markets: cell phones, desktop computers, and notebook computers. Sales dropped 3% in fiscal 2010, but the company is projecting fiscal 2011 revenues to increase about 25%.

Targeting the communications infrastructure market, Semtech acquired Sierra Monolithics for about $180 million in cash, plus employee stock options and equity incentives, in 2009. Sierra Monolithics makes high performance analog chips and microwave modules for the wireline and wireless communications and defense industries. The company sells to major telecom OEMs and optical module customers, specializing in wireless networking access equipment and defense applications. The acquisition boosts Semtech's portfolio of wireless communications offerings and adds a business that is growing by 20%-30% a year.

With its fabless manufacturing model, the company doesn't make its own chips. Semtech relies on nine third-party manufacturers in China, Malaysia, the Philippines, and the US for production. To reduce risk, Semtech balances sales among the computer, communications, consumer, and industrial markets.

In late 2010 the company agreed to pay $20 million to settle a class-action lawsuit over allegations of backdating securities options. The settlement would resolve claims against the company and its current and former officers and directors. No parties admit any wrongdoing as part of the proposed settlement.

Semtech phased out its line of what it calls human input devices — touch-screen and touchpad controllers, pointing stick devices, and battery management circuits it acquired in its 1999 acquisition of USAR Systems. The company made a strategic decision against investing more R&D on those products.

HISTORY

Founded in 1960, Semtech was the second semiconductor startup in as many years for Gustav Franzen and Harvey Stump. It went public in 1967. Catering to military customers enabled Semtech to reach $15 million in sales by the end of its second decade. When the price of silver, one of Semtech's raw materials, rose tenfold in 1979 and 1980, the panicked company switched to copper, which didn't work as well. Facing mounting troubles, in 1985 Semtech tapped former Silicon General executive John Poe as CEO (replacing Franzen, who was on vacation at the time).

Poe cut costs, raised capital, and brought in new management; by the early 1990s he had moved Semtech into commercial markets. The acquisitions of Lambda Semiconductors in 1990 and Modupower in 1992 boosted the company's power regulation business.

Diversified industrial firm Allegheny Teledyne, which had once owned nearly a fourth of Semtech, sold most of its stake in 1997 (Allegheny Teledyne's operations were sold off separately in 1999). That year Semtech began providing chips to the fast-growing automated test equipment market when it bought Edge Semiconductor.

Semtech made two acquisitions in 1999: Practical Sciences, a designer of high-speed communications components and analog integrated circuits (ICs), and USAR Systems, a maker of input device and systems management ICs for PCs and portable electronics. In 2002 Semtech announced plans to close its last wafer fabrication plant as part of its strategy to outsource all wafer manufacturing operations.

COO Jason Carlson succeeded Poe as CEO in 2003. Poe remained chairman. In 2004 the company named Tony Giraudo as COO; Giraudo joined Semtech from TelASIC Communications, where he was CEO, and previously worked at Atmel, Honeywell, IBM, and NCR.

In 2005 the company acquired XEMICS, a Swiss developer of ultralow-power analog, radio-frequency, and digital ICs, for $43 million in cash, plus future earnout payments. XEMICS became Semtech's Wireless and Sensing Products business unit.

After two years Carlson left the board and the company. Poe stepped in as interim CEO. Mohan Maheswaran, formerly an EVP/GM at Intersil, was named president and CEO in 2006. Later that year, Poe was succeeded as chairman by Rockell Hankin, who previously served as Semtech's vice chairman for eight years and was on the board since 1988.

John Poe stated his intention to resign from the board in 2006, effective once Semtech completed its restatement of historical financial results. The company was reviewing its past practices in granting stock options, partly during a period when Poe served as CEO. He previously took a leave of absence from the board to avoid the appearance of a conflict in interests while the board investigated option granting practices. Poe's resignation finally took effect in 2007.

EXECUTIVES

Chairman, Rockell N. (Rock) Hankin, age 64
President, CEO, and Director, Mohan R. Maheswaran, age 47, $3,001,804 total compensation
VP Worldwide Operations, Clemente (Clay) Beltran, age 41
VP Information Technology and CIO, Jonathan Hahn
VP and CFO, Emeka Chukwu, age 48, $1,140,609 total compensation

VP Worldwide Sales and Marketing, James J. Kim, age 54, $1,065,597 total compensation

VP and General Manager Power Management Product Group, Simon Prutton, age 47

VP Marketing, Sameer Vuyyuru

VP Worldwide Sales Operation, Distribution and Power Discretes, Jose Vargas, age 54

VP Human Resources, Kenneth J. Barry, age 63

VP Test and Measurement Products, Mark R. Drucker, age 47

VP Business, Portable Products, Edward Y. (Eddie) Yeow, age 47

VP Engineering, Power Management Products, Lawrence A. (Larry) King, age 52

VP Strategy and Business Development, R. Nejo Necar, age 68

VP Quality, Reliability, and Technology, Kevin P. Caffey, age 52

SVP Business Development and CTO, J. Michael (Mike) Wilson, age 55

Marketing Director, Protection Products, Rick Hansen

Investor Relations, Chris Rogers

Vice President, General Counsel, and Secretary, Randall H. Holliday, age 61

SVP and General Manager, Advanced Communication and Sensing Products, Alain Dantec, age 61, $833,539 total compensation

SVP and General Manager, Protection Products, Jeffrey T. (Jeff) Pohlman, age 61, $990,647 total compensation

Marketing Communications Manager, Terry Sears

Director Advanced Communications, Stewart Kelly

Director Protection Products, Tom Dugan

Auditors: Ernst & Young LLP

LOCATIONS

HQ: Semtech Corporation
200 Flynn Rd., Camarillo, CA 93012-8790
Phone: 805-498-2111 **Fax:** 805-498-3804
Web: www.semtech.com

2010 Sales

	$ mil.	% of total
Asia/Pacific	165.9	58
North America	72.8	25
Europe	47.8	17
Total	**286.5**	**100**

PRODUCTS/OPERATIONS

2010 Sales

	$ mil.	% of total
High-end consumer	113.2	40
Industrial	66.4	23
Communications	66	23
Computer	40.9	14
Total	**286.5**	**100**

Selected Products

Standard
 Advanced communication (chips for fiber-optic transmission and for timing and synchronization functions in local area networks, wide area networks, and cellular phone base stations)
 High performance (pin electronics, timing, clock distribution, and parametric measurement products used in automated test equipment instrumentation)
 Power management (linear regulators, switching voltage regulators, combination regulators, and smart regulators)
 Protection (transient voltage suppressors and related filters and termination devices)
Rectifier and assembly (used for military, aerospace and medical applications)
 Assemblies (standard and custom rectifier assembly packages)
 Rectifiers

COMPETITORS

Advanced Analogic Technologies	Maxim Integrated Products
Analog Devices	Micrel
Dialog Semiconductor	Microsemi
Exar	Monolithic Power Systems
Fairchild Semiconductor	National Semiconductor
Hittite Microwave	NXP Semiconductors
Infineon Technologies	O2Micro
Inphi	Oki Semiconductor
Integrated Device Technology	ON Semiconductor
International Rectifier	Power Integrations
	Silicon Labs
Intersil	Siliconix
IXYS	STMicroelectronics
Linear Technology	Texas Instruments
	Volterra Semiconductor

HISTORICAL FINANCIALS

Company Type: Public

Income Statement

FYE: Sunday nearest January 31

	REVENUE ($ mil.)	NET INCOME ($ mil.)	NET PROFIT MARGIN	EMPLOYEES
01/11	454.5	72.6	16.0%	982
01/10	286.6	1.0	0.3%	915
01/09	294.8	37.5	12.7%	827
01/08	284.8	47.8	16.8%	781
01/07	252.5	31.1	12.3%	689
Annual Growth	**15.8%**	**23.6%**	**—**	**9.3%**

2011 Year-End Financials

Debt ratio: —
Return on equity: 13.7%
Cash ($ mil.): 119.0
Current ratio: 3.77
Long-term debt ($ mil.): —

No. of shares (mil.): 63.9
Dividends
 Yield: —
 Payout: —
Market value ($ mil.): 1,395.9

	STOCK PRICE ($) FY Close	P/E High/Low	PER SHARE ($) Earnings	Dividends	Book Value
01/11	21.83	22 13	1.12	0.00	8.27
01/10	14.98	958 541	0.02	0.00	6.62
01/09	11.75	30 14	0.61	0.00	6.26
01/08	12.77	30 16	0.71	0.00	5.43
01/07	13.70	48 26	0.42	0.00	6.65
Annual Growth	**12.4%**	**— —**	**27.8%**	**—**	**5.6%**

Senior Housing Properties

Senior Housing Properties Trust (SHPT) offers those in their golden years a place to rest their weary heads. The real estate investment trust (REIT) owns some 300 health care-related properties in more than 30 states and Washington, DC. Its portfolio includes senior apartments, independent and assisted living facilities, nursing homes, medical office buildings, biotechnology laboratories, rehabilitation hospitals, and gymnasiums. Tenants, such as Sunrise Senior Living and Brookdale Senior Living, sign triple-net leases, which require them not only to pay rent, but to also pay operating expenses, remove hazardous waste, and carry insurance on their properties.

SHPT was spun off from HRPT Properties Trust in 1999 when that REIT sold off its health facilities in order to focus on office and industrial properties. SHPT's business strategy is primarily focused on acquiring upscale senior living properties, where the majority of residents pay rent through their own resources rather than through government programs. In 2008 and 2009 the company diversified its properties by purchasing nearly 50 medical office, clinic and biotech laboratory buildings in a dozen states from HRPT for some $565 million. In 2011 SHPT arranged to buy 20 senior living facilities in the Southeast for more than $300 million. In another deal announced later in the year, the company agreed to buy 13 medical office properties from Commonwealth REIT for $167 million. The properties are scattered throughout AZ, CA, IL, MN, NY, OH, PA, and SC.

SHPT created Five Star Quality Care in 2000 to operate properties that it repossessed from other tenants. The management company was spun off the follwoing year, but remains SHPT's largest tenant and accounts for more than half of the REIT's annual rent. Reit Management Research, a limited liability company owned by Barry Portnoy and his son Adam (who are also managing trustees of SHPT), manages the day-to-day activites of SHPT, HRPT, Five Star Quality Care, and two other publicly traded REITs, Hospitality Properties Trust and Government Properties Income Trust.

Institutional investors, including Vanguard, Deutsche Bank, BlackRock, and Morgan Stanley, own more than 40% of SHPT's stock.

EXECUTIVES

President and COO, David J. Hegarty, age 55, $163,693 total compensation

CFO and Treasurer, Richard A. (Rick) Doyle Jr., age 43, $55,608 total compensation

VP Investor Relations, Timothy A. (Tim) Bonang

Manager Investor Relations, Katherine L. (Katie) Johnston

Director Internal Audit and Compliance, William J. Sheehan

Secretary, Jennifer B. Clark, age 49

Auditors: Ernst & Young LLP

LOCATIONS

HQ: Senior Housing Properties Trust
400 Centre St., Newton, MA 02458-2076
Phone: 617-796-8350 **Fax:** 617-796-8349
Web: www.snhreit.com

2009 Properties

	No.
Wisconsin	21
Massachusetts	20
California	19
Florida	17
Georgia	17
Nebraska	17
Pennsylvania	17
Texas	15
Virginia	15
Maryland	13
South Carolina	13
Indiana	11
Tennessee	10
Kentucky	9
Arizona	8
Colorado	8
Delaware	6
Iowa	6
North Carolina	6
Alabama	5
Michigan	5
Kansas	4
New Jersey	4
New Mexico	4

New York	4
Oklahoma	4
Illinois	3
Minnesota	3
South Dakota	3
Mississippi	2
Ohio	2
Washington, DC	2
Wyoming	2
Missouri	1
Rhode Island	1
Washington	1
Total	**298**

PRODUCTS/OPERATIONS

2009 Sales

	$ mil.	% of total
Residential care facilities	227.9	76
Medical office buildings	53.3	18
Other	16.6	6
Total	**297.8**	**100**

2009 Properties

	No.
Senior living facilities	230
Medical office buildings	56
Wellness centers	10
Rehabilitation hospitals	2
Total	**298**

COMPETITORS

Chartwell Seniors Housing	Legacy Healthcare
Extendicare REIT	LTC Properties
G & K Industries	National Health Investors
HCP	Omega Healthcare
Health Care REIT	Investors
Healthcare Realty Trust	Sabra Health Care
	Ventas

HISTORICAL FINANCIALS

Company Type: Public

Income Statement
FYE: December 31

	REVENUE ($ mil.)	NET INCOME ($ mil.)	NET PROFIT MARGIN	EMPLOYEES
12/10	339.0	116.5	34.4%	650
12/09	297.8	109.7	36.8%	600
12/08	235.5	106.2	45.1%	585
12/07	188.0	85.3	45.4%	500
12/06	179.8	66.1	36.8%	450
Annual Growth	**17.2%**	**15.2%**	**—**	**9.6%**

2010 Year-End Financials

Debt ratio: 56.6%
Return on equity: 5.5%
Cash ($ mil.): 10.9
Current ratio: 3.63
Long-term debt ($ mil.): 1,204.9

No. of shares (mil.): 141.9
Dividends
Yield: 6.6%
Payout: 159.3%
Market value ($ mil.): 3,112.3

	STOCK PRICE ($) FY Close	P/E High/Low		PER SHARE ($) Earnings	Dividends	Book Value
12/10	21.94	28	21	0.91	1.45	15.00
12/09	21.87	25	12	0.90	1.42	14.92
12/08	17.92	25	10	1.01	1.40	15.12
12/07	22.68	26	16	1.03	1.37	14.93
12/06	24.48	27	18	0.91	1.30	14.19
Annual Growth	**(2.7%)**	**—**	**—**	**(0.0%)**	**2.8%**	**1.4%**

Senomyx

Senomyx nose a good thing when it smells it. The company — through collaborations with the likes of Kraft, Nestlé, and Coca-Cola — hopes to take the flavor and fragrance industry to a whole new level. Senomyx has identified human receptor genes related to the detection of smells and tastes, and, using this genetic research, the company is developing sweet, salty, and savory flavor enhancers and bitter taste modulators. Potential products include agents that can block bitter tastes in coffee and make low-sodium snacks taste salty. The company also works with Japan's largest flavors company, Ajinomoto, opening up the Asian market for Senomyx.

In 2011 Senomyx entered into a collaborative agreement with Cadbury Adams USA, a unit of Kraft Foods, to develop and commercialize novel flavor modulators for potential use in the gum and medicated confectionery product categories. Senomyx has similar agreements with companies such as Firmenich, PepsiCo, Campbell's Soup, and others.

Under its collaboration agreements, Senomyx's partners are responsible for manufacturing, marketing, selling, and distributing their foods, beverages, or ingredient supplies that include Senomyx ingredients. This allows Senomyx to benefit from its collaborators' brand recognition, global market presence, sales and distribution channels, and other industry-specific expertise. Senomyx receives both upfront payments from food and beverage companies for researching and developing its products, and royalty payments for their continued use in the marketplace.

EXECUTIVES

Chairman and CEO, Kent Snyder, age 57, $1,456,584 total compensation
President and COO, John W. Poyhonen, age 51, $881,111 total compensation
VP and CFO, Antony E. (Tony) Rogers, age 44, $451,961 total compensation
VP Information Technology, Lorenzo Pe a
VP Human Resources, Susan R. (Susie) Firestone
VP, General Counsel, and Corporate Secretary, David B. Berger, age 41, $425,984 total compensation
VP Investor Relations and Corporate Communications, Gwen Rosenberg, age 51
VP Biology, David L. Linemeyer
SVP and Chief Commercial Development Officer, Sharon Wicker, age 55, $727,825 total compensation
SVP Discovery and Chief Scientific Officer, Donald S. (Don) Karanewsky, age 59, $726,323 total compensation
Auditors: Ernst & Young LLP

LOCATIONS

HQ: Senomyx, Inc.
4767 Nexus Centre Dr., San Diego, CA 92121
Phone: 858-646-8300 **Fax:** 858-404-0752
Web: www.senomyx.com

COMPETITORS

Firmenich	Symrise
Givaudan	Takasago International
International Flavors	USA
Redpoint Bio	Tate & Lyle
Sensient	

HISTORICAL FINANCIALS

Company Type: Public

Income Statement
FYE: December 31

	REVENUE ($ mil.)	NET INCOME ($ mil.)	NET PROFIT MARGIN	EMPLOYEES
12/10	28.7	(10.7)	—	113
12/09	15.5	(26.2)	—	108
12/08	17.2	(26.9)	—	129
12/07	18.2	(21.8)	—	118
12/06	12.2	(23.1)	—	112
Annual Growth	**23.8%**	**—**	**—**	**0.2%**

2010 Year-End Financials

Debt ratio: 15.8%
Return on equity: —
Cash ($ mil.): 21.3
Current ratio: 2.28
Long-term debt ($ mil.): 5.1

No. of shares (mil.): 39.1
Dividends
Yield: —
Payout: —
Market value ($ mil.): 278.7

	STOCK PRICE ($) FY Close	P/E High/Low		PER SHARE ($) Earnings	Dividends	Book Value
12/10	7.13	—	—	(0.28)	0.00	0.82
12/09	3.77	—	—	(0.85)	0.00	0.56
12/08	2.79	—	—	(0.88)	0.00	1.20
12/07	7.49	—	—	(0.72)	0.00	1.86
12/06	12.99	—	—	(0.77)	0.00	2.31
Annual Growth	**(13.9%)**	**—**	**—**	**—**	**—**	**(22.7%)**

ServiceSource

ServiceSource is hoping to bring a sense of renewal to its clients. Part sales professional staffer, part software developer, ServiceSource offers sales staff outsourcing and proprietary customer management software geared toward increasing sales contract renewals. Its software, which includes data management platforms and cloud applications, aggregates customer data from its clients' different enterprise systems (e.g. CRM, billing, order management) to facilitate customer management and analysis from a single, online location. Serving clients primarily in the technology sector, ServiceSource often markets its sales professionals in tandem with its software offerings. The company launched an IPO in 2011.

ServiceSource intends to use a portion of the proceeds it raises in its more than $100 million IPO to repay debt. The balance is being used for general corporate purposes, including funding the development of new technologies. ServiceSource is owned by entities affiliated with private equity firm General Atlantic (which holds a 21% stake), Housatonic Partners (15%), and other institutional investors.

Aside from investments in its technologies, ServiceSource is also considering investing in companies and other assets that would enhance its presence in international markets. The company, which operates in the US through offices in San Francisco, Denver, and Nashville, has a presence in Europe and Asia through its Dublin, Ireland; Liverpool, England; and Singapore offices. In 2010 it bolstered its Asian operations after opening an office in Kuala Lumpur, Malaysia.

Formed in 2002, ServiceSource has enjoyed a healthy rise in its profits in recent years, due in large part to growing revenues and a widening

Senior Director, Automotive, Entertainment, PC and Gaming, Mike Canevaro
Product Marketing Manager, Kurt Heiden
Auditors: Squar, Milner, Peterson, Miranda & Williamson, LLP

LOCATIONS

HQ: SRS Labs, Inc.
2909 Daimler St., Santa Ana, CA 92705
Phone: 949-442-1070   Fax: 949-852-1099
Web: www.srslabs.com

2010 Sales

	$ mil.	% of total
Asia/Pacific		
South Korea	13.7	44
Japan	4.9	16
China	2.0	6
Other countries	2.5	8
US	7.5	24
Europe	0.6	2
Total	**31.2**	**100**

PRODUCTS/OPERATIONS

2010 Sales

	% of total
Home entertainment	64
Personal computers	16
Personal telecom	10
Automotive	7
Portable media	3
Total	**100**

Selected Technologies

Audio, voice, and speaker technologies
AVT (acoustic vector technology for speakers)
Circle Surround (discrete channels of surround sound)
FOCUS (repositions stereo images for poorly located speakers)
Headphone (repositions sounds spatially)
NuVoice (technology for creating speech that sounds less mechanical)
SRS (three-dimensional sound from a standard stereo source)
TruBass (gives small speakers better bass sound)
TruSurround (multichannel sound through two speakers)
VIP (voice intelligibility technology)
WOW (audio enhancement technology)
WOW Voice (speech intelligibility enhancement)

COMPETITORS

Acacia Technologies	Kurzweil Technologies
Akustica	Lucasfilm
Andrea Electronics	QSound Labs
Creative Technology	Sony
Dolby	THX
DTS	

HISTORICAL FINANCIALS

Company Type: Public

Income Statement

FYE: December 31

	REVENUE ($ mil.)	NET INCOME ($ mil.)	NET PROFIT MARGIN	EMPLOYEES
12/10	31.2	3.0	9.6%	106
12/09	25.0	2.1	8.4%	86
12/08	18.3	0.3	1.6%	20
12/07	18.9	5.4	28.6%	42
12/06	18.5	4.7	25.4%	39
Annual Growth	**14.0%**	**(10.6%)**	**—**	**28.4%**

2010 Year-End Financials

Debt ratio: —
Return on equity: 5.5%
Cash ($ mil.): 10.7
Current ratio: 12.53
Long-term debt ($ mil.): —
No. of shares (mil.): 14.8
Dividends
  Yield: —
  Payout: —
Market value ($ mil.): 130.5

	STOCK PRICE ($) FY Close	P/E High/Low		PER SHARE ($) Earnings	Dividends	Book Value
12/10	8.81	55	36	0.19	0.00	3.70
12/09	7.33	55	31	0.14	0.00	3.32
12/08	4.77	363	178	0.02	0.00	2.77
12/07	5.35	49	16	0.32	0.00	2.89
12/06	10.90	39	15	0.30	0.00	2.70
Annual Growth	**(5.2%)**	**—**	**—**	**(10.8%)**	**—**	**8.2%**

STAG Industrial

If STAG Industrial were to show up alone at a party, it would likely be on the hunt for single tenants who seek to lease industrial space. Formed in 2010, the self-managed and self-administered real estate investment trust (REIT), acquires and manages single-tenant industrial properties located in more than 25 states. The company's portfolio consists primarily of 14 million sq. ft. of leasable warehouse, distribution, manufacturing, and office space located in secondary markets. It conducts most of its business through its operating partner, STAG Industrial Operating Partnership. STAG went public in 2011.

The company raised about $179 million and intends to use the proceeds from the public offering to repay debt and acquire interests in about 25 properties currently held in an investment fund managed by STAG Capital, a predecessor company. The properties will be part of the 90 properties in STAG Industrial's initial portfolio. Many of the portfolio's properties, which are currently organized in a handful of investment funds held by STAG Capital, STAG Investments, and other of STAG Industrial's predecessor companies, are located in Michigan, Ohio, Indiana, Kansas, and other eastern and midwestern states.

In keeping with its predecessor companies' collective business strategy, STAG Industrial intends to build on its initial portfolio by continuing to acquire direct and indirect ownership of industrial space in secondary markets, including small cities and towns and suburban areas. The company's CEO and founder, Benjamin S. Butcher, founded STAG Industrial's predecessor companies in 2003. Butcher and other investors formed STAG Industrial to consolidate the companies' assets under a REIT umbrella for tax purposes and to raise public funds.

EXECUTIVES

Chairman, President, and CEO, Benjamin S. Butcher, age 58
EVP and Director Real Estate Operations, David G. King, age 43
EVP, General Counsel, and Secretary, Kathryn Arnone, age 61
EVP and COO, Stephen C. Mecke, age 48
EVP, CFO, and Treasurer, Gregory W. Sullivan, age 57
Auditors: PricewaterhouseCoopers

LOCATIONS

HQ: STAG Industrial, Inc.
99 High St., 28th Fl., Boston, MA 02111
Phone: 617-574-4777   Fax: 617-574-0052
Web: www.stagreit.com

Selected States

Florida
Indiana
Iowa
Kansas
Kentucky
Maine
Massachusetts
Michigan
New York
North Carolina
Ohio
Pennsylvania
South Dakota
Texas
Virginia
Wisconsin

COMPETITORS

First Industrial Realty	Monmouth Real Estate
	ProLogis
Liberty Property Trust	Welsh Property Trust

HISTORICAL FINANCIALS

Company Type: Public

Income Statement

FYE: December 31

	REVENUE ($ mil.)	NET INCOME ($ mil.)	NET PROFIT MARGIN	EMPLOYEES
12/10	60.4	0.6	1.0%	25
12/09	30.2	(5.6)	—	23
12/08	31.3	(7.7)	—	0
Annual Growth	**38.9%**	**—**	**—**	**8.7%**

2010 Year-End Financials

Debt ratio: —
Return on equity: 0.4%
Cash ($ mil.): 1.0
Current ratio: 0.05
Long-term debt ($ mil.): —
No. of shares (mil.): —
Dividends
  Yield: —
  Payout: —
Market value ($ mil.): —

Steven Madden

Steven Madden elevates chunky heels to new heights. It operates through five business segments: wholesale footwear, wholesale accessories, retail, first cost, and licensing. Its wholesale business boasts seven divisions, such as Madden Girl, Steven, Steve Madden Men's, and Stevies, as well as its Daisy Fuentes, Betsey Johnson, and Olsenboye accessories business through licenses. Its retail operations include about 85 Steve Madden and Steven stores, along with several websites. Its Adesso-Madden unit (aka first cost) designs and sources private-label footwear, such as Candie's, for mass merchants. Steven Madden shoes are sold in the US and Canada through its own shops and such stores as Nordstrom and Dillard's.

Despite slogging through an economic downturn that hurt many of its fellow retailers, the company logged a record $635 million in sales in 2010 (a more than 25% increase from the previous year). It did so by concentrating on its wholesale business, which rose from 73% of total sales in 2008 to 79% in 2010. Steven Madden looks to department stores, specialty stores, and independent boutiques for the majority of its wholesale revenue. Shoe retailer DSW was Steven Madden's biggest customer in this sector, accounting for 12% of that unit's sales and 10% of overall company revenue. Net income also rose dramatically to $75 million, a 50% increase.

Looking to increase its private-label footprint, Steven Madden bought Topline Corp. for $55 million in May 2011. Topline, which rang up sales of about $189 million in 2010, sells private-label and branded footwear (Report, Report Signature, R2 by Report) primarily to specialty retailers and department stores.

Steven Madden-owned stores are located across the US, with noteworthy penetration in New York, California, and Florida. Its retail business, which brought in about 20% of the company's revenue, logged a 12% increase in same-store sales in 2010. To maintain this part of its business, Steven Madden consistently reviews and adjusts its stores portfolio by shuttering underperforming shops.

Steven Madden also has a foothold in areas beyond shoes, and the firm continues to invest in its accessories business. (The footwear maker's accessories business has eclipsed its men's business.) In 2011 it acquired the Cejon group of design and marketing companies for about $30 million. The purchase included Cejon Inc., Cejon Accessories, and New East Designs. The companies design scarves, wraps, winter accessories and other items, and expanded Steven Madden's accessories business beyond handbags and belts. Prior to its purchase, Cejon was a licensee of Steven Madden for winter weather and other accessories. In mid-2009 the company acquired the SML Brands' Zone 88 and Shakedown Street lines for $1.25 million. The move gave Steven Madden an extended reach into private-label accessories (mostly handbags) that sell to mass merchants and department stores. The company followed up the deal by purchasing handbags and belts maker Big Buddha in early 2010 for $11 million. Later that year Steven Madden made a bold move when it acquired the trademarks and intellectual property of fashion house Betsey Johnson, paying $27 million that had been outstanding on a $49 million loan. Steven Madden, which also received a 10% equity stake, agreed to contribute additional funds to Betsey Johnson, which began restructuring its operations. As part of their agreement, Steven Madden has allowed Betsey Johnson to continue running its eponymous retail stores in the US, Canada, and the UK, as well as manufacture its name-brand apparel collections.

Along with its accessories business, Steve Madden has grown its business through licensing to diversify its income and products portfolio. In late 2009, the firm entered an agreement with Dualstar Entertainment to use the Olsenboye trademark to sell footwear and accessories to JCPenney. It also generates revenue by licensing its name for the manufacture of women's fashion apparel and jewelry through deals it inked in 2009 and 2010.

After seven years as head of Steve Madden and amid declining profits, Jamieson Karson resigned in March 2008 as the company's chairman and CEO. He was replaced by Ed Rosenfeld, formerly EVP of strategic planning and finance. Founder Steven Madden, individually and through his BOCAP Corp., owns nearly 16% of the company.

EXECUTIVES

Chairman and CEO, Edward R. (Ed) Rosenfeld, age 35, $3,225,103 total compensation

CFO, Chief Accounting Officer and Secretary, Arvind Dharia, age 61, $924,242 total compensation
EVP Wholesale, Amelia Newto Varela, age 39, $1,400,638 total compensation
COO, Awadhesh K. Sinha, age 65, $1,460,170 total compensation
Creative and Design Chief, Steven (Steve) Madden
Auditors:

LOCATIONS

HQ: Steven Madden, Ltd.
52-16 Barnett Ave., Long Island City, NY 11104
Phone: 718-446-1800   **Fax:** 718-446-5599
Web: www.stevemadden.com

PRODUCTS/OPERATIONS

2010 Sales

	$ mil.	% of total
Wholesale		
Footwear	402.6	64
Accessories	98.5	15
Retail	134.3	21
Total	**635.4**	**100**

Licensed Products

Belts
Hair accessories
Handbags
Hosiery
Jewelry
Outerwear
Socks
Sportswear
Sunglasses

COMPETITORS

Bakers Footwear	Kenneth Cole
Brown Shoe	NIKE
Diesel SpA	Nine West
Donna Karan	R. Griggs
Guess?	Reebok
Iconix Brand Group	Skechers U.S.A.
Jimlar	

HISTORICAL FINANCIALS

Company Type: Public

Income Statement

FYE: December 31

	REVENUE ($ mil.)	NET INCOME ($ mil.)	NET PROFIT MARGIN	EMPLOYEES
12/10	635.4	75.7	11.9%	1,440
12/09	503.5	50.1	10.0%	1,370
12/08	457.0	28.0	6.1%	1,510
12/07	431.0	35.7	8.3%	1,510
12/06	475.2	46.3	9.7%	1,498
Annual Growth	**7.5%**	**13.1%**	**—**	**(1.0%)**

2010 Year-End Financials

Debt ratio: —	No. of shares (mil.): 42.0
Return on equity: 21.2%	Dividends
Cash ($ mil.): 66.2	Yield: —
Current ratio: 2.94	Payout: —
Long-term debt ($ mil.): —	Market value ($ mil.): 1,168.7

	STOCK PRICE ($) FY Close	P/E High/Low		PER SHARE ($) Earnings	Dividends	Book Value
12/10	27.81	18	10	1.79	0.00	8.50
12/09	18.33	17	5	1.21	0.00	6.51
12/08	9.48	19	9	0.67	0.00	5.13
12/07	8.89	21	10	0.75	0.00	4.76
12/06	15.60	21	9	0.93	0.00	4.48
Annual Growth	**15.5%**	**—**	**—**	**17.8%**	**—**	**17.4%**

Stifel Financial

Stifel Financial doesn't repress investors. The company serves individual, corporate, municipal, and institutional investors through more than 300 offices in the US, with a concentration in the Midwest and mid-Atlantic regions. It also has offices in Canada and Europe. Through subsidiaries Stifel Nicolaus (founded 1890), Thomas Weisel (acquired in 2010), Century Securities Associates, Stifel Bank & Trust, and others, the company provides asset management, financial advice, and banking services for private clients. Stifel also offers brokerage and mergers and acquisitions advisory services for corporate clients, underwrites debt and equity, and provides research on more than 1,000 US and European equities.

Hoping to take advantage of the demise of bulge-bracket investment banks such as Bear Stearns and Lehman Brothers, and turmoil in the industry in general, Stifel Financial has been growing vigorously via acquisitions. The Thomas Weisel deal, worth more than $300 million and one of Stifel Financial's largest to date, should boost the company's investment banking capabilities in the technology, health care, and energy sectors. Thomas Weisel's Canadian operations took on the Stifel Nicolaus name.

Stifel Financial has also built up its asset management and brokerage operations. In 2010, the company bought investment advisor Missouri Valley Partners from First Banks; the year before, it acquired more than 50 wealth management branches in the US from UBS Financial Services.

The acquisitions, along with improved market conditions, helped Stifel Financial achieve record revenues in 2010, the 15th consecutive year that the figure increased. However, net income was lower, dragged down by compensation costs and expenses related to the Thomas Weisel transaction.

Undaunted by that deal, the company bought Stone & Youngberg in 2011. Stone & Youngberg specializes in municipal bonds and fixed income securities; its purchase builds Stifel's public finance business in the West.

Previous acquisitions include the 2008 purchase of Butler Wick, an advisory firm and brokerage with some two dozen offices in the Ohio Valley region; mid-Atlantic investment bank and brokerage Ryan Beck and St. Louis-based FirstService Bank (now Stifel Bank and Trust) in 2007; and virtually all of the capital markets business of Legg Mason from Citigroup in 2005.

In addition to acquisitions, Stifel Financial also has strategies to grow organically. These include establishing trust services at Stifel Bank & Trust and utilizing the bank to cross-sell mortgages and securities-based loans to wealth management clients. Stifel Financial also wants to grow its private client business in the US and its institutional equity operations globally.

EXECUTIVES

Co-Chairman, Thomas W. (Thom) Weisel, age 70
Vice Chairman, Richard J. Himelfarb, age 69, $2,079,675 total compensation
Vice Chairman, Ben A. Plotkin, age 55, $2,416,926 total compensation
Co-Chairman, President, and CEO, Ronald J. (Ron) Kruszewski, age 52, $4,155,460 total compensation
SVP and Director Syndicate, Stifel Nicolaus, Thomas R. Kendrick IV
SVP and General Counsel, David M. Minnick, age 54

SVP and Director St. Louis Public Finance, Stifel
Nicolaus, J. Joseph Schlafly III
SVP and Director Denver Public Finance, Stifel
Nicolaus, Stephen H. Bell
SVP and Director Equity Research, Stifel Nicolaus,
Hugo J. (Hugh) Warns III
SVP, CFO, Treasurer, and Director, James M.
Zemlyak, age 51, $1,755,233 total compensation
SVP and Director, Thomas P. Mulroy, age 49,
$2,454,033 total compensation
SVP, David D. Sliney, age 41
SVP and Managing Director, Denver Municipal
Trading, Stifel Nicolaus, Michael F. Imhoff
Co-Head Capital Markets and Director Investment
Banking, Victor J. Nesi, age 51
Auditors: Ernst & Young LLP

LOCATIONS

HQ: Stifel Financial Corp.
501 N. Broadway, St. Louis, MO 63102-2102
Phone: 314-342-2000
Web: www.stifel.com

PRODUCTS/OPERATIONS

2010 Sales

	$ mil.	% of total
Principal transactions	453.5	32
Commissions	445.3	32
Investment banking	218.1	16
Asset management & service fees	193.2	14
Interest	65.3	5
Other	19.8	1
Total	**1,395.2**	**100**

Selected Subsidiaries

Broadway Air Corp.
Butler Wick & Co., Inc.
Century Securities Associates, Inc.
  CSA Insurance Agency, Incorporated
Choice Financial Partners, Inc.
First Service Financial Company
  Stifel Bank & Trust
Hanifen, Imhoff Inc.
Missouri Valley Partners
Ryan Beck Holdings, L.L.C.
Stifel Nicolaus Canada Inc.
Stifel Asset Management Corp.
Stifel, Nicolaus & Company, Incorporated
  Ryan Beck Holdings, LLC
  Stifel, Nicolaus Insurance Agency, Incorporated
Stifel Nicholas Limited (UK)
Thomas Weisel Partners Group, Inc.

COMPETITORS

Bank of America	Oppenheimer Holdings
Cowen Group	Piper Jaffray
Edward Jones	Raymond James
Goldman Sachs	Financial
Jefferies Group	Robert W. Baird & Co.
JMP Group	SWS Group
Lazard	Wells Fargo Advisors
Morgan Stanley	

HISTORICAL FINANCIALS

Company Type: Public

Income Statement

FYE: December 31

	REVENUE ($ mil.)	NET INCOME ($ mil.)	NET PROFIT MARGIN	EMPLOYEES
12/10	1,395.2	1.9	0.1%	4,906
12/09	1,102.9	75.8	6.9%	4,434
12/08	888.8	55.5	6.2%	3,371
12/07	793.1	32.2	4.1%	2,834
12/06	471.4	15.4	3.3%	2,809
Annual Growth	**31.2%**	**(40.7%)**	**—**	**15.0%**

2010 Year-End Financials

Debt ratio: 7.2% No. of shares (mil.): 50.6
Return on equity: 0.2% Dividends
Cash ($ mil.): 253.5 Yield: 0.0%
Current ratio: — Payout: —
Long-term debt ($ mil.): 90.7 Market value ($ mil.): 2,092.3

	STOCK PRICE ($) FY Close	P/E High/Low	PER SHARE ($) Earnings	Dividends	Book Value
12/10	41.36	1263 854	0.03	0.00	24.79
12/09	39.49	25 12	1.57	0.00	19.22
12/08	30.57	31 12	1.32	0.00	15.42
12/07	23.36	34 20	0.84	0.00	12.46
12/06	17.44	40 27	0.49	0.00	8.45
Annual Growth	**24.1%**	**— —**	**(50.3%)**	**—**	**30.9%**

STRATTEC

STRATTEC SECURITY has your car under lock
and key. The company designs and manufactures
mechanical security locks, electro-mechanical locks
and keys, and ignition lock housings primarily for
global automakers. It also makes access control
products, including door handles, latches, power
sliding doors, and power lift gates. Chrysler, Ford,
and General Motors account for the majority of
STRATTEC's annual sales. In addition to cars and
light trucks, its products are used in the heavy
truck and recreational vehicle markets, as well as
in precision die castings. With facilities in the US
and Mexico, STRATTEC delivers products mainly
in North America, but also abroad in Asia, Europe,
and South America.

STRATTEC, along with fellow automotive product suppliers WIITE Automotive and ADAC Automotive, is a member of the Vehicle Access Systems
Technology (VAST) Alliance. This alliance allows
members to act as each others' sales, marketing,
manufacturing, and support representatives in
North America and Europe. Members also own a
joint venture, Vehicle Access Systems Technology
LLC, which operates manufacturing facilities in
China and Brazil and supports sales in the
Asia/Pacific and Latin America regions.

Through a joint venture with ADAC Automotive
called ADAC-STRATTEC LLC, STRATTEC also
supplies door handle components and related vehicle access hardware. In 2009 STRATTEC
formed a new subsidiary with WIITE Automotive
called STRATTEC Power Access LLC (SPA) to acquire the North American business of Delphi's
Power Products group. SPA produces power access systems for sliding doors, lift gates, and trunk
lids. Current customers for this set of products are
Chrysler, Ford, GM, and Taiwan-based Yulon.

As STRATTEC tries to grow its footprint geographically through these ventures, it's also moving beyond its traditional lock and key products
and diversifying with a more sophisticated set of
power access control products. Purely mechanical
devices are on the out and out. The company views
electro-mechanical devices for vehicles — mechanical locks, keys, housings, and latches that are enhanced by built-in electronics — as the future.
These include devices that incorporate user bio-
identification systems, keys with remote entry capabilities, and ignition interfaces with passive start
capabilities, among other technologies.

Following the global economic crisis, STRAT-
TEC faced a dismal performance in fiscal 2009, as

two of its largest customers (Chrysler and GM)
faced bankruptcy and the US auto industry was
near collapse. Economic forecasts for auto production were very low compared to pre-2009 levels, and industry analysts generally agreed that
any recovery would be long and slow. But despite
these negative conditions, STRATTEC weathered
the storm and managed to turn a small profit in
fiscal 2010, an achievement compared to the losses
of 2009. With vehicle production rates recovering
faster than forecasted, the company's sales are
likewise showing improvement, especially in terms
of access control products.

EXECUTIVES

Chairman and CEO, Harold M. Stratton II, age 63,
$415,600 total compensation
President, COO, and Board Member, Frank J. Krejci,
age 61
VP Marketing and Sales, Dennis A. Kazmierski, age
59, $362,542 total compensation
VP Product Development and Management, Brian J.
Reetz, age 53
VP Mexican Operations, Rolando J. Guillot, age 43,
$272,360 total compensation
VP Milwaukee Operations, Kathryn E. Scherbarth, age
55, $226,929 total compensation
SVP, CFO, Secretary, and Treasurer, Patrick J.
Hansen, age 52, $304,895 total compensation
Auditors: Grant Thornton LLP

LOCATIONS

HQ: STRATTEC SECURITY CORPORATION
3333 W. Good Hope Rd., Milwaukee, WI 53209
Phone: 414-247-3333 Fax: 414-247-3329
Web: www.strattec.com

PRODUCTS/OPERATIONS

2010 Sales by Customer

	$ mil.	% of total
Chrysler	68.2	33
General Motors	51.7	25
Ford Motor	18.4	9
Other customers	69.7	33
Total	**208.0**	**100**

COMPETITORS

AISIN World Corp.	Tokai Rika
Huf North America	Valeo
Automotive	Visteon
Magna International	

HISTORICAL FINANCIALS

Company Type: Public

Income Statement

FYE: Sunday nearest June 30

	REVENUE ($ mil.)	NET INCOME ($ mil.)	NET PROFIT MARGIN	EMPLOYEES
06/11	260.9	5.4	2.1%	2,556
06/10	208.0	3.4	1.6%	2,280
06/09	126.1	(6.1)	—	1,655
06/08	159.6	3.3	2.1%	2,000
06/07	167.7	8.2	4.9%	2,150
Annual Growth	**11.7%**	**(9.9%)**	**—**	**4.4%**

2011 Year-End Financials

Debt ratio: — No. of shares (mil.): 3.3
Return on equity: 6.3% Dividends
Cash ($ mil.): 17.3 Yield: 0.0%
Current ratio: 1.85 Payout: —
Long-term debt ($ mil.): — Market value ($ mil.): 69.4

	STOCK PRICE ($)	P/E		PER SHARE ($)		
	FY Close	High/Low	Earnings	Dividends	Book Value
06/11	21.13	23 11	1.63	0.00	26.24
06/10	22.10	27 13	1.04	0.00	22.63
06/09	13.80	— —	(1.86)	0.30	21.89
06/08	35.00	54 37	0.94	0.60	27.56
06/07	47.00	22 15	2.30	0.00	29.10
Annual Growth	(18.1%)	— —	(8.2%)	—	(2.6%)

Strayer Education

Students who wander from the traditional learning path can turn to Strayer Education. The company's Strayer University has about 90 campuses in some 20 states in the eastern US and Washington, DC. Founded in 1892, the university serves roughly 60,000 students, mostly working adults seeking associate's, bachelor's, and master's degrees in fields such as business administration, computer information systems, and computer networking. Strayer Education offers internet-based classes through its Strayer University Online, which offers both synchronous (real-time) and asynchronous class formats. Generation Investment Management (co-founded by former US Vice President Al Gore) owns about 6% of Strayer Education.

Strayer's growth strategy primarily involves opening campuses in markets where demand for university programs is high; at the same time the company limits its campus expansion to geographic locations in which it already has a nearby presence. The rationale being that academic deans and administrators don't have to travel great distances to keep tabs on educational activities and can instead focus on increasing academic quality. Strayer opened about a dozen new campuses in 2010 and intends to open eight more in 2011.

To keep its campuses staffed, the company plans to hire one full-time faculty member and one adjunct for every 50 students it enrolls. If it sticks to that plan, Strayer will have a student-teacher ratio of about 20:1.

Of course, physical growth can only be a component of an educational institution's expansion strategy. It also has to grow to meet its students educational needs. In order to do that, Strayer introduces new courses and programs as demand warrants. It launched the Writing Across the Curriculum program to help Strayer students improve their writing skills across all disciplines including business, computer science, and the arts. It also started offering a bachelor's degree in criminal justice.

These days students also expect to complete at least some of their education online, so Strayer has expanded in that area as well. It operates two Global Online Operations Centers through which its roughly 43,000 online students can attend classes and complete their degrees online.

In a move to add "name brand" education to its offerings, in 2011 Strayer Education agreed to buy the Jack Welsh Management Institute, an online business education program. Its executive MBA program and certification programs are based on the management lessons of the former General Electric Chairman and CEO, and are geared for both individual students and corporations seeking continuing education for their executives.

The company had an unusually large amount of capital expenditures in 2010 as it worked to keep up with demand and improving operational efficiency. Strayer spent more than 7% of its revenue on opening the aforementioned campuses, investing in classroom technology, and finishing construction on its second Global Online Operation Center in Salt Lake City, Utah. Strayer also consolidated its headquarters operations from four different locations in the Washington, D.C. area into one building. It expects keep spending at a more normal 5% in 2011.

EXECUTIVES

Chairman and CEO, Robert S. Silberman, age 53, $5,580,080 total compensation

President and COO, Karl McDonnell, age 44, $3,409,093 total compensation

President, Strayer University, Sondra F. Stallard, age 61, $798,299 total compensation

EVP and CFO, Mark C. Brown, age 51, $1,109,720 total compensation

VP Human Resources, Deborah Keller

VP Operations, Strayer University, James F. McCoy Jr., age 50

VP Operations, Strayer University, Dean R. Sippel

VP Financial Planning and Corporate Development, Strayer University, Daniel W. Jackson, age 34

VP Operations, Strayer University, Carter J. Smith

SVP and Chief Business Officer, Kelly J. Bozarth, age 42

SVP and Deputy General Counsel; General Counsel, Strayer University, Catherine R. Guttman-McCabe, age 42

Dean, Schools of Business and Information Systems, Strayer University, Deborah Snyder

SVP Operations, Strayer University, Chad D. Nyce

SVP Corporate Communications, Sonya G. Udler, age 43

Provost and Chief Academic Officer, Michael Plater, age 54

Senior Vice Provost Academic Administration, Randi Reich Cosentino, age 37

SVP Operations, Strayer University, Randall T. Jones

General Counsel and Secretary, Viet D. Dinh, age 43

Auditors: PricewaterhouseCoopers LLP

LOCATIONS

HQ: Strayer Education, Inc.
2303 Dulles Station Blvd., Herndon, VA 20171
Phone: 703-561-1600
Web: www.strayereducation.com

PRODUCTS/OPERATIONS

2010 Enrollment by Term

Term	Enrollment
Winter	55,106
Spring	55,970
Summer	52,221
Fall	60,711
Average	**56,002**

Selected Degrees and Programs

Master of Business Administration (M.B.A.) Degree
Master of Education (M.Ed.) Degree
Master of Health Services Administration (M.H.S.A.) Degree
Master of Public Administration (M.P.A.) Degree
Master of Science (M.S.) Degree
　Information Systems (with multiple concentrations)
　Professional Accounting
Executive Graduate Certificate Programs
　Business Administration
　Information Systems
　Professional Accounting
Bachelor of Science (B.S.) Degree
　Accounting

Information Systems
Economics
International Business
Criminal Justice
Bachelor of Business Administration (B.B.A.) Degree
Associate in Arts (A.A.) Degree
　Accounting
　Acquisition and Contract Management
　Business Administration
　Criminal Justice
　Information Systems
　Economics
　General Studies
　Marketing
Diploma Programs
　Accounting
　Acquisition and Contract Management
　Information Systems
Undergraduate Certificate Programs
　Accounting
　Business Administration
　Information Systems

COMPETITORS

Apollo Group	DeVry
Argosy Education	Education Management
Bridgepoint Education	ITT Educational
Cardean Learning Group	Kaplan
Career Education	Lincoln Educational
Corinthian Colleges	Services

HISTORICAL FINANCIALS

Company Type: Public

Income Statement

FYE: December 31

	REVENUE ($ mil.)	NET INCOME ($ mil.)	NET PROFIT MARGIN	EMPLOYEES
12/10	636.7	131.3	20.6%	2,099
12/09	512.0	105.1	20.5%	3,447
12/08	396.3	80.8	20.4%	2,407
12/07	318.0	64.9	20.4%	1,699
12/06	263.6	52.3	19.8%	2,177
Annual Growth	24.7%	25.9%	—	(0.9%)

2010 Year-End Financials

Debt ratio: —
Return on equity: 74.6%
Cash ($ mil.): 64.1
Current ratio: 1.28
Long-term debt ($ mil.): —
No. of shares (mil.): 13.3
Dividends
　Yield: 2.1%
　Payout: 33.5%
Market value ($ mil.): 2,027.1

	STOCK PRICE ($)	P/E		PER SHARE ($)		
	FY Close	High/Low	Earnings	Dividends	Book Value
12/10	152.22	27 13	9.70	3.25	13.22
12/09	212.52	31 19	7.60	2.25	13.60
12/08	214.41	42 25	5.67	1.63	12.38
12/07	170.58	44 23	4.47	1.31	13.00
12/06	106.05	33 24	3.61	1.06	11.94
Annual Growth	9.5%	— —	28.0%	32.3%	2.6%

Stream Global Services

This company can handle a torrent of customer service calls. Stream Global Services is a leading provider of business process outsourcing (BPO) services, such as customer care and technical support. The company maintains about 50 call centers in more than 20 countries, from which it works with its customers' customers over the telephone, via e-mail, and through online chat sessions in 35 different languages. In addition to customer service, Stream offers sales support and order processing. In late 2009, Stream made a significant move to expand when it acquired rival BPO services provider eTelecare Global Solutions in a stock-for-stock deal. The combined entity retained the Stream Global Services name.

As part of the merger, Stream gained access to eTelecare's expertise in the financial services, retail, and consumer products sectors. The deal diversified Stream's client base so that it didn't have to rely solely on the technology sector — high-tech clients Dell and Hewlett-Packard accounted for 16% and 12% of its sales, respectively, in 2010. When compared to 2009, Stream's revenues increased roughly 37% in 2010; it attributes the spike in revenue to the eTelecare acquisition. However, on the flip side, the company reported net losses for 2009 ($28.5 million) and 2010 ($53.5 million). It cites the direct costs associated with integrating eTelecare as factors contributing to the years of unprofitability. Stream officially completed the integration of eTelecare in April 2010.

The combination with eTelecare is just another notch in the evolution of Stream Global Services. It took its current form in 2008 when Stream was acquired for $200 million by Global BPO Services, a publicly traded entity formed to buy BPO providers, which changed its name to Stream Global Services. The new Stream Global Services is being led by Kathryn Marinello, who was hired as the company's chairman and top executive in mid-2010. Marinello formerly served as the chairman and CEO of payroll provider Ceridian Corporation.

In late 2008, Stream Global Services extended its geographic reach into Latin America when it acquired a contact center in San Salvador, El Salvador. It is using the center as a jumping off point for expanding its services into Central and South America. Stream is also looking to Brazil, China, and Japan as regions for future growth.

EXECUTIVES

Chairman, CEO and President, Kathryn V. (Kathy) Marinello, age 54
EVP and COO, Brian J. Delaney, age 53
EVP and CFO, Dennis J. Lacey, age 57
EVP Global Human Resources, Andrew J. Suchoff
EVP Operations, Americas, Jeff Bishop
EVP Global Sales and Marketing, Robert T. (Bob) Dechant, age 49, $2,601,610 total compensation
EVP Operations, EMEA, Harry Jackson
VP New Client Sales Development, Jeff Dixon
VP Product Management, Michelle Brown
Vice Chairman, Alfredo I. (Fred) Ayala, age 49
Director Marketing Communications, Sally Comollo
Auditors: Ernst & Young LLP

LOCATIONS

HQ: Stream Global Services, Inc.
Wellesley Office Park, 20 William St., Ste. 310, Wellesley, MA 02481
Phone: 781-304-1800   **Fax:** 781-304-1701
Web: www.stream.com

2010 Sales

	$ mil.	% of total
Americas	588.0	73
Europe, the Middle East & Africa	212.2	27
Total	**800.2**	**100**

PRODUCTS/OPERATIONS

Selected Services

Post-sales customer services
Pre-sales customer services
Professional and consulting services
Sales and marketing services
Technical support services

COMPETITORS

Accenture	Sutherland Global
Aditya Birla Minacs	Services
APAC Customer Services	Sykes Enterprises
Convergys	TechTeam
HP Enterprise Services	Teleperformance
IBM Global Services	TeleTech
Infosys	Transcom WorldWide
Keane	TRG Customer Solutions
NCO Group	Unisys
Perot Systems	West Corporation
Sitel Worldwide	Wipro Technologies
StarTek	WNS (Holdings)

HISTORICAL FINANCIALS

Company Type: Public

Income Statement

FYE: December 31

	REVENUE ($ mil.)	NET INCOME ($ mil.)	NET PROFIT MARGIN	EMPLOYEES
12/10	800.2	(53.5)	—	30,000
12/09	584.8	(28.6)	—	30,000
12/08	211.4	0.8	0.4%	17,000
Annual Growth	**94.6%**	**—**	**—**	**32.8%**

2010 Year-End Financials

Debt ratio: 87.7%	No. of shares (mil.): 80.1
Return on equity: —	Dividends
Cash ($ mil.): 18.5	Yield: —
Current ratio: 1.99	Payout: —
Long-term debt ($ mil.): 227.7	Market value ($ mil.): 316.4

	STOCK PRICE ($) FY Close	P/E High/Low	PER SHARE ($) Earnings	Dividends	Book Value
12/10	3.95	— —	(0.67)	0.00	3.24
12/09	5.95	— —	(3.46)	0.00	3.81
12/08	4.11	— —	(2.20)	0.00	0.18
00/00	7.30	104 102	0.07	0.00	(0.00)
Annual Growth	**(18.5%)**	**— —**	**—**	**—**	**—**

SuccessFactors

SuccessFactors believes it has a recipe for business success. The company provides software designed to help align business strategies, boost employee productivity, and manage development and performance. Its Business Execution Software provides everyone from *FORTUNE* 500 companies to small businesses with a Software-as-a-Service (SaaS) platform that automates goal planning, progress tracking, and performance reviews. The company targets customers in markets ranging from financial services (Equifax, Fannie Mae) and health care (Ascension Health) to education (Texas A&M), retail (The Gap), and technology (Sun Microsystems).

SuccessFactors is expanding primarily through acquisitions. In 2011 the company bought Jambok, a provider of hosted learning software that enabled organizations use mobile video, podcasting, and other social media tools to create business communities. The purchase extended SuccessFactors software portfolio to include collaborative content creation and learning tools. It also added customers from a wide range of industries including NIKE, Sandia National Laboratories, Mitsubishi Electric, and AAA. In a complementary deal the same year, SuccessFactors paid $145 million for human resources management software developer Plateau Systems, which offered a hosted HR software package similar to SuccessFactor's product. The deal broadened the company's customer base and improved its ability to offers its products as hosted applications on a subscription basis.

In 2010 the company acquired Inform Business Impact. The deal added analytics and workforce planning applications to SuccessFactors' portfolio of business planning and execution software. It also increased the company's customer list by about 130 clients, including Comcast and The McGraw-Hill Companies. It also bought online collaboration software maker CubeTree that year in a move to build its portfolio of products for remote communication and work sharing.

SuccessFactors generates revenue primarily from subscription fees and configuration services. Initially focused on the enterprise market, the company has expanded to serve small and midsized businesses. SuccessFactors utilizes a direct sales forces, though it does generate some channel sales through partners, including Ceridian and IBM.

The majority of SuccessFactors' sales are in the Americas, but the company has identified international expansion as a key part of its growth strategy. It expanded its list of international clients in 2009, when it added France Telecom's Orange wireless unit to its roster. The company also opened a development center in India in 2009.

EXECUTIVES

CFO, Bruce C. Felt Jr., age 52, $875,278 total compensation
President, Douglas (Doug) Dennerline
CEO and Director, Lars Dalgaard, age 43, $2,918,757 total compensation
VP and Controller, Brian Kinion
VP Global Sales Operations, Namdar (Alex) Saleh, age 50
VP Eastern Area Sales, Philip H. Carty, age 52
VP Financial Planning and Analysis, Eric McCluskey
VP Security, William Harmer III
VP Mergers and Acquisitions Integration, Judy Blegen
VP, Peter Howes
VP Product Management, Dmitri Krakovsky
VP New Business Operations, Conrad Voorsanger
VP Professional Services, Robert Block
VP Global Enterprise Sales, James B. (Jay) Larson, age 52, $1,154,390 total compensation
VP Operations and CIO, Randall J. (Randy) Womack, age 46, $611,551 total compensation
VP Global Customer Success, Patrick Saeger
VP Cloud Computing, Tom Fisher
VP Professional Services, EMEA, Christopher Nowell
VP Engineering, Mohan Sankaran
VP Engineering, Hong Yuan
VP Enterprise Sales, EMEA, Peter Prestele
VP Sales, Asia Pacific, Murray Sargant
VP Information Technology, Jeremy Bauer
CTO, Luen (Aaron) Au, age 37
Chief Marketing Officer, Darryl Dickens
Chief People Officer, Jeffrey W. Diana
Senior Director Global Small Business Sales, Marjorie Toucas
General Counsel and Secretary, Hillary B. Smith
Director Public and Investor Relations, Dominic Paschel
General Manager, Small Business Unit, Shelly K. Davenport, age 47
Auditors: Ernst & Young LLP

LOCATIONS

HQ: SuccessFactors, Inc.
1500 Fashion Island Blvd., Ste. 300, San Mateo, CA 94404
Phone: 650-645-2000   **Fax:** 650-645-2099
Web: www.successfactors.com

2009 Sales

	$ mil.	% of total
Americas	132.2	86
Europe	16.4	10
Asia/Pacific	4.5	4
Total	**153.1**	**100**

COMPETITORS

Callidus Software	Salary.com
Cornerstone OnDemand	SAP
Halogen Software	Softscape
Kenexa	SumTotal
Kronos	Synygy
Oracle	Taleo
Peopleclick Authoria	Workscape
Sage Software	Workstream

HISTORICAL FINANCIALS

Company Type: Public

Income Statement

FYE: December 31

	REVENUE ($ mil.)	NET INCOME ($ mil.)	NET PROFIT MARGIN	EMPLOYEES
12/10	205.9	(12.4)	—	1,047
12/09	153.1	(12.6)	—	664
12/08	111.9	(65.0)	—	596
12/07	63.3	(75.5)	—	736
12/06	32.6	(32.0)	—	524
Annual Growth	**58.5%**	**—**	**—**	**18.9%**

2010 Year-End Financials

Debt ratio: —
Return on equity: —
Cash ($ mil.): 75.4
Current ratio: 1.69
Long-term debt ($ mil.): —
No. of shares (mil.): 77.1
Dividends
 Yield: —
 Payout: —
Market value ($ mil.): 2,233.9

	STOCK PRICE ($) FY Close	P/E High/Low		PER SHARE ($) Earnings	Dividends	Book Value
12/10	28.96	—	—	(0.17)	0.00	3.52
12/09	16.58	—	—	(0.21)	0.00	2.82
12/08	5.74	—	—	(1.21)	0.00	(0.10)
12/07	11.82	—	—	(8.35)	0.00	0.40
Annual Growth	**34.8%**	**—**	**—**	**—**	**—**	**106.3%**

Summer Infant

Summer Infant makes products for infants and children that can be used in any season. Through its operating subsidiaries, Summer Infant develops and markets health and wellness products for children from birth to 3 years old under the Summer Infant name. Some of its products include booster seats, audio and video monitors, bed rails, safety gates, bedding, and durable bath items. It also licenses products under the Disney and Carter's brands. The company earns the majority of its revenue from the North American market, selling through retailers such as Toys "R" Us, Target, Wal-Mart, and Amazon.com. (European retailers ac-

count for less than 10% of sales.) CEO Jason Macari formed Summer Infant in 2001.

Since its inception, the company has pursued a product-centric growth strategy, which emphasizes the development of new product lines and selling more of its existing products in new retail environments. Summer Infant would like to add new products, such as car seats and strollers, to its existing categories. Expanding through acquisitions has also been key to Summer Infant's growth strategy. In 2009 the company acquired Classy Kid, a Las Vegas-based maker of placemats, bibs, and other hygiene products, as well as Butterfly Living, a crib manufacturer based in Pennsylvania.

Summer Infant has seen tremendous growth in recent years, thanks to its expanded product assortment. The company posted nearly $195 million in sales in 2010, a roughly 25% gain from the year before. Interestingly, 51% of its 2010 sales came from just one customer — Toys "R" Us. Profits also climbed from $5 million to $6 million during this time. (Those figures are a substantial improvement from years earlier — in 2006 revenues were just $1 million and profits hovered near $700,000.) Even more impressive has been Summer Infant's continued growth amid the global economic downturn, which has hit the firm's core US market especially hard. Child care products have proven to be relatively resistant to the tough economic times — market analysts suggest that consumers view many items in the category as necessities for their growing little ones. The company keeps expenditures under control by using third-party manufacturers, most of whom are based in Asia, to produce goods.

Summer Infant operates offices and warehouses in the US, Canada, and the UK. The company also hopes to eventually move into new geographic markets, such as Japan, Mexico, and Australia.

CEO Macari owns about 20% of Summer Infant's stock. Wynnefield Capital Management holds a roughly 10% stake.

EXECUTIVES

Chairman, President, and CEO, Jason P. Macari, age 47, $507,445 total compensation
President, Summer Infant Canada, Stephen Orleans
CFO and Treasurer, Joseph Driscoll, age 45, $301,116 total compensation
COO, Jeffrey L. Hale, age 48
General Manager of SIE, Rachelle Harel
Human Resource Manager, Kathy Augaitis
UK Sales Director, Richard Trott
Communications Director, Cynthia Barlow
Auditors: McGladrey & Pullen, LLP

LOCATIONS

HQ: Summer Infant, Inc.
1275 Park East Dr., Woonsocket, RI 02895
Phone: 401-671-6550   **Fax:** 401-671-6562
Web: www.summerinfant.com

2010 Sales

	$ mil.	% of total
North America	180.7	93
Other	13.8	7
Total	**194.5**	**100**

PRODUCTS/OPERATIONS

Selected Subsidiaries

Summer Infant (USA), Inc.
Summer Infant Canada, Ltd.
Summer Infant Europe, Limited
Summer Infant Asia, Ltd.

COMPETITORS

Dorel Industries	Kid Brands
Evenflo	Mattel
Graco Children's Products	RC2 Corporation

HISTORICAL FINANCIALS

Company Type: Public

Income Statement

FYE: December 31

	REVENUE ($ mil.)	NET INCOME ($ mil.)	NET PROFIT MARGIN	EMPLOYEES
12/10	194.5	6.6	3.4%	218
12/09	153.5	5.7	3.7%	178
12/08	132.4	4.9	3.7%	170
12/07	68.1	3.1	4.6%	105
12/06	1.5	0.7	46.7%	3
Annual Growth	**237.4%**	**75.2%**	**—**	**192.0%**

2010 Year-End Financials

Debt ratio: 68.0%
Return on equity: 8.6%
Cash ($ mil.): 1.1
Current ratio: 2.65
Long-term debt ($ mil.): 52.0
No. of shares (mil.): 15.5
Dividends
 Yield: —
 Payout: —
Market value ($ mil.): 117.1

	STOCK PRICE ($) FY Close	P/E High/Low		PER SHARE ($) Earnings	Dividends	Book Value
12/10	7.58	22	11	0.40	0.00	4.95
12/09	4.49	15	3	0.36	0.00	4.49
12/08	2.15	19	6	0.33	0.00	4.13
12/07	4.88	25	17	0.23	0.00	3.83
12/06	5.50	94	87	0.06	0.00	3.72
Annual Growth	**8.3%**	**—**	**—**	**60.7%**	**—**	**7.4%**

SunCoke Energy

If you're looking for a new soda product, look elsewhere; if you're looking to produce steel, SunCoke Energy's products may be right up your alley. One of North America's largest coke producers, SunCoke produces metallurgical coke (a coal-derived fuel used in steel production) for steel companies. Its five owned and operated plants — located in Virginia, Indiana, Ohio, Illinois, and Vitória, Brazil (operated only) — can produce an aggregate 5 million tons of coke per year. To support its coke production, the company also has coal mining operations in Virginia and West Virginia. Major customers have included ArcelorMittal, US Steel, and AK Steel. SunCoke, a spinoff from Sunoco, went public in 2011.

SunCoke raised some $186 million in its IPO. The proceeds were issued to initial debt exchange parties, which also received the option to purchase shares of company's common stock. In connection to the IPO, SunCoke was spun-off as an independent company and is no longer a Sunoco subsidiary. Sunoco sold SunCoke to focus on its other businesses and growth opportunities and to reduce its debt.

Going forward SunCoke, which traces its roots back to the 1960s, intends to increase its metallurgical coke production capabilities, bolster its presence in North America and Brazil, and expand into key international markets like China, Eastern Europe, and India. The company is building a new coke-producing facility in Middletown, Ohio, that would increase its overall production capacity to nearly 6 million tons per year. The facility, expected to produce 550,000 tons of coal per year, is set to open in October 2011.

In order to support the increase in production, SunCoke will also ramp up production in its coal mines and expand its mining operations through acquisitions. In early 2011 it acquired HKCC Companies and its related mining assets in Virginia. The purchase added 21 million tons of proved and probable coal reserves and brought the company's overall reserves to 106 million tons.

SunCoke uses its coal for its own operations, but it does generate some revenue through the sale of coal to outside parties. Aside from its core metallurgical coke sales, other sources of revenue for the company include sales of steam and electricity to Sunoco and other parties, as well as fees related to operating the Brazilian plant.

SunCoke also earns revenue through licensing fees for its proprietary coal-producing technologies, which includes coke ovens (used to produce its coke) that differ from more traditional by-product coke ovens. Unlike by-product ovens, which recover production-related waste used to make by-products like oil and coal tar, SunCoke's production process uses waste generated during coke production to produce steam and electricity.

Though the company's revenues were up in 2010, SunCoke's profits were down, due in part to the absence of a one-time investment tax credit it received the previous year for one of its plants.

EXECUTIVES

Chairman and CEO, Frederick A. (Fritz) Henderson, age 52
President and COO, Michael J. (Mike) Thomson, age 52
VP and Controller, Fay West, age 42
SVP, Corporate Strategy and Business Development, Matthew McGrath
SVP, Operations, Michael White
Secretary and Director, Stacy L. Fox, age 56
Auditors: Ernst & Young LLP

LOCATIONS

HQ: SunCoke Energy, Inc.
1011 Warrenville Rd., 6th Fl., Lisle, IL 60532
Phone: 630-824-1000   **Fax:** 865-288-5280
Web: www.suncoke.com

PRODUCTS/OPERATIONS

2010 Sales

	mil $	% of total
Metallurgical coke sales	1237.2	94
Steam and electricity sales	40.4	3
Operating and licensing fees	38.4	3
Metallurgical coal sales/other	.6	–
Total	**1316.6**	**100**

COMPETITORS

China Minmetals   Walter Coke
Oxbow Carbon
Severstal North
  America

HISTORICAL FINANCIALS

Company Type: Public

Income Statement

FYE: December 31

	REVENUE ($ mil.)	NET INCOME ($ mil.)	NET PROFIT MARGIN	EMPLOYEES
12/10	1,326.6	139.2	10.5%	1,140
12/09	1,145.0	189.7	16.6%	0
12/08	840.3	132.9	15.8%	0
Annual Growth	**25.6%**	**2.3%**	**—**	**—**

2010 Year-End Financials

Debt ratio: —
Return on equity: 37.7%
Cash ($ mil.): 40.1
Current ratio: 0.18
Long-term debt ($ mil.): —

No. of shares (mil.): —
Dividends
  Yield: —
  Payout: —
Market value ($ mil.): —

SunPower

SunPower won't keep you in the dark. The company makes solar cells and panels for governmental, residential, and commercial customers; and also sells imaging and infrared detector products made using SunPower's thin-wafer manufacturing process. Leading customers include Conergy, FPL, MMA Renewable Ventures, SolarPack, and Solon. Customers in Europe account for more than half of the company's sales. Cypress Semiconductor distributed to its shareholders all of SunPower's Class B common shares in 2008, ending its voting control over the former subsidiary. In 2011 French oil giant TOTAL agreed to buy a controlling stake in SunPower for around $1.4 billion.

With the transaction TOTAL plans to buy up to 60% of SunPower's Class A shares and 60% of the company's Class B shares. (The rest of the shares will remain publicly traded.) The deal also includes a $1 billion line of credit. TOTAL is looking to boost its presence in the renewable energy sector, especially in the solar and biofuel sectors. SunPower will benefit from access to cash and credit that will allow it to accelerate plans to expand solar panel production and develop large-scale solar farms. The company is one of a small group of US and European solar firms that has been able to compete for market share with the rapidly growing Chinese panel makers.

SunPower is building a solar cell manufacturing facility in Malaysia. Fab 3 came on line in October 2010. That year AU Optronics and SunPower agreed to operate Fab 3 as a 50/50 joint venture. SunPower's other plants are in the Philippines and the US.

Also in 2010 the company acquired SunRay, a European-based solar power plant developer, for around $277 million in cash, credit, and promissory notes. SunRay brings with it a project pipeline of solar photovoltaic products that spans Europe and the Middle East. The acquisition also adds to SunPower's investment in North American power plant development.

The company extended its international reach in 2008 through the acquisition of Solar Sales Pty Ltd., an Australian distributor and photovoltaic systems integrator. SunPower also acquired PowerLight (now SunPower Systems) to bring the company closer to end-users of its solar cells and panels, and help drive down the cost of solar power, making it more competitive with electrical power from other sources, without government tax incentives or subsidies.

SunPower has entered into multiyear polysilicon supply agreements with OCI Company (Korea), Hemlock Semiconductor Corp. (US), Jupiter Qingdao DTK Industries (China), and NorSun AS (Norway). SunPower also formed a joint venture with NorSun and its partners to build a polysilicon plant in Saudi Arabia.

EXECUTIVES

Chairman, President, and CEO, Thomas H. (Tom) Werner, age 51, $4,226,989 total compensation
President Emeritus and CTO, Richard M. (Dick) Swanson, age 65
President, Utility and Power Plants, Howard J. Wenger, age 51, $1,481,969 total compensation
Chairman, CEO, and CTO, SunPower Corporation, Systems, Thomas (Tom) Dinwoodie, age 56, $20,322,348 total compensation
EVP Human Resources and Corporate Services, Douglas J. (Doug) Richards, age 52, $1,066,051 total compensation
EVP Public Policy and Corporate Communications, Julie Blunden
EVP and CFO, Dennis V. Arriola, age 50, $2,174,198 total compensation
VP and Chief Marketing Officer, Jan Soderstrom
VP Technology and Development, William P. Mulligan
VP Corporate Strategy, Peter C. Aschenbrenner, age 54
VP and Treasurer, Navneet Govil
VP and General Manager, Utilities and Power Plants, EMEA, Gian Maria Ferrero
VP Global Quality and Customer Satisfaction, Surinder S. Bedi
VP and Controller, Eric Branderiz
VP and General Manager, North American Utilities and Power Plants, Jean M. Wilson
COO, Marty T. Neese, age 48, $1,109,346 total compensation
CIO, Jorg Heinemann
Managing Director, Australia, Bob Blakiston
Managing Director Market Development Southern Europe, Luis Torres
General Counsel and Secretary, Bruce R. Ledesma, age 43, $1,815,193 total compensation
Managing Director, Bill Kelly
Auditors: PricewaterhouseCoopers LLP

LOCATIONS

HQ: SunPower Corporation
3939 N. 1st St., San Jose, CA 95134
Phone: 408-240-5500   **Fax:** 408-240-5400
Web: www.sunpowercorp.com

2009 Sales

	% of total
US	43
Europe	
Italy	22
Germany	21
Spain	3
Other countries	7
Other regions	4
Total	**100**

PRODUCTS/OPERATIONS

2009 Sales

	$ mil.	% of total
Components	934.8	61
Systems	589.5	39
Total	**1,524.3**	**100**

COMPETITORS

Avago Technologies	Hamamatsu Photonics
BP Solar	IBERDROLA
Caterpillar	JA Solar
Conergy	Kyocera Solar
Conergy, Inc.	MEMC Electronic
Cummins Power	Materials
Generation	Q-Cells
DayStar Technologies	ROHM
Elecnor	SANYO Semiconductor
EMCORE	SCHOTT Solar
Energy Conversion	Sharp Corp.
Devices	Shell Renewables
Entech Solar	Solarfun
Evergreen Solar	Solon
FCC Barcelona	Suntech Power
First Solar	Vishay Intertechnology
GE Energy	

HISTORICAL FINANCIALS

Company Type: Public

Income Statement

FYE: Sunday closest to December 31

	REVENUE ($ mil.)	NET INCOME ($ mil.)	NET PROFIT MARGIN	EMPLOYEES
12/10	2,219.2	178.7	8.1%	5,150
12/09	1,524.3	33.2	2.2%	5,160
12/08	1,434.9	92.3	6.4%	5,400
12/07	774.8	9.2	1.2%	3,530
12/06	236.5	26.5	11.2%	1,572
Annual Growth	75.0%	61.1%	—	34.5%

2010 Year-End Financials

Debt ratio: 38.7%	No. of shares (mil.): 97.9
Return on equity: 10.8%	Dividends
Cash ($ mil.): 605.4	Yield: —
Current ratio: 2.28	Payout: —
Long-term debt ($ mil.): 641.9	Market value ($ mil.): 1,256.0

	STOCK PRICE ($) FY Close	P/E High/Low		PER SHARE ($) Earnings	Dividends	Book Value
12/10	12.83	15	5	1.75	0.00	16.93
12/09	23.68	129	55	0.36	0.00	14.18
12/08	37.00	118	17	1.09	0.00	11.91
12/07	130.39	1495	329	0.11	0.00	10.31
12/06	37.17	122	64	0.37	0.00	7.06
Annual Growth	(23.4%)	—	—	47.5%	—	24.4%

Super Micro Computer

Super Micro Computer strives for super macro computer sales. The company manufactures motherboards based on Intel's x86 architecture, plus complete server systems utilizing Intel's Pentium and Xeon microprocessors, as well as AMD's Opteron processors. Other products include chassis enclosures for rack-mounted servers and power supplies that feature redundant cooling systems. Customers include Juniper Networks, Lawrence Livermore National Laboratory, and Siemens. Super Micro also resells third-party cables, cooling fans, RAID (redundant array of independent disks) port cards, and other computer accessories. About two-thirds of Super Micro's sales are to customers in the US.

The company sells primarily through distributors and resellers (roughly two-thirds of sales), but it also markets to manufacturers and directly to end users.

The global recession dinged Super Micro's sales and profits in 2009. The company's revenues depend on the continued adoption of application-optimized servers for the critical business applications of its customers and end users. Competition from general-purpose, lower-cost servers and components is a challenge to the company. Super Micro must contend for business with such tech behemoths as Dell, Hewlett-Packard, IBM, and Intel.

Chairman, president, and CEO Charles Liang and his wife own about 27% of Super Micro Computer. VP and director Yih-Shyan (Wally) Liaw holds nearly 10% of the company.

EXECUTIVES

Chairman, President, and CEO, Charles Liang, age 53, $506,802 total compensation
CFO, Howard Hideshima, age 52, $539,965 total compensation
VP International Sales, Secretary, and Director, Yih-Shyan (Wally) Liaw, age 56, $225,754 total compensation
VP Operations, Treasurer, and Director, Chiu-Chu Liu (Sara) Liang, age 49, $175,960 total compensation
VP Worldwide Sales, Phidias Chou, age 53, $212,423 total compensation
SVP Investor Relations, Perry Hayes
Senior Manager Corporate Marketing Programs, Angela Rosario
Auditors: Deloitte & Touche LLP

LOCATIONS

HQ: Super Micro Computer, Inc.
980 Rock Ave., San Jose, CA 95131
Phone: 408-503-8000   **Fax:** 408-503-8008
Web: www.supermicro.com

2010 Sales

	$ mil.	% of total
US	433.6	60
Europe	156.3	22
Asia	106.9	15
Other regions	24.6	3
Total	**721.4**	**100**

PRODUCTS/OPERATIONS

2010 Sales

	$ mil.	% of total
Server systems	245.2	34
Subsystems & accessories	476.2	66
Total	**721.4**	**100**

Selected Products

Chassis enclosures (pedestal, rack-mount, tower)
Motherboards (desktop, server, workstation)
Power supplies
Servers (rack-mount, tower)

COMPETITORS

Celestica	Intel
Dell	Quanta Computer
Flextronics	Silicon Graphics
Hewlett-Packard	International
Hon Hai	Wistron
IBM	

HISTORICAL FINANCIALS

Company Type: Public

Income Statement

FYE: June 30

	REVENUE ($ mil.)	NET INCOME ($ mil.)	NET PROFIT MARGIN	EMPLOYEES
06/11	942.6	40.2	4.3%	1,272
06/10	721.4	26.9	3.7%	1,036
06/09	505.6	16.1	3.2%	865
06/08	540.5	25.4	4.7%	818
06/07	420.4	19.3	4.6%	624
Annual Growth	22.4%	20.1%	—	19.5%

2011 Year-End Financials

Debt ratio: 9.6%	No. of shares (mil.): 40.3
Return on equity: 14.0%	Dividends
Cash ($ mil.): 69.9	Yield: —
Current ratio: 2.63	Payout: —
Long-term debt ($ mil.): 27.6	Market value ($ mil.): 648.1

	STOCK PRICE ($) FY Close	P/E High/Low		PER SHARE ($) Earnings	Dividends	Book Value
06/11	16.09	21	9	0.93	0.00	7.13
06/10	13.50	30	11	0.65	0.00	6.07
06/09	7.66	27	9	0.41	0.00	5.07
06/08	7.38	16	10	0.65	0.00	4.67
06/07	10.01	21	15	0.57	0.00	3.83
Annual Growth	12.6%	—	—	13.0%	—	16.8%

Sutron

Through its Hydromet unit and other divisions, Sutron makes equipment that collects and transmits water and weather data. The company also provides related hydrological services. Customers use Sutron products to manage water resources, to obtain early warning of potentially disastrous floods or storms, and to help hydropower plants operate as efficiently as possible. The company's largest customer is the US government. Other customers include state and local governments, engineering companies, and power companies. Sutron markets its products internationally, and customers outside the US account for about 40% of sales. CEO Raul McQuivey owns 19% of the company.

EXECUTIVES

Chairman, President, and CEO, Raul S. McQuivey, age 72, $236,913 total compensation
CFO and Treasurer, Sidney C. Hooper, age 52, $211,742 total compensation
SVP, Ashish Raval, age 39, $231,874 total compensation
SVP and Director, Daniel W. Farrell, age 58, $200,534 total compensation
Director Operations and ISO Management Representative, Cecilia Oh
Auditors: Thompson, Greenspon & Co., P.C.

LOCATIONS

HQ: Sutron Corporation
21300 Ridgetop Cir., Sterling, VA 20166
Phone: 703-406-2800   **Fax:** 703-406-2801
Web: www.sutron.com

2007 Sales

	$ mil.	% of total
US	11.4	60
Asia	3.2	17
Middle East	2.5	13
Central & South America	0.6	3
Other regions	1.2	7
Total	**18.9**	**100**

PRODUCTS/OPERATIONS

2007 Sales

	$ mil.	% of total
Hydromet Products	10.0	53
Integrated Systems	6.3	33
Hydrological Services	2.0	11
Sutron India	0.6	3
Total	**18.9**	**100**

HISTORICAL FINANCIALS

Company Type: Public

Income Statement				FYE: December 31
	REVENUE ($ mil.)	NET INCOME ($ mil.)	NET PROFIT MARGIN	EMPLOYEES
12/10	23.0	3.0	13.0%	92
12/09	20.9	2.2	10.5%	90
12/08	15.9	0.5	3.1%	85
12/07	18.9	2.1	11.1%	95
12/06	19.4	2.4	12.4%	90
Annual Growth	**4.3%**	**5.7%**	**—**	**0.6%**

2010 Year-End Financials

Debt ratio: —
Return on equity: 16.5%
Cash ($ mil.): 9.6
Current ratio: 5.86
Long-term debt ($ mil.): —
No. of shares (mil.): 4.6
Dividends
  Yield: —
  Payout: —
Market value ($ mil.): 30.2

	STOCK PRICE ($) FY Close	P/E High/Low		PER SHARE ($) Earnings	Dividends	Book Value
12/10	6.61	14	10	0.60	0.00	3.96
12/09	7.19	22	8	0.45	0.00	3.29
12/08	4.45	103	28	0.10	0.00	2.78
12/07	10.62	32	15	0.41	0.00	2.68
12/06	6.81	19	13	0.51	0.00	2.32
Annual Growth	**(0.7%)**	**—**	**—**	**4.1%**	**—**	**14.4%**

Swisher Hygiene Inc.

Swisher Hygiene sweeps away the competition in the corporate world. The company provides commercial cleaning services, equipment, and supplies to more than 50,000 businesses in North America and abroad. Recognized for its restroom cleaning and disinfection services, Swisher also sells soap, cleaning chemicals, and paper products, and it rents facility service items (such as floor mats and mops). The company sells, rents, and maintains commercial dishwashers and other cleaning equipment. Swisher has expertise in serving customers in the foodservice, hospitality, health care, industrial, and retail industries. It boasts a global network of about 80 company-owned operations, 10 franchises, and 10 master licensees.

In a substantial move to expand its operations, in May 2011 Swisher Hygiene acquired ProClean of Arizona, an independent hygiene and chemical provider serving more than 4,000 customers throughout the Southwest. ProClean primarily provides warewashing (method for cleaning dishes, glasses, pots, pans, etc.), general cleaning, and laundry and housekeeping services to the foodservice and hospitality industries. Swisher Hygiene its combining its Southwest operations with ProClean's, a move that will bolster its presence in the markets of Albuquerque, El Paso, Las Vegas, Los Angeles, Phoenix, San Diego, and Tucson. In a move to expand into the deep South, the company acquired the Mississippi-based Gulf Coast Laundry Services late in the year. Gulf Coast provides linen and uniform rentals and laundry services to the hospitality industry in Alabama, Louisiana, and Mississippi.

Formerly named CoolBrands International, the company adopted the Swisher Hygiene moniker in late 2010 after combining with cleaning services provider Swisher International, which became a subsidiary. As part of the arrangement, former CoolBrands shareholders own 52% of the entity, and former Swisher International shareholders control the remaining 48%. The combined company is led by Swisher's primary shareholders, Wayne Huizenga (who serves as chairman) and Steve Berrard (who is CEO).

Once a leading maker of ice cream, yogurt, and other frozen treats, CoolBrands had been chilling as a publicly traded shell company since 2007, when it finished disposing of all its operating units. The company's portfolio included such popular brands as Eskimo Pie, Godiva, and Yoplait. It also operated and franchised retail outlets under the banners I Can't Believe It's Yogurt, Tropicana Smoothies, and Yogen Früz. CoolBrands was formerly controlled by the families of former chairmen Michael Serruya and Richard Smith.

EXECUTIVES

Chairman, President, and CEO, Michael Serruya, age 46
CFO, Ken McKenzie, age 55
President, Value America Flavors and Ingredients, William J. Weiskopf
President, Eskimo Pie Food Service, Craig L. Hettrich
VP Marketing, Matthew P. Smith
VP Operations, John R. LeSauvage
VP, SamPack Flexible Packaging, Paul C. Samuel
VP Manufacturing and Quality Assurance, Timothy Timm
VP Sales, Foodservice, Fred J. Fullerton
Vice Chairman and COO, David M. Smith, age 44
CIO, Daniel Heschke, age 48
SVP Sales and Marketing, John M. Kaczynski
Controller, Gabe Merle
SVP Operations, Americana Foods, Stacy L. Pugh
Auditors: BDO USA, LLP

LOCATIONS

HQ: Swisher Hygiene Inc.
4725 Piedmont Row Dr., Ste. 400, Charlotte, NC 28210
Phone: 704-364-7707
Web: www.swisherhygiene.com

COMPETITORS

ABM Industries	Rentokil Initial
ARAMARK	ServiceMaster
Ecolab	

HISTORICAL FINANCIALS

Company Type: Public

Income Statement				FYE: December 31
	REVENUE ($ mil.)	NET INCOME ($ mil.)	NET PROFIT MARGIN	EMPLOYEES
12/10*	63.7	(17.6)	—	1,077
08/10	0.5	0.4	80.0%	0
08/09	1.3	1.8	138.5%	0
08/06	99.3	(70.2)	—	1,033
08/05	385.1	(74.1)	—	1,305
Annual Growth	**(30.2%)**	**—**	**—**	**(3.8%)**

*Fiscal year change

2010 Year-End Financials

Debt ratio: —
Return on equity: —
Cash ($ mil.): 38.9
Current ratio: 2.23
Long-term debt ($ mil.): —
No. of shares (mil.): 114.0
Dividends
  Yield: 0.0%
  Payout: —
Market value ($ mil.): 539.3

	STOCK PRICE ($) FY Close	P/E High/Low		PER SHARE ($) Earnings	Dividends	Book Value
12/10*	4.73	—	—	(0.26)	0.00	0.40
08/10	2.48	320	85	0.01	0.00	1.03
08/09	0.94	37	12	0.03	0.00	0.99
08/06	0.71	11	7	0.09	0.00	0.99
08/05	0.96	—	—	(0.34)	0.00	0.90
Annual Growth	**49.0%**	**—**	**—**	**—**	**—**	**(18.3%)**

*Fiscal year change

SXC

SXC Health Solutions puts the "sexy" in prescription drug benefits. The company's pharmacy benefit management (PBM) software, called informedRx, manages and administers claims and offers cost control, Medicare Part D services, pharmacy network management, drug review and analysis, and reporting and information analysis. Customers include health plans such as Blue Cross/Blue Shield, managed care organizations, pharmacy benefit managers, and retail pharmacy chains. Top customers Boston Medical Center and the state of Hawaii together account for about a quarter of revenue. SXC Health Solutions also owns a mail-order pharmacy and a specialty service pharmacy (Ascend SpecialtyRx).

The company primarily offered IT-related health care services until 2008, when it bought pharmacy benefit management company National Medical Health Card Systems (NMHC) for $144 million in cash and stock. The acquisition enabled SXC to broaden its core claims processing and other pharmacy benefits management-related offerings. As a result, the company saw a dramatic increase in revenue — from $93 million in 2007 to a whopping $1.4 billion in 2009.

Proving that health care is big business, SXC was named the sixth-fastest growing company in the US by FORTUNE in 2010. And investors want in — in late 2009 it raised an additional $200 million in a public offering of 5,000 shares of its common stock, and in 2010 it offered a two-for-one stock split to increase the number of outstanding shares from 30 million to 60 million.

SXC's pharmacy benefit management software accounts for more than 90% of the company's revenues. In 2010 it landed new client HealthSpring, which offers Medicare Advantage plans in seven southern states. SXC will provide HealthSpring with its informedRx PBM software suite as well as mail-order and specialty pharmacy services. Later in the year SXC won a three-year, $720 million contract with an unnamed health plan that operates on the East Coast.

The smaller portion of SXC's revenue comes from offering health care IT (HCIT) services, including its online claims processing flagship product RxCLAIM, as well as products for pharmacy data warehousing, rebate management, and Web portal deployment. RxCLAIM processes more than 1 billion transactions every year for providers such as the Mayo Foundation. RxCLAIM and Rx-TRACK, its data warehousing and analysis tool, is marketed to resident care management providers such as long-term care facilities and institutionally based pharmacies. Subsidiary Health Business Systems (HBS), which offers pharmacy management software, operates under the HCIT segment.

In addition to bolstering its existing businesses, the company hopes to grow through acquisitions that diversify its services. In 2008 it enhanced its product offerings after acquiring the assets of Zynchros, a provider of formulary management products and Medicare Part D compliance-management products. SXC acquired MedfusionRX in late 2010 for $100 million in cash in order to build its specialty pharmaceuticals business. MedfusionRX specializes in drugs for chronic diseases such as multiple sclerosis, rheumatoid arthritis, and hepatitis C. In 2011 SXC paid about $77 million for PTRx, a pharmacy benefits manager that includes mail-order pharmacy delivery among its services. The company intends to use its growing product line to attract new customers, especially state-level public organizations and small to midsized retail pharmacy companies.

SXC was founded in 1993 as Systems Xcellence and changed its name in 2007. The company has one major institutional shareholder — asset manager Wellington Management Company controls 14% of its stock.

EXECUTIVES

Chairman, President, and CEO, Mark A. Thierer, age 51, $2,741,000 total compensation
EVP and CFO, Jeffrey (Jeff) Park, age 39, $1,397,000 total compensation
EVP Research Development and CTO, John Romza, age 55, $1,010,000 total compensation
VP Sales, Mark Mateka
SVP Industry Relations, Russell Annunziata
SVP PBM Operations, Kelly Kettlewell
SVP Public Sector and Resident Care Management, Dan Hardin
SVP Sales, B. Greg Buscetto, age 49, $1,000,000 total compensation
SVP Mail and Specialty, Mark A. Adkison, age 47
SVP, General Counsel, and Corporate Secretary, Clifford E. (Cliff) Berman, age 51
Auditors: KPMG LLP

LOCATIONS

HQ: SXC Health Solutions Corp.
2441 Warrenville Rd., Ste. 610, Lisle, IL 60532-3642
Phone: 630-577-3100   **Fax:** 630-577-3101
Web: www.sxc.com

PRODUCTS/OPERATIONS

2009 Sales

	$ mil.	% of sales
Pharmacy benefit management	1,336	92
Health care IT	102.6	8
Total	**1,438.6**	**100**

Selected Software

Ascend SpecialtyRx (specialty medication management)
HBS Retail Pharmacy Management System (pharmacy management)
informedMAIL (mail order pharmacy)
informedRx (pharmacy benefits management)
integrail (risk analysis)
RxAUTH (prior authorization management)
RxCLAIM (claims processing)
RxEXPRESS (pharmacy management)
RxMAX (rebate management system)
RxPORTAL (web portal for patients)
RxTRACK (data warehousing and analysis)
Zynchros (Medicare Part D management)

COMPETITORS

Affiliated Computer Services
Allscripts
Argus
BioScrip
Caremark Pharmacy Services
Catalyst Health Solutions
Cerner
Eclipsys
Express Scripts
First Health Group
Health Management Systems
IMS Health
Magellan Medicaid Administration
McKesson
Medco Health
MediSolution
NovoLogix
Prescription Solutions

HISTORICAL FINANCIALS

Company Type: Public

Income Statement

FYE: December 31

	REVENUE ($ mil.)	NET INCOME ($ mil.)	NET PROFIT MARGIN	EMPLOYEES
12/10	1,948.4	64.7	3.3%	1,216
12/09	1,438.6	46.1	3.2%	935
12/08	862.9	15.1	1.7%	940
12/07	93.2	13.1	14.1%	429
12/06	80.9	13.5	16.7%	426
Annual Growth	**121.5%**	**48.0%**	**—**	**30.0%**

2010 Year-End Financials

Debt ratio: —
Return on equity: 11.7%
Cash ($ mil.): 321.3
Current ratio: 2.18
Long-term debt ($ mil.): —
No. of shares (mil.): 61.6
Dividends
  Yield: —
  Payout: —
Market value ($ mil.): 2,640.3

	STOCK PRICE ($) FY Close	P/E High/Low		PER SHARE ($) Earnings	Dividends	Book Value
12/10	42.86	44	22	1.03	0.00	8.98
12/09	26.98	33	9	0.86	0.00	7.63
12/08	9.34	29	15	0.32	0.00	4.04
12/07	7.25	52	19	0.31	0.00	3.28
12/06	10.09	30	13	0.34	0.00	2.73
Annual Growth	**43.6%**	**—**	**—**	**31.9%**	**—**	**34.7%**

Sykes Enterprises

When that software won't install, Sykes can take your call. Sykes Enterprises operates more than 80 technical help and customer support centers in 24 countries across Africa, the Americas, Asia, and Europe that use phone, e-mail, and chat to serve those in need of help. Sykes specializes in customer service and inbound technical support and also provides large corporations with technical staffing and consulting relating to customer relationship management. Sykes predominantly serves the communications, consumer, financial services, and technology industries. In early 2010, Sykes achieved significant growth when it acquired rival ICT Group.

Sykes bought ICT Group for $263 million, and the deal created a combined company with revenues of more than $1.2 billion, significantly expanded its portfolio of clients, and extended its global reach to 24 countries by adding 34 call centers to its network. By the fiscal year end of 2010, Sykes experienced a substantial 42% increase in revenue; however, its net income underwent a steep decline, mostly as a result from losses associated with discontinued operations stemming from the ICT Group acquisition. The company was able to realize approximately $28 million in synergies because of the deal, though.

Sykes' experience and depth in international operations serves the company well as customers worldwide continue to shift outsourced CRM teleservices overseas to markets with cheaper labor pools. Like most companies in the industry, Sykes' efforts to cut costs have included layoffs and call center closures. (After its acquisition of ICT Group, the company had to shut down four centers in the Philippines and consolidate space in some US centers due to overlap.) Its overall growth strategy includes adding to its call center seat capacity and expanding the number of service lines and markets it serves internationally.

Former chairman and CEO John Sykes founded the company in 1977. His son Charles Sykes now leads the company as president and CEO.

HISTORY

Originally based in North Carolina, Sykes Enterprises was founded in 1977 to provide design and engineering services; it often acted as a temp agency for technical professionals. In 1992 Sykes' merger with programming firm Forrest Ford Consultants boosted the company's software services division. The big shift came in 1993, when Sykes moved its headquarters to Florida and refocused its operations on information technology outsourcing services. The company opened two call centers in 1994 and added two more the following year. It went public in 1996.

Targeting Europe as a market for growth, Sykes acquired Scotland's McQueen International Limited, Germany's Telcare, and TAS — all technical support companies — in 1997. In 1998 the company started its employee benefits administration joint venture with HealthPlan Services and soon bought out its partner's interest (it sold all but 7% in 2000 to investment firm Welsh, Carson, Anderson & Stowe).

In early 2000 the company restated 1999 second and third quarter earnings due to irregularities related to delays in the recognition of software revenues. A class-action shareholder lawsuit followed the announcement. In 2001 Iain Macdonald resigned from the board of directors. Founder, chairman, and CEO John Sykes retired from the company in 2004; his son Charles Sykes was appointed president and CEO.

Sykes acquired an Argentina-based operator of call centers, Centro de Interaccion Multimedia SA (known as Apex), for $27 million in 2006. It also sold its SHPS subsidiary, which provided employee benefits administration services, to health care industry investment firm Welsh, Carson, Anderson & Stowe.

After years of focusing on its core business and reducing costs, the company acquired rival ICT Group in early 2010.

EXECUTIVES

Chairman, Paul L. Whiting, age 67
President, CEO, and Director, Charles E. (Chuck) Sykes, age 48, $2,321,778 total compensation
EVP and CIO, David L. Pearson, age 52, $588,519 total compensation
EVP Global Sales and Client Management, Lawrence R. (Lance) Zingale, age 55, $931,601 total compensation
EVP, General Counsel, and Corporate Secretary, James T. Holder, age 52
EVP Global Operations, James C. Hobby, age 60, $932,866 total compensation
EVP Human Resources, Jenna R. Nelson, age 47
EVP and CFO, W. Michael Kipphut, age 57, $1,294,698 total compensation
EVP Global Strategy, Daniel L. Hernandez, age 44
VP and Corporate Controller, William N. Rocktoff, age 48
Director Marketing Communications, Andrea M. Burnett Thomas
Global VP Finance and Investor Relations, Subhaash Kumar
Auditors: Deloitte & Touche LLP

LOCATIONS

HQ: Sykes Enterprises, Incorporated
400 N. Ashley Dr., Ste. 2800, Tampa, FL 33602
Phone: 813-274-1000   **Fax:** 813-273-0148
Web: www.sykes.com

2010 Sales

	$ mil.	% of total
Americas		
US	293.2	25
Philippines	249.0	22
Canada	195.3	17
Costa Rica	89.8	8
El Salvador	35.4	3
Mexico	20.5	2
Argentina	7.8	1
Other	43.4	4
International		
Germany	65.1	5
UK	46.8	4
Spain	36.8	3
Sweden	27.3	2
The Netherlands	14.0	1
Hungary	8.2	1
Romania	3.7	-
Other	22.4	2
Total	**1,158.7**	**100**

PRODUCTS/OPERATIONS

2010 Sales

	$ mil.	% of total
Outsourced customer contact management services	1,133.7	98
Fulfillment services	16.9	1
Enterprise support services	8.1	1
Total	**1,158.7**	**100**

COMPETITORS

24/7 Customer	Keane
Accenture	NCO Group
Aegis Communications	SFN Group
Amdocs	Sitel Worldwide
APAC Customer Services	StarTek
Atento Brasil	Stream Global Services
Atos	Sutherland Global
Computer Generated	Services
Solutions	TechTeam
Computer Sciences	Teleperformance
Corp.	TeleTech
Concentrix	TRG Customer Solutions
Convergys	vCustomer
DecisionOne	West Corporation
HP Enterprise Services	Wipro Infotech
Infosys	

HISTORICAL FINANCIALS

Company Type: Public

Income Statement

FYE: December 31

	REVENUE ($ mil.)	NET INCOME ($ mil.)	NET PROFIT MARGIN	EMPLOYEES
12/10	1,158.7	(10.3)	—	43,400
12/09	846.0	43.2	5.1%	49,200
12/08	819.2	60.6	7.4%	32,940
12/07	710.1	39.9	5.6%	29,560
12/06	574.2	42.3	7.4%	26,210
Annual Growth	**19.2%**	**—**	**—**	**13.4%**

2010 Year-End Financials

Debt ratio: —
Return on equity: —
Cash ($ mil.): 189.8
Current ratio: 2.98
Long-term debt ($ mil.): —

No. of shares (mil.): 47.0
Dividends
　Yield: —
　Payout: —
Market value ($ mil.): 951.9

	STOCK PRICE ($) FY Close	P/E High/Low		PER SHARE ($) Earnings	Dividends	Book Value
12/10	20.26	—	—	(0.22)	0.00	12.41
12/09	25.47	26	13	1.05	0.00	10.86
12/08	19.12	15	8	1.48	0.00	9.31
12/07	18.00	21	15	0.98	0.00	8.95
12/06	17.64	21	11	1.05	0.00	7.19
Annual Growth	**3.5%**	**—**	**—**	**—**	**—**	**14.6%**

Syms

Syms sells fancy names at not-so-fancy prices. The company sells designer-label clothing through about 50 Syms and Filene's Basement (acquired in 2009) stores in some 15 states. The stores cater predominantly to middle-income women with branded slacks, skirts, blazers, and dresses with such labels as Liz Claiborne and to men by offering suits, sports jackets, slacks, shoes, and tuxedos. The apparel retailer also sells children's casual clothing and formalwear, as well as handbags, luggage, and other accessories. Sym (and its subsidiary Filene's Basement) filed for Chapter 11 bankruptcy protection in November 2011 and plans to liquidate the business.

The company has faced an uphill struggle in light of the economic downturn, curbed consumer spending, and the highly competitive field coming from large department stores and private label discount chains. With such competitive and financial struggles (2010 net income $8.3 million vs. 2011 net income -$32.8 million), Syms decided to go

through the liquidation process and expects to have its stores and real estate sold by the end of January 2012.

In May 2009 Syms acquired Filene's Basement out of Chapter 11 bankruptcy. The acquisition allowed Syms to pluck Filene's Basement out of Chapter 11 bankruptcy, which it had entered in May 2009. As part of the agreement, which was valued at $65 million, Syms purchased substantially all of the assets of Filene's Basement, including more than two dozen operating Filene's Basement store leases, store fixtures, and inventory. Syms also partnered with real estate developer Vornado Realty Trust, which funded the acquisition with more than $8 million in exchange for a renewed lease agreement at the Filene's Basement Manhattan location at a minimum increase of $1.5 million in annual rent. (The property is at 4 Union Square South and spans three stories and 90,000 sq. ft.)

Filene's Basement complements the unique retailing culture that Syms has established during more than 50 years in business. Indeed, the purchase of Filene's "feminized" the company in that it greatly increased the percentage of sales the retailer makes to women. Whereas prior to the Filene's acquisition men's apparel and accessories accounted for more than 50% of sales, in fiscal 2010 (ends February) sales to women overtook sales to males. Syms also plans to maintain long-held traditions, such as its annual "Running of the Brides," at 100-year-old Filene's Basement, as well as its name and many of the company's employees.

Syms is distinctive in that it's known for its 10-day automatic markdown pricing policy designed to move women's dresses (which typically have a shorter shelf life than other merchandise) off the selling floor. After every 10-day period a dress goes unsold, its price is reduced a total of three times over 30 days. Seeking to combine the best of both brands, in 2009 the company opened its first co-branded store in Fairfield, Connecticut. The hybrid store is divided into two areas and contains a Syms and a Filene's store. An additional three co-branded stores — named fbSY (pronounced fib-SEE) — debuted in mid-September 2010. The new stores are located in Manhattan, Westchester Country, and on Long Island and feature an expanded selection of American and European designer labels.

Founder Sy Syms, who opened his first retail clothing store in 1959, died at the age of 83 in November 2009 due to complications from heart disease. In January 2010 Marcy added chairman to her titles of president and CEO. Marcy joined the family-owned firm in 1978, becoming president in 1983 and CEO in 1998. She owns about 55% of the company's stock.

EXECUTIVES

Chairman, President, and CEO, Marcy Syms, age 60, $582,309 total compensation
VP Children's, Karen Day, age 52
VP Ladies, Mary A. Mann, age 60, $202,956 total compensation
VP Information Technology, Elyse Marks, age 57
VP Operations, James Donato, age 54
VP Human Resources, John Tyzbir, age 56
VP and Divisional Merchandise Manager, Men's Tailored Clothing, Myra Butensky, age 51, $205,542 total compensation
COO, Joel Feigenbaum, age 54
SVP and General Merchandise Manager, Jason Somerfeld
SVP, CFO, and Chief Administrative Officer, Seth L. Udasin, age 54
Auditors: BDO Seidman, LLP

LOCATIONS

HQ: Syms Corp
1 Syms Way, Secaucus, NJ 07094
Phone: 201-902-9600   **Fax:** 201-902-9874
Web: www.syms.com

2011 Stores

	No.
New York	10
Massachusetts	8
Florida	6
Maryland	4
District of Columbia	3
Georgia	3
Illinois	3
Connecticut	2
New Jersey	2
Ohio	2
Michigan	1
Pennsylvania	1
Texas	1
Virginia	1
Total	**47**

PRODUCTS/OPERATIONS

2011 Sales

	% of total
Women's dresses, suits, separates & accessories	46
Men's tailored clothing & haberdashery	38
Luggage, domestics & fragrances	6
Children's apparel	5
Shoes	5
Total	**100**

COMPETITORS

Brooks Brothers	Kohl's
Burlington Coat	Loehmann's
Factory	Macy's
Casual Male Retail	Men's Wearhouse
Group	Nordstrom
Dillard's	Ross Stores
Jos. A. Bank	TJX Companies

HISTORICAL FINANCIALS

Company Type: Public

Income Statement

FYE: Saturday nearest last day in February

	REVENUE ($ mil.)	NET INCOME ($ mil.)	NET PROFIT MARGIN	EMPLOYEES
02/11	445.1	(32.9)	—	2,500
02/10	377.3	8.3	2.2%	3,000
02/09	242.0	(3.4)	—	1,400
02/08	267.1	0.8	0.3%	1,700
02/07	281.2	9.5	3.4%	1,704
Annual Growth	**12.2%**	**—**	**—**	**10.1%**

2011 Year-End Financials

Debt ratio: 18.8%
Return on equity: —
Cash ($ mil.): 2.3
Current ratio: 1.46
Long-term debt ($ mil.): 30.2
No. of shares (mil.): 14.4
Dividends
Yield: 0.0%
Payout: —
Market value ($ mil.): 96.2

	STOCK PRICE ($) FY Close	P/E High/Low		PER SHARE ($) Earnings	Dividends	Book Value
02/11	6.66	—	—	(2.27)	0.00	11.14
02/10	9.95	18	7	0.57	0.00	13.36
02/09	5.42	—	—	(0.23)	0.00	12.75
02/08	13.45	442	185	0.05	0.00	13.17
02/07	19.20	33	22	0.65	0.00	14.03
Annual Growth	**(23.3%)**	**—**	**—**	**—**	**—**	**(5.6%)**

Synchronoss

Synchronoss Technologies hopes to help you synch up a variety of customer service efforts. The company provides hosted software and services that communications service providers use to manage tasks such as service activation and customer transactions, including additions, subtractions, and changes to service plans. Synchronoss' customers have included service providers AT&T Mobility (formerly Cingular), Vonage, Cablevision, and Time Warner Cable, as well as equipment manufacturers such as Dell, Apple, and Nokia. The company is targeting service providers in markets including wireless and wireline communications, as well as Voice over Internet Protocol (VoIP) markets.

In 2010 the company acquired FusionOne for about $40 million. The deal expanded Synchronoss' customer base and allowed it to offer an integrated package for managing transactions and mobile content delivery.

AT&T is responsible for about 65% of the company's sales, with Synchronoss' five largest customers accouning for 84% of its total revenues. Reliance on a relatively small number of customers for a majority of sales can be risky for companies such as Synchronoss, as the loss of a single customer can dramatically impact sales. To that end Synchronoss has been working to diversify its customer base in recent years, which has grown past its core base of telecom service providers to include mobile device makers such as Apple and Nokia. While the majority of the company's sales come from North America, Synchronoss has announced strategic plans to expand its international sales, with a focus on Europe, Latin America, and Asia Pacific..

EXECUTIVES

Chairman, President, and CEO, Stephen G. Waldis, age 43, $1,012,242 total compensation
President, International, Robert Sean Parkinson, age 52
EVP, CFO, and Treasurer, Lawrence R. Irving, age 54, $589,617 total compensation
EVP Marketing and Chief Marketing Officer, Omar Téllez, age 42, $335,623 total compensation
EVP Business Development, Daniel Rizer, age 47
EVP and COO, Robert E. (Bob) Garcia, age 42, $814,578 total compensation
EVP Research and Development and CTO, Patrick J. (Pat) Doran, age 37
EVP InterconnectNow, Mark A. Mendes, age 48
VP and CIO, S. Andrew Cox, age 45
EVp and Chief Sales Officer, Christopher S. (Chris) Putnam, age 42, $412,010 total compensation
Media Relations, Stacie Hiras
Investor Relations, Tim Dolan
Leader, Installed Accounts Unit, Michael S. (Mike) Arnold
SVP, General Counsel, and Secretary, Ronald J. Prague, age 47
Auditors: Ernst & Young LLP

LOCATIONS

HQ: Synchronoss Technologies, Inc.
750 Rte. 202 South, Ste. 600, Bridgewater, NJ 08807
Phone: 866-620-3940
Web: www.synchronoss.com

COMPETITORS

Accenture	IBM Global Services
Amdocs	Motive, Inc.
CSG Systems	NeuStar
International	VeriSign
HP Enterprise Services	

HISTORICAL FINANCIALS

Company Type: Public

Income Statement

FYE: December 31

	REVENUE ($ mil.)	NET INCOME ($ mil.)	NET PROFIT MARGIN	EMPLOYEES
12/10	166.0	3.9	2.3%	758
12/09	128.8	12.3	9.5%	511
12/08	111.0	11.9	10.7%	443
12/07	123.5	23.8	19.3%	232
12/06	72.4	10.1	14.0%	170
Annual Growth	**23.1%**	**(21.2%)**	**—**	**45.3%**

2010 Year-End Financials

Debt ratio: 3.2%
Return on equity: 1.3%
Cash ($ mil.): 180.4
Current ratio: 9.10
Long-term debt ($ mil.): 9.2
No. of shares (mil.): 36.9
Dividends
Yield: —
Payout: —
Market value ($ mil.): 984.6

	STOCK PRICE ($) FY Close	P/E High/Low		PER SHARE ($) Earnings	Dividends	Book Value
12/10	26.71	248	122	0.12	0.00	7.81
12/09	15.81	41	20	0.39	0.00	4.71
12/08	10.66	93	15	0.37	0.00	4.04
12/07	35.44	68	19	0.71	0.00	3.90
12/06	13.72	45	18	0.35	0.00	2.98
Annual Growth	**18.1%**	**—**	**—**	**(23.5%)**	**—**	**27.3%**

Synovics

Synovics Pharmaceuticals (formerly Bionutrics) is looking for a new edge. The company is focused on marketing over-the-counter pharmaceuticals and bringing new generic products to market in the US. Synovics brings in revenue from over-the-counter drugmaker Kirk Pharmaceuticals, which it acquired in 2006. Kirk makes private-label OTC versions of analgesics (Tylenol, Bayer), cold and allergy medicines (Benadryl, Chlor-Trimeton), and other medicines. The company also aims to market low-cost versions of prescription pharmaceuticals through partnerships with other manufacturers. Private Indian drug firm Maneesh Pharmaceuticals owns a 51% stake in Synovics.

Maneesh Pharmaceuticals invested in Synovics in mid-2008. The two companies also entered a joint venture agreement in which Maneesh will provide consulting services to Synovics for one year. The deal also provides for possible future licensing arrangements in which Kirk Pharmaceuticals may manufacture and market Maneesh's products.

The company was previously focused on developing generics and improved formulations of already-approved prescription drugs through a licensing partnership with Nostrum Pharmaceuticals, but the two companies ended their partnership in 2007 after a legal dispute.

EXECUTIVES

CFO, Mahendra (Manny) Desai, age 62, $10,384 total compensation
Chairman and Secretary, Ronald H. (Ron) Lane, age 66, $582,163 total compensation
VP Business Development, Kirk Pharmaceuticals, John S. Copanos, age 40, $232,932 total compensation
Interim CEO and Director, Jyotindra Gange, age 62
Controller, Aldo Rodriguez, $120,000 total compensation
Director Technical Operations, Kirk Pharmaceuticals, Joe Esposito, $190,500 total compensation
Auditors: Miller, Ellin & Company, LLP

LOCATIONS

HQ: Synovics Pharmaceuticals, Inc.
5360 NW 35th Ave., Fort Lauderdale, FL 33309
Phone: 954-486-4590
Web: www.synovics.com

PRODUCTS/OPERATIONS

Selected Subsidiaries
ANDAPharm, Inc.
Kirk Pharmaceuticals, Inc.

COMPETITORS

Bayer AG	Perrigo
Bristol-Myers Squibb	Pfizer
Forest Labs	Procter & Gamble
GlaxoSmithKline	Ranbaxy Laboratories
Hoffmann-La Roche	Sandoz International
Johnson & Johnson	GmbH
Mylan	Teva
Novartis	Watson Pharmaceuticals

HISTORICAL FINANCIALS

Company Type: Public

Income Statement
FYE: October 31

	REVENUE ($ mil.)	NET INCOME ($ mil.)	NET PROFIT MARGIN	EMPLOYEES
10/08	26.0	(4.0)	—	155
10/07	23.5	(20.9)	—	140
10/06	10.5	(8.6)	—	120
10/05	0.0	(2.9)	—	4
10/04	0.1	(1.1)	—	2
Annual Growth	301.6%	—	—	196.7%

2008 Year-End Financials
Debt ratio: 92.1%
Return on equity: —
Cash ($ mil.): 0.1
Current ratio: 0.53
Long-term debt ($ mil.): 3.8
No. of shares (mil.): 25.8
Dividends
Yield: —
Payout: —
Market value ($ mil.): 9.0

	STOCK PRICE ($) FY Close	P/E High/Low	Earnings	Dividends	Book Value
10/08	0.00	— —	(0.00)	0.00	(0.00)
10/07	0.35	— —	(0.17)	0.00	0.19
10/06	0.80	— —	(1.09)	0.00	(0.27)
10/05	2.00	— —	(0.33)	0.00	0.50
Annual Growth	—	— —	—	—	—

Synta Pharmaceuticals

Synta Pharmaceuticals doesn't fill stockings, but it might eventually fill the medical need of treating cancer. The drug development company has a handful of candidates in clinical and pre-clinical development stages. Its ganetespib and elesclomol compounds are in clinical trials as possible treatments for several types of cancer, including non-small cell lung cancer (NSCLC) and colorectal, pancreatic, ovarian, and breast cancers. Synta's preclinical research efforts include potential therapies for autoimmune diseases, inflammatory conditions, and cancerous tumors.

The company's ganetespib (formerly STA-9090) candidate is being evaluated for the treatment of about a dozen forms of cancer (including NSCLC, gastrointestinal, and colorectal), and as such, is Synta's lead contender for reaching commercialization. Elesclomol is in trials for NSCLC and ovarian cancer, as well as leukemia.

To help fund its development efforts, the company pursues strategic collaboration and licensing agreements with other drugmakers. For instance, Synta has a strategic agreement with Roche Holdings for its preclinical development program targeting rheumatoid arthritis and other autoimmune and inflammatory conditions.

The company also had a partnership with GlaxoSmithKline on elasclomol; however, that partnership was terminated in 2009 after a late-stage clinical trial on the candidate for melanoma was halted due to disappointing results. As a result, Synta laid off about 40% of its workforce. Afterwards, Synta evaluated the trial results, determined that the drug still held promise for many patients, and laid out plans for fresh trials.

The company has no manufacturing facilities and relies upon contract manufacturing organizations to produce its supplies for clinical trials. As a development-stage firm, Synta has yet to turn a profit and doesn't expect to do so until it completes trials on (and gains FDA approval to market) one of its candidates.

Investment firm Caxton Corporation is the company's largest shareholder, controlling a 20% stake. Synta cofounders Lan Bo Chen (a company director) and Safi Bahcall (CEO) own 8% and 6% stakes in the company, respectively.

EXECUTIVES

Chairman, Keith R. Gollust, age 65
President, CEO, and Director, Safi R. Bahcall, age 42, $1,152,639 total compensation
VP Human Resources, Arthur J. McMahon
VP Drug Disposition and Preclinical Safety, Andrew J. Sonderfan
VP Clinical Research, Iman El-Hariry
VP Investor Relations and Corporate Communications, Robert (Rob) Kloppenburg
VP Drug Product Development, Suresh R. Babu
VP Finance and Administration and CFO, Keith S. Ehrlich, age 60, $546,861 total compensation
VP Chemistry, Lijun Sun
VP Intellectual Property and Legal Affairs, Secretary. and General Counsel, Wendy E. Rieder, age 43
SVP Program Management and Clinical Operations, Jeremy G. Chadwick, age 48
SVP Drug Development, Keizo Koya, age 53, $719,991 total compensation
SVP Business and Commercial Development, Amar Singh, age 53

SVP Clinical Research and Regulatory Affairs and Chief Medical Officer, Vojo Vukovic
Senior Director Regulatory Affairs, David Noskowitz
Auditors: KPMG LLP

LOCATIONS

HQ: Synta Pharmaceuticals Corp.
45 Hartwell Ave., Lexington, MA 02421
Phone: 781-274-8200   **Fax:** 781-274-8228
Web: www.syntapharma.com

PRODUCTS/OPERATIONS

Selected Drug Candidates
Elesclomol (formerly STA-4783, mitochondria metabolism inhibitor for cancer)
Ganetespib (formerly STA-9090, Hsp90 inhibitor for cancer)
IL-12/23 inhibitor (inflammation)
Oral CRACM ion channel inhibitor (autoimmune diseases and inflammation)
STA-9584 (vascular disrupting agent for cancer)

COMPETITORS

Abbott Labs	Kyowa Hakko Kirin
Amgen	Myrexis
Biogen Idec	Novartis
Curis	Pharmaceuticals
EpiCept	OXiGENE
Exelixis	Pfizer
Infinity	Sanofi
Pharmaceuticals	YM BioSciences
Johnson & Johnson	

HISTORICAL FINANCIALS

Company Type: Public

Income Statement
FYE: December 31

	REVENUE ($ mil.)	NET INCOME ($ mil.)	NET PROFIT MARGIN	EMPLOYEES
12/10	14.8	(37.5)	—	112
12/09	144.2	79.1	54.9%	127
12/08	2.6	(92.6)	—	129
12/07	0.7	(63.5)	—	175
12/04	0.2	(45.9)	—	135
Annual Growth	104.9%	—	—	(3.1%)

2010 Year-End Financials
Debt ratio: 49.8%
Return on equity: —
Cash ($ mil.): 31.3
Current ratio: 3.08
Long-term debt ($ mil.): 11.7
No. of shares (mil.): 42.1
Dividends
Yield: —
Payout: —
Market value ($ mil.): 257.6

	STOCK PRICE ($) FY Close	P/E High/Low	Earnings	Dividends	Book Value
12/10	6.12	— —	(0.93)	0.00	0.56
12/09	5.06	4 1	2.32	0.00	0.73
12/08	6.12	— —	(2.75)	0.00	(1.73)
12/07	6.70	— —	(3.76)	0.00	0.73
Annual Growth	(3.0%)	— —	—	—	(8.8%)

Synthesis Energy Systems

Synthesis Energy Systems (SES) prefers it when a little waste is produced posthaste. The company owns a coal gasification plant in China that began production in 2008. (Coal gasification converts low-rank coal and coal waste into fuels such as synthetic natural gas, methanol, ammonia, and dimethyl ether, which are used to make gasoline). SES leases the technology behind the plant from the Gas Technology Institute. The company has four more coal gasification plants under development — two in China with AEI, and two in the US with North American Coal Corporation and CONSOL Energy.

EXECUTIVES

Chairman, Lorenzo C. Lamadrid, age 60
President, CEO, and Director, Robert Rigdon, age 52, $1,102,437 total compensation
VP Investor Relations, Ann Tanabe
Chief Accounting Officer and Corporate Controller, Kevin Kelly, age 47, $281,101 total compensation
CTO, Francis Lau, age 63
Managing Director, Chinese Operations, Foon Lee Leow, age 53
SVP Global Business Development and Licensing, William E. Preston, age 51
SVP Engineering and Project Operations, John D. Winter, age 56
Auditors: KPMG LLP

LOCATIONS

HQ: Synthesis Energy Systems, Inc.
3 Riverway, Ste. 300, Houston, TX 77056
Phone: 713-579-0600   **Fax:** 713-579-0610
Web: www.synthesisenergy.com

COMPETITORS

Changing World Technologies	Global Energy
Dakota Gasification	Global Environmental
	Syntroleum

HISTORICAL FINANCIALS

Company Type: Public

Income Statement

FYE: June 30

	REVENUE ($ mil.)	NET INCOME ($ mil.)	NET PROFIT MARGIN	EMPLOYEES
06/11	10.2	(15.5)	—	189
06/10	9.3	(21.7)	—	197
06/09	2.1	(28.6)	—	160
06/08	0.3	(27.4)	—	201
Annual Growth	**224.0%**	**—**	**—**	**(2.0%)**

2011 Year-End Financials

Debt ratio: 4.8%	No. of shares (mil.): 50.9
Return on equity: —	Dividends
Cash ($ mil.): 32.2	Yield: —
Current ratio: 4.36	Payout: —
Long-term debt ($ mil.): 4.7	Market value ($ mil.): 95.1

	STOCK PRICE ($) FY Close	P/E High/Low	PER SHARE ($) Earnings	Dividends	Book Value
06/11	1.87	— —	(0.32)	0.00	1.92
06/10	1.10	— —	(0.45)	0.00	2.16
06/09	1.15	— —	(0.60)	0.00	2.57
06/08	9.00	— —	(0.80)	0.00	4.13
Annual Growth	**(40.8%)**	**— —**	**—**	**—**	**(22.6%)**

Taleo

Taleo knows how to handle talent. The company offers staffing management software designed to help large companies establish and manage staffing processes for professional, hourly, and temporary employees. Taleo's application suite, which it offers as a hosted subscription service, includes tools for adhering to regulatory requirements and aligning tasks with the available skills of the workforce. The company's professional services division provides implementation and technical support. Taleo serves customers in a range of industries, including Dow Chemical, Hewlett-Packard, and UnitedHealth Group.

Taleo's sales in both its software and service business segments rose in 2010 over 2009, but losses for the year jumped by more than 400% due to increased operating expenses in a number of business areas. The company had higher costs largely because of its increased headcount resulting from its acquisitions in 2010 as well as the hiring of new sales personnel; additional expenses were tied to pay raises and other incentive compensation.

Most of Taleo's sales are made in the US and Canada, but the company markets its products worldwide, particularly in Europe. It has identified international expansion as a key part of its strategy. Taleo is focusing on countries where it already has customers and a local presence, including Australia, France, New Zealand, and the UK.

Acquisitions have played a key role in Taleo's product development and international growth. In 2011 the company bought Jobpartners, a European developer of recruiting software, for $38 million. The purchase doubled both Taleo's customer base and its sales and service staff in Europe. The deal included an R&D center in Poland and a customer service center in Scotland. Jobpartners' cloud-based software is used in more than 50 countries and is available in 28 languages. Also that year the company bought rival human resource software maker Cytiva for about $11 million. The transaction added a number of customers for Taleo's cloud-based product suite in North America.

In 2010 the company acquired Worldwide Compensation for about $14 million in cash. Taleo had made a previous equity investment in Worldwide Compensation, which provides compensation management software. Also that year Taleo purchased strategic partner Learn.com for about $125 million in cash. The deal expanded Taleo's Talent management suite to include applications for managing training and education activities throughout organizations as well as to customers and partners. The addition of Learn.com boosted Taleo's customer base to around 5,000.

EXECUTIVES

Chairman, President, and CEO, Michael (Mike) Gregoire, age 45, $2,392,995 total compensation
EVP and CFO, Douglas C. (Doug) Jeffries, age 55
EVP Global Services, Guy Gauvin, age 43, $852,678 total compensation
EVP Worldwide Field Operations and Chief Customer Officer, Neil Hudspith, age 53, $1,096,257 total compensation
VP Research, Alice Snell
SVP and General Counsel, Jonathan Faddis, age 39
SVP, Small and Medium Business and Talent Grid, Michael Boese
Press Contact, EMEA South, Christine Ducos-Restagno
Press Contact, EMEA North, Susan Graeme
Press Contact, Asia Pacific, Lynne Salmon
SVP Strategy and Corporate Development, Hans Lidforss
Press Contact, North America, Mary Jo Rose
SVP Products and Technology, Jason Blessing
SVP Operations, Paul Pronsati
Group VP People and Talent, Chris Lee
SVP and Chief Marketing Officer, Shail Khiyara
Investor Relations, Mike Magaro
Auditors: Deloitte & Touche LLP

LOCATIONS

HQ: Taleo Corporation
4140 Dublin Blvd., Ste. 400, Dublin, CA 94568
Phone: 925-452-3000   **Fax:** 925-452-3001
Web: www.taleo.com

2010 Sales

	% of total
US	83
Europe	9
Canada	4
Other countries	4
Total	**100**

PRODUCTS/OPERATIONS

2010 Sales

	$ mil.	% of total
Application	199.3	84
Consulting	38.0	16
Total	**237.3**	**100**

COMPETITORS

ADP	Pilat Technologies
Bernard Hodes	International
Cornerstone OnDemand	ProcureStaff
Elance	Saba Software
Fieldglass	Salary.com
Halogen Software	SAP
iCIMS	SilkRoad technology
Kenexa	Stepstone
Kronos	SuccessFactors
Monster Worldwide	SumTotal
Oracle	Talent Technology
Peopleclick Authoria	Workstream

HISTORICAL FINANCIALS

Company Type: Public

Income Statement

FYE: December 31

	REVENUE ($ mil.)	NET INCOME ($ mil.)	NET PROFIT MARGIN	EMPLOYEES
12/10	237.3	0.4	0.2%	1,164
12/09	198.4	1.3	0.7%	916
12/08	168.4	(8.2)	—	878
12/07	127.9	3.9	3.0%	656
12/06	97.0	(2.6)	—	585
Annual Growth	25.1%	—	—	18.8%

2010 Year-End Financials

Debt ratio: 0.0%
Return on equity: 0.1%
Cash ($ mil.): 141.6
Current ratio: 1.65
Long-term debt ($ mil.): 0.0
No. of shares (mil.): 40.7
Dividends
  Yield: —
  Payout: —
Market value ($ mil.): 1,124.6

	STOCK PRICE ($) FY Close	P/E High/Low		PER SHARE ($) Earnings	Dividends	Book Value
12/10	27.65	3266	1917	0.01	0.00	9.06
12/09	23.52	638	171	0.04	0.00	8.54
12/08	7.83	—	—	(0.30)	0.00	5.54
12/07	29.78	263	92	0.13	0.00	3.94
12/06	13.67	—	—	(0.13)	0.00	3.27
Annual Growth	19.3%	—	—	—	—	29.0%

Tangoe

Tangoe dances to a telecom tempo. The company provides telecommunications expense management software and consulting services, enabling organizations to manage their voice, data, and wireless communications services and control the costs associated with them. Its flagship Communications Management Platform software includes a knowledge base of industry reference metrics and tools to support service provisioning, inventory, carrier contracts management, billing, auditing, reporting, and analysis. Tangoe also offers such services as expense consulting, contract negotiation, bill auditing, and carrier migration. Its directors and executives collectively own about 52% of the company. Tangoe completed an IPO in 2010.

Proceeds from the public offering are slated primarily for paying down debt and funding the company's day-to-day operations. Tangoe's revenue more than doubled between 2007 and 2009 from a combination of organic growth and acquisitions, but the company did not turn a profit during those years.

Tangoe acquired the complementary software business of rival Telwares in 2011 in order to boost its market share. The companies concurrently formed a partnership to combine Tangoe's software products with Telwares' expertise in providing related corporate communications expense management and IT services. The deal gave Tangoe ownership of Telwares' invoice management, call accounting, and mobile device management product lines.

Also that year, the company acquired the fixed and mobile expense management business of HCL Technologies, as well as the associated processing and support operations located in Alpharetta, Georgia and East Rutherford, New Jersey, to extend the capacity of its customer service organization.

Tangoe established its European headquarters in Amsterdam in 2011 to better serve its growing customer base in the region. Tangoe has US offices in Connecticut, Massachusetts, New Jersey, New York, and Texas.

In late 2008 the company purchased InterNoded, a provider of mobile device management software, for $3.2 million. The deal added nearly 400 customers to Tangoe's client list and added mobile device management capabilities to its product line, enabling customers to provision and support smart devices. Also that year, the company bought New Jersey-based Information Strategies Group for $11.8 million in a move to build up its expense processing services and products. Tangoe bought Austin-based wireless expense management specialist Traq-wireless in 2007.

The company was founded as TelecomRFQ in 2000 by CEO Albert Subbloie. It changed its name to Tangoe the following year. The company has received venture capital financing from Comerica.

EXECUTIVES

Chairman, President, and CEO, Albert R. (Al) Subbloie Jr., age 50, $712,606 total compensation
CFO, Gary R. Martino, age 50, $429,268 total compensation
EVP Global Sales, Albert M. (Al) Rossini, age 54, $396,782 total compensation
VP Fixed Operations, Don Farias
VP Marketing, Jacques Wagemaker
CTO, Steven Shwartz
SVP Mobile Device Management Solutions, Julie Palen
SVP Professional Services, Robert Whitmore
SVP Fixed Solutions, George Germano
General Manager Europe, Larry D. Velez
SVP Marketing, Paul Schmidt
SVP Fixed Solutions, Charles D. (Charlie) Gamble, age 50, $233,233 total compensation
SVP Sales, Christopher (Chris) Mezzatesta
SVP Mobile Solutions, Scott E. Snyder, age 46, $301,035 total compensation
Auditors: BDO USA, LLP

LOCATIONS

HQ: Tangoe, Inc.
  35 Executive Blvd., Orange, CT 06477
Phone: 203-859-9300   **Fax:** 203-859-9427
Web: www.tangoe.com

COMPETITORS

Amdocs	ProfitLine
Ariba	Research In Motion
BroadSource	Sybase
CSG Systems International	Symphony Technology Group, LLC
Good Technology	Telwares
Invoice Insight	Ventyx
PAETEC	WidePoint

HISTORICAL FINANCIALS

Company Type: Public

Income Statement

FYE: December 31

	REVENUE ($ mil.)	NET INCOME ($ mil.)	NET PROFIT MARGIN	EMPLOYEES
12/10	68.5	(1.8)	—	757
12/09	55.9	(2.6)	—	439
12/08	37.5	(7.0)	—	0
12/07	21.0	(9.7)	—	0
Annual Growth	48.3%	—	—	72.4%

Debt ratio: 0.0%
Return on equity: 0.1%
Cash ($ mil.): 141.6
Current ratio: 1.65
Long-term debt ($ mil.): 0.0
No. of shares (mil.): 40.7
Dividends
  Yield: —
  Payout: —
Market value ($ mil.): 1,124.6

Targacept

Depressed because you can't smoke anymore? Targacept might be able to help as it researches how to put the nervous system's nicotinic receptors to good use. The biotechnology company is the result of nicotine research conducted by R.J. Reynolds Tobacco, which spun off the firm in 2000. Targacept's pipeline of drug candidates are being developed to address conditions related to cognitive impairment, depression, and pain by targeting neuronal nicotinic receptors (NNRs) in the nervous system using non-nicotine compounds. The firm hopes its drug candidates in clinical and pre-clinical development will reproduce the therapeutic effects of NNR interaction without the side effects of nicotine.

Targacept's leading candidate in clinical development, TC-5214, is being touted as the next big thing in antidepressants. TC-5214 is being presented as an alternative to the current leading category of antidepressants, called selective serotonin reuptake inhibitors (Prozac and Paxil are examples). In 2009 AstraZeneca jumped in with an agreement to pay Targacept $200 million up front plus an additional $1 billion if the drug gets regulatory clearance and meets sales targets.

Targacept and AstraZeneca also have partnered to investigate another candidate, AZD3480, as a possible treatment for ADHD. Trials to evaluate the drug for schizophrenia were halted in late 2008 when they failed to meet endpoint criteria.

GlaxoSmithKline has also partnered with Targacept over the years, bringing in some $45 million in payments. In addition to such partnerships, the company also seeks out research grants, and hires out as a subcontract researcher on larger grants. Under one such arrangement, the company has provided research into using NNRs to assist with smoking cessation therapies.

In 2009 the company discontinued marketing its one market-approved product, Inversine. Targacept bought the marketing rights to Inversine in 2002 from Layton BioScience. The drug received FDA approval to treat moderately severe to severe hypertension. Targacept marketed it for this use while simultaneously investigating it as a possible treatment for neuropsychiatric disorders, including autism and bipolar disorder, in children and adolescents.

The company launched its initial public offering in April 2006 and used the proceeds to fund development of its clinical and preclinical candidates and cover general operating expenses. New Enterprise Associates controls 16% of the company's stock, and holds a seat on the board of directors. R.J. Reynolds Tobacco no longer holds a stake in Targacept.

EXECUTIVES

Chairman, Mark B. Skaletsky, age 63
President, CEO, and Director, J. Donald (Don) deBethizy, age 60, $761,957 total compensation
VP Finance and Corporate Systems, and Controller, Mauri K. Hodges, age 53

VP Human Resources, Karen A. Hicks, age 59

SVP Business and Commercial Development, and Chief Business Officer, Jeffrey P. (Jeff) Brennan, age 53, $481,727 total compensation

SVP Legal Affairs, General Counsel, and Secretary, Peter A. Zorn, age 41

SVP Clinical Development and Regulatory Affairs, and Chief Medical Officer, Geoffrey C. Dunbar, age 64, $512,821 total compensation

SVP Preclinical Research, Merouane Bencherif, age 56, $438,644 total compensation

SVP Drug Discovery and Development, William S. Caldwell, age 57

Executive Assistant to the CEO and Administrative Coordinator, Jo A. Peay

SVP Finance and Administration, CFO, Treasurer, and Assistant Secretary, Alan A. Musso, age 49, $468,093 total compensation

Auditors: Ernst & Young LLP

LOCATIONS

HQ: Targacept, Inc.
200 E. 1st St., Ste. 300, Winston-Salem, NC 27101-4165
Phone: 336-480-2100   **Fax:** 336-480-2107
Web: www.targacept.com

COMPETITORS

AstraZeneca	Johnson & Johnson
Bristol-Myers Squibb	Novartis
Eli Lilly	Pfizer
Forest Labs	Sanofi
GlaxoSmithKline	Shire

HISTORICAL FINANCIALS

Company Type: Public

Income Statement

FYE: December 31

	REVENUE ($ mil.)	NET INCOME ($ mil.)	NET PROFIT MARGIN	EMPLOYEES
12/10	85.7	10.9	12.7%	132
12/09	25.1	(39.4)	—	116
12/08	20.1	(25.7)	—	113
12/07	11.6	(28.1)	—	102
12/06	27.5	2.1	7.6%	89
Annual Growth	32.9%	50.9%	—	10.4%

2010 Year-End Financials

Debt ratio: 1.5%	No. of shares (mil.): 28.9
Return on equity: 11.9%	Dividends
Cash ($ mil.): 165.9	Yield: —
Current ratio: 2.21	Payout: —
Long-term debt ($ mil.): 1.3	Market value ($ mil.): 765.1

	STOCK PRICE ($) FY Close	P/E High/Low		PER SHARE ($) Earnings	Dividends	Book Value
12/10	26.50	77	49	0.36	0.00	3.18
12/09	20.90	—	—	(1.54)	0.00	2.44
12/08	3.56	—	—	(1.04)	0.00	2.30
12/07	8.26	—	—	(1.42)	0.00	2.52
12/06	9.05	—	—	(0.09)	0.00	3.40
Annual Growth	30.8%	—	—	—	—	(1.6%)

Teavana Holdings

Teavana Holdings hopes its customers become steeped in its tea stores. Through more than 145 company-owned retail stores, Teavana Holdings sells gourmet loose-leaf teas, including white, green, and black teas imported from Asia and other regions, as well as hand-crafted teapots and other teaware. Its stores, located in malls and high-end shopping centers in 34 states, are imbued with a healthy-living "Eastern" ambiance and provide an interactive environment designed to cater to tea enthusiasts. While it does most of its business in the US, the company also has a presence in Mexico through 15 franchised stores. Teavana was founded in 1997 by CEO Andrew Mack and his wife Nancy. The firm went public in mid-2011.

Teavana intends to use a portion of the proceeds that it raises in its initial public offering (up to $100 million) to buy outstanding shares of preferred stock held by Teavana Investment LLC. It will also use some of the proceeds to repay debt and fund general corporate activity. Prior to the filing, Andrew Mack held a 69% controlling stake in company. Teavana Investment held a 24% stake before the filing.

Teavana filed its IPO during a time of significant growth for the company. Between 2006 and 2011, the company tripled its retail store locations from 47 to 146. Similarly, its revenues and profits increased during that time, due in large part to its retail store expansion and increasing sales at existing stores. The company's bottom line has also benefited from an uptick in sales through its e-commerce site. Other efforts that have bolstered profits include a long-term plan to reduce its stock of tea merchandise while increasing its selection of teas, as sales from teas inherently have a higher profit margin than more expensive, hand-made merchandise.

As part of its growth strategy, Teavana plans to continue aggressive store expansion and hopes to increase the number to some 500 stores by 2015. (It's planning to open 50 stores by the end of 2011.) This includes expansion into new markets in the US and Mexico by opening both company-owned and franchised locations.

In addition to its retail operations, Teavana supports its network of stores though a handful of facilities, including a support center in Atlanta and a distribution warehouse in Stratford, Connecticut. The company sources its teas to more than 100 international and domestic vendors.

EXECUTIVES

Chairman and CEO, Andrew T. Mack, age 46
EVP, Operations, Peter M. Luckhurst, age 56
EVP and CFO, Daniel P. Glennon, age 42
VP, Distribution, Juergen W. Link, age 50
VP, Real Estate, Robert A. Shapiro, age 64
Auditors: Grant Thornton LLP

LOCATIONS

HQ: Teavana Holdings, Inc.
3630 Peachtree Rd. NE, Ste. 1480, Atlanta, GA 30326
Phone: 404-995-8200
Web: www.teavana.com

PRODUCTS/OPERATIONS

2011 Sales

	% of total
Tea	56
Merchandise	40
Beverage	4
Total	**100**

COMPETITORS

Celestial Seasonings	R.C. Bigelow
Dean & DeLuca	Republic of Tea
GourmetFoodMall.com	Whole Foods

HISTORICAL FINANCIALS

Company Type: Public

Income Statement

FYE: Sunday nearest to January 31

	REVENUE ($ mil.)	NET INCOME ($ mil.)	NET PROFIT MARGIN	EMPLOYEES
01/11	124.7	12.0	9.6%	1,819
01/10	90.3	5.3	5.9%	0
01/09	63.9	1.2	1.9%	0
Annual Growth	39.7%	216.2%	—	—

Debt ratio: 1.5%	No. of shares (mil.): 28.9
Return on equity: 11.9%	Dividends
Cash ($ mil.): 165.9	Yield: —
Current ratio: 2.21	Payout: —
Long-term debt ($ mil.): 1.3	Market value ($ mil.): 765.1

Technical Communications

Technical Communications Corporation, also known as TCC, helps its customers keep their secrets to themselves. The company makes secure communications equiment that enables users to digitally encrypt and transmit information. It also makes receivers used to decipher the data. TCC's products protect transmissions sent by radios, telephones, fax machines, computer networks, the Internet, fiber-optic cables, and satellite links. The company subcontracts much of its manufacturing and caters largely to government agencies, but it also serves financial institutions and other corporations. It derives the bulk of its sales from a very small number of customers, including the US Army.

EXECUTIVES

Chairman, President, and CEO, Carl H. Guild Jr., age 66, $317,466 total compensation
CFO, Treasurer, and Assistant Secretary, Michael P. Malone, age 51, $169,216 total compensation
Auditors: Vitale, Caturano & Company, Ltd.

LOCATIONS

HQ: Technical Communications Corporation
100 Domino Dr., Concord, MA 01742-2892
Phone: 978-287-5100   **Fax:** 978-371-1280
Web: www.tccsecure.com

PRODUCTS/OPERATIONS

Selected Products

Government systems
  High-speed data encryptors
  Narrowband radio security systems
  Secure fax and office communications encryption systems
Network security systems
  Frame relay and IP network encryptors (Cipher)
  Network security management software (Keynet)
Secure office systems
  Fax security systems
  Secure portable telephone attachments

COMPETITORS

Alcatel-Lucent	General Dynamics
Cisco Systems	Motorola Solutions
Crypto	Omnisec
EF Johnson	SafeNet
Technologies	Thales

HISTORICAL FINANCIALS

Company Type: Public

Income Statement

FYE: Saturday nearest September 30

	REVENUE ($ mil.)	NET INCOME ($ mil.)	NET PROFIT MARGIN	EMPLOYEES
09/10	21.6	7.9	36.6%	35
09/09	7.8	0.9	11.5%	34
09/08	6.9	1.1	15.9%	29
09/07	4.9	0.8	16.3%	26
09/06	3.9	(0.1)	—	23
Annual Growth	53.4%	—	—	11.1%

2010 Year-End Financials

Debt ratio: —	No. of shares (mil.): 1.8
Return on equity: 67.9%	Dividends
Cash ($ mil.): 11.0	Yield: 2.2%
Current ratio: 4.44	Payout: 4.6%
Long-term debt ($ mil.): —	Market value ($ mil.): 16.9

	STOCK PRICE ($) FY Close	P/E High/Low		PER SHARE ($) Earnings	Dividends	Book Value
09/10	9.25	3	1	4.33	0.20	6.34
09/09	4.50	10	5	0.58	0.00	4.62
09/08	5.45	12	6	0.63	0.00	3.96
09/07	4.50	11	5	0.55	0.00	3.03
09/06	3.30	—	—	(0.07)	0.00	2.35
Annual Growth	29.4%	—	—	—	—	28.1%

TeleCommunication Systems

TeleCommunication Systems (TCS) enhances the mobile communication experience and keeps government agencies connected. The company develops software and provides services for wireless carriers and voice-over-IP service providers. TCS's software lets carriers deliver enhanced 9-1-1 service, text messaging, location information, and other Internet content to wireless phones. Its network operation centers provide its software on a hosted basis. The company also provides the Defense Dept. and other agencies with communications systems integration and IT services through its government division, which accounts for almost 60% of revenue. Founder and CEO Maurice Tosé controls about 33% of TCS's voting power.

TCS's commercial segment, which makes up the remaining 40% of sales, charges customers monthly usage payments for its hosted applications. It also provides software development services. The company is focused on messaging and location determination technologies to grow its commercial business. It handles about 30% of all text messages in the US, delivering some 700 billion in 2009, up from 260 billion in 2008. TCS's commercial clients include wireless carriers AT&T Wireless, Hutchison Whampoa, Sprint, T-Mobile,

and Verizon. VoIP networks that use its enhanced 9-1-1 service include Comcast, Level 3, and Vonage, while telematics providers such as DENSO use its electronic mapping technology.

The company's government sector specializes in satellite communication technology. TCS operates teleports in Manassas, Virginia, that are connected to the public switched phone network, and the company resells access to satellite airtime. In addition to the DoD, TCS counts the US Department of Homeland Security, the City of Baltimore, and Northrop Grumman among its government sector clients.

The company is also one of six vendors selected by the Army to provide secure satellite services and systems under a Worldwide Satellite Systems (WWSS) contract through 2012. In 2010, it was awarded more than $100 million in contracts by the Army (as well as a $269 million contract for the Marines and a $315 million contract for the Air Force), which helped its government division overtake its commercial segment in terms of sales.

Along with the Army contracts, the company has grown through a flux of acquisitions. In late 2010 it agreed to acquire California-based Trident Space & Defense for an undisclosed amount of cash and 3 million shares of stock. Trident provides solid-state drives (SSDs), electronic components, and ground systems services for military and industrial applications. Trident earned about $40 million in 2010.

TCS bought four complementary companies in 2009, beginning with LocationLogic, a top provider of location-based services, for $25 million in cash and stock. In November it bought two companies, Solvern Solutions and Sidereal Solutions, for its government segment. Solvern Solutions provides computer security training and other technology services to the DoD, while Sidereal Solutions provides technology engineering and maintenance services to the satellite industry. TCS said the purchases will boost its areas of secure network communications and encryption in support of its satellite communications and wireless carrier businesses. Finally, it bought Networks In Motion (NIM), a provider of GPS navigation software for mobile devices, for $170 million. Along with LocationLogic, the deal improved its ability to offer location-based products and services.

The acquisitions haven't disrupted TCS's bottom line, with overall sales growing more than 35% in 2009. By the third quarter of 2010, sales were up 37% year-over-year, and the company is enjoying record revenue and profit.

EXECUTIVES

Chairman, President, and CEO, Maurice B. Tosé, age 54, $3,742,519 total compensation
EVP, COO, and Director, Richard A. Young, age 64, $2,008,136 total compensation
VP Strategic Programs, Government, Allen Green
VP North America Sales, Sam D. Collura
VP Government Systems, Jude T. Panetta, age 50
SVP Solvern Innovations, Andre J. Gudger
SVP and General Manager, Government Solutions, Michael D. Bristol Sr.
SVP Navigation and Telematics, Doug Antone
SVP and CTO, Drew A. Morin, age 50, $1,537,676 total compensation
SVP, General Counsel, and Secretary, Bruce A. White
Senior Director Corporate Communications, Meredith Allen
SVP Service Bureau Operations, Chris Nabinger
SVP and Chief Marketing Officer, Timothy J. (Tim) Lorello, age 53, $1,221,771 total compensation

SVP, CFO, and Director, Thomas M. (Tom) Brandt Jr., age 59, $1,627,742 total compensation
Auditors: Ernst & Young LLP

LOCATIONS

HQ: TeleCommunication Systems, Inc.
275 West St., Ste. 400, Annapolis, MD 21401
Phone: 410-263-7616   **Fax:** 410-263-7617
Web: www.telecomsys.com

2009 Sales

	$ mil.	% of total
US	290.7	97
Other countries	9.4	3
Total	**300.1**	**100**

PRODUCTS/OPERATIONS

2009 Sales

	$ mil.	% of total
Commercial segment		
Services	89.7	30
Systems	37.6	12
Government segment		
Services	62.2	21
Systems	110.6	37
Total	**300.1**	**100**

Selected Services

Commercial mobile alert system (CMAS)
Cyber security training
Location-based applications and infrastructure
Navigation and telematics
Public safety services (wireless E9-1-1, E1-1-2)
SwiftLink deployable communications
Text messaging

COMPETITORS

CACI International	Globecomm
Computer Sciences	Intrado
Corp.	Motorola Solutions
Comtech	Nokia
Telecommunications	Openwave Systems
Converse Technology	Siemens AG
Ericsson	ViaSat
General Dynamics	VT iDirect

HISTORICAL FINANCIALS

Company Type: Public

Income Statement

FYE: December 31

	REVENUE ($ mil.)	NET INCOME ($ mil.)	NET PROFIT MARGIN	EMPLOYEES
12/10	388.8	15.9	4.1%	1,205
12/09	300.1	28.3	9.4%	1,048
12/08	220.1	57.6	26.2%	585
12/07	144.2	(1.3)	—	500
12/06	124.9	(21.7)	—	600
Annual Growth	32.8%	—	—	19.0%

2010 Year-End Financials

Debt ratio: 63.1%	No. of shares (mil.): 53.5
Return on equity: 7.4%	Dividends
Cash ($ mil.): 45.2	Yield: —
Current ratio: 1.90	Payout: —
Long-term debt ($ mil.): 136.0	Market value ($ mil.): 249.8

	STOCK PRICE ($) FY Close	P/E High/Low		PER SHARE ($) Earnings	Dividends	Book Value
12/10	4.67	38	11	0.28	0.00	4.03
12/09	9.68	20	12	0.53	0.00	3.54
12/08	8.59	7	2	1.23	0.00	2.59
12/07	3.56	—	—	(0.03)	0.00	1.05
12/06	3.10	—	—	(0.54)	0.00	0.88
Annual Growth	10.8%	—	—	—	—	46.1%

TeleNav

TeleNav can make an overachiever of your mobile phone. The company offers a platform and suite of applications that enables wireless navigation and tracking services delivered to mobile phone users primarily in the US. TeleNav's customers include wireless carriers and telematics service providers; Sprint Nextel and AT&T are the company's biggest clients by a large margin; other customers include Ford Motor, Intermec, and T-Mobile. Flagship product TeleNav GPS Navigator transmits voice and onscreen driving directions to mobile phones and smartphones. Its TeleNav Track product enables visual GPS navigation, electronic timesheet reporting, and interactive dispatching.

The company completed an IPO in 2010. Poceeds from the public offering were slated for general corporate purposes, including potential acquisitions and working capital.

Sprint offers TeleNav's location-based services (LBS) as part of its Simply Everything data services and voice communications package. The company's exclusive contract to provide the TeleNav GPS Navigator service to the wireless carrier (which markets the service as Sprint Navigation) expired at the end of 2010. Sprint had lost more than 3 million monthly subscribers in 2009 and may continue to lose money in the near future (it hasn't posted an annual profit since 2006), which could jeopardize the carrier's relationship with TeleNav in 2011 and beyond. TeleNav's other big customer, AT&T, isn't required to provide the company's LBS, and TeleNav's exclusive contract to provide GPS navigation services to AT&T expires in early 2011. Monthly subscription fees for the TeleNav GPS Navigator account for most of the company's revenues.

TeleNav acquired Boston-based local Web search service and mobile location-based software developer goby in 2011 to supplement its own navigation products and services.

The 24 Global Positioning System (GPS) satellites circling the Earth do not directly pinpoint the exact location of a mobile phone or navigation device. The satellites transmit a precise time to the GPS receiver in a phone or other gadget, and then the mobile device processes the satellite signals to determine your geographic location. To provide directions, the phone sends a signal to the nearest cell phone tower, which connects the device to TeleNav's servers. Those servers then provide updated maps, guides to local businesses, fuel prices, and other data to the phone.

Menlo Ventures (which owns about 13% of the company), iGlobe Partners, and Sycamore Ventures are among TeleNav's primary investors.

EXECUTIVES

Chairman, President, and CEO, H. P. Jin, age 47
CFO, Douglas S. (Doug) Miller, age 54
VP Business Development and Carrier Sales, Hassan Wahla, age 39
VP Research and Development, Y. C. Chao, age 47
VP Marketing, Dariusz Paczuski, age 45
VP Enterprise Solutions, Tom Erdman
VP Products and Marketing, Salman (Sal) Dhanani, age 38
VP Enterprise Solutions, Thomas (Tom) Erdman
CTO, Robert (Bob) Rennard, age 67
Media Contact, Mary Beth Lowell
General Manager, Longxue Li
General Counsel and Secretary, Loren E. Hillberg, age 53
Auditors: Ernst & Young LLP

LOCATIONS

HQ: TeleNav, Inc.
 1130 Kifer Rd., Sunnyvale, CA 94086
Phone: 408-245-3800   **Fax:** 408-245-0238
Web: www.telenav.com

2010 Sales

	$ mil.	% of total
US	166.3	97
Other countries	4.9	3
Total	**171.2**	**100**

COMPETITORS

ATX Group	TeleCommunication
Garmin	Systems
Google	TomTom
Hemisphere GPS	Trimble Navigation
Ituran	Vodafone
MapQuest	Webraska
Microsoft	WirelessCar
Nokia	Yahoo!
Parrot S.A.	

HISTORICAL FINANCIALS

Company Type: Public

Income Statement

FYE: June 30

	REVENUE ($ mil.)	NET INCOME ($ mil.)	NET PROFIT MARGIN	EMPLOYEES
06/11	210.5	42.6	20.2%	1,039
06/10	171.2	41.4	24.2%	942
06/09	110.9	15.7	14.2%	735
06/08	48.1	1.9	4.0%	0
06/07	27.7	(9.6)	—	0
Annual Growth	66.0%	—	—	18.9%

2011 Year-End Financials

Debt ratio: —
Return on equity: 22.6%
Cash ($ mil.): 24.1
Current ratio: 3.63
Long-term debt ($ mil.): —
No. of shares (mil.): 41.8
Dividends
 Yield: —
 Payout: —
Market value ($ mil.): 741.5

	STOCK PRICE ($) FY Close	P/E High/Low		PER SHARE ($) Earnings	Dividends	Book Value
06/11	17.73	20	5	0.94	0.00	4.51
06/10	8.39	14	9	0.83	0.00	3.54
Annual Growth	111.3%	—	—	13.3%	—	27.4%

Teradyne

Teradyne has the anodyne for electronics makers concerned about quality and consistency. The company is a leading supplier of automated test equipment, and the #1 maker of systems for testing semiconductors. Teradyne caters to electronics manufacturing services suppliers, as well as OEMs who use Teradyne's test systems to analyze complex electronics used in the computing, consumer electronics, military/aerospace, and telecommunications industries. Customers include Boeing, government contractors, and the US government. Teradyne has operations in Asia, Europe, and North America; international sales account for about three-fourths of its business.

Sales of semiconductors fell off a cliff in 2009, as the global recession helped dramatically cut sales for computers and consumer electronics. As the chip industry fares, so goes Teradyne. Semiconductor test systems represent approximately two-thirds of the company's sales. Teradyne's sales fell by one-quarter for the year, as semi test system sales plummeted due to excess test capacity at most chip makers, and the company marked its second straight year in the red. Teradyne laid off almost a quarter of its worldwide staff and implemented a 20% temporary pay cut for executive officers.

But the company impressively returned to profitablity in 2010, doubling its revenue and recording a positive net income that year. To focus on strengthening its semiconductor testing business, in 2011 the company sold its Automotive Diagnostics Solutions unit to SPX for an undisclosed amount. To the same end that year Teradyne acquired wireless production line testing equipment LitePoint for about $580 million in cash and tax benefits

The test equipment market is highly competitive, due to years of industry consolidation and the limited customer base. Most semiconductor companies don't make or test their chips, turning those chores over to outside contractors, many of which are based in Asia. Teradyne takes advantage of that outsourcing trend, as well, contracting production and testing of its FLEX and J750 products to Singapore-based Flextronics International, which does the work in China.

Teradyne's divisions are Semiconductor Test and Systems Test (assembly test and vehicle diagnostic systems). Semiconductor Test's performance is often tied to growth in the system-on-a-chip (SoC) market.

Teradyne has operations in China, Japan, the Philippines, Taiwan, the UK, and the US.

HISTORY

College pals Nicholas DeWolf and Alexander d'Arbeloff (who met in an alphabetical ROTC lineup at MIT) founded Teradyne in 1960 to develop industrial-grade electronic test equipment. The name combines "tera" (10 to the 12th power) and "dyne" (a unit of force); to the founding duo, it meant "rolling a 15,000-ton boulder uphill." The company's first headquarters was a loft over Joe & Nemo's hot dog stand in downtown Boston. In 1961 the company sold its first product — an automatic tester for semiconductor diodes called a go/no-go diode tester — to Raytheon for $5,000.

Teradyne grew rapidly during the 1960s as it introduced new products, including testers for integrated circuits, resistors, transistors, and diodes. In the latter part of the decade, the company began using computers to speed up the testing process, helping create the automatic test equipment (ATE) industry. It formed Teradyne Components (later Teradyne Connection Systems) in 1968 to produce electronics connection assemblies.

Teradyne went public in 1970. That year, with the first slump in the semiconductor industry, the company laid off 15% of its workforce and began diversifying its customer base. DeWolf departed Teradyne in 1971, leaving d'Arbeloff to run operations. The market quickly recovered, and the company grew and prospered again. In 1972 it began working on a telephone system testing device, the 4Tel. However, the market slumped again, and in 1975 Teradyne cut its staff by 15% a second time.

When trouble hit again in the mid-1980s, Teradyne suffered back-to-back annual losses. Meanwhile, Japanese companies overtook US semiconductor makers, leaving Teradyne short of customers for its testers. Teradyne fought back in the late 1980s by lowering prices to undercut the competition and by pushing into the Japanese market. In addition, the company formed a computer-aided engineering group by purchasing and combining Aida Corporation and Case Technologies.

The cycle continued in the early 1990s as military spending fell, leading to further staff cuts, salary freezes, and even a temporary suspension of production. Through the mid-1990s, a $63 million contract from the German national telephone system, an upgrade in Teradyne's ATE line, and a release of the TestMaster software development tool had Teradyne growing again.

High demand for PCs elevated sales of the company's semiconductor testing equipment, helping it top $1 billion in sales for the first time in 1995. However, the next year another semiconductor industry downturn caused a drop in profits, and Teradyne laid off about 300 workers. In 1997 president George Chamillard succeeded d'Arbeloff as CEO. (D'Arbeloff remained chairman until 2000, when Chamillard succeeded him in that post, as well.)

Teradyne turned a profit for 1998 despite one of the chip industry's worst-ever downturns. As chip sales and Asian economies rebounded, Teradyne booked more than $2 billion in sales in 1999. Riding the crest of a chip industry boom, Teradyne in 2000 posted record sales and its highest revenue growth in more than 25 years.

In the closing days of 2000, Teradyne sold its software testing division to a group of private investors led by Matrix Partners; that business became Empirix.

In 2001 Teradyne acquired GenRad for about $260 million in stock and debt assumption. GenRad was later renamed Teradyne Diagnostic Solutions. Also that year it laid off about 1,000 employees (about 11% of its workforce) and reduced managerial salaries in response to a sharp downturn in the worldwide chip industry.

In 2004 George Chamillard stepped down as CEO (he remained chairman); president Michael Bradley took on the additional title of CEO.

To focus on its test systems business, the company sold its Connection Systems division to Amphenol for about $390 million in 2005; Connection Systems accounted for about 20% of its revenue in 2004.

In 2006 the company moved out of its high-rise headquarters in downtown Boston, relocating operations to its campus in suburban North Reading. Teradyne sold the HQ building to Nordic Properties for nearly $35 million. It sold another Boston building in 2006 to Millennium Partners.

Co-founder Nick DeWolf died in 2006, at the age of 77. At the end of 2006 George Chamillard retired from the board of directors, after working at Teradyne for more than 35 years. Patricia Wolpert, a director since 1996 and a retired IBM executive, was named to succeed him as chairman.

In 2007 Teradyne acquired memory test assets from MOSAID Technologies, a memory device testing technology developer, for $17 million in cash. That same year, it also sold its broadband test product line and related assets to competitor Tollgrade Communications for about $12 million.

Co-founder Alex d'Arbeloff died in 2008, at the age of 80.

Complementing its strength in SoC test, the company moved into flash memory testing with the 2008 acquisition of Nextest Systems, which got more than 80% of its sales from flash memory testers. Teradyne spent about $325 million to buy Nextest, which became a business unit of the Semiconductor Test division. Also that year Teradyne purchased another competitor, Eagle Test Systems, which specialized in testing analog and power management chips. It became a business unit of the Semiconductor Test division. Teradyne spent about $250 million to acquire Eagle Test. Both deals were expected to help Teradyne compete against the combination of two leading test vendors, Credence Systems and LTX, which merged in 2008 to form LTX-Credence Corporation.

EXECUTIVES

Chairman, Albert Carnesale, age 74
President, CEO, and Director, Michael A. Bradley, age 62, $2,456,677 total compensation
President, Semiconductor Test Division, Mark E. Jagiela, age 50, $758,538 total compensation
President, Systems Test Group, Jeffrey R. (Jeff) Hotchkiss, age 63, $714,461 total compensation
VP, CFO and Treasurer, Gregory R. (Greg) Beecher, age 53, $787,183 total compensation
VP, General Counsel, and Secretary, Charles R. Gray, age 49
VP Corporate Relations, Andrew Blanchard
Auditors: PricewaterhouseCoopers LLP

LOCATIONS

HQ: Teradyne, Inc.
600 Riverpark Dr., North Reading, MA 01864
Phone: 978-370-2700   **Fax:** 978-370-1440
Web: www.teradyne.com

PRODUCTS/OPERATIONS

Selected Products

Semiconductor test systems
  Memory test
  Microcontroller test
  Mixed-signal test (A5 line)
  System-on-a-chip test (Catalyst and Tiger lines)
  Very large scale integration (VLSI) chip test
Circuit board test and inspection systems
  Automated optical inspection
  In-circuit and functional board test
  Software

COMPETITORS

Advantest	LTX-Credence
Agilent Technologies	Mitsui
Camtek	National Instruments
Cascade Microtech	Orbotech
FormFactor	Tektronix
Hitachi	Xyratex
High-Technologies	Yokogawa Electric
KLA-Tencor	

HISTORICAL FINANCIALS

Company Type: Public

Income Statement

FYE: December 31

	REVENUE ($ mil.)	NET INCOME ($ mil.)	NET PROFIT MARGIN	EMPLOYEES
12/10	1,608.7	379.7	23.6%	3,000
12/09	819.4	(133.8)	—	2,900
12/08	1,107.0	(397.8)	—	3,800
12/07	1,102.3	77.7	7.0%	3,600
12/06	1,376.8	198.8	14.4%	3,800
Annual Growth	4.0%	17.6%	—	(5.7%)

2010 Year-End Financials

Debt ratio: 13.4%   No. of shares (mil.): 182.0
Return on equity: 33.8%   Dividends
Cash ($ mil.): 397.7   Yield: —
Current ratio: 3.24   Payout: —
Long-term debt ($ mil.): 150.2   Market value ($ mil.): 2,555.8

	STOCK PRICE ($) FY Close	P/E High/Low		PER SHARE ($) Earnings	Dividends	Book Value
12/10	14.04	8	5	1.73	0.00	6.16
12/09	10.73	—	—	(0.77)	0.00	3.80
12/08	4.22	—	—	(2.33)	0.00	4.17
12/07	10.34	44	24	0.42	0.00	7.08
12/06	15.17	18	11	1.01	0.00	7.17
Annual Growth	(1.9%)	—	—	14.4%	—	(3.7%)

Tesla Motors

Tesla Motors intends to spark the public's passion and eco-conscience for electric vehicles. Founded in 2003, the company designs, manufactures, and markets high-performance electric cars and powertrain components. Tesla stylish Roadster is its flagship model, which the company continues to upgrade. The Roadster's operating specs include zero to 60 in less than four seconds and a top speed of 125 mph. The fuel-efficient, fully electric vehicle recharges its lithium-ion batteries from an outlet, and, depending on a driver's speed, is capable of 245 miles per charge. Roadsters are based on Lotus' Elise model; their UK assembly is shifting to a California facility. In mid-2010 Tesla became a publicly-held company.

The company's initial public offering raised more than $200 million; it was the first IPO for a carmaker since Ford's in 1956. Half of the proceeds serve as a reservoir for expenditures otherwise funded by a US Department of Energy $465 million loan, which was authorized in mid-2009 under the federal government's Advanced Technology Vehicles Manufacturing program. Specifically, Tesla expects that the cash infusion from investors will cover construction costs not funded by the loan. Some $33 million is earmarked for developing powertrains and building future vehicle models.

The company's luxury Tesla Roadster, and its subsequent upgrades, the Tesla Roadster 2, Roadster Sport, and Roadster 2.5, are the first in a line of electric vehicles offered largely in the US, Europe, and Canada via its 16 Tesla-owned stores, at corporate events, and through the Internet. And while sales and customer reservations for the cars have soared (The company sold about 1,500 of the high-priced vehicles in 2010.), so too have costs.

Despite efforts to trim its operating expenses, the company continues to operate at a loss, due in large part to high sales and R&D costs.

Looking ahead, Tesla is focused on boosting revenues by expanding its line of automobiles. Its strategy includes developing new electric vehicles, such as the Model S and Model X, for a wider consumer base. To that end, Tesla acquired the NUMMI (an acronym for New United Motor Manufacturing) assembly plant in California, formerly operated via a Toyota-GM joint venture, for $42 million. Tesla intends to leverage the former NUMMI's resources to build the Model S and other planned vehicles. The plant's strategic location in a decidedly pro-green state promises a built-in market for Tesla's electric offerings. Tesla intends to launch its Model S by mid 2012; its Model X, a cross-over built on the Model S platform, is expected to follow.

The company is also focused on developing electric vehicles and components alongside other carmakers. Tesla, which recently received a $50 million private placement for its stock from Toyota, teamed up with the #1 carmaker to jointly develop electric vehicles and share production techniques. In a separate agreement, Tesla signed on to develop an electric powertrain for Toyota's RAV4 compact SUV.

Other key collaborative agreements between Tesla and OEMs include developing powertrains for Daimler. Tesla also supplies lithium-ion battery packs and charging electronics for the German carmaker's electric smart car. In 2010 it agreed to develop and produce a battery pack and charger for a pilot fleet of Daimler's A-Class electric vehicles, set to launch in Europe in 2011. For Daimler affiliate Freightliner, Tesla is supplying modular battery packs to power electric vans. In late 2010 Japan-based electronics manufacturer Panasonic agreed to acquire a small stake in Tesla for $30 million. The two companies will also team up to develop electric-vehicle batteries.

Tesla Motors is named for Nikola Tesla (1856-1943), the renowned Serbian-American engineer and inventor. Founder and CEO Elon Musk is the electric vehicle maker's largest shareholder, holding more than a 28% stake in the company.

EXECUTIVES

CFO, Deepak Ahuja, age 47
Chairman, CEO, and Product Architect, Elon Musk, age 39
VP Business Development, Diarmuid O'Connell
VP and Chief Engineer, Vehicle Engineering, Peter Rawlinson
VP Communications, Ricardo Reyes, age 37
VP Manufacturing, Gilbert Passin
VP Finance, Mike Taylor
VP Human Resources, Arnnon Geshuri
VP and Controller, Matt Au
VP European Sales and Operations, Cristiano Carlutti
VP Sales and Ownership Experience, George Blankenship, age 58
VP Powertrain Hardware Engineering, Jim Dunlay
VP North America Sales and Marketing, John Walker, age 48
CTO, Jeffrey B. (JB) Straubel, age 34
Program Director, Model S, Henry Brice
Chief Designer, Franz von Holzhausen, age 43
General Counsel and Secretary, Eric S. Whitaker, age 41
Auditors: PricewaterhouseCoopers LLP

LOCATIONS

HQ: Tesla Motors, Inc.
  3500 Deer Creek, Palo Alto, CA 94304
Phone: 650-681-5000
Web: www.teslamotors.com

2010 Sales

	$ mil.	% of total
Europe	70.5	60
Americas	41.9	36
Asia	4.3	4
Total	**116.7**	**100**

COMPETITORS

BMW	Kia Motors
BYD	Mitsubishi Motors
Chrysler	Nissan
Daimler	Pininfarina
Fisker Automotive	Ronn Motor Company
Ford Motor	Subaru of America
General Motors	Suzuki Motor
Honda	Toyota
Hyundai Motor	Volkswagen
Isuzu	ZAP

HISTORICAL FINANCIALS

Company Type: Public

Income Statement
FYE: December 31

	REVENUE ($ mil.)	NET INCOME ($ mil.)	NET PROFIT MARGIN	EMPLOYEES
12/10	116.7	(154.3)	—	899
12/09	111.9	(55.7)	—	514
12/08	14.7	(82.8)	—	514
12/07	0.1	(78.2)	—	0
12/06	0.0	(30.0)	—	0
Annual Growth	—	—	—	32.3%

2010 Year-End Financials

Debt ratio: 34.9%	No. of shares (mil.): 94.9
Return on equity: —	Dividends
Cash ($ mil.): 99.6	Yield: —
Current ratio: 2.76	Payout: —
Long-term debt ($ mil.): 72.3	Market value ($ mil.): 2,527.4

	STOCK PRICE ($) FY Close	P/E High/Low		PER SHARE ($) Earnings	Dividends	Book Value
12/10	26.63	—	—	(3.04)	0.00	2.18
Annual Growth	—	—	—	—	—	—

Tii Network Industries

Tii products keep an eye on the sky. Tii Network Technologies makes overvoltage surge protection devices used by telecommunications companies to protect their equipment during lightning strikes and power surges. Products include the Totel Failsafe brand modular station protectors and In-Line brand broadband coaxial cable protectors. Tii also makes gas tubes (an integral part of overvoltage surge suppressors), custom network interface devices, and electronic products used to test the integrity of voice and data lines remotely. The company's customers include Verizon, DIRECTV, Power & Telephone Supply, and TE Connectivity.

In 2010 the company bought the Copper Products Division of Porta Systems (now known as

North Hills Signal Processing) for about $8 million in cash. The division designs and makes connectivity blocks, housings, and surge protection modules for the telecom industry. The acquisition includes Porta's subsidiaries in Mexico and the UK; Tii subsequently sold the majority interest in the Mexican subsidiary for $1 million in cash to its principal contract manufacturer, which will operate the Mexican manufacturing facility.

EXECUTIVES

Chairman, Charles H. (Chuck) House, age 70
President, CEO, and Director, Kenneth A. Paladino, age 54, $527,174 total compensation
VP Technology Development, David E. Foley, age 47, $302,757 total compensation
VP Sales and Marketing, Walter R. Fay
VP Engineering and Materials, Thomas J. (Tom) Smith
VP and Chief Scientist, Nisar A. Chaudhry, age 65
VP Finance, Treasurer, Secretary, and CFO, Jennifer E. Katsch, age 35, $200,124 total compensation
VP Quality Assurance, Christopher D. (Chris) James
Auditors: KPMG LLP

LOCATIONS

HQ: Tii Network Technologies, Inc.
  141 Rodeo Dr., Edgewood, NY 11717
Phone: 631-789-5000   **Fax:** 631-789-5063
Web: www.tiinettech.com

PRODUCTS/OPERATIONS

Selected Products

AC powerline and dataline protectors
Broadband coaxial cable protectors
Gas tubes
Modular station protectors
Network interface devices (NIDs)
Solid-state overvoltage surge protectors

COMPETITORS

Belkin	ONEAC
Bourns	SL Industries
Channell Commercial	Surge Technologies
Corning Cable Systems	TE Connectivity
LEA International	

HISTORICAL FINANCIALS

Company Type: Public

Income Statement
FYE: December 31

	REVENUE ($ mil.)	NET INCOME ($ mil.)	NET PROFIT MARGIN	EMPLOYEES
12/10	54.5	2.2	4.0%	75
12/09	27.4	0.1	0.4%	46
12/08	35.2	0.6	1.7%	38
12/07	46.8	6.4	13.7%	54
12/06	39.1	2.7	6.9%	99
Annual Growth	8.7%	(5.0%)	—	(6.7%)

2010 Year-End Financials

Debt ratio: —	No. of shares (mil.): 14.6
Return on equity: 5.4%	Dividends
Cash ($ mil.): 1.6	Yield: —
Current ratio: 2.75	Payout: —
Long-term debt ($ mil.): —	Market value ($ mil.): 40.5

STOCK PRICE ($) FY Close	P/E High/Low		PER SHARE ($) Earnings	Dividends	Book Value
12/10 2.78	19	8	0.16	0.00	2.81
12/09 1.25	138	49	0.01	0.00	2.66
12/08 0.63	54	14	0.04	0.00	2.69
12/07 1.94	6	4	0.48	0.00	2.64
12/06 2.49	18	10	0.20	0.00	2.14
Annual Growth 2.8%	—	—	(5.4%)	—	7.0%

Titan Energy

Titan Energy Worldwide provides power in a pinch. The company is a distributor of standby and emergency power equipment and a manufacturer of disaster relief systems. It offers power generators from such manufacturers as Generac Power Systems. It also makes and markets the Sentry 5000 mobile utility system, an all-in-one trailer unit that provides electrical power, heating and cooling, water purification, communication, and lighting. Titan Energy markets these products to first responders, relief agencies, defense and homeland security agencies, and municipalities. Those that depend on backup power — banks, data centers, hospitals, hotels, schools, and telcos — are also counted as customers.

EXECUTIVES

Chairman and CEO, Jeffrey W. (Jeff) Flannery, age 54, $108,000 total compensation
CFO, James J. Fahrner, age 59, $143,585 total compensation
President, Northeast Operations, Clifford J. Macaylo
COO and Director, Thomas Black, age 47, $183,150 total compensation
COO, Titan Energy Systems, Thomas Vagts
Service Manager, Titan Energy Systems, Kyle Gillett
Auditors: UHY LLP

LOCATIONS

HQ: Titan Energy Worldwide, Inc.
55800 Grand River Ave., Ste. 100, New Hudson, MI 48165-8713
Phone: 248-446-8557   **Fax:** 248-446-8196
Web: titanenergy.com

COMPETITORS

Aggreko	Cummins Power Systems
Baldor Electric	Tradewinds Power
Cooper Electric	

HISTORICAL FINANCIALS

Company Type: Public

Income Statement

FYE: December 31

	REVENUE ($ mil.)	NET INCOME ($ mil.)	NET PROFIT MARGIN	EMPLOYEES
12/10	14.0	(3.7)	—	60
12/09	10.6	(2.9)	—	49
12/08	9.3	(1.7)	—	27
12/07	8.8	(3.4)	—	32
12/06	0.0	(0.7)	—	7
Annual Growth	—	—	—	71.1%

2010 Year-End Financials

Debt ratio: 60.8%	No. of shares (mil.): 28.7
Return on equity: —	Dividends
Cash ($ mil.): 1.0	Yield: —
Current ratio: 0.63	Payout: —
Long-term debt ($ mil.): 0.2	Market value ($ mil.): 9.2

STOCK PRICE ($) FY Close	P/E High/Low		PER SHARE ($) Earnings	Dividends	Book Value
12/10 0.32	—	—	(0.16)	0.00	0.01
12/09 0.45	—	—	(0.20)	0.00	0.11
12/08 0.06	—	—	(0.15)	0.00	0.23
12/07 1.10	—	—	(2.50)	0.00	(0.00)
12/06 1.05	—	—	(0.00)	0.00	(0.00)
Annual Growth (25.7%)	—	—	—	—	—

Titan Machinery

For getting the job done, Titan Machinery is one titanic dealer. Titan owns one of North America's largest full-service networks that supply construction and agricultural equipment. Its more than 80 stores sell and rent new and used machinery and attachments, parts, as well as service equipment. The company represents equipment by CNH's Case IH, New Holland Agriculture, Case Construction, and New Holland Construction. Titan offers excavators, seeders, tillers, and tractors to customers from large-scale farmers to home gardeners. Other products include earthmoving equipment and cranes, used for heavy construction and light industrial jobs, in commercial or residential building, roadwork, forestry, and mining.

Titan continues to expand its network of independent stores, supported by a centralized administrative, finance, and marketing management. In tandem, the company's full-service, multi-point dealership approach is designed to leverage cross-selling equipment opportunities to a diverse group of customers.

Earnings have grown, save for 2010 when they were dented by weak demand for construction equipment coupled with the market's dismal activity. (Titan's construction segment suffered a net loss, pressuring year-over-year profits down by more than 10%.) Cash generated from operations, however, has dwindled drastically under mounting inventories (largely from acquired businesses) along with the net impact of declining accounts payable and customer deposits, and fixed expenses and long-term liabilities.

In 2011 Titan has pursued several strategic acquisitions in its agricultural segment and its construction segment. The company in mid-2011 purchased St. Joseph Equipment's construction business. The deal, comprising four locations, represented Titan's first construction equipment dealership in Wisconsin. Hard on its heels, Titan took over ABC Rental, a Montana-based independent construction rental yard with a large customer base that spans Montana, North Dakota, South Dakota, and Wyoming. Titan also acquired construction equipment dealer Carlson Tractor and Equipment, in Minnesota, which is the home turf of just-acquired Schoffman's, an agriculture equipment dealership. Early in 2011 Titan had scooped up Tri-State Implement, which serves the farming communities in and around Sioux Falls, South Dakota.

Titan targeted the Midwest in 2010, completing two acquisitions: Fairbanks International, an agricultural equipment dealer with six franchises in Nebraska, and Hubbard Implement, a Case IH brand agriculture equipment dealership in Iowa.

Chairman, and CEO David Meyer founded Titan in 1980. Meyer owns just shy of 20% of the company.

EXECUTIVES

Chairman and CEO, David J. Meyer, age 58, $704,646 total compensation
President, CFO, and Director, Peter Christianson, age 54, $704,646 total compensation
VP Finance and Treasurer, Ted Christianson, $304,559 total compensation
Human Resources Specialist, Josh Koehnen
Auditors: Eide Bailly LLP

LOCATIONS

HQ: Titan Machinery Inc.
644 East Beaton Dr., Fargo, ND 58078-2648
Phone: 701-356-0130   **Fax:** 701-356-0139
Web: titanmachinery.com

PRODUCTS/OPERATIONS

2011 Sales

	$ mil.	% of total
Equipment	855.4	78
Parts	141.0	13
Service	74.5	7
Other	23.5	2
Total	**1,094.4**	**100**

Selected Products

Agricultural
Application equipment
Attachments
Combines
Forage equipment
Hay equipment
Planting equipment
Precision farming technology
Seeding
Sprayers
Tillage equipment
Tractors
Construction
Articulated trucks
Compact track loaders
Compaction equipment
Cranes
Crawler dozers
Excavators
Forklifts
Loader/backhoes
Loader/tool carriers
Motor graders
Skid steer loaders
Telehandlers
Wheel loaders

COMPETITORS

AGCO	Deere
Caterpillar	RDO Equipment

HISTORICAL FINANCIALS

Company Type: Public

Income Statement
FYE: January 31

	REVENUE ($ mil.)	NET INCOME ($ mil.)	NET PROFIT MARGIN	EMPLOYEES
01/11	1,094.5	22.3	2.0%	1,874
01/10	838.8	15.7	1.9%	1,491
01/09	690.4	18.1	2.6%	1,288
01/08	433.0	5.2	1.2%	716
01/07	292.6	3.6	1.2%	555
Annual Growth	39.1%	57.8%	—	35.6%

2011 Year-End Financials

Debt ratio: 15.6%	No. of shares (mil.): 17.9
Return on equity: 10.4%	Dividends
Cash ($ mil.): 76.1	Yield: —
Current ratio: 1.43	Payout: —
Long-term debt ($ mil.): 33.4	Market value ($ mil.): 434.1

	STOCK PRICE ($) FY Close	P/E High/Low		PER SHARE ($) Earnings	Dividends	Book Value
01/11	24.23	20	9	1.23	0.00	11.98
01/10	11.02	19	9	0.88	0.00	10.72
01/09	10.15	32	7	1.08	0.00	9.85
01/08	16.48	28	14	0.67	0.00	5.70
Annual Growth	13.7%	—	—	22.4%	—	28.1%

Tix Corporation

Tix Corporation has got a ticket to ride. Through its Tix4Tonight subsidiary, the company sells discounted same-day tickets to Las Vegas shows from about a dozen locations in Las Vegas. Tix4Tonight also includes Tix4Dinner (discounted dinners on the Vegas strip) and Tix4Golf (discounted golf reservations in the Las Vegas area). The company's Exhibit Merchandising sells branded merchandise (souvenir posters, memorabilia) related to museum exhibits and theatrical productions. Sales are made in temporary specialty stores set up in conjunction with the touring event.

The company continuously focuses on beefing up its ticketing and event merchandising. In 2010 it purchased the assets of All Access Entertainment, a discount ticket service with five facilities in Las Vegas. It converted the locations to its Tix4Tonight brand. The company made the acquisition to gain greater coverage of the Las Vegas area. Also in 2010 Exhibit Merchandising formed agreements to operate stores for three exhibitions, including "Tutankhamen and The Golden Age of the Pharaohs."

In 2010 the firm sold its Tix Production subsidiary, which produced live entertainment — including plays and staged events such as *Walking with Dinosaurs*, *David Copperfield*, *Rain*, and *Lord of the Dance* — to members of Tix Production's management. The subsidiary was formed in 2008 with the purchase of live entertainment producers Magic Arts and Entertainment and NewSpace Entertainment. Tix Corporation made the divestiture after a strategic review of operations, determining that it would be in the best interests of its stockholders to focus on its core discount ticket operations.

Chairman and CEO Mitchell Francis owns more than 10% of Tix Corporation, while private equity firm Baker Street Capital has approximately 22% of the shares outstanding.

EXECUTIVES

Chairman, President, and CEO, Mitchell J. (Mitch) Francis, age 56, $388,000 total compensation
CFO, Steven D. (Steve) Handy, age 42
President, Tix Productions, John Ballard, $153,000 total compensation
VP Marketing, Tix Productions, Bruce Granath
COO, Kimberly Simon, age 43, $1,115,000 total compensation
Co-CEO, Tix Productions, Lee Marshall, $352,000 total compensation
Co-CEO, Tix Productions and Director, Joseph B. (Joe) Marsh
COO, Tix Productions, Steve Boulay, $152,000 total compensation
Auditors: Weinberg & Company, P.A.

LOCATIONS

HQ: Tix Corporation
12001 Ventura Place, Ste. 340, Studio City, CA 91604
Phone: 818-761-1002   **Fax:** 818-761-1072
Web: www.tixcorp.com

PRODUCTS/OPERATIONS

2009 Sales

	$ mil.	% of total
Live entertainment	54.4	67
Ticketing services	18.3	22
Exhibit merchandising	9.1	11
Total	**81.8**	**100**

COMPETITORS

Live Nation Entertainment
Shubert Organization
StubHub
TicketCity.com
Tickets.com
TicketsNow

HISTORICAL FINANCIALS

Company Type: Public

Income Statement
FYE: December 31

	REVENUE ($ mil.)	NET INCOME ($ mil.)	NET PROFIT MARGIN	EMPLOYEES
12/09	81.8	(0.6)	—	172
12/08	69.5	(34.7)	—	150
12/07	18.6	(16.3)	—	76
12/06	5.4	—	—	50
12/05	2.7	(1.0)	—	29
Annual Growth	134.6%	—	—	56.1%

2009 Year-End Financials

Debt ratio: 0.1%	No. of shares (mil.): 31.1
Return on equity: —	Dividends
Cash ($ mil.): 9.9	Yield: —
Current ratio: 1.94	Payout: —
Long-term debt ($ mil.): 0.0	Market value ($ mil.): 54.2

	STOCK PRICE ($) FY Close	P/E High/Low		PER SHARE ($) Earnings	Dividends	Book Value
12/09	1.74	—	—	(0.02)	0.00	0.68
12/08	2.15	—	—	(1.09)	0.00	0.71
12/07	5.85	—	—	(0.70)	0.00	1.66
12/06	4.42	—	—	(0.00)	0.00	0.01
12/05	0.27	—	—	(0.10)	0.00	(0.08)
Annual Growth	59.3%			—	—	—

TNS

TNS helps voices, money, and payments move around the world. The international data communications firm provides secure data and voice transmission services for financial institutions, retailers, payment processors, and telecommunications companies. The company has a multiple data network system that operates independently of other carriers. TNS provides services in more than 40 countries around the globe and is a leading provider of data communication services to processors of credit card, debit card, and ATM transactions. The company operates in three global divisions: payments, telecommunications services, and financial services.

TNS markets its products and services under several brand names such as TNSConnect, TNS FusionPoint, and TNSPay Gateway. Its Secure Trading Extranet product is a data service that supports the Financial Information eXchange (FIX) protocol for the financial services industry.

The company has been expanding aggressively through acquisitions both domestically and abroad. Its most recent focus has been on the telecommunications sector. TNS acquired VeriSign's Communication Services Group in 2009 for $230 million. The unit, which was integrated into TNS' Telecommunication Services segment, provides caller identification and wireless roaming-related services to telecommunications companies. The acquisition proved to be transformative for TNS. It strengthened the company's telecommunications product offering, opened opportunities in new markets, and boosted company revenues by nearly 40% in 2009. TNS then acquired Cequint, a provider of mobile caller ID products and services, for an initial payment of $49 million (in a deal that will potentially cost $118 million).

Customers are increasingly operating on a global scale. As a result, the international market is expanding with increased use of credit and debit card transactions. TNS also is aiming to bring its broadened telecommunications services to non-US markets. The company is focusing its international growth in countries where it already has operations such as Australia, France, Italy, Spain and the UK.

EXECUTIVES

Chairman, John B. (Jack) Benton, age 68
CEO and Director, Henry H. Graham Jr., age 60, $2,765,988 total compensation
EVP, CFO, and Treasurer, Dennis L. Randolph Jr., age 31, $1,456,980 total compensation
EVP and President, Payments Division, Raymond (Ray) Low, age 54, $2,178,871 total compensation
EVP; President Telecommunication Services Division, Daniel P. (Dan) Dooley III
EVP; President, Financial Services Division, Alan R. Schwartz, age 49, $1,052,550 total compensation
EVP, General Counsel, and Secretary, James T. McLaughlin, age 44, $1,450,021 total compensation
COO, Michael Q. Keegan, age 44, $2,249,878 total compensation
CTO, Craig E. Conway, age 45
SVP and Chief Systems Officer, Scott E. Ziegler, age 53
Chief Network Officer, Mark G. Cole, age 45
SVP and General Manager, Mainland Europe, Payment Division, Martin Croot

SVP and General Manager, TNS Payments Division, Asia Pacific Region, John Banfield
Chief Strategy Officer, Christopher F. Penny, age 43
SVP, Chief Accounting Officer, and Corporate Controller, David A. Neal, age 38
Manager Public Relations, Clare Cockroft
Auditors: Ernst & Young LLP

LOCATIONS

HQ: TNS, Inc.
11480 Commerce Park Dr., Ste. 600, Reston, VA 20191-1406
Phone: 703-453-8300   Fax: 703-453-8599
Web: www.tnsi.com

2010 Sales

	$ mil.	% of total
North America	376.8	71
Europe	114.0	22
Asia/Pacific	36.3	7
Total	**527.1**	**100**

PRODUCTS/OPERATIONS

2010 Sales by Segment

	$ mil.	% of total
Telecommunications Services	260,715	49
Payments	200,190	38
Financial Services	66,230	13
Total	**527.1**	**100**

COMPETITORS

Apriva	Reuters
AT&T	SAVVIS
Bloomberg L.P.	Syniverse
BT	Telefónica
BT Radianz	Telstra
France Telecom	VeriSign
MegaPath	Verizon

HISTORICAL FINANCIALS

Company Type: Public

Income Statement

FYE: December 31

	REVENUE ($ mil.)	NET INCOME ($ mil.)	NET PROFIT MARGIN	EMPLOYEES
12/10	527.1	8.5	1.6%	1,237
12/09	474.8	(2.1)	—	1,163
12/08	344.0	3.5	1.0%	783
12/07	325.6	(2.8)	—	687
12/06	286.2	(9.9)	—	622
Annual Growth	**16.5%**	**—**	**—**	**18.8%**

2010 Year-End Financials

Debt ratio: 334.1%
Return on equity: 7.4%
Cash ($ mil.): 56.7
Current ratio: 1.55
Long-term debt ($ mil.): 385.1

No. of shares (mil.): 25.4
Dividends
  Yield: —
  Payout: —
Market value ($ mil.): 527.5

	STOCK PRICE ($) FY Close	P/E High/Low		PER SHARE ($) Earnings	Dividends	Book Value
12/10	20.80	87	45	0.32	0.00	4.55
12/09	25.69	—	—	(0.08)	0.00	4.70
12/08	9.39	181	45	0.14	0.00	4.24
12/07	17.75	—	—	(0.12)	0.00	3.80
12/06	19.25	—	—	(0.41)	0.00	7.43
Annual Growth	**2.0%**	—	—	—	—	**(11.6%)**

Torotel

Torotel is a military magnet. The company's Torotel Products subsidiary makes more than 32,000 magnetic components used to control electrical voltages and currents in aviation, missile guidance, communication, navigational, and other systems. Products include transformers, inductors, chokes, and toroidal coils. Subsidiary Electronika designs and sells ballast transformers to the airline industry. Torotel sells its products primarily in the US to commercial customers (including those in the health care, oil, public safety, and financial services industries), but most of the company's sales come from the aerospace and military markets.

EXECUTIVES

Chairman, President, and CEO, Dale H. (Herb) Sizemore Jr., age 59, $157,800 total compensation
VP Finance and CFO, H. James (Jim) Serrone, age 56, $122,600 total compensation
VP, Torotel Products, Kent O. Klepper, age 51, $70,500 total compensation
VP, Torotel Products, Benjamin E. Ames Jr., age 57, $137,200 total compensation
Auditors: Mayer Hoffman McCann P.C.

LOCATIONS

HQ: Torotel, Inc.
620 N. Lindenwood Dr., Olathe, KS 66062
Phone: 913-747-6111   Fax: 913-747-6110
Web: www.torotelprod.com

PRODUCTS/OPERATIONS

COMPETITORS

Bel Fuse	Q-Tran
Espey Mfg.	SL Industries
ILC Industries	STC Microwave Systems
Pulse Electronics	Vishay Intertechnology

HISTORICAL FINANCIALS

Company Type: Public

Income Statement

FYE: April 30

	REVENUE ($ mil.)	NET INCOME ($ mil.)	NET PROFIT MARGIN	EMPLOYEES
04/11	11.1	1.2	10.8%	143
04/10	7.1	—	—	113
04/09	7.2	0.3	4.2%	96
04/08	6.1	0.2	3.3%	85
04/07	5.1	(0.1)	—	80
Annual Growth	**21.5%**	**—**	**—**	**15.6%**

2011 Year-End Financials

Debt ratio: 27.3%
Return on equity: 37.4%
Cash ($ mil.): 0.5
Current ratio: 2.29
Long-term debt ($ mil.): 0.9

No. of shares (mil.): 5.8
Dividends
  Yield: —
  Payout: —
Market value ($ mil.): 3.3

	STOCK PRICE ($) FY Close	P/E High/Low		PER SHARE ($) Earnings	Dividends	Book Value
04/11	0.56	5	1	0.21	0.00	0.57
04/10	0.30	—	—	(0.01)	0.00	0.34
04/09	0.28	15	4	0.05	0.00	0.33
04/08	0.55	30	11	0.03	0.00	0.26
04/07	0.50	—	—	(0.02)	0.00	0.24
Annual Growth	**2.9%**	—	—	—	—	**23.9%**

Tower Bancorp

Tower Bancorp is the holding company for Graystone Tower Bank, which has about 50 branches in central and southeastern Pennsylvania and neighboring portions of Maryland. The bank offers standard retail products, including checking and savings accounts, money market accounts, and credit and debit cards. It uses funds from deposits mainly to write residential and commercial mortgage loans, which account for more than three-quarters of its loan portfolio. Wealth management services are offered through an agreement with UVEST Financial Services, a division of LPL Financial. Susquehanna Bancshares is buying Tower Bancorp for approximately $343 million.

Tower Bancorp has grown through acquisitions itself. The company merged with Graystone Financial in 2009 and bought First Chester County Corporation the following year. The latter deal nearly doubled Graystone Tower Bank's branch network, while the Graystone Financial acquisition brought in Graystone Bank, which has nearly 10 locations and kept its name as a division of Graystone Tower Bank.

EXECUTIVES

President and CEO, Andrew S. Samuel, age 49
EVP; President and CEO, Graystone Bank, Janak Amin
EVP and CFO, Mark Merrill
EVP and COO, Jeffrey Renninger
EVP, John Duffey
EVP; President and CEO, Tower Bank, Jeffrey B. (Jeff) Shank, age 55, $276,408 total compensation
VP, Donald G. (Don) Kunkle, age 61
VP and Treasurer, Franklin T. Klink III, age 55, $147,015 total compensation
Vice Chairman, Tower Bancorp and The First National Bank of Greencastle, Frederic M. Frederick, age 54
SEVP and Secretary, John H. McDowell Sr., age 61, $187,448 total compensation
SVP, Margaret Kobel
Auditors: Smith Elliott Kearns & Company, LLC

LOCATIONS

HQ: Tower Bancorp Inc.
112 Market St., Harrisburg, PA 17101
Phone: 717-231-2700
Web: www.towerbancorp.com

COMPETITORS

Codorus Valley Bancorp	M&T Bank
Fidelity Bancorp (PA)	Mid Penn Bancorp
Fulton Financial	Orrstown Financial
Juniata Valley Financial	Susquehanna Bancshares

HISTORICAL FINANCIALS

Company Type: Public

Income Statement

FYE: December 31

	ASSETS ($ mil.)	NET INCOME ($ mil.)	INCOME AS % OF ASSETS	EMPLOYEES
12/10	2,747.3	1.2	0.0%	912
12/09	1,470.6	3.7	0.3%	322
12/08	556.5	3.2	0.6%	188
12/07	561.6	7.0	1.2%	183
12/06	542.2	6.1	1.1%	183
Annual Growth	50.0%	(33.4%)	—	49.4%

2010 Year-End Financials

Equity as % of assets: —
Return on assets: 0.0%
Return on equity: 0.5%
Long-term debt ($ mil.): 87.8
No. of shares (mil.): 12.0

Dividends
Yield: 5.1%
Payout: 700.0%
Market value ($ mil.): 263.8
Sales ($ mil.): 88.5

	STOCK PRICE ($) FY Close	P/E High/Low		PER SHARE ($) Earnings	Dividends	Book Value
12/10	22.04	175	111	0.16	1.12	21.44
12/09	22.85	52	26	0.72	1.12	23.01
12/08	22.50	30	14	1.37	1.12	30.56
12/07	41.10	15	14	2.99	1.06	33.76
12/06	44.75	17	15	2.87	0.74	34.60
Annual Growth	(16.2%)	—	—	(51.4%)	10.9%	(11.3%)

Tower Group

Tower Group is hoping to rise high in the insurance business. Through more than 15 subsidiaries, the firm sells specialty commercial and personal property/casualty insurance to individuals and to small and midsized businesses, primarily in the northeastern US. Its commercial products include auto, general liability, and workers' compensation coverage in the retail, wholesale, service, real estate, and construction industries. Its personal insurance lines focus on home and automobile policies. Tower's products are distributed through retail and wholesale agents. Its services division offers underwriting, claims, and reinsurance to other insurers.

Through acquisitions, Tower Group is expanding its operations outside of its core operating territories, as well as into new product segments. The company is looking to purchase small regional insurance companies to create a national presence across the US. Targeted regions for future growth include the West and Southwest.

In 2009 it acquired Hermitage Insurance, a specialty property/casualty provider in the Southeast, from Brookfield Asset Management for $130 million. That purchase expanded Tower Group's network of wholesale agents in the region. It has also bought Specialty Underwriters' Alliance, which provides commercial policies for niche industries in the Midwest, for $107 million.

Tower Group also broadened its specialty operations in early 2009 when it acquired reinsurance provider CastlePoint Holdings (which it helped form in 2005). It already owned about 7% of CastlePoint; Tower Group purchased the remaining interest in CastlePoint in a stock and cash transaction worth $490 million. CEO Michael Lee, who owns about 8% of Tower Group, also helms

the reinsurance provider. The company aims to expand its revenue sources, increase shareholder value, and cut costs through the deal. CastlePoint will continue to handle reinsurance contracts for Tower Group and other customers.

Tower's 2010 acquisition of OneBeacon's personal lines business further enriched its Northeastern holdings; the company spent $167 million to obtain several OneBeacon insurance and management subsidiaries that primarily offer private auto and homeowners coverage in the region.

Through its general agency subsidiary Tower Risk Management, Tower Group earns commissions on policies it sells for other providers. Tower Risk Management also provides underwriting, claims administration, and reinsurance intermediary services.

EXECUTIVES

Chairman, President, and CEO, Michael H. Lee, age 53, $4,437,698 total compensation
VP Operations, Joe Chamberlain
VP Commercial Lines Small Business, Josephine Saenz-DeViteri
VP Insurance Regulatory Counsel, Adam Perri
VP Information Technology, Matt Bates
VP Personal Lines, Edward A. Blomquist
VP IT Governance, Michael J. Mihalik
VP Reinsurance, Marina Contiero
VP Home Office Operations, Rick Lustri
VP Information Technology, Saeed Fotovat
VP and Corporate Counsel, Susan Eylward
SVP and CFO, William E. Hitselberger, age 53
SVP, Chief Actuary, and Strategic Planning, Joel S. Weiner, age 61, $737,446 total compensation
SVP and Chief Underwriting Officer, Gary S. Maier, age 46, $925,157 total compensation
SVP and CIO, Salvatore V. Abano, age 47
SVP Specialty Business, Courtney C. Smith, age 63
SVP Operations, Laurie Ranegar, age 49
Managing VP Corporate Development, Thomas (Tom) Song
Managing VP, West Zone, Larry Rogers
Managing VP, Midwest Zone and Specialty Underwriting, Fred Fontein
Managing VP, Corporate Planning and Development and Reinsurance, James Roberts
Managing VP Claims, Scott T. Melnik
Managing VP Human Resources, Catherine M. Wragg
Managing VP, Specialty Underwriting and Customized Solutions, David Brodsky, age 67
Managing VP, Personal Lines, Dan Liparini
Managing VP, Commercial Lines Executive, Mark Smith
Managing VP, Specialty Underwriting, Robert Hedges
Managing VP Planning, Angelica Facchini
Managing VP, East Zone, Bruce Sanderson, $390,405 total compensation
SVP, General Counsel, and Secretary, Elliot S. Orol, age 55, $622,590 total compensation
SVP Marketing and Distribution, Christian K. Pechmann, age 61
Managing VP Commercial Lines, Brian Hosey
Auditors:

LOCATIONS

HQ: Tower Group, Inc.
120 Broadway, 31st. Fl., New York, NY 10271
Phone: 212-655-2000   **Fax:** 212-655-2199
Web: www.twrgrp.com

PRODUCTS/OPERATIONS

2009 Sales

	$ mil.	% of total
Brokerage insurance	662.2	67
Specialty business	239.4	24
Investments	76.4	8
Insurance services	5.1	1
Total	**983.1**	**100**

2009 Sales

	$ mil.	% of total
Net premiums earned	854.7	87
Net investment income	74.9	8
Ceding commission revenue	43.9	4
Insurance services revenue	5.1	1
Policy billing fees	3.0	-
Net realized gain on investments	1.5	-
Total	**983.1**	**100**

Selected Subsidiaries

American Resources Insurance Consultants, LLC
CastlePoint Insurance Company
Hermitage Insurance Company
HIG, Inc.
Kodiak Insurance Company
Mountain Valley Indemnity Company
North Atlantic Underwriters, Inc.
North East Insurance Company
Ocean I Corporation
Preserver Group, Inc.
SUA Insurance Services, Inc.
Tower Insurance Company of New York
Tower National Insurance Company
Tower Risk Management Corp.

COMPETITORS

ACE Limited	NYCM
AIG	Philadelphia Insurance Companies
Allied World Assurance	
Allstate	Preferred Mutual
Chubb Corp	Progressive Corporation
CNA Financial	
Erie Insurance Exchange	Safeco
	Selective Insurance
GNY Mutual Insurance	State Farm
Hanover Insurance	The Hartford
Harleysville Group	Travelers Companies
Magna Carta Companies	Utica Mutual Insurance
Middlesex Mutual	W. R. Berkley
Nationwide	

HISTORICAL FINANCIALS

Company Type: Public

Income Statement

FYE: December 31

	ASSETS ($ mil.)	NET INCOME ($ mil.)	INCOME AS % OF ASSETS	EMPLOYEES
12/10	4,214.2	118.0	2.8%	1,360
12/09	3,313.0	109.3	3.3%	987
12/08	1,533.0	57.5	3.8%	588
12/07	1,354.6	45.1	3.3%	549
12/06	954.1	36.8	3.9%	403
Annual Growth	45.0%	33.8%	—	35.5%

2010 Year-End Financials

Equity as % of assets: 25.81%
Return on assets: 2.8%
Return on equity: 10.8%
Long-term debt ($ mil.): 374.3
No. of shares (mil.): 41.5

Dividends
Yield: 1.5%
Payout: 14.4%
Market value ($ mil.): 1,062.0
Sales ($ mil.): 1,458.7

	STOCK PRICE ($) FY Close	P/E High/Low		PER SHARE ($) Earnings	Dividends	Book Value
12/10	25.60	10	7	2.70	0.39	26.22
12/09	23.41	11	7	2.76	0.26	23.35
12/08	28.21	13	6	2.47	0.15	14.38
12/07	33.40	19	12	1.93	0.15	13.34
12/06	31.07	20	9	1.82	0.10	11.21
Annual Growth	(4.7%)	—	—	10.4%	40.5%	23.7%

TowerStream

TowerStream maintains a commanding view of the wireless landscape. The company provides wireless broadband network services to businesses over its network comprised of rooftop and tower-mounted antennas. Its networks can be accessed by customers within a 10-mile radius. The company has about 900 business customers, including retailers, educational institutions, and banks. Charging a monthly subscription fee, TowerStream provides service in twelve US markets: Boston, Chicago, Las Vegas, Los Angeles, Miami, Nashville, New York City, Reno, San Francisco, and Seattle, as well as Newport and Providence, Rhode Island.

In a move to expand its network in 2010, the company paid $1.6 million to Sparkplug Communications for assets in Chicago and Nashville, including its network facilities and customers accounts. The deal served to introduce the TowerStream brand to Nashville and increase its existing presence in Chicago. Also that year Towerstream bought the Boston and Providence-based assets of Pipeline Wireless to boost its presence on the Eastern seaboard.

In 2011 Towerstream entered the Nevada market with the purchase of the Las Vegas and Reno-based operations of wired and wireless business networking services provider One Velocity. Later in the year, Towerstream agreed to it largest acquisition yet. It will pick up the customer contracts, network infrastructure, and their related assets from California-based wireless Internet service provider Color Broadband. The acquisition will make Los Angeles Towerstream's largest market, boosting that area's customer base by about 60%, annual revenue by 70%, and network coverage area by 20%.

EXECUTIVES

Chairman, Philip Urso, age 52
CFO, Joseph P. Hernon, age 51, $376,413 total compensation
President, CEO, and Director, Jeffrey M. (Jeff) Thompson, age 47, $389,628 total compensation
VP Human Resources, Philip Mongada
VP Engineering and Network Operations, Arthur G. Giftakis, age 45
Chief Revenue Officer, Melvin L. (Mel) Yarbrough, age 45, $384,847 total compensation
Auditors:

LOCATIONS

HQ: TowerStream Corporation
55 Hammarlund Way, Middletown, RI 02842
Phone: 401-848-5848
Web: www.towerstream.com

COMPETITORS

AT&T	MegaPath
Clearwire	Speakeasy, Inc.
Comcast	Sprint Nextel
Covad Communications Group	Verizon
	WildBlue
Hughes Network	XO Holdings

HISTORICAL FINANCIALS
Company Type: Public

Income Statement
FYE: December 31

	REVENUE ($ mil.)	NET INCOME ($ mil.)	NET PROFIT MARGIN	EMPLOYEES
12/10	19.6	(5.6)	—	132
12/09	14.9	(8.6)	—	127
12/08	10.7	(13.4)	—	170
12/07	6.9	(8.5)	—	157
12/06	6.3	(0.8)	—	49
Annual Growth	32.8%	—	—	28.1%

2010 Year-End Financials

Debt ratio: 0.1%	No. of shares (mil.): 42.1
Return on equity: —	Dividends
Cash ($ mil.): 23.2	Yield: —
Current ratio: 6.25	Payout: —
Long-term debt ($ mil.): 0.1	Market value ($ mil.): 171.0

	STOCK PRICE ($) FY Close	P/E High/Low		PER SHARE ($) Earnings	Dividends	Book Value
12/10	4.06	—	—	(0.16)	0.00	0.95
12/09	1.94	—	—	(0.25)	0.00	0.73
12/08	0.69	—	—	(0.39)	0.00	0.96
12/07	3.07	—	—	(0.29)	0.00	1.31
Annual Growth	9.8%	—	—	—	—	(10.2%)

TPC Group

TPC Group makes the stuff that helps to make your car your car. The company manufactures building-block chemicals that are used as gasoline additives, go into tires, and make up carpet fibers. TPC's product line focuses on C4 hydrocarbons, including butadiene (for synthetic rubber), butene-1 (used in ethylene production), high-purity isobutylene (an intermediate for lube oils), and diisobutylene (an ingredient for surfactants). The company used to get about half its sales from the production of methyl tertiary butyl ether (MTBE), a prominent oxygenate used in gasolines. However, though it still makes MTBE as a byproduct, it closed its production units in 2008 after regulations limited its use in many states.

After a tough 2009 that included a two-month shutdown due to Hurricane Ike and an overall poor economy, TPC Group saw its both its revenues and income recover in 2010. Revenues were up 23% due primarily to increased sales volumes as well as improved selling prices, particularly for C4 product lines. Net income swung to $30.5 million in 2010 from a $23 million loss the previous year.

TPC Group began growing its highly reactive polyisobutylene (HR-PIB) line in 2008. That product is used to produce fuel and lubricant additives as well as caulks, adhesives, sealants, and in packaging materials. TPC Group, which holds several patents related to its production and is the prod-uct's sole merchant in North America, is ramping up HR-PIB production with plans to expand its sales into both domestic and foreign markets.

As a reflection of this focus on downstream products, the company changed its name from Texas Petrochemicals to the TPC Group in 2010.

EXECUTIVES

Chairman, Michael E. Ducey, age 62
President, CEO, and Director, Michael T. McDonnell, age 53
VP Strategic Planning, Mike Bloesch
VP Human Resources, Paula Sharp
VP and General Manager for C4 Processing, Glenn E. Bohny
VP and Controller, Roger D. Wollenberg
VP and General Manager, Performance Products, Sandra S. Davis
VP Finance and Treasurer, Robert R. (Bob) Whitlow Jr.
SVP and CFO, Miguel A. Desdin, age 45
SVP Commercial, Russ Crockett
SVP Operations, Luis E. Batiz
Investor Relations, Scott Phipps
Human Resources, Kathryn Wentz
Deputy General Counsel and Secretary, Shannon B. Weinberg
SVP Global Portfolio Growth, Gerald M. (Jerry) Law
Director Environmental Health, Safety, and Security, Marise Textor
Manager Corporate Communications and Media Relations, Sara Cronin
Auditors: Grant Thornton LLP

LOCATIONS

HQ: TPC Group Inc.
5151 San Felipe, Ste. 800, Houston, TX 77056-1935
Phone: 713-627-7474   **Fax:** 713-626-3650
Web: www.tpcgrp.com

PRODUCTS/OPERATIONS

2010 Sales

	$ mil.	% of total
C4 processing	1,328.7	79
Performance products	359.8	21
Total	**1,688.5**	**100**

Selected Products
C4 products
  Butadiene
  Butene-1
  Raffinates (blendstock used in the production of gasoline)
Performance products
  Isobutylene
    High purity isobutylenes
    Isobutylene concentrates
  Diisobutylene
  Nonene
  Polyisobutylene
    Conventional polyisobutylene
    Highly reactive polyisobutylene
  Tetramer

COMPETITORS

Braskem	Innospec
Dow Chemical	Methanex
Enterprise Products	Shell Chemicals
Equistar Chemicals	Sunoco Chemicals
ExxonMobil Chemical	Valero Energy

HISTORICAL FINANCIALS

Company Type: Public

Income Statement

FYE: December 31

	REVENUE ($ mil.)	NET INCOME ($ mil.)	NET PROFIT MARGIN	EMPLOYEES
06/07	1,781.5	23.7	1.3%	0
06/06	1,237.7	38.7	3.1%	0
06/05	936.3	24.7	2.6%	0
06/04	646.2	173.4	26.8%	0
06/03	708.2	(188.9)	—	0
Annual Growth	25.9%	—	—	—

Debt ratio: 0.1%
Return on equity: —
Cash ($ mil.): 23.2
Current ratio: 6.25
Long-term debt ($ mil.): 0.1

No. of shares (mil.): 42.1
Dividends
  Yield: —
  Payout: —
Market value ($ mil.): 171.0

Transcend Services

Transcend Services helps make sense of doctors' gibberish. The medical transcription company uses Internet-based technology to turn doctors' audio patient records into written text. Its home-based medical transcriptionists convert the physicians' recorded notes (made using either Transcend Services' proprietary BeyondTXT technology or the clients' own systems) into text documents. The company is increasingly using speech recognition software to automatically convert voice to text, after which the documents are edited by transcriptionists. Transcend Services counts some 330 hospitals, clinics, and physician group practices among its customers.

Operating in what is a highly fragmented industry, Transcend Services has grown by acquiring smaller medical transcription businesses. For example in 2010 the company bought Spryance, which has extensive operations in India where Transcend Services outsources a good portion of its business. Of its 2,400 medical language transcriptionists, 30% are based in India. Transcend Services intends to continue to grow its offshore-based services (hence the purchase of Spryance) because of faster turn around times resulting in a higher customer retention rate (95% in 2010).

In 2011, Transcend Services courted and won medical transcription firm DTS America. The $9.5 million deal gave Transcend Services an array of clinical documentation tools from standard transcription services to speech recognition tools.

In addition to acquisitions, the company pursues growth organically by winning new customers, focusing its marketing efforts on community hospitals with more than 100 beds, as well as by enhancing its transcription technologies. Transcend Services expects to reap the benefits of increased use of electronic medical records (EMR) because some of the data and content created by Transcend Services make up key parts of the EMR systems.

Transcend Services currently offers two primary service delivery options: In-house in which the customer partners with Transcend Services to receive medical transcription services on the customer's platform; and, Outsourcing, in which the customer outsources the entire transcription process from beginning to end. However, it is developing a third

Software as a Service option called Encore, in which customers with their own transcription departments can use Transcend Services' speech recognition-enabled platform, when needed.

Of Transcend Services' customers its top 10 are hospitals that account for nearly 17% of the company's transcription income. Transcend Services has a multi-year agreement with Health Management Associates (HMA) that also accounts for about 17% Transcend Services' revenue. Transcend Services has reported positive operating income since 2005.

EXECUTIVES

Chairman and CEO, Larry G. Gerdes, age 62, $272,500 total compensation
President and COO, Sue McGrogan, age 44, $622,500 total compensation
CFO, Lance T. Cornell, age 45, $483,050 total compensation
VP Information Technology, Scott Robertson
SVP Business Development, Jeff Felshaw
Auditors: Grant Thornton LLP

LOCATIONS

HQ: Transcend Services, Inc.
  1 Glenlake Pkwy., Ste. 1325, Atlanta, GA 30328
Phone: 678-808-0600   **Fax:** 678-808-0601
Web: www.transcendservices.com

COMPETITORS

3M HIS	Nuance Communications
Acusis	Precyse Solutions
Keystrokes	SPi Global Solutions
MedQuist Holdings	Sten-Tel
NCO Group	

HISTORICAL FINANCIALS

Company Type: Public

Income Statement

FYE: December 31

	REVENUE ($ mil.)	NET INCOME ($ mil.)	NET PROFIT MARGIN	EMPLOYEES
12/10	94.3	8.5	9.0%	891
12/09	71.8	6.8	9.5%	2,081
12/08	48.7	5.8	11.9%	1,172
12/07	42.5	11.5	27.1%	1,005
12/06	32.9	1.5	4.6%	877
Annual Growth	30.1%	54.3%	—	0.4%

2010 Year-End Financials

Debt ratio: —
Return on equity: 12.1%
Cash ($ mil.): 6.2
Current ratio: 4.55
Long-term debt ($ mil.): —

No. of shares (mil.): 10.6
Dividends
  Yield: —
  Payout: —
Market value ($ mil.): 207.0

	STOCK PRICE ($) FY Close	P/E High/Low		PER SHARE ($) Earnings	Dividends	Book Value
12/10	19.59	27	15	0.79	0.00	6.64
12/09	21.37	29	12	0.76	0.00	5.67
12/08	9.99	23	13	0.65	0.00	2.59
12/07	16.25	19	3	1.31	0.00	2.07
12/06	3.59	21	10	0.18	0.00	0.55
Annual Growth	52.8%	—	—	44.7%	—	86.5%

Tri-S Security

Keeping others fully guarded keeps Tri-S Security in business. Through its Paragon Systems subsidiary, the company provides contract security guard services to US government agencies. Its guards are used for activities such as access control, crowd control, perimeter security, personal protection, and surveillance. In 2009 Tri-S Security sold its Cornwall Group subsidiary, a provider of security and investigative services such as armed and unarmed uniformed guards and alarm monitoring throughout the Miami-Dade, Broward, and Palm Beach counties of Florida. Chairman, president, and CEO Ronald Farrell controls nearly 40% of Tri-S Security.

Nearly 75% of the Tri-S Security's business comes from contracts with the Federal government. Major customers include the Department of Homeland Security (about 25% of sales) and the Social Security Administration (nearly 20% of sales). The company is focused on growing its business by obtaining new Federal government contracts, as well as new commercial and residential customers.

Tri-S Security sold Cornwall in order to reduce its debt, improve its balance sheet ratios, and save interest expense. The sale reduced the company's debt by approximately $7 million.

EXECUTIVES

Chairman, President, and CEO, Ronald G. Farrell, age 67
CFO, Nicolas V. Chater, age 57
President, Paragon Systems, Leslie (Les) Kaciban Jr.
Auditors: Tauber & Balser, P.C.

LOCATIONS

HQ: Tri-S Security Corporation
  Royal Centre One, 11675 Great Oaks Way, Ste. 120, Alpharetta, GA 30022
Phone: 678-808-1540   **Fax:** 678-808-1551
Web: www.trissecurity.com

PRODUCTS/OPERATIONS

2008 Sales

	$ mil.	% of total
Paragon Systems	104.3	74
Cornwall	37.0	26
Total	**141.3**	**100**

COMPETITORS

AlliedBarton Security	Security Consultants
G4S Wackenhut	Group
Guardsmark	Shield Security, Inc.
Inter-Con Security	

HISTORICAL FINANCIALS

Company Type: Public

Income Statement

FYE: December 31

	REVENUE ($ mil.)	NET INCOME ($ mil.)	NET PROFIT MARGIN	EMPLOYEES
12/08	141.3	(15.8)	—	3,000
12/07	88.9	(4.3)	—	2,600
12/06	75.7	(3.8)	—	2,400
12/05	42.0	(2.3)	—	2,500
12/04	25.4	(1.6)	—	760
Annual Growth	53.6%	—	—	41.0%

2008 Year-End Financials

Debt ratio: — No. of shares (mil.): 4.2
Return on equity: — Dividends
Cash ($ mil.): 1.2 Yield: —
Current ratio: 0.61 Payout: —
Long-term debt ($ mil.): 9.0 Market value ($ mil.): 2.3

	STOCK PRICE ($) FY Close	P/E High/Low		PER SHARE ($) Earnings	Dividends	Book Value
12/08	0.55	—	—	(3.77)	0.00	(2.35)
12/07	1.54	—	—	(1.02)	0.00	1.14
12/06	2.21	—	—	(1.11)	0.00	1.63
12/05	4.40	—	—	(0.74)	0.00	2.48
Annual Growth	(50.0%)	—	—	—	—	—

Triangle Capital

Triangle Capital lends to companies, but they must be of a certain shape and size. An internally managed business-development company, Triangle provides loans to and invests in lower-middle-market US companies with annual revenues of $20 million-$100 million. The company, which likes to partner with its portfolio companies' management, prefers to invest in established businesses with stable financial histories. Triangle most often invests in senior and subordinated debt securities and usually takes a equity interest; it contributes between $5 million and $15 million per transaction. The company's portfolio includes some 50 manufacturers, business services, food services, and other types of enterprises.

Its portfolio comprises a diverse spread of businesses ranging from Ann's House of Nuts to Great Expressions Dental Center. Many of its investments are in companies that manufacture food products or equipment, chemicals, industrial goods, or textiles.

The company targets lower-midsized companies because it believes such businesses are underserved by the business lending industry (which generally tends to lend capital to larger commercial enterprises). Formed in 2006, Triangle Capital has grown over the years by serving smaller midsized enterprises.

Triangle Capital's investment activity reached record levels in 2010. The company funded more than $170 million in investments that year (compared to about $49 million the year before). Its number of portfolio companies also increased by about 30% in 2010. As the economy slowly recovers, Triangle is looking to make more investments in new and existing portfolio companies.

EXECUTIVES

Chairman, President, and CEO, Garland S. Tucker III, age 62
CFO, Secretary, Treasurer, and Director, Steven C. Lilly, age 40
VP, Matthew A Young
VP, James J. Burke
VP and Principal Accounting Officer, C. Robert Knox Jr.
VP Investor Relations, Sheri B. Colquitt
Chief Investment Officer and Director, Brent P.W. Burgess, age 44
Auditors: Ernst & Young LLP

LOCATIONS

HQ: Triangle Capital Corporation
3700 Glenwood Ave., Ste. 530, Raleigh, NC 27612
Phone: 919-719-4770
Web: www.tcap.com

PRODUCTS/OPERATIONS

2010 Sales

	$ in mil.	% of total
Loan interest, fee & dividend income	29.7	83
Total paid-in-kind interest income	6.0	17
Interest income from cash & cash equivalent investments	0.3	-
Total	**36.0**	**100**

Selected Portfolio Companies

Ambient Air Corporation
American De-Rosa Lamparts & Hallmark Lighting, LLC
Ann's House of Nuts, Inc
AP Services
Art Headquarters, Inc.
Botanical Laboratories
Brantley Transportation
Carolina Beer and Beverage
CRS Reprocessing Services
CV Holdings, LLC
Cyrus Networks, LLC
Dyson Corporation
Emerald Waste Services
Energy Solutions
Equisales, LLC
ESP
Fire Sprinkler Systems
Fischbein, LLC
Flint Acquisition
Garden Fresh Restaurant Corp.
Genapure (QC Labs)
Gerli & Company
Great Expressions Dental Center
Hatch
An Industrial Distributor
Inland Pipe Rehabilitation
Jenkins Restorations
Library Systems & Services
Media Temple
Minco Technology Labs
Syrgis Holdings, Inc.
TrustHouse Services Group
Tulsa Inspection Resources
Twin Star International
Wholesale Floors Inc.
Yellowstone Landscape Group
Zoom Systems

COMPETITORS

American Capital	Gladstone Capital
Ares Management	MCG Capital
Fifth Street Finance	MVC Capital
Full Circle Capital	Solar Capital

HISTORICAL FINANCIALS

Company Type: Public

Income Statement

FYE: December 31

	REVENUE ($ mil.)	NET INCOME ($ mil.)	NET PROFIT MARGIN	EMPLOYEES
12/10	36.0	25.4	70.6%	17
12/09	27.8	4.0	14.4%	14
12/08	21.4	7.6	35.5%	14
12/07	15.2	8.8	57.9%	11
12/03	0.0	(1.2)	—	0
Annual Growth	—	—	—	15.6%

2010 Year-End Financials

Debt ratio: 112.2% No. of shares (mil.): 14.9
Return on equity: 14.1% Dividends
Cash ($ mil.): 54.8 Yield: 8.7%
Current ratio: — Payout: 82.9%
Long-term debt ($ mil.): 202.5 Market value ($ mil.): 283.7

	STOCK PRICE ($) FY Close	P/E High/Low		PER SHARE ($) Earnings	Dividends	Book Value
12/10	19.00	11	6	1.99	1.65	12.09
12/09	12.09	28	11	0.47	1.62	11.03
12/08	10.20	12	4	1.11	1.44	13.22
12/07	12.40	12	8	1.31	0.98	13.74
Annual Growth	15.3%	—	—	15.0%	19.0%	(4.2%)

Trico Marine

Trico Marine Services was a workhorse under the water. The company provided subsea engineering support to the offshore oil and gas industry in the US and abroad. Its vessels provided subsea services, including trenching and installation services, as well towing and supply services. Trico Marine's fleet operated in the Gulf of Mexico as well as in such international markets as the North Sea, West Africa, Mexico, Brazil, and Southeast Asia. In 2009 the company decided to exit the offshore supply vessel business in favor of the subsea services segment. Facing heavy debts, in 2010 Trico Marine placed its US operations under Chapter 11 bankruptcy protection and sought liquidation in 2011.

Subsea services was seen as a market with more growth potential than Trico Marine's traditional towing and supply business. In this regard the company acquired two subsea service providers — the UK's CTC Marine Projects and Norway's Deep-Ocean for about $1.1 billion — in 2008. Those deals broadened its service offerings (especially in cable laying and trenching), its customer base, and its fleet of subsea vessels and equipment.

The expansion of its subsea services division was intended to help stabilize Trico Marine's cash flow as it dealt with reducing a large debt load through 2011. However, the company saw its debt grow with the downturn of the economy in 2009 and the weakening of demand for oil and gas exploration and production activity, as revenues could not outstrip the increased costs stemming from its 2008 subsea purchases. To help pay down debt, the company sold two of its supply vessels and other assets for about $70 million, and suspended the delivery of four new vessels, but in 2010 Trico Marine also needed to seek Chapter 11 protection for some of its units.

Unable to met its financial obligations, in 2011 the company spun off its marine supply and shipping businesses and filed a bankruptcy liquidation plan in US Bankruptcy Court.

EXECUTIVES

Chairman and Interim CEO, Richard A. Bachmann, age 65
President, DeepOcean AS, Mads Bardsen
President, Subsea Protection Division, Daryl Lynch
CEO Eastern Marine Services Ltd. (Shanghai), Michael Wallace
VP and General Counsel, Suzanne B. Kean
VP International Operations, Gerald A. Gray, age 67

VP Human Resources, Tricia Young
Interim COO, D. Michael Wallace, age 59
General Counsel and Secretary, Brett Cenkus
Chief Accounting Officer, Jeff Favret, age 51
Regional Manager; Global Sales and Marketing Mexico, Scott Worhington
Global Sales and Marketing Brazil, Jimmy De Souza
Group Treasurer and Director Financial Planning, Stephen L. (Steve) Morrell
Regional Manager; Global Sales and Marketing West Africa, Nick Anderson
Global Director, Technical Services, Ray Hoover, age 55
Global Director Sales and Marketing, Tomas R. Salazar, age 48
Sales and Marketing US, Tony Stokes
Auditors: PricewaterhouseCoopers LLP

LOCATIONS

HQ: Trico Marine Services, Inc.
10001 Woodloch Forest Dr., Ste. 610, The Woodlands, TX 77380
Phone: 713-780-9926   **Fax:** 713-780-0062
Web: www.tricomarine.com

COMPETITORS

C & C Technologies
Global Industries
GulfMark Offshore
Hornbeck Offshore
Oceaneering International
SEACOR
Subsea 7
Tidewater Inc.

HISTORICAL FINANCIALS

Company Type: Public

Income Statement

FYE: December 31

	REVENUE ($ mil.)	NET INCOME ($ mil.)	NET PROFIT MARGIN	EMPLOYEES
12/09	642.2	(145.3)	—	1,780
12/08	556.1	(111.2)	—	2,022
12/07	256.1	62.9	24.6%	659
12/06	248.7	58.7	23.6%	834
12/05	182.3	(41.3)	—	836
Annual Growth	37.0%	—	—	20.8%

2009 Year-End Financials

Debt ratio: 686.0%	No. of shares (mil.): 19.5
Return on equity: —	Dividends
Cash ($ mil.): 53.0	Yield: —
Current ratio: 0.88	Payout: —
Long-term debt ($ mil.): 681.3	Market value ($ mil.): 88.7

	STOCK PRICE ($) FY Close	P/E High/Low		PER SHARE ($) Earnings	Dividends	Book Value
12/09	4.54	—	—	(7.60)	0.00	5.08
12/08	4.47	—	—	(7.54)	0.00	9.22
12/07	37.02	10	7	4.16	0.00	25.99
12/06	38.31	10	7	3.86	0.00	21.13
12/05	26.00	—	—	(2.40)	0.00	15.20
Annual Growth	(35.4%)	—	—	—	—	(23.9%)

Trident Microsystems

This Trident can't stir up the oceans or shatter rocks like Poseidon's model, but its chips are behind some pretty powerful displays. Trident Microsystems offers integrated circuits (ICs) for digital televisions, LCD TVs, and digital set-top boxes. The company's video processors enhance the quality of both analog and digital TV outputs, while its encoder chips optimize the display of computer images on TV. Trident outsources its manufacturing (mainly to United Microelectronics) and sells primarily to OEMs located in Asia and Europe. The company's top customers are Philips, Samsung Electronics, Sharp, and Sony.

Trident has a limited number of customers, with the top three accounting for the majority of its sales. The company's focus on consumer electronics could be a boon as the global recession slowly fades and purchases of electronics are reviving, but it was a liability in fiscal 2009, as sales declined more than two-thirds due to lower demand driven by the recession, which crimped sales of TVs and the chips that go into them. Quite apart from general economic trends, the semiconductor industry is also subject to volatile cyclicality.

In late 2009, the company's board decided to shift its fiscal year from ending on June 30 to the calendar year. For the latter six months of 2009, Samsung Electronics resumed its place as a leading customer, representing 29% of sales, and LG Electronics was behind 15%.

After years of focusing on chips for notebook computers and desktop PCs, Trident set its sights on the digital TV market. Trident restructured its remaining operations by combining its digital media division with its Trident Technologies subsidiary in Taiwan.

In keeping with its ambitions for global dominance in the digital home entertainment arena, Trident acquired the TV systems and set-top box portfolios of NXP Semiconductors in 2010. The deal places Trident as one of the top three providers of both lines. It also gives NXP a 60% equity stake in Trident. In 2009 Trident picked up three product lines from Micronas Semiconductor in exchange for 7 million shares of Trident common stock, giving Micronas an equity stake of about 10% in Trident. The frame-rate-converter, demodulator, and audio product lines broaden Trident's DTV product and intellectual property portfolio, while expanding its base of tier-one customers. Trident hired about 150 employees from Micronas and opened three design centers in Europe as a result.

With the Micronas and NXP transactions, Trident went from being mostly a Silicon Valley venture to a truly global enterprise — and a much bigger company in terms of headcount. Its number of employees increased from 640 at the end of 2009 to 1,626 with the closing of the NXP transaction. How well the company can integrate and manage such growth — and whether the nascent economic recovery will help support a significantly larger and more geographically dispersed enterprise — remains to be seen.

The company is facing investigations by the SEC and the US Department of Justice regarding its past practices in granting stock options. Trident is cooperating with both inquiries. In addition, the IRS is making an inquiry into the company's finances.

HISTORY

Frank Lin, co-founder of graphics products maker Genoa Systems, started Trident Microsystems in 1987. The company shipped its first graphics-standard controller the next year. It opened a Taiwan office in 1989 and another in Hong Kong in 1992. That year Trident went public, introduced a chip for nonalphanumeric alphabets such as Chinese and Korean, and shipped a chipset for PC-based video production.

In 1995 Trident invested $60 million in a Taiwanese joint venture fabrication plant, which later became part of Taiwanese silicon foundry United Microelectronics Corporation (UMC). Two years later the company beefed up its marketing efforts in the US by opening sales offices and R&D centers.

In fiscal 1998 Trident posted its first annual loss, thanks in part to the Asian economic crisis of that year; a 10% workforce reduction followed. The company continued to introduce new product lines, including digital television video processors, in 1999 and 2000, and fared much better than many chip companies as it weathered dismal market conditions in fiscal 2001 and 2002.

In 2003 Trident transferred its graphics division to XGI Technology, a Silicon Integrated Systems spinoff, in order to focus on chips for digital television applications. Trident restructured its remaining operations by combining its digital media division with its Trident Technologies, Inc. (TTI) subsidiary. TTI was liquidated in 2006.

Following an internal investigation by a special board committee into the company's past practices in granting stock options, founder Frank Lin resigned as chairman and CEO in 2006. Glen Antle, a director of Trident since 1992, was named chairman and acting CEO to succeed Lin.

Among other measures adopted following the stock-options probe, which found that the company used incorrect measurement dates in granting options to officers and employees from 1994 to 2006, the Trident board voted to separate the positions of chairman and CEO.

The board's probe apparently cleared other Trident officers of responsibility in the stock-options problems, which resulted in the company taking noncash charges for stock-based compensation expenses of nearly $56 million; a nonexecutive employee who reported to Lin also resigned as the probe committee wrapped up its work. The board also relieved Peter Jen, the chief accounting officer, from his position, and determined that he would have no responsibilities or oversight in finance, human resources, or information systems.

Trident was also facing an audit of its 401(k) plan by the US Department of Labor following the internal inquiry; the Labor Department took no enforcement action.

Sylvia Summers, an EVP of Spansion and a former AMD executive, was named CEO in 2007. Summers was also named to a seat on the Trident board.

In 2008 the company laid off about 100 employees, a reduction in force of around 15%. Trident cited the challenges of a rapidly evolving market and an increasingly competitive environment in the DTV chip business.

EXECUTIVES

Chairman, David H. Courtney, age 52
President, CEO, and Director, Bami Bastani, age 57
EVP Research and Development, Saeid Moshkelani
EVP and CFO, Pete J. Mangan, age 52, $593,441 total compensation
EVP, Secretary, and General Counsel, David L. Teichmann, age 55, $569,567 total compensation
VP Human Resources, Shirley Olerich
VP IT, Patty Riley
VP Operations, Mark Newton
VP Worldwide Operations, Uri Kreisman, age 44
VP Business Integration and Quality, Shekhar Khandekar
VP and Controller, Richard H. Janney, age 52

CTO, J. Duane Northcutt, age 53
SVP and General Manager, Set-Top Box Business, Tony Francesca
Regional VP EMEA and India, Dirk Wieberneit, age 47
SVP Worldwide Sales, Paul Sandberg
SVP; General Manager, TV Business Unit, Christophe (Chris) Chene, age 44, $280,820 total compensation
Director Corporate Finance and Investor Relations, John Swenson, age 48
SVP Greater China, Hungwen Li, age 60, $500,981 total compensation
Auditors: PricewaterhouseCoopers LLP

LOCATIONS

HQ: Trident Microsystems, Inc.
1170 Kifer Rd., Sunnyvale, CA 94086-5303
Phone: 408-962-5000
Web: www.tridentmicro.com

2009 Sales

	$ mil.	% of total
Asia/Pacific		
Japan	41.6	55
South Korea	5.8	8
Other countries	14.1	18
Europe	13.9	18
Americas	0.4	1
Total	**75.8**	**100**

PRODUCTS/OPERATIONS

Selected Products

TV encoders
TV systems and set-top boxes
TV video processors

COMPETITORS

Broadcom	Pixelworks
Cirrus Logic	Renesas Electronics
ESS Technology	SANYO Semiconductor
Gennum	Silicon Image
Himax	STMicroelectronics
Imagination	Techwell
Technologies	Toshiba Semiconductor
Matrox Electronic	Tvia
Systems	VIA Technologies
MediaTek	ZiiLABS

HISTORICAL FINANCIALS

Company Type: Public

Income Statement
FYE: June 30

	REVENUE ($ mil.)	NET INCOME ($ mil.)	NET PROFIT MARGIN	EMPLOYEES
12/10*	557.2	(128.9)	—	1,522
06/09	75.8	(70.2)	—	690
06/08	257.9	10.2	4.0%	624
06/07	270.8	30.3	11.2%	520
06/06	171.4	24.4	14.2%	417
Annual Growth	**34.3%**	**—**	**—**	**38.2%**

*Fiscal year change

2010 Year-End Financials

Debt ratio: —	No. of shares (mil.): 177.0
Return on equity: —	Dividends
Cash ($ mil.): 93.2	Yield: —
Current ratio: 1.94	Payout: —
Long-term debt ($ mil.): —	Market value ($ mil.): 315.1

STOCK PRICE ($) FY Close	P/E High/Low	PER SHARE ($) Earnings	Dividends	Book Value
12/10* 1.78	— —	(0.79)	0.00	1.27
06/09 1.74	— —	(1.12)	0.00	2.76
06/08 3.65	122 23	0.16	0.00	3.89
06/07 18.35	53 31	0.48	0.00	3.50
06/06 18.98	75 27	0.42	0.00	2.66
Annual Growth (44.7%)	— —	—	—	(16.9%)

*Fiscal year change

Trio-Tech

Three's certainly company, if the company is Trio-Tech. Performing a trio of functions related to semiconductor manufacturing and testing, Trio-Tech International lives up to its name. First, the company makes its own chip manufacturing and test equipment; its front- and back-end testing products include temperature-controlled chucks, centrifuges, leak detectors, and burn-in equipment. Second, Trio-Tech provides outsourced testing services for chip manufacturers. Third, it distributes semiconductor manufacturing and testing equipment made by other companies. Trio-Tech's top customers are Advanced Micro Devices (42% of sales), Freescale Semiconductor (34%), and Infineon Technologies.

In 2006 Trio-Tech International acquired a burn-in testing facility in China to accommodate business in that country. The company closed its testing facility in Ireland in 2005.

Company insiders own about 30% of Trio-Tech's equity. CEO Siew Yong holds around 11% of Trio-Tech, while chairman Charles Wilson has an equity stake of nearly 8%. Director Richard Horowitz owns almost 10%.

EXECUTIVES

Chairman, A. Charles Wilson, age 87
President, CEO, and Director, Siew Wai Yong, age 58, $404,682 total compensation
VP Testing, Hwee Poh (Richard) Lim, age 51, $122,127 total compensation
VP, CFO, and Director, Victor H. M. Ting, age 56, $217,488 total compensation
Sales Manager, Jon Easterson
Auditors: Mazars LLP

LOCATIONS

HQ: Trio-Tech International, Inc.
14731 Califa St., Van Nuys, CA 91411
Phone: 818-787-7000
Web: www.triotech.comTrio-Tech International has operations in China, Malaysia, Singapore, Thailand, and the US.

2008 Sales

	$ mil.	% of total
Singapore	17.1	42
Malaysia	13.6	34
US	4.7	11
Thailand	2.0	5
China	1.1	3
Other countries	1.9	5
Adjustments	(0.1)	-
Total	**40.3**	**100**

PRODUCTS/OPERATIONS

2008 Sales

	$ mil.	% of total
Manufacturing	21.7	54
Testing services	18.2	45
Distribution	0.4	1
Total	**40.3**	**100**

Testing Services

Component reclaim
Constant acceleration
Electrical testing
Gross and fine leak tests
Highly accelerated stress testing (HAST)
Lead conditioning
Programming
Stabilization bake
Static and dynamic burn-in tests
Tape and reel
Temperature cycling

Distributed Products

Antistatic ionizers
Drop testers
Ellipsometers
Environmental chambers
Flip-chip bonders
High-temperature furnaces
Humidity chambers
Incubator/sterilizing ovens
Infrared conveyor ovens
Parametric component testers
Pick and place systems
PIND (particle impact noise detection) testers
Printed circuit board diagnostic and repair equipment
Probing stations
Shakers and vibration systems
Shock test systems
Solderability testers
Stress screening chambers
Temperature cycling chambers
Temperature shock chambers
Transport simulators
Vacuum/corrosion chambers
Wet-bench and cleaning systems

Manufactured Products

Autoclave systems
Burn-in board testers
Burn-in systems
Centrifuge systems
Component leak detection systems
HAST (highly accelerated stress testing) equipment
Rate/position tables
Temperature-controlled wafer chucks
Wet-process stations

COMPETITORS

Aehr Test Systems	Mirae
Aetrium	Reliability
Agilent Technologies	Incorporated
Amkor	Rockwood Holdings
ASE Test	STATS ChipPAC
Hitachi	Teradyne
inTEST	Tokyo Electron
KLA-Tencor	UTAC
LTX-Credence	

HISTORICAL FINANCIALS

Company Type: Public

Income Statement
FYE: Last Friday in June

	REVENUE ($ mil.)	NET INCOME ($ mil.)	NET PROFIT MARGIN	EMPLOYEES
06/11	35.5	(0.7)	—	501
06/10	36.9	(0.4)	—	418
06/09	20.0	(2.0)	—	423
06/08	40.3	(1.0)	—	480
06/07	46.8	3.3	7.1%	658
Annual Growth	**(6.7%)**	**—**	**—**	**(6.6%)**

2011 Year-End Financials

Debt ratio: 13.8%   No. of shares (mil.): 3.3
Return on equity: —   Dividends
Cash ($ mil.): 3.3   Yield: —
Current ratio: 2.01   Payout: —
Long-term debt ($ mil.): 3.0   Market value ($ mil.): 10.9

	STOCK PRICE ($) FY Close	P/E High/Low		PER SHARE ($) Earnings	Dividends	Book Value
06/11	3.29	—	—	(0.21)	0.00	6.63
06/10	3.84	—	—	(0.12)	0.00	6.28
06/09	2.57	—	—	(0.61)	0.00	6.15
06/08	5.08	—	—	(0.30)	0.00	6.86
06/07	20.24	22	6	1.02	0.00	6.64
Annual Growth	(36.5%)	—	—	—	—	(0.1%)

TriQuint

TriQuint fills it up with GaAs. TriQuint Semiconductor uses specialized materials — such as gallium arsenide (GaAs), gallium nitride, and quartz — instead of silicon as the substrate for its analog, digital, and mixed-signal integrated circuits (ICs). GaAs ICs operate at greater speeds than silicon chips, or at the same speeds with less power consumption. TriQuint's ICs are used in aerospace, automotive, communications, navigation, radar, cable TV, and wireless networking applications. Customers have included Futaihua Industrial (affiliate of Foxconn International) and Samsung Electronics. TriQuint also offers contract design and fabrication services. More than 60% of sales come from outside the US.

TriQuint's business is affected by general economic conditions around the world, including the global recession and credit crunch. The semiconductor industry in general has been in a recession-driven downturn, with consumers buying fewer electronics products. Companies in the industry — including TriQuint — are cautiously optimistic that better times are ahead in 2010, as demand for networking equipment and smartphones has started to rebound.

In addition, the company supplies high-power, wideband amplifiers for the F-22 Raptor and Joint Strike Fighter (JSF) aircraft programs; the US Department of Defense under the Obama administration is pushing to wind down F-22 production while accelerating testing and deployment of the JSF, also known as the F-35 Lightning II. TriQuint has dealt with uncertainty over aerospace applications in its defense business by developing products for unmanned drones, radar, and guidance systems.

In 2009 TriQuint acquired TriAccess Technologies, a maker of integrated circuits for the CATV and fiber optic video markets, as part of its strategy to strengthen its product offerings for multimedia applications. TriQuint formerly provided foundry services to TriAccess.

In 2008 TriQuint acquired competitor WJ Communications for about $69 million in cash. The purchase helped the company broaden its portfolio of radio-frequency components for wireless communications infrastructure.

TriQuint Semiconductor has facilities in China, Costa Rica, Finland, Japan, Germany, Malaysia, the Philippines, South Korea, Sweden, Taiwan, and the US.

EXECUTIVES

Chairman, Steven J. (Steve) Sharp, age 69
President, CEO, and Director, Ralph G. Quinsey, age 55, $1,015,540 total compensation
VP Oregon Operations, J. David Pye, age 60
VP Commercial Foundry, Glen A. Riley, age 48
VP Worldwide Operations, Steven R. Grant, age 51
VP Human Resources, Deborah (Debbie) Burke, age 56
VP Mobile Devices Design Engineering, Thomas Meier
VP Mobile Devices, Timothy A. (Tim) Dunn, age 49, $475,146 total compensation
VP Business Development, Bruce R. Fournier, age 54
VP Florida Operations and Costa Rica Operations, Azhar Waseem, age 57
VP Defense and Aerospace, Thomas V. (Tom) Cordner, age 66, $398,822 total compensation
VP Finance, CFO, and Secretary, Steven J. (Steve) Buhaly, age 54, $452,576 total compensation
VP, Texas Operations, Howard S. Witham
VP Global Sales, Strategic Development, and Customer Service, Todd A. DeBonis, age 46, $853,734 total compensation
VP Networks, Brian P. Balut, age 45
Head, TriQuint Colorado, Bill McCalpin
Networks Product Marketing Director, Dan Green
Director Marketing, Commercial Foundry, Mike Peters
Marketing Communications Manager, Shannon Rudd
Military Products Marketing Director, Gailon Brehm
Foundry Applications Engineering Director, Paul Litzenberg
Auditors: KPMG LLP

LOCATIONS

HQ: TriQuint Semiconductor, Inc.
2300 NE Brookwood Pkwy., Hillsboro, OR 97124
Phone: 503-615-9000   **Fax:** 503-615-8900
Web: www.tqs.com

2009 Sales

	$ mil.	% of total
US	238.3	36
China	225.6	35
Hong Kong	70.5	11
Other countries	119.9	18
Total	**654.3**	**100**

PRODUCTS/OPERATIONS

2009 Sales

	% of total
Wireless devices	63
Networks	25
Military & aerospace	12
Total	**100**

Selected Products

Amplifiers
    Driver amplifiers
    Gain block amplifiers
    High-power amplifiers
    Low-noise amplifiers
    Power amplifiers and amplifier modules
    Variable gain amplifiers
    Wideband amplifiers
Control devices
    Attenuators
    Limiters
    Oscillators
    Phase shifters
    Switches
Custom application-specific integrated circuits (ASICs)
Discrete field-effect transistors (FETs)
Filters
    Duplexers
    Intermediate frequency (IF) filters
    Radio-frequency filters
Frequency converters
    Doublers and triplers

Mixers
Receivers
Optical networking devices
    Modulator drivers
    Physical layer (PHY) devices
    Transimpedance amplifiers
Passive devices
    Attenuators
    Couplers
Radio-frequency integrated circuits (RFICs)
    Receivers
    Transmitters

Services

Assembly
Design
Package engineering
Test engineering
Testing
Wafer fabrication

COMPETITORS

ANADIGICS	MRV Communications
Applied Micro Circuits	Murata Manufacturing
Avago Technologies	Oki Semiconductor
Cree	America
CTS Corp.	Panasonic Electronic
Dover Corp.	Devices
EPCOS	Raytheon
Filtronic	RF Micro Devices
Freescale	RF Monolithics
Semiconductor	Silicon Labs
Fujitsu Semiconductor	Skyworks
Hittite Microwave	ST-Ericsson
Infineon Technologies	STMicroelectronics
Maxim Integrated	Sumitomo Electric
Products	Device Innovations
Microsemi	Vitesse Semiconductor

HISTORICAL FINANCIALS

Company Type: Public

Income Statement

FYE: December 31

	REVENUE ($ mil.)	NET INCOME ($ mil.)	NET PROFIT MARGIN	EMPLOYEES
12/10	878.7	190.8	21.7%	2,777
12/09	654.3	16.2	2.5%	2,393
12/08	573.4	(14.6)	—	2,297
12/07	475.8	23.4	4.9%	1,883
12/06	401.8	21.8	5.4%	1,780
Annual Growth	21.6%	72.0%	—	11.8%

2010 Year-End Financials

Debt ratio: —   No. of shares (mil.): 161.5
Return on equity: 22.9%   Dividends
Cash ($ mil.): 192.5   Yield: —
Current ratio: 4.29   Payout: —
Long-term debt ($ mil.): —   Market value ($ mil.): 1,887.5

	STOCK PRICE ($) FY Close	P/E High/Low		PER SHARE ($) Earnings	Dividends	Book Value
12/10	11.69	11	5	1.17	0.00	5.17
12/09	6.00	78	17	0.11	0.00	3.77
12/08	3.44	—	—	(0.10)	0.00	3.61
12/07	6.63	44	24	0.16	0.00	3.64
12/06	4.50	40	25	0.15	0.00	3.41
Annual Growth	27.0%	—	—	67.1%	—	11.0%

TTM Technologies

At TTM Technologies, it's Time To Market. TTM provides contract printed circuit board (PCB) manufacturing services, primarily for the networking, communications, high-end computing, aerospace and defense, medical, industrial, and instrumentation markets, as well as to electronics manufacturing service providers that serve those markets. In addition to prototype production, TTM offers both quick-turn production — limited quantities delivered in a shortened timeframe — and standard volume production services. Its top OEM customers include Cisco Systems, Huawei, Apple, Ericsson, and IBM. TTM gets about two-thirds of sales from customers outside the US; nearly half of sales come from China.

The electronics industry provides the majority of TTM's business. That industry is characterized by intense price competition, short product life-cycles, and fluctuations in product demand. The global economic downturn affected demand for its customer's products, which in turn affected demand for TTM's products. In the early part of 2010, TTM's backlog levels and capacity utilization rose, as demand for electronic products began to recover.

More importantly, the company began to see the results of its acquisition of Hong Kong-based PCB producer Meadville Holdings. For 2010, TTM's sales more than doubled on a year-over-year basis and the company reported record profits. The purchase boosted its reach in the computing and cell phone communications markets. It also added significant manufacturing operations in China and Hong Kong, where production costs are lower, as well as an expanded customer base concentrated in the region. TTM paid about $521 million in cash and stock for the 72% interest in Meadville held by Tang Hsiang Chien, giving Tang a 33% stake in TTM. Tang is the father of TTM director and executive, Tom Tang.

Because TTM previously had only one plant in China, when TTM made boards for big suppliers of computers and networking equipment, it shipped the boards to electronic manufacturing services (EMS) providers working under contract to those OEM customers. TTM's largest EMS customers, most of whom have significant Asian operations, include Celestica, Flextronics, Hon Hai, Jabil, and Plexus.

Many of the company's competitors also have large operations in Asia, which prior to the Meadville acquisition gave them an advantage in standard volume PCB production. To counteract this, the company used its quick-turn and prototyping services to get involved in the product development process early, giving it an advantage in becoming the preferred vendor for new and existing customers. It also gave customers the advantage of shortening the time required to develop and bring new products to market. The purchase of Meadville gives TTM the ability to compete as a one-stop shop for both standard and quick-turn volume contracts.

EXECUTIVES

Chairman, Robert E. Klatell, age 65
President, CEO, and Director, Kenton K. (Kent) Alder, age 61
EVP, Douglas L. Soder, age 50
EVP and COO, Shane S. Whiteside, age 45
EVP, CFO, and Secretary, Steven W. (Steve) Richards, age 46

VP Information Technology, Dale Knecht
VP Finance and Treasurer, Todd Amy
VP and Corporate Controller, Anthony Sanchez
VP Human Resources, Jeanette Newman
SVP Sales and Marketing, O. Clay Swain, age 48
Director; Managing Director, Asia Pacific, Chung (Tom) Yen Tang, age 51
SVP Human Resources, Grace Lee
Director Environmental, Health, and Safety, Lee Wilmot
Auditors: KPMG LLP

LOCATIONS

HQ: TTM Technologies, Inc.
2630 S. Harbor Blvd., Santa Ana, CA 92704
Phone: 714-327-3000   **Fax:** 714-241-0708
Web: www.ttmtech.com

2010 Sales

	$ mil.	% of total
China	497.3	42
US	416.2	35
Malaysia	64.7	6
Other countries	201.5	17
Total	**1,179.7**	**100**

PRODUCTS/OPERATIONS

2010 Sales

	% of total
Networking & communications	35
Computing, storage & peripherals	21
Aerospace & defense	20
Cellular phone	10
Medical, industrial & instrumentation	9
Other	5
Total	**100**

Selected Services

Backplanes
Commercial assembly (assembling backplanes into subassemblies and other devices)
Custom subsystem assemblies
Heat sink assemblies
Printed circuit board (PCB) fabrication
Prototype production
Radio-frequency (RF) and microwave interconnects
Quick-turn production
Standard volume production

COMPETITORS

Amphenol	Foxconn Technology
Benchmark Electronics	IBIDEN
Catalyst Manufacturing Services	Multek Flexible Circuits
Celestica	Plexus
DDi Corp.	Sanmina-SCI
Elec & Eltek	Simclar Group
Endicott Interconnect	TT electronics
Flextronics	Viasystems

HISTORICAL FINANCIALS

Company Type: Public

Income Statement

FYE: December 31

	REVENUE ($ mil.)	NET INCOME ($ mil.)	NET PROFIT MARGIN	EMPLOYEES
12/10	1,179.7	71.5	6.1%	17,448
12/09	582.5	4.9	0.8%	3,037
12/08	681.0	(35.3)	—	3,585
12/07	669.5	34.7	5.2%	3,609
12/06	369.3	35.0	9.5%	4,009
Annual Growth	**33.7%**	**19.6%**	**—**	**44.4%**

2010 Year-End Financials

Debt ratio: 65.7%		No. of shares (mil.): 80.3	
Return on equity: 9.8%		Dividends	
Cash ($ mil.): 216.1		Yield: —	
Current ratio: 1.62		Payout: —	
Long-term debt ($ mil.): 478.7		Market value ($ mil.): 1,197.5	

	STOCK PRICE ($) FY Close	P/E High/Low		PER SHARE ($) Earnings	Dividends	Book Value
12/10	14.92	16	8	1.01	0.00	9.07
12/09	11.53	114	35	0.11	0.00	7.90
12/08	5.21	—	—	(0.83)	0.00	7.15
12/07	11.66	18	11	0.81	0.00	7.75
12/06	11.33	21	10	0.83	0.00	6.84
Annual Growth	**7.1%**	**—**	**—**	**5.0%**	**—**	**7.3%**

U.S. Auto Parts

U.S. Auto Parts Network puts its customers in the fast lane. The company offers about 2 million aftermarket auto parts for all makes and models of domestic and foreign cars and trucks. Its inventory includes replacement, performance, body, and engine parts, as well as accessories (such as seat covers, alarms). U.S. Auto Parts also sells products for motorcycles, all-terrain vehicles, and RVs. The company generates the bulk of its revenue online; a pair of stores and mail-order catalogs also bring in sales. The company ships parts to more than 160 countries. It also distributes a private-label line of mirrors to auto parts stores nationwide and runs a wholesale program for body shops in Southern California.

In mid-2010 it acquired direct marketer Automotive Specialty Accessories and Parts. The deal, valued at $27 million, included Automotive Specialty's Illinois-based Whitney Automotive Group and Ohio-based Stylin' Trucks retailing operations. Each unit operates a brick-and-mortar store location, catalogs, and e-commerce sites, though Whitney accounts for the larger portion of business. Indeed, Automotive Specialty's successful e-commerce business and distribution facility in Illinois were attractive because they complemented U.S. Auto Parts' own operations and will provide a foundation for continued growth. (With Whitney's facility in its distribution network, U.S. Auto Parts is able to ship orders to 95% of its customers in the US within two days of purchase.) The acquisition also expanded U.S. Auto Parts' inventory to include products for ATVs, motorcycles, and recreational vehicles, and deepened its niche offerings for the Jeep and Volkswagen brands. As part of the deal, Automotive Specialty became a subsidiary of U.S. Auto Parts Network.

Picking up Automotive Specialty helped to boost U.S. Auto Parts' revenue. Sales rose above $260 million in 2010, a nearly 50% increase from $176 million the year before. Yet the purchase also brought restructuring charges and higher operating expenses that, together with increased freight costs, contributed to a nearly $14 million loss in 2010. To jump-start its bottom line, U.S. Auto Parts rolled out a new pricing strategy (basically, increasing prices on items to gauge whether consumers would continue to buy them), and the move is expected to boost margins higher than 30% in 2011.

The company, which boasts a variety of after-market supplies, often refines its offerings by removing low-selling products and updating them with new lines of merchandise. Included in that mix is U.S. Auto Parts' own private-label brand of mirror products called Kool-Vue. The bulk of its merchandise is supplied by manufacturers in China and the US. U.S. Auto Parts Network undertakes some of its own online marketing efforts, which include paid search advertising, affiliate programs, and e-mail promotions. It outsources website development, catalog management, and phone sales to its operations in the Philippines. The firm's Canadian subsidiary sells its products in Canada.

Directors Sol Khazani and Mehran Nia founded U.S. Auto Parts in 1995. Director Fredric Harman, who is a partner of Oak Investment Partners, owns 27% of the company's shares.

EXECUTIVES

Chairman, Robert J. Majteles, age 46
President, CEO, and Director, Shane Evangelist, age 37, $1,524,597 total compensation
CFO, Theodore R. (Ted) Sanders Jr., age 56
VP Marketing, Houman Akhavan, age 33, $570,010 total compensation
COO, Aaron E. Coleman, age 36, $347,394 total compensation
SVP Purchasing, Charles Fischer, age 53, $230,450 total compensation
Auditors: Deloitte & Touche LLP

LOCATIONS

HQ: U.S. Auto Parts Network, Inc.
17150 S. Margay Ave., Carson, CA 90746
Phone: 310-735-0553   **Fax:** 310-632-1681
Web: www.usautoparts.net

PRODUCTS/OPERATIONS

Selected Product Categories
Body Parts
  A/C condensers
  Bumpers
  Door handles
  Fenders
  Floor mats
  Fog lights
  Head & taillight assemblies
  Mirrors
  Mud flaps
  Radiators
  Seat belts
  Wheels
  Window regulators
Engine Parts
  Air filters
  Brake discs & pads
  Catalytic converters
  Clutch parts
  Condensers
  Engine mounts
  Exhaust gaskets
  Fuel filters & pumps
  Mufflers
  Oil filters
  Radiator hoses
  Sock absorbers
  Water pumps
Performance Parts
  Car wash supplies
  Dash and door bars
  Dual exhaust pipe kits
  Hitch mounts and rails
  Light bar mounting kits
  Sport tubes
  Turbochargers
Replacement Parts
  Alternators
  Clocks
  Distributor rotors
  Fan motors

Fuel gauges
Headlight covers
Oxygen sensors
Radiators
Tail pipes
Water pumps
Vehicle Accessories
  Car covers
  Dash & interior trims
  Gauges
  Hitches
  Seat covers
  Sun shields
  Toolboxes
  Visors

COMPETITORS

Advance Auto Parts	Genuine Parts
Amazon.com	Keystone Automotive
AutoZone	Industries
CARQUEST	LKQ
eBay	O'Reilly Automotive
Fisher Auto Parts	Pep Boys
General Parts	

HISTORICAL FINANCIALS
Company Type: Public

Income Statement
FYE: December 31

	REVENUE ($ mil.)	NET INCOME ($ mil.)	NET PROFIT MARGIN	EMPLOYEES
12/10	262.3	(13.9)	—	1,612
12/09	176.3	1.3	0.7%	1,022
12/08	153.4	(16.9)	—	800
12/07	161.0	(3.6)	—	748
12/06	120.1	3.5	2.9%	451
Annual Growth	21.6%	—	—	37.5%

2010 Year-End Financials
Debt ratio: 24.8%
Return on equity: —
Cash ($ mil.): 17.6
Current ratio: 1.35
Long-term debt ($ mil.): 18.1

No. of shares (mil.): 30.4
Dividends
  Yield: —
  Payout: —
Market value ($ mil.): 255.4

	STOCK PRICE ($) FY Close	P/E High/Low		PER SHARE ($) Earnings	Dividends	Book Value
12/10	8.40	—	—	(0.46)	0.00	2.39
12/09	5.20	159	25	0.04	0.00	2.77
12/08	1.39	—	—	(0.57)	0.00	2.60
12/07	8.11	—	—	(0.13)	0.00	3.07
Annual Growth	1.2%	—	—	—	—	(8.0%)

U.S. Energy

U.S. Energy (USE) has put its energy in many places, including oil and gas exploration and production, geothermal energy projects, and molybdenum mining. It operates oil and gas wells on the coast of the Gulf of Mexico and in Texas. The company bought a quarter stake in Standard Steam Trust in 2008, giving USE entry into the geothermal energy market. It also is developing a molybdenum mining project in Colorado. U.S. Energy has an agreement with Thompson Creek Metals to fund development of the project. The company had owned almost half of Sutter Gold Mining but sold most of its stake in the gold miner in 2008.

EXECUTIVES

Chairman and CEO, Keith G. Larsen, age 52, $396,800 total compensation
President, COO, and Director, Mark J. Larsen, age 48, $432,100 total compensation
Secretary and General Counsel, Steven R. Youngbauer, age 61, $318,500 total compensation
Director Investor Relations, Reggie Larsen
Auditors: Moss Adams, LLP

LOCATIONS

HQ: U.S. Energy Corp.
877 N. 8th West, Riverton, WY 82501
Phone: 307-856-9271   **Fax:** 307-857-3050
Web: www.usnrg.com

HISTORICAL FINANCIALS
Company Type: Public

Income Statement
FYE: December 31

	REVENUE ($ mil.)	NET INCOME ($ mil.)	NET PROFIT MARGIN	EMPLOYEES
12/10	27.2	(0.8)	—	19
12/09	9.6	(8.2)	—	18
12/08	2.3	(1.4)	—	19
12/07	1.2	56.4	4700.0%	20
12/06	0.8	1.1	137.5%	26
Annual Growth	141.5%	—	—	(7.5%)

2010 Year-End Financials
Debt ratio: 0.3%
Return on equity: —
Cash ($ mil.): 6.0
Current ratio: 1.59
Long-term debt ($ mil.): 0.4

No. of shares (mil.): 27.1
Dividends
  Yield: —
  Payout: —
Market value ($ mil.): 164.6

	STOCK PRICE ($) FY Close	P/E High/Low		PER SHARE ($) Earnings	Dividends	Book Value
12/10	6.08	—	—	(0.03)	0.00	4.83
12/09	5.93	—	—	(0.38)	0.00	4.89
12/08	1.64	—	—	(0.06)	0.00	5.00
12/07	4.25	3	2	2.54	0.00	5.46
12/06	5.05	147	66	0.05	0.00	1.67
Annual Growth	4.7%	—	—	—	—	30.3%

Ubiquiti

Ubiquiti Networks isn't concerned with "the green mile" so much as "the last mile." The company and its subsidiaries design, manufacture, and sell a portfolio of wireless broadband networking products based on proprietary technologies that are intended to help provide connectivity in underserved markets, particularly areas of the world known as "the last mile" that can't support infrastructure for wired networking. Products include AirMax antennas, Bullet outdoor radio devices, NanoStation integrated wireless devices, and SuperRange embedded radios. It primarily sells to network operators and service providers through a network of distributors, resellers, and OEMs. Ubiquiti Networks filed to go public in 2011.

Ubiquiti Networks plans to use net proceeds from its $200 million IPO and existing cash and cash equivalents to help cover costs associated with becoming a public company. It may also use a portion to acquire other businesses, products, services, or technologies, although in the short-term it intends to invest in short-term, interest-bearing, investment-grade securities.

With subsidiaries in Hong Kong, India, and Lithuania, Ubiquiti Networks' business model revolves around trying to penetrate emerging markets and remote areas where individuals and small and midsized enterprises do not have access to the benefits of carrier-class broadband networking. Its radios, antennas, and management tools are designed to deliver carrier-class performance for wireless networking in the unlicensed radio frequency (RF) spectrum.

Instead of employing a traditional direct sales force, the company relies on an online community of network operators, service providers, and distributors known as the Ubiquiti Community to drive awareness and demand through viral information dissemination. Members of this community also help to provide its engineers with product feedback central to its research and development efforts. This unconventional model enables substantial cost savings, but it's also a risky move to rely on a single, largely customer-driven channel for everything from sales and marketing to product development and technical support.

Ubiquiti Networks eventually plans to expand into new product areas, such as enterprise wireless local area network (WLAN) and video surveillance equipment, which may make its financial future even more uncertain. New product development costs could negatively affect its profitability, and it will also face competitors with more capabilities and resources. Because it began operating at a time when the market was rapidly expanding, Ubiquiti Networks reported historical growth rates from fiscal 2006 to 2010. However, the company has said that it doesn't expect that same growth rate to continue as the global wireless broadband market matures and becomes constrained.

EXECUTIVES

CFO, John Ritchie, age 45
CEO and Director, Robert J. Pera, age 33
VP Business Development, Benjamin Moore, age 34
CTO, John R. Sanford, age 47
Chief Counsel and Assistant Secretary, Steven J. Hanley, age 52
Auditors: PricewaterhouseCoopers LLP

LOCATIONS

HQ: Ubiquiti Networks, Inc.
91 E. Tasman Dr., San Jose, CA 95134
Phone: 408-942-3085   **Fax:** 408-351-4973
Web: www.ubnt.com

COMPETITORS

Alvarion	Harris Corp.
Ceragon Networks	Motorola Mobility
Cisco Systems	PCTEL
CommScope	Proxim Wireless
DragonWave	

HISTORICAL FINANCIALS
Company Type: Public

Income Statement
FYE: June 30

	REVENUE ($ mil.)	NET INCOME ($ mil.)	NET PROFIT MARGIN	EMPLOYEES
06/11	197.9	49.7	25.1%	92
06/10	137.0	(6.9)	—	84
06/09	63.1	9.9	15.7%	0
06/08	22.4	4.7	21.0%	0
Annual Growth	106.7%	119.5%	—	9.5%

Debt ratio: 0.3%
Return on equity: —
Cash ($ mil.): 6.0
Current ratio: 1.59
Long-term debt ($ mil.): 0.4

No. of shares (mil.): 27.1
Dividends
 Yield: —
 Payout: —
Market value ($ mil.): 164.6

Ultra Clean Technology

Ultra Clean Holdings helps chip makers handle gases under ultraclean conditions. The company, which does business as Ultra Clean Technology (UCT), designs, engineers, manufactures, and tests customized gas, liquid, and catalytic steam generation delivery systems used in the production of semiconductors. It developed a catalytic steam generator designed for use in several chip production steps that call for high-purity steam. UCT, which was founded as a subsidiary of Mitsubishi Corporation in 1991, draws almost 90% of its sales from Applied Materials, Intuitive Surgical, Lam Research, and Novellus Systems. The company gets nearly all of its sales in the US.

Though the industry experienced a widespread downturn in 2008 and 2009, the company views the situation as an opportunity to expand market share and transferred additional manufacturing operations to Asia. Suffering from lower sales and a net loss in the fourth quarter of 2008, UCT consolidated most US manufacturing at its plant in Hayward, California, closing two US facilities and downsizing another. Starting in 2008 and continuing into 2009, the company reduced its workforce by 32%, and it plans further actions to align its resources with market demand by adjusting production scheduling.

In 2010 UCT officially opened a plant in the Woodlands Industrial Estate of Singapore. The company acquired the facility in 2009 and expanded the plant's manufacturing capacity and capability. As part of the upgrading, UCT installed a 7,000-sq.-ft. cleanroom for making gas and liquid chemical delivery systems and the assembly of complex subsystems.

UCT operates from five wholly owned subsidiaries, including Ultra Clean Technology Systems and Service, UCT-Sieger Engineering, and Shanghai subsidiaries Ultra Clean Technology and Ultra Clean Micro-Electronics Equipment. In addition to semiconductor capital equipment, the company also develops components for similar markets such as the flat-panel display, medical device, and solar industries.

The company's gas delivery systems allow for the precise amount of specialty gases to be delivered at the appropriate time during the semiconductor manufacturing process. These steps include depositing, etching, cleaning, and annealing. Gas delivery systems include CMP (chemical mechan-

ical planarization) which is used to polish off high spots on wafers or films deposited on wafers. Chemical delivery modules dispense gases and reactive chemicals, while top-plate assemblies etch films on the wafer.

EXECUTIVES

Chairman and CEO, Clarence L. Granger, age 62, $1,012,418 total compensation
President and COO, Gino (Gino) Addiego, age 51
VP Technology and CTO, Sowmya Krishnan, age 42
SVP Sales, Deborah Hayward, age 49, $386,591 total compensation
SVP Engineering, Bruce Wier, age 62, $331,493 total compensation
SVP, CFO, and Principal Accounting Officer, Kevin C. (Casey) Eichler, age 51
Auditors: Deloitte & Touche LLP

LOCATIONS

HQ: Ultra Clean Holdings, Inc.
26462 Corporate Ave., Hayward, CA 94545
Phone: 510-576-4400   **Fax:** 510-576-4401
Web: www.uct.com

2008 Sales

	$ mil.	% of total
US	262.2	98
Asia & Europe	4.7	2
Total	266.9	100

COMPETITORS

Air Products	L'Air Liquide
Allegro MicroSystems	Matheson Tri-Gas
ATMI	Praxair
Benchmark Electronics	Sanmina-SCI
Ebara	Wolfe Engineering
Flextronics	

HISTORICAL FINANCIALS
Company Type: Public

Income Statement
FYE: December 31

	REVENUE ($ mil.)	NET INCOME ($ mil.)	NET PROFIT MARGIN	EMPLOYEES
12/10	443.1	20.1	4.5%	1,241
12/09	159.8	(20.0)	—	901
12/08	266.9	(52.4)	—	819
12/07	403.8	15.9	3.9%	1,027
12/06	337.2	16.3	4.8%	1,005
Annual Growth	7.1%	5.4%	—	5.4%

2010 Year-End Financials

Debt ratio: 28.0%
Return on equity: 23.0%
Cash ($ mil.): 34.7
Current ratio: 2.68
Long-term debt ($ mil.): 24.5

No. of shares (mil.): 22.3
Dividends
 Yield: —
 Payout: —
Market value ($ mil.): 207.6

	STOCK PRICE ($) FY Close	P/E High/Low		PER SHARE ($) Earnings	Dividends	Book Value
12/10	9.31	13	7	0.87	0.00	3.92
12/09	6.99	—	—	(0.94)	0.00	2.85
12/08	2.01	—	—	(2.43)	0.00	3.69
12/07	12.20	28	17	0.72	0.00	6.02
12/06	12.35	17	8	0.83	0.00	5.13
Annual Growth	(6.8%)	—	—	1.2%	—	(6.5%)

Under Armour

Under Armour is proving its mettle as an apparel warrior. Since its foray into the sports apparel market, the maker of performance athletic undies and apparel has risen to the top of the industry pack, boasting a big portion of the compression garment market. It is gaining a foothold in footwear, too. As of 2011, Under Armour is the official footwear supplier of MLB. Specializing in sport-specific garments, the company dresses its consumers from head (COLDGEAR) to toe (Team Sock). Most products are made from its moisture-wicking and heat-dispersing fabrics, able to keep athletes dry during workouts. Under Armour sells its products online, by catalog, and in more than 23,000 sporting goods stores worldwide.

Under Armour broke the billion-dollar-sales-mark in 2010 (up from just $281 million five years ago). Indeed, sales rose 24% in 2010 vs. the year earlier period. In 2011 the company is looking to grow its revenues by about 25%. The performance apparel maker has grown rapidly by introducing new items each year, entering new product categories (such as basketball shoes in 2010), heavily promoting its products, and expanding its wholesale distribution. Still, the company has a long way to go in its race to catch market leaders NIKE ($19 billion in sales) and adidas ($14.8 billion).

To compete against its larger rivals, Under Armour spends heavily to promote its products, forming endorsement deals with athletes across multiple sports. Its strategy is to identify the next generation of stars, such as skier Lindsey Vonn and Milwaukee Bucks point guard Brandon Jennings, and sign them to multiyear endorsement deals. The firm also spends about 13% of its net income each year on marketing. It spends its money on commercials and print ads, as well as sponsorships for leagues, teams, players, and events.

Under Armour generated 73% of its 2010 sales through its wholesale business. Its customers include the likes of Cabela's and the Army and Air Force Exchange, as well as Dick's Sporting Goods and The Sports Authority, which as a pair accounted for 27% of Under Armour's 2010 revenue. The company's direct to consumer business is growing rapidly as a percentage of total sales. In 2010 it logged an increase of about 57% with the help of about 20 stores added during the year. Under Armour operates about 55 of its own factory house and specialty stores. While North America accounts for more than 90% of sales, Under Armour is growing in Western Europe and has a licensing deal with Dome Corporation to sell its brand in Japan.

In a rare defeat for the company, footwear sales — which had been on the rise — declined by about $9 million in 2010, due to a decline in running and training shoes. Cash flow from operations also took a dive in 2010, due to higher inventory levels and investments in new products.

To date, Under Armour's primary consumer segment has been men, but it is actively working to expand its apparel offerings for women and children. Product lines are sold to almost 400 women's sports teams at NCAA Division I-A colleges.

Chairman and CEO Kevin Plank added the president's title to his job description following David McCreight's departure in mid-2010. Plank, a former college football player who founded Under Armour in 1996, is the company's largest shareholder. He controls about 75% of the voting shares.

EXECUTIVES

Chairman, President, and CEO, Kevin A. Plank, age 38, $748,061 total compensation
CFO, Brad Dickerson, age 46, $368,515 total compensation
President and Managing Director, Under Armour Europe, Peter Mahrer, age 51, $859,794 total compensation
EVP Product, Kip J. Fulks, age 38
EVP Global Brand and President, International, Mark Dowley
VP Retail, Daniel J. Sawall, age 56
VP Sales and Interim VP Footwear, Adam Peake
VP Operations and Facilities, Michael F. Fafaul Sr.
VP and General Manager, E-commerce, John S. Rogers
COO, Wayne A. Marino, age 50, $462,693 total compensation
CIO, Joseph D. (Jody) Giles
Chief Supply Chain Officer, James E. (Jim) Calo, age 48
SVP Footwear, Eugene R. (Gene) McCarthy, age 54, $1,105,677 total compensation
SVP Brand, Stephen J. (Steve) Battista, age 37
SVP Apparel, Henry Stafford
SVP Sales, North America and Interim Head of Wholesale Apparel, North America, Matthew C. Mirchin, age 51
SVP Retail, J. Scott Plank, age 45
SVP Talent, Melissa A. Wallace, age 52
SVP Consumer Insights, Kevin M. Haley, age 42
Auditors: PricewaterhouseCoopers LLP

LOCATIONS

HQ: Under Armour, Inc.
1020 Hull St., 3rd Fl., Baltimore, MD 21230-2080
Phone: 410-454-6428   **Fax:** 410-468-2516
Web: www.underarmour.com

2010 Sales

	$ mil.	% of total
US	952.9	90
Canada	44.9	4
Other countries	66.1	6
Total	**1,063.9**	**100**

PRODUCTS/OPERATIONS

2010 Sales

	$ mil.	% of total
Apparel	853.5	80
Footwear	127.1	12
Accessories	43.9	4
Licensing	39.4	4
Total	**1,063.9**	**100**

COMPETITORS

adidas	NIKE
Calvin Klein	North Face
Columbia Sportswear	Patagonia, Inc.
Fruit of the Loom	Victoria's Secret
Hanesbrands	Stores
Jockey International	Warnaco Swimwear
L.L. Bean	

HISTORICAL FINANCIALS

Company Type: Public

Income Statement

FYE: December 31

	REVENUE ($ mil.)	NET INCOME ($ mil.)	NET PROFIT MARGIN	EMPLOYEES
12/10	1,063.9	68.5	6.4%	3,900
12/09	856.4	46.8	5.5%	3,000
12/08	725.2	38.2	5.3%	2,200
12/07	606.6	52.6	8.7%	1,400
12/06	430.7	39.0	9.1%	979
Annual Growth	**25.4%**	**15.1%**	**—**	**41.3%**

2010 Year-End Financials

Debt ratio: 1.8%   No. of shares (mil.): 51.2
Return on equity: 13.8%   Dividends
Cash ($ mil.): 203.9   Yield: —
Current ratio: 3.73   Payout: —
Long-term debt ($ mil.): 9.1   Market value ($ mil.): 2,805.6

	STOCK PRICE ($) FY Close	P/E High/Low		PER SHARE ($) Earnings	Dividends	Book Value
12/10	54.84	45	18	1.34	0.00	9.71
12/09	27.27	36	13	0.92	0.00	7.96
12/08	23.84	61	21	0.77	0.00	6.72
12/07	43.67	70	39	1.05	0.00	5.75
12/06	50.45	68	33	0.79	0.00	4.50
Annual Growth	**2.1%**	—	—	**14.1%**	**—**	**21.2%**

Unify Corporation

Unify helps disparate forces such as databases, client/server applications, and the Web exist together in harmony. Software developers, value-added resellers, systems integrators, and IT departments use the company's software to create and deploy applications that integrate data from older legacy systems with newer enterprise applications. Unify also sells client/server development tools and database management software; Composer for Lotus Notes and Sabertooth; application development product families NXJ Developer, Team Developer, ACCELL, and VISION; and data management software such as SQLBase and DataServer.

Unify is building out its product lineup and expanding its customer base through acquisitions. In mid-2009 the company acquired AXS-One, a provider of integrated content archiving software. It bought legal data services provider and software developer Daegis the following year for about $38 million in a move to better address the market for electronic data management tools used by corporate legal departments and law firms.

EXECUTIVES

Chairman, Steven D. (Steve) Whiteman, age 60
President, CEO, and Director, Todd E. Wille, age 48, $653,525 total compensation
EVP and COO, Kurt A. Jensen, age 45
VP Marketing and Chief Marketing Officer, Glenn Rhodes
VP Product Development and CTO, Duane V. George Sr., age 53, $269,147 total compensation
VP Oracle Migration Practice, Jennifer McNeill
VP Business Development, Steve L. Soren
VP Sales, AXS-One, Kevin R. Kane, age 43

VP Finance and Administration, CFO, and Secretary, Steven D. Bonham, age 55, $297,205 total compensation
VP Americas and APAC Sales, Frank Verardi, age 62, $265,179 total compensation
SVP EMEA Sales, Mark T. Bygraves, age 54, $400,355 total compensation
Auditors: Grant Thornton LLP

LOCATIONS

HQ: Unify Corporation
1420 Rocky Ridge Dr., Ste. 380, Roseville, CA 95661
Phone: 916-928-6400   **Fax:** 916-928-6404
Web: www.unify.com

PRODUCTS/OPERATIONS

2009 Sales

	$ mil.	% of total
Services	11.7	57
Software licenses	6.4	31
Migration solutions	2.5	12
Total	**20.6**	**100**

Selected Software

Application development
  Database applications (Accell/SQL)
  Internet integration applications (Accell/Web)
  Integrated development system (Accell/IDS)
  E-commerce applications (VISION)
Business Web applications (Unify NXJ)
Database management
  Enterprise data management system (DataServer)
  Relational database management (DataServer ELS)
  Thin client data access system (DBIntegrator)

Selected Services

Consulting
Maintenance
Training

COMPETITORS

CA, Inc.	OpenLink
Hewlett-Packard	Oracle
IBM	Progress Software
Information Builders	Sybase
Microsoft	TIBCO Software

HISTORICAL FINANCIALS

Company Type: Public

Income Statement

FYE: April 30

	REVENUE ($ mil.)	NET INCOME ($ mil.)	NET PROFIT MARGIN	EMPLOYEES
04/11	47.0	(16.7)	—	204
04/10	28.6	(1.8)	—	127
04/09	20.6	2.4	11.7%	89
04/08	19.8	1.6	8.1%	71
04/07	11.2	(2.4)	—	63
Annual Growth	**43.1%**	**—**	**—**	**34.1%**

2011 Year-End Financials

Debt ratio: 137.1%
Return on equity: —
Cash ($ mil.): 4.6
Current ratio: 1.20
Long-term debt ($ mil.): 24.7
No. of shares (mil.): 14.6
Dividends
  Yield: —
  Payout: —
Market value ($ mil.): 42.3

	STOCK PRICE ($) FY Close	P/E High/Low		PER SHARE ($) Earnings	Dividends	Book Value
04/11	2.90	—	—	(1.23)	0.00	1.24
04/10	3.60	—	—	(0.18)	0.00	1.76
04/09	2.93	20	4	0.32	0.00	1.24
04/08	6.40	31	9	0.23	0.00	0.80
04/07	2.50	—	—	(0.41)	0.00	0.14
Annual Growth	**3.8%**	**—**	**—**	**—**	**—**	**72.0%**

Union First Market Bankshares

Union First Market Bankshares is the holding company for Union Bank & Trust, which operates approximately 100 branches in central, northern, and coastal portions of Virginia. The bank offers standard services such as checking and savings accounts, credit cards, and certificates of deposit. Union Bank & Trust maintains a diverse loan portfolio: Commercial real estate loans make up more than 30%, while one- to four-family residential mortgages and construction loans account for approximately 15% and 20%, respectively. The bank also originates personal and business loans.

Other financial services are provided through subsidiaries Union Investment Services (brokerage and investment advisory services), Union Insurance Group (long-term care and business owner coverage), and Union Mortgage Group, which provides mortgage brokerage services through about 15 offices in Virginia, Maryland, and the Carolinas.

Union Bank and Trust acquired First Market Bank from Ukrops Super Markets and Markel Corporation in early 2010, nearly doubling its branch total. It merged First Market with Union Bank & Trust to create the newly branded Union First Market Bank. The holding company also added "First Market" to its name. Further consolidating its bank subsidiaries to create operating efficiencies, Union First Market Bankshares later merged subsidiaries Northern Neck State Bank and Rappahannock National Bank into Union First Market Bank. In 2008 Union Bankshares merged Prosperity Bank & Trust into Union Bank & Trust; it did the same with another banking unit, Bay Community Bank.

The company has also grown through *de novo* branching and through purchases of branches and related companies. It acquired an existing branch in Harrisonburg, plus some $74 million in loan assets, from NewBridge Bank in 2011. The bank is also opening up new locations inside Martin's grocery stores, where it already has more than 20 in-store branches. The acquisition of Prosperity Bank & Trust in 2006 expanded Union Bankshares' geographic reach northward.

EXECUTIVES

Chairman, Ronald L. Hicks, age 64
President, Union Investments, Bernard (Bern) Mahon Jr.
President and CEO, Northern Neck State Bank, N. Byrd Newton
President, Northern Virginia, Union Bank &Trust, Mark E. Wright

Chairman, President, and CEO, Prosperity Bank & Trust, Robert J. McDonough
President, Rappahannock National Bank, Michael T. Leake
President, Bay Community Bank, Robert L. Bailey
CEO and Director; CEO, Union First Market Bank, G. William Beale, age 61, $505,196 total compensation
President and CEO, Union Mortgage, Herbert W. Engler
President and Director; EVP and Chief Banking Officer, Union First Market Bank, David J. Fairchild
EVP and Director Information Technology and Operations, Rex A. Hockemeyer, age 57, $112,989 total compensation
EVP and Chief Credit Officer, Douglas F. Wooley III
EVP and CFO, D. Anthony Peay, age 51, $270,717 total compensation
EVP and Director Information Technology and Data Management, David S. (Smokey) Wilson, age 69
EVP Consumer Financial Services, Myles W. H. Gaythwaite
EVP and Director Retail Banking, Elizabeth M. Bentley, age 50, $165,541 total compensation
EVP and Chief Banking Officer; President, Union First Market Bank, John C. Neal, age 61, $334,910 total compensation
EVP, General Counsel, and Secretary, Janis Orfe
VP and Director Human Resources, Rita Bartol
VP and Controller, William E. (Bill) Davis
VP, George Washington Jr.
VP Investments and Fund Management, John A. Lane
Vice Chairman, W. Tayloe Murphy Jr., age 78
SVP and Chief Marketing Officer, Olen Thomas
Director Internal Audit, Rawley H. Watson III
Auditors: Yount, Hyde & Barbour, P.C.

LOCATIONS

HQ: Union First Market Bankshares Corporation
111 Virginia St., Ste. 200, Richmond, VA 23219
Phone: 804-633-5031
Web: www.ubsh.com

PRODUCTS/OPERATIONS

2010 Sales

	$ mil.	% of total
Interest		
Loans, including fees	169.5	71
Taxable securities, including dividends	14.0	6
Other	6.3	3
Noninterest		
Gains on sales of loans	22.2	9
Service charges on deposit accounts	9.1	4
Other service charges, commissions & fees	11.4	5
Other	4.6	2
Total	**237.1**	**100**

Selected Subsidiaries

Carmel Church Properties, LLC
Union First Market Bank
Union Insurance Group, LLC
Union Investment Services, Inc.
Union Mortgage Group, Inc.

COMPETITORS

Bank of America	PNC Financial
BB&T	Regions Financial
C&F Financial	SunTrust
Eastern Virginia Bankshares	TowneBank
JPMorgan Chase	Wells Fargo

HISTORICAL FINANCIALS

Company Type: Public

Income Statement

FYE: December 31

	ASSETS ($ mil.)	NET INCOME ($ mil.)	INCOME AS % OF ASSETS	EMPLOYEES
12/10	3,837.2	22.9	0.6%	1,005
12/09	2,587.3	8.4	0.3%	662
12/08	2,551.9	14.5	0.6%	670
12/07	2,301.4	19.8	0.9%	690
12/06	2,092.9	26.0	1.2%	646
Annual Growth	16.4%	(3.1%)	—	11.7%

2010 Year-End Financials

Equity as % of assets: 11.16%
Return on assets: 0.6%
Return on equity: 5.8%
Long-term debt ($ mil.): 215.2
No. of shares (mil.): 26.0

Dividends
Yield: 1.7%
Payout: 30.1%
Market value ($ mil.): 384.3
Sales ($ mil.): 237.1

	STOCK PRICE ($) FY Close	P/E High/Low		PER SHARE ($) Earnings	Dividends	Book Value
12/10	14.78	22	13	0.83	0.25	16.46
12/09	12.39	130	47	0.19	0.30	15.31
12/08	24.80	27	11	1.07	0.74	20.25
12/07	21.14	20	12	1.47	0.73	15.84
12/06	30.59	17	13	1.94	0.63	15.02
Annual Growth	(16.6%)	—	—	(19.1%)	(20.6%)	2.3%

United Financial Banking

United Financial Banking Companies is getting down to business. The firm is the holding company for The Business Bank, which primarily targets small and medium-sized businesses out of a handful of branch locations in northern Virginia. The bank offers standard deposit products, including checking and savings accounts, money market accounts, and CDs to both commercial and personal customers. Insurance products, including auto, commercial property, and workers' compensation, are offered through Bankers Insurance, a subsidiary. The bank also provides investment and real estate (mortgage and title) services.

EXECUTIVES

Chairman, Jeffery T. Valcourt, age 56
CFO, United Financial Banking and The Business Bank, Lisa M. Porter, age 49
President, United Title, Christie Peck
President, CEO, and Director; President, CEO, and Chairman, The Business Bank, Harold C. Rauner, age 58
EVP, The Business Bank, Laurence Baker
EVP, United Financial Banking, The Business Bank, Business Venture Capital; President, Business Bank, Sharon A. Stakes, age 46
SVP, The Business Bank, Gail Edmonds
SVP, The Business Bank, Terry R. Frey
Auditors: Goodman & Company, L.L.P.

LOCATIONS

HQ: United Financial Banking Companies, Inc.
133 Maple Ave., Vienna, VA 22180
Phone: 703-938-2500   **Fax:** 703-938-5315
Web: www.businessbankva.com

COMPETITORS

BB&T
Capital One
Central Virginia Bankshares

Potomac Bancshares, Inc.
SunTrust

HISTORICAL FINANCIALS

Company Type: Public

Income Statement

FYE: December 31

	ASSETS ($ mil.)	NET INCOME ($ mil.)	INCOME AS % OF ASSETS	EMPLOYEES
12/05	205.8	1.4	0.7%	67
12/04	174.3	1.2	0.7%	54
12/03	142.9	0.8	0.6%	42
12/02	109.3	0.7	0.6%	33
12/01	85.5	2.0	2.3%	0
Annual Growth	24.6%	(8.5%)	—	26.6%

2005 Year-End Financials

Equity as % of assets: 7.33%
Return on assets: 0.7%
Return on equity: 9.0%
Long-term debt ($ mil.): 6.9
No. of shares (mil.): —

Dividends
Yield: —
Payout: —
Market value ($ mil.): —
Sales ($ mil.): 11.9

	STOCK PRICE ($) FY Close	P/E High/Low		PER SHARE ($) Earnings	Dividends	Book Value
12/05	22.05	20	16	1.23	0.00	(0.00)
12/04	20.25	20	17	1.05	0.00	(0.00)
12/03	18.05	24	21	0.75	0.00	(0.00)
12/02	15.25	22	16	0.68	0.00	(0.00)
12/01	10.25	5	5	1.90	0.00	(0.00)
Annual Growth	21.1%	—	—	(10.3%)	—	—

United Therapeutics

United Therapeutics hopes its products will be in vein. Its injectable drug Remodulin treats pulmonary hypertension, which affects the blood vessels between the heart and lungs. The product is marketed directly and through distributors in North America, Europe, and other regions. Other hypertension treatments include Adcirca and Tyvaso. The company's development pipeline includes additional treatments for cardiovascular disease, as well as various cancers, respiratory conditions, and infectious diseases. United Therapeutics has divested its cardiac monitoring division.

Remodulin accounted for about two-thirds of the company's 2010 sales, with the US being the drug's largest market. Remodulin accounted for an even larger portion (about 90%) of sales in 2009, but the company gained a more diverse pharmaceutical revenue base after it received FDA approval that year for its two other cardiovascular drugs, Adcirca and Tyvaso. The addition of new products, as well as increased Remodulin sales, created a significant jump in overall company revenue and net income levels in 2010.

Adcirca (tadalafil) is an oral treatment for pulmonary arterial hypertension licensed from Eli Lilly, while Tyvaso is an inhaled version of treprostinil (the primary ingredient of Remodulin). United Therapeutics is also developing an oral version of treprostinil for pulmonary hypertension, as well as for treatment for peripheral vascular disease, which affects blood vessels in the legs. The company has additional cardiovascular research and development programs, some of which are conducted through its Lung Rx unit. Lung Rx also formed a partnership with R&D firm ImmuneWorks in 2010 to develop respiratory disease candidates.

The company's development pipeline includes an investigational cancer drug licensed from the Memorial Sloan-Kettering Cancer Center. The antibody candidates aim to treat metastatic brain cancer. A second candidate (for neuroblastoma) was returned to Memorial Sloan-Kettering in 2010 when United Therapeutics partnered on a different neuroblastoma candidate with the National Cancer Institute. United Therapeutics also has antiviral agents under development for treatment of ailments including hepatitis C. The company has additional early stage research programs, and it regularly evaluates opportunities to license additional compounds for development.

To focus on core operations, United Therapeutics divested its non-pharmaceuticals division, Medicomp, in 2011 by spinning it off in a management-led buyout transaction. United Therapeutics retained a non-controlling minority stake in the unit through the transaction. Medicomp provides cardiac monitoring services over the phone and Internet using its CardioPAL event monitors, which detect heart arrhythmias and ischemic heart disease; it served hospitals and physicians, as well as managed care organizations. Medicomp had been conducting development work to expand its product offerings and launched a wireless version of its CardioPAL event monitor in 2010.

Eli Lilly owns a minority stake (about 10%) in United Therapeutics.

EXECUTIVES

Chairman and CEO, Martine A. Rothblatt, age 56, $17,591,098 total compensation
President, COO, and Director, Roger Jeffs, age 49, $8,672,264 total compensation
CFO and Treasurer, John M. Ferrari, age 56, $5,673,540 total compensation
EVP Pharmaceutical Development and Chief Manufacturing Officer, David Zaccardelli
EVP, General Counsel, and Corporate Secretary, Paul A. Mahon, age 47, $6,583,196 total compensation
Vice Chairman, Christopher Patusky, age 47
CIO, Shola Oyewole
Chief Strategic Officer and Deputy General Counsel, Andrew (Andy) Fisher
Chief Medical Officer, United Therapeutics and Lung Rx, Eugene Sullivan
SVP Human Resources, Alyssa Friedrich
Auditors: Ernst & Young LLP

LOCATIONS

HQ: United Therapeutics Corporation
1040 Spring St., Silver Spring, MD 20910
Phone: 301-608-9292   **Fax:** 301-608-9291
Web: www.unither.com

2010 Sales

	$ mil.	% of total
US	546.7	91
Other countries	57.1	9
Total	**603.8**	**100**

PRODUCTS/OPERATIONS

2010 Sales

	$ mil.	% of total
Cardiovascular products		
Remodulin	403.6	67
Tyvasco	151.8	25
Adcirca	36.3	6
Telemedicine services & products	10.9	3
License fees	1.2	-
Total	**603.8**	**100**

Selected Products

Marketed
Remodulin (pulmonary arterial hypertension)
Tyvaso (pulmonary arterial hypertension)
Adcirca (pulmonary arterial hypertension)
In Development
8H9 MAb (metastatic brain cancer)
Beraprost (cardiovascular disease)
Ch14.18 (neuroblastoma)
Miglustat and other Glycobiology Antiviral Agents
(hepatitis C and other infectious diseases)
IW001 (pulmonary disease)
Treprostinil (oral form for pulmonary arterial
hypertension and peripheral vascular disease)

Selected Subsidiaries

Lung RX, Inc.
Lung RX, Ltd. (UK)
United Therapeutics Europe, Ltd. (UK)
Unither Biotech Inc. (Canada)
Unither Neurosciences, Inc.
Unither Pharma, Inc.
Unither Pharmaceuticals, Inc.
Unither Telmed, Ltd.
Unither Therapeutik, GmbH (Germany)
Unither Virology, LLC
Unither.com Inc.

COMPETITORS

Abbott Labs	Eli Lilly
Actelion	Gilead Sciences
American HealthChoice	GlaxoSmithKline
Anadys Pharmaceuticals	Novartis
Ark Therapeutics Group	Pfizer
AstraZeneca	Teva
Bayer HealthCare	
Pharmaceuticals	

HISTORICAL FINANCIALS

Company Type: Public

Income Statement

FYE: December 31

	REVENUE ($ mil.)	NET INCOME ($ mil.)	NET PROFIT MARGIN	EMPLOYEES
12/10	603.8	105.9	17.5%	520
12/09	369.8	19.5	5.3%	410
12/08	281.5	(42.8)	—	360
12/07	210.9	19.9	9.4%	320
12/06	159.6	74.0	46.4%	285
Annual Growth	**39.5%**	**9.4%**	**—**	**16.2%**

2010 Year-End Financials

Debt ratio: 7.8%
Return on equity: 12.0%
Cash ($ mil.): 252.2
Current ratio: 1.78
Long-term debt ($ mil.): 68.9

No. of shares (mil.): 57.6
Dividends
Yield: —
Payout: —
Market value ($ mil.): 3,638.7

	STOCK PRICE ($) FY Close	P/E High/Low		PER SHARE ($) Earnings	Dividends	Book Value
12/10	63.22	36	26	1.78	0.00	15.36
12/09	52.65	153	78	0.35	0.00	12.04
12/08	31.27	—	—	(0.94)	0.00	10.93
12/07	48.83	126	54	0.44	0.00	6.96
12/06	27.18	23	15	1.53	0.00	4.41
Annual Growth	**23.5%**	**—**	**—**	**3.9%**	**—**	**36.6%**

UniTek Global Services

UniTek Global Services has a variety of ways to keep the lines of communications companies open. A provider of outsourced infrastructure services, UniTek offers technical, engineering and design, repair, construction, and other services to major US satellite, cable, wired telecom, and wireless communications companies. Its services range from residential and commercial installation to design and construction of fiber optic networks. The company, which operates through offices in Texas, Florida, California, and the northeastern US, has counted Clearwire, T-Mobile, and Ericsson as customers. UniTek Global Services was formed in early 2010 when Berliner Communications merged with UniTek Holdings.

The merger consolidated the service offerings of both Berliner, which provided installation and construction services to wireless companies, and UniTek, a provider of engineering and construction management services to cable, satellite, and wireline companies. The consolidation, in part, was made to expand the combined company's service offerings and, more specifically, shift more of its focus to the large and growing wireless communications market. To that end, UniTek Global Services is making an effort to expand its customer base (both Berliner and UniTek earned revenue from only a handful of customers) by bolstering its service offerings to cell phone companies and other wireless service providers. The company is also continuing to provide installation, design, construction, and technical services to its other customer segments.

UniTek Global Services acquired two-way radio and wireless communications systems integtrator Pinnacle Wireless in 2011 for $20 million, with another $30 million payable based on performance over two years. The company is using the acquisition to expand into more technical market sectors such as in-building wireless systems and land-mobile radio (LMR) technology.

UniTek Global Services is majority-owned by private equity firm HM Capital and its affiliates, which collectively hold an 80% stake. HM Capital had owned UniTek Holdings prior to the merger.

EXECUTIVES

Chairman and President, Peter Giacalone, age 50
CEO and Director, C. Scott Hisey, age 45
CFO, Ronald J. Lejman, age 42
CEO, UniTek Canada, Kevin Peters
CEO, DirectSAT USA, Daniel Yannantuono, age 37
CEO, FTS USA, Christopher Perkins, age 47
CEO, Advanced Communications USA, Scott Lochhead, age 39
CIO, Norman (Norm) Snell
General Counsel and Corporate Secretary, Kyle M. Hall, age 53
Chief Administrative Officer, Elizabeth Downey, age 40
Auditors: Ernst & Young LLP

LOCATIONS

HQ: UniTek Global Services, Inc.
1777 Sentry Pkwy., West, Blue Bell, PA 19422
Phone: 267-464-1700
Web: www.unitekglobalservices.com

COMPETITORS

Dycom	MasTec
EMCOR	Quanta Services
Integrated Electrical Services	

HISTORICAL FINANCIALS

Company Type: Public

Income Statement

FYE: December 31

	REVENUE ($ mil.)	NET INCOME ($ mil.)	NET PROFIT MARGIN	EMPLOYEES
12/10	402.2	(30.6)	—	5,000
12/09*	278.1	(65.6)	—	5,200
06/09	54.5	(3.4)	—	432
06/08	128.4	8.5	6.6%	342
06/07	55.1	1.1	2.0%	333
Annual Growth	**94.0%**	**—**	**—**	**146.7%**

*Fiscal year change

2010 Year-End Financials

Debt ratio: 95.6%
Return on equity: —
Cash ($ mil.): 17.7
Current ratio: 1.38
Long-term debt ($ mil.): 107.3

No. of shares (mil.): 15.2
Dividends
Yield: —
Payout: —
Market value ($ mil.): 148.8

	STOCK PRICE ($) FY Close	P/E High/Low		PER SHARE ($) Earnings	Dividends	Book Value
12/10	9.82	—	—	(11.43)	0.00	7.40
12/09*	42.00	—	—	(7.28)	0.00	46.57
06/09	0.00	—	—	(0.00)	0.00	(0.00)
06/08	61.60	7	3	17.36	0.00	61.95
Annual Growth	**(45.8%)**	**—**	**—**	**—**	**—**	**(50.7%)**

*Fiscal year change

Universal Display

Universal Display is putting organic technology on display. The company, through sponsored research agreements with Princeton University, the University of Southern California, and the University of Michigan, is developing organic light-emitting diodes (OLEDs) for flat-panel displays, solid-state lighting, and other applications. Its OLED technologies use organic semiconductor materials to overcome limitations in LCDs, such as poor image and color quality. Universal Display is licensing its technology to makers of televisions, computer screens, and consumer electronics devices. The company gets the majority of its revenues outside North America.

Universal Display is expanding through development and licensing agreements with partners such as AU Optronics, AIXTRON, Idemitsu Kosan, Nippon Steel Chemical, PPG Industries, Samsung Mobile Display (about 31% of sales), Seiko Epson, Sony, and the US government. The company is researching applications for the US Army that include head-mounted displays, displays on durable metal foil, and pen-like communication devices with roll-up displays. Universal Display owns, exclusively licenses, or has the sole right to sublicense more than 1,000 issued and pending patents.

Universal Display is also expanding its research efforts into related OLED display technologies such as phosphorescent OLEDs (PHOLEDs), printable PHOLEDs, flexible OLEDs (FOLEDs), and transparent OLEDs (TOLEDs), as well as organic vapor phase deposition tools for manufacturing the displays. Universal Display is providing red PHOLED chemicals to Tohoku Pioneer, a subsidiary of Pioneer Corp., for use in passive-matrix OLED cell phone displays.

Many applications for the company's products involve consumer electronics, sales of which were severely depressed during the global recession. In addition, the markets for flat-panel displays and lighting products are highly competitive. PPG Industries is the company's sole supplier for OLED materials, and their supply contract is scheduled to expire at the end of 2011. Universal Display has never made money and carries an accumulated deficit of about $197 million. The company may require additional funding for R&D and commercialization of its OLED technologies.

EXECUTIVES

Chairman, Sherwin I. Seligsohn, age 75, $728,258 total compensation
President, CEO, and Director, Steven V. Abramson, age 59, $1,187,749 total compensation
EVP, Dean L. Ledger
EVP, CFO, Secretary, Treasurer, and Director, Sidney D. Rosenblatt, age 63, $1,193,620 total compensation
VP Strategic Product Development and General Manager, OLED Lighting and Custom Displays, Michael G. Hack, age 54
VP Technology Commercialization and General Manager, Materials Supply Business, Janice K. Mahon, age 53, $407,081 total compensation
SVP and CTO, Julia J. Brown, age 50, $816,409 total compensation
Auditors: KPMG LLP

LOCATIONS

HQ: Universal Display Corporation
375 Phillips Blvd., Ewing, NJ 08618
Phone: 609-671-0980   **Fax:** 609-671-0995
Web: www.universaldisplay.com

2009 Sales

	% of total
North America	30
Other regions	70
Total	**100**

PRODUCTS/OPERATIONS

2009 Sales

	$ mil.	% of total
Developmental revenue	9.7	61
Commercial revenue	6.1	39
Total	**15.8**	**100**

COMPETITORS

AU Optronics	LG Electronics
BASF SE	Merck KGaA
Canon	Microvision
Chimei Innolux	Mitsubishi Chemical
Chunghwa Picture Tubes	NEC
Dow Chemical	Nippon Sheet Glass
DuPont	Pioneer Corporation
E Ink	Planar Systems
Eastman Kodak	Samsung Electronics
eMagin	SANYO
Epson	Sharp Corp.
FUJIFILM	Sony
Fujitsu	Sumitomo Chemical
Hitachi Displays	TDK
Idemitsu Kosan	Texas Instruments
LG Display	Toshiba

HISTORICAL FINANCIALS

Company Type: Public

Income Statement

FYE: December 31

	REVENUE ($ mil.)	NET INCOME ($ mil.)	NET PROFIT MARGIN	EMPLOYEES
12/10	30.5	(19.9)	—	86
12/09	15.8	(20.5)	—	84
12/08	11.1	(19.1)	—	80
12/07	11.3	(16.0)	—	64
12/06	11.9	(15.2)	—	64
Annual Growth	**26.5%**	**—**	**—**	**7.7%**

2010 Year-End Financials

Debt ratio: —
Return on equity: —
Cash ($ mil.): 20.4
Current ratio: 3.29
Long-term debt ($ mil.): —
No. of shares (mil.): 38.9
Dividends
Yield: —
Payout: —
Market value ($ mil.): 1,193.4

	STOCK PRICE ($) FY Close	P/E High/Low		PER SHARE ($) Earnings	Dividends	Book Value
12/10	30.65	—	—	(0.53)	0.00	1.47
12/09	12.36	—	—	(0.56)	0.00	1.62
12/08	9.45	—	—	(0.53)	0.00	2.13
12/07	20.67	—	—	(0.47)	0.00	2.53
12/06	15.01	—	—	(0.49)	0.00	1.74
Annual Growth	**19.5%**	**—**	**—**	**—**	**—**	**(4.1%)**

Universal Manufacturing

Parts are the best part of Universal Manufacturing. The company is a remanufacturer and distributor of automotive parts, including fuel pumps, engines, and master cylinders. Universal Manufacturing sells its remanufactured products wholesale — under the brand name ReTech — to automotive dealers, warehouse distributors, and parts supply stores in the midwestern US. The firm also distributes remanufactured engines. Although specializing in the car and truck industry, it also has facilities for serving the marine, railroad, aircraft, motor sport, and industrial engine markets. Universal Manufacturing was founded in 1946.

EXECUTIVES

President and Director, Donald D. (Don) Heupel
Controller, Lanelda Bollinger
Product Development Manager, Roger Rouse
Shipping and Warehouse Manager, Dale Plathe
Quality Manager, Quality Office and Technical Support, Robert Nord
Director Sales and Marketing, Lance Frame
National Sales Manager, Ken Schuneman
Director Purchasing, Laura Ziesman
Auditors: Deloitte & Touche LLP

LOCATIONS

HQ: Universal Manufacturing Co.
405 Diagonal St., Algona, IA 50511-0190
Phone: 515-295-3557   **Fax:** 515-295-5537
Web: www.universalmanf.com

PRODUCTS/OPERATIONS

Selected Remanufactured Products

A/C compressors
A/C compressor clutches
Alternators
Brake parts
Carburetors
Distributors
Engines
Fuel pumps
Steering pumps
Water pumps
Window lift motors

COMPETITORS

CARQUEST	Keystone Automotive
Dana Holding	Operations
Federal-Mogul	Motorcar Parts
Hahn Automotive	Uni-Select

HISTORICAL FINANCIALS

Company Type: Public

Income Statement

FYE: July 31

	REVENUE ($ mil.)	NET INCOME ($ mil.)	NET PROFIT MARGIN	EMPLOYEES
07/01	32.4	0.1	0.3%	163
07/00	21.6	0.5	2.3%	68
07/99	19.5	0.5	2.6%	72
07/98	19.4	1.1	5.7%	84
07/97	19.1	1.2	6.3%	84
Annual Growth	**14.1%**	**(46.3%)**	**—**	**18.0%**

Debt ratio: —
Return on equity: —
Cash ($ mil.): 20.4
Current ratio: 3.29
Long-term debt ($ mil.): —
No. of shares (mil.): 38.9
Dividends
Yield: —
Payout: —
Market value ($ mil.): 1,193.4

US Global Investors

It may be a small world, but U.S. Global Investors wants to make it a little greener, after all. Primarily serving the U.S. Global Investors Funds and the U.S. Global Accolade Funds, the company is a mutual fund manager providing investment advisory, transfer agency, broker-dealer, and mailing services. It offers a family of no-load mutual funds generally geared toward long-term investing. The company also engages in corporate investment activities. U.S. Global Investors has more than $5.4 billion in assets under management.

EXECUTIVES

Chairman, Jerold H. Rubinstein, age 72
President and General Counsel, Susan B. McGee, age 50
CFO, Catherine A. Rademacher, age 49
CEO, Chief Investment Officer, and Director, Frank E. Holmes, age 56
Vice Chairman, Roy D. Terracina, age 65
COO, Shannon Neill
Director Marketing, Susan K. Filyk
Chief Compliance Officer and Associate General Counsel, James L. Love
Research Director and Portfolio Manager, John W. Derrick
Communications Director, Terry Badger

Portfolio Manager, U.S. Global Accolade Eastern European Fund, Andrew Wiles
Portfolio Manager, Charlemagne Capital, Stefan Böttcher
Portfolio Manager Global Strategist, Jack Dzierwa
Portfolio Manager, Julian Mayo
Portfolio Manager Quantitative Analyst, Tim Steinle
Equity Research Analyst, Bernard Austin
Portfolio Manager, Ralph P. Aldis
Institutional Services Director, Michael Dunn
Portfolio Manager, Brian K. Hicks
Portfolio Manager, Evan W. Smith
Asia Research Analyst, Xian Liang
Portfolio Manager, Romeo A. Dator
Director, Institutional Services, Michael S. Dunn, age 48
Auditors: BDO Seidman, LLP

LOCATIONS

HQ: U.S. Global Investors Funds
7900 Callaghan Rd., San Antonio, TX 78229
Phone: 210-308-1234   **Fax:** 210-308-1223
Web: www.usfunds.com

PRODUCTS/OPERATIONS

2008 Sales

	$ mil.	% of total
Mutual fund advisory fees	39.5	71
Other advisory fees	6.5	12
Transfer agent fees	8.5	15
Investments	1.4	2
Other	0.1	-
Total	**56.0**	**100**

Selected Mutual Funds

All American Equity Fund
China Region Opportunity Fund
Eastern European Fund
Global Resources Fund
Gold and Precious Metals Fund
Holmes Growth Fund
Near-Term Tax Free Fund
Tax Free Fund
U.S. Government Securities Savings Fund
U.S. Treasury Securities Cash Fund
World Precious Minerals Fund

Selected Subsidiaries

U.S. Global Brokerage, Inc.
U.S. Global Investors (Bermuda) Limited
U.S. Global Investors (Guernsey) Limited
United Shareholder Services, Inc.

COMPETITORS

AGF Management	Oak Associates
Atalanta Sosnoff	PIMCO
Eaton Vance	Putnam
FMR	T. Rowe Price
Franklin Templeton	The Vanguard Group
Janus Capital	TIAA-CREF
MFS	Westwood Holdings
Nuveen	

HISTORICAL FINANCIALS

Company Type: Public

Income Statement

FYE: June 30

	REVENUE ($ mil.)	NET INCOME ($ mil.)	NET PROFIT MARGIN	EMPLOYEES
06/11	41.9	7.8	18.6%	88
06/10	35.0	5.3	15.1%	83
06/09	23.1	(2.2)	—	79
06/08	56.0	10.8	19.3%	93
06/07	58.6	13.8	23.5%	82
Annual Growth	**(8.0%)**	**(13.3%)**	**—**	**1.8%**

2011 Year-End Financials

Debt ratio: —
Return on equity: 19.1%
Cash ($ mil.): 27.2
Current ratio: 7.59
Long-term debt ($ mil.): —

No. of shares (mil.): 15.4
Dividends
  Yield: 3.3%
  Payout: 47.1%
Market value ($ mil.): 111.1

	STOCK PRICE ($) FY Close	P/E High/Low	Earnings	PER SHARE ($) Dividends	Book Value
06/11	7.21	21 11	0.51	0.24	2.66
06/10	5.55	42 15	0.35	0.22	2.36
06/09	9.26	— —	(0.15)	0.22	2.18
06/08	16.75	37 17	0.71	0.21	2.57
06/07	22.66	40 10	0.90	0.27	2.04
Annual Growth	**(24.9%)**	**— —**	**(13.2%)**	**(2.9%)**	**6.9%**

USA Technologies

Since you can't get much from a vending machine with a quarter these days, USA Technologies decided to make them take plastic. Its ePort device attaches onto vending machines and its eSuds works on washing machines and clothes dryers to allow them to accept debit and credit cards. With the Business Express device, hotels, libraries, and universities can run their business centers as self-pay operations; customers simply swipe their cards to use a PC, fax machine, or copier. USA Technologies also sells energy-saving devices for such "always-on" appliances as vending machines and office equipment. Information from the company's remote devices is transmitted through the company's USALive network.

Thanks mainly to good results in the company's license and transaction fees segment, especially of ePort units connected to the USALive network, USA Technologies' revenue rose 45% in fiscal 2011 over the previous year. Connections to the USALive network grew from about 82,000 in fiscal 2010 to some 119,000 in 2011. USA Technologies has partnered with AT&T Mobility, Verizon Wireless, and Rogers Wireless to supply USALive services.

Besides card processing, the company's ePort product also offers online sales reports, machine-dysfunction alerts, and other retail-related services. The company's ePort device can also be configured to work with contactless cards, a type of debit or credit card with a microchip that allows transactions to be completed through wireless means, rather than swiping a card through a magnetic-strip reader.

Customers have included Marriott International, Sony Electronics, ARAMARK, and PepsiCo. USA Technologies has partnerships with Verizon Wireless, Visa, and VIVOtech.

The company holds more than 70 patents for its technology.

EXECUTIVES

Chairman and CEO, George R. Jensen Jr., age 61, $959,865 total compensation
CFO, David M. DeMedio, age 39, $343,292 total compensation
President, COO, and Director, Stephen P. Herbert, age 47, $742,170 total compensation
VP, Business Development Strategic Partners, John McLaughlin, $271,427 total compensation

VP, Sales and Business Development, Michael Lawlor, $282,930 total compensation
Auditors: McGladrey & Pullen, LLP

LOCATIONS

HQ: USA Technologies, Inc.
100 Deerfield Lane, Ste. 140, Malvern, PA 19355
Phone: 610-989-0340   **Fax:** 610-989-0344
Web: www.usatech.com

PRODUCTS/OPERATIONS

2011 Sales

	$ mil.	% of total
License & transaction fees	16.5	72
Equipment sales	6.4	28
Total	**22.9**	**100**

COMPETITORS

Crane Co.	Radiant Systems
Equinox Payments	TNS
Gemalto	TransAct Technologies
Ingenico	VeriFone
Mac-Gray	Wincor Nixdorf
NCR	

HISTORICAL FINANCIALS

Company Type: Public

Income Statement

FYE: June 30

	REVENUE ($ mil.)	NET INCOME ($ mil.)	NET PROFIT MARGIN	EMPLOYEES
06/11	22.9	(6.5)	—	45
06/10	15.8	(11.6)	—	41
06/09	12.0	(13.7)	—	40
06/08	16.1	(16.4)	—	59
06/07	9.2	(17.8)	—	83
Annual Growth	**25.6%**	**—**	**—**	**(14.2%)**

2011 Year-End Financials

Debt ratio: 0.4%
Return on equity: —
Cash ($ mil.): 13.0
Current ratio: 2.68
Long-term debt ($ mil.): 0.1

No. of shares (mil.): 32.3
Dividends
  Yield: —
  Payout: —
Market value ($ mil.): 71.7

	STOCK PRICE ($) FY Close	P/E High/Low	Earnings	PER SHARE ($) Dividends	Book Value
06/11	2.22	— —	(0.26)	0.00	0.81
06/10	0.50	— —	(0.55)	0.00	0.89
06/09	3.04	— —	(0.95)	0.00	1.29
06/08	5.95	— —	(1.21)	0.00	2.15
06/07	10.75	— —	(2.13)	0.00	2.29
Annual Growth	**(32.6%)**	**— —**	**—**	**—**	**(22.9%)**

Valence Technology

If you charged Valence Technology with battery, you'd be right. The company's rechargeable lithium polymer batteries are designed for use in industrial, military, and motive and stationary electrical power applications. Valence touts its Saphion (patented technology) lithium iron magnesium phosphate (LiFeMgPO4) energy storage systems as having a longer life and being safer and more stable under extreme conditions than lithium-ion batteries that use oxide-based cathode materials.

Valence derives over 60% of its sales from Segway (46%) and The Tanfield Group (16%). Customers in the US account for about 60% of sales.

Battery technology is a live wire and charging new innovations as quickly as you can turn a light on or off. For this reason, the company pulls the plug on product lines as newer, more efficient technology is discovered. It has discontinued its N-Charge power system as well as its Epoch brand to focus on its next generation U-Charge LiFeMgPO4 energy storage system (due out in 2010) as well as its standard and custom battery packs. N-Charge and Epoch technology will be incorporated into the new revision of U-Charge.

U-Charge power system is in its third generation of development. Its features support extended-life lithium phosphate storage systems, utilizing phosphate-based cathode material; the features are suited for electric and hybrid vehicle applications. Additional development is underway on the company's patented lithium vanadium phosphate and lithium vanadium phosphate fluoride cathode materials for use in large, high-capacity cells suitable for the aerospace, automotive, military, and telecommunications sectors.

The company has transitioned from a developer of technology to a commercial provider of energy storage systems, and it is beginning to pay off — 2009 sales saw an increase of over 25%. The company has multi-year manufacturing agreements to provide lithium phosphate energy systems to companies such as Brammo, Oxygen S.p.A., and PVI. Additionally, Valence signed an agreement to develop modular energy storage systems for Siemens' Elfa marine hybrid propulsion systems. It has also partnered with Red Electrica and S&C Electric to develop and evaluate energy storage systems.

Valence will be sailing over the bounding seas in 2010 on the five-year deal it inked in February with Bénéteau Group, a yacht manufacturer based in France. Bénéteau plans to outfit all of its hybrid electric boats that use a hybrid drive system with Valence's rechargeable batteries. The deal has the potential to net over $45 million in revenue for Valence, which has not realized a profit since it started in 1989.

Valence's four market groups include Motive, Stationary, Industrial, and Military. Motive addresses the power needs of vehicles from commercial delivery to personal hybrid cars, scooters, and trams. Stationary energy storage systems regulate voltage and provide power during outages. The Industrial sector focuses on power that lifts rather than propels an object, such as floor cleaners, medical carts, defibrillators, wheelchairs, and industrial tools. Military applications are focused on communications, robotics, and survey equipment. Military motive applications include armored vehicles as well as aviation, marine, and submarine.

Chairman Carl Berg and his brother, Clyde, own nearly 54% of Valence Technology.

EXECUTIVES

Chairman, Carl E. Berg, age 73
President, CEO, and Director, Robert L. (Bob) Kanode, age 61, $337,500 total compensation
CFO, Ross A. Goolsby, age 44, $471,970 total compensation
VP Sales and Marketing, Randall J. Adleman, age 53
VP Legal, General Counsel, and Assistant Secretary, Roger A. Williams, age 63, $200,000 total compensation
CTO, Khoon Cheng Lim, age 66, $83,231 total compensation

Director HR, Cheryl Logan
Auditors: Deloitte & Touche LLP

LOCATIONS

HQ: Valence Technology, Inc.
  12303 Technology Blvd., Ste. 950, Austin, TX 78727
Phone: 512-527-2900   **Fax:** 512-527-2910
Web: www.valence.com

2009 Sales

	$ mil.	% of total
US	15.6	60
Other countries	10.5	40
Total	**26.1**	**100**

PRODUCTS/OPERATIONS

2009 Sales

	$ mil.	% of total
Battery & system sales	24.8	95
Licensing & royalty revenue	1.3	5
Total	**26.1**	**100**

Selected Products

Battery modules (U-Charge Power System)
Cathode material (lithium iron magnesium phosphate cathode materials)
Cells (Valence 18650 cylindrical cells)
Custom systems

COMPETITORS

A123 Systems	Panasonic Corp
Arotech	SAFT
China BAK	SANYO
Ener1	Sharp Corp.
Exide	Solicore
Hitachi	Sony
Johnson Controls Power Solutions	Toshiba
NEC	Ultralife

HISTORICAL FINANCIALS
Company Type: Public

Income Statement
FYE: March 31

	REVENUE ($ mil.)	NET INCOME ($ mil.)	NET PROFIT MARGIN	EMPLOYEES
03/11	45.9	(12.7)	—	433
03/10	16.1	(23.0)	—	349
03/09	26.2	(21.2)	—	366
03/08	20.8	(19.4)	—	490
03/07	16.7	(22.3)	—	311
Annual Growth	**28.8%**	—	—	**8.6%**

2011 Year-End Financials

Debt ratio: —	No. of shares (mil.): 155.0
Return on equity: —	Dividends
Cash ($ mil.): 2.9	Yield: —
Current ratio: 1.22	Payout: —
Long-term debt ($ mil.): 65.2	Market value ($ mil.): 241.7

	STOCK PRICE ($) FY Close	P/E High/Low	PER SHARE ($) Earnings	Dividends	Book Value
03/11	1.56	— —	(0.09)	0.00	(0.41)
03/10	0.85	— —	(0.18)	0.00	(0.61)
03/09	2.13	— —	(0.18)	0.00	(0.48)
03/08	4.41	— —	(0.18)	0.00	(0.59)
03/07	1.18	— —	(0.22)	0.00	(0.63)
Annual Growth	**7.2%**	— —	—	—	—

Vasomedical

Vasomedical's noninvasive treatments for angina and congestive heart failure get patients' blood pumping. The company's main product is the EECP (enhanced external counterpulsation) system, which is also approved to treat coronary artery disease and cardiogenic shock. During the company's Medicare-covered treatments, cuffs attached to the patient's calves and thighs inflate and deflate in sync with the patient's heartbeat, increasing and decreasing aortic blood pressure. After about 35 treatments, patients may experience years of symptomatic relief. Vasomedical sells the system to hospitals, clinics, and other health care providers worldwide through a direct sales force and independent distributors.

EXECUTIVES

President, CEO, and Director, Jun Ma, age 46, $108,400 total compensation
CFO, Jonathan Newton
VP Sales and Marketing, Larry Liebman
Vice Chairman and CTO, John C. K. Hui, age 65, $197,629 total compensation
Auditors: Miller, Ellin & Company, LLP

LOCATIONS

HQ: Vasomedical, Inc.
  180 Linden Ave., Westbury, NY 11590
Phone: 516-997-4600   **Fax:** 516-997-2299
Web: www.vasomedical.com

2008 Sales

	$ mil.	% of total
US	4.4	85
Other countries	0.8	15
Total	**5.2**	**100**

PRODUCTS/OPERATIONS

2008 Sales

	$ mil.	% of total
Equipment rentals & services	3.1	60
Equipment sales	2.1	40
Total	**5.2**	**100**

COMPETITORS

ABIOMED	Medtronic
Boston Scientific	Scott Fetzer Co.
CardioVascular BioTherapeutics	St. Jude Medical

HISTORICAL FINANCIALS
Company Type: Public

Income Statement
FYE: May 31

	REVENUE ($ mil.)	NET INCOME ($ mil.)	NET PROFIT MARGIN	EMPLOYEES
05/11	16.4	(3.9)	—	109
05/10	4.2	(1.9)	—	84
05/09	4.5	(1.5)	—	25
05/08	5.2	(0.7)	—	25
05/07	6.4	(1.6)	—	19
Annual Growth	**26.5%**	—	—	**54.8%**

2011 Year-End Financials

Debt ratio: —
Return on equity: —
Cash ($ mil.): 8.1
Current ratio: 1.20
Long-term debt ($ mil.): —

No. of shares (mil.): 117.1
Dividends
Yield: —
Payout: —
Market value ($ mil.): 59.7

	STOCK PRICE ($) FY Close	P/E High/Low		PER SHARE ($) Earnings	Dividends	Book Value
05/11	0.51	—	—	(0.04)	0.00	0.02
05/10	0.22	—	—	(0.02)	0.00	0.00
05/09	0.08	—	—	(0.02)	0.00	0.02
05/08	0.07	—	—	(0.01)	0.00	0.03
05/07	0.07	—	—	(0.02)	0.00	0.02
Annual Growth	64.3%	—	—	—	—	9.6%

VaxGen

diaDexus (formerly VaxGen) has moved beyond its vaccine operations and into the field of cardiovascular diagnostics. The diagnostic company's products test for heart disease and other conditions. Its flagship product, the PLAC test, is FDA-approved to detect a specific enzyme linked to coronary heart disease and ischemic stroke, and is useful in predicting risk in patients with otherwise low to moderate cholesterol levels. Other development products in diaDexus' pipeline include simple blood tests which may ultimately detect molecules associated with cancer in its earliest stages. The company changed its name after acquiring fellow drug development firm, diaDexus, in 2010.

The company believed that the purchase of diaDexus would provide for a new avenue of future revenue growth, and it plans to build up PLAC commercialization efforts while developing additional diagnostic products. The former-VaxGen's shareholders retained 62% ownership of the combined entity through the acquisition, which was completed through a stock-for-stock merger transaction. diaDexus' officers, including CEO Patrick Plewman, took the helm of the former-VaxGen (CEO James Panek remains on the board of directors).The company previously agreed to be acquired by cancer therapeutic development firm OXiGENE in 2009 in a stock merger transaction; however, the agreement was terminated early the following year when shareholders rejected the deal. It then stated that it would pursue an alternative strategic transaction, but that the company would examine the potential liquidation of its operations if no opportunities had arisen by the end of 2010. Soon after that, the agreement with diaDexus was reached.Way back when it was still VaxGen, the company was the first big winner of the Project BioShield Act of 2004, winning a contract worth some $880 million to produce an anthrax vaccine for the US government's civilian stockpile. However, the Department of Health and Human Services terminated the contract in 2007 after the troubled program missed a clinical trial deadline. The company also terminated a smallpox vaccine development program that year due to a lack of funding.After losing its anthrax contract, the company attempted in 2008 to merge with privately held Raven Biotechnologies, a developer of monoclonal antibodies designed to fight cancer, but that deal also fell through. As a result, it cut its remaining staff by about 75% and then sold its anthrax pro-

gram to rival Emergen BioSolutions in 2008. diaDexus has potential milestone payment and royalty rights on the vaccine should it become a commercial product.Following the well-publicized failure, CEO Lance Gordon resigned and was replaced by James Panek. The company began looking for potential acquisitions to help it get a new start. It raised some money (about $50 million) by selling almost all of its interest in Celltrion, a South Korea-based biologics start-up. It also got about $11 million in a settlement with the US government over the anthrax contract termination.

The company's history can be traced back to its roots as Genentech's in-house AIDS vaccine research operation and was launched as a separate company in 1995. The AIDS vaccine program was later licensed to developer Global Solutions for Infectious Disease, and diaDexus retains some commercialization rights related to the HIV/AIDS candidates.

EXECUTIVES

President, CEO, and Director, Patrick Plewman, age 44
EVP and Chief Scientific Officer, Robert Wolfert
EVP and Chief Commercial Officer, Bernard M. (Dino) Alfano
EVP, CFO, and Secretary, David J. Foster, age 53
Auditors: PricewaterhouseCoopers LLP

LOCATIONS

HQ: diaDexus, LLC
349 Oyster Point Blvd., Ste. 10, South San Francisco, CA 94080
Phone: 650-624-1000   **Fax:** 650-624-4785
Web: www.diadexus.com

COMPETITORS

Avecia
CEL-SCI
Celldex Therapeutics
Crucell
Emergent BioSolutions
GlaxoSmithKline

Novartis Corporation
Novavax
Pfizer
Sanofi
Vical

HISTORICAL FINANCIALS

Company Type: Public

Income Statement
FYE: December 31

	REVENUE ($ mil.)	NET INCOME ($ mil.)	NET PROFIT MARGIN	EMPLOYEES
12/10	11.8	(8.4)	—	56
12/09	0.0	(6.2)	—	3
12/08	0.3	(12.6)	—	3
12/07	5.0	(44.2)	—	216
12/06	14.8	37.6	254.1%	216
Annual Growth	(5.5%)	—	—	(28.6%)

2010 Year-End Financials

Debt ratio: 19.9%
Return on equity: —
Cash ($ mil.): 20.4
Current ratio: 7.49
Long-term debt ($ mil.): 3.6

No. of shares (mil.): 53.1
Dividends
Yield: —
Payout: —
Market value ($ mil.): 15.4

	STOCK PRICE ($) FY Close	P/E High/Low		PER SHARE ($) Earnings	Dividends	Book Value
12/10	0.29	—	—	(0.25)	0.00	0.34
12/09	0.49	—	—	(0.19)	0.00	0.91
12/08	0.43	—	—	(0.38)	0.00	1.09
12/07	0.55	—	—	(1.33)	0.00	1.42
12/06	1.90	11	1	1.15	0.00	2.69
Annual Growth	(37.5%)	—	—	—	—	(40.5%)

Vector Group

Vector Group is small potatoes next to Big Tobacco, but it's reaching into new niches. The holding company's Liggett Group makes discount cigarettes under brands including Liggett Select, Grand Prix, Pyramid, and Eve, and several private-label brands of cigarettes for other companies, including the USA brand. The group is also engaged in developing "reduced risk cigarette products" through its Vector Tobacco (VT) subsidiary. VT launched the QUEST brand, a line of low-nicotine and nicotine-free cigarette products, in 2003 but exited the business in 2009. The firm's real estate arm, New Valley, owns a 50% stake in the New York City broker Douglas Elliman Realty. It's looking to acquire other properties.

Following the discontinuation of the manufacturing and sale of QUEST brand cigarettes, the company's discount and private-label cigarette lines generate all of its sales. While Liggett's sales appeared to have soared in 2009 — rising about 42% over the year earlier period — the increase was primarily due to price increases in 2008 and 2009 on all of its brands in conjunction with user fees imposed by the passage of the bill that granted the US Food and Drug Administration jurisdiction over tobacco in mid-2009. (Liggett's tobacco profits actually declined by about 2.5% in 2009 vs. 2008.)

Recently Liggett's discount niche — which it pioneered back in the 1980s — has become increasingly crowded and competitive as makers of premium cigarettes have begun selling the brands at discount prices and launching discount brands of their own. (Altria's 2008 spinoff of its international unit, Philip Morris International, sparked increased competition for Vector by pushing Altria into the discount niche.) Indeed, discount cigarettes have been the fastest-growing segment of the US tobacco industry for more than a decade. (Liggett held about 9% of the overall discount market segment in 2009.)

Being small, relative to its heavyweight competitors, has its benefits. Under the Master Settlement Agreement (MSA) reached in 1998, the three largest cigarette makers must make settlement payment to 46 US states based on how many cigarettes they sell annually. Smaller companies, such as Liggett, need only make payments if their market share exceeds 1.65% of the US cigarette market. In 2009 Liggett and Vector Tobacco accounted for about 2.7% of the total cigarettes shipped in the US. Because it exceeded the threshold, it paid about $45.5 million under the MSA.

Liggett's "Partner Brands" program makes and supplies private-label brand cigarettes to convenience stores operators. It makes MONTEGO-brand discount cigarettes for Circle K Stores, SILVER

EAGLE cigarettes for Sunoco, and BRONSON cigarettes for QuikTrip.

Chairman and former CEO Bennett LeBow owns about 12% of Vector, while investor Carl Icahn and his associates own about 19%. Phillip Frost owns about 12% of the shares.

HISTORY

Former computer analyst Bennett LeBow founded Brooke Partners in 1980 (renamed Brooke Group in 1990) to acquire troubled companies and turn them around. Many of LeBow's early investments were in the computer industry. He eventually expanded into other areas, including tobacco (with the purchase of Liggett in 1986).

Founded in 1822 by the Liggett family as a snuff maker and joined by George Myers in 1873, Liggett & Myers produced several popular cigarette brands, including L&M and Chesterfield. Liggett slipped during the 1950s and 1960s by failing to exploit the market for filtered and low-tar cigarettes. Although Liggett launched a successful discount brand under LeBow (Pyramid), its US market share continued to dwindle.

Like Liggett, many of LeBow's other businesses were slipping. In 1993 Western Union (bought in 1987 and renamed New Valley) and computer maker MAI Systems (bought in 1985) entered Chapter 11 bankruptcy. That year LeBow paid about $20 million to Brooke Group shareholders who sued a group of company officers who they believed were stripping assets and using the company for personal loans.

Frustrated in the US, Brooke Group turned to developing new markets. In 1993 the company began a joint venture with Russian cigarette maker Ducat. In 1995 New Valley emerged from bankruptcy.

In 1997 the company made deals with 41 states regarding tobacco-related Medicaid payments. But most of Liggett's state deals were negated when in late 1998 it joined a $206 billion settlement hammered out with 46 states by its much larger rivals. As part of the deal, Liggett did not have to chip in as long as its market share stayed below its 1997 level of 1.67%.

To cut debt, Liggett sold its L&M, Chesterfield, and Lark brands to Philip Morris for $300 million in 1999. (The deal also kept Liggett's market share well below 1.67%.) Also in 1999 an Alabama court rejected an agreement that would have allowed Liggett to settle tobacco-related lawsuits with a limited fund. That year the US government filed a massive lawsuit against the Big Tobacco companies to recover health care costs and profits allegedly derived from fraud.

In 2000 the firm changed its name to Vector Group to remove the old name's stigma of sick-smoker lawsuits. The company said it would appeal a Florida's $790 million verdict against it. Later Vector Group sold its Liggett-Ducat subsidiary (Russia) to cigarette manufacturer Gallaher for $400 million. A Florida judge upheld the July 2000 verdict; meanwhile Vector angled for a global settlement of all punitive cases, payable to a public health trust fund over a 30-year period.

The company, along with Brown & Williamson, Lorillard (Carolina Group), Philip Morris, and R.J. Reynolds, faced paying Florida smokers $145 billion after losing a lengthy court battle in 2000. Three years later a state appeals court threw out the case, saying that the thousands of Florida smokers named in the case could not lump their complaints in a single lawsuit. That decision is now under review by the Florida Supreme Court.

In late 2001 Vector launched OMNI, a reduced-carcinogen cigarette, which received a lukewarm acceptance and hit a slow burn in sales. OMNI generated a disappointing $5.1 million in revenue for 70.7 million units. (Vector gave up on the product several years later.)

The next year the company created Liggett Vector Brands, a new unit that combines the sales and marketing functions of its Liggett Group and Vector Tobacco subsidiaries. Vector also bought The Medallion Company, a discount cigarette manufacturer (USA and Marlin brands), for $110 million.

Vector closed its Timberlake, North Carolina, production plant and laid off 150 workers in 2003. The company moved operations to a nearby cigarette plant in Mebane, North Carolina.

Vector announced in August 2004 that it would sell its reduced-nicotine cigarette brand, QUEST, on the Internet beginning in 2005 and is seeking FDA approval to sell QUEST as a device for quitting smoking. (In 2009 the company decided against seeking FDA approval of Quest as a smoking cessation aide, citing the significant time and expense involved in seeking it.) However, it switched gears in November 2004 by putting an indefinite hold on a national rollout of QUEST. The company said a review of marketing data made such a move necessary. Vector laid off approximately 330 full-time and 135 part-time positions that December.

In March 2005 the company began supplying Montego deep-discount brand cigarettes exclusively to more than 2,200 Circle K and Mac's convenience stores in the US. In November it entered into a similar deal with Sunoco, which operates 800-plus Sonoco APlus convenience stores, to make and supply Silver Eagle brand cigarettes to its stores.

Howard Lorber succeeded LeBow as CEO in 2006. Later that year Vector entered into a settlement with the Internal Revenue Service that called for the company to pay about $42 million related to a gain stemming from a 1998 and 1999 deal with Philip Morris.

To tap the popular and more politically correct smokeless tobacco market, Vector launched Grand Prix-branded snus in May 2008. The pouched tobacco product is made in Sweden and rolls out in a trio of varieties.

EXECUTIVES

Chairman, Bennett S. LeBow, age 73, $8,689,923 total compensation
President, CEO, and Director, Howard M. Lorber, age 62, $17,081,276 total compensation
President and CEO, Liggett Group and Liggett Vector Brands and Director, Ronald J. Bernstein, age 57, $1,870,710 total compensation
EVP, Richard J. (Dick) Lampen, age 57, $2,564,617 total compensation
VP, CFO, and Treasurer, J. Bryant Kirkland III, age 45, $1,127,715 total compensation
VP, General Counsel, and Secretary, Marc N. Bell, age 50, $1,193,942 total compensation
Investor Relations, Carrie Bloom
Auditors: PricewaterhouseCoopers LLP

LOCATIONS

HQ: Vector Group Ltd.
100 SE 2nd St., Miami, FL 33131
Phone: 305-579-8000   **Fax:** 305-579-8001
Web: www.vectorgroupltd.com

PRODUCTS/OPERATIONS

2009 Sales

	$ mil.	% of total
Liggett	800.0	100
Vector Tobacco	1.5	-
Total	**801.5**	**100**

Selected Cigarette Brands
Eve
Grand Prix
Jade (licensed)
Liggett Select
Pyramid
USA

Primary Holdings
Liggett Group LLC
Liggett Vector Brands Inc.
New Valley Corporation
Vector Tobacco Inc.

COMPETITORS

800-JR Cigar	Philip Morris USA
Commonwealth Brands	Reynolds American
Lorillard	Smokin Joes

HISTORICAL FINANCIALS
Company Type: Public

Income Statement
FYE: December 31

	REVENUE ($ mil.)	NET INCOME ($ mil.)	NET PROFIT MARGIN	EMPLOYEES
12/10	1,063.3	54.1	5.1%	512
12/09	801.5	24.8	3.1%	435
12/08	565.2	60.5	10.7%	430
12/07	555.4	73.8	13.3%	430
12/06	506.3	42.7	8.4%	430
Annual Growth	**20.4%**	**6.1%**	**—**	**4.5%**

2010 Year-End Financials

Debt ratio: —
Return on equity: (117.0)%
Cash ($ mil.): 299.8
Current ratio: 2.32
Long-term debt ($ mil.): 506.1

No. of shares (mil.): 78.7
Dividends
Yield: 9.0%
Payout: 220.0%
Market value ($ mil.): 1,297.9

	STOCK PRICE ($) FY Close	P/E High/Low		PER SHARE ($) Earnings	Dividends	Book Value
12/10	16.50	28	18	0.68	1.49	(0.59)
12/09	12.70	47	30	0.31	1.38	(0.06)
12/08	11.77	24	14	0.69	1.28	0.44
12/07	16.50	21	15	0.93	1.22	1.37
12/06	14.30	26	20	0.56	1.15	1.31
Annual Growth	**3.6%**	**—**	**—**	**5.0%**	**6.7%**	**—**

Veeco Instruments

Veeco Instruments gives high-tech components the VIP treatment. The company offers precision equipment for manufacturing, measuring, and testing microelectronic components, such as thin-film magnetic heads, photovoltaic solar cells, and semiconductor devices. Its deposition, etching, coating, and lapping and dicing systems are used to make semiconductors, data storage, and other products. The company is exploring applications in nanotechnology and the biosciences, but its focus is on the LED, solar, and data storage markets. LG Electronics represents 20% of sales. Veeco gets about three-quarters of its sales outside the US.

The company has a limited number of customers, the five largest of which account for 39% of sales. Veeco's customers make components that go into consumer electronics, a market that was severely depressed by the global recession in 2009. The company has struggled with profitability in the past decade, affected by industry downturns and recessions.

Veeco's business segments include LED & Solar Process Equipment and Data Storage Process Equipment. LED & Solar Process Equipment is the largest segment and has experienced a high rate of growth, even in the recessionary year of 2009. It manufactures different types of deposition systems, such as web coaters, which it sells to manufacturers of high-brightness light-emitting diodes (HB-LEDs), photovoltaic solar cells, and telecommunications components. While the majority of the solar industry is using older silicon technologies, Veeco supports using thin-film CIGS (copper, indium, gallium, selenide) technology, which yields lower manufacturing costs and higher efficiency. To capitalize on CIGS technology, the company in 2008 purchased Mill Lane Engineering, a manufacturer of web coating technology, which is used to make flexible CIGS solar cells. The firm was rechristened Veeco Solar Equipment.

Its Data Storage Process Equipment segment designs and manufactures ion beam etch and deposition systems, along with other process instruments necessary to create thin-film magnetic heads that read and write data on hard-disk drives.

Veeco is allocating additional R&D spending toward end markets that it believes offer significant growth opportunities, such as LEDs, optical communications, photovoltaic solar cells, wireless networking, and other communications applications. It uses acquisitions as a means of extending its reach into specialized semiconductor markets. Deteriorating business conditions in late 2008 caused data storage and LED customers to reduce orders for 2009, citing industry overcapacity, financing constraints, and a weak business outlook for the year ahead. Veeco responded by implementing a variety of cost-cutting measures, which included layoffs (16% of the workforce) and executive salary cuts. Sales in 2009 were down about 14% from the prior year.

As part of its strategy to focus on its LED, solar, and data storage businesses, in 2010 Veeco sold its metrology instruments business to Bruker for about $229 million in cash. The business includes atomic force and scanning probe microscopes for surface inspection and measurement and optical industrial metrology instruments. Veeco reasoned that the division, which is profitable and growing, will be a better fit as part of a company that plans to continue to focus on developing scientific instruments, such as Bruker. The sale also gives Veeco the financial flexibility to make acquisitions and expand customer support for its business in Asia.

The company serves customers worldwide through its sales and service organizations located throughout Asia, Europe, and the US. In addition to its products, the company offers services such as consulting, maintenance, and training.

HISTORY

Albert Nerken, a civil engineer in the Manhattan Project, and Frank Raible founded Veeco Instruments in 1945 to make equipment that detected microscopic leaks. The next year the company received its first order from the University of Rochester.

During the 1960s Veeco supplied critical parts for the space race. Raible died in 1975. In 1989 Nerken retired as chairman and sold the company for more than $250 million to UK-based Unitech, which wanted its power supply business. Chairman and CEO Ed Braun and other Veeco executives bought the instrumentation business in 1990 in a leveraged buyout.

In 1993 the company began reselling IBM's SXM atomic force microscopes to semiconductor manufacturers. Veeco went public a year later. In 1995 Veeco developed an ion beam deposition tool for microelectronic films. The next year the company debuted a direct-deposit ion beam system for depositing diamond-like carbon coatings for disk drive read-write heads. In 1997 Veeco acquired Materials Research Corp.'s ion deposition and etching equipment division. That year Veeco also acquired Wyko Corp., a leading maker of optical measurement systems.

In 1998 Veeco acquired measurement device maker Digital Instruments. In 1999 the company acquired OptiMag (inspection equipment for thin-film magnetic heads) and Ion Tech (ion beam deposition systems for dense wavelength division multiplexing).

In 2000 the company bought privately held Monarch Labs (data storage test and measure products). It also purchased rival CVC Inc., a maker of deposition equipment used to manufacture semiconductors and thin-film recording heads.

In 2001 Veeco acquired Applied Epi, a maker of specialized epitaxy equipment used in the manufacture of high-speed networking semiconductors, for $120 million in cash and stock. The harsh industry downturn, however, forced the company to lay off about 15% of its staff, consolidate some operations, and reduce executive pay.

In 2002, facing continuing market weakness, Veeco closed plants and cut another 20% of its staff in an effort to control costs. Although the company announced plans in 2002 to acquire FEI Company, a maker of electron microscopes, the companies agreed to terminate the $1 billion deal in 2003, citing continuing poor market conditions in the semiconductor equipment industry.

Later in 2003 Veeco expanded its offerings by acquiring a line of chemical vapor deposition equipment from EMCORE. It also acquired privately held Advanced Imaging (Aii), a maker of bar lapping equipment used to make thin-film magnetic heads, for about $60 million. In 2004 Veeco purchased privately held Manufacturing Technology Inc. (MTI), a maker of slicing and dicing equipment for the data storage market, for close to $10 million. Veeco formed a Slider Process Equipment division, which consisted of Aii and MTI.

In 2005 Veeco licensed atomic layer deposition (ALD) technology from ASM International, giving the company another process tool in its hard-disk drive manufacturing equipment line. This led to Veeco offering an ALD tool, the NEXUS.

In 2006 the company formed a Process Equipment Group to capitalize on opportunities in the data storage and high-brightness light-emitting diode industries. Also that year Ed Braun signaled his intention to retire as Veeco's CEO, once a successor could be identified. In 2007 the board tapped John Peeler, the one-time CEO of Acterna (acquired by JDS Uniphase in 2005) and president of JDSU's Communications Test and Measurement business, as the CEO, with Braun remaining as chairman.

In 2006 the company merged two operating segments, the Ion Beam and Mechanical Process Equipment segment and the Epitaxial Process Equipment segment, into one Process Equipment

segment. Veeco later divided Process Equipment into two segments: Data Storage and LED & Solar.

In 2010, as part of a plan to focus on its Data Storage and LED & Solar businesses, Veeco sold its Metrology Instruments division to Bruker Corporation for around $229 million in cash. The sale included Veeco's scanning probe microscope, atomic force microscope, and optical metrology product lines.

EXECUTIVES

Chairman, Edward H. Braun, age 71
CEO and Director, John R. Peeler, age 56, $3,658,484 total compensation
EVP LED & Solar, William J. (Bill) Miller
EVP Metrology and Instrumentation, Mark Munch, age 49, $880,433 total compensation
EVP and CFO, David D. Glass, age 51
EVP Data Storage, Robert P. Oates, age 57, $1,297,578 total compensation
EVP Compound Semi, William J. Miller
VP Metrology Strategic Marketing and Development, Andrew Masters
VP and General Manager, CIGS Solar Equipment Business, David Bruns
VP and General Manager, Veeco Metrology and Instrumentation, Ross Q. Smith
SVP Finance, Chief Accounting Officer, and Corporate Controller, John P. Kiernan, age 49, $629,492 total compensation
SVP Human Resources, Robert W. Bradshaw
SVP Corporate Communications, and Investor Relations, Debra A. Wasser
Senior Director, Applications Development, Stephen Minne
Sales Director, China, Wa Mo
SVP, General Counsel, and Secretary, Gregory A. Robbins
CTO, CIGS Solar Equipment Business, Johannes Segner
Senior Director Marcom, Fran Brennen
SVP Worldwide Sales and Service, Peter Collingwood, age 51
Auditors: Ernst & Young LLP

LOCATIONS

HQ: Veeco Instruments Inc.
Terminal Drive, Plainview, NY 11803
Phone: 516-677-0200   **Fax:** 516-714-1200
Web: www.veeco.com

2009 Sales

	$ mil.	% of total
Asia/Pacific		
South Korea	101.1	27
China	38.8	10
Japan	19.6	5
Other countries	52.1	14
Americas		
US	87.5	23
Other countries	3.0	1
Europe, Middle East & Africa	78.0	20
Total	**380.1**	**100**

PRODUCTS/OPERATIONS

2009 Sales

	$ mil.	% of total
LED & solar process equipment	205.1	54
Metrology	97.7	26
Data storage process equipment	77.3	20
Total	**380.1**	**100**

Selected Products

Light-Emitting Diode (LED) and Solar Process Equipment
  Cluster tools (NEXUS family; system for combining etch and deposition modules)

Metal organic chemical vapor deposition
Molecular beam epitaxy systems and components
Web and glass coating deposition systems for solar cells
Data Storage
Ion beam etch and ion beam deposition equipment
Lapping and dicing systems
Physical layer deposition equipment

COMPETITORS

Agilent Technologies	Lam Research
AIXTRON	MKS Instruments
Amtech Systems	Oerlikon
Applied Materials	OTB Group
Canon	Oxford Instruments
centrotherm	PANalytical
Dainippon Screen	Shimadzu
FEI	Singulus
GT Advanced	Taiyo Nippon Sanso
Technologies	Tegal
Hitachi	Tokyo Electron
High-Technologies	Xyratex

HISTORICAL FINANCIALS

Company Type: Public

Income Statement

FYE: December 31

	REVENUE ($ mil.)	NET INCOME ($ mil.)	NET PROFIT MARGIN	EMPLOYEES
12/10	933.2	361.8	38.8%	1,023
12/09	380.1	(15.6)	—	1,005
12/08	442.8	(71.1)	—	1,195
12/07	402.5	(17.4)	—	1,216
12/06	441.0	14.9	3.4%	1,279
Annual Growth	20.6%	122.0%	—	(5.4%)

2010 Year-End Financials

Debt ratio: 0.3%	No. of shares (mil.): 40.3
Return on equity: 47.4%	Dividends
Cash ($ mil.): 245.1	Yield: —
Current ratio: 2.67	Payout: —
Long-term debt ($ mil.): 2.7	Market value ($ mil.): 1,732.9

	STOCK PRICE ($) FY Close	P/E High/Low		PER SHARE ($) Earnings	Dividends	Book Value
12/10	42.96	6	3	8.51	0.00	18.90
12/09	33.04	—	—	(0.48)	0.00	9.21
12/08	6.34	—	—	(2.27)	0.00	6.67
12/07	16.70	—	—	(0.56)	0.00	8.62
12/06	18.73	57	36	0.48	0.00	9.07
Annual Growth	23.1%	—	—	105.2%	—	20.2%

Vera Bradley

Vera Bradley loves women with lots of baggage. The company designs, makes and sells quilted handbags and travel bags, as well as accessories, such as cosmetic bags, curling iron covers, and wallets. Its goods are available at 3,300 gift and specialty stores and about 35 Vera Bradley full-price stores in 25 US states. It also operates several outlet shops and an online store. In addition to its core products, the firm licenses its name for use on Vera Bradley-branded rugs, eyewear, stationery, and home decor items. The business was founded as Vera Bradley Designs in 1982 by Patricia Miller and Barbara Bradley Baekgaard when

they recognized a need for good-looking women's luggage. In 2010 the company went public.

In its first year as a public company Vera Bradley enjoyed strong sales growth, with net revenue up more than 26% in fiscal 2011 (ends January) vs. the previous year. Sales got a boost from the opening of nine full-price and three outlet stores. Net income rose by nearly 7%. Since its launch in 2006, the company's e-commerce site (verabradley.com) has experienced strong sales growth (adding nearly $23 million in sales in fiscal 2011) and the company hopes to increase e-commerce sales even more through the use of social networking sites such as Facebook and Twitter.

Vera Bradley operates through two channels: Direct and Indirect. Its Direct Channel (about 40% of sales) consists of sales generated by the Vera Bradley full-price stores and sales from its website. It also operates four outlet stores. The larger Indirect portion of the business consists of sales of Vera Bradley products at 3,300 independent retailers, select national retailers, and through third-party e-commerce sites.

The accessory retailer (which changed its name to Vera Bradley, Inc., when it became a publicly traded company) is using the proceeds from the IPO, which was priced at $16 per share in October 2010, to expand its network of full-price and outlet stores. (The company believes the US market can eventually support at least 300 Vera Bradley full-price stores, about ten times the number it operated upon going public.) Growth with respect to the location of its stores is another company concern — it intends to position new stores in underpenetrated markets, mainly in the Midwest, Southwest, and West. The company is also looking abroad for additional sales, launching an international marketing campaign in early 2011 to increase its brand awareness in Japan.

The Vera Bradley name has a strong brand identity and courts an upscale market with its range of product offerings; the stylish, inviting décor of its stores; and its knowledgeable staff and personalized services. Its visual displays try to create the feeling of hominess and warmth, all of which appeals to the shopper with discretionary money.

Co-founders Baekgaard and Miller own nearly 22% and 18% of the company's shares, respectively. The investment firm FMR LLC owns more than 14% of the shares.

EXECUTIVES

CEO and Director, Michael C. Ray, age 50
EVP Operations, Matthew C. Wojewuczki, age 41
EVP, CFO, Chief Administrative Officer and Secretary, Jeffrey A. (Jeff) Blade, age 50
EVP Philanthropy and Community Relations, Jill Nichols, age 50
EVP Strategy and Business Development, C. Roddy Mann, age 41
EVP Design, Kimberly F. (Kim) Colby, age 49
VP Direct Sales, David O. Thompson, age 47
National Spokesperson and Director, Patricia R. Miller, age 72
Chief Creative Officer and Director, Barbara Bradl Baekgaard, age 72
Senior Marketing Creative Director, Monica Edwards
Auditors: PricewaterhouseCoopers LLP

LOCATIONS

HQ: Vera Bradley, Inc.
2208 Production Rd., Fort Wayne, IN 46808
Phone: 260-482-4673   **Fax:** 260-484-2278
Web: www.verabradley.com

2011 Full-Price Stores

	No.
California	4
Texas	4
Massachusetts	3
Florida	2
Illinois	2
New Jersey	2
Alabama	1
Colorado	1
Connecticut	1
Delaware	1
Georgia	1
Hawaii	1
Indiana	1
Kansas	1
Maryland	1
Michigan	1
New York	1
North Carolina	1
Ohio	1
Rhode Island	1
Tennessee	1
Virginia	1
Washington	1
Wisconsin	1
Total	**35**

PRODUCTS/OPERATIONS

2011 Sales

	% of total
Handbags	49
Accessories	32
Travel & leisure items	13
Other	6
Total	**100**

2011 Sales

	$ mil.	% of total
Indirect	214.9	59
Direct	151.1	41
Total	**366.0**	**100**

Selected Brands, Collections, and Products

Accessories
  Eyewear
  ID cases
  Wallets
Baekgaard
  Cufflinks
  Leather accessories
  Pocket squares
  Ties
Handbags
  Purses
  Specialty bags
  Totes
Stationery
Travel and leisure
  Duffel bags
  Garment bags
  Weekend bags

COMPETITORS

Christian Dior	Liz Claiborne
Coach, Inc.	LVMH
Dillard's	Macy's
Dooney & Bourke	Nine West
Gucci	Polo Ralph Lauren
Laura Ashley	

HISTORICAL FINANCIALS

Company Type: Public

Income Statement

FYE: Saturday nearest January 31

	REVENUE ($ mil.)	NET INCOME ($ mil.)	NET PROFIT MARGIN	EMPLOYEES
01/11	366.1	46.2	12.6%	1,427
01/10	288.9	43.2	15.0%	1,059
01/09	238.6	23.7	9.9%	0
01/08*	39.6	13.6	34.3%	0
12/07	281.1	50.2	17.9%	0
Annual Growth	6.8%	(2.1%)	—	34.7%

*Fiscal year change

2011 Year-End Financials

Debt ratio: 104.1%
Return on equity: 71.8%
Cash ($ mil.): 14.0
Current ratio: 2.34
Long-term debt ($ mil.): 66.9

No. of shares (mil.): 40.5
Dividends
Yield: —
Payout: —
Market value ($ mil.): 1,393.2

	STOCK PRICE ($) FY Close	P/E High/Low		PER SHARE ($) Earnings	Dividends	Book Value
01/11	34.40	33	18	1.25	0.00	1.59
Annual Growth	—	—	—	—	—	—

ViroPharma

ViroPharma didn't want to wait until its drugs were finished to start making money, so instead it bought some already approved ones. The biopharmaceutical development firm discovers drugs to combat viral infections and other serious diseases. To finance its development, the company markets the antibiotic Vancocin, which treats conditions of *C. difficile*, *Staphylococcus*, and other hospital-related infections. The company also markets Cinryze, a drug made from human plasma to combat heriditary angiodema (HAE, a potentially fatal genetic disease that causes swelling of the skin or hives). ViroPharma's distributes its products through wholesalers and specialty pharmacies in the US.

ViroPharma's hopes for revenue growth are pinned on expanding markets and uses for Cinryze, which has US exclusivity rights under the Orphan Drug Act to treat certain conditions of HAE, as well as on receiving marketing approval for its other development candidates. While Vancocin, which was acquired from Eli Lilly in 2004, still accounts for more than two-thirds of annual revenues, the company's first commercial product is facing increasing levels of generic competition.

Cinryze was added to ViroPharma's repertoire in 2008 when the company acquired Lev Pharmaceuticals, a biotech developer and marketer of inflammatory disease treatments, in a $617 million deal shortly after the drug received FDA approval. The purchase also expanded ViroPharma's portfolio of serious disease treatments under development for niche customer markets. In 2010 ViroPharma acquired the rights to commercialize Cinryze in Europe and other global territories from German firm Sanquin; the company hopes to launch Cinryze in the European Union in 2011.

To further this goal, the company purchased UK specialty pharma company Auralis in 2010. The acquisition allowed ViroPharma to establish a commercial presence in the region; it also added pain therapy drug Diamorphine, which is marketed in the UK by Auralis, and other drugs under development. In 2011 the company agreed to buy Sweden-based DuoCort Pharma AB, a privately held company that makes orphan drug Plenadren, a hydrocortisone treatment for adult adrenal insufficiency. The drug is expected to receive European Commission approval before year-end. Closing of the deal depends on this approval, at which time ViroPharma will pay 220 million SEK ($33.6 million) with the added potential of 860 million SEK (about $131 million) in regulatory and commercial milestone payments.

ViroPharma's products under development include versions of Cinryze that are being tested for treatment of additional genetic and viral diseases. Other candidates include a potential antiviral agent to treat viral infection *C. difficile*. The firm's intranasal candidate Pleconaril is licensed to Merck & Co. for development as a treatment for the common cold. The company is also seeking other licensing, partnership, or acquisition opportunities to further expand its product development and marketing operations.

However, the drug development game always comes with failed ventures. For instance, the company discontinued development of investigational hepatitis C drug HCV-796, which it was developing in collaboration with Wyeth (now part of Pfizer), because of safety concerns in 2008. In addition, in 2009 it halted development of Maribavir for the treatment of cytomegalovirus (CMV) when the candidate failed to meet goals during clinical trials; the firm is evaluating results to determine whether to pursue further development of the drug.

EXECUTIVES

Chairman, President, and CEO, Vincent J. (Vinnie) Milano, age 47, $1,754,879 total compensation
VP and Chief Scientific Officer, Colin Broom, age 55, $1,254,875 total compensation
VP and General Manager, ViroPharma Europe, Thierry J. P. Darcis
VP Strategic Initiatives, Thomas F. Doyle, age 50, $1,229,880 total compensation
VP, General Counsel, and Secretary, J. Peter Wolf, age 41
VP Human Resources, Thomas G. (Tom) MacNamara
VP Corporate Communications, William C. (Will) Roberts
VP Information Technology and Facilities, Thomas Lembck
VP Plasma Operations, John C. Carlisle
VP Clinical Research and Development, Stephen (Steve) Villano
VP and CFO, Charles A. (Charlie) Rowland Jr., age 52, $1,234,658 total compensation
VP Clinical Development Programs, Steven P. (Steve) Gelone
VP and COO, Daniel B. (Dan) Soland, age 52, $1,460,465 total compensation
VP Business Development and Project Management, R. Clayton Fletcher
VP Sales, Peter A. Galiano
VP Clinical Pharmacology and Non-Clinical Development, Judith A. Johnson
VP Technology Development and Operations, James A. Nash
VP and Director Reimbursement and Managed Care, Paul E. Firuta
VP Global Regulatory Affairs and Quality, Robert G. (Bob) Pietrusko, age 62, $1,252,716 total compensation
VP and Chief Accounting Officer, Richard S. Morris, age 37
Assistant Director Investor Relations, Robert A. (Bob) Doody Jr.
Associate Director Public Relations and Advocacy, Kristina Broadbelt
Auditors: KPMG LLP

LOCATIONS

HQ: ViroPharma Incorporated
730 Stockton Dr., Exton, PA 19341
Phone: 610-458-7300   **Fax:** 610-458-7380
Web: www.viropharma.com

PRODUCTS/OPERATIONS

2009 Sales

	$ mil.	% of total
Vancocin	213.2	69
Cinryze	97.3	31
Total	**310.5**	**100**

COMPETITORS

Achillion	Merck
Amgen	Optimer
AstraZeneca	Pharmasset
CSL	Pharming
Cubist Pharmaceuticals	Roche Holding
Dyax	Salix Pharmaceuticals
Genzyme	Shire
Gilead Sciences	Teva
GlaxoSmithKline	Theravance
Idenix Pharmaceuticals	Vertex Pharmaceuticals
MedImmune	Vical

HISTORICAL FINANCIALS

Company Type: Public

Income Statement

FYE: December 31

	REVENUE ($ mil.)	NET INCOME ($ mil.)	NET PROFIT MARGIN	EMPLOYEES
12/10	439.0	125.6	28.6%	232
12/09	310.4	(11.1)	—	188
12/08	232.3	67.6	29.1%	201
12/07	203.8	95.4	46.8%	115
12/06	167.2	66.7	39.9%	67
Annual Growth	27.3%	17.1%	—	36.4%

2010 Year-End Financials

Debt ratio: 16.4%
Return on equity: 14.1%
Cash ($ mil.): 426.7
Current ratio: 8.78
Long-term debt ($ mil.): 145.7

No. of shares (mil.): 78.1
Dividends
Yield: —
Payout: —
Market value ($ mil.): 1,353.4

	STOCK PRICE ($) FY Close	P/E High/Low		PER SHARE ($) Earnings	Dividends	Book Value
12/10	17.32	12	6	1.47	0.00	11.40
12/09	8.39	—	—	(0.14)	0.00	9.69
12/08	13.02	18	10	0.83	0.00	8.40
12/07	7.94	15	6	1.21	0.00	7.11
12/06	14.64	25	7	0.95	0.00	5.91
Annual Growth	4.3%	—	—	11.5%	—	17.8%

VirtualScopics

VirtualScopics makes medical imaging analysis tools that help clinical researchers speed up the drug development process. Its patented algorithms let researchers analyze data from computed tomography, MRI, PET, and ultrasound scans, with the aim of helping pharmaceutical, biotech, and medical device companies determine how an investigational drug is working (or not working). The company also hopes its products can be used to develop diagnostic tools to help with disease treatment and surgery. VirtualScopics provides services for many large pharmaceutical companies, including GlaxoSmithKline and Johnson & Johnson; its largest customer is Pfizer (which also holds a minority stake).

EXECUTIVES

Chairman, Robert G. (Bob) Klimasewski, age 68
President, CEO, and Director, L. Jeffrey (Jeff) Markin, age 52, $896,101 total compensation
VP Technology and Product Development, Jonathan Riek
VP Business Development, Rosemary J. Shull
SVP, CFO, and Chief Business Officer, Molly Henderson, $261,324 total compensation
Director Clinical Affairs, Mark W. Tengowski
Director Quality Assurance and Regulatory Affairs, Toni Handzel
Chief Scientific Officer, Edward Ashton
Director Software Development, Colin Rhodes
Auditors: Marcum & Kliegman LLP

LOCATIONS

HQ: VirtualScopics, Inc.
350 Linden Oaks, Rochester, NY 14625
Phone: 585-249-6231   **Fax:** 585-218-7350
Web: www.virtualscopics.com

COMPETITORS

BioClinica	Pharmaceutical Product
Covance	Development
Duke University	PRA International
ICON	Quintiles
Nordion	Transnational
PAREXEL	Synarc
Penn	UCSF
Perceptive Informatics	Vital Images

HISTORICAL FINANCIALS

Company Type: Public

Income Statement

FYE: December 31

	REVENUE ($ mil.)	NET INCOME ($ mil.)	NET PROFIT MARGIN	EMPLOYEES
12/10	13.4	(0.6)	—	88
12/09	10.4	(1.0)	—	66
12/08	7.1	(2.6)	—	53
12/07	5.6	(4.3)	—	55
12/06	4.7	(3.7)	—	62
Annual Growth	29.9%	—	—	9.1%

2010 Year-End Financials

Debt ratio: —	No. of shares (mil.): 27.4
Return on equity: —	Dividends
Cash ($ mil.): 4.6	Yield: —
Current ratio: 1.60	Payout: —
Long-term debt ($ mil.): —	Market value ($ mil.): 58.7

	STOCK PRICE ($) FY Close	P/E High/Low	PER SHARE ($) Earnings	Dividends	Book Value
12/10	2.14	— —	(0.03)	0.00	0.18
12/09	1.01	— —	(0.05)	0.00	0.19
12/08	0.55	— —	(0.13)	0.00	0.23
12/07	0.92	— —	(0.25)	0.00	0.31
12/06	1.91	— —	(0.17)	0.00	0.27
Annual Growth	2.9%	— —	—	—	(9.4%)

Vitacost

Vitacost.com hopes to capitalize on convenience, low cost, and people's unending desire for better health. The online retailer offers about 32,000 products (from algae to zinc), including dietary supplements, health food, and body care items, at discounted prices. In addition to selling name brands (such as Atkins and Burt's Bees), the firm makes and sells its own Nutraceutical Sciences Institute (NSI) brand of nutritional products. Customers can also shop by phone or mail order, but online orders account for the majority of Vitacost.com's sales. The company operates a call center, manufacturing plant, and two distribution facilities in the US. Founded in 1994, Vitacost went public in 2009.

Vitacost's post-IPO performance has been stormy, marked by delays in filing financial reports, a shareholder lawsuit, a temporary halt in the trading of its shares, and the departure of directors and top level executives, including its CFO and CEO in 2010. The executive departures came on the heels of an operating loss of $2 million in the second quarter of 2010. Jeffrey Horowitz, founder and former CEO of rival Vitamin Shoppe, joined the company as a director and interim CEO following the resignation of CEO Ira Kerker in August 2010 and was named to the position permanently in early 2011. Under Horowitz, the company's sales performance has improved (up 15% vs. 2009), but the profits have not. Indeed, the company lost money in 2010 for the first time in since 2005.

In May 2011 Vitacost settled a shareholder lawsuit alleging top company officials made false and misleading statements in connection with the 2009 IPO. The lawsuit filed in July 2010 claimed certain officers made "overly optimistic" statements about the company's business and failed to disclose problems before and after the IPO. In December 2010 trading of Vitacost's shares was halted after the firm disclosed that an internal investigation found financial statements dating back more than a decade to be unreliable.

A resurgent IPO market had breathed life back into the online vitamin and health supplement retailer's public offering, filed back in 2007. Priced at $12 per share in September, the IPO raised about $132 million, which Vitacost used to repay debt, further develop its manufacturing capacity, and expand and improve its distribution operations. To that end, the company opened a new West Coast distribution center in spring 2010. The 155,000-sq.-ft. facility in Las Vegas replaces a smaller facility there, which was closed.

The online retailer looks to grow as consumers (especially the aging baby boomer population) increasingly shift their focus from health care treatment to prevention and incorporate dietary supplements, vitamins, and other wellness products into

their lifestyles. As part of its strategy, Vitacost plans to broaden the range of nutritional items from its own NSI brand as well as other manufacturers. It also aims to develop an international presence in order to reach a wider audience. (International customers accounted for 3% of sales in 2010, up from 2% in 2009.)

Vitacost executives, directors, and their affiliates own about 25% of its shares.

EXECUTIVES

Chairman, Michael A. Kumin, age 38
CEO and Director, Jeffrey J. Horowitz, age 60
VP Information Technology and CIO, Robert D. Hirsch, age 51
Inteirm CFO, Stephen E. Markert Jr., age 59
Chief Marketing Officer, Sonya L. Lambert, age 45, $440,861 total compensation
Director Customer Service, Jason Henne
Director Investor Relations, Kathleen M. Reed
General Counsel and Corporate Secretary, Mary L. Marbach, age 44
Director Manufacturing, John Young
Auditors: McGladrey & Pullen, LLP

LOCATIONS

HQ: Vitacost.com, Inc.
5400 Broken Sound Blvd., NW, Ste. 500, Boca Raton, FL 33487-3521
Phone: 561-982-4180   **Fax:** 800-347-6898
Web: www.vitacost.com

PRODUCTS/OPERATIONS

2010 Sales

	$ mil.	% of total
Third-party products	147.1	67
Proprietary products	59.2	27
Billed shipping & handling	14.4	6
Total	**220.7**	**100**

Selected Products

Bodybuilding & sports
Natural care products
Natural & organic food
Vitamins, minerals, herbs & supplements

COMPETITORS

Amazon.com	Rite Aid
CVS Caremark	Safeway
GNC	Target Corporation
Herbalife Ltd.	USANA Health Sciences
Kmart	Vitamin Shoppe
Kroger	Wal-Mart
NBTY	Walgreen
PureTek	Whole Foods

HISTORICAL FINANCIALS

Company Type: Public

Income Statement

FYE: December 31

	REVENUE ($ mil.)	NET INCOME ($ mil.)	NET PROFIT MARGIN	EMPLOYEES
12/10	220.7	(15.2)	—	415
12/09	191.8	5.9	3.1%	292
12/08	143.6	—	—	266
12/07	99.3	1.8	1.8%	0
12/06	66.4	0.2	0.3%	160
Annual Growth	35.0%	—	—	26.9%

2010 Year-End Financials

Debt ratio: —
Return on equity: —
Cash ($ mil.): 14.6
Current ratio: 1.57
Long-term debt ($ mil.): —

No. of shares (mil.): 27.8
Dividends
Yield: —
Payout: —
Market value ($ mil.): 158.3

	STOCK PRICE ($) FY Close	P/E High/Low		PER SHARE ($) Earnings	Dividends	Book Value
12/10	5.70	—	—	(0.55)	0.00	2.24
12/09	10.42	51	29	0.24	0.00	2.71
Annual Growth	(45.3%)	—	—	—	—	(17.4%)

Volcano Corporation

Volcano aims to get your heart's blood flowing as smoothly as lava down a mountain. The company makes a variety of medical imaging devices used in the diagnosis and treatment of heart disease. Volcano's intravascular ultrasound (IVUS) systems give information about the condition of arteries as well as plaque and lesions. Its functional measurement (FM) products measure characteristics of blood around plaque in arteries. The company also sells related single-use disposable catheters and guidewires. Volcano sells its products to physicians, hospitals, and other health care providers worldwide through a direct sales force and distributors.

The company, does most of its business in the US (about half of sales), Japan (about 30%), and Europe, the Middle East, and the rest of Asia, where it employs direct sales employees. Products are marketed through independent distributors in about 40 additional countries; the company has about 6,000 consoles installed at facilities worldwide and is working to expand its distribution network in emerging markets. In recent years its sales in Japan have seen significant growth, thanks in part to its contractual relationship with Johnson & Johnson, which distributes Volcano's IVUS products there. Volcano gets more than 70% of its revenues from sales of the disposable catheters and guidewires used with its IVUS and FM systems.

The company makes continuous improvements on its products (especially its top-selling IVUS systems), hoping to improve the diagnosis of heart conditions and take advantage of the growing trend of using minimally invasive surgical treatment procedures. As part of a development program that aimed to allow the company's products to network with interventional devices made by other manufacturers, Volcano has developed an IVUS console (s5i) customized for use in cardiac catheterization laboratories in hospital surgery suites.

Along with in-house research and development, Volcano grows through acquisitions, such as the 2010 purchase of Fluid Medical, a company that develops imaging technology for use in various structural heart applications including mitral valve repair. Fluid Medical's technology is being used to develop a Forward-Looking Intra-Cardiac Echo, or FLICE, catheter to expand Volcano's minimally invasive structural heart applications. The $4 million purchase also enhances the company's suite of visualization products

To further grow its interventional cardiology development pipeline, the company purchased IVUS

technology firm Novelis for $12 million in 2008. Novelis' development-stage FLIVUS technology also to widened Volcano's product applications in minimally invasive heart procedures.

By acquiring marketing rights to the Xtract line of thrombus aspiration catheters from private medical device firm Lumen Biomedical in 2010, the company expanded into the clot removal market. Through similar acquisitions and development efforts, Volcano aims to offer diagnostic and treatment options for a wide range of vascular conditions.

The company's subsidiary AXSUN Technologies manufactures lasers and optical engines used in OCT imaging systems. It also is responsible for Volcano's activities in the telecommunications market, where AXSUN sells spectrometers and optical channel monitors to telecom firms.

EXECUTIVES

President, CEO, and Director, R. Scott Huennekens, age 46, $2,009,762 total compensation
President, IVUS and FM Business Units, David M. Sheehan, age 47
President and Managing Director, Volcano Japan, Junichi Osawa
CFO and Secretary, John T. Dahldorf, age 54, $1,435,332 total compensation
EVP Marketing and General Manager, Functional Measurement and IGT, Joseph M. (Joe) Burnett, age 34
EVP Global Sales, Jorge J. (George) Quinoy, age 56, $1,742,144 total compensation
VP, Scientific Affairs and Chief Medical Director, M. Pauliina Margolis
VP Clinical and Scientific Affairs and Advanced Research and Development, D. Geoffrey Vince
Group President Advanced Imaging Systems, Clinical and Scientific Affairs, and EMEA Operations, Michel E. Lussier, age 54, $1,116,549 total compensation
Auditors: Ernst & Young LLP

LOCATIONS

HQ: Volcano Corporation
3661 Valley Centre Dr., Ste. 200, San Diego, CA 92130
Phone: 916-638-8008 **Fax:** 858-720-0325
Web: www.volcanocorp.com

2010 Sales

	$ mil.	% of total
US	134.6	46
Japan	79.2	27
Europe, Middle East & Africa	57.6	19
Other countries	22.6	8
Total	**294.1**	**100**

PRODUCTS/OPERATIONS

2010 Sales

	$ mil.	% of total
Medical		
IVUS single-procedure disposables	167.0	57
FM single-procedure disposables	46.5	16
Consoles	40.6	14
Other medical	16.9	5
Industrial	23.0	8
Total	**294.1**	**100**

COMPETITORS

Abbott Labs	Cordis
Aegis Corp.	Covidien
Bard	Edwards Lifesciences
Becton, Dickinson	Medtronic
Boston Scientific	CardioVascular

CONMED Corporation St. Jude Medical
Cook Group Terumo

HISTORICAL FINANCIALS

Company Type: Public

Income Statement

			FYE: December 31

	REVENUE ($ mil.)	NET INCOME ($ mil.)	NET PROFIT MARGIN	EMPLOYEES
12/10	294.1	5.2	1.8%	1,144
12/09	227.9	(29.0)	—	969
12/08	171.5	(13.7)	—	883
12/07	130.6	(26.6)	—	639
12/06	103.0	(8.6)	—	505
Annual Growth	30.0%	—	—	22.7%

2010 Year-End Financials

Debt ratio: 33.3%
Return on equity: 1.9%
Cash ($ mil.): 43.4
Current ratio: 5.41
Long-term debt ($ mil.): 91.2

No. of shares (mil.): 51.4
Dividends
Yield: —
Payout: —
Market value ($ mil.): 1,402.8

	STOCK PRICE ($) FY Close	P/E High/Low		PER SHARE ($) Earnings	Dividends	Book Value
12/10	27.31	289	180	0.10	0.00	5.34
12/09	17.38	—	—	(0.60)	0.00	4.40
12/08	15.00	—	—	(0.29)	0.00	4.81
12/07	12.51	—	—	(0.66)	0.00	4.98
12/06	16.40	—	—	(0.41)	0.00	3.91
Annual Growth	13.6%	—	—	—	—	8.1%

Volterra Semiconductor

Volterra Semiconductor aims to usher in a new era in voltage control for microchips. The fabless semiconductor company designs and markets low-voltage power supply chips, primarily voltage regulators for the data networking, computer, consumer electronics, servers and storage, and telecomm industries. Its products are designed to replace several power management components with a single device. Volterra outsources fabrication of its products, primarily to GLOBAL-FOUNDRIES and Taiwan Semiconductor Manufacturing, among other contractors. IBM and Hon Hai are top customers of Volterra. Nearly all of the company's sales come from international customers.

While the company is a relatively small semiconductor supplier, it has grown steadily and is consistently profitable. In 2010 sales rose 46% compared to 2009 (when sales were up 1% in spite of the global economic downturn). The company is reducing its dependency on distributors, which handled 27% of its sales in 2010, down from 37% in 2009 and 54% the prior year. Though Volterra makes analog and mixed-signal chips, it works with the developers of digital semiconductors that are driving demand for power management products. About two-thirds of sales in 2010 came from power management semiconductors for the server and storage market.

The company takes its name from Italian mathematician and physicist Vito Volterra. There is also a Tuscan town named Volterra.

EXECUTIVES

Chairman, Christopher B. (Chris) Paisley, age 59
President, CEO, and Director, Jeffrey (Jeff) Staszak, age 58, $1,008,694 total compensation
VP Legal Affairs, General Counsel, and Secretary, David Oh
VP IC Technology and Process Development, Marco Zuniga
VP World Wide Operations, David Ng
VP World Wide Sales, Thomas Truman
VP Finance, CFO, and Treasurer, Mike Burns, age 45, $514,631 total compensation
VP Quality and Reliability, Manufacturing Engineering, Achilleas Veziris
VP Research and Development, Advanced Circuit Design, David Lidsky, age 44, $399,390 total compensation
SVP Advanced Research and Development, Anthony Stratakos, age 39
SVP New Product Development, William (Bill) Numann, age 54, $465,234 total compensation
SVP Operations, Manufacturing Engineering, and Quality Assurance, Craig Teuscher, age 42, $484,488 total compensation
Investor Relations, Heidi Flannery
Auditors: KPMG LLP

LOCATIONS

HQ: Volterra Semiconductor Corporation
47467 Fremont Blvd., Fremont, CA 94538-6537
Phone: 510-743-1200 **Fax:** 510-743-1600
Web: www.volterra.com

2010 Sales

	% of total
China	50
Singapore	38
Japan	4
Taiwan	3
Germany	2
US	2
Other countries	1
Total	**100**

2009 Sales

	% of total
Singapore	47
China	42
Taiwan	4
US	2
Japan	2
Other countries	3
Total	**100**

PRODUCTS/OPERATIONS

Selected Products
Voltage regulator chipsets (VT1000, VT1300)
Voltage regulator semiconductors (VT100, VT200, VT300)

COMPETITORS

Advanced Analogic Technologies	Marvell Technology
Alpha and Omega	Maxim Integrated Products
Analog Devices	Microsemi
Infineon Technologies	ON Semiconductor
International Rectifier	Semtech
Intersil	Summit Microelectronics
Linear Technology	Texas Instruments

HISTORICAL FINANCIALS

Company Type: Public

Income Statement
FYE: December 31

	REVENUE ($ mil.)	NET INCOME ($ mil.)	NET PROFIT MARGIN	EMPLOYEES
12/10	153.6	28.4	18.5%	274
12/09	104.9	10.9	10.4%	205
12/08	104.2	14.3	13.7%	182
12/07	74.7	0.6	0.8%	164
12/06	74.6	6.9	9.2%	151
Annual Growth	**19.8%**	**42.4%**	**—**	**16.1%**

2010 Year-End Financials

Debt ratio: 0.4%
Return on equity: 22.1%
Cash ($ mil.): 86.9
Current ratio: 8.62
Long-term debt ($ mil.): 0.5

No. of shares (mil.): 24.4
Dividends
 Yield: —
 Payout: —
Market value ($ mil.): 564.7

	STOCK PRICE ($) FY Close	P/E High/Low	PER SHARE ($) Earnings	Dividends	Book Value
12/10	23.16	27 16	1.10	0.00	5.27
12/09	19.12	45 14	0.45	0.00	3.94
12/08	7.15	31 11	0.57	0.00	3.02
12/07	11.03	1675 1055	0.01	0.00	2.64
12/06	15.00	75 49	0.26	0.00	2.96
Annual Growth	**11.5%**	**— —**	**43.4%**	**—**	**15.5%**

Walker & Dunlop

When it comes to its commercial real estate loans, Walker & Dunlop has the government on its side. The company provides commercial real estate financial services — mainly multifamily loans for apartments, health care properties, and student housing — to real estate owners and developers across the US. It originates and sells its products (e.g. mortgages, supplemental financing, construction loans, and mezzanine loans) primarily through government-sponsored enterprises (GSEs) like Fannie Mae and Freddie Mac, as well as through HUD. To a lesser extent, the company originates loans for insurance companies, banks, and institutional investors. Founded in 1937, Walker & Dunlop went public via a 2010 IPO.

The company raised some $100 million from the offering. It is using the proceeds for general corporate purposes and for acquisitions of complementary businesses and products. Its strategies for growth include expanding staff, boosting its health care lending, and broadening its product line.

Walker & Dunlop has shaped its growth strategy (and timed its IPO) around certain opportunities in the commercial real estate market on which it believes it can capitalize. The company is expecting a rebound in the commercial real estate sector (which, like the residential real estate sector, suffered during the 2009 economic downturn); as such, it intends to invest in origination activities and products to meet the expected increase in demand for real estate financing. In addition, Walker & Dunlop's focus on growing its services to health care facilities is centered on an expected rise in the demand for health care real estate loans. It hopes to serve an expected increased demand for such facilities as baby boomers reach retirement age. The company is also motivated by the fact that

many commercial health care loans are sought after through GSE and HUD programs.

Walker & Dunlop's relationship with government-related housing finance companies began in the late 1980s after it started originating, underwriting, and selling loans through Fannie Mae. In 2008 it began working with Freddie Mac and HUD after acquiring a loan servicing portfolio worth $5 billion from Column Guaranteed LLC. The acquisition served to widen Walker & Dunlop's revenue base and increase its sales volume; consequently, the company saw its overall revenue figures rise dramatically in 2009.

Prior to its IPO filing, Walker & Dunlop was owned and managed by members of the Walker family. William Walker, the company's CEO, represents the third generation of family leadership for the company.

EXECUTIVES

Chairman, President, and CEO, William M. Walker, age 44, $1,107,331 total compensation
EVP, COO, and Director, Howard W. Smith III, age 52, $982,331 total compensation
SVP and Chief Underwriter, Richard C. Warner, age 56, $652,859 total compensation
SVP, CFO, Secretary, and Treasurer, Deborah A. Wilson, age 55, $660,359 total compensation
Auditors: KPMG LLP

LOCATIONS

HQ: Walker & Dunlop, Inc.
7501 Wisconsin Ave., Ste. 1200, Bethesda, MD 20814
Phone: 301-215-5500 **Fax:** 301-634-2151
Web: web.walkerdunlop.com

PRODUCTS/OPERATIONS

Selected Products and Services
Capital Markets and Investment Services
Construction loans
Equity investments
FHA Finance
First mortgage loans
Healthcare Finance
Mezzanine loans
Multifamily Finance
Second trust loans
Supplemental financings
Underwriting

COMPETITORS

Arbor Commercial	MetLife
Deutsche Bank	Wells Fargo
Deutsche Bank Berkshire Mortgage	

HISTORICAL FINANCIALS

Company Type: Public

Income Statement
FYE: December 31

	REVENUE ($ mil.)	NET INCOME ($ mil.)	NET PROFIT MARGIN	EMPLOYEES
12/10	121.8	8.2	6.7%	157
12/09	88.8	28.7	32.3%	150
12/08	49.2	8.7	17.7%	0
12/07	50.3	16.3	32.4%	0
Annual Growth	**34.3%**	**(20.5%)**	**—**	**4.7%**

2010 Year-End Financials

Debt ratio: 228.6%   No. of shares (mil.): 21.4
Return on equity: 6.6%   Dividends
Cash ($ mil.): 33.3   Yield: —
Current ratio: 11.02   Payout: —
Long-term debt ($ mil.): 285.0   Market value ($ mil.): 216.0

	STOCK PRICE ($) FY Close	P/E High/Low		PER SHARE ($) Earnings	Dividends	Book Value
12/10	10.09	18	16	0.55	0.00	5.82
Annual Growth	—			—	—	—

Walter Investment Management

Walter Investment Management deals with the credit-challenged. The company owns and services residential mortgages, particularly those of the sub-prime and nonconforming variety. Walter Investment Management services a $38 billion loan portfolio. It operates through subsidiaries: Walter Mortgage Company; Hanover Capital; and Best Insurors. In 2011 Walter Investment Management dramatically increased its assets under management and transformed into a fee-based service provider when it paid $1 billion for GTCS Holdings, the parent of Green Tree Servicing. Green Tree specializes in high-touch, third-party credit servicing.

As a result of the deal, Walter Investment Management no longer qualified as a real estate investment trust (REIT). Walter Investment hopes to tap into growing demand from big lenders looking to shift its debt servicing functions to outside firms such as Green Tree.

Walter Investment Management was created in 2009 when Hanover Capital Mortgage merged with the home financing business of Walter Industries (now Walter Energy). Walter Energy was spun off after the closure of troubled homebuilder Jim Walter Homes.

Since its formation, Walter Investment Management has made acquisitions in order to grow and better define itself. It added to its capabilities when it acquired mortgage servicing firm Marix from Marathon Asset Management in 2010.

EXECUTIVES

Chairman and CEO, Mark J. O Brien, age 68
President and COO, Charles E. Cauthen Jr., age 52
VP, CFO, and Treasurer, Kimberly A. Perez, age 43
VP, General Counsel, and Secretary, Stuart Boyd
Director Investor Relations, Whitney Finch
Vice Chairman and EVP, Denmar J. Dixon
Auditors: Grant Thornton LLP

LOCATIONS

HQ: Walter Investment Management Corp.
3000 Bayport Dr., Ste. 1100, Tampa, FL 33607
Phone: 813-421-7600
Web: www.walterinvestment.com

PRODUCTS/OPERATIONS

COMPETITORS

Annaly Capital Management	DVL
Capstead Mortgage	Newcastle Investment
CIFC	Redwood Trust
	Resource Capital

HISTORICAL FINANCIALS

Company Type: Public

Income Statement   FYE: December 31

	REVENUE ($ mil.)	NET INCOME ($ mil.)	NET PROFIT MARGIN	EMPLOYEES
12/10	180.9	37.1	20.5%	349
12/09	187.4	113.8	60.7%	219
12/08	54.3	(15.1)	—	16
12/07	27.4	(80.0)	—	17
12/06	25.9	(2.9)	—	53
Annual Growth	62.6%	—	—	60.2%

2010 Year-End Financials

Debt ratio: 230.7%   No. of shares (mil.): 25.8
Return on equity: 6.7%   Dividends
Cash ($ mil.): 114.4   Yield: 11.1%
Current ratio: —   Payout: 144.9%
Long-term debt ($ mil.): 1,281.6   Market value ($ mil.): 462.6

	STOCK PRICE ($) FY Close	P/E High/Low		PER SHARE ($) Earnings	Dividends	Book Value
12/10	17.94	14	10	1.38	2.00	21.54
12/09	14.33	10	1	5.25	1.50	22.16
12/08	4.55	—	—	(87.00)	0.00	(234.89)
12/07	19.00	—	—	(484.00)	7.50	(148.02)
12/06	248.50	—	—	(17.50)	35.00	348.42
Annual Growth	(48.2%)	—	—	—	(51.1%)	(50.1%)

Washington Banking

Washington Banking is the holding company for Whidbey Island Bank, which serves individuals and businesses through some 30 branches in north-western Washington. The bank offers standard deposit services, such as checking and savings accounts, CDs, and IRAs. It primarily originates commercial mortgages and consumer and construction loans. To a lesser extent, the bank offers one- to four-family residential mortgages and business loans. Whidbey Island Bank sells investment and insurance products through agreements with third-party providers. The bank added about a dozen branches in 2010 from the acquisitions of failed financial institutions City Bank and North County Bank in separate FDIC-assisted transactions.

EXECUTIVES

Chairman, Washington Banking Company and Whidbey Island Bank, Anthony B. (Tony) Pickering, age 63, $57,140 total compensation
President and CEO; President and CEO, Whidbey Island Bank, John L. (Jack) Wagner, age 67, $276,779 total compensation
EVP and Chief Credit Officer, Whidbey Island Bank, Joseph W. Niemer, age 59, $274,884 total compensation

---

EVP and CFO; EVP and CFO, Whidbey Island Bank, Richard A (Rick) Shields, age 51, $295,084 total compensation
EVP and COO, Whidbey Island Bank, Bryan MacDonald, age 40
VP and Controller, Washington Banking Company and Whidbey Island Bank, Darin J. Johnson
VP and Marketing Manager, Whidbey Island Bank, Mary Bailey
SVP and Executive Administrative Officer, Washington Banking Company and Whidbey Island Bank, Shelly L. Angus
SVP Retail and Operations Administrator, Whidbey Island Bank, Dale F. Smith
Payroll Administrator, Whidbey Island Bank, Cary Aliberti
SVP Human Resources Director, Whidbey Island Bank, Lynn Garrison
SVP and Senior Credit Administrator, Whidbey Island Bank, Robert Schutte
Auditors: Moss Adams, LLP

LOCATIONS

HQ: Washington Banking Company
450 SW Bayshore Dr., Oak Harbor, WA 98277
Phone: 360-679-3121   **Fax:** 360-675-7282
Web: www.wibank.com

PRODUCTS/OPERATIONS

2007 Sales

	$ mil.	% of total
Interest		
Loans, including fees	61.4	88
Investment securities & other	1.0	2
Noninterest		
Service charges & fees	3.1	4
Electronic banking	1.3	2
Other	3.1	4
Total	**69.9**	**100**

COMPETITORS

Bank of America	U.S. Bancorp
Banner Corp	Washington Federal
KeyCorp	

HISTORICAL FINANCIALS

Company Type: Public

Income Statement   FYE: December 31

	ASSETS ($ mil.)	NET INCOME ($ mil.)	INCOME AS % OF ASSETS	EMPLOYEES
12/10	1,704.5	25.6	1.5%	448
12/09	1,045.9	6.2	0.6%	281
12/08	899.6	8.3	0.9%	258
12/07	882.3	9.4	1.1%	283
12/06	794.5	9.5	1.2%	324
Annual Growth	21.0%	28.1%	—	8.4%

2010 Year-End Financials

Equity as % of assets: 10.66%   Dividends
Return on assets: 1.5%   Yield: 1.0%
Return on equity: 16.4%   Payout: 8.7%
Long-term debt ($ mil.): 25.8   Market value ($ mil.): 210.1
No. of shares (mil.): 15.3   Sales ($ mil.): 109.5

STOCK PRICE ($)		P/E		PER SHARE ($)		
	FY Close	High/Low		Earnings	Dividends	Book Value
12/10	13.71	10	7	1.55	0.14	11.86
12/09	11.94	28	13	0.46	0.18	10.43
12/08	8.70	20	6	0.88	0.19	8.49
12/07	15.79	21	13	0.99	0.23	7.83
12/06	16.89	19	14	1.00	0.20	7.15
Annual Growth	(5.1%)	—	—	11.6%	(8.5%)	13.5%

Wave Systems

Wave Systems develops digital security applications. Designed to work with security chips from such manufacturers as Broadcom and STMicroelectronics, its software enables information encryption and identity protection. Wave Systems' EMBASSY products are used in devices including notebook computers made by Dell and hard drives from Seagate Technology. The company also offers tools for securing wireless networks and for secure electronic document management. Wave Systems acquired Tel Aviv-based data loss protection software maker Safend in 2011 to expand its product line and reseller network, giving it better access to markets in Europe and the Middle East.

EXECUTIVES

Chairman, John E. Bagalay Jr., age 76
President, CEO, and Director, Steven K. Sprague, age 46, $827,564 total compensation
EVP Sales and Marketing, Brian D. Berger
EVP Business Development, Lark Allen, age 65
VP European Operations, Bruno Leconte
CTO, Len Veil
CIO, SVP Production and Services, Ed Green
SVP Finance and Administration, CFO, and Secretary; Director, Wavexpress, Gerard T. Feeney, age 52, $645,383 total compensation
Auditors: KPMG LLP

LOCATIONS

HQ: Wave Systems Corp.
480 Pleasant St., Ste. 3, Lee, MA 01238
Phone: 413-243-1600   **Fax:** 413-243-0045
Web: www.wave.com

2007 Sales

	$ mil.	% of total
US	6.0	94
Europe	0.2	4
Asia	0.1	2
Total	**6.3**	**100**

PRODUCTS/OPERATIONS

2009 Sales

	$ mil.	% of total
Licensing	18.0	96
Services	0.8	4
Total	**18.8**	**100**

COMPETITORS

CA, Inc.	Microsoft
Entrust	Phoenix Technologies
Hewlett-Packard	RSA Security
HP Enterprise Services	SafeNet
IBM	Symantec
Identive Group	VeriSign

Infineon Technologies
Intertrust
Technologies

HISTORICAL FINANCIALS

Company Type: Public

Income Statement

FYE: December 31

	REVENUE ($ mil.)	NET INCOME ($ mil.)	NET PROFIT MARGIN	EMPLOYEES
12/10	26.1	(4.1)	—	129
12/09	18.9	(3.3)	—	102
12/08	8.8	(20.5)	—	90
12/07	6.3	(20.0)	—	70
12/06	3.1	(18.8)	—	96
Annual Growth	**70.3%**	**—**	**—**	**7.7%**

2010 Year-End Financials

Debt ratio: 4.3%	No. of shares (mil.): 81.4
Return on equity: —	Dividends
Cash ($ mil.): 3.6	Yield: —
Current ratio: 1.20	Payout: —
Long-term debt ($ mil.): 0.1	Market value ($ mil.): 320.6

STOCK PRICE ($)		P/E		PER SHARE ($)		
	FY Close	High/Low		Earnings	Dividends	Book Value
12/10	3.94	—	—	(0.05)	0.00	0.03
12/09	1.42	—	—	(0.05)	0.00	(0.02)
12/08	0.37	—	—	(0.38)	0.00	(0.10)
12/07	1.45	—	—	(0.43)	0.00	0.05
12/06	2.53	—	—	(0.51)	0.00	0.14
Annual Growth	11.7%	—	—	—	—	(30.3%)

WebMD Health

House calls are a browser click away thanks to this online doctor. WebMD Health is a leading Web publisher of health information for consumers and health care professionals. Its WebMD.com portal gives consumers information on common health ailments, as well as articles and features on staying healthy through diet and exercise. WebMD's Medscape is a Web portal with clinical information for doctors and other health care professionals. All total, The WebMD Health Network (including WebMD.com, Medscape.com, and third-party sites) attracts more than 83 million users. The company also operates private portals for employers and health plans.

WebMD generates the lion's share of its revenue through its Public Portal Advertising and Sponsorship segment, which includes online advertising, marketing sponsorships, and licensing fees earned from The WebMD Health Network websites. Beyond digital media, the Public Portal Advertising and Sponsorship segment publishes *WebMD the Magazine*, which is distributed free of charge to physicians' office waiting rooms. The company's remaining revenues come from its Private Portals segment, which produces custom versions of its content for corporations (Wal-Mart, IBM) and health plans (Cigna, WellPoint) in order to manage their health and benefits Web portals.

In 2010 the company experienced revenue growth when compared to the prior year, mainly due to a recovery in the ad market, which allowed for higher advertising and sponsorship revenue from its Public Portals segment. That year rev-

enue grew 22% to $534.5 million from $438.5 million in 2009. Despite this increase, its overall net earnings fell because of substantial one time gains WebMD reported in 2009, mainly from a large income tax benefit. Specifically, profit fell 54% to $54.1 million in 2010 (from $117.3 million the prior year).

The company drives revenue growth by expanding its content offerings. In 2010 it launched The WebMD Community, a social networking service for consumers to connect with health experts and with other WebMD members to exchange information and support. The service joins its existing Physician Connect social networking service for doctors. WebMD also worked to expand its digital offerings in 2010 with the introduction of WebMD for iPad. The previous year the company launched Medscape Mobile.

In 2009 HLTH Corporation acquired the 20% of WebMD Health it didn't already own and completed a reverse merger with WebMD as the surviving company. Previously a medical practice services provider, HLTH divested most of its other operations to focus on its online content and services business. The merger, worth some $1.2 billion, was intended to reduce costs associated with both WebMD and HLTH operating as a publicly traded companies. HLTH and WebMD had previously planned to merge in 2008 but that deal, valued at $2.3 billion, was called off due to poor economic conditions and problems with obtaining financing.

EXECUTIVES

Chairman, Martin J. (Marty) Wygod, age 71, $5,862,524 total compensation
President, CEO, and Director, Wayne T. Gattinella, age 59, $1,000,065 total compensation
EVP and CTO, William E. (Bill) Pence, age 48
EVP, General Counsel, and Secretary, Douglas W. Wamsley, age 52
EVP Consumer Services, Nan-Kirsten Forte, age 48, $491,757 total compensation
EVP Professional Services, Steven L. (Steve) Zatz, age 54, $516,815 total compensation
EVP Health Services, Craig Froude, age 44
COO and CFO, Anthony (Tony) Vuolo, age 53, $2,430,693 total compensation
SVP and General Manager, Clare A. Martorana
SVP, Lewis H. Leicher
Medscape Educational/Grant Services Contact, Joan Arata
Publishing and Magazine Contact, Heidi Anderson
Editorial Contact, Sean Swint
Media Relations, Kate Hahn
Advertising Sales WebMD Consumer and Professional Networks Contact, Dorothy Gemmell
Investor Relations Contact, Risa Fisher
Auditors: Ernst & Young LLP

LOCATIONS

HQ: WebMD Health Corp.
111 8th Ave., New York, NY 10011
Phone: 212-624-3700   **Fax:** 212-624-3800
Web: www.wbmd.com

PRODUCTS/OPERATIONS

2010 Sales

	$ mil.	% of total
Public portal advertising & sponsorship	447.0	84
Private portal services	87.5	16
Total	**534.5**	**100**

Selected Offerings

The WebMD Health Network
Drugs.com

TheHeart.org
MedicineNet.com
Medscape.com
WebMD.com
WebMD the Magazine
WebMD Health Services (Online Private Portals)

COMPETITORS

AMA	Healthcommunities.com
Caremark Pharmacy	Healthline
Services	HealthStream
CDC	iVillage
Disney Online	Mayo Clinic
Ebix	MediZine
EBSCO	Medline Industries
Epocrates	New York Academy of
Everyday Health	Medicine
Health Fitness	Reed Elsevier Group
Corporation	

HISTORICAL FINANCIALS
Company Type: Public

Income Statement
FYE: December 31

	REVENUE ($ mil.)	NET INCOME ($ mil.)	NET PROFIT MARGIN	EMPLOYEES
12/10	534.5	54.1	10.1%	1,630
12/09	438.5	117.3	26.8%	1,400
12/08	382.8	26.7	7.0%	1,300
12/07	332.0	65.9	19.8%	1,175
12/06	253.9	4.5	1.8%	1,025
Annual Growth	20.5%	86.2%	—	12.3%

2010 Year-End Financials
Debt ratio: —
Return on equity: 7.2%
Cash ($ mil.): 400.5
Current ratio: 3.41
Long-term debt ($ mil.): —
No. of shares (mil.): 59.9
Dividends
Yield: —
Payout: —
Market value ($ mil.): 3,059.3

	STOCK PRICE ($) FY Close	P/E High/Low		PER SHARE ($) Earnings	Dividends	Book Value
12/10	51.06	60	43	0.88	0.00	12.57
12/09	38.49	19	9	2.07	0.00	11.09
12/08	23.59	93	30	0.45	0.00	10.98
12/07	41.07	58	35	1.10	0.00	10.56
12/06	40.02	591	357	0.08	0.00	8.85
Annual Growth	6.3%	—	—	82.1%	—	9.2%

Western Gas Partners

Western Gas Partners' style is to gather and go. The company gathers and transports natural gas for its largest customer and parent, Anadarko Petroleum. It pumps about 900 million cu. ft. of gas a day through nine gas gathering systems, six treating facilities, one natural gas liquids pipeline, and one interstate pipeline (totaling more than 4,620 miles across Wyoming, Utah, Texas, Oklahoma, and Kansas). Operating principally under long-term contracts, the company gathers natural gas from individual wells, after which it is compressed, treated, and ultimately delivered to end-users. Anadarko Petroleum spun off Western Gas Partners in 2008 and retains a controlling stake.

Western Gas Partners was formed to handle certain petroleum processing, storage, and trans-

port operations for Anadarko and to make complementary acquisitions.

In 2009 the company made its first acquisition, when it bought $210 million of midstream assets located in the Powder River Basin from its parent. It later acquired assets in the Uintah Basin in northeastern Utah for $107 million. In 2010 it acquired properties in southwest Wyoming from Anadarko for $254 million. That year it also agreed to buy natural gas assets in northeastern Colorado from its parent for about $498 million. In 2011 it acquired a natural gas processing plant and other assets in Colorado from Encana Oil and Gas (USA) for $303 million.

That year the company also acquired the Bison gas treating facility and related assets in the Powder River Basin from Anadarko Petroleum for $130 million.

In 2010 president Donald Sinclair was promoted to CEO and Robert Gwin rose to take on the chairman's role.

EXECUTIVES
Chairman, Robert G. Gwin, age 48, $879,686 total compensation
President, CEO, and Director, Donald R. Sinclair
VP and Treasurer, Jeremy M. Smith, age 38, $173,448 total compensation
VP, General Counsel, and Corporate Secretary, Amanda M. McMillian, $169,513 total compensation
SVP, CFO and Treasurer, Benjamin M. (Ben) Fink, age 41
Investor Relations, Chris Campbell
SVP and COO, Danny J. Rea, $351,906 total compensation
Auditors: KPMG LLP

LOCATIONS
HQ: Western Gas Partners, LP
1201 Lake Robbins Dr., The Woodlands, TX 77380-1046
Phone: 832-636-6000   **Fax:** 832-636-6001
Web: www.westerngas.com

PRODUCTS/OPERATIONS

2009 Sales

	$ mil.	% of total
Affiliates	219.7	90
Third parties	25.4	10
Total	**245.1**	**100**

COMPETITORS

DCP Midstream Partners	ONEOK Partners
Enbridge Energy	Questar
Kinder Morgan Energy	XTO Energy
Partners	

HISTORICAL FINANCIALS
Company Type: Public

Income Statement
FYE: December 31

	REVENUE ($ mil.)	NET INCOME ($ mil.)	NET PROFIT MARGIN	EMPLOYEES
12/10	503.3	126.1	25.1%	0
12/09	245.1	77.3	31.5%	174
12/08	311.6	65.3	21.0%	167
12/07	116.1	24.0	20.7%	117
12/06	81.2	9.7	11.9%	120
Annual Growth	57.8%	89.9%	—	13.2%

2010 Year-End Financials
Debt ratio: —
Return on equity: —
Cash ($ mil.): 27.1
Current ratio: 1.02
Long-term debt ($ mil.): 474.0
No. of shares (mil.): 77.6
Dividends
Yield: 4.6%
Payout: 84.8%
Market value ($ mil.): 2,350.5

	STOCK PRICE ($) FY Close	P/E High/Low		PER SHARE ($) Earnings	Dividends	Book Value
12/10	30.30	19	12	1.64	1.39	(0.00)
12/09	19.49	16	10	1.24	1.23	(0.00)
12/08	12.83	23	12	0.77	0.46	12.34
Annual Growth	53.7%	—	—	45.9%	73.8%	—

WidePoint

WidePoint stretches to provide a variety of IT services to government and enterprise customers. Once a provider of Y2K compliance support, the company has reinvented itself. WidePoint provides wireless telecom management services. Its cybersecurity segment provides identity management services including identity proofing, credential issuing, and public key infrastructure. The company also provides more traditional IT services such as application development, strategic planning, and vulnerability testing. WidePoint focuses its operations toward federal government clients including the Transportation Security Administration, the FBI, Department of Homeland Security, and the Treasury and Justice departments.

While WidePoint has never strayed far from its IT roots, the company has found opportunities to provide the services in growing segments of the market. Cyber security and homeland defense programs are two areas that it looks for additional opportunities to provide expanded on-site and outsourced service offerings. The company is also looking to use its experience working with Department of Defense agencies and other government entities to attract new customers and cross-sell its expanded services to existing clients.

Because the company targets a governmental customer base, the global economic downturn had little effect on its results. Revenues for 2009 increased by around 18%, driven by a 30% increase in its wireless mobility management segment and a 50% increase in its cybersecurity unit. The increases were offset by a small decrease in consulting segment sales, attributed to lower software resale revenues late in 2009. WidePoint's net income grew to $1.4 million in 2009 compared to a net loss of $1.1 the prior year, due in part to higher revenues, lower cost of sales, and higher profit margins related to the telecom management and security businesses acquired in 2008.

WidePoint has grown primarily through acquisitions that allow it to broaden its expertise by adding value to its existing operations. It acquired iSYS LLC, a provider of mobile telecom managed services to the US government, in 2008. In addition to managing the mobile telecom assets of customers, the subsidiary provides the RaptorID system to federal, state, and local government agencies to support law enforcement personnel with information system forensics. The same year it acquired Protexx, which provides software-based authentication and encryption services primarily to government, military, and emergency services organizations.

The company began operating in 1986 as Pandora, and has since changed its name three times, once dabbling in gold and oil exploration.

EXECUTIVES

Chairman and CEO, Steven L. (Steve) Komar, age 70, $105,533 total compensation
President, PROTEXX, Pater Letizia
EVP, CFO, Secretary, Treasurer, and Director, James T. (Jim) McCubbin, age 46, $190,417 total compensation
EVP Business Development and Director, Ronald S. (Ron) Oxley, age 64, $327,500 total compensation
VP and CTO; President and CEO, Operational Research Consultants, Daniel E. Turissini, age 51, $225,000 total compensation
Preisdent and CEO, iSYS, Jin Kang, age 46, $492,750 total compensation
Auditors: Moss Adams, LLP

LOCATIONS

HQ: WidePoint Corporation
1 Lincoln Centre, 18W140 Butterfield Rd., Ste. 1100, Oakbrook Terrace, IL 60181
Phone: 630-629-0003 **Fax:** 630-629-7559
Web: www.widepoint.com

PRODUCTS/OPERATIONS

2009 Sales

	$ mil.	% of total
Wireless Mobility	27.3	63
Consulting	10.3	24
Cybersecurity	5.7	13
Total	**43.3**	**100**

Selected Services

Wireless Mobility
  Outsourcing
  Telecom assets database
  Wireless telecommunications operations management
Consulting
  Application development, integration, and management
  IT architecture and strategic planning
  Infrastructure management
  Project management
  Software selection
  Systems engineering and integration
Cybersecurity
  Business and technical policy analysis
  Digital certificate credential
  Identity proofing
  Implementation of security devices
  Public key infrastructure authentication
  Security consulting and implementation
  Security risk assessment and mitigation planning
  System security planning
  Vulnerability testing and remediation

COMPETITORS

BAE Systems Inc.	Lockheed Martin
Booz Allen	ManpowerGroup
CACI International	Northrop Grumman
EDS UK	SAIC
HP Enterprise Services	Tangoe
IBM Global Services	VeriSign

HISTORICAL FINANCIALS

Company Type: Public

Income Statement

FYE: December 31

	REVENUE ($ mil.)	NET INCOME ($ mil.)	NET PROFIT MARGIN	EMPLOYEES
12/10	50.8	6.4	12.6%	115
12/09	43.3	1.4	3.2%	92
12/08	35.5	(1.1)	—	90
12/07	14.1	(0.5)	—	52
12/06	18.0	(0.4)	—	61
Annual Growth	**29.6%**	**—**		**17.2%**

2010 Year-End Financials

Debt ratio: 2.7%	No. of shares (mil.): 62.7
Return on equity: 29.0%	Dividends
Cash ($ mil.): 5.8	Yield: —
Current ratio: 1.52	Payout: —
Long-term debt ($ mil.): 0.6	Market value ($ mil.): 84.0

	STOCK PRICE ($) FY Close	P/E High/Low		Earnings	PER SHARE ($) Dividends	Book Value
12/10	1.34	16	6	0.10	0.00	0.35
12/09	0.75	50	9	0.02	0.00	0.24
12/08	0.21	—	—	(0.02)	0.00	0.22
12/07	1.07	—	—	(0.01)	0.00	0.14
12/06	2.22	—	—	(0.01)	0.00	0.16
Annual Growth	**(11.9%)**	**—**	**—**	**—**	**—**	**21.8%**

Wilhelmina International

Wilhelmina International has a new face. Formerly a billing services and software provider serving the telecommunications industry, New Century Equity Holdings reinvented itself as a holding company and in 2009 acquired Wilhelmina International - the company responsible for the iconic modeling agency Wilhelmina Models. The $30 million transaction also included affiliates Wilhelmina Miami, Wilhelmina Film & TV, and Wilhelmina Artist Management. Upon the deal's closure, New Century changed its name to Wilhelmina International, reflecting its new primary business focus. The Wilhelmina deal came after more than four years of scouting new investment opportunities.

Mark E. Schwartz was named CEO of Wilhelmina in 2009.

HISTORY

Chairman and CEO Parris "Butch" Holmes started U.S. Long Distance (USLD) as a small pay-telephone business in his Houston garage in 1985 with an investment of $50,000. Unwilling to pay local monopolies for billing services, Holmes started an in-house operation. The company turned billing into a profit center by offering the service to other carriers through three billing subsidiaries (Zero Plus Dialing, 1988; US Billing, 1993; and Enhanced Services Billing, 1994). Billing quickly became USLD's cash cow. In 1996 the billing operations were spun off to USLD stockholders as Billing Information Concepts.

While gaining market share in its primary business, the company strengthened its presence in billing services by acquiring Computer Resources Management in 1997. Billing software and equipment gained in the acquisition allowed Billing Information Concepts to expand into other metered billing services (such as utility billing). The acquisition also brought with it an alliance with IBM.

In 1998 the company changed its name to Billing Concepts and bought Communications Software Consultants, which specializes in billing services for local and wireless operators. Billing Concepts also purchased 22% of Princeton Tele-Com (now Princeton eCom), which specializes in billing through the Internet.

In 1999 Billing Concepts announced it would split its billing clearinghouse operations and its software division into separate companies. However, after writing off $2.3 million owed by a former customer, taking a $1.8 million expense for pending litigation, and racking up additional costs for restructuring and moving its software business to Austin, Texas, the company backed off. Also that year the company acquired FIData, which provides the financial services industry with Internet-based automated loan approval products. In 2000 Billing Concepts acquired, then sold, call center operator OSC; it also sold software business Aptis and its local exchange carrier billing subsidiaries to Platinum Equity Holdings.

The company changed its name to New Century Equity Holdings in 2001. It sold its stakes in all companies acquired under the old regime. As part of a long-term tie-up with Intuit, Princeton eCom that year acquired Intuit's Quicken Bill Manager. It also sold off FIData in 2001 and its interest in Tanisys in 2003.

In 2004 the company pondered a complete liquidation of its holdings after selling its 29% stake in bill payment services firm Princeton eCom. Instead, it sold a controlling stake of itself to Dallas-based investment firm Newcastle Partners. Upon the acquisition by Newcastle, founder Parris Holmes resigned from the company and its board, as did CFO David Tusa and directors Gary Becker and Steven Wagner.

In 2008 New Century purchased Wilhelmina International for $30 million and changed its name to Wilhelmina International.

EXECUTIVES

Chairman and CEO, Mark E. Schwarz, age 50
CFO, John Murray, age 39
General Counsel, Secretary, and Director, Evan D. Stone, age 39
Auditors: Burton McCumber & Cortez, LLP

LOCATIONS

HQ: Wilhelmina International, Inc.
300 Crescent Ct., Ste. 1400, Dallas, TX 75201
Phone: 214-661-7488
Web: www.wilhelmina.com

COMPETITORS

DWS Investments	Putnam
GAMCO Investors	TCW
Old Mutual (US)	The Vanguard Group

HISTORICAL FINANCIALS

Company Type: Public

Income Statement

FYE: December 31

	REVENUE ($ mil.)	NET INCOME ($ mil.)	NET PROFIT MARGIN	EMPLOYEES
12/10	49.0	1.0	2.0%	78
12/09	32.5	(3.3)	—	79
12/06	0.1	(0.6)	—	2
12/05	0.0	(0.5)	—	2
12/02	10.0	(7.2)	—	6
Annual Growth	22.0%	—	—	37.8%

2010 Year-End Financials

Debt ratio: —	No. of shares (mil.): 129.4
Return on equity: 4.8%	Dividends
Cash ($ mil.): 1.7	Yield: —
Current ratio: 0.84	Payout: —
Long-term debt ($ mil.): —	Market value ($ mil.): 19.4

	STOCK PRICE ($) FY Close	P/E High/Low		PER SHARE ($) Earnings	Dividends	Book Value
12/10	0.15	16	8	0.01	0.00	0.16
12/09	0.09	—	—	(0.03)	0.00	0.15
12/06	0.13	—	—	(0.02)	0.00	0.23
12/05	0.19	—	—	(0.00)	0.00	0.25
12/02	0.22	—	—	(0.02)	0.00	0.25
Annual Growth	(9.1%)	—	—	—	—	(10.5%)

Winnebago

A pioneer in the world of recreational vehicles, Winnebago Industries makes products intended to encourage exploration and outdoor escape. Almost all of the company's sales come from its motor homes and towables, which are sold via independent dealers throughout the US and Canada under the Winnebago, Itasca, SunnyBrook, and ERA brands. Winnebago Industries also sells RV parts and provides related services; in addition, the company produces OEM parts, such as extruded aluminum components, for other RV manufacturers and for use in commercial vehicles. Winnebago Industries makes most of its sales in the US.

After a two year slump in 2008-2009 (when sales sank some 75% from 2007 totals), 2010 and 2011 have both posted stronger numbers, though the company has not yet reached the same heights. Gains are largely due to stronger sales volumes and parts purchases, a mix of higher-priced RVs, along with retail and other incentives, and a reduction in losses on motor home repurchases.

Winnebago is working to diversify by acquiring companies that complement its existing portfolio, as evidenced by its acquisition of the assets of SunnyBrook RV in late 2010 for a $4.7 million. The deal increased the company's portfolio of fifth wheel and towable RVs to include established brand names such as Bristol Bay, Brookside, Edgewater, Harmony, and Sunset Creek. Towable units are cheaper than motorized ones, and because of this the towable market has not been hit as hard and should be larger than the market for motorized units in 2011.

HISTORY

During a mid-1950s economic downturn, furniture store owner John Hanson convinced Forest City officials to welcome a local subsidiary of California trailer maker Modernistic Industries. The company's first trailer rolled off the line in 1958. Hanson later bought the plant and in 1960 named the business Winnebago Industries after Forest City's home county. Winnebago Industries went public in 1966. Sales took off when the company offered less-expensive RVs than its competitors.

The 1970s energy crisis and increased competition eroded the company's sales, prompting it to make lower-cost, more fuel-efficient motor homes. Hanson retired in 1972; he returned in 1979 and in 1986 diversified Winnebago Industries by buying Cycle Video (renamed Cycle-Sat; operations discontinued beginning in 1996) for distributing TV and radio commercials via satellite.

Winnebago Industries' sales suffered again during the early 1990s when recession hit and gas prices increased in response to the Gulf War. Sales rebounded in 1992, but remained stagnant for several years. Hanson died in 1996. That year and the next the company divested non-RV assets and sold its European operations.

During an industry-wide slump, Winnebago Industries and other RV makers formed the Go RVing Coalition (1997), targeting baby boomers with a $15 million ad campaign. Lower gas prices and interest rates fed RV demand in 1998 and 1999. In 2000 the company spent $14.5 million on upgrading its equipment and expanding its manufacturing facilities.

In 2003 Winnebago ceased manufacturing its EuroVan RV. Also that year, the company sold its dealer financing business to GE Commercial Distribution Finance. A new shipping facility located at its Charles City, Iowa, Class C motor home manufacturing plant was opened in 2004.

Winnebago weathered the economic crisis in 2008 and 2009 and managed to get on a positive trajectory in 2010 as demand for big-ticket items slowly returned.

EXECUTIVES

Chairman, Robert J. (Bob) Olson, age 60, $403,099 total compensation
President and CEO, Randy J. Potts, age 52
VP and CFO, Sarah N. Nielsen, age 38, $237,546 total compensation
VP Administration, Robert L. Gossett, age 60
VP Sales and Marketing, Roger W. Martin, age 51, $239,585 total compensation
VP, General Counsel, and Secretary, Raymond M. Beebe, age 69, $255,444 total compensation
VP Manufacturing, Daryl W. Krieger, age 48
VP Product Development, William J. O'Leary, age 62, $240,636 total compensation
Treasurer, Donald L. Heidemann, age 39
Controller, Brian J. Hrubes, age 60
Manager Public Relations and Investor Relations, Sheila Davis
Auditors: Deloitte & Touche LLP

LOCATIONS

HQ: Winnebago Industries, Inc.
605 W. Crystal Lake Rd., Forest City, IA 50436
Phone: 641-585-3535   **Fax:** 641-585-6966
Web: www.winnebagoind.com

PRODUCTS/OPERATIONS

2011 Sales

	$ mil.	% of total
Motor homes	443.2	89
Towables	16.7	3
Motor home parts & services	13.1	3
Other manufactured products	23.4	5
Total	**449.4**	**100**

2011 Sales by Units

	Units sold	% of total
Class A	2,436	56
Class B	103	2
Class C	1,856	42
Total	**4,395**	**100**

Selected Products

ERA
  ERA
Itasca
  Cambria
  Ellipse
  Impulse
  Impulse Silver
  Meridian
  Meridian V Class
  Navion
  Navion IQ
  Reyo
  Suncruiser
  Sunova
  Sunstar
Winnebago
  Access
  Access Premier
  Adventurer
  Aspect
  Journey
  Journey Express
  Sightseer
  Tour
  Via
  View
  View Profile
  Vista

COMPETITORS

Airstream	Newmar Corporation
Elixir Industries	Patrick Industries
Featherlite	Prevost Car
Forest River	Rexhall Industries
Gulf Stream Coach	Skyline
Jayco, Inc.	Supreme Industries
Keystone RV	Thor Industries
Monaco RV	Tiffin Motorhomes
Motor Coach Industries	TRIGANO

HISTORICAL FINANCIALS

Company Type: Public

Income Statement

FYE: Last Saturday in August

	REVENUE ($ mil.)	NET INCOME ($ mil.)	NET PROFIT MARGIN	EMPLOYEES
08/11	496.4	11.8	2.4%	2,130
08/10	449.5	10.2	2.3%	1,950
08/09	211.5	(78.8)	—	1,630
08/08	604.4	2.8	0.5%	2,250
08/07	870.2	41.6	4.8%	3,310
Annual Growth	(13.1%)	(27.0%)	—	(10.4%)

2011 Year-End Financials

Debt ratio: —	No. of shares (mil.): 29.1
Return on equity: 10.9%	Dividends
Cash ($ mil.): 69.3	Yield: 0.0%
Current ratio: 3.21	Payout: —
Long-term debt ($ mil.): —	Market value ($ mil.): 228.7

	STOCK PRICE ($)	P/E		PER SHARE ($)		
	FY Close	High/Low	Earnings	Dividends	Book Value
08/11	7.85	40	15	0.41	0.00	3.73
08/10	8.58	50	23	0.35	0.00	3.35
08/09	12.10	—	—	(2.71)	0.00	3.17
08/08	11.35	324	91	0.10	0.48	5.98
08/07	26.67	28	19	1.32	0.42	7.05
Annual Growth	(26.3%)	—	—	(25.3%)	—	(14.7%)

Woodstock Financial

Woodstock Financial Group offers up financial advice, but just don't expect to hear about hippie stock picks. The company, formerly Raike Financial Group, brokers support services for brokers. Founded in 1995, the company provides licensing, clearing, IT support, education, and various administrative services to a network of independent financial planners, insurance agents, and traditional and discount securities brokers. Woodstock handles a range of investment products, including stocks, bonds, mutual funds, annuities, and life insurance. Online trading is offered through its Woodstock Discount Brokerage division. Founder and CEO William Raike owns about 80% of the company.

EXECUTIVES

Chairman, President, and CEO, William J. Raike III, age 52
Treasurer, CFO, and Director, Melissa L. Whitley, age 34
Auditors: Porter Keadle Moore, LLP

LOCATIONS

HQ: Woodstock Financial Group, Inc.
117 Town Lake Pkwy., Ste. 200, Woodstock, GA 30188
Phone: 770-516-6996 **Fax:** 770-516-8169
Web: www.woodstockfg.com/

PRODUCTS/OPERATIONS

2007 Sales

	$ mil.	% of total
Commissions	7.0	86
Interest and dividends	0.3	4
Other fees	0.8	10
Total	**8.1**	**100**

COMPETITORS

Detwiler Fenton
Edward Jones
LPL Investment
  Holdings
TD Ameritrade

HISTORICAL FINANCIALS

Company Type: Public

Income Statement

FYE: December 31

	REVENUE ($ mil.)	NET INCOME ($ mil.)	NET PROFIT MARGIN	EMPLOYEES
12/10	12.7	0.3	2.4%	118
12/09	8.9	(0.2)	—	123
12/08	8.1	—	—	125
12/07	8.1	(0.4)	—	11
12/06	9.3	0.3	3.2%	79
Annual Growth	8.1%	0.0%	—	10.6%

2010 Year-End Financials

Debt ratio: 76.0%
Return on equity: 22.6%
Cash ($ mil.): 1.0
Current ratio: 1.59
Long-term debt ($ mil.): 0.9
No. of shares (mil.): 17.7
Dividends
  Yield: —
  Payout: —
Market value ($ mil.): 1.2

	STOCK PRICE ($)	P/E		PER SHARE ($)		
	FY Close	High/Low	Earnings	Dividends	Book Value
12/10	0.07	14	3	0.01	0.00	0.07
12/09	0.08	—	—	(0.02)	0.00	0.07
12/08	0.01	—	—	(0.00)	0.00	0.08
12/07	0.10	—	—	(0.02)	0.00	(0.00)
12/06	0.16	15	8	0.02	0.00	(0.00)
Annual Growth	(18.7%)	—	—	(15.9%)	—	—

World Energy

World Energy Solutions offers its customers some protection from the world of hurt that is rising energy prices. The company offers energy procurement, market analysis, and risk management services for industrial and commercial customers and government entities in deregulated regions of the US. World Energy Solutions analyzes clients' energy needs and provides savings on electricity and natural gas supply contracts through its online reverse auction platforms; it also manages bill payments and monitors energy usage after the auction process. The company's more than 300 customers include Cargill Energy Marketing, Ford, SAIC, and the US Postal Service.

World Energy Solutions operates the World Energy Exchange, an online power and gas brokerage, and the World Green Energy Exchange, a similar auction platform focused on supporting alternative energy products, such as renewable energy certificates and certified emission reductions.

In 2009 retail product sales accounted for 80% of the company's total revenues, although the company is also trying to grow its wholesale line as a significant revenue stream (13% in 2009, up from 10% in 2008).

In 2010 World Energy Solutions launched a third auction platform, World DR Exchange, to auction demand response (monetized power reduction programs) at times of stress on the US power grid. The platform is the first such online marketplace for power customers.

Growing its portfolio, in 2011 the company bought the energy procurement business of software firm Co-eXprise, for an undisclosed price and privately-held energy efficiency company Northeast Energy Solutions. Later in the year it acquired GSE Consulting for an estimated $8.6 million. GSE

---

provides energy management and consulting services in Texas and provides World Energy with a foothold in the largest de-regulated market in the US.

CEO Richard Domaleski owns 22% of the company.

EXECUTIVES

Chairman, Edward T. Libbey, age 64
CEO and Director, Richard M. Domaleski, age 41, $375,000 total compensation
President and COO, Philip V. Adams, age 52, $464,301 total compensation
CFO, Treasurer, and Secretary, James F. (Jim) Parslow, age 45, $302,655 total compensation
CIO and Chief Architect, World Energy Exchange, Robert J. (Rob) Hartwell
SVP Environmental and Wholesale Operations, Andrew J. Thomas
Auditors:

LOCATIONS

HQ: World Energy Solutions, Inc.
446 Main St., Worcester, MA 01608
Phone: 508-459-8100 **Fax:** 508-459-8101
Web: www.worldenergy.com

COMPETITORS

APX
CHOICE! Energy
EnerNOC

HISTORICAL FINANCIALS

Company Type: Public

Income Statement

	REVENUE ($ mil.)	NET INCOME ($ mil.)	NET PROFIT MARGIN	EMPLOYEES
12/10	18.0	(0.1)	—	60
12/09	14.6	(2.3)	—	54
12/08	12.4	(6.8)	—	55
12/07	9.2	(8.6)	—	0
12/06	5.8	(0.5)	—	0
Annual Growth	32.7%	—	—	4.4%

2010 Year-End Financials

Debt ratio: 0.0%
Return on equity: —
Cash ($ mil.): 3.6
Current ratio: 1.97
Long-term debt ($ mil.): 0.0
No. of shares (mil.): 9.2
Dividends
  Yield: —
  Payout: —
Market value ($ mil.): 25.6

	STOCK PRICE ($)	P/E		PER SHARE ($)		
	FY Close	High/Low	Earnings	Dividends	Book Value
12/10	2.80	—	—	(0.01)	0.00	1.22
12/09	3.10	—	—	(0.27)	0.00	1.16
12/08	4.00	—	—	(0.08)	0.00	0.13
12/07	8.00	—	—	(0.11)	0.00	0.20
12/06	11.50	—	—	(0.01)	0.00	0.23
Annual Growth	(29.8%)	—	—	—	—	51.2%

WorldGate Communications

WorldGate Communications has its eye on the video phone market. The company markets the Ojo video phone, which uses broadband Internet connections and video screens to allow people to see one another while chatting. The Ojo includes a cordless handset and a display unit with a camera, video screen, and interface ports. The product is targeted at both residential and business users. The Ojo is also intended for use by people with hearing disabilities, as it enables them to use American Sign Language to communicate. WorldGate sells through distributors, broadband service providers, and retailers.

The company's goal of having its video phones replace the ordinary home or business phone hit a snag in 2008, when it reported severe cash shortfalls. It was forced to layoff staff and briefly shut down operations when it entered into a payment dispute with its largest customer, Aequus Technologies. WorldGate resumed operations after Aequus agreed to paid $5 million for support and training to keep the company afloat, and to purchase $1.5 million worth of Ojo video phones.

To maintain interest in its products, WorldGate in 2010 introduced an updated version of its phone, known as the Ojo Vision. That year, the company announced that telecommunications services reseller ACN had adopted the new Ojo model to enable its video phone service.

While WorldGate's revenues declined in 2009 due to weak demand, the company lost less money that year due to a $6.5 million investment by WGI Investor which gave WGI a 63% stake in the company. WGI's backers include ACN.

EXECUTIVES

Chairman, Robert Stevanovski
CEO, George E. Daddis Jr.
SVP Legal and Regulatory, General Counsel, and Secretary, Christopher V. (Chris) Vitale
SVP Finance, CFO, and Treasurer, James G. Dole, age 50
SVP Sales, Marketing, and Business Development, Allan Van Buhler
Auditors: Marcum & Kliegman LLP

LOCATIONS

HQ: WorldGate Communications, Inc.
3190 Tremont Ave., Trevose, PA 19053
Phone: 215-354-5100 **Fax:** 215-354-1049
Web: www.wgate.com

PRODUCTS/OPERATIONS

2009 Sales

	$ mil.	% of total
Direct to manufacturer	1.4	82
Consumer services	0.3	18
Total	**1.7**	**100**

COMPETITORS

8x8	Logitech
Apple Inc.	Polycom
Cisco Systems	Skype
Creative Technology	Sony
D-Link	Sorenson
Intel	TANDBERG
Leadtek	Vialta

HISTORICAL FINANCIALS

Company Type: Public

Income Statement

FYE: December 31

	REVENUE ($ mil.)	NET INCOME ($ mil.)	NET PROFIT MARGIN	EMPLOYEES
12/10	17.8	(12.7)	—	50
12/09	1.8	(6.3)	—	40
12/08	3.0	(9.3)	—	27
12/07	3.4	(14.7)	—	39
12/06	2.8	(17.6)	—	70
Annual Growth	**58.8%**	**—**	**—**	**(8.1%)**

2010 Year-End Financials

Debt ratio: —   No. of shares (mil.): 339.5
Return on equity: —   Dividends
Cash ($ mil.): 0.9   Yield: —
Current ratio: 0.14   Payout: —
Long-term debt ($ mil.): —   Market value ($ mil.): 73.9

	STOCK PRICE ($) FY Close	P/E High/Low		PER SHARE ($) Earnings	Dividends	Book Value
12/10	0.22	—	—	(0.03)	0.00	(0.01)
12/09	0.75	—	—	(0.02)	0.00	(0.01)
12/08	0.38	—	—	(0.13)	0.00	(0.09)
12/07	0.19	—	—	(0.32)	0.00	(0.03)
12/06	1.34	—	—	(0.44)	0.00	0.05
Annual Growth	**(36.3%)**	**—**	**—**	**—**	**—**	**—**

Xponential

Xponential is the holding company for Pawn-Mart, which makes small short-term loans secured by personal property, such as jewelry, electronics, tools, and cars. The shops specialize in lending on heavy equipment, boats, and motorcycles. Pawn-Mart typically makes loans of less than $500, charges annual interest rates of 24%-300%, and sells the property if the customer defaults. To compete with discount retailers, the company operates clean, well-lit stores in suburban areas, and sells no handguns or rifles. PawnMart has about 25 locations in Georgia and North Carolina.

PawnMart filed for bankruptcy in 2001 and emerged from bankruptcy the next year on the heels of a merger with Texas-based C/M Holdings, Inc. Changes included relocating corporate headquarters from Fort Worth, Texas, to Smyrna, Georgia; the naming of new board members and executives; and the announcement of a new independent auditor. Finally, the newly formed company, named Xponential, Inc. in 2003, set PawnMart up as a subsidiary to allow for the entry into other lines of business.

Xponential Real Estate Holdings was formed in 2005 to acquire land on which the company's pawn shops are located. Xponential also owned a nearly 20% stake in American IronHorse Motorcycle Company. The motorcycle maker was forced into Chapter 11 bankruptcy by investors and creditors in 2008 and was later acquired by AIH Acquisition.

EXECUTIVES

Chairman and VP, Jeffrey A. Cummer
CEO, PawnMart Inc., Thomas K. Haas
EVP, CFO, and Director, Robert W. (Bob) Schleizer
Auditors: Grant Thornton LLP

LOCATIONS

HQ: Xponential, Inc.
6400 Atlantic Blvd., Ste. 190, Norcross, GA 30071
Phone: 678-720-0670   **Fax:** 678-720-0671
Web: www.xponential.us

COMPETITORS

Cash America	Kmart
Check Into Cash	Sears
DGSE Companies	Target Corporation
EZCORP	Wal-Mart
First Cash Financial	Winmark
Services	World Acceptance

HISTORICAL FINANCIALS

Company Type: Public

Income Statement

FYE: June 30

	REVENUE ($ mil.)	NET INCOME ($ mil.)	NET PROFIT MARGIN	EMPLOYEES
06/07	19.2	(8.5)	—	0
06/03*	17.1	12.1	70.8%	166
01/97	7.9	(3.1)	—	110
01/96	4.4	(2.8)	—	0
Annual Growth	**14.3%**	**—**	**—**	**7.1%**

*Fiscal year change

Debt ratio: —   No. of shares (mil.): 339.5
Return on equity: —   Dividends
Cash ($ mil.): 0.9   Yield: —
Current ratio: 0.14   Payout: —
Long-term debt ($ mil.): —   Market value ($ mil.): 73.9

ZAGG

ZAGG hopes to stand in the way when a little zig threatens to scratch your iPhone. Short for "Zealous About Great Gadgets," ZAGG designs, manufactures, and distributes protective coverings and other products for electronic devices. Its flagship product, invisibleSHIELD, is a thin, scratch-resistant polyurethane film covering that's custom cut to fit invisibly on the screens and displays of Apple iPhones and other smartphones, laptops, GPS devices, and watch faces. ZAGG also offers additional accessories, including headphones for iPods and MP3 players and decorative cases for phones. It sells its products through retailers like Best Buy and RadioShack, mall kiosks, and its own website.

Tracing its roots back to 2004, ZAGG has traditionally focused on distributing through sales channels like kiosk vendors and through its e-commerce site; however, in recent years, it has brought in more and more income through retailers. In fact the company saw a dramatic revenue increase in 2009 that was largely attributed to hefty sales generated by retail channels. Ultimately, demand for its products has been driven by the growing popularity of iPhones and other smartphones (iPhone accessories are its biggest sellers). This trend is particularly pronounced in the US, where ZAGG does most of its business. The company also sells throughout Europe and other global regions through international distributors.

In a move that at once broadens its brand and product portfolio and increases its retail reach, ZAGG in mid-2011 acquired iFrogz, a maker and distributor of protective cases, headphones and earbuds, and other accessories for smartphones, tablets, and other mobile devices under the iFrogz and EarPollution brands. ZAGG paid $50 million in cash, acquired 4.4 million restricted shares of ZAGG common stock, and assumed about $5 million in debt in the deal that closed in June. Utah-based iFrogz will operate as a wholly-owned subsidiary of ZAGG. iFrogz counts Wal-Mart amongst its customers.

Going forward, ZAGG hopes to keep its growth momentum swinging in an upward direction by expanding its sales channels to include more telecom companies like U.S. Cellular and retailers like Amazon.com. It has also been broadening its range of accessories for the mobile phone market by adding car chargers and power supplies to its product offerings. Other growth strategies include focusing its sales and marketing efforts on cross-selling accessories to customers that purchase its invisibleSHIELD products.

A publicly-traded company, ZAGG is controlled in part by CEO Robert G. Pedersen, who owns 20% of its stock.

EXECUTIVES

Chairman and CEO, Robert G. Pedersen II, age 43
CFO, Brandon T. O'Brien, age 39
VP Sales and Marketing, Derek Smith
Media Contact, Nathan Nelson
Auditors: KPMG LLP

LOCATIONS

HQ: ZAGG Inc.
3855 S. 500 West, Ste. J, Salt Lake City, UT 84115-4279
Phone: 801-263-0699
Web: www.zagg.com

2009 Sales

	% of total
US	85
Europe	8
Other regions	7
Total	**100**

PRODUCTS/OPERATIONS

Selected Brands

EarPollution
iFrogz
invisibleSHIELD (film coatings)
ZAGGbuds (audio headphones)
ZAGGskins (cell phone cases and covers)
ZAGGsmartbuds (audio headphones)

COMPETITORS

Apple Inc.	Kyocera Communications
Bose	Motorola Mobility
Dooney & Bourke	Otterbox
Forward Industries	Plantronics

HISTORICAL FINANCIALS

Company Type: Public

Income Statement

FYE: December 31

	REVENUE ($ mil.)	NET INCOME ($ mil.)	NET PROFIT MARGIN	EMPLOYEES
12/10	76.1	10.0	13.1%	183
12/09	38.4	3.4	8.9%	122
12/08	19.8	2.1	10.6%	74
12/07	5.1	(0.8)	—	76
12/06	2.8	(0.1)	—	35
Annual Growth	**128.3%**	**—**	**—**	**51.2%**

2010 Year-End Financials

Debt ratio: —	No. of shares (mil.): 23.9
Return on equity: 33.0%	Dividends
Cash ($ mil.): 2.4	Yield: —
Current ratio: 2.02	Payout: —
Long-term debt ($ mil.): —	Market value ($ mil.): 182.3

	STOCK PRICE ($) FY Close	P/E High/Low		PER SHARE ($) Earnings	Dividends	Book Value
12/10	7.62	22	5	0.41	0.00	1.26
12/09	3.92	53	6	0.15	0.00	0.64
12/08	0.93	11	5	0.11	0.00	0.30
12/07	0.75	—	—	(0.05)	0.00	(0.00)
Annual Growth	**116.6%**	**—**	**—**	**—**	**—**	**—**

Zalicus

Zalicus is working to reduce pain and inflammation 'round the clock. The company develops new combinations or improved versions of drugs to improve their effectiveness and safety. It prefers to work with previously approved compounds, with the hopes of moving them more quickly and inexpensively through the drug development process. Its Exalgo extended-release painkiller product received FDA approval in 2010. Zalicus' pipeline of drug candidates includes Synavive, which is in clinical development to address such immuno-inflammatory diseases as rheumatoid arthritis and osteoarthritis. Its preclinical candidates are potential analgesics based upon ion channel blockers.

Formerly known as CombinatoRx, the company has seen several major changes in the past few years. Due to economic conditions and a lack of available funding in the biotech market in late 2008, the company announced a restructuring of its operations to conserve cash. It proceeded to cut two-thirds of its workforce, sold off a subsidiary in Singapore, and focused on its core development operations.

The slimmed-down company merged with privately held, Canadian drug developer Neuromed Pharmaceuticals in 2009. The two companies combined their assets to push forward the development of Neuromed's leading candidate Exalgo, an extended-release formulation of pain-killer hydromorphone. Despite earlier FDA concerns that the drug might be too easily abused, Exalgo received approval in 2010.

Exalgo will be competing not only with the original hydromorphone formulation, sold under the brand name Dilaudid and widely available as a generic, but also with other extended-release formulations of opioids such as the Duragesic patch and OxyContin.

Contract manufacturer ALZA produces the Exalgo while Covidien holds the license to market the drug in the US. Before the drug was even approved Covidien put $15 million up front to secure the marketing rights. It then made a milestone payment of $40 million when the drug was approved and gained intellectual property rights.

The company changed its name from CombinatoRx to Zalicus in mid-2010 to reflect its broader focus on not only combination drug formulations, but also on improved versions of single drugs.

Zalicus maintains several collaborative agreements to develop compounds. An agreement with Novartis is focused on oncology compounds while another agreement with Sanofi subsidiary Fovea

Pharmaceuticals is developing Prednisporin, an ophthalmic anti-inflammatory drug. Under an agreement with Amgen the company is researching potential cancer drug combinations and it is also researching Alphavirus infections on behalf of the US Army Medical Research Institute for Infectious Diseases.

As part of the 2009 merger terms, Neuromed's CEO Christopher Gallen became CEO of the company and Robert Forrester, who had served as interim CEO of CombinatoRx, assumed the role of COO. However, just a few short weeks after the deal with Neuromed closed, the company underwent a shakeup in its management team. Forrester resigned as COO, and Gallen was moved into the position of EVP of research and development; at the same time director Mark Corrigan, who previously led R&D efforts at Sunovion (formerly Sepracor), took over the CEO post.

EXECUTIVES

Chairman, Frank W. Haydu III, age 63
President, CEO, and Director, Mark H. N. Corrigan, age 53
EVP Research and Development, Christopher C. Gallen, age 60
VP Corporate Communications and Investor Relations, Gina Nugent
SVP and Chief Development Officer, Eugene Wright
SVP Commercial Development, John Randle, age 54, $475,480 total compensation
SVP and Chief Scientific Officer, Terrance Snutch
SVP, Secretary and General Counsel, Jason F. Cole, age 38, $741,411 total compensation
SVP, CFO, and Treasurer, Justin A. Renz, age 39
Auditors: Ernst & Young LLP

LOCATIONS

HQ: Zalicus Inc.
245 1st St., 3rd Fl., Cambridge, MA 02142
Phone: 617-301-7000   **Fax:** 617-301-7010
Web: www.zalicus.com

PRODUCTS/OPERATIONS

2010 Revenue

	$ mil.	% of total
Collaborations	45.9	98
Government contracts & grants	0.8	2
Total	**46.7**	**100**

COMPETITORS

Akela	Pain Therapeutics
BioDelivery Sciences International	Purdue Pharma
	Sandoz International
Cephalon	GmbH
Mylan	Watson Pharmaceuticals

HISTORICAL FINANCIALS

Company Type: Public

Income Statement

FYE: December 31

	REVENUE ($ mil.)	NET INCOME ($ mil.)	NET PROFIT MARGIN	EMPLOYEES
12/10	46.7	(35.0)	—	58
12/09	17.3	15.4	89.0%	51
12/08	14.1	(65.1)	—	73
12/07	14.9	(53.3)	—	164
12/06	13.3	(34.3)	—	144
Annual Growth	**36.9%**	**—**	**—**	**(20.3%)**

Debt ratio: 6.3%   No. of shares (mil.): 89.1
Return on equity: —   Dividends
Cash ($ mil.): 2.8   Yield: —
Current ratio: 5.29   Payout: —
Long-term debt ($ mil.): 4.0   Market value ($ mil.): 140.8

	STOCK PRICE ($) FY Close	P/E High/Low		PER SHARE ($) Earnings	Dividends	Book Value
12/10	1.58	—	—	(0.42)	0.00	0.71
12/09	0.83	6	1	0.41	0.00	0.45
12/08	0.62	—	—	(1.87)	0.00	0.45
12/07	4.44	—	—	(1.78)	0.00	2.16
12/06	8.66	—	—	(1.26)	0.00	3.02
Annual Growth	(34.6%)	—	—	—	—	(30.5%)

Zillow

Wonder how much your home is really worth? Zillow has the answer. Its website for homeowners and buyers provides a free estimated market value using its proprietary formula ("Zestimate") for more than 70 million homes across America. Users enter an address into a search field, and Zillow computes the Zestimate and overlays it on a satellite map. The company also provides listings and neighborhood information, photos, purchase and sale data, and rental price estimates on more than 100 million US homes, and offers services to find real estate agents and mortgage rates. Zillow was established in 2004 by Expedia founder Rich Barton and former Expedia exec Lloyd Frink. It filed to go public in 2011.

Observers have questioned the timing of Zillow's IPO, as the housing market has yet to recover from the downturn. Thanks to a temporary federal tax credit for homebuyers that was instituted in 2010, residential real estate experienced a slight uptick during the first half of the year; however, demand slowed in the latter part of 2010 and has remained lackluster since then. Zillow raised about $69 million through the offering (higher than the previously estimated $52 million figure), and is using the proceeds for general corporate purposes, as well as to fund possible acquisitions or investments that complement its business.

The company provides listings and neighborhood information, photos, purchase and sale data, and rental price estimates on more than 100 million US homes. It provides Zestimates on more than 70 million US homes. In 2010, Zillow's revenues jumped to $30.5 million from $17.5 million the year before, representing 74% growth. Part of the increase was due to its ability to attract more visitors to the site. Zillow had an average of more than 12 million monthly unique users in the last three months of 2010, an increase of more than 65% from the same period in 2009. Like other startups, it has yet to post a profit while it incurs costs to expand the business. However, its net loss narrowed significantly to $6.8 million from $12.9 million in 2009 as it increased sales.

Another reason for the company's positive earnings in 2010 was its increase in revenues outside of display advertising, which historically had earned Zillow nearly all of its money. Now, however, fees and subscription sales to lenders and agents are becoming a more important source of revenue. The company's Zillow Mortgage Marketplace connects borrowers with verified and rated lenders, while its Premier Agent program provides a directory of real estate agents. Together these products are classified as marketplace revenues, and accounted for more than 40% of sales in 2010 (up from about 20% in 2009 and 1% in 2008).

Zillow has been expanding its offerings through strategic partnerships, acquisitions, and product development. It formed a deal with Yahoo! in 2011 through which it places home listings and ads from local real estate brokers on Yahoo!. Later in 2011 it acquired the assets of Postlet, a real estate agent and rental property manager marketing service. Postlet created a platform that makes it easier for agents, property managers, and landlords to distribute listings on real estate and social media sites across the Web. The previous year the company launched Zillow Mobile, which publishes a real estate app for iPhone, iPad, Android, and BlackBerry products.

In 2010 Barton relinquished the CEO role to Spencer Rascoff, the company's former COO and a co-founder of the online travel service Hotwire.com. Barton had been the company's CEO since it was founded, and remains with Zillow as executive chairman. The CEO appointment was an early signal of the firm's upcoming IPO, as Rascoff is comfortable communicating with outside investors and the public.

The two co-founders together own most of the company; Barton controls about 47% of votes, while Frink controls some 38%. Before its IPO, the company raised about $87 million in funding from venture capital groups such as Benchmark Capital, Technology Crossover Ventures, Legg Mason, and PAR Capital Management.

The name "Zillow" combines the words pillow (where you lay your head at night) and zillions (the number of data points the firm desires to provide).

EXECUTIVES

Chairman, Richard N. (Rich) Barton, age 43
CFO and Treasurer, Chad M. Cohen, age 36
CEO and Director, Spencer M. Rascoff, age 35
VP Product Teams, Garrett McAuliffe
VP Product Teams, Christopher Roberts
VP, Sales Strategy and Operations, Tony Small
VP Product Teams, Kristin Acker
VP, IT and Operations, Chris Staats
VP Local Advertising Sales, Doug Slotkin
VP, Product Management and Strategy, Chloe Harford
Vice Chairman and President, Lloyd D. Frink, age 46
CTO, David A. Beitel, age 42
Chief Economist, Stan Humphries
Chief Marketing Officer, Amy Bohutinsky, age 36
Chief Revenue Officer, Greg M. Schwartz, age 38
General Counsel, Kathleen Philips, age 44
Auditors: Ernst & Young LLP

LOCATIONS

HQ: Zillow, Inc.
999 3rd Ave., Ste. 4600, Seattle, WA 98104
Phone: 206-470-7000
Web: www.zillow.com

PRODUCTS/OPERATIONS

2010 Sales

	$ mil.	% of total
Display advertising	17.2	56
Marketplace	13.3	44
Total	**30.5**	**100**

Selected Products & Operations

Website and Mobile Offerings
  Local information (neighborhoods, schools, demographics)
  Sale and rental listings
  Zestimate values (determines a home's worth)
  Zillow Mobile (real estate app for smart phones)
Marketplace Offerings
  Mortgage Marketplace (instant loan quotes)
  Premier Agent (real estate agent listing)

COMPETITORS

Classified Ventures   Move, Inc.
craigslist   PropertyInfo
Google   RE/MAX
HomeGain.com   Zaio
Market Leader

HISTORICAL FINANCIALS

Company Type: Public

Income Statement

FYE: December 31

	REVENUE ($ mil.)	NET INCOME ($ mil.)	NET PROFIT MARGIN	EMPLOYEES
12/10	30.5	(6.8)	—	252
12/09	17.5	(12.9)	—	0
12/08	10.6	(21.2)	—	0
Annual Growth	69.6%	—	—	—

Debt ratio: 6.3%   No. of shares (mil.): 89.1
Return on equity: —   Dividends
Cash ($ mil.): 2.8   Yield: —
Current ratio: 5.29   Payout: —
Long-term debt ($ mil.): 4.0   Market value ($ mil.): 140.8

Zipcar

Zipcar empowers pedestrians. The company rents cars under the Zipcar and Streetcar names by the hour or day, rather than by the week. It offers more than 550,000 members access to about 8,000 vehicles parked in designated spaces throughout large cities in the US, Canada, and Europe, and among some 100-plus North American universities. Drivers (aka Zipsters) pay a fee to use Zipcar's reservation system; they unlock a vehicle using a keyless-entry Zipcard. Hourly rates cover mileage, fuel, and insurance. Founded in 2000, the company typically targets individuals who are supplementing the use of public transportation through car rentals. Zipcar went public in early 2011.

Through its IPO, estimated at $89 million, Zipcar intends to pay down debt incurred from past purchases. The company also plans to expand its business, as well as invest in complementary technologies and add-on businesses. While the car service operates in more than a dozen major metropolitan areas across North America and the UK, Zipcar is looking to extend its reach internationally in both existing and new markets. It has identified more than 100 metro areas worldwide and hundreds of universities as car-sharing markets to target. The company's strategy is to maintain and acquire new members who live in large, densely populated areas where it's expensive to own or park a car.Zipcar, which is banking on the success of its car-sharing concept to keep competitors such as Hertz and Enterprise at bay, hopes to achieve sales of $1 billion by 2018. The firm, which has not yet reached profitability, generated 90% of its revenue from vehicle usage; the balance of its business came from membership fees. The big-city service provider, which supplies its members with a variety of cars from Hondas to Toyotas, has boosted its revenue from $3.7 million in 2005 to $127.5 million in 2009. As Zipcar enters more markets, it's jockeying for position with other car-sharing companies such as Car2Go, which has been busy inking deals with cities for reserved spaces. To Zipcar's benefit, however, it offers its customers more than a handful of car choices while some competitors have only one: Smart's fortwo. The company's move to go public follows its aggressive expansion since late 2009. Zipcar gained a firm foothold in Europe through its 2010 purchase of UK's Streetcar. The car provider acquired Streetcar, the UK's fastest-growing car-sharing club, in a deal valued at about $50 million with no assumption of debt. (In 2009, Streetcar logged about $25 million in revenue.) The deal created the first global car-sharing network, gave Streetcar members access to Zipcar vehicles in the US and Canada, and built a foundation for Zipcar to expand to an additional dozen European markets in the long term. Zipcar, which has operated in London since 2006, more than quadrupled its stable of UK members by buying Streetcar. As part of the agreement, Streetcar will eventually adopt the Zipcar brand name. Zipcar also plans to leverage Streetcar's investments in technology and branding, as well as exercise its increased bargaining power for insurance rates and access to financing. Also, Streetcar founders and executives Andrew Valentine and Brett Akker joined the Zipcar executive team.The acquisition of Streetcar bolsters Zipcar's previous minority investment in Barcelona's Catalunya Carsharing, known as Avancar, the largest car-sharing company in Spain, in late 2009. Keeping its options open in Spain, Zipcar in early 2011 inked a deal that gives it until the end of the year to boost ownership in Avancar to a majority holding.Investment firm Revolution (headed by director and AOL co-founder Steve Case) owns 23% of Zipcar. Board member Robert Kagle and his Benchmark Capital Partners hold nearly 13% of the company.

EXECUTIVES

Chairman and CEO, Scott W. Griffith, age 52, $600,000 total compensation
President and COO, Mark D. Norman, age 43, $450,475 total compensation
CFO, Edward G. (Ed) Goldfinger, age 49, $311,507 total compensation
EVP, Corporate Development, Jon Zeitler
VP, International University Operations, Matthew Malloy
VP, Human Resources, Sean Quimby
VP, Engineering, Doug Williams
CTO, Luke Schneider
Executive, Streetcar, Brett Akker, age 31
Executive, Streetcar, Andrew Valentine, age 32
General Manager, Vancouver, John Macsween
General Manager, New York, Charlie Irons
General Manager, Seattle, Carla Archambault
Chief Marketing Officer, Robert J. (Rob) Weisberg, age 39
General Manager, Washington, D.C., Ellice Perez
General Manager, Portland, Bill Scott
General Manager, Boston, Dan Curtin
General Manager, Philadelphia, Jeremy Nelson
General Manager, Chicago, Jonathan Gonsky
General Manager, Toronto, Michael Lende
General Manager, San Francisco, Michael Uribe
Auditors: PricewaterhouseCoopers LLP

LOCATIONS

HQ: Zipcar, Inc.
25 First St., 4th Fl., Cambridge, MA 02141
Phone: 617-995-4231   **Fax:** 617-995-4300
Web: www.zipcar.com

2009 Sales

	$ mil.	% of total
North America	127.5	97
UK	3.7	3
Total	**131.2**	**100**

PRODUCTS/OPERATIONS

2009 Sales

	$ mil.	% of total
Vehicle usage	117.6	90
Fees	13.5	10
Total	**131.2**	**100**

Select Cities

US
  Atlanta
  Boston
  Chicago
  Philadelphia
  Pittsburgh
  Portland
  New York
  San Francisco
  Seattle
  Washington, DC
Canada
  Toronto
  Vancouver
Europe
  Bristol
  Cambridge
  London
  Oxford
  Southampton

COMPETITORS

AMERCO
Avis
Daimler
Dollar Thrifty
  Automotive

Enterprise Rent-A-Car
Hertz
Penske Truck Leasing

HISTORICAL FINANCIALS

Company Type: Public

Income Statement

FYE: December 31

	REVENUE ($ mil.)	NET INCOME ($ mil.)	NET PROFIT MARGIN	EMPLOYEES
12/10	186.1	(14.1)	—	712
12/09	131.2	(4.6)	—	426
12/08	106.0	(14.5)	—	0
12/07	57.8	(14.4)	—	0
Annual Growth	**47.7%**	**—**	**—**	**67.1%**

2010 Year-End Financials

Debt ratio: 60.8%	No. of shares (mil.): —
Return on equity: —	Dividends
Cash ($ mil.): 43.0	Yield: —
Current ratio: 0.92	Payout: —
Long-term debt ($ mil.): 68.0	Market value ($ mil.): —

Hoover's Handbook of

Emerging Companies

Master Index for all 2012 Hoover's Handbooks

Index by Industry

Advertising & Marketing Services
Groupon, Inc.
interclick, inc.
KIT digital, Inc.
Local.com Corporation
ReachLocal, Inc.
Responsys, Inc.

Aerospace Products & Parts Manufacturing
Environmental Tectonics Corporation

Aircraft Maintenance & Repair
Butler National Corporation

Ambulatory Health Care Services
Conmed Healthcare Management, Inc.
Healthways, Inc.
IPC The Hospitalist Company, Inc.

Analog Chip Manufacturing
International Rectifier Corporation
Linear Technology Corporation
Maxim Integrated Products, Inc.
Power Integrations, Inc.
Volterra Semiconductor Corporation

Apparel Accessories Manufacturing
Vera Bradley, Inc.

Apparel Manufacturing
G-III Apparel Group, Ltd.
Under Armour, Inc.

Asset Management
Och-Ziff Capital Management Group LLC

Audio & Video Equipment Manufacturing
DEI Holdings, Inc.
LRAD Corporation
Skullcandy, Inc.

Audio Chip & Board Manufacturing
Cirrus Logic, Inc.

Auto & Other Vehicle Insurance Carriers
Baldwin & Lyons, Inc.

Auto Lending
Credit Acceptance Corporation
First Investors Financial Services Group, Inc.

Automobile Dealers
CarBiz Inc.

Automobile Manufacturing
Tesla Motors, Inc.

Automobile Parts Manufacturing
Amerigon Incorporated
Azure Dynamics Corporation
STRATTEC SECURITY CORPORATION

Automobile Rental & Leasing
Zipcar, Inc.

Automotive Parts & Accessories Stores
Universal Manufacturing Co.
U.S. Auto Parts Network, Inc.

Baby Supplies & Accessories Manufacturing
Summer Infant, Inc.

Banks & Credit Unions
1st United Bancorp, Inc.
Allied First Bancorp, Inc.
American Bank Holdings, Inc.
American Business Bank
ASB Financial Corp.
Bank of Commerce Holdings
BCB Bancorp, Inc.
Blue River Bancshares, Inc.

BNC Bancorp
BofI Holding, Inc.
Burke & Herbert Bank & Trust Company
CalWest Bancorp
Carolina Trust Bank
CCF Holding Company
CenterState Banks, Inc.
Cherokee Banking Company
Citizens South Banking Corporation
Clarkston Financial Corporation
Coast Bancorp
Community Bankers Trust Corporation
Community Financial Corporation
Eagle Bancorp, Inc.
East West Bancorp, Inc.
First Bancorp of Indiana, Inc.
First Financial Bancorp
First Niagara Financial Group, Inc.
First Savings Financial Group, Inc.
First South Bancorp, Inc.
First Trust Bank
Georgia Bancshares, Inc.
Hampton Roads Bankshares, Inc.
IBERIABANK Corporation
Idaho Independent Bank
Investors Bancorp, Inc.
KS Bancorp, Inc.
Lafayette Community Bancorp
Meridian Interstate Bancorp, Inc.
Millennium Bankshares Corporation
Mission Bancorp
Monarch Financial Holdings, Inc.
New York Community Bancorp, Inc.
Peapack-Gladstone Financial Corporation
Premier Financial Bancorp, Inc.
PSB Holdings, Inc.
Roma Financial Corporation
SCBT Financial Corporation
Signature Bank
South Street Financial Corp.
Southern Missouri Bancorp, Inc.
Southern National Bancorp of Virginia, Inc.
Tower Bancorp Inc.
Union First Market Bankshares Corporation
United Financial Banking Companies, Inc.
Washington Banking Company

Battery Manufacturing
A123 Systems, Inc.
Ener1, Inc.
Evergreen Solar, Inc.
Valence Technology, Inc.

Billing & Service Provisioning Software
BroadSoft, Inc.
Synchronoss Technologies, Inc.
Tangoe, Inc.

Biopharmaceuticals & Biotherapeutics Manufacturing
Acorda Therapeutics, Inc.
Alexion Pharmaceuticals, Inc.
Anika Therapeutics, Inc.
Ardea Biosciences, Inc.
ARIAD Pharmaceuticals, Inc.
ArQule, Inc.
AVEO Pharmaceuticals, Inc.

Celldex Therapeutics, Inc.
Cleveland BioLabs, Inc.
Curis, Inc.
Dendreon Corporation
Emergent BioSolutions Inc.
Exelixis, Inc.
Halozyme Therapeutics, Inc.
Human Genome Sciences, Inc.
InterMune, Inc.
Medivation, Inc.
NeoStem, Inc.
Neurocrine Biosciences, Inc.
Onyx Pharmaceuticals, Inc.
Osiris Therapeutics, Inc.
Regeneron Pharmaceuticals, Inc.
Seattle Genetics, Inc.
SIGA Technologies, Inc.
Synta Pharmaceuticals Corp.
Targacept, Inc.
United Therapeutics Corporation
diaDexus, LLC
ViroPharma Incorporated

Biotechnology Product Manufacturing
Bacterin International Holdings, Inc.
Momenta Pharmaceuticals, Inc.

Biotechnology Research Equipment Manufacturing
Fluidigm Corporation
Illumina, Inc.

Breweries
Craft Brewers Alliance, Inc.

Building Services
Swisher Hygiene Inc.

Business Intelligence Software
Qlik Technologies, Inc.

Business Service Centers & Copy Shops
Document Security Systems, Inc.

Business Services Sector
Iconix Brand Group, Inc.
RPX Corporation

Casual Restaurants
Buffalo Wild Wings, Inc.

Cigarette, Cigar & Smokeless Tobacco Product Manufacturing
Vector Group Ltd.

Clothing Stores
Francesca's Holdings Corporation
rue21, inc.
Syms Corp

Coal Mining
Alliance Holdings GP, L.P.
Alliance Resource Partners, L.P.
Hallador Energy Company
L & L Energy, Inc.
Oxford Resource Partners, LP
SunCoke Energy, Inc.

Coffee & Tea Manufacturing
Green Mountain Coffee Roasters, Inc.

Coin Conversion
Green Dot Corporation
NetSpend Holdings, Inc.

Colleges & Universities
American Public Education, Inc.
Bridgepoint Education, Inc.
Broadview Institute, Inc.
Corinthian Colleges, Inc.
DeVry Inc.

Grand Canyon Education, Inc.
National American University Holdings, Inc.
Strayer Education, Inc.

Commercial & Heavy Construction Contractors
Cavico Corp.
Energy Services of America Corporation
Primoris Services Corporation

Commercial & Industrial Equipment Rental & Leasing
Essex Rental Corp.

Commercial Insurance Carriers
Tower Group, Inc.

Commercial Real Estate & Construction Lending
Walker & Dunlop, Inc.

Commercial Real Estate Management
EACO Corporation
Hudson Pacific Properties, Inc.

Communications Chip Manufacturing
Entropic Communications, Inc.
InterDigital, Inc.
MaxLinear, Inc.
Semtech Corporation

Communications Testing Equipment Manufacturing
Ixia
JDS Uniphase Corporation
ORBIT/FR, Inc.

Computer & Office Equipment Wholesalers
Bsquare Corporation
INX Inc.

Computer Display & Projector Manufacturing
eMagin Corporation

Computer Peripheral Equipment Manufacturing
Comarco, Inc.

Computer Software
Cornerstone OnDemand, Inc.
ExlService Holdings, Inc.
Premier Alliance Group, Inc.
ServiceSource International, Inc.

Consumer Electronics & Appliances Stores
hhgregg, Inc.

Consumer Electronics Manufacturing
ZAGG Inc.

Consumer Lending
DFC Global Corp.
EZCORP, Inc.
Xponential, Inc.

Content & Document Management Software
OmniComm Systems, Inc.
ProtoSource Corporation
Rovi Corporation

Contract Electronics Manufacturing
DDi Corp.
IEC Electronics Corp.
Simclar, Inc.
TTM Technologies, Inc.

Control, Electromedical, Measuring & Navigational Instruments Manufacturing

Aerosonic Corporation

Cosmetics, Beauty Supply & Perfume Stores
FragranceNet.com, Inc.

Credit Reporting & Collections Services
Encore Capital Group, Inc.
FirstCity Financial Corporation
Portfolio Recovery Associates, Inc.

Customer Relationship Management, Marketing & Sales Software
Constant Contact, Inc.
LivePerson, Inc.
Pegasystems Inc.
salesforce.com, inc.

Database & File Management Software
The Active Network, Inc.
Informatica Corporation

Deep Sea Freight Transportation
Eagle Bulk Shipping Inc.

Development Tools, Operating Systems & Utilities Software
Red Hat, Inc.

Diagnostic Substance Manufacturing
Genomic Health, Inc.
Neogen Corporation
Response Genetics Inc.

Direct Broadcast Services Providers
Multiband Corporation

Direct Marketing Services
QuinStreet, Inc.
Stream Global Services, Inc.
Sykes Enterprises, Incorporated

Discrete & Passive Semiconductor Manufacturing
Diodes Incorporated
Maxwell Technologies, Inc.

Display Component Manufacturing
Cree, Inc.
ProPhotonix Limited
Rubicon Technology, Inc.
Universal Display Corporation

Drug Delivery System Manufacturing
Alexza Pharmaceuticals, Inc.
CPEX Pharmaceuticals, Inc.
Depomed, Inc.

Drug Wholesalers
Amexdrug Corporation
MWI Veterinary Supply, Inc.

E-commerce Software
Pacific WebWorks, Inc.

Education & Training Services
Archipelago Learning, Inc.
Cambium Learning Group, Inc.
EVCI Career Colleges Holding Corp.
ITT Educational Services, Inc.
Lincoln Educational Services Corporation
The Princeton Review, Inc.

Electric Power Distribution
EnerNOC, Inc.

Electric Utilities
Acorn Energy, Inc.

Electromedical, Electrotherapeutic & X-Ray Apparatus Manufacturing
Alphatec Holdings, Inc.
Cardiovascular Systems, Inc.
DexCom, Inc.
Endologix, Inc.
Insulet Corporation
MAKO Surgical Corp.
NuVasive, Inc.
NxStage Medical, Inc.
Solta Medical, Inc.

Electronic Component Manufacturing
API Technologies Corp.
CPS Technologies Corporation

Electronic Component Wholesalers
CUI Global, Inc.

Electronic Payment Systems
Meta Financial Group, Inc.

Electronic Test & Measurement Instruments Manufacturing

Teradyne, Inc.

Energy Trading & Marketing
AMEN Properties, Inc.
World Energy Solutions, Inc.

Enterprise Application Integration Software

Unify Corporation

Enterprise Resource Planning Software
RealPage, Inc.

Enterprise Telecommunications Equipment Manufacturing
eOn Communications Corporation
ShoreTel, Inc.

Environmental Consulting Services
Sutron Corporation

Fabricated Metal Product Manufacturing
Electric & Gas Technology, Inc.

Film & Video
Dolby Laboratories, Inc.
DTS, Inc.

Financial Planners & Investment Advisers
Stifel Financial Corp.

Financial Services
IntercontinentalExchange, Inc.
TNS, Inc.

Financial Services, Legal & Government Software
Ebix, Inc.

Financial Transaction Processing
Higher One Holdings, Inc.

Fixed-Income Trading
MarketAxess Holdings Inc.

Footwear Manufacturing
Deckers Outdoor Corporation
Skechers U.S.A., Inc.
Steven Madden, Ltd.

Freight Forwarding Services
Pacific CMA, Inc.
Sino-Global Shipping America, Ltd.

Fuel Oil Dealers
Able Energy, Inc.

Furniture Manufacturing
Decorize, Inc.

Gambling Resorts & Casinos
Full House Resorts, Inc.
Nevada Gold & Casinos, Inc.

Generic Drug Manufacturing
Hi-Tech Pharmacal Co., Inc.
Impax Laboratories, Inc.
Par Pharmaceutical Companies, Inc.

Geophysical Surveying & Mapping Services
U.S. Energy Corp.

Glass & Glass Product Manufacturing
Dynasil Corporation of America

Gold & Silver Mining
Atna Resources Ltd.
Coeur d'Alene Mines Corporation
Golden Star Resources Ltd.
Hecla Mining Company
Jaguar Mining Inc.
North Bay Resources Inc.
Royal Gold, Inc.

Graphics/Video Chip & Board Manufacturing
Trident Microsystems, Inc.

Gun & Ammunition Manufacturing
Sturm, Ruger & Company, Inc.

Hazardous Waste Services
Clean Harbors, Inc.

Health Care Management Software
athenahealth, Inc.
Medidata Solutions, Inc.
Merge Healthcare Incorporated
Quality Systems, Inc.
SXC Health Solutions Corp.

Health Care REITs
Senior Housing Properties Trust

Health Insurance Carriers
Access Plans, Inc.
The Amacore Group, Inc.

Almost Family, Inc.
LHC Group, Inc.

Human Resources & Workforce Management Software
SuccessFactors, Inc.
Taleo Corporation

Industrial Chemical Manufacturing
Amyris, Inc.
BioFuel Energy Corp.
Clean Diesel Technologies, Inc.
Codexis, Inc.
Green Plains Renewable Energy, Inc.
KMG Chemicals, Inc.
Synthesis Energy Systems, Inc.
TPC Group Inc.

Industrial Equipment Wholesalers
Titan Machinery Inc.

Industrial REITs
Duke Realty Corporation
STAG Industrial, Inc.

Information Collection & Delivery
DG FastChannel, Inc.
MSCI Inc.

Information Technology Services
Allin Corporation
Datalink Corporation
DuPont Fabros Technology, Inc.
The KEYW Holding Corporation
Limelight Networks, Inc.
NCI, Inc.
Spearhead Limited, Inc.
WidePoint Corporation

Institutional Asset Management
Epoch Holding Corporation

Insurance Agencies & Brokerages
eHealth, Inc.

Internet Content Providers
Ancestry.com Inc.
Demand Media, Inc.
LinkedIn Corporation
OpenTable, Inc.
Shutterfly, Inc.
WebMD Health Corp.
Zillow, Inc.

Internet Educational Services
Capella Education Company
K12 Inc.

Internet Music Distribution & Downloads
Pandora Media, Inc.

Internet Search & Navigation Services
InfoSpace, Inc.

Internet Service Providers
TowerStream Corporation

Investment Banking
Evercore Partners Inc.
Gleacher & Company, Inc.
JMP Group Inc.
KBW, Inc.
Piper Jaffray Companies
Rodman & Renshaw Capital Group, Inc.

Investment Firms
Ares Capital Corporation
ICG Group, Inc.
Main Street Capital Corporation
Prospect Capital Corporation
Wilhelmina International, Inc.

Legal Services
The Dolan Company

Life Insurance Carriers
American Equity Investment Life Holding Company
FBL Financial Group, Inc.
Life Partners Holdings, Inc.
National Western Life Insurance Company

Lighting Equipment Manufacturing
Energy Focus, Inc.
Lighting Science Group Corporation

Logic Device Manufacturing
Altera Corporation

Logistics Services

AutoInfo, Inc.
Echo Global Logistics, Inc.
Radiant Logistics, Inc.

LP Gas Dealers
Chesapeake Utilities Corporation

Machinery Manufacturing
Global Power Equipment Group Inc.

Managed Application & Network Services
Equinix, Inc.
Rackspace Hosting, Inc.

Manufacturing, Warehousing & Industrial Software
GSE Systems, Inc.

Market Research & Polling Services
comScore, Inc.

Medical & Diagnostic Laboratories
Bio-Reference Laboratories, Inc.
NeoGenomics, Inc.

Medical Equipment & Supplies Manufacturing
Antares Pharma, Inc.
Cerus Corporation
Cytori Therapeutics, Inc.
Electromed, Inc.
ICU Medical, Inc.
Intuitive Surgical, Inc.
Patient Safety Technologies, Inc.
Vasomedical, Inc.
VirtualScopics, Inc.
Volcano Corporation

Medical Practice Management & Services
Accretive Health, Inc.
Birner Dental Management Services, Inc.
ExamWorks Group, Inc.
HMS Holdings Corp.
MedAssets, Inc.
MedQuist Holdings Inc.
Transcend Services, Inc.

Memory Chip & Module Manufacturing
Dataram Corporation
GSI Technology, Inc.
OCZ Technology Group, Inc.
Rambus Inc.
Silicon Mountain Holdings, Inc.

Messaging, Conferencing & Communications Software
NeuLion, Inc.

Microprocessor, Microcontroller & Digital Signal Processor Manufacturing
Cavium, Inc.
Microchip Technology Incorporated

Mining
Globe Specialty Metals, Inc.
Molycorp, Inc.

Mortgage & Investment REITs
American Capital Agency Corp.
Hatteras Financial Corp.
RAIT Financial Trust
Redwood Trust, Inc.

Mortgage Banking
DJSP Enterprises, Inc.
Ellington Financial LLC
Walter Investment Management Corp.

Motion Picture Equipment Manufacturing
Ballantyne Strong, Inc.
RealD Inc.

Motorcycle & Other Small-Engine Vehicle Manufacturing
Advanced Battery Technologies, Inc.

Multimedia, Graphics & Publishing Software
Digimarc Corporation

Music, Video, Book & Entertainment Retail
Coinstar, Inc.
Netflix, Inc.

Mutual Fund Management
Diamond Hill Investment Group, Inc.
U.S. Global Investors Funds

Natural Gas Gathering & Processing Systems

Index by Headquarters

ARGENTINA

Buenos Aires
YPF W450

AUSTRALIA

Bella Vista
Woolworths Limited W444

Docklands
Australia and New Zealand Banking
W44
National Australia Bank W269

Hawthorn
Amcor W29

Macquarie Park
Metcash W255

Mascot
Qantas W317

Melbourne
BHP Billiton W65
Rio Tinto Limited W329
Telstra W399

Sydney
Commonwealth Bank of Australia
W104
Westpac Banking W442

Tooronga
Coles Group W102

AUSTRIA

Vienna
Erste Bank W147
OMV W298
STRABAG SE W381

BELGIUM

Brussels
ageas SA/NV W14
Dexia W124
KBC W216
Umicore W423

Leuven
Anheuser-Busch InBev W32

BRAZIL

Rio de Janeiro
PETROBRAS W305
Vale W429

São Paulo
AmBev W28

CANADA

Aurora
Magna International W246

Brampton
Loblaw W241

Calgary
Imperial Oil W196

Montreal
Bombardier W72

Stellarton
Empire Company W138

Toronto
Barrick Gold W55
BMO Financial Group W66
CIBC W96
George Weston W169
RBC Financial Group W321
Rogers Communications W333
TD Bank W393

Verdun
BCE W61

CHINA

Beijing
Bank of China W51

Shanghai
Sinopec Shanghai Petrochemical
W366

DENMARK

Copenhagen
A.P. Møller - Mærsk W3
Danske Bank W115
ISS A/S W204

FINLAND

Espoo
Nokia W283

Helsinki
Kesko W218
Stora Enso W379
UPM-Kymmene W427

FRANCE

Asni res-sur-Seine
EIFFAGE W135

Blagnac
Airbus W17

Boulogne-Billancourt
Colas W100
Renault W324

Clermont-Ferrand
Michelin W257

Clichy
L'Oréal W232

Courbevoie
GDF SUEZ W167
Saint-Gobain W346
TOTAL W412

Croix
Auchan W42

Issy-les-Moulineaux
Sodexo W371

Laval
Lactalis W233

Levallois-Perret
ALSTOM W27
Carrefour W87

Nanterre
Faurecia W150

Neuilly-sur-Seine
Thales W405

Paris
Alcatel-Lucent W21
AXA W47
BNP Paribas W69
Bouygues W73
Capgemini W86
Christian Dior W94
CNP Assurances W98
Crédit Agricole W109
Danone W114
Electricité de France W136
France Telecom W157
L'Air Liquide W230
La Poste W233
Lafarge W235
LVMH W245
Natixis W271
Pernod Ricard W303
Peugeot W306
PPR SA W313
Rallye W319
SAFRAN W345
Sanofi W351
SNCF W368
Société Générale W369

Sonepar W374
Valeo W430
Veolia Environnement W431
Vivendi W435

Roissy
Air France W16

Rueil-Malmaison
Schneider Electric W357
VINCI W432

Saint-Étienne
Casino Guichard W88

GERMANY

Bad Homburg
Fresenius Medical Care W159

Berlin
Bayer HealthCare Pharmaceuticals
W59
Deutsche Bahn W119

Bonn
Deutsche Post W121
Deutsche Telekom W123

Cologne
Lufthansa W242
REWE W326

Darmstadt
Merck KGaA W254

Düsseldorf
E.ON W130
ERGO W144
Henkel W180
METRO AG W256

Essen
ALDI W22
Arcandor W33
HOCHTIEF W185
RWE W341
ThyssenKrupp W406

Frankfurt
Commerzbank W103
Deutsche Bank W120
KfW W219
DZ BANK W129

Friedrichshafen
ZF Friedrichshafen W451

Gütersloh
Bertelsmann W62

Hamburg
Edeka Zentrale W133
Otto Group W299

Hanau
Heraeus Holding W181

Credit Suisse W108
Holcim W187
Migros W258
Swiss Re W388
UBS W421
Zurich Financial Services W453

TAIWAN

Hsichih
Acer W8

Hsinchu
TSMC W415

THE NETHERLANDS

Amstelveen
KPMG W224

Amsterdam
ABN AMRO Group W5
Akzo Nobel W19
CNH Global W97
Heineken W177
ING W201
Philips Electronics W308
Royal Ahold W336

Delft
IKEA W195

Diemen
Randstad Holding W320

Heerlen
DSM W128

Leiden
EADS W132

The Hague
AEGON W13
KPN W225
Royal Dutch Shell W339

Utrecht
Rabobank W318

TURKEY

Istanbul
Sabanci W342

UNITED KINGDOM

Bristol
Imperial Tobacco W198

Chertsey
Compass Group W105

Cheshunt
Tesco W402

Crawley
TUI Travel W417

Edinburgh
Royal Bank of Scotland W338
Standard Life W377

Hemel Hempstead
Dixons Retail W127

Leeds
ASDA W37
UK National Health Service W422

London
Anglo American W31
Associated British Foods W38
AstraZeneca W40

Aviva W46
BAE SYSTEMS W49
Balfour Beatty W50
Barclays W53
BP W75
British Airways W78
British American Tobacco W79
BT W81
BUPA W83
Diageo W125
Ernst & Young Global W146
GlaxoSmithKline W171
HSBC W191
J Sainsbury W208
John Lewis W213
Johnson Matthey W214
Kingfisher W220
Legal & General Group W236
Lloyds Banking Group W240
Marks & Spencer W249
National Grid W270
Old Mutual W297
PricewaterhouseCoopers W314
Prudential plc W316
Rolls-Royce W334
Royal Mail W340
SABMiller W343
Unilever W426
Virgin Group W433

Manchester
Co-operative Group W99

Newbury
Vodafone W436

Newcastle
Northern Rock (Asset Management)
  W288

Perth
Scottish and Southern Energy W358

Reading
BG Group W63

Slough
Reckitt Benckiser W323

Theale
Wolseley W443

Windsor
Centrica W92

UNITED STATES

ALABAMA

Birmingham
EBSCO A317
Protective Life A715
Regions Financial A738
Vulcan Materials A922
Drummond Company P191
Alabama Power P20
EBSCO P195
McWane P390
Protective Life and Annuity
  Insurance P487
O'Neal Steel P450
University of Alabama at
  Birmingham P627

Madison
Intergraph P315

ALASKA

Anchorage
Arctic Slope Regional
  Corporation P42

ARIZONA

Chandler
Amkor A61
Bashas' P66
Microchip Technology E243

Phoenix
Apollo Group A73
Avnet A93
Freeport-McMoRan A370
PetSmart A691
Pinnacle West A696
Republic Services A742
Swift Transportation A827
Banner Health P62
SkyMall P550
Shamrock Foods P537
Cavco E62
Grand Canyon Education E161

Scottsdale
Discount Tire P182
Fender Musical Instruments P215
Kyocera Solar P354
Hunt Construction P303
Kahala P337
Services Group of America P537
The Dial Corporation P592
JDA Software E204

Tempe
Insight Enterprises A462
US Airways A906
MicroAge P409
SRP P561
Amtech Systems E29
Limelight E220

Tucson
ASARCO P45

ARKANSAS

Bentonville
Wal-Mart A928

Fort Smith
Golden Horizons A395
Golden Horizons P251

Little Rock
Dillard's A284
Windstream A954

Lowell
J.B. Hunt A479

Siloam Springs
Allens P22

Springdale
Tyson Foods A876

CALIFORNIA

Anaheim
EACO E113
DDi Corp. E95

Arcadia
Vons P650

Bakersfield
Aera Energy P16
Mission Bancorp E245

Beverly Hills
Live Nation Entertainment A538
LFP P363
Platinum Equity P483
Amexdrug E28
RealD E297

Brea
Beckman Coulter A115

Brisbane
InterMune E195

Burbank
Disney A290
Aramark Uniform and Career
  Apparel P41
Warner Bros. P657

Calabasas
DTS E110
Ixia E202

Camarillo
Power-One E284
Semtech E315

Carlsbad
Jenny Craig P328
HomeFed E177
MaxLinear E234
Onsite Energy E270
Alphatec Spine E17

Carson
U.S. Auto Parts E361

Chatsworth
Capstone Turbine E60

Chino Hills
Jacuzzi Brands P325

Commerce
Unified Grocers A881
Smart & Final P550
Unified Grocers P620
Joe's Jeans E208

Compton
Ralphs Grocery P496

Concord
Cerus E66

Culver City
Sony Pictures Entertainment P555

Cupertino
Apple Inc. A74

Cypress
Vans P645

Dublin
Taleo E344

El Segundo
DIRECTV A286
Mattel A568
International Rectifier E196

Emeryville
Pixar P482
Onyx Pharmaceuticals E270
Amyris E30

Foothill Ranch
Oakley P451

Foster City
Gilead Sciences A394
Visa Inc A917
Visa U.S.A. P647
QuinStreet E292
SciClone E313

Fountain Valley
Kingston Technology A505
Hyundai Motor America P306
CAM Commerce Solutions P107
Kingston Technology P342

Fremont
Lam Research A518
Ikanos E184

Lincolnshire
Quill Corporation P493

Lisle
Molex A601
SunCoke Energy E336
SXC E339

Lombard
Veolia Environmental Services North
America P646

Mettawa
HSBC Finance P302

Moline
Deere A272

Mt. Sterling
Dot Foods P184

Mundelein
Medline Industries P394

Naperville
Nalco A613
Nicor A638
OfficeMax A660
Eby-Brown P196

Northbrook
Allstate A43
Euromarket Designs P206
Kapstone Paper and Packaging E210

Northfield
Kraft Foods A512

Oak Brook
Ace Hardware A9
McDonald's A575
Dominick's P183
Ace Hardware P12
Advocate Health Care P15

Oakbrook Terrace
WidePoint E381

Oswego
Allied First Bancorp E15

Park Ridge
Koch Foods P346

Peoria
Caterpillar A181
OSF Healthcare System P456

River Grove
Follett A362
Follett P225

Riverwoods
CCH Incorporated P126

Rosemont
U.S. Foodservice A879
Reyes Holdings P509
U.S. Foodservice P617

Schaumburg
Motorola Solutions A607
USRobotics P642
Zurich American P680
Sagent Pharmaceuticals E310

Skokie
Topco Associates LLC A867
Peapod, LLC P469
Topco Associates LLC P602

Urbana
Flex-N-Gate P220
University of Illinois P630

Vernon Hills
CDW A189
CDW P126

Warrenville
Navistar International A617
Navistar P425

Westchester
Insurance Auto Auctions P314

Westmont
SIRVA P546

Wheaton
Wheaton Franciscan Services P666

INDIANA

Bloomington
Indiana University P311
Cook Group P151

Carmel
CNO Financial A219
ITT Educational E202

Clarksville
First Savings Financial E146

Columbus
Cummins A259

East Chicago
ArcelorMittal USA P42

Evansville
Berry Plastics P77
First Bancorp of Indiana E143

Fort Wayne
Do it Best P182
Vera Bradley E374

Indianapolis
Brightpoint A143
Eli Lilly A324
Simon Property Group A789
WellPoint A939
Consona CRM P150
ProLiance Energy P487
Duke Realty E111
Baldwin & Lyons E44
hhgregg E172

Lafayette
Lafayette Community Bancorp E217

Merrillville
NiSource A641

Mishawaka
Quality Dining P491

Shelbyville
Blue River Bancshares E49

Warsaw
Biomet A128
Biomet P79

IOWA

Algona
Universal Manufacturing E368

Ankeny
Casey's General Stores A179

Des Moines
MidAmerican Energy A597
Principal Financial A709
Iowa Health System P319

Forest City
Winnebago E383

Johnston
Pioneer Hi-Bred P481

Pella
Pella P469

Storm Lake
Meta Financial Group E243

West Des Moines
Hy-Vee P305
Kum & Go P353
American Equity Investment Life
Holding Company E25
FBL Financial E140

KANSAS

Hutchinson
Collins Industries P145

Kansas City
Associated Wholesale Grocers A85
Associated Wholesale Grocers P51

Olathe
NIC E262
Torotel E353
Butler National E56

Overland Park
Ferrellgas Partners A350
Sprint Nextel A806
YRC Worldwide A964
Black & Veatch P81

Shawnee Mission
Seaboard A778

Topeka
Payless ShoeSource P468

Wichita
Koch Industries, Inc. A508
Cessna P131
Hawker Beechcraft P279
Koch Industries, Inc. P348

KENTUCKY

Bowling Green
Houchens P297
Fruit of the Loom P235
Russell Brands P516

Covington
Ashland Inc. A84
Omnicare A662

Highland Heights
General Cable A379

Lexington
Lexmark A531

Louisville
Brown-Forman A152
Humana A452
Kindred Healthcare A503
YUM! A965
AAF-McQUAY P6
Long John Silver's P368
Steel Technologies P569
Res-Care P507
Industrial Services of America E189
Almost Family E16

LOUISIANA

Baton Rouge
Shaw Group A783
Blue Cross and Blue Shield of
Louisiana P85
Turner Industries P613

Lafayette
IBERIABANK E179
LHC Group E218

Metairie
OrthoSynetics P456

Monroe
CenturyLink A191

Morgan City
Conrad Industries E83

New Orleans
Entergy A332

MAINE

Scarborough
Hannaford Bros. A415
Hannaford Bros. P275

MARYLAND

Adelphi
University of Maryland P630

Annapolis
TeleCommunication Systems E347

Baltimore
Constellation Energy Group A243
Legg Mason A523
T. Rowe Price A831
Johns Hopkins P332
University of Maryland Medical
System P631
Whiting-Turner P668
Under Armour E364

Bethesda
Host Hotels & Resorts A449
Lockheed Martin A541
Marriott A558
Clark Enterprises P141
NIH P444
American Bank Holdings E22
Walker & Dunlop E378
American Capital Agency Corp. E24
Eagle Bancorp (MD) E113

Chevy Chase
Howard Hughes Medical
Institute P299

Columbia
W. R. Grace A923
MedStar Health P395
Osiris Therapeutics E273
Sourcefire E327

Gaithersburg
MedImmune P394
Sodexo USA P552
BroadSoft E53

Hagerstown
JLG Industries P329

Hanover
Allegis Group P22
TEKsystems P582
Conmed Healthcare E82
KEYW E211

Landover
Giant Food P247

Marriottsville
Bon Secours Health P91

Owings Mills
Medifast E238

Memphis
AutoZone A88
FedEx A350
International Paper A470
ServiceMaster A783
American Residential Services P32
FedEx Express P212
FedEx Freight P212
Medtronic Sofamor Danek P396
Dunavant Enterprises P192
MLGW P411
Morgan Keegan P413
ServiceMaster P536
ThyssenKrupp Elevator
  Americas P597
GTx E167

Nashville
HCA A424
Ardent Health P43
Gibson Guitar P248
Baldwin Piano P61
Ingram Industries P313
Cat Financial P115
Thomas Nelson P596
Vanderbilt University Medical
  Center P645
Sitel Worldwide P547
Vanderbilt University P644

Tullahoma
Jacobs Technology P324

TEXAS

Addison
Mary Kay A562
Mary Kay P383
Dresser, Inc. P188

Angleton
Benchmark Electronics A122

Austin
Freescale Semiconductor A371
Temple-Inland A837
Texas Lottery A845
University of Texas System A899
Whole Foods A950
Freescale Semiconductor P232
Schlotzsky's P525
University of Texas System P636
HomeAway E176
American Campus Communities E23
MV Oil Trust E250
NetSpend E258
SolarWinds E324
Active Power E9
Cirrus Logic E69
EZCORP E138
National Western E252
Valence Technology E369

Bedford
Warrantech P659

Carrollton
McLane Foodservice A579
BeautiControl P71
McLane Foodservice P390
RealPage E298

College Station
Texas A&M P586

Dallas
Affiliated Computer Services A21
Army and Air Force Exchange A79
AT&T A86
Brinker A146
Comerica A229
Dean Foods A270
Energy Future A330

HollyFrontier A443
Neiman Marcus A622
Southwest Airlines A800
Tenet Healthcare A838
Texas Instruments A844
Turner Corporation A873
7-Eleven P4
Chase Paymentech Solutions P134
Energy Future P203
Glazer's Wholesale Drug P250
Austin Industries P53
Dal-Tile P171
HM Capital Partners P292
Hunt Consolidated P303
Army and Air Force Exchange P44
FedEx Office P213
Haggar P272
Interstate Batteries P317
Turner Corporation P613
Neiman Marcus P431
Sammons Enterprises P520
Trammell Crow Company P605
National Dairy Holdings P421
Primoris E286
Archipelago Learning E34
Cambium Learning Group E58
Diodes E107
Holly Energy Partners E175
Wilhelmina International E382

Fort Worth
AMR Corp. A63
Burlington Northern Santa Fe A157
D.R. Horton A262
RadioShack A729
Ben E. Keith P75
Justin Brands P336
TPG P604

Garland
Electric & Gas Technology E120

Grapevine
GameStop A374

Houston
Apache A72
Baker Hughes A98
Calpine A167
CenterPoint Energy A190
ConocoPhillips A238
Cooper Industries A244
Diamond Offshore A282
Dynegy A307
El Paso Corporation A321
Enron A331
Enterprise Products A333
EOG A335
GenOnEnergy A386
Halliburton A413
Marathon Oil A556
McDermott A573
Motiva Enterprises A606
Plains All American Pipeline A699
Schlumberger A773
Shell Oil A785
Southern Union A798
Sysco A830
Union Carbide A882
Waste Management A936
CEMEX Inc. P128
Goodman Manufacturing P254
Grocers Supply P261
American Air Liquide P28
American General P30
Enron P204
GDF SUEZ Energy North
  America P239
Gulf States Toyota P267
King Ranch P341
Memorial Hermann Healthcare P398
Goodman Global P253
Landmark Graphics P357

M. D. Anderson Cancer Center P372
Petrobras America P479
Republic National Distributing
  Company P507
Randall's P497
Shell Oil P541
Tauber Oil P579
United Space Alliance P623
Wyman-Gordon P673
Motiva Enterprises P414
Philip Services P479
American Spectrum Realty E26
Boardwalk Pipeline E50
C&J Energy Services E57
Cheniere Energy Partners E68
Crestwood Midstream Partners
  LP E91
Exterran Partners E138
KMG Chemicals E213
PAA Natural Gas Storage E275
Spectra Energy Partners E329
Synthesis Energy Systems E344
Cheniere Energy E67
El Paso Pipeline Partners E120
Houston American Energy E177
INX Inc. E199
LaPolla Industries E217
Magnum Hunter Resources E228
Niska E262
Oasis Petroleum E265
BPZ Resources E51
First Investors Financial
  Services E144
Francesca's Holdings E150
Main Street Capital E228
Nevada Gold & Casinos E260
Oiltanking Partners E268
TPC Group E355

Hurst
Bell Helicopter P74

Irving
Commercial Metals A230
Exxon Mobil A343
Fluor A359
Hostess Brands A450
Kimberly-Clark A502
Pioneer Natural Resources A696
ACE Cash Express P11
Aegis Communications P16
CHRISTUS Health P137
Lehigh Hanson P360
Michaels Stores P407
Hostess Brands P296
NEC of America P430
DG FastChannel E104

Katy
Academy Sports P10

McKinney
Blockbuster A130
Torchmark A868

Midland
AMEN Properties E21
Concho E82

Plano
J. C. Penney A478
Rent-A-Center A741
Frito-Lay P234
HP Enterprise Services P300
Lone Star Steakhouse P368
Denbury Resources E99

Richardson
Lennox A528
MetroPCS A591

Round Rock
Dell A275

San Antonio
H-E-B A412
Tesoro A842
USAA A908
Valero Energy A912
Clear Channel P143
CPS Energy P160
H-E-B P270
Kinetic Concepts P340
Taco Cabana P579
USAA P641
Whataburger P666
Zachry Inc. P679
Rackspace E293
US Global Investors E368

Southlake
Sabre Holdings A760
Sabre Holdings P518

Sugar Land
Imperial Sugar E186

Temple
McLane P389

Texarkana
Truman Arnold P610

The Woodlands
Anadarko Petroleum A65
Chevron Phillips Chemical P135
Western Gas Partners E381
Trico Marine E357

Tyler
Brookshire Grocery P98

Waco
Curves International P165
FirstCity Financial E148
Life Partners Holdings E219

UTAH

Midvale
Ally Bank P25

Ogden
Autoliv ASP, Inc. P55

Park City
Park City Group E278
Skullcandy E324

Provo
Ancestry.com E31

Salt Lake City
Zions Bancorporation A966
Huntsman International P304
Intermountain Health Care P316
Associated Food P49
Smith's Food & Drug P551
Sinclair Oil P545
Fusion-io E152
Pacific WebWorks E276
FX Energy E152
ZAGG E385

St. George
SkyWest A790

VERMONT

Burlington
Burton P102

Montpelier
National Life Insurance P422

Waterbury
Green Mountain Coffee E163

Index of Executives

A

Aab, Richard T. P462
Aach, Joel A267
Aadland, Todd P210
Aagaard, Hans Christian W2
Aagaard, Ken P123
Aaholm, Sherry A. A349
Aakio, Seppo W217
Aakre, D. Scott A447
Aamir, Mir A761
Aanestad, Ola M. W378
Aardsma, David A. A935
Aarhaug Gundersen, Lill
    Christin W378
Aaron, Barth F. E151
Aaron, Henry L. P52
Aaron, Mark L. A860
Aaron, Roger S. P548
Aaron, Sammy E153
Aaronson, Daniel R. P210
Aaronson, Michael J. E138
Aasen, Cambra P532
Aasen, Thomas H. E5
Aasheim, Hilde M. W287
Abadie, Laurent W300
Abadir, Jeffrey A249
Abalakin, Sergey W25
Abano, Salvatore V. E354
Abate, Christopher J. E300
Abate, Peter (E. & J. Gallo) A309
Abate, Peter (E. & J. Gallo) A309
Abbasi, Osama W107
Abbasi, Sohaib E190
Abbass, Mike A602
Abbate, Mark L. E241
Abberger, Robert P604
Abbey, Richard E. A829
Abbey, Stephen L. E288
Abbott, Bradley S. A662
Abbott, Frederick C. A887
Abbott, James R. A966
Abbott, Jeff P312
Abbott, John W339
Abbott, Mark A734
Abbott, Michael A824
Abbott, Mike P102
Abbott, Tom P520
Abbrecht, Todd M. P595
Abbruzzese, James P372
Abdalla, Zein A684
Abdelmessih, Vivian W392
Abdelnour, Gaby A. A494
Abdessamad, Hicham P291
Abdi, Behrooz E258
Abdoo, Elizabeth A. A449
Abdul-Latif, Saad A684
Abdulla Al Qubaisi, Khadem W298
Abdullah, Daud Vicary (Deloitte) A276
Abdullah, Daud Vicary (Deloitte) A276
Abdun-Nabi, Daniel J. E124
Abe, Daisaku W266
Abe, Hideo P140
Abe, Hironobu W260
Abe, Ken W265

Abe, Yasushi W273
Abe, Yasuyuki W381
Abe, Yutaka W162
Abel, Bob P495
Abel, Gregory E. (Berkshire
    Hathaway) A123
Abel, Gregory E. (MidAmerican
    Energy) A597
Abel, Gregory E. (PacifiCorp) A676
Abel, James E. A704
Abel, Steven R. E49
Abel, Virginia K. A668
Abelenda, Gustavo H. A512
Abeles, Jon C. P120
Abella, Roland W125
Abello, Vincent W87
Abels, Stephen J. (Mutual of
    Omaha) A609
Abels, Stephen J. (Mutual of
    Omaha) A609
Abenante, Frank W32
Abendschein, Robert D. A65
Abercrombie, George B. W331
Aberle, Derek K. A724
Aberman, Michael E301
Abernathy, Kathleen Q. A372
Abernathy, Robert E. A502
Abernethy, David S. P200
Abess, Leonard P632
Abeyta, David (W.L. Gore) A924
Abeyta, David (W.L. Gore) A924
Abi-Karam, Leslie R. A697
Abinder, Susan P307
Abington, Bill P394
Abiteboul, Jean E67
Abji, Minaz B. A449
Able, Michael W268
Ables, Buddy (Pro-Build) A710
Ables, Buddy (Pro-Build) A710
Abney, David P. A902
Abney, Jeff (Cox
    Communications) A251
Abney, Jeff (Cox
    Communications) A251
Aboud, Mark (SAP America) P521
Aboud, Mark (SAP) W354
Abraham, Chad R. E280
Abraham, Cori P428
Abraham, Deborah A932
Abraham, Jay P420
Abraham, Jeff (Random House) A733
Abraham, Jeff (Random House) A733
Abraham, Joseph W44
Abraham, Karen P634
Abraham, Linda Bolan E80
Abraham, Magid M. E80
Abraham, Thomas R. A301
Abraham, Todd (Endologix) E126
Abraham, Todd (Kraft Foods) A512
Abrahams, Kees P554
Abrahamson, James A. E156
Abrahamson, Ted (S.C. Johnson) A759
Abrahamson, Ted (S.C. Johnson) A759
Abrahamsson, Jonas W130
Abramowicz, Daniel A. A256
Abramowitsch, Peter E237

Abrams, David L. P81
Abrams, Denis S. P76
Abrams, Edward B. E222
Abrams, Jim P394
Abrams, Karen A163
Abrams, Robert P548
Abrams, S. Thomas P521
Abramson, David (Hallmark) A414
Abramson, David (Hallmark) A414
Abramson, Jenny A934
Abramson, Joel A18
Abramson, Nancy P186
Abramson, Rick P173
Abramson, Sara J. P399
Abramson, Steven V. E368
Abravanel, Isaac W403
Abreu, Claudio F. P70
Abril Abadín, Antonio W199
Abril Pérez, Luis W395
Abrol, Abhishek A283
Abrutyn, David P309
Abruzzese, Joseph A287
Abruzzi, Michael (Burlington Coat
    Factory) A156
Abruzzi, Michael (Burlington Coat
    Factory) A156
Abshire, Scott E67
Abston, Larry J. A65
Abts, Douglas C. E52
Abu-Ali, Amjad A379
Abu-Hadba, Walid A595
Abu-Hakima, Ihab E242
Abud, Joao A283
Abughazaleh, Cizar Nazee P318
Abunaser, Bashar P306
Abusamra, Gary A278
Acamovic, Bob P210
Accardo, John A152
Acciari, Luciano W155
Accordino, Daniel T. P579
Acevedo, Alejandro A595
Acevedo, Cecilia (MasTec) E230
Acevedo, Cecilia (MasTec) E230
Acevedo, Jorge A. A338
Achaibar, Gowton W145
Achatz, Reinhold W363
Achermann, Hubert W224
Acheson, Eleanor D. (Amtrak) A64
Acheson, Eleanor D. (Amtrak) A64
Acheson Luther, Lisa P84
Achleitner, Paul W25
Ackart, Jennifer C. A734
Acker, Andreas P565
Acker, Jim P125
Acker, Kristin E387
Acker-Blardo, Margaret (Cox
    Communications) A251
Acker-Blardo, Margaret (Cox
    Communications) A251
Ackerman, Carolina P357
Ackerman, Chuck P496
Ackerman, Jay R. E318
Ackerman, Monti P222
Ackerman, Paul R. A940
Ackerman, Steve P523

Ackermann, Josef (Deutsche
    Bank) W119
Ackermann, Josef (Siemens AG) W363
Ackermann, Josef (Zurich Financial
    Services) W452
Ackerson, James C. A186
Ackley, Sheri A900
Acone, Adam (NHL) A637
Acone, Adam (NHL) A637
Acosta, Alan (Stanford University) A810
Acosta, Alan (Stanford University) A810
Acosta, Juan M. A157
Acosta, Maria G. E114
Acquaviva, Riccardo W155
Acree, Allan L. E114
Acree, Bill P52
Acs, Magdolna A340
Acton, Elizabeth S. A228
Acton, John C. P181
Acton, Nicole E108
Acuɑa, Bilda A901
Acworth, Fiona W443
Adachi, Hiroshi W327
Adachi, Michio W116
Adachi, Naoki W409
Adachi, Tamotsu (The Carlyle
    Group) A847
Adachi, Tamotsu (The Carlyle
    Group) A847
Adachi, Toshio W361
Adachi, Yoroku W83
Adade, Mauricio W128
Adair-Potts, Janna A832
Adam, Donald F. A122
Adami, Norman J. W343
Adamitis, Thomas J. (Anheuser-
    Busch) P38
Adamitis, Thomas J. (Anheuser-Busch
    InBev) W32
Adamo, Nicholas A. A210
Adamopoulos, William P226
Adams, Angela S. A489
Adams, Anthony P618
Adams, Barry P391
Adams, Bill P665
Adams, Chris P221
Adams, Clint B. P43
Adams, Craig L. A338
Adams, D. Scott A715
Adams, Deborah G. A238
Adams, Donna M. P532
Adams, Dwayne P96
Adams, Edward A334
Adams, Gerald A391
Adams, Graham W37
Adams, Gregory A. (Kaiser Foundation
    Health Plan) A496
Adams, Gregory A. (Kaiser Foundation
    Health Plan) A496
Adams, Heather D. P596
Adams, J. Milton P636
Adams, Joe A883
Adams, John (Calpine) A167
Adams, John B. (Interpublic
    Group) A471
Adams, John (Marriott) A557

Atkins, Aileen P419
Atkins, C. Richard P85
Atkins, Chris W80
Atkins, Colin (The Carlyle Group) A847
Atkins, Colin (The Carlyle Group) A847
Atkins, Stephen E. P303
Atkinson, Arthur P207
Atkinson, Carolyn (Pro-Build) A710
Atkinson, Carolyn (Pro-Build) A710
Atkinson, Graham W. A930
Atkinson, Matt W401
Atkinson, Michael P. (BJ's Wholesale Club) A121
Atkinson, Michael P. (BJ's Wholesale Club) A129
Atkinson, Mike P222
Atkinson, Preston L. P665
Atkinson, Ray A695
Atkinson, Susan (Stater Bros.) A819
Atkinson, Susan (Stater Bros.) A819
Atkinson, Tracy A817
Atlas, Ilana W442
Aton, Neal R. A940
Atondo, Angel E64
Atorf, Lars A711
Atra, Chandrashekara (Maxim Integrated Products) E233
Atra, Chandrashekara (Maxim Integrated Products) E233
Atsumi, Masanori W385
Attal, Laurent W231
Attaway, John A. (Publix) A719
Attaway, John A. (Publix) A719
Atterbury, Rick R. P401
Attinger, Per-Olof W331
Attridge, Harold W. P675
Attwood, James A. (The Carlyle Group) A847
Attwood, James A. (The Carlyle Group) A847
Attwooll, Jon P130
Atwell, William L. A207
Atwood, Tara P600
Au, Gregory H. P543
Au, Luen E335
Au, Matt E350
Au, Paul W103
Au Yeung, Steve A666
Au, Yun P432
Au-Yeung, Ricky A749
Aubee, Debi P93
Auberger, Luc-Emmanuel W271
Aubin, John F. E273
Aubrejuan, Paco A666
Aubuchon, Myra K. P546
Auclair, Dave P257
Audagna, Guido (The Carlyle Group) A847
Audagna, Guido (The Carlyle Group) A847
Audan, Fabrice W303
Audet, John P. E40
Audette, Matthew J. A308
Audia, Damon J. A400
Audiffred, J. Douglas P386
Audvard, Yves W324
Aue, Walter J. A63
Auer, Thomas H. P91
Auer, Werner W363
Aufranc, Roberta P162
Augaitis, Kathy E336
Augsburger, Blake A419
August-deWilde, Katherine E146
Augustin, Jeffrey G. A489
Augustsson, Tommy R. A380
Aulagnon, Thierry W369
Aulbaugh, Carrol P398
Auld, David A262
Aulds, James (H-E-B) A412
Aulds, James (H-E-B) A412
Aulds, Steven P569
Ault, T. Scott (Mutual of Omaha) A609
Ault, T. Scott (Mutual of Omaha) A609
Auman, Greg F. P416
Auque, François W131

Auray, Robert R. P240
Aurello, Joseph P416
Aurich, Thomas A278
Auriemma, Marco W153
Auris, Jan-Dirk W180
Ausick, Richard M. A151
Ausiello, Dennis A. P465
Ausnit, Peter A322
Ausseil, Georges W100
Austell, Theodore A135
Austen, W. Kim (Nationwide) A615
Austen, W. Kim (Nationwide) A615
Austen, William F. A121
Austenfeld, Steve A216
Austin, Bernard E368
Austin, Charlie E. A254
Austin, Gabrielle A910
Austin, Gail A186
Austin, Jay A814
Austin, Jeff P480
Austin, Jill D. P644
Austin, Karen A. A694
Austin, Mike W99
Austin, Neil D. (KPMG L.L.P.) P349
Austin, Neil D. (KPMG) W224
Austin, Russell P. (Battelle Memorial) A107
Austin, Russell P. (Battelle Memorial) A107
Austin, Ski (NBA) A618
Austin, Ski (NBA) A618
Austin, Terri A576
Austin-King, Nona P452
Austrian, Neil R. A658
Ausura, Maureen K. A543
Autenrieth, Dana P76
Auton, Sylvia P600
Auyeung, Rex A709
Avadhany, Nagesh E251
Avallone, Thomas P482
Avedon, Marcia J. W202
Avenía, Cesare W145
Avera, Stephen R. A357
Averbeck, Richard W112
Averell, Donna M. E130
Averett, Kirk E293
Averill, Howard (Time Warner) A862
Averill, Howard (Time Inc.) P600
Averitt, Richard G. A734
Averre, Adrian W69
Avery, David A954
Avery, James (Golden Horizons) A395
Avery, James (Golden Horizons) A395
Avery, John A391
Avery, Keith P. E138
Avery, Reginald S. P630
Avey, Dustin E280
Avidan, Amos (Bechtel) A114
Avidan, Amos (Bechtel) A114
Avila, Joaquín (The Carlyle Group) A847
Avila, Joaquín (The Carlyle Group) A847
Avila, José A. W106
Avila, Mari E302
Avila, Omar W320
Aviles, Alan D. (New York City Health and Hospitals) A624
Aviles, Alan D. (New York City Health and Hospitals) A624
Aviles, Marisol E47
Avise, William A. A524
Avner, Kenneth S. (HCSC) A426
Avner, Kenneth S. (HCSC) A426
Avril, Matthew E. A815
Avrin, William N. A261
Awad, Azmy A47
Awad, George A213
Axelrod, Elizabeth L. A316
Axmacher, Thomas P148
Axmann, Michael W363
Axson, Harry B. A648
Ayala, Alfredo I. E335
Ayala, Carlos (Perdue Incorporated) A686

Ayala, Carlos (Perdue Incorporated) A686
Ayala, Daniel L. A940
Ayala, Orlando A595
Ayat, Simon A772
Aycock, Coleman E111
Aydemir, Mevlüt W342
Ayer, William S. (Alaska Air) A33
Ayer, William S. (Puget Energy) P490
Ayerbe, Guillermo A340
Ayers, Chris L. A35
Ayers, Doug P293
Ayers, Kevin D. P165
Ayers, Mark H. P17
Ayers, Rick L. P532
Ayling, Bruce P276
Aylor, James H. P636
Aylward, George P675
Aymerich, Philippe W369
Ayotte, Robert J. A845
Ayre, David J. A640
Ayres, David A. A186
Ayuso García, Joaquín W152
Ayuso, Jill P563
Ayyoubi, Silvia W331
Azagra Blázquez, Pedro W194
Azar, Alex M. A324
Azar, Tony P242
Azarloza, Armando A471
Azbell, Michael T. A502
Azel, Jose P632
Azema, David W368
Azersky, Mike E248
Azevedo, John M. P105
Aziz, Gamal A592
Azmon, Dan A516
Azmy, Nahla A. A650
Azuhata, Shigeru W184
Azuma, Kazunori W327
Azuma, Takeshi W295
Azumi, Tooru W293
Azzam, Henry W119
Azzara, C. Daniel A434
Azzari, Gerard J. A366

B

Baars, Molly P642
Baba, Fawaz R. W53
Baba, Kengo W205
Baba, Marietta L. P408
Babani, Susie W44
Babb, Ralph W. A228
Babbs, Gareth W186
Babby, Kenneth R. A934
Babcock, Ernest J. A380
Babcock, Gordon E77
Babcoke, George F. A890
Babe, Gregory S. (Bayer Corp.) P70
Babe, Gregory S. (Bayer AG) W57
Babeau, Emmauel W357
Babiceanu, Geanina W233
Babin, Jean-Christophe W245
Babins, Sandi A. A249
Babitsch, George P200
Babson-Smith, Stacey A841
Babu, Amar W237
Babu, Suresh R. (Synta Pharmaceuticals) E343
Babu, Suresh (Great Lakes Cheese) P259
Babyak, Barry P53
Baca, Joe P336
Baca, Vicki E16
Bacardit, Ramón W180
Bacchetta, Paolo W142
Bach, Chuck (TVA) A874
Bach, Chuck (TVA) A874
Bach, Paul D. P244
Bach, Richard C. (Turner Corporation) A873
Bach, Richard C. (Turner Corporation) A873
Bacharach, Hal P416

Bachelor, Alex (Dairy Farmers of America) A263
Bachelor, Alex (Dairy Farmers of America) A263
Bacher, Lars C. W378
Bacher, Lawrence C. P249
Bachman, Merle S. P282
Bachmann, Jay W234
Bachmann, Lisa M. A126
Bachmann, Richard A. (Trico Marine) E357
Bachmann, Richard H. (Enterprise Products) A333
Bachmeyer, Kurt P325
Bachrach, Christine A. P443
Bachus, Daniel E. E162
Baciarelli, Renato V. (Catholic Healthcare West) A185
Baciarelli, Renato V. (Catholic Healthcare West) A185
Bacica, Brian P428
Bacidore, Becky A638
Backer, Shaju A587
Backes, Roland P70
Backes, Theresa E150
Backhurst, Jane P671
Backman, Cathy L. W392
Backus, Glenn (Topco Associates LLC) A867
Backus, Glenn (Topco Associates LLC) A867
Bacon, A. Raymond P210
Bacon, Andrew W80
Bacon, Bruce W. P300
Bacon, Caryn P474
Bacon, Christopher (E. & J. Gallo) A309
Bacon, Christopher (E. & J. Gallo) A309
Bacon, Craig A876
Bacon, Darryl F. A179
Bacon, Ken P129
Bacon, Kenneth J. (Fannie Mae) A345
Bacon, Paul P166
Bacus, Lisa R. (American Family Insurance) A54
Bacus, Lisa R. (American Family Insurance) A54
Badagliacca, Mark P463
Badalian, Joseph A838
Badame, Jay (Tishman Construction) A865
Badame, Jay (Tishman Construction) A865
Badani, Bipin P236
Bade, Brian M. A126
Baden, Colin P451
Baden, Erik P30
Bader, Jeffrey D. P8
Bader, Troy P170
Bader-Michel, Natalie W245
Badger, Terry E368
Badrinarayan, Madapusi K. A247
Badrinath, Vivek W157
Badylak, Theresa P520
Baehman, Schuyler (NHL) A637
Baehman, Schuyler (NHL) A637
Baehren, James W. A673
Baek, Hwang W349
Baekgaard, Barbara Bradl E374
Baer, Amy A188
Baer, Brian A761
Baer, Dave (Wakefern Food) A927
Baer, Dave (Wakefern Food) A927
Baer, Timothy R. A832
Baer, Ulrich P449
Baer, Werner A703
Baerg, Bill A321
Baessler, Mike P32
Baez, Ramon F. A502
Bagai, Pavan E137
Bagalay, John E. E380
Bagan, Brian A312
Bagan, Dan P473
Bagan, John P267

Balthazor, Steven R. E156
Baltz, Jeffrey D. P39
Balut, Brian P. E360
Balz, Manfred W122
Balzar, Robert M. (TVA) A874
Balzar, Robert M. (TVA) A874
Bamba, Ryoichi W83
Bambawale, Ajai W392
Bamberger, Thomas W354
Bamert, Peter W258
Bamrick, Michael A482
Banas, Mike A641
Banatao, Diosdado P. (Ikanos) E184
Banatao, Diosdado P. (Inphi) E191
Banati, Amit A512
Banbury, Lee P170
Bancarz, Gloria P13
Bancroft, Charles A. A147
Bandas, Mark P644
Bandel, Bob (Mars, Incorporated) A559
Bandel, Bob (Mars, Incorporated) A559
Bandera, Alberto (Dairy Farmers of America) A263
Bandera, Alberto (Dairy Farmers of America) A263
Bandler, Ronald S. A11
Bandlow, Joseph L. A293
Bandyopadhyay, Kalyan A498
Banek, Amy L. A416
Banerjee, Anup R. A794
Banerjee, Gautam W314
Banerjee, Prith A438
Banerjee, Saurav W266
Banerjee, Sumit W186
Banfi, Carlo W133
Banfield, Colin W284
Banfield, John E352
Bang, Lars W285
Banga, Ajaypal S. A567
Bangert, Richard E. A674
Bangs, Nelson A. (Neiman Marcus) A622
Bangs, Nelson A. (Neiman Marcus) A622
Banholzer, William F. A299
Banikarim, Maryam A375
Banister, Gaurdie E. P16
Banke, Barbara R. P324
Banker, Beth P524
Banks, Andy P663
Banks, Carol A. P294
Banks, David D. (CarMax) A176
Banks, David (Cumberland Farms) P164
Banks, Edward E134
Banks, Erica (USAA) A908
Banks, Erica (USAA) A908
Banks, Hunter P394
Banks, Lee C. A678
Banks, Maureen P465
Banks, Michelle A851
Banks, Richard L. W288
Banks, Tony C. A355
Bannell, Scott A811
Banner, Roderick W445
Bannigan, Gabriel W51
Bannister, Michael E. A365
Banovich, Mark M. P358
Banowetz, Don A372
Bansal, Arun W145
Bansch, J.L. A328
Banse, Amy L. A227
Bansil, Lee A711
Banskota, Arun A650
Banta, John E. P629
Bantle, Gayanne A391
Bantom, Michael A. (NBA) A618
Bantom, Michael A. (NBA) A618
Bantz, Charles R. P311
Banu, John E. A580
Baptista Filho, Benjamin M. W34
Bar-Cohen, Barak E212
Barahona, Pablo (Liberty Mutual) A534
Barahona, Pablo (Liberty Mutual) A534
Barahona, Pedro W60

Baraibar, Gonzalo Gomez W9
Barak, Deborah P123
Barakat, Richard R. P399
Baran, David S. P171
Baran, Richard L. P123
Baranda, Pedro P459
Baranes Cohen, Florence W87
Baranov, Andrey W165
Barash, Igor E93
Baratelli, Yves A677
Barba, Glenn P. A217
Barbagello, John A. A714
Barbalas, Michael A398
Barbari, Patricia L. (New York Life) A625
Barbari, Patricia L. (New York Life) A625
Barbarite, Joseph E277
Barbaro, Donna A. P439
Barbaroux, Olivier W431
Barbasch, Annette P416
Barbassa, Almir G. W304
Barbeau, Anthony A312
Barbee, Anthony W. A720
Barbee, Sheila S. E327
Barber, Dennis A386
Barber, Douglas E. A254
Barber, Gary P405
Barber, Michael J. A376
Barber, Mike (Perdue Incorporated) A686
Barber, Mike (Perdue Incorporated) A686
Barber, Ralph G. W190
Barber, Roger L. P529
Barber, Stephen E. (Pension Benefit Guaranty) A682
Barber, Stephen E. (Pension Benefit Guaranty) A682
Barber, Timothy C. A340
Barber, Tina P45
Barbercheck, Richard S. E143
Barberis, L. W142
Barbi, Glenn A117
Barbier, Brian E83
Barbier, Denis W324
Barbier, Francois W156
Barbier, Gonzalo Chico A754
Barbier, Peter W85
Barbieri, Pierlaurent W11
Barbieri, Scott P102
Barbir, Karim P238
Barbizet, Patricia W313
Barbon, Gonzalo W119
Barbon, Renato A267
Barbosa, Fabio de Ol W63
Barbosa, Flavio (Springs Global US) A805
Barbosa, Flavio (Springs Global US) A805
Barbosa, Gustavo P478
Barbosa, Otavio P663
Barbour, Bob W54
Barbour, Sondra A541
Barbour, Steve P189
Barboza, Ana Paula A5
Barbu, Anca W426
Barbusca, Juergen (Cox Communications) A251
Barbusca, Juergen (Cox Communications) A251
Barbuto, Jeff A. E193
Barbé, Pierre W411
Barceló, Nancy P633
Barclay, Bronwen W296
Barclay, Kathleen S. A514
Barcome-King, Dena A577
Bard, James V. A890
Bardgett, Edward R. P679
Bardin, Michael P530
Bardis, John A. E236
Bardon, Ursula W70
Bardos, Jeff A211
Bardos, Kevin E226
Bardsen, Mads E357

Bare, R. Kirk A940
Bareket, Ran E215
Bareksten, Jim A203
Baresich, Michael A211
Baret, Mark A749
Barge, Alan W40
Barge, Robert H. A43
Barger, Jack P545
Bargerhuff, Rita P4
Barhydt, Kevin E306
Baril, Noel R. P286
Baril, Thierry W17
Barin, Ronald E. A35
Bario, Holly P188
Barish, Robert J. A914
Barkauskas, Steven E50
Barkell, Susan L. (Blue Cross Blue Shield of Michigan) A133
Barkell, Susan L. (Blue Cross Blue Shield of Michigan) A133
Barker, Andy P650
Barker, Brandon P336
Barker, Calvin E. A111
Barker, David A293
Barker, Donna A344
Barker, Geoffrey T. E306
Barker, Gordon D. A888
Barker, Greg P20
Barker, Heidi A574
Barker, Jason P563
Barker, Jay A228
Barker, John R. (ONEOK) A664
Barker, John D. (Wendy's) A943
Barker, John D. (Wendy's International, Inc.) P662
Barker, Julie A627
Barker, Kenneth A. A322
Barker, Michael P554
Barker, Paul (Hallmark) A414
Barker, Paul (Hallmark) A414
Barker, Peter A494
Barker, Randolph H. P140
Barker, Robert P. A678
Barker, Shawn M. A99
Barker, Steve P547
Barker, Steven (Guilford Mills) P266
Barker, Thomas B. A945
Barker, Timothy J. E298
Barkin, Alan P190
Barkley, Barb A278
Barkley, Howard W321
Barkley, James M. A789
Barkley, Michael T. A674
Barkmann, Steve E3
Barkov, Anatoly A. W243
Barlik, Len (Cox Communications) A251
Barlik, Len (Cox Enterprises) A252
Barlik, Len (Cox Communications) A251
Barlik, Len (Cox Enterprises) A252
Barlow, Brett E324
Barlow, Charles P545
Barlow, Colin P624
Barlow, Cynthia E336
Barlow, Gary T. A32
Barlow, James F. A39
Barlow, Jon P660
Barlow, Simon (Carlson Companies) A175
Barlow, Simon (Carlson Companies) A175
Barman, Christine L. (Chrysler) A201
Barman, Christine L. (Chrysler) A201
Barna, Jeff A339
Barna, Peter P180
Barnabé, Pierre W21
Barnard, Janet H. (Cox Communications) A251
Barnard, Janet H. (Cox Communications) A251
Barnard, Mark P294
Barnard, Randall L. A952
Barnard, Ray F. A359
Barnden, Marsha P13

Barner, Andreas W70
Barner, Coleman C. E96
Barner, Mark D. (Ascension Health) A82
Barner, Mark D. (Ascension Health) A82
Barner, Ray A842
Barnes, Casilda E277
Barnes, Chuck P219
Barnes, David R. (American Express) A53
Barnes, David A. (UPS) A902
Barnes, Eric J. P502
Barnes, George P. P488
Barnes, Gerald P. (DDi Corp.) E96
Barnes, Gerald A. (Neiman Marcus) A622
Barnes, Gerald A. (Neiman Marcus) A622
Barnes, Greg P545
Barnes, Lee R. A648
Barnes, Louis E. E273
Barnes, Lynn M. A50
Barnes, Mark (Volkswagen Group of America) P649
Barnes, Mark (Volkswagen) W438
Barnes, Michael P173
Barnes, Nancy P565
Barnes, Peter (Emory University) P201
Barnes, Peter (BT) W80
Barnes, Peter L. (Metcash) W254
Barnes, Rayford L. A111
Barnes, Samuel G. A351
Barnes, Thomas C. A829
Barnes, Virginia A. P623
Barnes, W. Brian A204
Barnes, William P164
Barnet, Andy P583
Barnetson, Alex E8
Barnett, Barbara P215
Barnett, Catherine A628
Barnett, Charles J. (Ascension Health) A82
Barnett, Charles J. (Ascension Health) A82
Barnett, Hoyt R. (Publix) A719
Barnett, Hoyt R. (Publix) A719
Barnett, Jeffrey L. A319
Barnett, John P. A798
Barnett, Kerry E. P506
Barnett, Maria W37
Barnett, Megan P675
Barnett, Michele P. A377
Barnett, Nancy A366
Barnett, Phillip S. A338
Barnett, Richard K. A646
Barnett, Robert A844
Barnett Sarpalius, Jenny (Catholic Health East) A182
Barnett Sarpalius, Jenny (Catholic Health East) A182
Barnette, K. Gary E168
Barney, Kathleen A410
Barney, Robin T. (Biomet) A127
Barney, Robin T. (Biomet) A127
Barney, Steven M. P562
Barnhardt, J. Brett E66
Barnhardt, Thomas M. E147
Barnhart, Ann M. A427
Barnhart, John P460
Barnhart, Randy P556
Barnhart, Steven D. P61
Barnhill, Mark P483
Barnhill, Matthew P82
Barnholt, Edward W. A506
Barnum, Gregory T. E95
Barnum, Michael P. A500
Barnwell, Martha W. A713
Barollier, Pascal W351
Baron, Barry L. A340
Baron, Martin A628
Baron, Melissa P309
Baron, Sergio P478
Barone, Claudio A71
Barone, Scott E184

Benson, Robert L. A612
Benson, Tim A438
Benstead, Bob P312
Bent, Ritchie W212
Bent, S. David A892
Bentas, Lily Haseo P164
Bente, David P374
Bentegeat, Renaud W432
Benten, R. Anthony A628
Bentitou, Laurent J. E74
Bentler, Martin W363
Bentley, Barry P196
Bentley, David E185
Bentley, Elizabeth M. E365
Bentley, Eric J. P532
Bentley, Fred P281
Bentley, Maria W420
Bentley, Pam (The Carlyle Group) A847
Bentley, Pam (The Carlyle Group) A847
Bentley, Phillip K. W92
Bentley, Rebecca A299
Benton, Cory P207
Benton, John B. E352
Benton, Lauren P449
Benton, Tom E220
Benun, Bary P38
Benusa, Gerry W. (American Family Insurance) A54
Benusa, Gerry W. (American Family Insurance) A54
Benvenuti, Mike E85
Benway, Aaron (The Carlyle Group) A847
Benway, Aaron (The Carlyle Group) A847
Benz, Gary D. A355
Benzecry, Oliver W6
Benítez, Francisco Cresp A221
Beran, David R. A44
Beran, Robin D. A181
Berardesco, Charles A. A243
Berberich, Christine P127
Berchtold, Walter W107
Bercovici, Val A623
Berczi, Peter W333
Berdick, Edward P576
Berding, John B. A56
Berelowitz, Raymond W296
Berencreutz, Mats W387
Berengolts, Michael J. E50
Berens, Gregg P339
Bereswill, Ted A666
Berg, Achim A595
Berg, Carl E. E370
Berg, Charles G. P461
Berg, Corii P554
Berg, Donald C. A152
Berg, Doug P646
Berg, Ian P223
Berg, Jason A. A49
Berg, Jeremy M. P443
Berg, Julie Dexte A825
Berg, Kevin (Bechtel) A114
Berg, Kevin (Bechtel) A114
Berg, Kevin (CBS) P123
Berg, Leanne P537
Berg, Marc E158
Berg, Mark S. A696
Berg, Ronald C. A892
Bergant, Paul R. A479
Bergareche Busquet, Santiago (CEPSA) W93
Bergareche Busquet, Santiago (Ferrovial) W152
Bergdoll, Andrew J. A944
Bergdoll, Susan E111
Berge, Elizabeth A. (General Re) A385
Berge, Elizabeth A. (General Re) A385
Bergen, John D. A35
Bergen, Paul (Harvard University) A421
Bergen, Paul (Harvard University) A421
Bergenhem, Nils E87
Berger, Brian D. E380
Berger, Cindi A471
Berger, Darryl D. P644

Berger, David B. E317
Berger, Dennis G. (CDW) A189
Berger, Dennis G. (CDW) A189
Berger, Elliott P116
Berger, Eric P554
Berger, Geneviève B. W426
Berger, Harvey J. E36
Berger, JC E257
Berger, John S. A842
Berger, Kenneth A855
Berger, Larry L. A318
Berger, Laurence J. P439
Berger, Mark P624
Berger, Marlene P315
Berger, Michael P181
Berger, Nancee R. A945
Berger, Steve (Guardian Life) A407
Berger, Steve (Guardian Life) A407
Berger-Gross, Victoria A860
Bergerand, Christophe W306
Bergeron, Kathy E208
Bergeron, Mario (Amtrak) A64
Bergeron, Mario (Amtrak) A64
Bergeron, Renee A461
Bergeron, Robert A772
Bergeron, Tom A398
Berget, Jørn W63
Bergevin, Paul A464
Bergevin, Pierre P166
Berggren, Anders P380
Berggren, Marie N. (University of California) A897
Berggren, Marie N. (University of California) A897
Bergh, Charles V. (Levi Strauss) A530
Bergh, Charles V. (Levi Strauss) A530
Berghausen, Rainer W90
Bergin, Bill A744
Bergland, Bruce W. P311
Bergman, Christer P236
Bergman, Greg A771
Bergman, Maili A408
Bergman, Rebecca M. A583
Bergman, Rick A48
Bergman, Stanley M. A433
Bergmann, J. David A265
Bergmann, Leon A825
Bergmann, Thomas E. P34
Bergmark, Thomas W195
Bergner, Kevin J. (USAA) A908
Bergner, Kevin J. (USAA) A908
Bergquist, Betty A. (American Family Insurance) A54
Bergquist, Betty A. (American Family Insurance) A54
Bergren, Byron L. A136
Bergren, Scott O. A965
Bergsrud, Mark A887
Bergstein, Joseph P. A704
Bergstrom, Bengt E38
Bergstrom, Craig A. P353
Bergström, Thomas W195
Berguson, Amy A724
Berigan, Karen E. A256
Berisford, John L. A576
Berk, Celia P677
Berk, Jeffrey L. A363
Berkeley, Richard M. E298
Berkemeyer, Thomas G. A17
Berkenhagen, Ulf W43
Berkery, Rosemary T. W420
Berkett, Neil A. A916
Berkley, John E302
Berkley, Rosalind A462
Berkley, William R. P449
Berklich, Pamela M. A499
Berko, Edward M. A715
Berkowitz, Bobbie P261
Berkowitz, Jeffrey A930
Berkowitz, Mortimer E18
Berkowitz, Philip A484
Berkowitz, Ronald M. E320
Berkowski, Larry P65
Berland, Leslie A53
Berlien, Olaf W406

Berlin, John E. A174
Berlin, Scott L. (New York Life) A625
Berlin, Scott L. (New York Life) A625
Berlind, David P618
Berlinsky, Robert J. E112
Berman, Adam P433
Berman, Bernard D. E141
Berman, Beverly A. P595
Berman, Bill A87
Berman, Clifford E. E340
Berman, Don A274
Berman, Ira P. (General Dynamics) A380
Berman, Ira P. (Gulfstream Aerospace) A409
Berman, Ira P. (Gulfstream Aerospace) A409
Berman, Lance E87
Berman, Richard K. A117
Berman, Robert L. A312
Berman, Saul J. A456
Bermingham, Robert P. P679
Bernabe, Mike A135
Bernabé, Franco W394
Bernacchi, Terri P311
Bernaden, John A. A749
Bernanke, Ben S. P209
Bernard, Alain W16
Bernard, Andrea A224
Bernard, Dane P339
Bernard, Daniel J. (Dow Jones) P186
Bernard, Daniel (Kingfisher) W220
Bernard, Edward C. A831
Bernard, Gordon R. P644
Bernard, Jim P379
Bernard, Laurel P229
Bernard, Nicole P229
Bernard, Peter J. P91
Bernard, Robert J. P752
Bernard, Scott A744
Bernard, Tom P554
Bernardini, Anthony V. P550
Bernardino, Pamela E116
Bernardoni, Lonnie (Pro-Build) A710
Bernardoni, Lonnie (Pro-Build) A710
Bernasconi, Pierluigi W149
Bernasek, Brian A. (The Carlyle Group) A847
Bernasek, Brian A. (The Carlyle Group) A847
Bernauer, Dieter W389
Bernd, David L. P533
Bernd, Douglas R. P569
Berndt, Carole A403
Berndt, Wolfgang C. G. W298
Berne, Robert P449
Bernens, David A711
Berner, G. Gary E145
Berner, Reto A749
Berner, Robert F. W333
Berney, Arnold A524
Berney, Rand C. A238
Bernhard, Allan E45
Bernhard, James M. A783
Bernhard, Wolfgang W112
Bernhardt, David L. P638
Bernheim, Antoine W245
Bernhoerster, Michael P117
Bernick, Alan (Andersen Corporation) A68
Bernick, Alan (Andersen Corporation) A68
Bernie, Brent E80
Bernier, Jean A912
Bernier, Steve P272
Berning, Melvin P6
Berninger, Matthias (Mars, Incorporated) A559
Berninger, Matthias (Mars, Incorporated) A559
Berninghaus, Ernst Dieter W258
Bernini, Alessandro W142
Bernis, Valérie W167
Bernkopf, Helmut W423

Bernon, Alan J. (Dairy Farmers of America) A263
Bernon, Alan J. (Dean Foods) A269
Bernon, Alan J. (Dairy Farmers of America) A263
Bernosky, Richard E. E121
Berns, Paul L. E16
Bernscherer, Erich A461
Bernstein, Bill P65
Bernstein, David A178
Bernstein, Eric P125
Bernstein, Harvey (Skechers U.S.A.) E323
Bernstein, Harvey M. (McGraw-Hill) A576
Bernstein, Joel (SAP America) P521
Bernstein, Joel (SAP) W354
Bernstein, Marc L. A940
Bernstein, Marvin E323
Bernstein, Mike A267
Bernstein, Ronald J. E372
Bernstein, Scot B. P171
Bernstein, Stephen J. E108
Bernt, Duane L. A536
Bernthal, Eric L. P358
Berntzen, Petter E111
Berolatti, Rebecca Jane S. E71
Beroleit, Björn W416
Berquist, Carl T. A557
Berres-Olivotti, Ann P227
Berrill, Nick (Parsons Corporation) A679
Berrill, Nick (Parsons Corporation) A679
Berrios, Edwin A. E174
Berrios, Sean P363
Berroeta, Iñaki W436
Berry, Candace P624
Berry, Chris A33
Berry, G. Dennis (Cox Enterprises) A252
Berry, G. Dennis (Cox Enterprises) A252
Berry, Jeff E. P85
Berry, Joseph S. E211
Berry, Michael J. E325
Berry, Shane A7
Berry, Tamara P102
Berry, Tracy P129
Berry, Tyler A391
Berry, William E. (American Tire Distributors) P32
Berry, William (Southwire) P557
Berryman, David H. P248
Berryman, Donald B. P547
Berryman, Kevin C. A468
Bersani, Jamie A535
Bersch, Steven P593
Berselli, Carlo W203
Bersin, Alan D. P181
Berson, David (CBS Corp) A188
Berson, David (CBS) P123
Berson, Jory A. A170
Berstein, David L. E36
Bertamini, Andrew M. A940
Bertelsen, Mike P219
Bertero, John B. A720
Berthelot, Phil P598
Bertheuil, Julien W8
Berthiaume, Joanne P93
Bertini, Bob (Wendy's) A943
Bertini, Bob (Wendy's International, Inc.) P662
Bertière, François W73
Bertke, Norman P. A453
Bertling, Lutz W131
Bertner, Sherry L. A117
Bertolami, Charles N. P449
Bertolami, Mark S. A711
Bertoldo, Frederick A. A940
Bertoli, Nadia P153
Bertolini, Joseph M. A224
Bertolini, Mark T. A19
Bertolissi, Mario W203
Bertolone, Giovanni W155

Bertolucci, Helen P493
Bertoluzzo, Paolo W436
Bertomeu, Luiz C. A885
Bertram, Irvving S. A33
Bertrand, Greg D. A829
Bertrand, James A. A278
Bertrand, Jenny P129
Bertrand, Kenneth L. E15
Bertrand, Philippe W271
Bertrand, William C. P393
Bertsch, Guy A901
Bertsch, Jan A. A140
Berube, Brian A. A163
Berwager, Syd P92
Berwick, Frances P428
Besanko, Bruce H. A660
Besançon, Michael A950
Besbeas, Nick E223
Besecker, Beck P117
Beshar, Peter J. A561
Beshore, Lance G. A524
Besio, Gregory J. A70
Beslity, Steve A70
Besnier, Emmanuel W233
Bespalov, Alexander D. W165
Bessant, Catherine P. A100
Bessant, Dennis J. P223
Bessaud, Geoffroy W351
Bessel, Shelley P219
Besselièvre, Caroline W124
Besser, David J. P162
Bessette, Andy F. A871
Bessette, Diane J. A526
Bessey, Kerry (Time Warner) A862
Bessey, Kerry (Time Inc.) P600
Bessinger, Kris P55
Besson, Thomas W281
Bessy, Patrick W27
Best, Robert O. A901
Best, Thierry W27
Besten, C. Henry A78
Betbeze, Jean-Paul W109
Beth, Scott A473
Bethancourt, John E. A197
Bethards, Brandon C. (Babcock & Wilcox) A95
Bethards, Brandon C. (McDermott) A573
Bethke, Amy E279
Betman, Mitzi R. (US Postal Service) A907
Betman, Mitzi R. (US Postal Service) A907
Betsch, Deborah P254
Bettamio, Alexandre P403
Betten, Herman W128
Bettencourt, Ken E23
Betteridge, David W79
Betterley, Laurence L. E62
Betti-Berutto, Andrea E157
Bettiga, Michael J. P542
Bettinelli, Greg A538
Bettinger, Walter W. A194
Bettini, John A. E114
Bettman, Gary B. (NHL) A637
Bettman, Gary B. (NHL) A637
Bettman, Suzanne S. A728
Betts, Bill A384
Betts, Douglas D. (Chrysler) A201
Betts, Douglas D. (Chrysler) A201
Betts, Roy (US Postal Service) A907
Betts, Roy (US Postal Service) A907
Betts, Steve A70
Betty, Scott P451
Betz, Hans-Georg E12
Betz, Wolfgang W248
Betzner, Ray P584
Beuerle, Mark P39
Beuerlein, Bob P30

Beuers, Joerg W422
Beuke, Richard A. A703
Beumer, Markus W102
Beutner, René W255
Bevan, George P. A783
Bevan, Rich A726
Bevash, Joseph A. P358
Beverido Lomelín, Rafael W302
Beverin, Miro P416
Bevier, Deborah L. E78
Bevil, W. Larry A387
Bevilacqua, Randy P563
Bevilaqua, Joseph P. P412
Bevill, Rick A920
Bevin, Bryan A729
Bevington, Susan E. A595
Bevins, William C. (MacAndrews & Forbes) A547
Bevins, William C. (MacAndrews & Forbes) A547
Bewkes, Jeffrey L. A862
Bewley, Jason A31
Beyen, Kris A244
Beyer, Leslie P553
Beyer, Richard M. (Freescale Semiconductor) A371
Beyer, Richard M. (Freescale Semiconductor) A371
Beyer, Richard E. (J.E. Dunn Construction Group) P322
Beyer, Uwe W320
Beyers, Dan A934
Beynio, Wolfgang W180
Beynon, Ann W80
Beyra, Annabel (Kingston Technology) A504
Beyra, Annabel (Kingston Technology) A504
Beyssade, Jacques W271
Beytout, Nicolas W245
Bezaire, George E. W196
Bezek, Don A296
Bezney, Michael A. P120
Bezos, Jeffrey P. A45
Bhagat, Karan W53
Bhagat, Nancy A464
Bhakhri, Sandeep A335
Bhalla, Vikas E137
Bhanap, Nina E292
Bhandair, Bobby P219
Bhandari, Shailendra W200
Bhappu, Ross R. E247
Bhargava, Amit P222
Bhargava, Pankaj E42
Bhargava, Sameer (The Carlyle Group) A847
Bhargava, Sameer (The Carlyle Group) A847
Bhasin, Puneet A935
Bhasin, Sanjay P215
Bhatia, Karan A376
Bhatia, Vishant A280
Bhatnagar, Ashok S. (TVA) A874
Bhatnagar, Ashok S. (TVA) A874
Bhatnagar, Atul E203
Bhatnagar, Vijay K. W34
Bhatt, Ajay V. A464
Bhatt, Prat A210
Bhattacharya, Sudipta P670
Bhattal, Jasjit S. W284
Bhayani, Amyn P144
Bhojani, Kiran W130
Bhojwani, Gary C. W25
Bialik, Gary D. P115
Bialis, David (Cox Communications) A251
Bialis, David (Cox Communications) A251
Bialosky, David L. A400
Biancarelli, Jean-Louis W148
Bianchi, Franco P280
Bianchi, Frank P267
Bianchi, John P127
Bianchi, S. W347
Bianco, Dino A512

Bianco, Robert L. A235
Bianconi, Salvatore W155
Biancuzzo, Frank (Hearst Corporation) A430
Biancuzzo, Frank (Hearst Corporation) A430
Biandrino, Pierluigi W133
Biau, Patrick W324
Bibaud, Scott A. A149
Bible, Daryl N. A111
Bible, Gary G. E245
Bick, Mayer E134
Bickers, Amy A646
Bickerstaffe, Katie W127
Bickert, Bob (EBSCO) A317
Bickert, Bob (EBSCO) A317
Bickerton, David W92
Bickett, Dan A176
Bickett, Kenneth R. E138
Bickford, Mark P552
Bickham, John R. A161
Bicknell, Simon M. W171
Bidart, John P105
Biddle, Kevin B. A264
Bide, Richard W99
Bidmead, Nigel (First Data) A354
Bidmead, Nigel (First Data) A354
Bidwell, James A903
Bidwell, Jon A204
Bie, Roy W. E206
Bieber, Christopher P411
Bieber, Eric P626
Biechler, George E. A704
Bieder, Andrea P416
Biediger, Ralph P679
Biedzinski, Rene A431
Biegel, John E45
Biegen, Richard S. (TIAA-CREF) A859
Biegen, Richard S. (TIAA-CREF) A859
Biegun, Stephen E. A365
Biehn, Doug P89
Bielat, Jack (BJ's Wholesale Club) A129
Bielat, Jack (BJ's Wholesale Club) A129
Bielen, Richard J. (Protective Life) A715
Bielen, Richard (Protective Life and Annuity Insurance) P487
Bielinski, Robert A211
Bienenstock, Arthur (Stanford University) A810
Bienenstock, Arthur (Stanford University) A810
Bierley, Mark R. A853
Bierman, James L. A670
Bierman, R. Craig A387
Bierman, Steven W97
Biery, Michael P352
Biever, Angela M. A734
Bifulk, Ed P401
Bigbee, Bryant E. A464
Bigelow, Andrew E208
Bigelow, Chandler P607
Bigelow, John R. A57
Bigelow, Michael P654
Biggar, Grant E193
Biggers, Jerry W. A387
Biggs, John A232
Biggs, Penelope J. A646
Bigland, Reid (Chrysler) A201
Bigland, Reid (Chrysler) A201
Biglari, Hamid A213
Bigler, Barbara P15
Biglieri, Susan P343
Biglin, Robert M. A437
Bignon, Jean-Yves W100
Bigwood, Karen A871
Bihuniak, Peter E167
Bik, Otto A480
Bikman, Samuel G. P253
Bilbrey, John P. A434
Bilder, Sheila P156
Bilen, Faruk W342
Bilik, Jerry P214
Biljan, Marko W354
Bill, Johan P459

Bill-Peter, Marco E300
Billeci, Michael F. A940
Biller, Odd I. W287
Billet, Van P78
Billeter, Tobias W452
Billhartz, Gregory A. A731
Billiel, Jack P300
Billing, Duncan J. A422
Billings, Scott (Guardian Industries) A406
Billings, Scott (Guardian Industries) A406
Billington, Sarah W78
Billman, Andrew J. A957
Billmeyer, Sam J. A179
Billot, Thierry W303
Billotti, Nicholas E. (Turner Corporation) A873
Billotti, Nicholas E. (Turner Corporation) A873
Bills, David G. A305
Bills, Jai A939
Bilney, Jody L. (OSI Restaurant Partners) A669
Bilney, Jody L. (OSI Restaurant Partners) A669
Bilodeau, Noel E206
Bilotta, James P. E13
Bilstrom, Jon W. A228
Bimblick, Warren N. P473
Bimson, Paul W80
Binaghi, Christian W119
Bindal, Harshendu A367
Binder, David B. E191
Binder, Jeffrey R. (Biomet) A127
Binder, Jeffrey R. (Biomet) A127
Binder, Steven G. A447
Binder, Thomas P. A11
Binetti, Craig F. A305
Bing, Richard N. P449
Bing, Roger A267
Binger, Janice K. A11
Bingham, H. Raymond W156
Bingham, John P372
Bingham, Michael E330
Bingol, Selim A384
Bingxun, Zhang W51
Bingöl, Mehmet W342
Binkley, David A. A949
Binkley, Kevin C. (Belk) A119
Binkley, Kevin C. (Belk) A119
Binks, David A349
Binks, Ian W80
Binning, Paviter S. W169
Binns, Kristin A939
Binstock, Martin L. P395
Bion, Joel A210
Biosca, Salvador W287
Birak, Donald J. E77
Biran, Danny K. E19
Birch, Adolpho (NFL) A635
Birch, Adolpho (NFL) A635
Birch, Andy P312
Birch, Christine P188
Birchall, C. William D. W54
Birckhead, Lynda W. P636
Bird, Andy A290
Bird, Christopher M. A503
Bird, Damien W63
Bird, Gary P577
Bird, Julian L. E211
Bird, Neil (Grant Thornton International) A403
Bird, Neil (Grant Thornton International) A403
Bird, Rachel A157
Bird, Shelley A171
Bird, Stacia E88
Bird, Stephen A213
Bird, T. Gary E168
Bird, Thomas P253
Bird, Zoe W220
Birden, Ray P242
Birdsong, Jerre E. A50
Birenberg, Allan M. P395

Carroll, Anne Marie P416
Carroll, Barry E179
Carroll, Christopher F. A471
Carroll, Cynthia B. W30
Carroll, Dan (PulteGroup) A720
Carroll, Dan (Shamrock Foods) P537
Carroll, David M. (Wells Fargo) A940
Carroll, David (Quicken Loans) P492
Carroll, John M. (Satcon
  Technology) E312
Carroll, John M. (Merck) A587
Carroll, Kevin J. (Brinker) A146
Carroll, Kevin (GROWMARK) P261
Carroll, Kristin E8
Carroll, Mary Beth A355
Carroll, Matt (Baker & Taylor) A97
Carroll, Matt (Baker & Taylor) A97
Carroll, Michael J. P569
Carroll, Milton (CenterPoint
  Energy) A190
Carroll, Milton (HCSC) A426
Carroll, Milton (HCSC) A426
Carroll, Patrick M. P569
Carroll, Sean P416
Carroll, Steve P526
Carroll, Teresa S. A499
Carroll, Terry P208
Carroll, Thomas A663
Carroll-Solomon, Pamela (Catholic
  Health East) A182
Carroll-Solomon, Pamela (Catholic
  Health East) A182
Carron, René W109
Carrozza, Anthony E321
Carruthers, Court D. A926
Carruthers, R. Michael E38
Carsky, Jack (Visa Inc) A917
Carsky, Jack (Visa U.S.A.) P647
Carson, John C. (Regions
  Financial) A738
Carson, John C. (Morgan Keegan) P413
Carson, Johnnie (US Department of
  State) P638
Carson, Lee H. (The Carlyle
  Group) A847
Carson, Lee H. (The Carlyle
  Group) A847
Carson, Neil A. (Fusion-io) E152
Carson, Neil A. P. (Johnson
  Matthey) W214
Carson, Paul W47
Carson, Ray H. (Highmark) A440
Carson, Ray H. (Highmark) A440
Carson, Sandra A. A829
Carson, Thomas E305
Carswell, Mark A. E71
Carswell, Shirley A934
Cartegena, Noela P294
Cartellone, Pat P514
Carter, Andrew J. E32
Carter, Benjamin R. P608
Carter, Brett C. A304
Carter, Brian E74
Carter, C. Michael A291
Carter, Cary V. A387
Carter, Dave P274
Carter, David J. (Cornerstone
  OnDemand) E86
Carter, David W. (Magellan
  Health) A550
Carter, David (Fresenius Medical
  Care) W158
Carter, Deon P65
Carter, Douglas A138
Carter, Evelyn P661
Carter, Ian R. (Hilton Worldwide) A441
Carter, Ian R. (Hilton Worldwide) A441
Carter, J. Braxton A591
Carter, Jim A63
Carter, John P. (Columbia
  University) A226
Carter, John D. (Schnitzer Steel) A775
Carter, John P. (Columbia
  University) A226
Carter, Larry W. P315

Carter, Lonnie N. P521
Carter, Lynn A. A170
Carter, Marshall N. A656
Carter, Mary D. (Andersen
  Corporation) A68
Carter, Mary D. (Andersen
  Corporation) A68
Carter, Matthew A806
Carter, Michael (Energy Future) A330
Carter, Michael G. (Northwestern
  Mutual) A649
Carter, Michael (Energy Future) A330
Carter, Michael G. (Northwestern
  Mutual) A649
Carter, Mike (Skullcandy) E324
Carter, Mike (Winn-Dixie) A955
Carter, Pamela L. A258
Carter, Patrick A577
Carter, Paul A394
Carter, Regina A95
Carter, Rex L. P291
Carter, Richard P. A359
Carter, Robert B. (FedEx) A349
Carter, Robert B. (FedEx Express) P212
Carter, Ron P221
Carter, Stephen A. W21
Carter, Terry W. (PostRock
  Energy) E283
Carter, Terry (DHL Express
  (USA)) P181
Carter, Theodore N. A186
Carter, Tim P680
Carter, Timothy L. (Piper Jaffray) E280
Carter, Todd A757
Carter, Virginia E. P636
Carter, Wayne A224
Carter, William H. (Momentive
  Performance Materials) P412
Carter, William H. (Momentive) P412
Carthew, Michael L. A197
Cartiaux, Xavier A771
Cartmill, Craig A589
Cartolari, Antonio A431
Cartoni, James E. E169
Cartwright, David W44
Carty, Philip H. E335
Caruana, Ken A752
Carucci, Richard T. A965
Carufe, Peter P553
Caruso, Christopher J. P180
Caruso, Dominic J. A487
Caruso, Frank A. P571
Caruso, Joe A161
Caruso, John P551
Caruso, Rebecca A. P354
Caruso, Thomas (Blue Tee) P89
Caruso, Thomas J. (Insurance Auto
  Auctions) P314
Carvajal y Urquijo, Jaime W152
Carvalho, Jack A484
Carvalho, Orlando D. A541
Carver, Mary Lynn P630
Carvette, Anthony M. P571
Carvill, Jon P250
Carvill, Mel W168
Cary, Dennis M. P61
Cary, Jeff P215
Cary, William H. A376
Cary-Brown, Richard L. (Parsons
  Corporation) A679
Cary-Brown, Richard L. (Parsons
  Corporation) A679
Casacuberta, Antonio E302
Casados, Heather P219
Casady, Paul A587
Casala, Georges A512
Casale, Carl M. A203
Casale, Robert J. (MassMutual) A564
Casale, Robert J. (MassMutual) A564
Casale, Vincent P553
Casaletto, Daniel J. A464
Casalou, Robert P608
Casanova, Vincent P607
Casartelli, Aldo R. A934
CasaSanta, Daniel J. A140

Casati, Gianfranco W6
Casazza, William J. A19
Cascapera, Judy P432
Cascio, Bill P250
Case, Gregory C. A70
Case, Jessica A690
Case, Joe (Nationwide) A615
Case, Joe (Nationwide) A615
Case, Kendra E218
Case, Mark E298
Case, Richard J. A181
Case, Rob P432
Case, Thurman K. E70
Casebier, Mike A249
Casella, Bruce A. (Army and Air Force
  Exchange) A79
Casella, Bruce A. (Army and Air Force
  Exchange) A79
Casella, Michael J. A204
Caselli, G. W347
Caselli, Marilyn A234
Casely-Hayford, Margaret W213
Caserta, John E273
Casey, Allyson A473
Casey, Catherine M. P449
Casey, Charles H. P633
Casey, Darlene (US Postal
  Service) A907
Casey, Darlene (US Postal
  Service) A907
Casey, Don B. A63
Casey, Donald J. (Realogy) P502
Casey, J. Phillip P351
Casey, John P. A380
Casey, Leo F. E312
Casey, Lesley W80
Casey, Linda E2
Casey, Mabel P280
Casey, Phillip G. A391
Casey, Sister Juliana M. (Catholic
  Health East) A182
Casey, Sister Juliana M. (Catholic
  Health East) A182
Casey, T. Michael (JM Family
  Enterprises) A486
Casey, T. Michael (JM Family
  Enterprises) A486
Casey, Thomas W. P143
Casey, Tom A595
Casey, Wally P163
Casey, William E. P186
Cash, Stella P408
Cash, Tanisha L. P416
Cashill, Robert M. E199
Cashin, Richard M. A494
Cashman, Chuck P165
Cashman, Denis G. A326
Cashman, George D. A211
Casillas, Federico W441
Caskey, Davis E174
Caslow, Diane L. P395
Casnelli, Chris P39
Cason, Thomas W. E12
Casper, Andrea J. A104
Casper, Bradley A. (The Dial
  Corporation) P592
Casper, Bradley A. (Henkel) W180
Casper, David R. W66
Casper, John A416
Casper, Marc N. A855
Casper, Michele P358
Caspers, Freddy W323
Caspers, Rod (University of Texas
  System) A899
Caspers, Rod (University of Texas
  System) A899
Caspersen, Daniel A869
Casperson, Finn M.W. E279
Cass, Jim (Mars, Incorporated) A559
Cass, Jim (Mars, Incorporated) A559
Cassady, Steven J. A11
Cassagne, John R. (New York
  Life) A625
Cassagne, John R. (New York
  Life) A625

Cassarino, Melissa P233
Cassato, Robert T. P332
Cassel, James S. E217
Casselblad, Christopher W285
Cassella, James V. E14
Cassels, Scott L. (Peter Kiewit
  Sons') A689
Cassels, Scott L. (Peter Kiewit
  Sons') A689
Casseri, Amy L. P644
Cassetta, Carmella E85
Cassidy, Gerald S. J. A471
Cassidy, Jay A224
Cassidy, Joe W119
Cassidy, Kathryn A. A376
Cassidy, Patrick A71
Cassidy, Rick W415
Cassileth, Barrie R. P399
Cassin, B. J. E66
Cassinerio, Pete P105
Cassirer, Christopher E59
Cassoni, Marisa W213
Cast, William R. P311
Castagna, David E280
Castagna, Eugene A. A118
Castagna, Giuseppe W203
Castagnola, Dave A398
Castaneda, Jeannette (Wakefern
  Food) A927
Castaneda, Jeannette (Wakefern
  Food) A927
Castel, Carolyn A260
Castelino, Sanjay E325
Castellanos, Andria P439
Castelletti, Luigi W423
Castello, Augusto V. E198
Caster, Lori P526
Castex, Celine W69
Castiel, Mercedes P399
Castilla, John D. P249
Castillo, Daniel (General Re) A385
Castillo, Daniel (General Re) A385
Castillo, Francisco E3
Castillo, Joe P238
Castle, Fran P65
Castle, John K. P115
Castle-Smith, Howard A29
Castles, James B. (Motiva
  Enterprises) A606
Castles, James B. (Motiva
  Enterprises) A606
Castonguay, Michael R. E22
Castor, Lawrence W. P45
Castor, Richard L. P244
Castorina, Ed P323
Castro, Christine P241
Castro, John W. P401
Castro, Manuel W60
Castro, Michael J. P178
Castro, Rene A138
Castro, Rick (Catholic Healthcare
  West) A185
Castro, Rick (Catholic Healthcare
  West) A185
Castro, Ron D. A400
Castro-Wright, Eduardo A928
Caswell, James L. P638
Caswell, Richard S. P545
Cat, Felipe A920
Catalani, Robert P573
Catalano, David E. E202
Catalano, Mark J. P671
Cataldo, Robert A866
Catanach, Dave A328
Catanese, George A734
Catani, Thomas P. A878
Catania, Claudio (The Carlyle
  Group) A847
Catania, Claudio (The Carlyle
  Group) A847
Catanzano, Keith A138
Cater, Charles B. A857
Cates, Rudolph A. E321
Cathalifaud, François W41
Cathcart, Alasdair (Bechtel) A114

A = AMERICAN BUSINESS
E = EMERGING COMPANIES
P = PRIVATE COMPANIES
W = WORLD BUSINESS

Dozier, Alvin M. A254
Drabinsky, Cyril (MacAndrews & Forbes) A547
Drabinsky, Cyril (MacAndrews & Forbes) A547
Drablos, Craig A452
Drachman, Jonathan E315
Draeger, Klaus W67
Draft, Howard A471
Dragics, David A164
Dragish, Bruce E181
Drago, Dana A. A228
Dragone, Allan (Unisource) A884
Dragone, Allan (Unisource) A884
Dragone, Elia P131
Dragonetti, Christina (HMS Holdings) E175
Dragonetti, Christina (Health Management Systems) P283
Dragonetti, John P663
Dragt, Bruce (First Data) A354
Dragt, Bruce (First Data) A354
Draheim, John L. A420
Drain, John J. (Hearst Corporation) A430
Drain, John J. (Hearst Corporation) A430
Drake, David P604
Drake, Denny P319
Drake, Eileen P. A893
Drake, Gavin P492
Drake, Lorin E310
Drake, Michael V. (University of California) A897
Drake, Michael V. (University of California) A897
Drake, Miles P. A947
Drake, R. Glenn A872
Drake, Scott A268
Drake, Teri Ann (Hallmark) A414
Drake, Teri Ann (Hallmark) A414
Drake, Timothy J. (Norfolk Southern) A644
Drake, Timothy J. (Norfolk Southern Railway) P446
Drake, Tom E248
Drane, Susan A480
Drapeau, Annie A474
Draper, Anne P92
Draper, Preston A249
Drass, M. Joy P395
Drazkowski, Mark P508
Dreano, Philippe W303
Dreasher, John L. P145
Drebin, Greg P657
Drees, Jeff W357
Drehobl, Stephen V. E244
Dreiling, Richard W. A293
Drelick, Robert P85
Drell, Persis (Stanford University) A810
Drell, Persis (Stanford University) A810
Drendel, Frank M. (CommScope) A231
Drendel, Frank M. (CommScope) A231
Drennan, Robert F. A713
Drennen, William A437
Drescher, Jennifer A. E330
Dresser, Scott A916
Dressman, Laura A711
Dreux, Thierry W430
Dreves, Frank W43
Drew, Ina R. A494
Drew, Sande E119
Drew, Sue P45
Drexler, John T. A78
Drexler, Millard S. P321
Dreyer, Alec G. E81
Dreyer, David C. E278
Dreyer, Michael L. (Visa Inc) A917
Dreyer, Michael L. (Visa U.S.A.) P647

Dreyfus, Andrew (Blue Cross and Blue Shield of Massachusetts) A132
Dreyfus, Andrew (Blue Cross and Blue Shield of Massachusetts) A132
Dreyfus, Nicolas W41
Dreyfuss, Lawrence J. A699
Dries, Robert E. A662
Drieselmann, Ralf W422
Driggers, Timothy K. A335
Drillock, David M. A261
Dring, John E282
Drinon, Bob P573
Driscart, Kathleen P166
Driscoll, Brian J. (Hostess Brands) A450
Driscoll, Brian J. (Hostess Brands) A450
Driscoll, Erica P6
Driscoll, Jackie P129
Driscoll, Jen (AllianceBernstein) A40
Driscoll, Jen (AllianceBernstein) A40
Driscoll, Jennifer (Campbell Soup) A168
Driscoll, Jennifer L. (Northern Trust) A646
Driscoll, John P. (Medco Health) A582
Driscoll, John P. (Medco Health) A582
Driscoll, Joseph E336
Driscoll, Lisa A. W392
Driscoll, Matt A945
Driskell, Cory E111
Driskill, Marc P45
Drislane, Judith C. A627
Driver, William D. E57
Drobny, Dane A. (Kmart) A507
Drobny, Dane A. (Kmart) A507
Drobny, Dane A. (Sears) P532
Droesch, Jérôme W47
Droesch, Patrick A. P367
Dromer, Alain W45
Drop, Jeffrey S. (Catholic Health Initiatives) A183
Drop, Jeffrey S. (Catholic Health Initiatives) A183
Drosos, Virginia C. A711
Drotleff, Andy A954
Drouet, Didier W245
Drouet, Dominique W186
Drouilhet, Timothy J. A786
Drouin, Joseph A499
Dru, Jean-Marie A663
Drucker, Mark R. E315
Drueckler, Ingeborg A340
Druffel, Elizabeth M. E77
Drugan, Thomas A. A293
Drum, Diane A391
Drummey, George L. A866
Drummond, Brad C. P41
Drummond, David C. A402
Drummond, Ed P191
Drummond, Garry N. P191
Drummond, Jose A. A949
Drummond, Kirk G. A829
Drummond, Lance F. A356
Drummond, Larry P191
Drummond, Robert A772
Drury, John E. E142
Drury, Larry (First Data) A354
Drury, Larry (First Data) A354
Drusebjerg, Paul W285
Drutz, Marla A934
Drwinga, Randall L. E244
Dryer, Richard W107
Drysdale, Derek A410
Drzik, John P. A561
Dréano, Philippe A. X. W303
du Mottay, Olivier P358
du Passage, Benoît A491
du Peloux, Cyrille W431
du Plessis Currie, John Alexander A143
du Plessis, Jan P. W329
du Pont, Lammot J. E112
Du Ree, Mark W11
du Toit, Philippus F. W34
Duale, Marc A. A474

Duane, Francis Kenne A721
Duarte, Gianni A284
Duarte, Helio W190
Duarte, Ira E86
Duarte, Jose W354
Duato, Joaquin A487
Dubbelman, Peter W254
Dubchak, Jason A. E262
Dubert, Patrick W27
Dubey, Atul P140
Dubik, Nikolay N. W165
Dubin, Thomas E13
Dubiner, Jay L. A932
Dubinett, Howard E47
Duboc, Jean Henri A. W88
Dubois, Loic W220
Dubois, Mark E61
DuBois, Molly M. A159
Dubois, Peter A811
DuBois, Raymond N. P372
DuBois, Tim P45
Dubos, Jean-François W435
Dubose, G. Dial P521
Dubourg, Saori W56
Dubree, Marilyn A. P644
duBrowa, Corey A814
Dubrulle, Christophe W41
Dubuisson, H. Raymond E100
Dubuisson, Ray E100
Duby, Cathy A955
Dubé, Robert L. P63
Duca, Denise J. E7
Ducar, Scott P92
Ducasse, Patrick (Boston Consulting) A141
Ducasse, Patrick (Boston Consulting) A141
Ducey, Charles E. A283
Ducey, Chris A63
Ducey, Michael E. E355
Duch-Pedersen, Alf W115
Duchamp, Anne-Sophie P153
DuCharme, James M. P277
Duchesne, Marc W72
Duck, Barbara F. A111
Duck, Bennie H. E144
Ducker, Michael L. P212
Duckett, W. David A699
Duckworth, Michael P266
Ducos-Restagno, Christine E344
Ducroix, Jean-Christophe W100
Ducré, Henri W167
Dudding, Theresa P387
Duddy, Jen P6
Duddy, John A135
Dude, Ken P198
Dudek, James F. A890
Duderstadt, Janet F. A35
Dudich, George A95
Dudick, David E. A382
Dudley, Alexander P600
Dudley, Bill (Bechtel) A114
Dudley, Bill (Bechtel) A114
Dudley, Jessica P165
Dudley, John C. A627
Dudley, Michael M. P533
Dudley, Rick A471
Dudley, Robert W. W74
Dudley, William C. (Federal Reserve) P209
Dudley, William C. (Federal Reserve Bank (NY)) P210
Dudley-Eshbach, Janet P630
Due, Adam W2
Duensing, James A. P115
Duersten, Althea L. A494
Duerwachter, Steven S. P34
Duey, Maria C. A563
Duff, Andrew S. E280
Duff, Jim P125
Duff, Michael P472
Duffaut, Eric W354
Duffey, John E353
Duffey, Michael S. P578
Duffin, Neil W. A343

Duffin-Maxwell, Kelly A269
Duffy, David J. P197
Duffy, Dennis A239
Duffy, Ian W195
Duffy, John G. E211
Duffy, Josh P87
Duffy, Kevin P. E98
Duffy, Mark A. A237
Duffy, Michael P. P134
Duffy, Mike A171
Duffy, Robert (GE) A376
Duffy, Robert (Sikorsky) P545
Duffy, Scott P679
Duffy, Sean P4
Duffy, Sharon (Catholic Health East) A182
Duffy, Sharon (Catholic Health East) A182
Duffy, Thomas P349
Duffy, Tom P236
Dufosse, Alain W303
Dufour, Daniele A577
Dufour, Jean-Frédéric W245
Dufour, Pierre W230
Dufour, Sandrine W435
Dufourcq, Nicolas W85
Dufresne, Pierre W19
Dugan, Barbara A832
Dugan, Brian W119
Dugan, Jim A181
Dugan, John C. P209
Dugan, Michael P226
Dugan, Tom E315
Duganier, Allen A. A944
Dugard, Brad P166
Dugas, Richard J. A720
Dugas, Robert P. (Chick-fil-A) A198
Dugas, Robert P. (Chick-fil-A) A198
Dugas, William A. P585
Duggal, Rajeev P. P548
Duggan, Frank W4
Duggan, Gary W53
Duggan, Michael J. P183
Dugi, Klaus W70
Dugle, Lynn A. A735
Duhamel, Jean-Michel W88
Duhamel, Nicholas W233
Duhamel, Pascal W87
Duhau de Berenx, Jean W271
Duhnkrack, Thomas W129
Duignan, Christopher C. E256
Duijser, Machiel P189
Duijzer, Dirk W318
Duke, Bebe P140
Duke, James B. E314
Duke, Michael T. A928
Duke, Randy P98
Duke, Warren P291
Dukes, Mark E111
Dul, John A. A69
Dulaney, Daryl D. P543
Dull, Stephen F. A915
Dulle, Catherine P137
Dulmage, Vicki P537
Dumais, Michael R. (United Technologies) A893
Dumais, Michael R. (Hamilton Sundstrand) P274
DuMars, Bert A629
Dumas, Debra A284
Dumas, Jacques (Casino Guichard) W88
Dumas, Jacques (Rallye) W319
Dumas, Paul A. P652
Dumbacher, Robert J. P494
Dumler, Dwight D. A741
Dumler, Jim M. A190
Dummer, Vicki P8
Dumond, Susan P8
DuMont, Gregory J. P298
Dumont, Lisa M. A163
Dumont, Nicolas P266
Dumont, Philippe W109
Dumont, Serge A663
Dumoulin, Sven (Akzo Nobel) W19

Dumoulin, Sven (Unilever) W426
Dunagin, C. Martin A437
Dunai, Julie P680
Dunant, Nicolas W331
Dunavant, William B. (Dunavant
  Enterprises) P192
Dunavant, William B. (Dunavant
  Enterprises) P192
Dunaway, Barry C. A793
Dunaway, Cambria W. P445
Dunbar, Carson J. P416
Dunbar, Geoffrey C. E345
Dunbar, Melody P333
Dunbar, Timothy N. A709
Dunbar-Johnson, Stephen A628
Duncan, Bruce W. A815
Duncan, Claudia P596
Duncan, David S. (Publix) A719
Duncan, David S. (Publix) A719
Duncan, Dean R. P561
Duncan, Galen (NFL) A635
Duncan, Galen (NFL) A635
Duncan, Gary A789
Duncan, Harold E143
Duncan, Jeffrey H. E95
Duncan, Jimmy P62
Duncan, John W340
Duncan, Philip J A711
Duncan, Rick A. E156
Duncan, Robert J. A713
Duncan, Scott J. E152
Duncan, Steven W. W24
Duncan, Wayne P669
Duncan-Poitier, Johanna A824
Duncomb, Vicki J. E109
Dundon, Gerry A66
Dundon, Tim P394
Dundrea, Matthew W. A71
Dungey, Channing P8
Dunham, Craig T. E113
Dunham, David (Catholic Healthcare
  West) A185
Dunham, David (Catholic Healthcare
  West) A185
Dunham, Robert H. A743
Dunham, Stephen S. P332
Dunie, Deborah B. A164
Dunifon, Jeff P655
Dunkel, Damon E142
Dunkerley, Luke W444
Dunlap, Anna Marie E85
Dunlap, James S. (Huntington
  Bancshares) A453
Dunlap, James H. (Michigan
  State) P408
Dunlap, Kathleen P. E131
Dunlap, London P472
Dunlap, Shep A607
Dunlap, Terry L. A37
Dunlay, Jim E350
Dunleavy, J.K. W214
Dunleavy, Michael F. A256
Dunlevie, Bruce W. E295
Dunlop, Alfred N. A913
Dunlop, Maurice A480
Dunmore, Stephen W371
Dunn, Bill P325
Dunn, Brian J. A124
Dunn, Bryan C. (Western & Southern
  Financial) P664
Dunn, Bryan C. (Western and Southern
  Life) P665
Dunn, Christi A307
Dunn, David W. E84
Dunn, Douglas (Army and Air Force
  Exchange) A79
Dunn, Douglas (Army and Air Force
  Exchange) A79
Dunn, Eric C.W. A473
Dunn, Hana W420
Dunn, James W. A516
Dunn, Kenneth E. A335
Dunn, Kevin P573
Dunn, Martin P499

Dunn, Michael (US Global
  Investors) E368
Dunn, Michael S. (US Global
  Investors) E368
Dunn, Michael (Hearst
  Corporation) A430
Dunn, Michael G. (PacifiCorp) A676
Dunn, Michael (Hearst
  Corporation) A430
Dunn, Michael (BT) W80
Dunn, Micheal G. A597
Dunn, Norma F. A167
Dunn, Paula E110
Dunn, Peter (CBS Corp) A188
Dunn, Peter (CBS) P123
Dunn, Reggie (BJ's Wholesale
  Club) A129
Dunn, Reggie (BJ's Wholesale
  Club) A129
Dunn, Rodney P579
Dunn, Rusty A181
Dunn, Stephen D. P322
Dunn, Steve P529
Dunn, Terrence P. P322
Dunn, Timothy A. E360
Dunn, Tracy A482
Dunn, William H. (J.E. Dunn
  Construction Group) P322
Dunn, William H. (J.E. Dunn
  Construction Group) P322
Dunne, Brett P556
Dunne, Gary W392
Dunne, Michael (Cox
  Communications) A251
Dunne, Michael (Cox
  Communications) A251
Dunne, Tom P204
Dunning, David R. A359
Dunning, James D. P231
Dunning, Rick (FirstGroup
  America) P219
Dunning, Rick E. (University of
  Maryland Medical System) P630
Dunoyer, Marc W171
Dunphey, Paul J. P439
Dunphy, Steve (Land O'Lakes) A519
Dunphy, Steve (Land O'Lakes) A519
Dunphy, William J. (Chick-fil-A) A198
Dunphy, William J. (Chick-fil-A) A198
Dunselman, Ange W307
Dunst, Bob P346
Duntz, Matt (Gulfstream
  Aerospace) A409
Duntz, Matt (Gulfstream
  Aerospace) A409
Dunwoodie, Matthew P200
Dupee, Michael E163
Duperreault, Brian A561
Dupety, Bruno W432
Duphorn, Helen W195
Duponchel, François W88
Dupont, Bo P399
DuPont, Mark E. A63
Duprat, Pierre W432
DuPree, C.H.R. A160
Duprey, David E. A228
Duprez, Franck W41
Duprieu, Jean-Pierre W230
Dupuy, Andy A783
Dupuy, Joseph L. A662
DuPuy, Robert A. (Major League
  Baseball) A551
DuPuy, Robert A. (Major League
  Baseball) A551
Dupéré, Simon E262
Duquette, Allison L. E34
Duquette, William P63
Durack, David T. A117
Duran, Ernesto A768
Duran, Gabriela E2
Durand, Cécile W306
Durand, Michael A651
Durand, Patrice W405
Durand, Philippe W100
Durant des Aulnois, Jean-Pierre W85

Durant, Martin A. A22
Durante, Nicandro W79
Duranton, Philippe A656
Durbin, Kathy (H-E-B) A412
Durbin, Kathy (H-E-B) A412
Durbin, Neil J. A295
Durcan, D. Mark A594
Durcan, Deborah A. A900
Dureau, Gaetan W72
Durekas, Ty P346
Durette, Peter C. A580
Durfey, Steven M. P210
Durgan, Beverly P633
Durgin, Robert E. (Biomet) A127
Durgin, Robert E. (Biomet) A127
Durham, Jennifer P134
Durham, Lynne A577
Durham, Marshall P148
Durie, James P309
Durie, John I. E322
Durkan, George T. E66
Durkan, John W101
Durkin, Dennis A595
Durkin, Joan P367
Durkin, Sean E110
Durney, Martin T. W214
Durnford, Andrew W392
Durning, Lucinda (Columbia
  University) A226
Durning, Lucinda (Columbia
  University) A226
Durocher, Philip A224
Durr, Michael W119
Durrani, Faisel A538
Durrant, Mark W282
Durrence, Neiciee A901
Durruthy, Rosanna M. A207
Dursi, Carolyn A161
Durso, Jerry P520
Durst, Ken A63
Durst, Sherri P4
Dusel, Thomas M. P223
Dusenbery, Jack P666
Dusenbury, Zack W. P521
Dushnisky, Kelvin P. M. W54
Dusi, Sam W237
Dussart, Marc A121
Dussek, Steven P. P445
Dussere, Jérôme W100
Dutiné, Gottfried W94
Dutkowsky, Robert M. A834
Dutra, Felipe W32
Dutta, Sugata W296
Duttenhaver, Scott E146
Duttenhofer, David A. P210
Dutton, Scott P150
Duty, Stuart M. E280
Duval, Bertrand W271
Duval, Jacques A471
Duvall, Judith Ann P456
Duvall, Marc A. A398
Duverne, Denis W47
Duvoisin, Jean-Marc W274
Duzich, Aly P523
Dvoracek, Barry A334
Dvorak, Bernard G. A532
Dvoroznak, Mark J. A786
Dwiggins, Ranny A475
Dworken, Jeffrey H. W146

Dworkin, Peter G. E301
Dwortz, David R. (Liberty
  Mutual) A534
Dwortz, David R. (Liberty
  Mutual) A534
Dwyer, Carrie E. A194
Dwyer, Daniel P. P608
Dwyer, James E. P405
Dwyer, Joanne A260
Dwyer, Joseph P. P49
Dwyer, Kathleen P680
Dwyer, Kevin P. P180
Dwyer, Richard P. A464
Dwyer, Shannon P563
Dwyer, Stacey H. A262

Dwyer, Thomas K. P200
Dwyer Vargas, Jennifer A94
Dyal, Gordon E. A397
Dyck, Jeffrey A775
Dyck, Tom W392
Dyckman, David L. P32
Dye, Darby E183
Dye, John R. A369
Dye, Justin P21
Dye, Robert J. A71
Dyer, Andrew (Boston
  Consulting) A141
Dyer, Andrew (Boston
  Consulting) A141
Dyer, Campbell R. (The Carlyle
  Group) A847
Dyer, Campbell R. (The Carlyle
  Group) A847
Dyer, Colin A491
Dyer, Erinne P590
Dyer, J. Michael (Cox
  Communications) A251
Dyer, J. Michael (Cox
  Communications) A251
Dyer, John M. (Cox Enterprises) A252
Dyer, John M. (Cox Enterprises) A252
Dyer, Mark P415
Dyer, Peggy (Red Cross) A737
Dyer, Peggy (Red Cross) A737
Dyer, Richard J. A264
Dyer, Robert W375
Dyer, Thomas P353
Dykes, Allison P201
Dykes, Jamie W65
Dykhouse, Richard R. A195
Dykhouse, Robin P10
Dykstra, Timothy A791
Dylla, Ellen M. A122
Dynes, Craig A. E279
Dyrbus, Robert W197
Dyrbye, Tomas W2
Dyrda, Christopher D. W392
Dyrstad, Joanell P208
Dzau, Victor J. P191
Dziadzio, Richard S. P57
Dziak, Donna M. P210
Dziedzic, Joseph W. A144
Dzierak, Thomas E205
Dzierwa, Jack E368
Dziki, Thomas A. A888
Dzina, Richard P. P210
D□Alba, Greg P612
D□Anna, John P98
D□Vorkin, Lewis P226
Dáger Gómez, David W441
Dänzer-Vanotti, Christoph W130
Dénes, Ferenc W267
Díaz Rato, Enrique W152
Dörig, Rolf W11
Dünhaupt, Aage W242
Dürheimer, Wolfgang (Porsche) W310
Dürheimer, Wolfgang
  (Volkswagen) W438
Dürig, Uta-Micaela W330

E

Eades, Ted M. P11
Eadon, Martin J. A. (Deloitte) A276
Eadon, Martin J. A. (Deloitte) A276
Eads, Ralph A484
Eagan, Anthony J. P160
Eagan, John T. A249
Eagle, A. Rae A652
Eagle, Donald E. P160
Eaglen, David E. (Liberty Mutual) A534
Eaglen, David E. (Liberty Mutual) A534
Eagleson, C. F. A328
Eaker, Norman L. (Edward Jones) A320
Eaker, Norman L. (Edward D.
  Jones) P198
Eaker, Norman L. (Edward Jones) A320
Ealet, Isabelle A397
Ealy, C. Cato A470

Evancho, John R. P456
Evangelist, Shane E362
Evangelisti, Joseph M. A494
Evanich, Craig (Andersen
 Corporation) A68
Evanich, Craig (Andersen
 Corporation) A68
Evanko, John C. P439
Evanoff, Douglas D. P210
Evanoff, Stephen A265
Evans, Aicha S. A464
Evans, Bob (Performance Food) A687
Evans, Bob (Performance Food) A687
Evans, Brynley W38
Evans, Calvin E. (Amtrak) A64
Evans, Calvin E. (Amtrak) A64
Evans, Carlos A940
Evans, Charles L. (Federal
 Reserve) P209
Evans, Charles L. (Federal Reserve
 Bank of Chicago) P210
Evans, Charles (Intergraph) P315
Evans, David C. (Scotts Miracle-
 Gro) A777
Evans, David (Mizuho Financial) W266
Evans, Deborah M. A254
Evans, Don P62
Evans, Donald L. (Energy Future) A330
Evans, Donald L. (Energy Future) A330
Evans, Doug P555
Evans, Edward A. P623
Evans, Elizabeth P92
Evans, Eric (Tenet Healthcare) A838
Evans, Eric D. (MIT) P411
Evans, G. Edward E260
Evans, G. Linn P175
Evans, Gareth (BUPA) W83
Evans, Gareth (Qantas) W317
Evans, Gary C. (Magnum Hunter
 Resources) E228
Evans, Gary (Meda
 Pharmaceuticals) P391
Evans, Ian (Grant Thornton
 International) A403
Evans, Ian (Grant Thornton
 International) A403
Evans, J. Michael A397
Evans, James E. A56
Evans, Jane P334
Evans, Jeffrey D. E211
Evans, John W37
Evans, Lisa P557
Evans, Marc P463
Evans, Mark D. (IBERIABANK) E179
Evans, Mark (Nestlé Waters North
 America) P432
Evans, Meryl D. E121
Evans, Michael (Red Hat) E300
Evans, Michael R. (Live Nation
 Entertainment) A538
Evans, Michael (MGM Resorts) A592
Evans, Molly P186
Evans, Neil E93
Evans, Paul (Hewlett-Packard) A438
Evans, Paul J. (AXA) W47
Evans, Paul (BT) W80
Evans, Richard A491
Evans, Rick P439
Evans, Russ P36
Evans, Russell A. (Access Business
 Group) P10
Evans, Russell A. (Alticor) P26
Evans, Scott P. (BB&T) A111
Evans, Scott C. (TIAA-CREF) A859
Evans, Scott C. (TIAA-CREF) A859
Evans, Simon W197
Evans, Stephen P395
Evans, Steve (Perdue
 Incorporated) A686
Evans, Steve (Perdue
 Incorporated) A686
Evans, Suzanne W80
Evans, Ted W442
Evans, Terry N. (Norfolk
 Southern) A644

Evans, Terry N. (Norfolk Southern
 Railway) P446
Evans, Tim W250
Evans, V. Lynn P411
Evans, William W44
Evans-Stacey, Jennifer E41
Evanson, Jim P48
Evanson, Paul J. A355
Evanson, Sandy E330
Evard, John E. W419
Eveland, Johan A484
Even, Daniel E. A265
Evens, Deirdre J. E74
Everaet, Karel A461
Everett, Bryan A832
Everett, J. Christopher E25
Everett, Michael A. E235
Everett, Nora M. A709
Everett, Roger D. A699
Everett, Teri A632
Everette, Bruce L. A761
Everetts, Kelley (First Data) A354
Everetts, Kelley (First Data) A354
Everitt, Laurence A646
Evers, John E. (Siemens Corp.) P543
Evers, John E. (Siemens AG) W363
Eversman, George P183
Everson, Shawn R. P313
Eves, David L. A958
Evnin, Anthony B. E42
Ewald, Thad A258
Ewanick, Joel A384
Ewbank, David G. A741
Ewer, Dan P678
Ewer, Galen E137
Ewert, Gregory C. E201
Ewing, Bradley S. A355
Ewing, Gary P380
Ewing, R. Stewart A191
Ewing, Robyn L. A952
Excell, Paul W80
Exline, John A739
Exner, Michael P. (Rock-Tenn) A747
Exner, Michael P. (RockTenn CP) A748
Eydenberg, John W119
Eyerly, Mark P584
Eylott, Malcolm W392
Eylward, Susan E354
Eynon, Richard R. A880
Eyrich, Keith P319
Eytchison, Brian R. A254
Ezell, Eden E218
Ezell, Jeff A117
Ezeta González, Xavier W441
Ezickson, Elan E42
Ezzat, Aiman W85
Ezzell, Donald G. E172

F

Faa, Jeremy A221
Fabara, Paul A53
Fabbri, Linda (University of
 California) A897
Fabbri, Linda (University of
 California) A897
Fabel, Paul D. P351
Faber, Emmanuel W114
Faber, Joachim W25
Faber, Terrance A. A69
Faber, Timothy J. A535
Fabian, Frank W438
Fabian, Heinz W181
Fabian, Jeff A842
Fabian, John E274
Fabiani, Matteo W203
Fabiano, Michael G. (Port Authority of
 New York and New Jersey) A701
Fabiano, Michael G. (Port Authority of
 New York and New Jersey) A701
Fabiano, Rocco J. A724
Fabius, Raymond J. A856
Fabre, Sandy A642
Fabrikant, Charles L. A779

Fabritiis, Edward A176
Fabrizio, Richard W. A58
Facchin, Claudio W4
Facchini, Angelica E354
Facciani, Jennifer P371
Facey, Paul D. E252
Factor, Mark A866
Faddis, Clifford P293
Faddis, Jonathan E344
Fadel, Mitchell E. A741
Fadool, John A267
Fady, Antoine W19
Faeste, Lars P312
Fafaul, Michael F. E364
Fagan, Elizabeth W24
Fagan, James P166
Fagan, Rob P667
Fagan, Shirley P450
Fagen, Richard E. P107
Fagen, Ron P207
Fagenson, Robert B. E108
Fager, Chris P637
Fagerlin, Karl Gunnar W174
Fagerstal, Dick A779
Faggert, Pamela F. A295
Fagin, Bari A118
Fago, John A461
Fagre, Nathan E. A802
Faherty, Richard L. E47
Fahey, John J. A889
Fahey, Thomas J. P399
Fahrner, James J. E351
Fahs, L. Reade P422
Fahy, Nick W51
Faigenbaum, Herman P166
Fain, Eric S. A809
Fain, Richard D. A754
Fain, T. Scott P8
Fainé Casas, Isidro (Repsol YPF) W325
Fainé Casas, Isidro (Telefónica) W395
Fair, Debra (Mars, Incorporated) A559
Fair, Debra (Mars, Incorporated) A559
Fair, Ron P624
Fairall, Ian W80
Fairbairn, Kevin E197
Fairbairn, Mark W270
Fairbairn, Sally W358
Fairbank, Richard D. A170
Fairbanks, Karen P315
Fairbrass, Nigel W343
Fairchild, David J. E365
Fairchild, Drew W339
Faircloth, Mark W392
Fairclough, Daniel W34
Fairfax, Daniel W. E54
Fairfield, Thomas L. P109
Fairhead, Alan W452
Fairl, William M. A164
Fairman, Francis E. E280
Fairweather, George R. W24
Faissola, Michele W119
Faith, David M. P529
Faith, Dean E234
Faith, Marshall E. P529
Faivre, William P117
Faivre-Duboz, Michel W324
Faja, Garry C. P608
Fakult, James V. A355
Falanga, Mark A921
Falberg, Kathryn E. E204
Falcetti, Charlie P554
Falcetti, Timothy E208
Falck, Alexandre W87
Falck, David P. A695
Falco, Charlie P127
Falco, Dominick A102
Falco, Randel A. P637
Falcone, Tommaso P590
Falcone, Valeria (The Carlyle
 Group) A847
Falcone, Valeria (The Carlyle
 Group) A847
Falconer, Marc W69
Falcones Jaquotot, Baldomero W151
Falconi, John J. A376

Faldyn, Rodney P10
Faley, David R. A631
Falick, Paul P307
Falk, Adam F. P332
Falk, Kathryn (Cox
 Communications) A251
Falk, Kathryn (Cox
 Communications) A251
Falk, Stephen T. A171
Falk, Thomas J. A502
Falkenburg, Morten W137
Falkenstrom, Lee J. A138
Falla, Charlotte E319
Falletti, Daphne A398
Fallick, Patti (NHL) A637
Fallick, Patti (NHL) A637
Falline, Brian A913
Fallis, Brendan P127
Fallmann, Sean R. P245
Fallon, Catriona A438
Fallon, Daniel A616
Fallon, Jim W66
Fallon, John A. (Blue Cross and Blue
 Shield of Massachusetts) A132
Fallon, John A. (Blue Cross and Blue
 Shield of Massachusetts) A132
Fallon, Mark D. P133
Fallon, Mike E90
Fallon, Timothy G. E105
Fallon, William J. E169
Fallowfield, Tim W208
Faltemier, Sharon K. E111
Falvey, Joseph L. (Unified
 Grocers) A881
Falvey, Joseph L. (Unified
 Grocers) A881
Falvey, Justin P188
Falvey, Samie Kim P8

Falézan, Franck (The Carlyle
 Group) A847
Falézan, Franck (The Carlyle
 Group) A847
Famularo, Adam A160
Fanandakis, Nicholas C. A305
Fancher, Scott A135
Fancke, Peter W103
Fandrich, Bill (Blue Cross and Blue
 Shield of Massachusetts) A132
Fandrich, Bill (Blue Cross and Blue
 Shield of Massachusetts) A132
Fanelli, Angelo W142
Fanelli, William G. P61
Fang, Karen P403
Fang, Min (The Carlyle Group) A847
Fang, Min (The Carlyle Group) A847
Fang, Pei Hsien E122
Fanjul, Oscar W234
Fannin, Kevin R. (Chick-fil-A) A198
Fannin, Kevin R. (Chick-fil-A) A198
Fannin, Richard L. A126
Fanning, Kathleen S. A960
Fanning, Michael R.
 (MassMutual) A564
Fanning, Michael R.
 (MassMutual) A564
Fanning, Sean A92
Fanning, Stephen J. E326
Fanning, Thomas A. A797
Fant, Paul V. A770
Fante, Rich (AstraZeneca
 Pharmaceuticals) P52
Fante, Rich (AstraZeneca) W40
Fantom, Lynn A471
Fanucchi, Richard E245
Far, Robert A. P164
Faraci, John V. A470
Faraci, Philip J. A312
Farage, Christopher M. A678
Farah, George J. A355
Farah, John M. A193
Farah, Roger N. A732
Farandou, Jean-Pierre W368
Faranetta, David (Energy Future) A330
Faranetta, David (Energy Future) A330

Fitzsimons, Shane A376
Fiuza, Murilo W428
Fivel, Steven E. A789
Fix, Alan D. P443
Fix, Chris P123
Fix, Dodie A176
Fiévet, Denis W303
Fjeldheim, Norm A724
Flach, Gloria A. A648
Flachman, Jennifer K. A49
Flack, Gregory D. (Schwan's) A776
Flack, Gregory D. (Schwan's) A776
Flack, Robert J. (Ag Processing Inc.) A23
Flack, Robert J. (Ag Processing Inc.) A23
Flagg, Claude A. A842
Flaharty, Gary R. A97
Flaherty, Dave A271
Flaherty, James E. (Cardiovascular Systems) E62
Flaherty, James P. (NBTY) A619
Flaherty, James P. (NBTY) A619
Flaherty, John A. (The Carlyle Group) A847
Flaherty, John A. (The Carlyle Group) A847
Flaherty, Kathy P460
Flaherty, Pamela P. (Citigroup) A213
Flaherty, Pamela P. (Johns Hopkins) P332
Flanagan, Alan A102
Flanagan, Cary A827
Flanagan, Craig E111
Flanagan, Glenda J. A950
Flanagan, J. Ryan A780
Flanagan, Joseph G. A76
Flanagan, Nicholas V. A254
Flanagan, Patrick M. P569
Flanagan, Robert J. P141
Flanagan, Thomas A866
Flanagan, Tom A80
Flanagin, David E. A438
Flanary, Ron P250
Flanders, Paul R. P579
Flanigan, John W. A293
Flanigan, Matthew C. A524
Flanigan, Melvin L. E111
Flanigan, Patrick A389
Flannelly, Barry P. E270
Flannery, Christopher E280
Flannery, Dion A906
Flannery, Heidi E378
Flannery, Jeffrey W. E351
Flannery, Jerry P305
Flannery, John L. A376
Flannery, Mary Ellen P456
Flannery, Matthew J. A889
Flater, Marybeth A338
Flatley, Jay T. E185
Flatley, Rob P180
Flatt, L. W. A328
Flavin, L. A. A328
Flavin, Laura A224
Flaws, James B. A247
Flaws, Jamie P565
Flax, Samuel A. E24
Flay, Gregory A650
Fleeher, Jeff P428
Fleerackers, Clare W125
Fleet, Clifford B. A44
Fleischer, John P439
Fleischhacker, James E. A600
Fleisher, Martin P399
Fleisher, Michael D. (Warner Music) A933
Fleisher, Michael D. (Warner Music) A933
Fleishman, Susan N. (Time Warner) A862
Fleishman, Susan N. (Warner Bros.) P657
Fleiss, Bradley A. P532
Fleming, Beverly J. A646
Fleming, Blair P499

Fleming, Bruce F. (Church & Dwight) A205
Fleming, Bruce E. (Nortek) P447
Fleming, Candace (Columbia University) A226
Fleming, Candace (Columbia University) A226
Fleming, Gregory J. A605
Fleming, James W420
Fleming, John A365
Fleming, Katherine E. P449
Fleming Kauffman, Alejandro W302
Fleming, Mary-Ann (NFL) A635
Fleming, Mary-Ann (NFL) A635
Fleming, Michael J. (Federal Reserve Bank (NY)) P210
Fleming, Michael P. (Deutsche Bank) W119
Fleming, Murray A249
Fleming, Richard H. A909
Fleming, Shane D. A261
Fleming, Suzanne E42
Fleming, Tim P403
Flemming, Michael D. A791
Flemming, William W367
Fletcher, James C. A335
Fletcher, John P. (Windstream) A954
Fletcher, John (Providence Health & Services) P487
Fletcher, Karen A. A305
Fletcher, Nick A482
Fletcher, R. Clayton E375
Fletcher, Rick P130
Flett, Angus W80
Flett, Steve P90
Fleuranges, Paul J. P436
Fleurant, John (New York Life) A625
Fleurant, John (New York Life) A625
Fleuriot, Elisabeth A498
Fleury, Lynda A901
Flexon, Robert C. A307
Fliegelman Olli, Amy A160
Flier, Jeffrey S. (Harvard University) A421
Flier, Jeffrey S. (Harvard University) A421
Fligge, Lori (Cargill) A172
Fligge, Lori (Cargill) A172
Flinchum, Brett P155
Flinn, Ronald T. P408
Flint, Charles W. P222
Flint, Douglas J. W190
Flint, John W190
Flispart, Staci E147
Fliss, Tim (Schneider National) A774
Fliss, Tim (Schneider National) A774
Fliss, Timothy S. (Bemis) A121
Flitman, David E. A613
Flocken, Jeffery A838
Flockhart, Alexander A. W190
Floeck, Scott J. (BJ's Wholesale Club) A129
Floeck, Scott J. (BJ's Wholesale Club) A129
Floersch, Richard R. A574
Floether, Karl-Heinz W6
Flohr, Ronny W112
Flombaum, Carlos D. P399
Flood, Amy A394
Flood, Bryan W. E209
Flood, Gary J. A567
Flora, Jon C. A514
Florance, Ken E257
FlorCruz, Ana P334
Florczak, James E. A78
Florczuk, Marek P26
Floren, Hans-Peter W130
Florence, Mark E264
Flores, Claudia P291
Flores, Debra A. P533
Flores, Gregorio R. A866
Flores, Jorge E. P443
Flores Montes, Javier P70
Flores, Rafael (Energy Future) A330
Flores, Rafael (Energy Future) A330

Florez, Fabian P65
Floriani, Lodovico W168
Floridia, Aaron G. A772
Florin, Daniel P. (Biomet) A127
Florin, Daniel P. (Biomet) A127
Floris, Jean-Pierre W346
Florness, Daniel L. A346
Flory, David W422
Floum, Joshua R. (Visa Inc) A917
Floum, Joshua R. (Visa U.S.A.) P647
Flowe, Ira M. E71
Flower, Craig A438
Flower, William C. A742
Flowers, Carolyn P368
Flowers, Garry W. A359
Flowers, Jeffry E61
Flowers, Kimberly D. A797
Flowers, Mark P609
Flowers, Melvin L. A595
Flowers, Stephen D. A902
Flowers, Tina (Giant Eagle) A392
Flowers, Tina (Giant Eagle) A392
Floyd, Dennis A135
Floyd, Eric A193
Floyd, H. Charles A455
Fludder, Steven A376
Flunger, Rudolf W388
Flur, Dorlisa K. A344
Flygare, Janet W387
Flynn Condon, Tara E33
Flynn, David A. E152
Flynn, Edward B. A15
Flynn, Gary A642
Flynn, George R. P546
Flynn, John J. P17
Flynn, Karen P43
Flynn, Kathleen P18
Flynn, Larry R. (General Dynamics) A380
Flynn, Larry (Gulfstream Aerospace) A409
Flynn, Larry (Gulfstream Aerospace) A409
Flynn, Liz P97
Flynn, Lucy A. A735
Flynn, Michael T. (Eagle Bancorp (MD)) E114
Flynn, Michael C. (Frontier Communications) A372
Flynn, Michael (Cushman & Wakefield) P166
Flynn, Michael (Soave) P551
Flynn, Nadine A224
Flynn, P. Lucas E114
Flynn, Patrick W200
Flynn, Thomas E. W66
Flynn, Timothy P. W224
Flynt, Larry P363
Flynt, Theresa P363
Flyte, Jonathan P558
Flórez, Federico W152
Flückiger, Reto W90
Foden, Hugh A258
Foe, Bryan D. A159
Foehr, Matthew J. A197
Foerderer, Norma P593
Fogarty, Stephen J. A224
Fogarty, Timothy J. P210
Fogel, Anthony A529
Fogel, Arthur (Live Nation Entertainment) A538
Fogel, Arthur J. (Northern Trust) A646
Fogel, Brad P260
Fogel, Glenn D. A708
Fogelman, Ronald R. A41
Fogelson, Adam (NBCUniversal) P428
Fogelson, Adam (Universal Studios) P626
Fogg, David H. A380
Fogle, Mitch P371
Fogo, Jim P553
Fok, Canning K. N. W192
Fok, Cecilia P291
Folan, McDara P. A743
Foland, Jeffrey T. A887

Folden, Dennis N. P353
Foley, Brendan A431
Foley, Carol E118
Foley, Dan W320
Foley, David E. (Tii Network Industries) E350
Foley, David (Regis Corporation) A739
Foley, Donough W307
Foley, Douglas A. E193
Foley, Ed P115
Foley, Henry C. P470
Foley, James W. A940
Foley, John (Barnes & Noble) A105
Foley, John (Austin Industries) P53
Foley, John (Prudential plc) W315
Foley, Joseph R. A901
Foley, Loretta E. A889
Foley, Melanie J. (Liberty Mutual) A534
Foley, Melanie J. (Liberty Mutual) A534
Foley, Mike (Group Health Cooperative (Puget Sound)) P261
Foley, Mike (Zurich American) P680
Foley, Mike (Zurich Financial Services) W452
Foley, Paul P624
Foley, Richard P449
Foley, S. Robert (University of California) A897
Foley, S. Robert (University of California) A897
Foley, Sean E319
Folger, Russell F. A864
Folkers, Gregory K. P443
Folkman, Ann (Cargill) A172
Folkman, Ann (Cargill) A172
Folkwein, Kristy J. (Dow Corning) A300
Folkwein, Kristy J. (Dow Corning) A300
Folland, Nick W220
Follett, Charles R. (Follett) A362
Follett, Charles R. (Follett) A362
Folley, Gregory S. A181
Folliard, Thomas J. A176
Follo, James M. A628
Folsom, Grant A438
Folz, Jeanine M. P659
Fomichev, Vadim A431
Fondren, Beth P521
Fondu, Karen P354
Fong, Chester P.W. A224
Fong, Clayton E216
Fong, Corliss A549
Fong, David J. A761
Fong, Ivan K. P181
Fong, Russell G. (CalPERS) A167
Fong, Russell G. (CalPERS) A167
Fong, William H. E115
Fong, Yuman P399
Fonseca, Miguel W413
Fonseca, Rodrigo (The Carlyle Group) A847
Fonseca, Rodrigo (The Carlyle Group) A847
Fonseca, Victor A338
Fonstein, Michael E75
Fontaine, Bryan P93
Fontaine, Dan P372
Fontaine, Dorrie K. P636
Fontaine, Elizabeth E. E143
Fontaine, Jean-Louis W72
Fontaine, R. Richard A374
Fontaine, Thomas J. (AllianceBernstein) A40
Fontaine, Thomas J. (AllianceBernstein) A40
Fontana, Bernard W34
Fontana, David G. P526
Fontana, John P676
Fontanes, A. Alexander (Liberty Mutual) P521
Fontanes, A. Alexander (Liberty Mutual) A534
Fontanet, Xavier W109
Fontein, Fred E354

Fonteyne, Paul W70
Fooshee, Margot P321
Foote, Christopher J. A219
Foote, William C. (USG) A909
Foote, William C. (Federal Reserve Bank of Chicago) P210
Foran, Robert E. (MTA) A608
Foran, Robert E. (MTA) A608
Forbau, Mike E283
Forbes, Christian V. (The Carlyle Group) A847
Forbes, Christian V. (The Carlyle Group) A847
Forbes, Christopher P226
Forbes, Dee A287
Forbes, J. Thomas P311
Forbes, Kathryn A. (Red Cross) A737
Forbes, Kathryn A. (Red Cross) A737
Forbes, Malcolm S. P226
Forbes, Michael S. A447
Forbes, Miguel P226
Forbes, Moira P226
Forbes, Ricardo P63
Forbes, Robert L. P226
Forbes, Stephen J. W95
Forbes, Timothy (Delphi Automotive) A278
Forbes, Timothy C. (Forbes) P226
Forbes, Wallace P226
Forbes, William P. E311
Forbidussi, Joseph M. A81
Forbis, Jeanne (Land O'Lakes) A519
Forbis, Jeanne (Land O'Lakes) A519
Force, Megan P336
Forch, Paul J. P636
Forcier, Jason M. E3
Ford, Ann P394
Ford, Barton D. P584
Ford, Beth E. A468
Ford, Carl E56
Ford, Charisse A336
Ford, Charlotte M. P439
Ford, Criscella J. E56
Ford, Daniel E92
Ford, Ed P553
Ford, Elena A365
Ford, Fred L. P546
Ford, Harold E. A605
Ford, Jeffrey J. (GT Advanced Technologies) E167
Ford, Jeffrey J. (IMS Health) P311
Ford, John L. P201
Ford, Judith V. (Ag Processing Inc.) A23
Ford, Judith V. (Ag Processing Inc.) A23
Ford, Lawrence G. E179
Ford, Luisa W269
Ford, Mark P600
Ford, Maureen A538
Ford, Michael C. (Hilton Worldwide) A441
Ford, Michael C. (Hilton Worldwide) A441
Ford, Mike P186
Ford, Milam P85
Ford, Monte E. A63
Ford, Phillip P145
Ford, Randall M. A524
Ford, Robert B. (Abbott Labs) A5
Ford, Robert C. (Casey's General Stores) A179
Ford, Rollin L. A928
Ford, Ryan P553
Ford, Steven J. A174
Ford, Timothy A. A841
Ford, William C. A365
Forde, David W177
Forde, Terry P129

Fordham, Ilona P328
Forehand, Cheryl A955
Forehand, J. P. A923
Forehand, Joe W. (First Data) A354
Forehand, Joe W. (First Data) A354
Forel, Jean-Yves W271
Foreman, Mark G. P584
Foreman, Robert B. A807
Foreman, Roger L. P85
Foreman, Steve P667
Forese, James A. A213
Forese, Laura L. P439
Foresti, Michele W119
Foresti, Ronaldo M. A531
Forestier, Jean-Pierre W405
Foret, John D. E57
Forger, James P408
Forget, Jason E188
Forgione, Elizabeth R. E320
Forkner, Tom P654
Forkovitch, James K. A230
Forlenza, Vincent A. A117
Forline, Joseph A. A717
Forliti, Alex A739
Forman, Gwen P164
Forman, Marc P245
Forman, Shari A53
Forman, Steven D. P439
Forman, Susan A194
Formica, Andrea W153
Formisano, Melina P434
Formusa, Joe (State Farm) A816
Formusa, Joe (State Farm) A816
Fornaro, Carlo W394
Forneck, Günter W57
Fornero, Elsa W203
Fornos, Josep A839
Forrest Ales, John (Hilton Worldwide) A441
Forrest Ales, John (Hilton Worldwide) A441
Forrest, David A5
Forrest, Gail A164
Forrest, H. Miles A628
Forrest, John A491
Forrest, Stephen R. P632
Forrester, Brian W51
Forrester, Craig W. A208
Forrester, Tom A817
Forsa, Bethlam P298
Forsberg, Steve A157
Forsee, Gary D. P633
Forshay, Steven E. E110
Forsman, Christopher K. P584
Forst, Edward C. A397
Forstall, Scott A74
Forster, Kevin G. A174
Forstmann, Theodore J. (Forstmann Little) P228
Forstmann, Theodore J. (IMG) P309
Forsyth, David W420
Forsyth, Michael E134
Forsythe, Daniel T. N. (Liberty Mutual) A534
Forsythe, Daniel T. N. (Liberty Mutual) A534
Forsythe, Greg A194
Fort, Farrel E75
Forte, Linda D. A228
Forte, Nan-Kirsten E380
Forte, Peter A66
Forte, Stephan (Gulfstream Aerospace) A409
Forte, Stephan (Gulfstream Aerospace) A409
Forte, Steven J. (US Postal Service) A907
Forte, Steven J. (US Postal Service) A907
Forth, J. Bradford E167
Fortin, Mary Jane B. P30
Fortin, Raymond D. A823
Fortis, Marco W133
Fortner, Jack L. P634
Fortner, Kris A577

Fortson-Bigby, Toni P109
Fortuna, Terri E134
Fortunato, Armine P89
Fortunato, Kim F. A168
Fortunato, Laura P211
Fortune, Beth P644
Fortune, Christie J. P137
Fortune, Darryll (Northwestern Mutual) A649
Fortune, Darryll (Northwestern Mutual) A649
Fortune, Mary A901
Foschi, Pier Luigi A178
Foshee, Douglas L. A321
Fosina, Michael J. P439
Foskey, Paul T. A557
Foss, Donald A. E89
Foss, Eric J. A684
Foss, Kristine E326
Foss, Linda L. A84
Foss, Michael E. (PETCO (Holding)) P477
Foss, Michael E. (PETCO) P476
Foss, Wendy L. A520
Fosse, Eric E139
Fossel, Jon S. A901
Fossenier, Patrick J. A235
Fossick, Chris A491
Fossum, Drew J. P584
Fossum, Tryggve A464
Foster, Anthony P630
Foster, Betsy A950
Foster, Bradley A. A281
Foster, Carol A71
Foster, Charles E. P159
Foster, Chris A735
Foster, Cynthia P166
Foster, David J. E371
Foster, Dennis E. A954
Foster, Derek W340
Foster, Erin A312
Foster, Jack A367
Foster, James (Clorox) A216
Foster, James J. (Computer Sciences Corp.) A232
Foster, Jeffrey H. E112
Foster, Jonathan F. (New York Power Authority) A626
Foster, Jonathan F. (New York Power Authority) A626
Foster, Kevin P499
Foster, Kirstie A382
Foster, Marie P550
Foster, Martin G. (HCSC) A426
Foster, Martin G. (HCSC) A426
Foster, Melanie P408
Foster, Mickey A349
Foster, Paul L. (University of Texas System) A899
Foster, Paul L. (University of Texas System) A899
Foster, Phillip L. (Catholic Health Initiatives) A183
Foster, Phillip L. (Catholic Health Initiatives) A183
Foster, Randall P529
Foster, Ron P228
Foster, Ronald C. (Micron Technology) A594
Foster, Scott E269
Foster, Stephen P500
Foster, Steven A589
Foster, Vincent D. E228
Foster, W. Kim A360
Foster, Wendell P8
Foth, Lynn A203
Fotopoulos, Thane W61
Fotovat, Saeed E354
Fotsch, Richard J. (Kohler) A510
Fotsch, Richard J. (Kohler) A510
Fouad, Sam W146
Foulkes, Anne M. A703
Foulkes, Helena B. A260
Foulkes, Hilary S. P548
Foulon, Koenraad C. P108

Foulon-Tonat, Martha E114
Fountain, David B. A713
Fountain, Jerald M. P127
Fountain, La-Verna J. (Columbia University) A226
Fountain, La-Verna J. (Columbia University) A226
Four, Valérie W374
Fournier, Annie W230
Fournier, Bruce R. E360
Fournier, Marcel P115
Fournier, Steve P182
Fournié, Patrick W405
Fourtou, Jean-René W435
Foussé, Thomas (The Carlyle Group) A847
Foussé, Thomas (The Carlyle Group) A847
Foust, Michael F. E107
Foustok, Farah W200
Fowke, Benjamin G. S. A958
Fowler, Bennie W. A365
Fowler, Cameron W66
Fowler, Fred J. E329
Fowler, J. B. W214
Fowler, Jamie P257
Fowler, John F. (Oracle) A666
Fowler, John C. (Quad/Graphics) A722
Fowler, Mark P604
Fowler, Richard G. A194
Fowler, Simon W213
Fowler, W. Randall A333
Fox, Anita A194
Fox, Beverly P115
Fox, Brad A761
Fox, Brent P7
Fox, C.H. (OSI Restaurant Partners) A669
Fox, C.H. (OSI Restaurant Partners) A669
Fox, Carl P161
Fox, Carla D. (BB&T) A111
Fox, Carolyn S. (Unified Grocers) A881
Fox, Carolyn S. (Unified Grocers) A881
Fox, Daniel P500
Fox, David S. P15
Fox, Frank A654
Fox, Fred L. (EZCORP) E139
Fox, Fred L. (Big Lots) A126
Fox, J.R. P537
Fox, Jackie P282
Fox, James M. P208
Fox, Jeremy E116
Fox, John F. (Cabot) A163
Fox, John (Royal Caribbean Cruises) A754
Fox, Keith A576
Fox, Kelly P163
Fox, Kimberley W196
Fox, Lynn S. P209
Fox, Marye Anne (University of California) A897
Fox, Marye Anne (University of California) A897
Fox, Mike A391
Fox, Pamela P663
Fox, Paul A711
Fox, Richard J. (Time Warner) A862
Fox, Richard J. (Warner Bros.) P657
Fox, Roy P92
Fox, Sheldon A. A420
Fox, Stacy L. (SunCoke Energy) E337
Fox, Stacy L. (Sunoco) A822
Fox, Stephen A. A934
Fox, T.J. P127
Fox, Tamara P227
Fox, Timothy S. E184
Fox, William J. (Lehman Brothers) A525
Fox, William (Soave) P551
Fox, Willy E279
Foxhall, Irene E. A887
Foxhall, Lewis E. P372
Foye, Brian A267

Furbish, Jeff (Guardian Life) A407
Furbish, Jeff (Guardian Life) A407
Furby, Randy L. P163
Furby, Richard P150
Furci, Carmelo W394
Furey, Tracy A147
Furihata, Toru W381
Furlan, Luiz F. A24
Furlano, David C. E5
Furlong, Mark P226
Furlong, Pete P394
Furlong, Robert J. P231
Furlong, William J. W392
Furman, Christopher (CHS) A203
Furman, Christopher (Mitsui) W265
Furman, Matthew S. A871
Furman, Roy L. A484
Furnas, Martha P239
Furnstahl, Lawrence J. (University of Chicago) A898
Furnstahl, Lawrence J. (University of Chicago) A898
Furrer, Lilian W11
Furrer, Robin R. P92
Furrer, Roger E143
Furrow, Samuel J. E208
Furtado, Robert E. A138
Furuhashi, Mamoru W413
Furuhashi, Michiaki W229
Furuichi, Takeshi W277
Furukawa, Toshimasa W265
Furumoto, Yoshiharu W221
Furusawa, Kiichiro W161
Furusawa, Masao W449
Furusho, Seiichi W385
Furuta, Kei E132
Furutama, Takashi W252
Furutani, Masahiko W266
Furuya, Kazuhiko W161
Furuya, Sadao W210
Furuya, Shigemi W110
Fusaro, James M. A61
Fusaro, Michael J. A387
Fusco, Jack A. A167
Fusco, Vincent A. A43
Fusignani, Franco W97
Fusile, Jeffrey P. A939
Fussell, Stephen R. A5
Fust, Matthew K. E270
Fuster, José M. W172
Fusté, Roberto W158
Futaki, Shiro W262
Futamura, Bun'yu W279
Futcher, Jack (Bechtel) A114
Futcher, Jack (Bechtel) A114
Fuyao, Tong W237
Fybel, Gary G. P530
Fyodorov, Igor Y. W165
Fyrwald, J. Erik A613
Fässler, Hanspeter W4
Fürer, Guido W388

G

Gaal, Elizabeth A841
Gabai-Pinsky, Veronique A336
Gabanna, Louis W100
Gabarró Serra, Salvador W164
Gabay, Russell (Major League Baseball) A551
Gabay, Russell (Major League Baseball) A551
Gabbard, Robert D. A704
Gabbe, Steve G. (Ohio State University) A661
Gabbe, Steve G. (Ohio State University) A661
Gabbe, Steven G. (Vanderbilt University Medical Center) P644
Gabel, Jim P505
Gabetti, Gianluigi W149
Gable, C. Lynn E156
Gable, Greg A194
Gable, Steve P607

Gabler, Erik W. E221
Gabriel, Andrew A812
Gabriel, Anthony A268
Gabriel, Dave G. W374
Gabriel, Ira P555
Gabriel, Michael A862
Gabriel, Yves W73
Gabrielli de Azevedo, José S. W304
Gabás, Antonio G. W164
Gadbois, Ben A629
Gaddis, Betty B. E71
Gaddis, Byron J. A707
Gaddy, Nancy L. A4
Gaddy, Rodney E. A713
Gade, Bernt W119
Gadeselli, Richard W153
Gadney, Oliver W420
Gaemperle, Chantal W245
Gaertner, Deborah E153
Gaertner, Frederick W. A204
Gaffner, Arlin E. (CBRE Group) A186
Gaffner, Arlin E. (Trammell Crow Company) P604
Gaffney, James J. E187
Gaffney, M. W214
Gaffney, Michael (RAIT Financial Trust) E294
Gaffney, Michael S. (Genuine Parts) A387
Gaffney, Steven F. P192
Gafford, Ronald J. P53
Gafinowitz, Martin A265
Gage, Audrey A238
Gage, Douglas M. A271
Gage, John P17
Gage Lofgren, Diane (Kaiser Foundation Health Plan) A496
Gage Lofgren, Diane (Kaiser Foundation Health Plan) A496
Gage, Timothy M. E63
Gagel, Robert F. P372
Gagelmann, Diethard W299
Gager, James A336
Gagliano, Gerald W. A890
Gagliano, Nancy J. A260
Gagne, Don A595
Gagnon, D. John E81
Gahan, Pattra A81
Gaherty, John B. A249
Gaier, David A650
Gailey, Karen P525
Gaillard, Clay A258
Gaillard, John A771
Gaines, Bennett L. A355
Gaines, Donald E. P490
Gaines, Phillip J. A964
Gainor, John P170
Gaither, Eva D. (Salvation Army) A764
Gaither, Eva D. (Salvation Army) A764
Gaither, Israel L. (Salvation Army) A764
Gaither, Israel L. (Salvation Army) A764
Gaither, J. Michael P32
Gajdos, Ludovit A230
Gajecka, Marta W148
Gal, Moshe A273
Galanis, Peter A438
Galanko, William A. (Norfolk Southern) A644
Galanko, William A. (Norfolk Southern Railway) P446
Galano, Camela P657
Galano, Raul I. E146
Galant, Paul A213
Galanti, Richard A. A249
Galasco, Antonella W153
Galasso, David A. A940
Galateri di Genola, Gabriele (Generali) W168
Galateri di Genola, Gabriele (Telecom Italia) W394
Galati, Philip P569
Galayev, Andrey W165
Galbato, Chan W. P438

Galbavy, Mary P642
Galdi, Scott P221
Galdon, Rafael W296
Gale, Fournier J. A738
Gale, Robert C. A916
Gale, William C. A209
Galen, Douglas J. E319
Galet, Sam P309
Galfetti, Kristen E20
Galia, Lynn A512
Galiano, Peter A. E375
Galica, James P. E208
Galifi, Vincent J. W246
Galik, Jeffrey A147
Galipeau, Linda W320
Galit, Scott E243
Galitz McTighe, Jenny A456
Galizzi, P. W347
Gallagher, Angela A271
Gallagher, Anna W51
Gallagher, Brian (W.L. Gore) A924
Gallagher, Brian T. (DRS Technologies) P190
Gallagher, Brian (W.L. Gore) A924
Gallagher, Chris (Guardian Life) A407
Gallagher, Chris (Guardian Life) A407
Gallagher, Christopher (Duke Realty) E111
Gallagher, Chuck P221
Gallagher, Dan P654
Gallagher, Dianne E250
Gallagher, Donald J. A215
Gallagher, Duncan P. P25
Gallagher, Gavin L. (H-E-B) A412
Gallagher, Gavin L. (H-E-B) A412
Gallagher, Gerry W197
Gallagher, Hugh J. A880
Gallagher, James D. A332
Gallagher, Jim P309
Gallagher, John (Tishman Construction) A865
Gallagher, John (Tishman Construction) A865
Gallagher, John (Royal Dutch Shell) W339
Gallagher, Kevin A. A835
Gallagher, Marie T. A684
Gallagher, Mary Lee A539
Gallagher, Michael P. P162
Gallagher, Michela P332
Gallagher, Philip R. A92
Gallagher, Stewart P452
Gallagher, Susan A50
Gallagher, Thomas C. A387
Gallagher, Tim A178
Gallagher, William T. (Crown Holdings) A256
Gallagher, William C. (Capmark) P109
Gallant, Gilles E178
Gallant, Michael J. A326
Gallardo, Luis (Deloitte) A276
Gallardo, Luis (Deloitte) A276
Gallart Gabás, Antonio W164
Galle, Jean-Loⁱc W405
Galledari, Arman P334
Gallegos, Lisa A367
Gallen, Christopher C. E386
Gallenberger, Mark J. E227
Gallentine, Jerry L. E252
Gallet, Gerard W41
Gallett, Scott D. A140
Galletta, Robert P210
Gallia, Fabio W69
Gallia, Franco W203
Gallick, Joseph K. P472
Galliher, Paul E323
Gallin, John I. P443
Gallina, John E. A939
Gallinari, D. W347
Gallo, A. C. A950
Gallo, Dominic P267
Gallo, Gina (E. & J. Gallo) A309
Gallo, Gina (E. & J. Gallo) A309
Gallo, John (E. & J. Gallo) A309
Gallo, John (E. & J. Gallo) A309

Gallo, Joseph E. (E. & J. Gallo) A309
Gallo, Joseph E. (E. & J. Gallo) A309
Gallo, Laurie A138
Gallo, Martha J. A494
Gallo, Matt (E. & J. Gallo) A309
Gallo, Matt (E. & J. Gallo) A309
Gallo, Michael G. (New York Life) A625
Gallo, Michael G. (New York Life) A625
Gallo, Robert J. (E. & J. Gallo) A309
Gallo, Robert J. (E. & J. Gallo) A309
Gallo, Stephanie (E. & J. Gallo) A309
Gallo, Stephanie (E. & J. Gallo) A309
Gallo-Aquino, Cristina A. A757
Gallois, Louis W131
Gallopoulos, Gregory S. A380
Gallot, Jean-Marc W245
Galloway, Brett D. A210
Galloway, Caroline P248
Galloway, Chuck P181
Galloway, David A. W66
Galloway, Dorcas P183
Galloway, James R. P223
Galloway, Jean E147
Galloway, Kenneth F. P644
Gally, John A484
Galmarini, Jeffrey M. (Giant Eagle) A392
Galmarini, Jeffrey M. (Giant Eagle) A392
Galovic, Scott L. A219
Galston, Matthew E156
Galt, Helen M. A716
Galuccio, Miguel A772
Galvagni, Agostino W388
Galvan, Michael S. E228
Galvanauskas, Mike P271
Galvanek, David P143
Galvanoni, Matthew R. A338
Galvez, Adrian E325
Galvin, Jeanie (Neiman Marcus) A622
Galvin, Jeanie (Neiman Marcus) A622
Galvin, Michael E38
Galvin, Mike W80
Galvin Morandi, Brandi L. E132
Galvin, Stacy (Genentech) P241
Galvin, Stacy (Roche Holding) W331
Galvin, Walter J. A328
Gambelli, Marianne P428
Gambina, Frank S. P4
Gamble, Brian R. P286
Gamble, Carol A. E204
Gamble, Charles D. E345
Gamble, John W. (Lexmark) A531
Gamble, John (NFL) A635
Gamble, John (NFL) A635
Gamble, Paul E142
Gamble, Sean E626
Gambrell, George (Springs Global US) A805
Gambrell, George (Springs Global US) A805
Games, Danny A196
Gami, Kapil P256
Gammell, Damian A221
Gammiere, Tom P530
Gammons, Chris P403
Gamoran, Reuben P672
Gampp, Michael L. E39
Gamson, Michael E223
Ganase, Kris A516
Ganczakowski, Helena W426
Gandhi, Arunkumar R. W390
Gandhi, Siddharth S. P532
Gandhi, Vikram W107
Gang, Xiao W51
Gange, Jyotindra E343
Gangestad, Nicholas C. A2
Gangwal, Rakesh A660
Gannaway, Michael T. A915
Gannon, Harold J. P416
Gannon, Thomas A. (Schneider National) A774
Gannon, Thomas A. (Schneider National) A774
Ganse, Shigeru W375

Gavant, David (Major League
  Baseball) A551
Gavant, David (Major League
  Baseball) A551
Gavazzi, Alberto W125
Gavegnano, Richard J. E241
Gavelin, Kirby P499
Gavell, Stefan M. A817
Gavenchak, Genie A632
Gavin, John F. (NSTAR) A651
Gavin, John T. (Wells Fargo) A940
Gavin, Kevin E318
Gavin, Mike W80
Gavino, Richard F. P659
Gaviria, Ruth P637
Gavras, Jonathan P84
Gavrielov, Moshe N. A961
Gavrilis, James A. P190
Gawaxab, Johannes W296
Gawkowski, John A666
Gawronski, Grant L. A244
Gay, Anthony A338
Gay, Katherine P499
Gay, Mary Chris A522
Gay, Vergel L. P585
Gay, William (Gulfstream
  Aerospace) A409
Gay, William (Gulfstream
  Aerospace) A409
Gaydoul, Philippe W258
Gaylor, Albert L. A829
Gaylor, Robert L. E245
Gaymard, Clara A376
Gaynor, Richard J. E167
Gaythwaite, Myles W. H. E365
Gazdag, Attila (NBA) A618
Gazdag, Attila (NBA) A618
Gazzard, William R. W392
Gazzaway, Trent P257
Gazzillo, Ada E47
Gburek, James B. E179
Ge, Neil W107
Geanacopoulos, David P649
Geanes, John E200
Gearhart, Bruce P573
Gearhart, Jeffrey J. A928
Geary, Bill P413
Geary, John (CNA Financial) A218
Geary, John (Energy Future) A330
Geary, John (Energy Future) A330
Geary, Reginald P325
Geary, Ronald G. P507
Geary, William J. E74
Geason, Paul W399
Geballe, Gordon T. P675
Gebbia, A. W347
Geber, Daniel E131
Gebert, Terry A749
Gebhardt, Paul E. P454
Gebhart, Jim P546
Geddes, Paul W337
Gedeon, Harvey A336
Gedge, William S. P674
Gee, David P300
Gee, Diana (University of
  California) A897
Gee, Diana (University of
  California) A897
Gee, E. Gordon (Ohio State
  University) A661
Gee, E. Gordon (Ohio State
  University) A661
Gee, Noriko P123
Gee, Patrick A871
Gee, Preston P608
Gee, Vera A379
Geekie, Matthew W. (Graybar
  Electric) A404
Geekie, Matthew W. (Graybar
  Electric) A404
Geelan, John W. E280
Geenty, Theresa P91
Geer, Boyce I. (FMR) A361
Geer, Boyce I. (FMR) A361
Geer, Lyn M. E25

Geerlings, Caroline A336
Geha, John P143
Gehl, Keith M. A344
Gehl, Walter N. W242
Gehlmann, Gregory A. E143
Gehr, Jim P207
Gehrig, Bruno W331
Gehring, Fred A721
Gehring, John F. A237
Gehringer, Elisabeth W. P502
Geib, Sally L. A398
Geier, Frank P254
Geiger, Hermann W388
Geiger, Jan D. (USAA) A908
Geiger, Jan D. (USAA) A908
Geiger, Jeffrey S. A380
Geiger, Richard A. A387
Geis, William L. P584
Geisel, Ellen A587
Geisler, David A. (Dairy Farmers of
  America) A263
Geisler, David A. (Dairy Farmers of
  America) A263
Geisler, Greg I. P584
Geisler, Jennifer P277
Geisler, John E. (Cargill) A172
Geisler, John E. (Cargill) A172
Geisler, Nancy C. (Unisource) A884
Geisler, Nancy C. (Unisource) A884
Geisser, Mindy P144
Geissler, Werner A711
Geist, Steve W95
Geith, Christine P408
Geißler, Nicole W106
Gejima, Toshimi W229
Gelbcke, Alex A839
Gelbien, Lawrence J. A651
Gelbke, C. Konrad P408
Geldart, Jonathan (Grant Thornton
  International) A403
Geldart, Jonathan (Grant Thornton
  International) A403
Geldmacher, Jay L. A328
Gelfo, Malia E3
Gelgota, William P649
Gellens, Luc W422
Geller, Harvey P624
Geller, Robert P674
Geller, Scott A494
Geller, Steven W149
Gellert, Jay M. A428
Gellert, John A779
Gelman, Mitch A375
Gelone, Steven P. E375
Gelormino, Michael K. A353
Gelsinger, Patrick P. A326
Gelston, Tom A841
Geltzeiler, Michael S. A656
Gembar, Richard P248
Gemignani, Gino J. P668
Gemkow, Stephan W242
Gemmell, Dorothy E380
Gemmill, Stacey McG P675
Gemuend, Markus P241
Gemzik, David E237
Genau, Michael C. P340
Gender, Maureen A. E236
Gendreau, Ronald R. A852
Gendreau, Steven C. A796
Gendregske, Mark P24
Gendron, Jeffrey C. P155
Gendron, Mark O. P92
Gendron, Teresa P445
Geneczko, Robert M. A704
Geneletti, Giuseppe A949
Genestar, Thierry W100
Genet, Peter P166
Geninatti, Mark E205
Genis, Arnaud A671
Genito, Anthony L. A802
Gennette, Jeffrey A549
Gennitti, John P107
Genovese, Frank A44
Genovese, Michael D. A247
Gent, Christopher Charl W171

Gentel, Gary P298
Genter, Werner W219
Gentile, Catherine A118
Gentile, David R. P85
Gentile, Jerry E206
Gentile, Michael G. A794
Gentile, Tony P49
Gentin, Nicolas E146
Gentle, Meg A. (Cheniere Energy) E67
Gentle, Meg A. (Cheniere Energy
  Partners) E68
Gentner, William J. W215
Genton, André P304
Gentry, Boyd P. E10
Gentry, Eugenie P675
Gentry, Greg A912
Gentry, Jeffery S. A743
Gentry, Phil P7
Gentry, Scott E. A664
Gentry, W. Marichal P675
Gentsu, Yukihiro W361
Genty, Dennis N. E49
Gentz, Julie A952
Gentz, Manfred W452
Gentzel, Fredrik W119
Gentzel, Kevin P226
Gentzkow, Paul F. A746
Gentzler, Roland G. A447
Geofroy, Diana A224
Geoghegan, Bernard E107
Geoghegan, Michael A186
George, Andy E8
George, Arthur A29
George, Boyd L. P21
George, Dave A372
George, David C. A267
George, Duane V. E364
George, Grant A595
George, Jacob P546
George, Jeffrey W289
George, Joe P377
George, John B. P45
George, K. Travis A600
George, Keith E130
George, Kevin A491
George, Nicole P45
George, Peter C. P352
George, Philip J. A663
George, Sean W119
George, Stephanie P600
George, Steve A453
George, Thomas A. (Deckers
  Outdoor) E97
George, Thomas F. (University of
  Missouri) P633
George, Walter N. A731
George, Warren S. P17
George, William J. E123
George, Willy A197
Georgen, Mary Jo C. (CDW) A189
Georgen, Mary Jo C. (CDW) A189
Georgens, Thomas A623
Georges, Christophe P649
Georges, William D. P294
Georgescu, Peter A. P439
Georgiadis, Margaret H. A402
Georgino, Damian C. E172
Georgiopoulos, Christos A464
Geppert, Michael P282
Geppert, William K. (Cox
  Communications) A251
Geppert, William K. (Cox
  Communications) A251
Gerace, Anthony J. P97
Gerace, Christopher P. P511
Geraci, Lucrezia W133
Geraghty, James A. A389
Geraghty, Liz P662
Gerard, Jeff P576
Gerard, Leo W. P17
Gerardu, Nico H. W128
Gerasoulis, Apostolos P49
Gerber, Brad P555
Gerber, Michel W4
Gerber, William J. A833

Gerberding, Julie Louis A587
Gerd Kühn, Thomas W180
Gerdes, Jürgen W121
Gerdes, Larry G. E356
Gerdes, Thelke W32
Gerds, Rob P260
Gereb, Mark L. A914
Gerencser, Mark J. A138
Gerend, Timothy J. (Northwestern
  Mutual) A649
Gerend, Timothy J. (Northwestern
  Mutual) A649
Gerhards, Tilmann W129
Gerhardsson, Peter E103
Gerhardus, Christian W185
Gerichter, Peggy A224
Geringer, Steven P675
Gerke, Thomas A. A964
Gerlach, James M. E25
Gerlach, Thomas B. (Turner
  Corporation) A873
Gerlach, Thomas B. (Turner
  Corporation) A873
Gerlin, Simon R. E74
Germain, Al P219
Germain, Drew A254
Germain, Jean-Pierre W41
German, Alston A348
German, Gary E. E203
Germano, Donald J. (Kmart) A507
Germano, Donald J. (Kmart) A507
Germano, Geno J. A692
Germano, George E345
Germany, Rhonda G. A446
Germeroth, Gary M. A167
Germiniani, Paolo W394
Gernand, Vivian L. A247
Gerner, Roland W181
Gerrand, Sarah W220
Gerrard, Paul W. E66
Gerrard, Ronald W. P304
Gerritsen, Marcel W318
Gerritsen, Nieke W426
Gerrond, Terry A964
Gersh, Bruce P8
Gershenhorn, Alan A902
Gershenson, Michael D. (The Carlyle
  Group) A847
Gershenson, Michael D. (The Carlyle
  Group) A847
Gershon, Peter W270
Gerson, James B. A932
Gerson, Jim P447
Gerson, Matthew P624
Gerspach, John C. A213
Gerstel, Jeffrey C. A81
Gerstenberg, Eric W. E74
Gerstenberger, Tom A623
Gerstenkorn, Petra W416
Gerstle, Mark R. A258
Gerstman, Ned I. A204
Gerstmayr, Julie
  (AllianceBernstein) A40
Gerstmayr, Julie
  (AllianceBernstein) A40
Gerstner, Louis V. P399
Gerszberg, Seth E181
Gertel, Eitan E142
Gerth, Erich W45
Gervais, Valerie W346
Gervasoni, Carlo W186
Gery, Yoav A557
Gerzema, John P677
Geschke, Charles M. A13
Geschwind, Ben J. W6
Geshuri, Arnnon E350
Geske, Rob (Menard) A586
Geske, Rob (Menard) A586
Gesten, Samuel J. A39
Gestin, Denis M. A809
Gethers, Peter (Random House) A733
Gethers, Peter (Random House) A733
Getman, Thomas P671
Getrajdman, George I. P399
Gettelfinger, Ron P17

Gillis, Ruth Ann M. A338
Gilliss, Catherine L. P191
Gillman, David D. A835
Gillman, Joan H. P600
Gillund, Laura A159
Gilman, Paul P156
Gilman, Steven C. E91
Gilman, Susan P495
Gilman, Warren W95
Gilmore, Anthony A761
Gilmore, Dennis J. A353
Gilmore, Jim P326
Gilmore, Timothy J. A265
Gilpin, Donald E. (Unified
  Grocers) A881
Gilpin, Donald E. (Unified
  Grocers) A881
Gilpin, Lorelle A249
Gilrain, David P577
Gilroy, Kevin J. (SAP America) P521
Gilroy, Kevin J. (SAP) W354
Gilsinger, Brett A372
Gilstrap, Douglas L. W145
Giltner, F. Phillips P537
Gimbe, Peter W367
Giménez, Enrique W92
Ginascol, John F. A5
Gineris, Peter A186
Ginger, Andrew R. A794
Gingerella, David P675
Gingo, Joseph M. E3
Gingrich, James A.
  (AllianceBernstein) A40
Gingrich, James
  (AllianceBernstein) A40
Gingrich, James A.
  (AllianceBernstein) A40
Gingrich, James
  (AllianceBernstein) A40
Gingrich, Karen A391
Ginoux, Stephane W17
Ginsberg, Alan S. E115
Ginsberg, Errol E203
Ginsberg, Frank A471
Ginsberg, Gary L. A862
Ginsburg, Dan P349
Ginsburg, Scott K. E104
Ginzburg, Assaf A273
Gioia, Mary E320
Gioia, Nancy A365
Giopatto, Joao P266
Giordano, Donna F. A514
Giordano, Phillip P678
Giordano, Thomas R. A938
Giordano, Trish P482
Giordo, Giuseppe W155
Giotta, Gregory J. E270
Giovanelli, Gabriele E181
Gipson, James P297
Gipson, Jim A196
Giraffa, Pietro D. P276
Girard, Martin P222
Girard, Scott W315
Girard, Sebastien W320
Giraud, C. William E82
Giraud, Hubert W85
Girdwood, Amy A287
Girgis, Gisele W258
Girodat, David A351
Giroir, Brett P585
Girolamo, Elizabeth A53
Giroldi, Sergio W400
Giron, César W303
Giroux, Daniel W271
Giroux, Dave W112
Giroux, David F. A900
Giroux, Marc S. A247
Girskis, Donald J. E318
Girsky, Stephen J. A384
Girvin, Steven M. P675
Giró Ribas, Jaume W325
Gisel, William G. P510
Gish, Kathy O. A829
Gish, Scott J. E135
Gish, Stephen J. P467

Gisi, John J. A966
Gitlin, David L. (United
  Technologies) A893
Gitlin, David L. (Hamilton
  Sundstrand) P274
Gitlin, ken A746
Gitlin, Mike A831
Gittoes, Derek A666
Giubin, Stephen W107
Giuffre, Amy S. A417
Giuliani, Rosella A851
Giuliano, Louis J. (US Postal
  Service) A907
Giuliano, Louis J. (US Postal
  Service) A907
Giuliano, Tony A660
Giuliante, Rosina L. (The Carlyle
  Group) A847
Giuliante, Rosina L. (The Carlyle
  Group) A847
Giusto, Mauro W168
Giusto, Phillip A81
Givans, Natalie M. A138
Given, Susanne W213
Givens, Gregg W. A301
Givens, Michelle R. P14
Giver, Lori E76
Giverholt, John W397
Givers, Conrad A11
Gjesdal, Tamera A111
Glabus, Wolfgang W310
Glaccum, Joann P76
Gladden, Brian T. A274
Gladden, Fran (Cox
  Communications) A251
Gladden, Fran (Cox
  Communications) A251
Gladden, Terry L. E71
Gladkowski, Daniel E. E312
Gladman, Philip W125
Glaeser, Scott A. A50
Glaesmann, Ronnie P165
Glancy, Marie J. P546
Glancy, W. John E175
Glander, Michelle P96
Glanding, Ken P556
Glanvill, Derek W. P386
Glaser, Brian J. E138
Glaser, Cynthia A249
Glaser, Daniel S. A561
Glaser, John P563
Glaser, Nancy A94
Glaser, William A. (Ericsson) W145
Glaser, William A. (Sony) W375
Glasgow, Dane A316
Glasgow, David M. A741
Glasgow, Terry W. E253
Glashow, Rebecca A287
Glasky, Dan G. A741
Glasnapp, J. (Andersen
  Corporation) A68
Glasnapp, J. (Andersen
  Corporation) A68
Glaspey, Roger P192
Glass, Alex A66
Glass, David D. E373
Glass, Dennis R. A536
Glass, G. Fred P311
Glass, Kevin W95
Glass, Robert W. A746
Glass, Roger I. P443
Glass, Sharon P117
Glass, Sherman J. A343
Glass, Steven C. P590
Glasscock, David A. A305
Glassell, Claes E66
Glasser, Susan A934
Glassgow, Perry A. A417
Glassman, Karl G. A524
Glassner, David A. E157
Glat, Daniel P480
Glat, Neil (NFL) A635
Glat, Neil (NFL) A635
Glauser, Jonathan P590

Glavin, Martin (The Carlyle
  Group) A847
Glavin, Martin (The Carlyle
  Group) A847
Glavin, William F. (MassMutual) A564
Glavin, William F. (MassMutual) A564
Glavina, David W168
Glaysher, Toby A646
Glazer, Bennett J. P250
Glazer, Jamie S. E200
Glazer, Melvin L. P85
Glazer, Mike P250
Glazer, R.L. P250
Glazunov, Oleg W217
Gleacher, Eric J. E158
Gleason, Bradley J. (American Family
  Insurance) A54
Gleason, Bradley J. (American Family
  Insurance) A54
Gleason, Cheryl A. P210
Gleason, John J. A757
Gleason, Krista A312
Gleeson, Bill P576
Gleim, Jeff P634
Gleises, Sylvie W47
Gleissner, Bernhard A654
Glen, Douglas S. A591
Glenday, Greg P143
Glendinning, Stewart A602
Glendon, David C. P57
Glenewinkel, Arlen O. A842
Glenewinkel, Gary P571
Glenn, Douglas J. E169
Glenn, John F. E326
Glenn, Jonathan H. E236
Glenn, Peterson E248
Glenn, Richard P42
Glenn, Robert J. P413
Glenn, Rose M. P286
Glenn, T. Michael A349
Glenn, Tiffany K. E169
Glenn, William H. A53
Glennon, Daniel P. E346
Glew, James P. E63
Glicenstein, Gilles W69
Glickman, Barry P188
Glickman, Jonathan P405
Glidewell, C. Douglas A366
Gliedman, Michael S. (NBA) A618
Gliedman, Michael S. (NBA) A618
Glitza-Stamberger, Silke W248
Globe, Brad (Time Warner) A862
Globe, Brad (Warner Bros.) P657
Glocer, Thomas H. A856
Glock, Uwe W330
Glode, Michael S. P609
Gloeckler, Michelle J. A928
Glogoff, Andrea Taske E131
Glomnes, Einar W287
Glorie, Michele P352
Glorioso, Lisa P98
Glosser, Cathy Hoffm P593
Gloth, Mark J. (Manor Care) A554
Gloth, Mark J. (Manor Care) A554
Glover, Daniel K. P20
Glover, Dean E159
Glover, Michael J. E191
Glover, Thomas E. A476
Glowacki, John A232
Glowinski, Irene B. P443
Gloyne, Peter A. A646
Gluchowski, Gregory J. A811
Gluck, Michelle H. P211
Gluscic, Gerald A631
Gluski, Andrés R. A18
Glyer, Paul A115
Glynn, Diana H. P416
Glynn, Thomas P. P465
Glück, Hartmut A. (The Carlyle
  Group) A847
Glück, Hartmut A. (The Carlyle
  Group) A847
Gmuer, Stefan A817
Gnagey, Laurel P632
Gnazzo, Patrick J. A160

Gnoodde, Richard J. A397
Gnudi, Piero W140
Go, Bob (Deloitte) A276
Go, Bob (Deloitte) A276
Go, Odette P241
Go, Yoshinori W284
Goachet, Pascal A348
Goad, Pierre W190
Goan, Takahiko W449
Goare, Douglas M. A574
Gobbetti, Marco W245
Gober, James P416
Gochman, David P10
Gockley, John C. A878
Gocmen, Mehmet W342
Godara, Michael P39
Godbold, Francis S. A734
Godby, Angela (University of Texas
  System) A899
Godby, Angela (University of Texas
  System) A899
Goddard, Mike A856
Goddard, Steven P669
Godec, Larry W. A353
Godfrey, Diana P550
Godfrey, Matthew P677
Godfrey, Michele S. P210
Godin, Barbara A738
Godkin, Glenn V. A940
Godleski, Christine (NBA) A618
Godleski, Christine (NBA) A618
Godley, William C. E147
Godsman, John P180
Godwin, Cliff A666
Godwin, David L. A947
Godwin, Ian D. W214
Godwin, Jerry H. A791
Godwin, Malcolm R. E156
Godwin, Ted G. E215
Godé, Pierre W245
Goebel, Maryann A356
Goeden, David W190
Goedken, Jolene P546
Goel, Manish A623
Goeler, Andy W32
Goelzer, Paulo (IGA) A458
Goelzer, Paulo (IGA) A458
Goenaga, Domingo A379
Goerck, Rui-Artur P65
Goering, Wynn P634
Goerke, Brian A700
Goerler, Raimund E. (Ohio State
  University) A661
Goerler, Raimund E. (Ohio State
  University) A661
Goersch, Klaus A31
Goesch, Thomas C. E127
Goessens, Jos H. W128
Goethe, Robert A. A655
Goettel, Ralf A264
Goetting, Pamela A351
Goettsch, Dennis B. A447
Goetz, Barbara M. A599
Goetz, Debra A375
Goetz, James H. A652
Goetz, William R. P600
Goetzee, Rudy (Motiva
  Enterprises) A606
Goetzee, Rudy (Motiva
  Enterprises) A606
Goetzeler, Martin W363
Goetzmann, Pete A11
Goewe, Jennifer W299
Goff, Alisha P583
Goff, Barbara J. P594
Goff, Carmen P58
Goff, Colby E51
Goff, Greg J. A842
Goff, Melissa A549
Goff, Phillip G. (TIAA-CREF) A859
Goff, Phillip G. (TIAA-CREF) A859
Goff, Stacey W. A191
Goff, Susan Gallo P450
Goff-Crews, Kimberly M. (University of
  Chicago) A898

A = AMERICAN BUSINESS
E = EMERGING COMPANIES
P = PRIVATE COMPANIES
W = WORLD BUSINESS

A = AMERICAN BUSINESS
E = EMERGING COMPANIES
P = PRIVATE COMPANIES
W = WORLD BUSINESS

Haley, Kevin M. E364
Halfhide, Jon (Catholic Healthcare West) A185
Halfhide, Jon (Catholic Healthcare West) A185
Halfmann, Scott A799
Halford, Andrew N. W436
Halkyard, Jonathan S. (Caesars Entertainment) A165
Halkyard, Jonathan S. (Caesars Entertainment) A165
Hall, Almon C. P447
Hall, Andrew (NBCUniversal) P428
Hall, Andrew (Woolworths Limited) W444
Hall, Bill (EBSCO) A317
Hall, Bill (EBSCO) A317
Hall, Bradley C. A880
Hall, Carol A817
Hall, Charles J. (HCA) A424
Hall, Charles M. (Renco) P506
Hall, Christopher S. A744
Hall, Craig (Mars, Incorporated) A559
Hall, Craig (Mars, Incorporated) A559
Hall, Dale P155
Hall, Daryl A369
Hall, David E. (Hallmark) A414
Hall, David E. (Hallmark) A414
Hall, David B. (Shamrock Foods) P537
Hall, David (HSBC) W190
Hall, David (Qantas) W317
Hall, Dennis G. P644
Hall, Dick P598
Hall, Donald J. (Hallmark) A414
Hall, Donald J. (Hallmark) A414
Hall, Donald J. (Hallmark) A414
Hall, Donald J. (Hallmark) A414
Hall, Doris P524
Hall, Edward A18
Hall, Erin A807
Hall, Frank W. A696
Hall, Gannon E212
Hall Gregg, Mary A726
Hall, H. Dale P638
Hall, Holly E10
Hall, J. Franklin E143
Hall, J. Scott A845
Hall, Jacque (Belk) A119
Hall, Jacque (Belk) A119
Hall, Jaronda P215
Hall, Jeffrey L. A342
Hall, Jennifer Jones A473
Hall, Jerry P75
Hall, John L. (Oracle) A666
Hall, John F. (Caltech) P107
Hall, John G. (Tenaska) P584
Hall, Jonathan W. P223
Hall, Keith E160
Hall, Kelley A640
Hall, Kenneth T. A690
Hall, Kyle M. E367
Hall, Ladd R. A652
Hall, Laura A546
Hall, Linda S. (Publix) A719
Hall, Linda S. (Publix) A719
Hall, Lori A. (BJ's Wholesale Club) A129
Hall, Lori A. (BJ's Wholesale Club) A129
Hall, Martin L. A355
Hall, Michael C. P257
Hall, Miles A207
Hall, Mollie M. A126
Hall, Neva L. (Neiman Marcus) A622
Hall, Neva L. (Neiman Marcus) A622
Hall, O. B. Grayson A738
Hall, Patricia P219
Hall, Randal C. A922
Hall, Richard F. E169

Hall, Ronald P386
Hall, Shawn L. P438
Hall, Spain (General Dynamics) A380
Hall, Spain (General Dynamics Information Technology) P242
Hall, Steve (7-Eleven) P4
Hall, Steve (Alex Lee) P21
Hall, Steve (Guilford Mills) P266
Hall, Terry P114
Hall, Todd B. (Cargill) A172
Hall, Todd B. (Cargill) A172
Hall, Veronica M. P286
Hall, William C. A295
Hallaba, Tarek S. P245
Hallahan, Michael D. A699
Hallal, David L. E13
Hallam, Cynthia P85
Hallam, Howard P75
Hallam, John P75
Hallam, Robert (Ben E. Keith) P75
Hallam, Robert (Ben E. Keith) P75
Hallamore, Brian G. W196
Hallar, James P92
Hallavo, Ilkka W115
Hallberg, Per (Scania) W356
Hallberg, Per (Volkswagen) W438
Halle, Bruce T. P182
Hallee, Garry W. E142
Hallen, Shane P462
Haller, Heinz A299
Haller, Jüerg W420
Haller, Michael E169
Hallerdin, Michelle A717
Hallett, Stewart E238
Hallgren, Wendy A359
Halliburton, Kent E297
Halligan, Mike P660
Hallihan, Daniel G. A920
Hallock, Bradley J. E92
Halloran, Brian A230
Halloran, Jean M. A26
Halloran, Jennifer E61
Halloran, Robert J. E290
Hallowell, Bryce A41
Hallowell, Harry H. (Nationwide) A615
Hallowell, Harry H. (Nationwide) A615
Halls, Ronald J. A363
Hallsey, James W. P551
Hallstrom, Craig A651
Hallum, Rob E245
Hallums, Bruce A. A254
Hally, Edward A. (CommScope) A231
Hally, Edward A. (CommScope) A231
Halmesmäki, Matti W217
Halnon, William G. A742
Halota, Stacey A934
Halperin, Pamela E45
Halpern, Allan C. P399
Halpern, Neil A. P399
Halpin, Gerard A. P543
Halpin, Kevin P. P186
Halsey, Casey S. P322
Halsey, Stephen F. P670
Haltebourg, Patrice W100
Halter, Hank A280
Halter, Kevin P91
Halter, Michael P. A838
Haluska, Frank G. E36
Haluska, Michael P553
Halverson, Bradley M. A181
Halverson, Craig E313
Halverson, Gary W54
Halvey, John K. A656
Halvin, Fred D. A447
Halvorsen, Per-Kristian A473
Halvorson, George C. (Kaiser Foundation Health Plan) A496
Halvorson, George C. (Kaiser Foundation Health Plan) A496
Halvorson, George C. (Kaiser Permanente) P339
Hama, Noriyuki W143
Hamaba, Masaaki W162
Hamada, Akio W188
Hamada, Kenichi W300

Hamada, Kenichiro (All Nippon Airways) W23
Hamada, Richard P. A92
Hamada, Shigeaki W385
Hamada, Toyosaku W381
Hamade, Ahmad J. P460
Hamaguchi, Chiaki W277
Hamaguchi, Tomokazu W292
Hamaker, Donald W. A775
Hamamoto, Yasuo W279
Hamann, Dennis J. P678
Hamano, Toshishige W361
Hamaoui, Isaac A249
Hamasaki, Yuji W384
Hamatsuka, Junichi W373
Hamblen, Don A344
Hamblen, Terry P579
Hambleton, Margaret P563
Hambley, Winthrop P. P209
Hamblin, Laura P21
Hambly, Alexander J. W315
Hambrick, James L. A546
Hamburg, Marc D. A123
Hamburger, Daniel M. E102
Hamburger, John E222
Hamdani, Kausar P210
Hamel, Matthew E. A152
Hamel, William P43
Hamelinck, Annemiek P654
Hamer, Mikey (Golden State Foods) A396
Hamer, Mikey (Golden State Foods) A396
Hamich, Lars P186
Hamill, Clare L. A640
Hamilton, Allan J. P665
Hamilton, Arthur A803
Hamilton, Cara P263
Hamilton, Carol J. P354
Hamilton, Edwin T. (Columbia University) A226
Hamilton, Edwin T. (Columbia University) A226
Hamilton, Gregory A576
Hamilton, Jerry J. (Follett) A362
Hamilton, Jerry J. (Follett) A362
Hamilton, Jim P413
Hamilton, Joanne G. A449
Hamilton, Joe H. (Liberty Mutual) A534
Hamilton, Joe H. (Liberty Mutual) A534
Hamilton, John A. (Patient Safety Technologies) E278
Hamilton, John (Electro-Motive) P200
Hamilton, John (Walsh Group) P655
Hamilton, Jonathon A5
Hamilton, Kathleen (CalPERS) A167
Hamilton, Kathleen (CalPERS) A167
Hamilton, Kevin P219
Hamilton, Lisa A746
Hamilton, Mark W224
Hamilton, Paul W. A634
Hamilton, Peter B. A153
Hamilton, Robert A. A380
Hamilton, Scott D. P143
Hamilton, Ted P14
Hamilton, Timothy D. E114
Hamilton, Trudy (Ascension Health) A82
Hamilton, Trudy (Ascension Health) A82
Hamilton, Yvette W92
Hamlin, Cassandra W317
Hamlin, Machell P239
Hamlin, Stephen E. P579
Hamm, Ranell A681
Hamm, Richard F. E100
Hamm, William R. P171
Hammarstrom, David A590
Hammer, Bonnie P428
Hammer, David A453
Hammer, Dennis J. P162
Hammer, Michelle P491
Hammer, Pete P556

Hammer, Wolfgang A188
Hammergren, John H. A577
Hammerle, David (Bechtel) A114
Hammerle, David (Bechtel) A114
Hammerly, Gregg M. P532
Hammerton, Andy W99
Hammett, Gary C. (Unified Grocers) A881
Hammett, Gary C. (Unified Grocers) A881
Hammond, Donald V. A209
Hammond, Neal P623
Hammond, Phyllis P96
Hammond, Thomas J. (IntercontinentalExchange) E193
Hammond, Thomas R. (Jacobs Engineering) A483
Hammonds, Evelynn (Harvard University) A421
Hammonds, Evelynn (Harvard University) A421
Hammonds, Kim A135
Hamnett, Marty W444
Hamon, Joël W100
Hamoui, Omar A402
Hamouly, Mona A53
Hamp, Julie A. A684
Hampel, Rupert P309
Hampton, Brian P596
Hampton, Donald P281
Hampton, Mark W445
Hampton, Philip W337
Hamre, Reid A24
Hamrick, Larry W. A794
Hamrock, Joseph A17
Han, Bernard L. A289
Han, Donald P166
Han-Yong, Park W311
Hanada, Yoshihiko W162
Hanafin, Mark W92
Hanagata, Shigeru W265
Hanai, Masayuki W373
Hanai, Takafumi W294
Hanan, Shelley A605
Hanaoka, Seiji W143
Hanatani, Shinji W375
Hance, James H. A806
Hance, Julie A475
Hance, Robert B. A5
Hance, William N. P644
Hancock, Chris P279
Hancock, Claire P492
Hancock, D. Keith A357
Hancock, Dale E129
Hancock, Debbie A422
Hancock, Mike P473
Hancock, Peter D. A27
Hancock, Terry E189
Hand, Erin B. (Cox Communications) A251
Hand, Erin B. (Cox Communications) A251
Hand, Fred (Burlington Coat Factory) A156
Hand, Fred (Burlington Coat Factory) A156
Hand, John (Guardian Life) A407
Hand, John (Guardian Life) A407
Handa, Pavan E33
Handcock, Todd E132
Handel, Bob P580
Handel, Paul B. (HCSC) A426
Handel, Paul B. (HCSC) A426
Handelsman, Edward L. P443
Handelsman, Harold S. P269
Handler, Richard B. A484
Handley, Mark P261
Handley, Terry W. A179
Handley, Thomas W. A318
Handlon, Carolyn B. A557
Handrick, Gabriele W175
Handy, Clay P315
Handy, Scott A456
Handy, Steven D. E352
Handzel, Toni E376

A	= AMERICAN BUSINESS
E	= EMERGING COMPANIES
P	= PRIVATE COMPANIES
W	= WORLD BUSINESS

Headrick, Michael S. A829
Healey, Ada M. P651
Healey, Bill P573
Healey, Jeff A438
Healey, John H. P399
Healey, Melanie Liddl A711
Healey, Michaela J. W269
Healey, Paul F. A102
Healey, Timothy G. E20
Healton, Ed P395
Healy, Andrew W115
Healy, C. Michael P366
Healy, Jim A376
Healy, Joseph (AllianceBernstein) A40
Healy, Joseph (AllianceBernstein) A40
Healy, Joseph (National Australia Bank) W269
Healy, Karen L. A278
Healy, Kevin P. A31
Healy, L. Russell P304
Healy, Michael E. E318
Healy, Robert P416
Healy, Thomas (Guardian Life) A407
Healy, Thomas F. (Parker-Hannifin) A678
Healy, Thomas (Guardian Life) A407
Healy, Timothy G. (EnerNOC) E129
Healy, Timothy R. (Primoris) E286
Healy, Timothy C. (US Postal Service) A907
Healy, Timothy C. (US Postal Service) A907
Healy, William J. (Catholic Health East) A182
Healy, William J. (Catholic Health East) A182
Heaps, Kenneth L. P358
Heard, David W. E206
Heard, James A529
Hearn, Shawn E. P407
Hearne, Ross A502
Hearst, George R. (Hearst Corporation) A430
Hearst, George R. (Hearst Corporation) A430
Hearst, Stephen T. (Hearst Corporation) A430
Hearst, Stephen T. (Hearst Corporation) A430
Heath, Brenton P78
Heath, Cynthia G. A328
Heath, George E. A786
Heath, Graham A70
Heath, Gregory F. E185
Heath, Joel E97
Heath, Jon A391
Heath, Malcolm P524
Heath, Ralph D. A541
Heath, Steven E237
Heath, Susan P644
Heath, William F. A324
Heathcott, Forrest (JM Family Enterprises) A486
Heathcott, Forrest (JM Family Enterprises) A486
Heatly, Danny J. A281
Heaton, Jon P309
Heatwole, Deirdre P631
Heavin, Diane M. P165
Heavin, H. Gary P165
Hebard, Douglas H. A122
Hebe, James L. A616
Hebeda, Dave E310
Heberle, Donald J. A102
Hebert, Robert P. E87
Hebich, Christian W331
Hebron, Anthony T. (Battelle Memorial) A107

Hebron, Anthony T. (Battelle Memorial) A107
Hebron, Robert J. (New York Life) A625
Hebron, Robert J. (New York Life) A625
Hecht, Audrey A271
Hecht, Beth P. P573
Hecht, Tom P527
Heck, Christopher (NBA) A618
Heck, Christopher (NBA) A618
Heck, John M. P529
Heck, Lowell P222
Heck, Scott M. A437
Heck, Sharon L. A123
Heckart, Christine A623
Heckel Kuhlmann, Sherri A602
Hecker, Andrew A913
Heckes, Howard C. A913
Heckman, Lauralee A428
Heckmann, Fritz-Jürgen W176
Heckmann, Norbert W447
Heckmann, Richard J. E172
Hed, Alan P434
Hedberg, Brian (HCSC) A426
Hedberg, Brian (HCSC) A426
Hedberg, John P89
Hedberg, Jonny W72
Hedde, Emmanuel W167
Hedding Galeana, Benjamín W302
Hede, Luke A538
Hedensio, Henrik A340
Hederick, Jeff (Unisource) A884
Hederick, Jeff (Unisource) A884
Hedge, Ramachandra A705
Hedge, Tom P527
Hedges, Derek E39
Hedges, James L. P8
Hedges, Michael A583
Hedges, Robert E354
Hediger, Gary P140
Hediger, Larry A722
Hedley, Paul W37
Hedrich, Anne A71
Hedrick, J. P4
Hedrick, Marc H. E94
Hedström, Tomas W387
Heebner, David K. A380
Heekin, James R. (Grey Group) P260
Heekin, James R. (WPP) W445
Heekin-Canedy, Scott H. A628
Heelan, Robert T. P399
Heenan, Christine (Harvard University) A421
Heenan, Christine (Harvard University) A421
Heenan, Timothy S. A705
Heer, Hans A4
Heere, Jan W249
Hees, Bernardo V. (Burger King) A155
Hees, Bernardo V. (Burger King) A155
Heffernan, C. Gamble E314
Heffernan, Christine (Topco Associates LLC) A867
Heffernan, Christine (Topco Associates LLC) A867
Heffernan, Marianne P545
Heffernan, Michael P. A416
Heffernan, Paul P434
Hefferon, Timothy W. P152
Heffington, Joe P105
Heffler, Mava K. A327
Heffron, Mike W48
Heflin, Adam C. A50
Heflin, Robert H. (Perdue Incorporated) A686
Heflin, Robert H. (Perdue Incorporated) A686
Hefner, Curt E111
Hefner, Linda P. A928
Hegarty, David J. E316
Hegarty, Kieran A841
Hegarty, Sean P. P226
Heger, Mary P. A50
Heggelund, Stig W287

Heggen, Elmar W62
Hegi, Frederick B. A892
Hegland, Sandra K. E243
Heichler, Elizabeth (International Data Group) A467
Heichler, Elizabeth (International Data Group) A467
Heid, Michael J. A940
Heidelman, Jim A920
Heidemann, Donald L. E383
Heidemann, Lyle G. P609
Heiden, Cara K. A940
Heiden, Clint P462
Heiden, Kurt E330
Heider, Michael L. P457
Heidmann, Eric P92
Heidrich, Gerson A796
Heidrich, Kevin E251
Heidt, Alex A420
Heigel, Catherine A304
Heigel, Douglas W. E326
Heil, Gene D. A284
Heil, John A. A802
Heil, Mike A546
Heilbron, Jonathan W245
Heilesen, Henry E. P315
Heilig, Tim A. (Norfolk Southern) A644
Heilig, Tim A. (Norfolk Southern Railway) P446
Heilman, Theodore A. E159
Heilmann, Matthias L. A758
Heim, Michael C. A324
Heim, Philippe W369
Heim, Tamara L. P596
Heimann, Sandra W. A56
Heimbach, Stephan W363
Heimbigner, Marc A475
Heimbrook, David A762
Heims, Heinrich W219
Hein Bax, Jan W320
Hein, Bill A538
Hein, Gail P622
Hein, Gernot W451
Hein, Leland J. A346
Heina, Patricia W452
Heincke, Roland A224
Heine, J. Michael A652
Heine, Tara A958
Heinemann, Jorg E337
Heinen, Winfried (General Re) A385
Heinen, Winfried (General Re) A385
Heinick, Rick (Bausch & Lomb) A108
Heinick, Rick (Bausch & Lomb) A108
Heinig, Stefan W400
Heinimann, Felix W445
Heininger, Ted P78
Heinmiller, John C. A809
Heinrich, Wolfgang (First Data) A354
Heinrich, Wolfgang (First Data) A354
Heinrichs, George K. A945
Heinricht, Frank W181
Heinsen, Hans H. P145
Heintz, Kenneth N. A648
Heintz, Mark E97
Heintz, Melanie L. P210
Heintz, Michael J. (E. & J. Gallo) A309
Heintz, Michael J. (E. & J. Gallo) A309
Heintz, Stanton E61
Heintzelman, Daniel C. A376
Heinz, James D. A940
Heinz, Jeffrey A375
Heinz, Michael W56
Heinz, Peter D. P623
Heinzer, Patrice P502
Heise, Michael W25
Heise, Rita J. (Cargill) A172
Heise, Rita J. (Cargill) A172
Heiselman, William J. A420
Heiser, Randy J. (Giant Eagle) A392
Heiser, Randy J. (Giant Eagle) A392
Heiser, Thomas P. E515
Heisey, Bradley K. P584
Heiskanen, Kari W217
Heisley, Michael E. P286
Heissenbuttel, William E305

Heith, Robert A844
Heitman, J. William A84
Heitmann, Frank A232
Heizmann, Jochem W438
Helayel, Tony A340
Helbig, Michael W219
Helck, Chester B. A734
Held, James P. A464
Held, Joe P502
Held, Michael A. P210
Helders, Bernard W85
Heldman, Paul W. A514
Heldreth, Tony P266
Helenyi, Judit W298
Helfand, Michael P554
Helfenstein, Dorothy A138
Helfer, Michael S. A213
Helfrich, Thomas E. A500
Helgesen, Terry P179
Helgeson, Bradford J. P156
Helgeson, Lonnie J. E123
Hellberg, Marita W145
Helleb□, Leif W287
Hellenthal, Markus W405
Heller Allen, Elizabeth A453
Heller, Andrew T. (Time Warner) A862
Heller, Andrew T. (Turner Broadcasting) P612
Heller, Brian E217
Heller, Bridgette P. A587
Heller, David J. (Boeing) A135
Heller, David B. (Goldman Sachs) A397
Heller, David S. (Latham & Watkins) P358
Heller, Frances K. E136
Heller, Greg P52
Heller, Jennifer J. A227
Heller, John S. (Caterpillar) A181
Heller, John (Harris Corp.) A420
Heller, Marjorie J. (Mutual of Omaha) A609
Heller, Marjorie J. (Mutual of Omaha) A609
Heller, Michael D. (Amscan) P33
Heller, Michael (Otto Group) W299
Heller, Paul P594
Hellerich, Randy P529
Hellman, David P325
Hellman, Steven W107
Hellmuth, Stephen M. (NBA) A618
Hellmuth, Stephen M. (NBA) A618
Hellrigel, Robert P487
Hellstern, Ursula A348
Hellyer, Nancy P608
Helm, Jeffry (Army and Air Force Exchange) A79
Helm, Jeffry (Army and Air Force Exchange) A79
Helm, Jim P52
Helm, Lucy Lee A814
Helm, Robert M. A380
Helmandollar, Brent P287
Helmbrecht, Steven M. A475
Helmers, Leo (The Carlyle Group) A847
Helmers, Leo (The Carlyle Group) A847
Helmi, Angie (The Carlyle Group) A847
Helmi, Angie (The Carlyle Group) A847
Helmlinger, Jayne P563
Helmont, Sue W45
Helmrich, Klaus W363
Helms, Christopher A. A641
Helms, Jody P336
Helms, L. Wade E119
Helms, Lloyd W. A335
Helms, Nick (Liberty Mutual) A534
Helms, Nick (Liberty Mutual) A534
Helms, Todd P. A387
Helms, W. Phil E119
Helsel, Bruce E. A940
Heltne, Jørn W334
Helton, Mike P420
Heltz, Sabrina P85
Helyer, Scott M. P584

Helz, Terrance V. A244
Hembree, Thomas R. P336
Hemenway, E. Allen A906
Hemingway Hall, Patricia A. (HCSC) A426
Hemingway Hall, Patricia A. (HCSC) A426
Hemingway, W. David A966
Hemink, D. C. A104
Hemken, Peter C. (DuPont) A305
Hemken, Peter C. (Pioneer Hi-Bred) P480
Hemlepp, Pat D. A17
Hemm, David P412
Hemmady, Gokul V. P445
Hemme, Brita W299
Hemme, Jan P551
Hemmelgarn, Terrance A90
Hemmer, J. Michael A883
Hemmings, Stuart P18
Hemmingsen, Claus V. W2
Hemnani, Rohit A491
Hempel, Karen P135
Hemphill, Neil P43
Hempson, David P. P379
Hemsley, Michael C. (Catholic Health East) A182
Hemsley, Michael C. (Catholic Health East) A182
Hemsley, Richard W337
Hemsley, Stephen J. A895
Hemus, Simon C. A872
Henchel, Gregory J. A451
Henchman, Robbie P309
Henck, Douglas C. W13
Hencker, Nathalia W354
Henderschedt, Robert R. P14
Henderson, Bob W339
Henderson, David (Lighting Science Group) E220
Henderson, David T. (Western & Southern Financial) P664
Henderson, Deborah A589
Henderson, Frederick A. (SunCoke Energy) E337
Henderson, Frederick A. (Sunoco) A822
Henderson, Gregg P107
Henderson, Harold R. (NFL) A635
Henderson, Harold R. (NFL) A635
Henderson, J. Michael P590
Henderson, James P. E213
Henderson, Jeffrey W. A171
Henderson, Jocelyn E. A934
Henderson, Judith A. (Mutual of Omaha) A609
Henderson, Judith A. (Mutual of Omaha) A609
Henderson, Julie A632
Henderson, Michael C. P92
Henderson, Michele A658
Henderson, Michelle W99
Henderson, Molly E376
Henderson, Rick (Parsons Corporation) A679
Henderson, Rick (Parsons Corporation) A679
Henderson, Scott M. A514
Henderson, Steve W80
Henderson, Thomas C. E77
Henderson, Wendy E. A943
Hendin, Barry J. P62
Hendler, David P554
Hendrick, Scott A777
Hendricker, Alan P116
Hendricks, Andy A772
Hendricks, Diane M. P7
Hendricks, Francis L. (Army and Air Force Exchange) A79
Hendricks, Francis L. (Army and Air Force Exchange) A79
Hendricks, John S. (Discovery Communications) A287
Hendricks, John (Tribune Company) P607

Hendricks, Kevin P7
Hendricks, Kim P7
Hendricks, Laura J. (ServiceMaster) A782
Hendricks, Laura J. (ServiceMaster) A782
Hendricks, Thomas E. P584
Hendrickson, Charles J. A484
Hendrickson, Erik A376
Hendrickson, Gary E. A913
Hendrickson, John T. A688
Hendrickson, Kenneth (Catholic Health East) A182
Hendrickson, Kenneth (Catholic Health East) A182
Hendrickson, Thomas T. (Sports Authority) A804
Hendrickson, Thomas T. (Sports Authority) A804
Hendrix, Clay A623
Hendry, Andrew D. A224
Hendry, David W99
Hendry, Lisa P165
Hendry, Steve P405
Hendry, Timothy G. A464
Henebry, Timothy M. A674
Heneghan, Bill E19
Heneghan, James M. A195
Henger, Chris P117
Hengst, Carla J. E17
Hengst, Paul T. A420
Hengst, Ted A420
Hengsterman, Stacey A824
Henigan, Mark P319
Henin, Roland P173
Henisse, Pascal W69
Henke, David E223
Henke, Paul E95
Henkel, Arthur P523
Henkel, Kathleen A. A590
Henkel, Oliver P590
Henkel, Robert J. (Ascension Health) A82
Henkel, Robert J. (Ascension Health) A82
Henkel, Scott M. E59
Henkels, Virginia A827
Henkle, Dan A851
Henle, Walter R. P548
Henley, Jeffrey O. A666
Henley, Robert W. A655
Henly, James B. (MTA) A608
Henly, James B. (MTA) A608
Hennah, James W80
Henne, Jason E376
Henne, Preston A. (General Dynamics) A380
Henne, Preston (Gulfstream Aerospace) A409
Henne, Preston (Gulfstream Aerospace) A409
Henneberry, Brian (Koch Industries, Inc.) A508
Henneberry, Brian (Koch Industries, Inc.) A508
Henneberry, Patrick D. E187
Hennefeld, Cheryl P469
Hennekes, David (Energy Future) A330
Hennekes, David (Energy Future) A330
Hennelly, Ben J. P57
Hennes, Amy P263
Hennessey, Amy S. P532
Hennessey, Mélanie E172
Hennessey, William E. P256
Hennessy, Brian J. A791
Hennessy, James R. P210
Hennessy, John (CNA Financial) A218
Hennessy, John L. (Stanford University) A810
Hennessy, John L. (Stanford University) A810
Hennessy, Karl A70
Hennessy, Sean P. A786
Hennessy, Tom (Catholic Healthcare West) A185

Hennessy, Tom (Catholic Healthcare West) A185
Henney, Herbert Raymo E7
Hennigan, Bryan E. A335
Henning, Bryan W53
Henning, Gary S. A794
Hennings, Dean A65
Henningsen, August-Wilhelm W242
Hennington, Donald L. P416
Hennon, Armand W303
Henny, Marinus N. P624
Henretta, Deborah A. A711
Henrich, Carolyn (University of California) A897
Henrich, Carolyn (University of California) A897
Henrich, Edward E302
Henrich, William L. (University of Texas System) A899
Henrich, William L. (University of Texas System) A899
Henrici, Peter G. A918
Henricks, Gwenne A. A181
Henriksen, Lisa (Giant Eagle) A392
Henriksen, Lisa (Giant Eagle) A392
Henrikson, C. Robert A590
Henriksson, Henrik W356
Henriques, Elisabete A278
Henriques, George L. A681
Henriquez, Margareth W245
Henry, Bob A650
Henry, Brent L. P465
Henry, Brian (Bristol-Myers Squibb) A147
Henry, Brian (Medtronic) A583
Henry, Brian J. (Terex) A841
Henry, Chris P337
Henry, Christian O. (Illumina) E185
Henry, Christopher (NFL) A635
Henry, Christopher (NFL) A635
Henry, Daniel R. (NetSpend) E258
Henry, Daniel T. (American Express) A53
Henry, David A. E27
Henry, Dee A. (Mutual of Omaha) A609
Henry, Dee A. (Mutual of Omaha) A609
Henry, Edouard-Malo W369
Henry, Francis J. A138
Henry, Jeff P291
Henry, Kathy P160
Henry, Kim E10
Henry, Larry L. A516
Henry, Maria A768
Henry, Michael A451
Henry, Patrick C. E129
Henry, Peter (Analog Devices) A66
Henry, Peter B. (NYU) P449
Henry, Pierre W371
Henry, Randy E111
Henry, Richard A. P386
Henry, Sam A238
Henry, Simon W339
Henry, Susan A. P154
Henry, Trent W146
Henschel, Laurel E. P548
Henschen, Gary M. A550
Hensel, Anthony D. A140
Hensing, John P62
Hensley, Edward H. A662
Hensley, Jonathan P506
Hensley, Susan (E. & J. Gallo) A309
Hensley, Susan (E. & J. Gallo) A309
Henson, Christopher L. A111
Henson, Daniel S. A376
Henson, Gregg L. A281
Henstenburg, Robert B. E130
Hentges, Harriet P247
Hentges, Mary M. A188
Hento, Merja W217
Hentschel, Steve E158
Henze, Kay P127
Henzler, Thomas A. A573
Hepps, Tammy P320
Hepvar, Ergun W342
Her, Michael H. E259

Heraeus, Jürgen W181
Herath, Kirk (Nationwide) A615
Herath, Kirk (Nationwide) A615
Herbel, Peter W411
Herbel, Vern D. A868
Herbert, C. Theodore A835
Herbert, Delker A871
Herbert, Gavin S. A39
Herbert, James H. (First Republic (CA)) E146
Herbert, James L. (Neogen) E255
Herbert, Jean-Marc W351
Herbert, Peter N. P674
Herbert, Stephen P. E369
Herbert-Jones, Siân W371
Herbkersman, John P84
Herbold, Chris A699
Herbst, Kai P352
Herbst, Steve P420
Herbst-Brady, Elizabeth A471
Herchenbach, Scott L. (Mutual of Omaha) A609
Herchenbach, Scott L. (Mutual of Omaha) A609
Herdiech, Ed E226
Herdman, Michael D. A99
Hereford, James P261
Herga, Gen A772
Hering, Alfred P551
Herington, Charles M. A94
Herington, Harry H. E262
Heris, Jean-François W36
Herkert, Craig R. A825
Herkins, Jon A476
Herko, Daniel J. A743
Herkströter, Cornelius A. J. W128
Herlache, Thomas L. P215
Herlihy, Donagh A94
Herman, Fred E. A741
Herman, Gary S. (Unified Grocers) A881
Herman, Gary S. (Unified Grocers) A881
Herman, John W. P208
Herman, Judy (Tishman Construction) A865
Herman, Judy (Tishman Construction) A865
Herman, Larry P413
Herman, Mark A138
Herman, Robert A. A238
Herman, Roberta (Harvard Pilgrim) P277
Herman, Scott P124
Herman, Theodore L. P416
Hermanek, Donald J. P314
Hermann, Wolfgang W363
Hermans, Johan P18
Hermelin, Paul W85
Hermens, Rosalee P609
Hermiz, Ramzi Y. A348
Hermosillo, Jeff P89
Hermreck, Immanuel W62
Hermógenes Rollano, Manuel W325
Hernandez, Adolfo W21
Hernandez, Bernardo A402
Hernandez, Carlos M. (Fluor) A359
Hernandez, Carlos M. (JPMorgan Chase) A494
Hernandez, Cecil A. E83
Hernandez, Dan A447
Hernandez, Daniel L. (Sykes Enterprises) E341
Hernandez, Enrique A642
Hernandez, John P255
Hernandez, Luis W91
Hernandez, Ricardo A512
Hernandez, Robert M. P634
Hernandez, Sandra A605
Hernandez-Lichtl, Javier P63
Hernberg, Neil P505
Herndon, Carol M. P175
Herndon, Charlotte A628
Herndon, D. Rogers A386
Hernon, Joseph P. E355

Holt, Allan M. (The Carlyle Group) A847
Holt, Bill A823
Holt, Bradford R. A790
Holt, Christopher A186
Holt, Douglas A. A646
Holt, John W. P. A15
Holt, Kenny P98
Holt, Matt P183
Holt, Paul A. E292
Holt, Sharon E. E295
Holt, William M. A464
Holtby, Jason A734
Holtcamp, Bob P662
Holte, Doug P319
Holter, Birgitte W287
Holter, Rod P279
Holtkamp, Bert A532
Holton, Martin L. A743
Holub, Robert C. P631
Holyfield, Jeff A217
Holzbacher, Enric W180
Holzem, John D. A829
Holzer, Sunita A204
Holzherr, Christian W90
Holzhey, Georg W427
Holzman, Elana W403
Holzman Graziano, Glori (The Carlyle Group) A847
Holzman Graziano, Glori (The Carlyle Group) A847
Holzman, Jac (Warner Music) A933
Holzman, Jac (Warner Music) A933
Holzschuh, Gunther W299
Homan, Richard P. (Turner Corporation) A873
Homan, Richard P. (Turner Corporation) A873
Homan, Todd P375
Homann, Bill A791
Homann, Timm W299
Hombach, Robert J. A110
Home, Ed (NHL) A637
Home, Ed (NHL) A637
Homer, David P. A382
Homfray, Christopher C. A256
Homlish, Martin A438
Homma, Mitsuru W352
Homma, Toshio W83
Hommen, Jan H. M. W200
Hommert, Douglas D. P39
Homrighaus, Barry P327
Homsey, Harvey H. H. P207
Hon Chew, Chan W365
Honaker, Jack P336
Honan, Bradley A471
Honan, Colleen P455
Honbo, Kenkichi W23
Honda, Daisaku W407
Honda, Haruhisa W83
Honda, Osamu W385
Honerkamp, P.J E204
Honeycutt, Bruce P87
Honeycutt, John A287
Honeyman, Eric A912
Hong, Arlene S. P321
Hong, Hak Pyo W238
Hong, Henry A476
Hong, James W107
Hong, Julie A761
Hong, Lingde W296
Hong, Peter A35
Hong, Richard A590
Hong, Shaw E269
Hong, Sung-Ho W238
Hong, Yin E322
Honggen, Li W366
Hongler, Markus W452
Hongo, Shousuke W384
Honig, Barry E193
Honig, Lawrence E. A7
Honig, Thomas W. A940
Honish, Gregory J. E275
Honjo, Masashi W294
Honnold, Scott A400

Honor, Robert A749
Honts, Gary A838
Hoo-Geun, Lee W311
Hood, Amy A595
Hood, Charles R. E230
Hood, Colin W358
Hood, Derek P219
Hood, Ernie P261
Hood, Henry J. A196
Hood, Lynn M. (Manor Care) A554
Hood, Lynn M. (Manor Care) A554
Hood, Mark (Apache) A71
Hood, Mark E. (Brown Shoe) A151
Hoogasian, Seth H. A855
Hoogenboom, Paul G. P. A755
Hoogmoed, David R. (Land O'Lakes) A519
Hoogmoed, David R. (Land O'Lakes) A519
Hook, Cynthia K. A227
Hook, Jonathan D. (Ohio State University) A661
Hook, Jonathan D. (Ohio State University) A661
Hooker, John T. A338
Hooks, Brian P293
Hooks, Craig E. P204
Hooks, Jacob T. A314
Hooks, M. Stacy E13
Hookstratten, Jon P229
Hooley, James L. E73
Hooley, Joseph L. A817
Hooley, Stephen C. A301
Hooper, Anna A267
Hooper, Brett E206
Hooper, Cindy P16
Hooper, John A947
Hooper, Marjorie W50
Hooper, Max D. A30
Hooper, Merritt S. E36
Hooper, Ned A210
Hooper, Sandy P8
Hooper, Sidney C. E338
Hoopes, John R. P561
Hoops, thomas K. A940
Hoover, Dennis A. A249
Hoover, Julie P8
Hoover, R. David A99
Hoover, Ray E357
Hoover, Richard A. E283
Hoover, Steve A960
Hoover, T. Wayne (Chick-fil-A) A198
Hoover, T. Wayne (Chick-fil-A) A198
Hoovestol, Wayne B. E164
Hope, Donald I. W296
Hope, Gustave W100
Hope, James D. A829
Hopf, A. Gidget P254
Hopf, Clarence J. P488
Hopgood, Daniel R. A589
Hopke, James C. E23
Hopkin, Daniel P292
Hopkins, Chris A772
Hopkins, Frank E. A696
Hopkins, Gordon (OSI Restaurant Partners) A669
Hopkins, Gordon (OSI Restaurant Partners) A669
Hopkins, Jennafer R. A594
Hopkins, John L. (Fluor) A359
Hopkins, John (Wyman-Gordon) P673
Hopkins, Joseph K. (Catholic Health East) A182
Hopkins, Joseph K. (Catholic Health East) A182
Hopkins, Laura P537
Hopkins, Nick A916
Hopkins, Paul N. W452
Hopkins, Roger J. E78
Hopkins, Sheila A. A224
Hopkins, Stephen W212
Hopkins, Thomas E. A786
Hopkins, Timothy J. A662
Hopkins, Vaugh K. W40
Hopko, Kathleen M. A893

Hoplamazian, Mark S. A455
Hopley, Peter J. (BJ's Wholesale Club) A129
Hopley, Peter J. (BJ's Wholesale Club) A129
Hopmans, John A538
Hopp, Daniel F. A949
Hopp-Michlosky, Kelli C. A247
Hoppe, Michael J. P210
Hopper, Doyle G. A652
Hopper, James W. E131
Hopper, Marilyn P430
Hopper, Scott E74
Hopwood, Andy W74
Horace, Bret P97
Horan, Ace P143
Horan, Christopher P241
Horan, Douglas S. A651
Horan, Jamey (NHL) A637
Horan, Jamey (NHL) A637
Horan, Jeanette A456
Horan, Terry P511
Horbach, Sandra J. (The Carlyle Group) A847
Horbach, Sandra J. (The Carlyle Group) A847
Horbaczewski, Henry Z. P363
Horbelt, Nicole W452
Horber, Felix W388
Horgan, John P387
Horger, Robert R. E313
Horie, Kiyohisa W327
Horin, David E304
Horioka, Hiroshi W410
Horiszny, Laurene H. A140
Horiszny, Vadim P433
Hormats, Robert D. P638
Horn, Alan F. (Time Warner) A862
Horn, Alan F. (Warner Bros.) P657
Horn, Alan (Randstad Holding) W320
Horn, Alan D. (Rogers Communications) W333
Horn, David C. A32
Horn, Jonathan W2
Horn, Kimberly K. P558
Horn, Michael E43
Horn, Patricia D. P203
Horn, Paul M. P449
Horn, Randall C. A901
Hornbuckle, William J. A592
Horne, Denise A. A574
Horne, James W. P144
Horne, Skip P358
Horne, Stephen C. P186
Horne, Terry P231
Horner, Caroline A289
Horner, Dawn M. E72
Horner, Digby A13
Horner, Jack A632
Horner, Jerald L. P11
Horner, Jill M. A748
Horner, Jody (Cargill) A172
Horner, Jody (Cargill) A172
Horner, Kim K. A126
Horner, Matt P671
Horner, Theresa A105
Horning, Al A224
Horning, Roxanne V. A375
Hornish, Thomas E. E274
Hornsby, Robert (Columbia University) A226
Hornsby, Robert (Columbia University) A226
Hornstein, Andreas L. P211
Hornstra, Peter E. A855
Hornung, Russ (W.L. Gore) A924
Hornung, Russ (W.L. Gore) A924
Horodniceanu, Michael (MTA) A608
Horodniceanu, Michael (MTA) A608
Horowitz, Howard B. E132
Horowitz, Jeffrey J. E376
Horowitz, Mark (AllianceBernstein) A40
Horowitz, Mark (AllianceBernstein) A40

Horowitz, Zach P624
Horrell, Jonathan A512
Horrell, Karen Holle A56
Horrell, Tony P144
Horrigan, Brian (IGA) A458
Horrigan, Brian (IGA) A458
Horsch, James A307
Horsham-Bertels, Helen A815
Horsley, Donald R. A797
Hortas, Laura A147
Hortensius, Peter D. W237
Horton, Chandler P339
Horton, Donald R. A262
Horton, Earl E. P141
Horton, Gary B. A49
Horton, Greg J. W296
Horton, Kevin W101
Horton, Michael (PPG Industries) A703
Horton, Michael (Universal Music Group) P624
Horton, Nehl P409
Horton, Peter W444
Horton, Rick A262
Horton, Thomas W. A63
Horton, Tim (First Data) A354
Horton, Tim (First Data) A354
Horton, William L. (Verizon) A914
Horton, William W. (Tenaska) P584
Horvath, Albert G. P470
Horvath, Peter Z. A535
Horváth, Ferenc W267
Horwitz, Steven E269
Horzepa, Joseph E. E199
Hosaka, Takemi W273
Hosang, Willem C. A. W177
Hosegood, Claire A885
Hosey, Brian E354
Hosfeld, Mark E111
Hosford, Chris P305
Hoshi, Hisamitsu W292
Hoshijima, Tokitaro W259
Hoshino, Asako W281
Hoshino, Kazuo W373
Hoshino, Masahide W284
Hoshstrasser, Kevin A135
Hosking, Graeme W44
Hosking, Robert A746
Hoskins, Adriana N. A778
Hoskins, Anne E. A717
Hoskins, Craig H. (Performance Food) A687
Hoskins, Craig H. (Performance Food) A687
Hoskins, Gary F. E71
Hoskins, John M. (TVA) A874
Hoskins, John M. (TVA) A874
Hoskins, Richard (Southern Missouri Bancorp) E328
Hoskins, Richard (Aviva) W45
Hoskinson, Carey P421
Hosoda, Ryutaro W161
Hosoi, Susumu W205
Hosp, Walter D. (HMS Holdings) E175
Hosp, Walter D. (Health Management Systems) P283
Host, Brian P180
Host, Kathleen E146
Hostler, Jeffrey N. P391
Hostler, Sharon L. P636
Hotchkiss, Jeffrey R. E349
Hotop, Tina A. A153
Hotson, Matt W236
Hotsuki, Keishi A605
Hotta, Satoru W352
Hottinger, Molly A779
Hou, Mingjuan A724
Houben, Luc G. P334
Houck, Jancy P675
Houdard, France P166
Houde, Rob E181
Hough, Benjamin M. E170
Hough, Jeffery G. E166
Hough, Michael R. E170
Hough, P.J. A595
Houghton, Michael A92

A = AMERICAN BUSINESS
E = EMERGING COMPANIES
P = PRIVATE COMPANIES
W = WORLD BUSINESS

Hutchison, Robert (CHEP) P135
Hutley, Lynn P15
Hutmacher, Heiko W19
Hutson, Carolyn P98
Hutson, William (EBSCO) A317
Hutson, William (EBSCO) A317
Hutterly, Jane M. (S.C. Johnson) A759
Hutterly, Jane M. (S.C. Johnson) A759
Huttle, Lawrence J. A858
Huttleston, Timothy S. A4
Huttner, Jack E157
Hutto, Peter S. E225
Huwiler, John E. A484
Huxtable, Laurie J. A181
Huybrecht, Viviane W216
Huyer, Paul W. W392
Huyghebaert, Jan W216
Huyhua, Juan Carlos P506
Huzii, Natsuki W76
Huët, Jean-Marc W426
Hviid, Frank W285
Hvisdas, James M. P462
Hwang, Angelina W8
Hwang, Hyeon Sik W238
Hwang, Ruey-Li A394
Hwang, Simon W8
Hwang, Teddy B. B. W238
Hwong, Jimmy P222
Hyams, Larry P8
Hyatt, Lawrence E. A254
Hyatt, Michael S. P596
Hydanus, Michael P. E252
Hyde, D. Cameron A960
Hyde, Joan A138
Hyde, Joseph R. E168
Hyde, Matthew G. E82
Hyde, Michael W. A484
Hyder, Rima (Energy Future) A330
Hyder, Rima (Energy Future) A330
Hygen, Odd Marius W378
Hyita, Bart J. A239
Hyland, Dave E81
Hyland, Seamus P127
Hyle, Charles S. A500
Hyle, Kathleen W. A243
Hylen, Jane A334
Hyman, Danny P511
Hyman, David E257
Hyman, Gary W334
Hyman, Steven E. (Harvard University) A421
Hyman, Steven E. (Harvard University) A421
Hynard, Andrew A491
Hynes, James P. E260
Hynes, Jane E310
Hynes, Kevin P571
Hynes, Ronald C. A567
Hynes, Toby N. P267
Hynick, Robert P170
Hyson, Kevin P31
Hyzak, Dwayne L E228
Hyzak, Randy A. (Freescale Semiconductor) A371
Hyzak, Randy A. (Freescale Semiconductor) A371
Hägglöf, Henrik W350
Hägglöv, Tobias W137
Häggström, Lars W379
Hänggi, Rolf W274
Hänle, Wolfgang W112
Hänninen, Pauli W427
Härnwall, Peter W356
Härter, Hans-Georg W451
Hébert, Susan P129
Hödl, Hubert W246
Hökby, Björn W285
Höttges, Timotheus W122
H⬜gsted, Peter W220

H⬜jlund, Carsten W204
Hübner, Thomas M. W87
Hübscher, Otmar W186
Hülskötter, Hans-Peter W62

I

Iacabucci, Tim A627
Iachini, Michael A194
Iaco, Steven A186
Iacobelli, Alphons A. (Chrysler) A201
Iacobelli, Alphons A. (Chrysler) A201
Iacobelli, Ronald V. E43
Iacobucci, Andrew W240
Iacovone, Gina M. (BJ's Wholesale Club) A129
Iacovone, Gina M. (BJ's Wholesale Club) A129
Iacozzilli, Venanzio W394
Iacullo, Bob P425
Iams, Bryan P70
Ianieri, Valerie P674
Ianni, Josie W254
Ianni, Mark A634
Iannicelli, Joseph W377
Ianniello, Joseph R. A188
Iannone, Jamie A105
Iannotti, Joseph P590
Iannotti, Thomas J. (Hewlett-Packard) A438
Iannotti, Thomas J. (HP Enterprise Services) P300
Iannucci, Patricia A677
Iardella, Carlo Alberto W155
Ibaraki, Akira W352
Ibarra, Alicia Bárce P621
Ibbetson, David A380
Ibbotson, Stephen A94
Iboshi, Tricia E212
Ibraghimov, Nail G. W391
Ibrahim, Christina A413
Ibsen, Marlene A871
Ibuchi, Yoshiaki W361
Icahn, Carl C. (Federal-Mogul) A348
Icahn, Carl C. (XO Holdings) P674
Ice, Carl R. A157
Icenhour, Kenneth A. E71
Ichikawa, Hiizu W262
Ichikawa, Junji W83
Ichikawa, Masakazu W182
Ichimaru, Yoichiro W413
Ichino, Naoshi W18
Ichishi, Masao W373
Icole, Jean-Yves W98
Ida, Yoshinori W205
Iddon, Mike W401
Ide, Akiko W293
Iden, Ronald L. A290
Idiart, Roger A. A340
Idrovo, Javier H. A434
Ielusic, Walter F. A376
Ienuso, Joseph A. (Columbia University) A226
Ienuso, Joseph A. (Columbia University) A226
Ierland, Sejal W48
Iersel, Erwin W11
Iftiniuk, Alan (Catholic Healthcare West) A185
Iftiniuk, Alan (Catholic Healthcare West) A185
Igarashi, Kazuhiro W162
Igarashi, Yasuharu W410
Igashira, Hiroshi W410
Iger, Robert A. A290
Iglesias, Anabell A502
Iglesias, Henry A860
Igli, Kevin J. A876
Ignaczak, Edward A342
Ignasher, Timothy J. P. E71
Ignatz, Craig (Giant Eagle) A392
Ignatz, Craig (Giant Eagle) A392
Igney, Natja E268

Igoe, Brian P647
Igoe, Jessica A53
Igrejas, Eduardo W41
Ihamuotila, Timo W282
Ihara, Katsumi W375
Ihara, Kenichi W263
Ihara, Yasumori W413
Ihlenfeld, Jay V. A2
Ihnken, N. William P580
Ihori, Kazutaka W361
Ihrie, Robert W543
Iida, Haruyuki W162
Iida, Satoshi W226
Iijima, Masami W265
Iijima, Shigekazu W327
Iino-Harvey, Jennifer A94
Iio, Norinao W265
Iio, Toshimitsu W449
Iiyama, Toshiyasu W284
Ike, Denisse P646
Ike, Fumihiko W188
Ikeda, Donna S. A367
Ikeda, Takashi W373
Ikeda, Tomohiko W160
Ikegai, Kenji W162
Ikegaya, Mikio W263
Ikemura, Toshio W184
Iker, John P374
Ikeuchi, Hiroshi W352
Ikeuchi, Mitsuo W294
Ikeura, Tmoihisa W259
Ikoma, Toshiaki W83
Ikuno, Hiroshi W250
Ikuno, Mitsuhiko W327
Ikuta, Shoichi W250
Ilar, Kristina A646
Ilderem, Vida A464
Ilek, Hartmut W299
Iles, T. Randall (Andersen Corporation) A68
Iles, T. Randall (Andersen Corporation) A68
Ilitch, Christopher P309
Ilitch, Marian (Ilitch Holdings) P309
Ilitch, Marian (Little Caesar's) P366
Ilitch, Michael (Ilitch Holdings) P309
Ilitch, Michael (Little Caesar's) P366
Iliya, Anthony W107
Illich, Jim (Bechtel) A114
Illich, Jim (Bechtel) A114
Ilyes, Amy P472
Ilyushin, Viktor V. W165
Im, Tony E314
Imada, Bill A471
Imai, Kazuki W252
Imai, Masamichi W273
Imai, Michiro W262
Imai, Takashi W277
Imaki, Hisakazu W252
Imakubo, Tetsuo W279
Imamura, Masashi W375
Imanaka, Mitsuru W229
Imanse, Andrew A858
Imatoki, Takeshi W284
Imauven, Claude W346
Imazu, Hidetoshi W281
Imbert, Frank W150
Imbert, Frederico W107
Imhoff, Michael F. E332
Imielinski, Mitch M. A30
Imielinski, Tomasz P49
Imler, Elia A176
Immelt, Jeffrey R. A376
Imperato, Donna (Young & Rubicam) P677
Imperato, Donna (WPP) W445
Impicciche, Joseph R. (Ascension Health) A82
Impicciche, Joseph R. (Ascension Health) A82
Imrie, Alastair W48
Imura, Kimihiko E234
In-Hwan, Oh W311
In-Kyung, Oh W311
Inaba, Nobuo W327

Inaba, Yoshimi W413
Inacker, Steve A171
Inamori, Kazuo (Japan Airlines) W209
Inamori, Kazuo (Kyocera) W229
Inamoto, Nobuhide W252
Inayama, Hideaki W384
Inbona, Yves W347
Incardona, Christopher E156
Inch, Donna A365
Inciarte, Juan R. W172
Indeglia, Maria E142
Indekeu, Jack E194
Indest, John L. E218
Ineci, Barbaros W342
Infante, Adelle A5
Infanti, Daniel A211
Infantino, Federico W119
Infantino, Frances P416
Ingall, Seth P239
Ingalls, Donald R. P284
Ingato, Robert J. A211
Inge, Carol P368
Ingelog, Michael W107
Ingemanson, Björn W439
Ingemansson, Björn W439
Ingenthron, Greg A664
Ingersoll, Kelly P314
Ingham, Gideon W37
Ingle, Raymond L. A335
Ingleby, Philip P166
Inglis, Craig W213
Inglis, Greg (NHL) A637
Inglis, Greg (NHL) A637
Inglis, I. Martin (Battelle Memorial) A107
Inglis, I. Martin (Battelle Memorial) A107
Ingold, Roger W6
Ingold, Scott P632
Ingoldsby, James J. A650
Ingraham, Tricia A355
Ingram, Duncan W80
Ingram, Edgar Waldo P667
Ingram, Kevin S. P223
Ingram, Lisa P667
Ingram, Louise W282
Ingram, Martha River P644
Ingram, Orrin H. P313
Ingram, Paul P116
Ingram, Richard A398
Ingram, Scott A722
Ingrao, Adam P108
Inlander, Todd L. A319
Inman, Emma P533
Inman, Gordon E. A351
Inman, Paul W334
Inman, Samuel M. E79
Innes, Jan L. W333
Innocenzi, Fabio W203
Ino, Hiroyuki W408
Inobe, Sadayuki W385
Inohara, Hiroyuki W381
Inoue, Haruo W263
Inoue, Hiroo W207
Inoue, Hisayuki W413
Inoue, Masahiro (Yahoo!) A963
Inoue, Masahiro (SOFTBANK) W372
Inoue, Nobuaki W161
Inoue, Osamu W384
Inoue, Shinichi W23
Inoue, Shuhei W373
Inoue, Takeshi W260
Inoue, Tamotsu W162
Inoue, Toshiki W182
Inoue, Yoichi W413
Inoue, Yoshiharu W76
Inoue, Yuji (Obayashi) W294
Inoue, Yuji (Ricoh Company) W327
Insall, Gerard (Avis Budget) A91
Insall, Gerard (Avis) P56
Insel, Thomas R. P443
Inserra, Andrea A138
Insignares, Felisa A711
Insogna, Anthony M. P334
Intemann, Greg A273

Jeffery, Scott W. A224
Jeffery, W. Jeremy A22
Jeffress, Rusty A595
Jeffrey, Bob W445
Jeffrey, David (Salvation Army) A764
Jeffrey, David (Salvation Army) A764
Jeffrey, John (Deloitte) A276
Jeffrey, John (Deloitte) A276
Jeffrey, Rick E211
Jeffries, Douglas C. E344
Jeffries, Jamie A640
Jeffries, Michael S. A7
Jeffries-Jones, Sharon A111
Jeffs, Roger E366
Jehn, Jennifer P186
Jelinek, W. Craig A249
Jelinkova, Klara (University of Chicago) A898
Jelinkova, Klara (University of Chicago) A898
Jelle, Dave P227
Jellinek, Michael S. P465
Jellison, Brian D. A751
Jellison, Douglas J. A652
Jelmini, David A443
Jemley, Charles A814
Jen, Chin-Our Jerry E166
Jenereaux, Joyce A375
Jeng, Megan A340
Jenkin, Thomas M. (Caesars Entertainment) A165
Jenkin, Thomas M. (Caesars Entertainment) A165
Jenkins, Antony W53
Jenkins, Bob P4
Jenkins, Bonnie D. P638
Jenkins, Brad P4
Jenkins, Charles W (Energy Future) A330
Jenkins, Charles H. (Publix) A719
Jenkins, Charles W (Energy Future) A330
Jenkins, Charles H. (Publix) A719
Jenkins, Chris (Universal Studios) P626
Jenkins, Chris (Thales) W405
Jenkins, Clay A151
Jenkins, D. Scott (The Carlyle Group) A847
Jenkins, D. Scott (The Carlyle Group) A847
Jenkins, Deborah A369
Jenkins, Derek L. A832
Jenkins, Ernest L. A683
Jenkins, James R. A271
Jenkins, Joe P673
Jenkins, John S. W419
Jenkins, Ken P671
Jenkins, Kent (Corinthian Colleges) E85
Jenkins, Les P537
Jenkins, Marc P420
Jenkins, Norman K. A557
Jenkins, Richard D. P43
Jenkins, Tony P84
Jenkins, William A326
Jenkyn, Oliver (Visa Inc) A917
Jenkyn, Oliver (Visa U.S.A.) P647
Jenner, Jan W48
Jenner, Shane A923
Jenness, James M. A498
Jennifer, Jackie R. P294
Jennings, Austin W51
Jennings, Brian (NHL) A637
Jennings, Brian (NHL) A637
Jennings, Donna N. E102
Jennings, Gary (Associated Wholesale Grocers) A85
Jennings, Gary (Associated Wholesale Grocers) A85
Jennings, Kyle P30
Jennings, Maurine P642
Jennings, Michael C. (HollyFrontier) A443
Jennings, Michael (PSEG Power) P488
Jennings, Scott S. A717

Jennings, William (Jefferies Group) A484
Jennings, William M. (Yale New Haven Health Services Corporation) P674
Jenny, Sacha E235
Jensen, Anders (Nordea Bank) W285
Jensen, Anders (Telenor) W397
Jensen, Andrea P129
Jensen, Anita K. (Catholic Health East) A182
Jensen, Anita K. (Catholic Health East) A182
Jensen, Brad A906
Jensen, Carol E. P660
Jensen, Carolyn (ASCAP) P45
Jensen, Dan W. A284
Jensen, Dennis P219
Jensen, Eric P396
Jensen, Erling W2
Jensen, George R. E369
Jensen, Harry P667
Jensen, James B. A790
Jensen, Jan P318
Jensen, Jim A930
Jensen, Julia A568
Jensen, Keith A. A56
Jensen, Kurt A. E364
Jensen, Larry P360
Jensen, Luke W208
Jensen, Mary P92
Jensen, Peder K. A587
Jensen, Peter P492
Jensen, Rick W. A473
Jensen, Steven P476
Jensen, Tony E305
Jenson, Mike P311
Jenson, Paul P306
Jenssen, Jens R. W378
Jeong-Woo, Choi W311
Jeppesen, Jon A. A71
Jerde, Garett P279
Jeremiah, Dai W80
Jerger-Stevens, Jan E. P237
Jerijervi, Tracey E122
Jermyn, Isadore (MassMutual) A564
Jermyn, Isadore (MassMutual) A564
Jernberg, Melker W356
Jernigan, Donald E. (TVA) A874
Jernigan, Donald L. (Adventist Health System) P14
Jernigan, Donald E. (TVA) A874
Jerome, Chris A901
Jerome, Harrison P565
Jerome, James P. E258
Jerschke, Tobias W228
Jervis, Lisa W314
Jervoe, Johan A464
Jerzyk, Timothy P. A965
Jesion, Paula J. A35
Jeske, Hans-O W248
Jesko, Mark A339
Jessar, Kevin (Red Cross) A737
Jessar, Kevin (Red Cross) A737
Jesse, David E165
Jesse, Sandra L. (Blue Cross and Blue Shield of Massachusetts) A132
Jesse, Sandra L. (Blue Cross and Blue Shield of Massachusetts) A132
Jester, Lisa H. A711
Jesudason, Rob W107
Jeter, Peter P92
Jetha, Yasmin W83
Jetmundsen, Norman A922
Jette, Al W392
Jeunet, Philippe W167
Jew, Kerri (Columbia University) A226
Jew, Kerri (Columbia University) A226
Jewell, Rick A666
Jewell, Tony W40
Jewett, Joshua R. A344
Jewett, Patrick A92
Jewkes, Brett P420
Jeworrek, Torsten W268
Jeyarajah, Praveen R. P500
Jezerinac, Daniel E. P188

Jha, Abhinav P595
Jha, Rajesh A595
Jha, Satya K P16
Jhanwar, Suresh C. P399
Jhi-Yong, Kim W311
Jian, Qiao W237
Jiang, Chao E69
Jiang, Wei-Ming W128
Jianglei, Wei W237
Jianping, Zhang W366
Jibilian, John P675
Jiga, Anthony P. P449
Jikumaru, Yusuke W23
Jimarez, Miguel A61
Jimenez, A. David P120
Jimenez, Augusto P191
Jimenez, Frank R. A476
Jimenez, Jose (Cox Communications) A251
Jimenez, Jose (Cox Communications) A251
Jimenez, Joseph (Novartis) W289
Jimenez, Linda A939
Jimenez, Rey Y. A355
Jimenez, Roberto I. (Cox Enterprises) A252
Jimenez, Roberto I. (Cox Enterprises) A252
Jimenez, Samuel D. E45
Jimenez, Trini M. A157
Jimenez-Hernandez, Iris (New York City Health and Hospitals) A624
Jimenez-Hernandez, Iris (New York City Health and Hospitals) A624
Jiménez, Rod W54
Jin, H. P. E348
Jin-Il, Kim W311
Jines, Michael L. A386
Jing-Shyh Su, Samuel A965
Jing-Wan, Kim W349
Jingming, Zhang W366
Jinno, Junichi W229
Jirgal, Robert A218
Jiron, Feliciano (Catholic Healthcare West) A185
Jiron, Feliciano (Catholic Healthcare West) A185
Jiufeng, Yu W153
Jiwanlal, Sharad B. P279
Joas, Irmgard W268
Jobkar, Kathi M. A37
Jobs, Ulrich W341
Jocham, Uwe E. P163
Joei, Bernard W452
Joerres, Jeffrey A. A555
Jog, Vikram E149
Joh, Bill A376
Johannesen, James A574
Johanneson, David (Navistar International) A616
Johanneson, David (Navistar) P425
Johannessen, Morten S. W378
Johannpeter, Guilherme A391
Johansen, Michael Holm A221
Johansen, Trond-Erik A238
Johanson, John P206
Johansson, Ann-Sofie W174
Johansson, Annica A512
Johansson, Christer W439
Johansson, Christian W439
Johansson, Jan C. W387
Johansson, Thomas O. A538
John, Andrew W417
John, Steve W83
Johns, Christopher P. A694
Johns, David L. A671
Johns, Derrick A. A318
Johns, Douglas A. P412
Johns, John D. A715
Johns, Michael M. E. P201
Johns, Tammy A555
Johnsen, Andrew K. A157
Johnsen, Cheryl M. P532
Johnsen, Constance R. A794
Johnsen, Kjell-Morten W397

Johnsen, Timothy J. P546
Johnson, Abigail P. (FMR) A361
Johnson, Abigail P. (FMR) A361
Johnson, Alan W426
Johnson, Andrea P351
Johnson, Andy P221
Johnson, Ardelle R. E307
Johnson, Ben F. P201
Johnson, Bill (AgriBank) P19
Johnson, Bill (Benjamin Moore) P76
Johnson, Bill (Intermountain Health Care) P315
Johnson Bolt, Jennifer M. A367
Johnson, Boyd P401
Johnson, Brent P315
Johnson, Brett W317
Johnson, Brian J. (Casey's General Stores) A179
Johnson, Brian D. (Hormel) A447
Johnson, Bruce (C&S Wholesale) A158
Johnson, Bruce D. (Regis Corporation) A739
Johnson, Bruce (C&S Wholesale) A158
Johnson, Bryan W451
Johnson, Carmen S. (JM Family Enterprises) A486
Johnson, Carmen S. (JM Family Enterprises) A486
Johnson, Carol M. (EBSCO) A317
Johnson, Carol M. (EBSCO) A317
Johnson, Carolyn M. (Protective Life) A715
Johnson, Catharine E247
Johnson, Charles B. (Franklin Templeton) A367
Johnson, Charles E. (MeadWestvaco) A580
Johnson, Charlotte P201
Johnson, Chris (Dillard's) A284
Johnson, Chris (Nestlé) W274
Johnson, Christine Cole (Henry Ford Health System) P286
Johnson, Christopher (Deutsche Bank Securities (USA)) P180
Johnson, Christopher (FM Global) P223
Johnson, Clarence D. E253
Johnson, Colin A642
Johnson, Craig R. (JMP Group) E207
Johnson, Craig A. (Altria) A44
Johnson, Craig (Guitar Center) P267
Johnson, Dan (Baker & Taylor) A97
Johnson, Dan (Baker & Taylor) A97
Johnson, Dan (COUNTRY Financial) P155
Johnson, Dana (Comerica) A228
Johnson, Daniel L. P371
Johnson, Darin J. E379
Johnson, David L. (Maxus Realty Trust) E234
Johnson, David L. (Dell) A274
Johnson, David A. (Jones Lang LaSalle) A491
Johnson, David D. (Molex) A600
Johnson, David (Nalco) A613
Johnson, Dean (Sodexo USA) P552
Johnson, Dean (Sodexo) W371
Johnson, Dennis (American Business Bank) E23
Johnson, Dennis A. (Comerica) A228
Johnson, Dennis (NFL) A635
Johnson, Dennis (NFL) A635
Johnson, Donald P. E23
Johnson, Dorine A367
Johnson, Doug P92
Johnson, E. Thomas (New York Life) A625
Johnson, E. Thomas (New York Life) A625
Johnson, Edward C. (FMR) A361
Johnson, Edward C. (FMR) A361
Johnson, Ellen T. A471
Johnson, Emilie A766
Johnson, Eric R. (CNO Financial) A219
Johnson, Eric (Oxbow) P460

Jones, Dawn (University of Texas System) A899
Jones, Derek A801
Jones, Dick (Quintiles Transnational) A727
Jones, Dick (Quintiles Transnational) A727
Jones, Donald G. P14
Jones, Douglas L. A30
Jones, Ebbert E. A940
Jones, Elizabeth P492
Jones, Ellen (Regions Financial) A738
Jones, Ellen (CHRISTUS Health) P137
Jones, Evon L. A539
Jones, Franklin B. A464
Jones, Garry P. A656
Jones, Gary P71
Jones, George S. A339
Jones, Graham W45
Jones, Gregg P421
Jones, Hal S. A934
Jones, Hannah A640
Jones, Hayden R. (The Carlyle Group) A847
Jones, Hayden R. (The Carlyle Group) A847
Jones, Hugh W. (Sabre Holdings) A760
Jones, Hugh W. (Sabre Holdings) A760
Jones, Ingrid Saund A221
Jones, J. Larry A254
Jones, James J. P204
Jones, Jamie E111
Jones, Jan P487
Jones, Janice M. (PulteGroup) A720
Jones, Janis L. (Caesars Entertainment) A165
Jones, Janis L. (Caesars Entertainment) A165
Jones, Jeffrey D. E78
Jones, Jill A. A152
Jones, Jim E277
Jones, Jody P600
Jones, Joel A963
Jones, John (CenturyLink) A191
Jones, John Alton (Smithfield Foods) A791
Jones, John (Boston Market) P96
Jones, John (K-VA-T Food Stores) P336
Jones, John F. (NIH) P443
Jones, Joseph M. P65
Jones, Juan C. A666
Jones, Katrina (Hilton Worldwide) A441
Jones, Katrina (Hilton Worldwide) A441
Jones, Keith (Pediatric Services of America) P469
Jones, Keith H. D. (Wolseley) W443
Jones, Ken P78
Jones, Keri A832
Jones, Kevin C. (Hormel) A447
Jones, Kevin (Wenner Media) P663
Jones, Laura Blake P632
Jones, Leslie M. A607
Jones, Loretha P82
Jones, M. Steven P626
Jones, Malcolm A224
Jones, Mark (Bonneville Power) P92
Jones, Mark A. (Structure Tone) P571
Jones, Mark (AstraZeneca) W40
Jones, Mary S. A883
Jones, Matt A375
Jones, Maurice D. A553
Jones, Michael (News Corp.) A632
Jones, Michael (Royal Caribbean Cruises) A754
Jones, Michael (United Space Alliance) P623
Jones, Michelle A483
Jones, Mike W. A138
Jones, Neal A557
Jones, Nicholas P. P332
Jones, Nicole S. A207
Jones, Paul J. (Harley-Davidson) A417
Jones, Paul (US Airways) A906

Jones, Peter P520
Jones, Phil (MidAmerican Energy) A597
Jones, Phil (Scotts Miracle-Gro) A777
Jones, Philip (Document Security Systems) E108
Jones, Philip (Telstra) W399
Jones, R. Todd (Publix) A719
Jones, R. Todd (Publix) A719
Jones, Rachael P166
Jones, Randall T. E334
Jones, Rhys W92
Jones, Richard H. (Pegasystems) E279
Jones, Richard M. (CBS Corp) A188
Jones, Richard (Tesco) W401
Jones, Robert C. (Fluidigm) E149
Jones, Robert L. (Onyx Pharmaceuticals) E270
Jones, Robert G. (Arch Coal) A78
Jones, Robert J. (University of Minnesota) P633
Jones, Roderick P222
Jones, Ron E167
Jones, Sheldon W289
Jones, Sheri E52
Jones, Sidney G. A387
Jones, Stephen J. (Air Products) A29
Jones, Stephen J. (Coca-Cola Refreshments) A223
Jones, Steve P668
Jones, Steven M. (Credit Acceptance) E89
Jones, Steven C. (NeoGenomics) E255
Jones, Tami A5
Jones, Terrie P92
Jones, Thomas A. A387
Jones, Tim (ConAgra) A237
Jones, Tim (Stanley Black and Decker) A811
Jones, Tom (Ryder System) A757
Jones, Tom (United Rentals) A889
Jones, Tony A912
Jones, Travis E220
Jones, W. Paul P542
Jones, W. Terrell P470
Jones, W. Wesley P245
Jones, Wendy A33
Jones, Wilson R. A668
Jong, Peter W200
Jong-Soo, Woo W311
Jong-Tae, Choi W311
Jongstra, Robert A711
Jonker, Niels E51
Jonsson, Haakan P70
Jonsson, Jonas W296
Jonsson, Lennart A314
Joo, Mike P403
Joo-Hyeon, Choi W349
Joon-Sik, Kim W311
Joon-Yang, Chung W311
Joos, David W. A217
Joos, Sven A461
Joosten, Ruud W19
Joppa, Sandra N. A296
Jordan, Boyd P508
Jordan, Chris P677
Jordan, Christopher J. (Wells Fargo) A940
Jordan, Debbie (NHL) A637
Jordan, Debbie (NHL) A637
Jordan, Elliot W208
Jordan, Gunther W119
Jordan, Henry K. A940
Jordan, J. Craig A703
Jordan, Jeffrey E271
Jordan, Ken A461
Jordan, Lani A203
Jordan, Linda A147
Jordan, Louis A814
Jordan, Lyriel P108
Jordan, Michael A577
Jordan, Nicole P48
Jordan, Phil P416
Jordan, Raymond C. (Johnson & Johnson) A487

Jordan, Raymond (TVA) A874
Jordan, Raymond (TVA) A874
Jordan, Rhonda A512
Jordan, Robert E. (AirTran Holdings) A31
Jordan, Robert E. (Southwest Airlines) A799
Jordan S., Glenn G. A221
Jordan, Sheila A210
Jordan, Tim P96
Jordan, Tina P219
Jordan, Vitol E328
Jordis, Theresa W147
Jorge, Robert (Golden State Foods) A396
Jorge, Robert (Golden State Foods) A396
Jorgensen, Blake J. (Levi Strauss) A530
Jorgensen, Blake J. (Levi Strauss) A530
Jorgensen, Erik A595
Jorgensen, Mark E181
Jorgensen, Steven C. P304
Jorgenson, Kevin J. E215
Jorgenson, Mary Ann P412
Josefsson, Lars W350
Joselove, Jonathan (Neiman Marcus) A622
Joselove, Jonathan (Neiman Marcus) A622
Joseph, Alex A. A265
Joseph, Charles S. P84
Joseph, James E. P454
Joseph, Keith A. P553
Joseph, Marc P272
Joseph, Pamela A. (U.S. Bancorp) A877
Joseph, Pamela A. (Elavon) P199
Joseph, Susan R. A228
Joseph, Tamara L. E91
Joseph, Thomas A. A208
Joseph, Tommy S. (International Paper) A470
Joseph, Tommy S. (Shorewood Packaging) P553
Josephs, Brian (Topco Associates LLC) A867
Josephs, Brian (Topco Associates LLC) A867
Josephson, Brian P498
Josephson, Richard C. A775
Josey, John A. E38
Joshi, Anant N. A557
Joshi, Prasoon A471
Joshi, Salil E205
Joshi, Vyomesh A438
Josi, Jean-Louis Laure W47
Josiah, Timothy W. A735
Joslin, Julie A. E75
Joslyn, James E. A934
Joss, Robert L. (Stanford University) A810
Joss, Robert L. (Stanford University) A810
Jost, Gerrit W158
Joswiak, Greg A74
José de Costa Flores, Ricardo W428
Jot, Jean-Marc E111
Jotwani, Pradeep A312
Jotwani, Tarun W284
Joubert, Philippe W27
Joubran, Robert J. P483
Jouet, Lionel (Bausch & Lomb) A108
Jouet, Lionel (Bausch & Lomb) A108
Jouffret, Christophe P108
Jourdaine, Thierry W73
Joussen, Friedrich P. W436
Jowers, Ronnie L. P201
Joy, Bill P343
Joy, John W. A84
Joy, Michelle P62
Joyce, Alan W317
Joyce, Brian P6
Joyce, David L. A376
Joyce, Derek P305
Joyce, Francis T. E246
Joyce, Glenn A71

Joyce, John J. E21
Joyce, Joseph M. A124
Joyce, Kenneth T. A61
Joyce, Mary P170
Joyce, Michael A541
Joyce, Paul A402
Joyce, R. Todd A938
Joyce, Richard W323
Joyce, Stephen T. P277
Joyce, Thomas P. (Danaher) A265
Joyce, Thomas P. (Public Service Enterprise Group) A717
Joyce, Thomas P. (U.S. Bancorp) A877
Joyce, Thomas P. (PSEG Power) P488
Joyce, Tony W190
Joyner, David S. P89
Joyner, Jackie A713
Juarez, Diego (First Data) A354
Juarez, Diego (First Data) A354
Juarez, Joe A673
Juarez, Ricardo E322
Juarez, Steve (University of California) A897
Juarez, Steve (University of California) A897
Jucker, Bernhard W4
Judd, Andrew P166
Judd, Norm P197
Judd, Penny (TVA) A874
Judd, Penny (TVA) A874
Judd, Russell (Catholic Healthcare West) A185
Judd, Russell (Catholic Healthcare West) A185
Juden, Alexander A772
Judet, Charlotte W313
Judge, Barry A124
Judge, James J. A651
Judge, John W. A355
Judge, Jonathan J. (First Data) A354
Judge, Jonathan J. (First Data) A354
Judge, Lola S. P210
Judge, Stephen A267
Jueckstock, Rainer A348
Juel, Steinar W285
Jufors, Staffan W439
Juhas, Peter A27
Juhl, Randy P. P634
Juhlke, David P. A447
Juj, Hardev P92
Julian, David F. (Norfolk Southern) A644
Julian, David F. (Norfolk Southern Railway) P446
Julian, James R. P631
Julian, Jerome E. P210
Julian, Mark A. A355
Julian, Paul C. A577
Julie, Russel W296
Julien, Jeffrey P. A734
Julien, Mark V. P352
Jun, Liu W237
Junck, Mary E. P50
June, Lee N. P408
Junemann, Gregory J. P17
Jung, Andrea A94
Jung, Franz W67
Jung, Joseph P610
Jung, Reinhard W438
Jung, Simon A340
Jung, Sonia A247
Jung, Steven E. P210
Jung Tsai, John Chieh A29
Jung-Sik, Lee W311
Jung-Soo, Shin W349
Jung-Suk, Shin W311
Junio, Marc A400
Junkroski, Robert M. E260
Junor, Duncan A413
Junqueira Leite, Agenor W304
Junqueiro, Steve P523
Jura, Anton A890
Juranek, Herbert W147
Juras, Lara P52
Jurasek, Jeanne P594

A = AMERICAN BUSINESS
E = EMERGING COMPANIES
P = PRIVATE COMPANIES
W = WORLD BUSINESS

Kessler, Eric A862
Kessler, Heinz W147
Kessler, Lisa (American Public Education) E25
Kessler, Lisa (Procter & Gamble) A711
Kessler, Stephen W. (CalPERS) A167
Kessler, Stephen W. (CalPERS) A167
Kessler, Steven P200
Kesson, Scott E82
Kesteloot, Thomas M. A829
Kestenbaum, Alan E159
Kestenbaum, Jay A30
Kestenbaum, Jerry A30
Kestenbaum, Michael P49
Kestler, M. Lee E112
Keswani, Sid A832
Keswick, Adam P. C. W212
Keswick, Benjamin W. W212
Keswick, Henry W212
Keswick, Simon L. W212
Ketchin, David W85
Kett, John W. P314
Kettels, Janet A39
Ketter, Stefan W153
Ketterer, Douglas J. A605
Kettering, Glen L. A641
Kettlewell, Kelly E340
Keup, Gregory J. P39
Keuper, Frank W47
Keur, P. C. W318
Kevelighan, Sean W452
Kevers, Charly A438
Key, David W374
Key, Matthew W395
Keyes, Michael J. A152
Keyes, Rick (Meijer) A584
Keyes, Rick (Meijer) A584
Keyes, Tony A232
Keys, Thomas C. A591
Keyser, Kate A87
Keziere, Russell E279
Kgosana, Moses W224
Khahaifa, Avido P607
Khail, Steven C. A553
Khaitan, Neeti P16
Khajasha, Inayat E269
Khalar, Rick (University of Texas System) A899
Khalar, Rick (University of Texas System) A899
Khaldi, Anan A577
Khalfan, Rizwan W392
Khan, Badar W92
Khan, Ejaz A. A922
Khan, Fareed A. A892
Khan, Mehmood A684
Khan, Omar A213
Khan, Ruhi E7
Khan, Shabana W354
Khan, Shahid P219
Khan, Zareen A379
Khandekar, Shekhar E358
Khani, David A239
Khanna, Roma P405
Khanzode, Atul P186
Khasbulatov, Khamzat A574
Khasis, Lev A928
Khattak, Farouque P10
Khattri, Sanjiv P156
Khaykin, Oleg E196
Khazam, Jonathan A464
Khemani, Rajiv E64
Khemlani, Neeraj (Hearst Corporation) A430
Khemlani, Neeraj (Hearst Corporation) A430
Khera, Rajesh E55
Khichi, Samrat S. P116
Khisamov, Rais S. W391

Khiyara, Shail E344
Khoba, Lyubov W243
Khomyakov, Sergey F, W165
Khoo, Shu W47
Khor, Jiak Woen A376
Khorana, Sunny K. E141
Khosla, Sanjay A512
Khosravi, Behzad A809
Khouri, Nick A. A303
Khourie, Matt A186
Khourie, Matthew S. (Trammell Crow Company) P604
Khoury Newcomb, Jennifer A227
Khoury, Philip S. P411
Ki-Hong, Park W311
Ki-Moon, Ban P621
Kiah, Chris A43
Kian Wah, Ng W365
Kiappes, John (Motiva Enterprises) A606
Kiappes, John (Motiva Enterprises) A606
Kibarian, Chris (Thomson Reuters) A856
Kibarian, Chris (Thomson West) A857
Kibben, Jeffrey J. A138
Kibbon, Larry J. P655
Kibby, Brian A576
Kibler, Tina P89
Kibsgaard, Paal A772
Kiczuk, William F. A735
Kidd, Chekesha C. A19
Kidd, John A. A623
Kidd, Ruthann A705
Kidd, Steven (E. & J. Gallo) A309
Kidd, Steven (E. & J. Gallo) A309
Kidder, C. Robert (Chrysler) A201
Kidder, C. Robert (Chrysler) A201
Kiddoo, Bruce E. (Maxim Integrated Products) E233
Kiddoo, Bruce E. (Maxim Integrated Products) E233
Kidowaki, Masaki W273
Kidwai, Naina L. W190
Kidwell, Stephen M. A50
Kiefer, David P114
Kieffer, Brad A428
Kieffer, Korry A53
Kiehn, Timothy E. P399
Kieley, Jim E330
Kielholz, Walter B. W388
Kieltyka, LeeAnn C. E290
Kiely, W. Leo (Molson Coors) A602
Kiely, W. Leo (MillerCoors) P409
Kiely, W. Leo (SABMiller) W343
Kiepura, Michael E. A747
Kier, Lynn A278
Kierlin, Robert A. A346
Kiernan, Brian G. E194
Kiernan, Dan A267
Kiernan, John P. E373
Kierspe, Thomas L. P521
Kiesel, Greg W119
Kiesel, Klaus-Armin W363
Kiesi, Esko W217
Kiessling, Thomas W122
Kifer, Ron A76
Kiffe, Mitchell W. A369
Kihn, Jean-Claude A400
Kiik, Matti P237
Kijima, Tsunao W260
Kikuchi, Katsuyori W23
Kikuchi, Kazuyuki W262
Kikuchi, Satoshi W207
Kikuchi, Takashi W205
Kikuyama, Hideki W209
Kilbane, Michael P. A741
Kilborn, Cheryl P511
Kilburg, William H. A111
Kilburn, Roger M. W214
Kilcoyne, Stacy A797
Kildahl, Jørgen W130
Kildare, Greg K. P368
Kilday, Pam A823
Kilduff, Larry P332

Kiley, Mary A739
Kilgannon, Susan B. A904
Kilgore, Jack C. P510
Kilgore, Leslie J. E257
Kilgore, Tom D. (TVA) A874
Kilgore, Tom D. (TVA) A874
Kilian, Axel W284
Kilibarda, Addison A405
Kilkowski, Bruce A478
Killackey, Maureen P399
Killebrew, Chad (New York Times) A628
Killebrew, Chad E. (Swift Transportation) A827
Killebrew, Flavius C. P585
Killen, Tracey W213
Killette, Delores J. (US Postal Service) A907
Killette, Delores J. (US Postal Service) A907
Killgore, Michael D. E286
Killian, John M. A228
Killilea, Kevin P. P551
Killinger, Clayton E. A912
Killingsworth, Mark A284
Killion, Robert L. A95
Killoy, Christopher J. E309
Kilmer, Raymond A35
Kilmer, Robert P432
Kilpatrick, Emily A724
Kilpi, Olli A574
Kilpin, Tim A568
Kilroe, Deborah A. P210
Kilroy, Thomas M. A464
Kim, Anthony P197
Kim, Bong Soo W238
Kim, Clara A287
Kim, Dong-Cheol W238
Kim, Eunice A324
Kim, Grace (Maxim Integrated Products) E233
Kim, Grace (Maxim Integrated Products) E233
Kim, Henry W72
Kim, HJ W80
Kim, Hoil E167
Kim, In Chull W238
Kim, James J. (Semtech) E315
Kim, James J. (Amkor) A61
Kim, James Y. (The Carlyle Group) A847
Kim, James Y. (The Carlyle Group) A847
Kim, James J. E. (LG Group) W238
Kim, Jenny B. P416
Kim, Jeong H. W21
Kim, John Y. (New York Life) A625
Kim, John Y. (New York Life) A625
Kim, Joo-Hyung W238
Kim, JooHo A61
Kim, Kyeong Hye W354
Kim, Matthew M. E68
Kim, Michael E274
Kim, Michelle W180
Kim, Neil Y. A149
Kim, O. C. E151
Kim, Peter S. (Merck) A587
Kim, Peter B. S. (LG Group) W238
Kim, Rene L. A194
Kim, Scott P49
Kim, Seungsoo A724
Kim, Stephen E. E105
Kim, Steven E330
Kim, Sue A913
Kim, Sung P638
Kim Wah, Yap W365
Kim, Yong Hyun (The Carlyle Group) A847
Kim, Yong Hyun (The Carlyle Group) A847
Kim, Youlee Y. (The Carlyle Group) A847
Kim, Youlee Y. (The Carlyle Group) A847
Kim, Young-Il W238

Kimata, Masatoshi W226
Kimata, Stephen A. P636
Kimball, David E325
Kimball, Kathleen R. P470
Kimball, Ken P551
Kimball, Kevin M. A557
Kimball, Stefan A650
Kimball, Walker (Bechtel) A114
Kimball, Walker (Bechtel) A114
Kimberlin, Cecilia L. A5
Kimberly, Dean A124
Kimble, Donald R. A453
Kimble, Eric W. E91
Kimble, Lewis P. A363
Kimbrell-Silva, Kerri P328
Kimbro, Kenneth J. A876
Kimbrough, Brad A738
Kimbrough, Mark A424
Kime, Jack P352
Kime, Jeffery L. A858
Kimishima, Tatsumi (Nintendo of America) P445
Kimishima, Tatsumi (Nintendo) W276
Kimler, Bill P375
Kimm, David A833
Kimmel, Mike P673
Kimmel, Sidney A490
Kimmes, Steve A. P353
Kimmitt, Joseph H. A668
Kimura, Hiroshi (Japan Tobacco) W210
Kimura, Hiroshi (Nippon Steel) W279
Kimura, Kazumasa (DENSO America) P179
Kimura, Kazumasa (DENSO) W116
Kimura, Keiji W375
Kimura, Kenji W284
Kimura, Masakazu W160
Kimura, Masao A480
Kimura, Shigeru (Kubota) W226
Kimura, Shigeru (Tokyo Electric) W408
Kimura, Shohei W281
Kimura, Takaaki W449
Kimura, Toshihide W384
Kimura, Yujiro W226
Kincaid, Cynthia A453
Kinder, Jacquelyn (Catholic Health East) A182
Kinder, Jacquelyn (Catholic Health East) A182
Kinder, Randy P452
Kindig, Karl W. A219
Kindy, Michael J. A293
Kinerk, Beth A. A662
King, Alexa E38
King, Andrew W. A868
King, Bob P92
King, Carolyn A715
King, David R. (JDA Software) E205
King, David G. (STAG Industrial) E331
King, Diana A853
King Dibble, Kelly A646
King, Donald R. P253
King, Donnie D. A876
King, Doug P396
King, Douglas (Blue Shield Of California) P89
King, Gale V. (Nationwide) A615
King, Gale V. (Nationwide) A615
King, Gene A410
King, Glenn E130
King, Gregory A. (IBERIABANK) E179
King, Gregory L. (Rock-Tenn) A747
King, Ian W48
King, James D. (Scotts Miracle-Gro) A777
King, James (Randstad Holding) W320
King, Janet (International Data Group) A467
King, Janet (International Data Group) A467
King, Janice E238
King, John (Lincoln Educational Services) E222
King, John J. (Lubrizol) A546

King, John L. (University of Michigan) P632
King, Jon J. (Benchmark Electronics) A122
King, Jon M. (Tiffany & Co.) A860
King, Justin W208
King, Karen A574
King, Kathleen S. P20
King, Kelly S. A111
King, Kenton J. P548
King, Kirby W. (First Bancorp of Indiana) E143
King, Kirby (Port Authority of New York and New Jersey) A701
King, Kirby (Port Authority of New York and New Jersey) A701
King, Kris A610
King, Lawrence A. E315
King, Liz W80
King, M. J. W. W190
King, Mark A. (Diodes) E107
King, Mark (Kellogg) A498
King, Mark (Rolls-Royce) W334
King, Mary W51
King, Matthew P173
King, Michael P221
King, Pamela A512
King, Philip E. P664
King, Raymond W83
King, Regina P228
King, Richard (Thomson West) A857
King, Richard L. (Associated Food) P49
King, Richard (Legal & General Group) W236
King, Richie P228
King, Rick P583
King, Robert P. (CONSOL Energy) A239
King, Robert P. (ACE Cash Express) P11
King, Robert R. (US Department of State) P638
King, Scott V. A311
King, Shauna R. P675
King, Simon W37
King, Spencer A334
King, Stephen P129
King, Steve P366
King, Thomas B. (Alexza) E14
King, Thomas A. (Progressive Corporation) A714
King, Thomas B. (National Grid) W270
King, Vivian (Roundy's Supermarkets) A753
King, Vivian (Roundy's Supermarkets) A753
King, W. Russell A370
King, Wal M. W185
King, William H. A265
King, Yolonda A22
King-Shaw, Ruben J. P631
Kingaby, Carolyn W392
Kingery, David A. (The Carlyle Group) A847
Kingery, David A. (The Carlyle Group) A847
Kingma, Todd W. A688
Kingsbury, Thomas A. (Burlington Coat Factory) A156
Kingsbury, Thomas A. (Burlington Coat Factory) A156
Kingsley, Linda A. (US Postal Service) A907
Kingsley, Linda A. (US Postal Service) A907
Kingswell-Smith, Charles A699
Kinion, Brian E335
Kinkead Reiling, Keith E30
Kinkela, David P255
Kinlaw, Scott S. E114
Kinlin, Clark S. A247
Kinloch, Leon A887
Kinnaird, Tom W445
Kinnas, Cynthia W320
Kinneberg, Eric A370

Kinnerk, Brian P543
Kinney, Al P300
Kinney, Patrick A871
Kinnings, Guy P309
Kinol, Jon W107
Kinoshita, Kenji W222
Kinoshita, Manabu W273
Kinoshita, Masayuki W265
Kinpara, Kazuya W449
Kinscherff, R. Paul A135
Kinsella, Bret A420
Kinsella, Erin E30
Kinser, Dennis (Associated Wholesale Grocers) A85
Kinser, Dennis (Associated Wholesale Grocers) A85
Kinsey, R. Steve A357
Kinsinger, David A516
Kinslow, Tim A656
Kinstle, Mike (Meijer) A584
Kinstle, Mike (Meijer) A584
Kintz, Gary P669
Kinukawa, Jun W260
Kinver, Peter J. W54
Kinzel, Donna J. A683
Kinzey, Cara D. A444
Kipfer, Hans Peter A666
Kiplin, Kimberly A844
Kipp, Bill A391
Kipphut, W. Michael E341
Kiral, Atilla A666
Kirbo, Holland C. A357
Kirbow, Donna W. (Chick-fil-A) A198
Kirbow, Donna W. (Chick-fil-A) A198
Kirby, Bob (CDW) A189
Kirby, Bob (CDW) A189
Kirby, Brent G. A543
Kirby, Carrie (Energy Future) A330
Kirby, Carrie (Energy Future) A330
Kirby, J. Scott A906
Kirby, John A31
Kirby, Michael E38
Kirby, Susan G. P583
Kircher, Chris A237
Kircher, Jerry F. A541
Kirchgässner, Johann W451
Kirchhof, Ina W144
Kirchhoff, Bruce C. E305
Kirchmaier, Thomas P242
Kirchmann, Albert W112
Kirchner, Alexander W118
Kirchner, Jon E. E111
Kirchner, Jörg P358
Kirchner, Stefanie W158
Kirgan, Danielle A267
Kiriaki, Sami A843
Kirianoff, Vassili W452
Kirk, Charles T. E279
Kirk, David B. A654
Kirk, J. Christopher A186
Kirk, Joe F. A940
Kirk, Katharine W38
Kirk, Matthew W436
Kirk, Percy J. (Cox Communications) A251
Kirk, Percy J. (Cox Communications) A251
Kirk, Robert F. E43
Kirk, Rose M. A914
Kirk, Stephen F. A546
Kirkby, Matthew W337
Kirkconnell, Kristin R. (American Family Insurance) A54
Kirkconnell, Kristin R. (American Family Insurance) A54
Kirkendall, Brian P514
Kirkendall, Donald L. E228
Kirkland, George L. A197
Kirkland, J. Bryant E372
Kirkpatrick, H. Scott E287
Kirkpatrick, R. James P408
Kirkpatrick, Ralph A376
Kirkpatrick, Thomas A. A864
Kirkpatrick, Wayne P173
Kirksey, Hugh P98

Kirkwood, David W. P584
Kirkwood, Karen A. A855
Kirloskar, Virendra A. A506
Kirmayer, Susan M. P452
Kirsch, Eric M. A22
Kirsch, Holger W451
Kirsch, Joel P543
Kirsch, Rodney P. P470
Kirsch, Wolfgang W129
Kirschke, Thorsten (Carlson Companies) A175
Kirschke, Thorsten (Carlson Companies) A175
Kirschner, Rainer A340
Kirschner, Ulrich W330
Kirsh, Jesse E174
Kirshner, David K. A437
Kirst, Fred L. P609
Kirtley, Melvyn A860
Kirwan, Ian (AllianceBernstein) A40
Kirwan, Ian (AllianceBernstein) A40
Kirwan, William E. P630
Kisaka, Toshiro W300
Kisaka, Yoshiyuki W259
Kiser, David A470
Kiser, Glenn P371
Kishida, Makoto W294
Kishida, Shoichi W117
Kishimoto, Kei E247
Kishino, Fukuju W266
Kishore, Sameer P312
Kislak, Todd E200
Kisling, Ronald W. E251
Kisling, Tim P180
Kissane, David W. P399
Kissane, James F. P598
Kisseberth, Mike (International Data Group) A467
Kisseberth, Mike (International Data Group) A467
Kissel, Frank A. E279
Kissel, W. Craig P605
Kissell, Felise G. A451
Kissick, John R. E139
Kissinger, James G. A964
Kissling, Kevin C. A244
Kissling, René W331
Kist, Ewald W128
Kistler, Matt A928
Kita, Osamu W250
Kitabwalla, Husein P552
Kitagawa, Mitsuo W279
Kitagawa, Nobuo W381
Kitajima, Keisuke W277
Kitajima, Yoshinari W110
Kitajima, Yoshitoshi W110
Kitamura, Hideo W410
Kitamura, Nobuo W229
Kitamura, Tadashi W293
Kitano, Masahiro W184
Kitao, Yuichi W226
Kitaoka, Masayoshi W226
Kitayama, Ryuichi W184
Kitayuguchi, Tatsuro W110
Kitchen, Carol (Land O'Lakes) A519
Kitchen, Carol (Land O'Lakes) A519
Kitchen, Larry P92
Kitchen, Louise P180
Kitching, Scott P130
Kitson, Frederick E111
Kittrell, Marty R. P188
Kitz, Edward G. (Roundy's Supermarkets) A753
Kitz, Edward G. (Roundy's Supermarkets) A753
Kitzelman, Lance P97
Kitzmiller, James P360
Kiuchi, Masaru W279
Kivelä, Aatos W217
Kivetz, Robert S. P449
Kivihuhta, Jari W285
Kiviniemi, Pertti W285
Kivisaari, Tero E. W398
Kiyoshi, Tatsuya W260
Kizer, Richard S. P521

Kizielewicz, James P352
Kizuka, Hiroshi W295
Kjaersgaard, Carl Erik P260
Klaas, Jeff E330
Klaeijsen, Bram C. (Cargill) A172
Klaeijsen, Bram C. (Cargill) A172
Klafter, Cary I. A464
Klag, Michael J. P332
Klahn, Markus P97
Klahn, Thomas P19
Klaif, Mitchell P600
Klaila, Cornelia W268
Klaiman, Joel P624
Klas, Todd A954
Klasing, Paul W. W374
Klasky, Helaine S. P675
Klatell, Robert E. E361
Klatt, David A. A629
Klatzkin, Terri D. P141
Klau, Kevin A. A265
Klauer, James A249
Klauer, Thomas D. A775
Klauser, Alexander W331
Klauser, Andreas W97
Klauser, Lisa W426
Klausner, Richard D. W351
Klausner, Ronald D. E58
Klauzner, Tatyana A522
Klawitter, Warren P239
Klayko, Michael E54
Klebe, Elizabeth L. A29
Kleber, Klee E293
Kleckner, James J. A65
Klee, Ann A376
Kleeman, Carl P598
Klefenz, Friedbert W330
Kleiderer, Karl A398
Kleifges, Mark L. E161
Kleijwegt, Rudi W318
Kleiman, Steve A623
Klein, Beth P428
Klein, Bob A417
Klein, Bruce A210
Klein, Cathy (Perdue Incorporated) A686
Klein, Cathy (Perdue Incorporated) A686
Klein, Christopher J. A112
Klein, David S. P160
Klein, Dean A. A594
Klein, Ed P76
Klein, Eduard (W.L. Gore) A924
Klein, Eduard (W.L. Gore) A924
Klein, Eric P590
Klein, Jason P399
Klein, Joel T. A632
Klein, John R. A789
Klein, Leon P537
Klein, Mark (Cargill) A172
Klein, Mark (Cargill) A172
Klein, Martin P675
Klein, Matt A31
Klein, Matthew (AXA Financial) P57
Klein, Matthew (AXA) W47
Klein, Michael F. (Travelers Companies) A871
Klein, Michael H. (LFP) P363
Klein, Peter S. A595
Klein, Philippe W324
Klein, Ronald A549
Klein, Steve W250
Klein, Thomas (Sabre Holdings) A760
Klein, Thomas F. (Federal Reserve Bank (NY)) P210
Klein, Thomas (Sabre Holdings) A760
Klein, Timothy M. P421
Klein, Torsten-Jörn W62
Kleinbaum, Linda G. (MTA) A608
Kleinbaum, Linda G. (MTA) A608
Kleiner, Rolf E. A499
Kleinerman, Eugenie S. P372
Kleinert, Robert W. A115
Kleinfeld, Klaus A35
Kleinhandler, David A186
Kleinhenz, Kenneth K. E94

Kulhanek, Tim P71
Kulig, James S. A95
Kulinets, Irina B. E32
Kull, Mike P170
Kullman, Ellen J. A305
Kulmala, Sari W217
Kulmann, Björn A99
Kulovaara, Harri U. A754
Kulp, Bruce A374
Kulsky, Jason S. E262
Kumada, Yasuhisa P6
Kumagai, Bunya W293
Kumagai, Les A914
Kumagai, Osamu W375
Kumano, Mikio W116
Kumar, Aneish A102
Kumar, Anil P595
Kumar, Biren A307
Kumar, Jaya A684
Kumar, Kris E107
Kumar, R. K. Krish W390
Kumar, Rajesh (DDi Corp.) E96
Kumar, Rajesh (Intel) A464
Kumar Saranam, Narendra W317
Kumar, Subhaash E341
Kumar, Sunil (University of
  Chicago) A898
Kumar, Sunil (University of
  Chicago) A898
Kumar, TLV P340
Kumar, V. Raman E239
Kumar, Vinod W390
Kumaresan, Swami E61
Kumbier, Michelle A417
Kumin, Michael A. E376
Kumm, Mark P474
Kummert, Ted A595
Kump, Eric J. (The Carlyle
  Group) A847
Kump, Eric J. (The Carlyle
  Group) A847
Kumpf, Robert J. P70
Kumura, Haruyoshi W281
Kun, Zsuzsanna W267
Kunath, Jan W326
Kunberger, George A. A483
Kuncl, Sharon P196
Kunde, Gerald R. A267
Kunes, Richard W. A336
Kung, Lawrence P556
Kung, Patrick S. W307
Kunieda, Toshinari W293
Kunihiro, Jim (ServiceMaster) A782
Kunihiro, Jim (ServiceMaster) A782
Kunikiyo, Takurni W385
Kunio, Takemitsu W273
Kunis, Suzanne A550
Kunish, Matt P162
Kunk, James E. A453
Kunkel, Gregory P. P584
Kunkel, Joseph S. A176
Kunkel, Thomas M. A871
Kunkle, Donald G. E353
Kunkler, Tom P206
Kunselman, Scott G. (Chrysler) A201
Kunselman, Scott G. (Chrysler) A201
Kunszabo, Steve E. E201
Kuntz, Edward L. A503
Kuntz, Kevin P386
Kuntz, Michael J. (Turner
  Corporation) A873
Kuntz, Michael J. (Turner
  Corporation) A873
Kuntz, Richard E. A583
Kuntz-Mayr, Christiane W354
Kunz, Barbara L. (Battelle
  Memorial) A107
Kunz, Barbara L. (Battelle
  Memorial) A107
Kunz, John E. A839
Kunz, Thomas S. (PNC Financial) A700
Kunz, Thomas (Danone) W114
Kunze, Hans-Peter W430
Kuo, Kimberly (Baker & Taylor) A97
Kuo, Kimberly (Baker & Taylor) A97

Kupatt, Wolf F. A110
Kupchella, Leslie (Carlson
  Companies) A175
Kupchella, Leslie (Carlson
  Companies) A175
Kuper, Debra A24
Kuperfarb, Gérard W234
Kuperman, Jason A663
Kupfer, Tilman W80
Kupferman, Susan L. (MTA) A608
Kupferman, Susan L. (MTA) A608
Kupiec, Andrew E74
Kuplic, David M. P532
Kupriyanov, Sergei W165
Kura, Brian A777
Kuranaka, Shin W266
Kurasaka, Katsuhide W384
Kuri, Camilo W374
Kurian, Thomas A666
Kurihara, Katsumi W327
Kurihara, Kazuhiro W184
Kurihara, Shinichi W262
Kurishima, Satoshi W292
Kurita, Nobuki W375
Kuritzkes, Andrew A817
Kurkcu, Cengiz S. A864
Kurkiewicz, Marc R. (Topco Associates
  LLC) A867
Kurkiewicz, Marc R. (Topco Associates
  LLC) A867
Kurlan, Terri P250
Kurland, Larry W202
Kurman, Michael R. E75
Kurmas, Steven E. A303
Kurnick, Robert H. (Penske) A683
Kurnick, Robert H. (Penske) A683
Kuroda, Hiroshi W262
Kuroda, Masami W277
Kuroda, Yujiro W110
Kuroki, Keisuke W279
Kuromoto, Kazunori W222
Kurosawa, Koji W252
Kurosawa, Tomohiro W293
Kuroyanagi, Nobuo W263
Kurpad, Umesh P611
Kurre, Adrian (Hilton Worldwide) A441
Kurre, Adrian (Hilton Worldwide) A441
Kurtenbach, Jeff P432
Kurtul, Zafer W342
Kurtulus, Cezmi W342
Kurtz, Christopher E14
Kurtz, George P. E279
Kurtz, Jim (TVA) A874
Kurtz, Jim (TVA) A874
Kurtz, Neil M. (Golden Horizons) A395
Kurtz, Neil M. (Golden Horizons) A395
Kurtz, Randy P180
Kurtz, Richard J. E217
Kurtz, Robert C. P399
Kurtz, Ryan (CDW) A189
Kurtz, Ryan (CDW) A189
Kurtzweil, John T. E90
Kurunsaari, Minna W217
Kurup, Veenod (Cox
  Communications) A251
Kurup, Veenod (Cox
  Communications) A251
Kurusu, Shigemi W209
Kurusz, Peggy (Ascension Health) A82
Kurusz, Peggy (Ascension Health) A82
Kuryak, Timothy A287
Kurz, Christian A287
Kurz, Steven P439
Kurz, Thomas P. A829
Kurzius, Lawrence E. A572
Kus, Alper E130
Kuschman, Thomas A372
Kush, Donna A883
Kushan, Ravi W103
Kushar, Kent (E. & J. Gallo) A309
Kushar, Kent (E. & J. Gallo) A309
Kushibab, Ken A748
Kushner, Michael P553
Kusserow, Paul B. A452
Kusuhashi, Toshinori W252

Kutchera, Kris M. A33
Kutscher, Christof W420
Kutsovsky, Yakov A163
Kutz, Tim (Unisource) A884
Kutz, Tim (Unisource) A884
Kuwabara, Tetsuro W260
Kuwayama, Nobuo W207
Kuwayama, Shoji W250
Kux, Barbara W363
Kuyper, Dirk E18
Kuzak, Derrick M. A365
Kuzevenkov, Dmitry A97
Kuznetsov, Vlad E319
Kuznetsova, Inna A456
Kuzuoka, Toshiaki W184
Kvalheim, P.□ W397
Kvamme, E. Floyd E284
Kwan, Kam (AllianceBernstein) A40
Kwan, Kam (AllianceBernstein) A40
Kwan-Rubinek, Veronika (Time
  Warner) A862
Kwan-Rubinek, Veronika (Warner
  Bros.) P657
Kwang-Jae, Yoo W311
Kwater, Sherry P546
Kweder, Amy A462
Kwek, Alan W19
Kwiatkoski, Virginia M. P416
Kwiecinski, Michal (Liberty
  Mutual) A534
Kwiecinski, Michal (Liberty
  Mutual) A534
Kwitowski, Jeff E209
Kwok, Bernard A828
Kwok, Ling E275
Kwok, Robby E223
Kwon, Samuel H. (The Carlyle
  Group) A847
Kwon, Samuel H. (The Carlyle
  Group) A847
Kwon, Young T. E247
Kwon, Young Soo (LG Group) W238
Kwong, Seck Wai A817
Kydd, Steven E99
Kyle, Angela T. (New York Life) A625
Kyle, Angela T. (New York Life) A625
Kyle, David L. A664
Kyle, Richard G. A864
Kyncl, Robert A402
Kyoung-Mok, Lee W311
Kyu-Seok, Choi W311
Kyu-Sung, Yeon W311
Kyung-Hoon, Lee W311
Kyung-Zoon, Min W311
Kyzer, Floyd (Shaw Industries) A785
Kyzer, Floyd (Shaw Industries) A785
K□rhus, Ragnar W397
Köhler, Roland W186
Köhler, Wolfgang W129
Köhn, Doris W219
König, Andreas A623
König, Peter W424
Körner, Ulrich W420
Köstlin, Ulrich W59
Küchler, Gunter W242
Küchler, Rainer W181
Külps, Hubertus W354
Kürstein, Peter A265

L

La Bruno, Laura A4
La Force, Hudson A923
La Perriere, Pierre A249
La Quaglia, Michael P. P399
La Rocca, Cathy A963
Laabs, Greg (Gulfstream
  Aerospace) A409

Laabs, Greg (Gulfstream
  Aerospace) A409
Laatsch, Michael J. (Western &
  Southern Financial) P664
Laatsch, Michael J. (Western and
  Southern Life) P665
Lababidi, Sami A322
Laban, Stefan A851
LaBarre, Michael J. E169
LaBarre, Ron W230
Labat, Kristen A332
Labate, John A. E161
LaBauve, Randall R. A634
Laben, Gary S. P677
Labenz, Thomas E. A484
Laber, Heinz W424
Laberge, Fred A19
Labetti, Joe (Columbia
  University) A226
Labetti, Joe (Columbia
  University) A226
Labeyrie, Christian W432
Labian, Paula (Giant Food) P247
Labian, Paula (Stop & Shop) P570
Labinger, Barry A. E178
Labonte, Ralph W406
Labosky, Mike (Golden State
  Foods) A396
Labosky, Mike (Golden State
  Foods) A396
Labovich, Gary D. A138
Laboy, Felix (Sabre Holdings) A760
Laboy, Felix (Sabre Holdings) A760
LaBrache, Sarah P123
Labriola, Pietro W394
Labrucherie, Gil M. E254
Labry, Edward A. (First Data) A354
Labry, Edward A. (First Data) A354
Lacaille, Rick A817
LaCalle, Maria P663
LaCapra, Louis J. (Port Authority of
  New York and New Jersey) A701
LaCapra, Louis J. (Port Authority of
  New York and New Jersey) A701
Lacassagne, Laurent W303
Lacchin, Louise M. W169
Lacertosa, Marie A478
Lacey, David L. A60
Lacey, Debra L. A489
Lacey, Dennis J. E335
Lacey, Diane E. (New York City Health
  and Hospitals) A624
Lacey, Diane E. (New York City Health
  and Hospitals) A624
Lacey, Jim (MassMutual) A564
Lacey, Jim (MassMutual) A564
Lacey, John A389
Lacey, Mark A646
Lacey, Roger H. D. A2
Lacey-Varona, Alina P3
Lachance, Margaret P. A721
LaChance, Susan M. (US Postal
  Service) A907
LaChance, Susan M. (US Postal
  Service) A907
LaChapelle, Trevor (BJ's Wholesale
  Club) A129
LaChapelle, Trevor (BJ's Wholesale
  Club) A129
Lachica, Victor P166
Lachman, Charles W44
Lachman, Henri W357
Lachman, Todd R. (Mars,
  Incorporated) A559
Lachman, Todd R. (Mars,
  Incorporated) A559
Lachmann, Henri W435
Lachmiller, Robert E. A673
Lack, Andrew R. (Bloomberg L.P.) A131
Lack, Andrew R. (Bloomberg L.P.) A131
Lack, Krystyna A4
Lacker, Jeffrey M. (Federal
  Reserve) P209
Lacker, Jeffrey M. (Federal Reserve
  Bank of Richmond) P211

Lee, Jessica Y. (The Carlyle
  Group) A847
Lee, Joel G. P644
Lee, John B. (CCF Holding) E65
Lee, John (East West Bancorp) E115
Lee, John J. (Peapack-Gladstone
  Financial) E279
Lee, Jong Sang W238
Lee, Joonho J. P210
Lee, Joseph P49
Lee, Keli P8
Lee, Kim W240
Lee, Kong Ann A480
Lee, Maria R. P166
Lee, Mary A. P487
Lee, Michael H. (Tower Group) E354
Lee, Michael D. (Nucor) A652
Lee, Michael P. (FlightSafety) P221
Lee, Michelle (Allstate) A43
Lee, Michelle Y. (Wells Fargo) A940
Lee, Ming-Yen A480
Lee, Myung Kwan W238
Lee, Nancy C. A557
Lee, Paul (L & L Energy) E216
Lee, Paul (ABC, Inc.) P8
Lee, Raymond E54
Lee, Rebecca F. A7
Lee, Regina R. A15
Lee, Robert E. (Chrysler) A201
Lee, Robert E. (Chrysler) A201
Lee, Roger A856
Lee, Sam W107
Lee, Samuel (Equinix) E132
Lee, Samuel K. (Northeast
  Utilities) A645
Lee, Sang-Cheol W238
Lee, Shao-Kang A247
Lee, Soo Ghee E90
Lee, Soo-Yon (Air Products) A29
Lee, Stanley E275
Lee, Stephen C. Y. W365
Lee, Suengliang E166
Lee, Sven P116
Lee, T.J. E107
Lee, Terry C. A293
Lee, Thai P553
Lee, Theresa K. A311
Lee, Thomas H. P465
Lee, Timothy E. A384
Lee, Tobin A473
Lee, Tommy A654
Lee, Trina A176
Lee, William A. (Gilead Sciences) A394
Lee, William K. (The Carlyle
  Group) A847
Lee, William K. (The Carlyle
  Group) A847
Lee, William J. (Quality Dining) P491
Lee, Woo-Jong W238
Lee, Yaun Mo W238
Lee, Yoon-Woo W349
Lee, Yun J. E151
Leebaw, Jeffrey J. A487
Leech, Steve E319
Leech, Wilson A646
Leeder, John W101
Leedle, Ben R. E171
Leedom, David W. E243
Leeds, Bruce P148
Leeds, Candace A542
Leeds, Doug P49
Leeds, Richard P148
Leeds, Robert P148
Leeds, Sarene P663
Leeds, Thomas V. P399
Leedy, Brian E78
Leeming, Chris P663
Leenaars, Eli P. W200
Leentjes, Hans A555
Leeper, Sarah A57
Leer, Steven F. A78
Lees, Andrew A595
Lees, Moira W99
Lees, Richard P452
Leese, Gail E. A271

Leese, Holly E. (Chrysler) A201
Leese, Holly E. (Chrysler) A201
Leet, Dennis P266
Leets, Karen L. A909
Lefebvre, Georges W233
Lefebvre, Marvin E74
Lefebvre, Pierre A387
Lefebvre, Pierre-Emmanuel
  (Aviva) W45
Lefebvre, Robert D. P163
Lefebvre, Vincent (Holcim) W186
Lefebvre, Vincent (Holcim) W186
Lefert, Jerry P562
Lefferson, C. Douglas E143
Lefkoff, Kyle A. E38
Lefkofsky, Eric P. E165
Lefler, Val P92
Lefor, Maggie E92
Lefort, Christian A297
Lefort, Tim E181
LeFrak, Harrison (LeFrak
  Organization) A521
LeFrak, Harrison (LeFrak
  Organization) A521
LeFrak, James (LeFrak
  Organization) A521
LeFrak, James (LeFrak
  Organization) A521
LeFrak, Richard S. (LeFrak
  Organization) A521
LeFrak, Richard S. (LeFrak
  Organization) A521
Leftwich, Gary P557
Legain, Arnaud P354
Legan, Brian M. A138
Leger, Jean C. P203
Leger, Manfred W50
Legg, Dexter R. (Liberty Mutual) A534
Legg, Dexter R. (Liberty Mutual) A534
Legg, Sarah W190
Legge, Michael H. P506
Leggio, Jennifer E149
Leghorn, Cynthia E146
LeGouguec, Laurence W234
Legrand, Olivier P186
Legree, Lance (NFL) A635
Legree, Lance (NFL) A635
Legros, Éric W87
LeGuluche, John A512
Lehane, Stephen W24
Lehane, Tracey P186
Lehanski, David (NHL) A637
Lehanski, David (NHL) A637
Lehfeld, Lindsay A950
Lehman, Arnold S. (LeFrak
  Organization) A521
Lehman, Arnold S. (LeFrak
  Organization) A521
Lehman, Joseph E. A296
Lehman, Kirk A372
Lehman, Matthew A714
Lehman, Neal F. A664
Lehman, Nicholas (iVillage) P320
Lehman, Nicholas
  (NBCUniversal) P428
Lehman, Robert P192
Lehmann, Axel P. W452
Lehmann, Mark L. E207
Lehmann, Mary A589
Lehmkuhl, W. Gregory P148
Lehmkuhle, Stephen P633
Lehner, Jean-Pierre W351
Lehner, John A102
Lehner, Ulrich (Deutsche
  Telekom) W122
Lehner, Ulrich (Novartis) W289
Lehnert, Markus A557
LeHocky, Mark A752
Lehr, Tom A471
Lehrman, Kenneth F. P470
Lehrmann, Jeffrey K. A197
Lehtinen, Olli-Petteri W285
Lehtiö, Raimo W356
Lei, Cao E322
Leib, Daniel N. A728

Leibenstern, Maurice E321
Leibholz, Daniel A66
Leibman, Maya A63
Leibold, Bob E111
Leibowitz, Gary W343
Leibowitz, Lawrence E. A656
Leibrand, Randy P537
Leibsla, Melvin D. A966
Leicher, Bruce A. E247
Leicher, Lewis H. E380
Leichtle, Robert P87
Leiden, Lisa (University of Texas
  System) A899
Leiden, Lisa (University of Texas
  System) A899
Leiden, Mark P256
Leidich, Gary R. (Allegheny
  Energy) A36
Leidich, Gary R. (FirstEnergy) A355
Leigh-Pemberton, James H. W107
Leighton, Allan L. (George
  Weston) W169
Leighton, Allan L. (Loblaw) W240
Leighton, James B. (Perdue
  Incorporated) A686
Leighton, James B. (Perdue
  Incorporated) A686
Leighton, Karen A. P532
Leighton, Nicholas John E170
Leighton, Robert M. A532
Leiman, Joan M. P439
Leimann, Ralph T. A480
Leimgruber, Wolfgang W310
Leino, David L. A7
Leinroth, Peter A471
Leipold, Dianne A84
Leiponen, Mika W217
Leisengang, Helen P124
Leisten, Heiner (Boston
  Consulting) A141
Leisten, Heiner (Boston
  Consulting) A141
Leitch, Alexander P. (BUPA) W83
Leitch, Alexander P. (Lloyds Banking
  Group) W239
Leitch, David G. A365
Leite, Eduardo C. P59
Leitner, Chris A. P584
Leitz, James P309
Lejman, Ronald J. E367
Lek, Bonnary A287
Leketa, Anthony F. (Parsons
  Corporation) A679
Leketa, Anthony F. (Parsons
  Corporation) A679
Leland, D. Mark A321
Leland, Dick E130
Lella, Janusz W220
Lem, Scott C. E36
Lema, Gerald A110
LeMaire, Joshua W. E135
LeMaitre, Yves E266
Lemarie, Christophe W303
Lematta, Claire P654
Lembck, Thomas E375
Lembo, Philip J. A651
Lemerise, Paul M. A853
Lemieux, Catharine P210
Leminen, Matti W217
Leming, Rudy P161
Lemire, Catherine P58
Lemkau, Kristin A494
Lemke, James P. A159
Lemke, Judith A. (Schneider
  National) A774
Lemke, Judith A. (Schneider
  National) A774
Lemke, Thomas P. A522
Lemley, Rich P204
Lemm, Michael R. P660
Lemme, Dave A69
Lemmo, Mark A. E194
Lemos, Silvio A391
Lemâne, Thierry W150
Lende, Michael E388

Lendino, Al A936
Lenhard, April A690
Lenhardt, David K. A690
Lenihan, Robert J. (AMC
  Entertainment) A47
Lenihan, Robert J. (AMC
  Entertainment) A47
Lenk, Toby A851
Lenker, Max P494
Lennartz, Frank W331
Lennie, William A444
Lennon, Aubree P663
Lennon, Frank T. A144
Lennox, Bill A398
Lennox, Peter T. P256
Lennox, Randy P624
Leno, Samuel R. A142
Lenormand, Jacques W109
Lenox, Selene P249
Lenser, Leslie A910
Lentsch, David E81
Lentz, James E. W413
Lentz, Kevin P165
Lentz, M. Alan P276
Lentz, Pamela M. A138
Lentz, Paul P5
Lenz, Brad A539
Lenz, Matthias W451
Lenz, Patrick J. (University of
  California) A897
Lenz, Patrick J. (University of
  California) A897
Lenz, Teresa P228
Lenzner, Julie W4
Leo, James P661
Leo, Koguan P553
Leon, Alfonso A71
Leon, George P554
Leon, Jonathan A. A144
Leon, Wynne P237
Leonard, Bernard F. A876
Leonard, J. Wayne A332
Leonard, James C. P610
Leonard, Jeff (Baker & Taylor) A97
Leonard, Jeff (Baker & Taylor) A97
Leonard, Jim P487
Leonard, John M. (Abbott Labs) A5
Leonard, John C. (UBS) W420
Leonard, Mary A. E78
Leonard, Richard J. A19
Leonard, Rob W92
Leonard, Robert A. (M. A.
  Mortenson) P371
Leonard, Roger F. P395
Leonard, Scott (Amtrak) A64
Leonard, Scott (Amtrak) A64
Leonard, Stephen P116
Leonard, Steven A326
Leonardi-Cattolica, Karyn (Motiva
  Enterprises) A606
Leonardi-Cattolica, Karyn (Motiva
  Enterprises) A606
Leone, Chris A666
Leone, Mario F. A461
Leone, Michael (ARAMARK) A77
Leone, Michael (ARAMARK) A77
Leone, Pietro P660
Leone, Rafaella W142
Leone, Robert A484
Leone, Thomas H. (Cox
  Communications) A251
Leone, Thomas H. (Cox
  Communications) A251
Leong, David (Kingston
  Technology) A504
Leong, David (Kingston
  Technology) A504
Leong, Michael A340
Leong, Tina P379
Leonhardt, Jearld L.
  (CommScope) A231
Leonhardt, Jearld L.
  (CommScope) A231
Leonidas, Robert G. P432
Leonsis, Theodore J. E165

Long, Alysia (Cox
  Communications) A251
Long, Alysia (Cox
  Communications) A251
Long, Andrew P. W190
Long, Annabelle W62
Long, Charles H. P675
Long, Christine G. E202
Long, Dan P6
Long, David H. (Liberty Mutual) A534
Long, David (Royal Caribbean
  Cruises) A754
Long, David H. (Liberty Mutual) A534
Long, Deborah J. A715
Long, Don P667
Long, George P. A700
Long, Hal (Shaw Industries) A785
Long, Hal (Shaw Industries) A785
Long, Henry P. A44
Long, Hugh C. A940
Long, James H. (INX Inc.) E199
Long, James M. (Veolia Environmental
  Services North America) P646
Long, Jeffrey R. A249
Long, Jo Anne C. P506
Long, John P183
Long, Michael J. A80
Long, Nancy P291
Long, Peter (Blue Shield Of
  California) P89
Long, Peter (TUI) W416
Long, Peter (TUI Travel) W417
Long, Philip P675
Long, Randall P242
Long, Randy A524
Long, Stephen J. A104
Long, Susan E17
Long, Tom (MillerCoors) P409
Long, Tom (SABMiller) W343
Long, Tony A186
Long, Tracey A711
Long, William C. (Diamond
  Offshore) A282
Long, William J. (Amcor) W29
Longacre, David L. A447
Longbottom, Eric E22
Longden, Larry E235
Longe, Kevin T. P581
Longerstaey, Jacques M. A817
Longhi Filho, Mário A391
Longhi, William G. A234
Longi, Mike A592
Longino, Donna A902
Longmore-Grund, Rhonda P485
Longo, Cheryl W95
Longo, Christopher M. E30
Longo, Peter (International Data
  Group) A467
Longo, Peter F. (United
  Technologies) A893
Longo, Peter (International Data
  Group) A467
Longstaff, David P. P334
Longstreet, Greg N. A447
Longwitz, Ina A489
Lonnquist, John E280
Lonon, Terrill A. P561
Lonsert, Michael W90
Lonsway, Michael A673
Looger, Lindell L. A335
Look, Bryon A545
Lookabaugh, Tom E129
Loomes, Oliver W125
Loomis, Lawrence P39
Loon, Mae A367
Looney, Bernard W74
Looney, Bob A203
Looney, Stacy P336
Looper, Becky E45
Loos, Steve P229
Loosli, Hansueli W389
Loparco, Michael J. A480
Lopdrup, Kim A. A267
Lopes, Jo□o W451
Lopez, Andres A673

Lopez, Claude L. A777
Lopez, David A. E260
Lopez, Fawn P160
Lopez, George A. E181
Lopez, Gerardo I. (AMC
  Entertainment) A47
Lopez, Gerardo I. (AMC
  Entertainment) A47
Lopez, Gustavo P624
Lopez, José W274
Lopez, Miguel-Angel W363
Lopez, Ramón A376
Lopez, Roberto E3
Lopez, Susan Nords P15
Lopez-Blazquez, Ana P63
Lopiano, Victor N. A704
Lopriore, Richard P. (Public Service
  Enterprise Group) A717
Lopriore, Richard P. (PSEG
  Power) P488
Lopus, Thomas A. E283
Lorang, Malcolm M. A591
Loranger, Steven R. A476
Lorat, Helmut A163
Lorber, Howard M. (Ladenburg
  Thalmann) E217
Lorber, Howard M. (Vector
  Group) E372
Lorberbaum, Jeffrey S. A599
Lorch, George A. A692
Lorch, Robert K. P380
Lord, Albert L. A763
Lord, Andy W78
Lord, Gene D. A357
Lord, William T. P641
Loreau, Dominique W100
Loree, James M. A811
Lorello, Benjamin D. A484
Lorello, Diane J. A434
Lorello, Timothy J. E347
Lorenc, Mike P250
Lorensen, Paul P148
Lorente, Jose A. A673
Lorenti, Paul J. P416
Lorentzen, □ivind A779
Lorenz, Mike P540
Lorenzen, Friederike W59
Lorenzen, Jeffrey D. E25
Lorenzi, Nancy M. P644
Lorenzo, Alain W245
Lorenzo, Antonio W239
Lori, Peter H. P637
Lorimer, Linda Koch P675
Loring, Kurt P222
Lorrain, Michel W100
Lorraine, Craig P266
Lorson, John W. A78
Lortie, Brian A. W171
LoRusso, Matthew (The Carlyle
  Group) A847
LoRusso, Matthew (The Carlyle
  Group) A847
Lorusso, Michael A211
Losada, A. M. W190
LoSardo, Christopher E174
Loscocco, Peter F. P412
Losh, Anthony J. A228
Losik, Timothy P. E288
Lospak, Mark P28
Loten, Moira A224
Lothrop, Dave A267
Lotman, Herbert P339
Lott, Hamilton A652
Lottefier, Vincent A491
Lotvin, Alan M. A550
Lou, Michael H. E265
Loucks, Nancy A817
Loucks, William D. P2
Louderback, R. Scott A443
Loudermilk, Joey M. A22
Louette, Pierre W157
Lougee, Anthony M. E95
Lougee, David T. A375
Lougee, Wendy Pradt P633

Loughlin, John P. (Hearst
  Corporation) A430
Loughlin, John P. (Hearst
  Corporation) A430
Loughlin, Michael J. A940
Loughlin, Patrick F. A29
Loughmiller, Eric M. P314
Loughrey, Dan W51
Loughridge, Mark A456
Louie, Keith W101
Louison, Mark W282
Louka, Marie W74
Loura, Ralph A216
Loureiro, Guilherme W426
Lousberg, Kenneth D. A841
Louv, Bill W171
Louvet, Patrice A711
Louwhoff, Roel W80
Lovallo, Anthony P325
Lovato, John P. A480
Love, Cathy A770
Love, Dan P394
Love, David (Levi Strauss) A530
Love, David (Guardian Building
  Products Distribution) P263
Love, David (Levi Strauss) A530
Love, Frank P369
Love, George W85
Love, Greg P369
Love, James L. E368
Love, Jim P544
Love, Jon A697
Love, Judy A228
Love, Lisa A. A208
Love Meyer, Jenny P369
Love, Nat (Meijer) A584
Love, Nat (Meijer) A584
Love, Sharon A663
Love, Tammy A681
Love, Ted W. E270
Love, Tim A663
Love, Tom P369
Love, William G. A312
Lovejoy, Mary F. A845
Lovejoy, Stephen A814
Lovejoy, Thomas B. E152
Lovelace, James J. A516
Lovelace, Lori L. W6
Loveless, Keith A33
Lovell, Craig L. P623
Lovell, Sandy P130
Loveman, Gary W. (Caesars
  Entertainment) A165
Loveman, Gary W. (Caesars
  Entertainment) A165
Loveridge, Debbie W320
Lovett, Melendy A843
Lovett, Michael J. A195
Lovette, Barry (EBSCO) A317
Lovette, Barry (EBSCO) A317
Lovette, William W. A695
Lovie, James S. W333
Lovig, Deb E90
Lovik, Kenneth E143
Loviska, Mike P632
Lovlien, Thomas A. P90
Lovsin, Bob P499
Low, John D. P45
Low, Raymond E352
Lowden, Simon A684
Lowe, Abby P137
Lowe, Alan S. (JDS Uniphase) E206
Lowe, Alan L. (Brunswick Corp.) A153
Lowe, Alistair A817
Lowe, Carol P. A174
Lowe, Challis M. (Ascension
  Health) A82
Lowe, Challis M. (Ascension
  Health) A82
Lowe, Edward A. A657
Lowe, Elizabeth T. E270
Lowe, Gregg A. A843
Lowe, Harry R. A652
Lowe, J. Mitchell E78
Lowe, Kim W213

Lowe, Leticia A190
Lowe, Monte E. P421
Lowe, Roger K. (Red Cross) A737
Lowe, Roger K. (Red Cross) A737
Lowe, Willis E. A223
Lowell, Bruce P468
Lowell, Kevin R. A878
Lowell, Mary Beth E348
Lowenstein, David E287
Lowenthal, Tina M. P107
Lowery, Donny (TVA) A874
Lowery, Donny (TVA) A874
Lowery, Kate A950
Lowery, Kevin A35
Lowery, Michael P114
Lowery, Steve P527
Lowes, D. Rick A909
Lowinger, Jeffrey P74
Lowis, Stephan W341
Lowman, David B. A494
Lowney, P. Geoffrey A464
Lowrance, Randy M. P249
Lowrey, Bill W339
Lowrey, Charles F. A716
Lowrey, Ray E34
Lowrey, William C. (Shell Oil) A785
Lowrey, William C. (Shell Oil) A785
Lowry, Benjamin P178
Lowry, Jennifer E. A243
Lowry, Ryan A623
Lowry, Scott T. A104
Lowson, Steven R. P535
Lowth, Simon W40
Lowther, Julie W80
Lox, Egbert W422
Loxam, Teri A147
Loxton, Debbie W296
Loya, Kathleen E200
Lozano, Guillermina P372
Lozano, Joe J. P679
Lozich, Tom A592
Lozier, Kurt P186
Lu, Carol A160
Lu, Kathryn P416
Lu, Keh-Shew E107
Lu, Luke A339
Lu, Qi A595
Lu, Sophie A949
Lubben, David J. P461
Lubben, Tom (HCSC) A426
Lubben, Tom (HCSC) A426
Lubbock, Geoffrey O. A651
Lubieniecki, Martin P144
Lubischer, Stephen A. E18
Lucarelli, Charles D. P399
Lucas, Christopher W53
Lucas, Earnell (Major League
  Baseball) A551
Lucas, Earnell (Major League
  Baseball) A551
Lucas, George W. P371
Lucas, Grant F. (USAA) A908
Lucas, Grant F. (USAA) A908
Lucas, Hinton J. A305
Lucas, John T. A541
Lucas, Jonathan A. A211
Lucas, Karen P668
Lucas, Melissa A531
Lucas, Michel W345
Lucas, Robert T. A304
Lucas, Tom A786
Lucas, Wes W. P546
Lucas, Wonya Y. A287
Lucchese, John J. A503
Lucchesi, Janice P20
Lucchini, Stefano W142
Luccock, Tom N. P408
Luce, Jason E293
Luce, Richard E. P201
Lucia, Bruce A. A514
Lucia, William C. (HMS
  Holdings) E175
Lucia, William C. (Health Management
  Systems) P283
Luciani, Luca W394

Lytle, Holly P199
Lytle, Shawn W420
Lytovchenko, Igor W397
Lyttle, Catherine M. A957
Lyublinsky, Michael W337
Lähdemäki, Pasi W217
Léger, Thierry W388
Léonard, Michael W233
Lépine, Jean A419
Lévy, Jean-Bernard (Activision
  Blizzard) A10
Lévy, Jean-Bernard (Vivendi) W435
Lévy, Jean-Marc W79
López Calvet, Francisco Javier W87
López Cernada, Abel W199
López García, Marcos W199
López Mozo, Ernesto W152
López Revuelta, Rafael W450
López Rodríguez, Ignacio W302
López Romero, Juan José W199
López Velarde, Antonio W302
López-Cano Ibarreche, Begoña W199
López-Piñol, José María W9
Löckle, Alfred W330
Löjdquist, Per W439
Löscher, Peter W363
Lööf, Torbjörn W195
Lübke, Gerhard Kurt W363
Lütt, Hans-Jürgen P358

M

M'Guinness, Thomas A. (Visa Inc) A917
M'Guinness, Thomas A. (Visa
  U.S.A.) P647
Ma, Christopher A934
Ma, Jun E370
Ma, Steven Y. (The Carlyle
  Group) A847
Ma, Steven Y. (The Carlyle
  Group) A847
Ma, Wayne W8
Maag, Allen W. A92
Maag, Maureen A235
Maag, Timothy L. P371
Maag-Spieler, Jacqueline W11
Maagero, Ashley M. A871
Maas Helvey, Kirsten E86
Maas, Rick P626
Maass, Paul A237
Maatta, John D. (Time Warner) A862
Maatta, John D. (Warner Bros.) P657
Mabbott, John P336
Mabe, Katherine A43
Mabon, David P240
Mabry, Curtis P646
Mabry, Joseph M. A543
Mabry, Rodney H. (University of Texas
  System) A899
Mabry, Rodney H. (University of Texas
  System) A899
Mabry, Steven A303
Mabuchi, Akira W160
Mac Naughton, Duncan C. A928
Macaddino, Laurie A. (Chrysler) A201
Macaddino, Laurie A. (Chrysler) A201
Macalus, Sam (Carlson
  Companies) A175
Macalus, Sam (Carlson
  Companies) A175
Macaluso, Charles E159
Macaluso, Dan P201
Macan, W. Andrew A204
Macapagal, Chito W426
Macari, Jason P. E336
MacArthur, Bob P473
MacArthur, Herbert A138
Macaulay, Bruce A. A514
Macaulay, Scott D. P24
Macaylo, Clifford J. E351
MacBain, Michael W. P499
MacBeath, Alex (Grant Thornton
  International) A403

MacBeath, Alex (Grant Thornton
  International) A403
Maccarone, Constance M. P664
Macchiarola, Doreen A. E279
Macchiaverna, Frank R. A644
MacCleary, Gerald F. P70
MacClellan, Clare (NHL) A637
MacClellan, Clare (NHL) A637
MacConnel, Melinda J. E268
MacCormack, Jean F. P631
MacCormick, Ron P530
MacDonald, Alan S. P140
MacDonald, Bradley T. E238
MacDonald, Brian (Microsoft) A595
MacDonald, Brian P. (Sunoco) A822
MacDonald, Bruce R. E227
Macdonald, Bruce P499
MacDonald, Bryan E379
MacDonald, David P668
MacDonald, Donald J. A356
MacDonald, J. Randall A456
MacDonald, Jack (Golden
  Horizons) A395
MacDonald, Jack (Golden
  Horizons) A395
Macdonald, Jeff E7
MacDonald, Jim (FMR) A361
MacDonald, Jim (FMR) A361
MacDonald, John (Bechtel) A114
MacDonald, John (Bechtel) A114
Macdonald, John Paul W72
MacDonald, Martin P66
MacDonald, Michael E211
Macdonald, Natalie-Jane W83
Macdonald, Roderick A379
MacDonald, S. Kelley A817
MacDonald, Scott A81
Macdonald, Thomas R. A464
MacDonald-Sheetz, Margaret E238
Mace, Roy W. E265
Macedo, Alex (Burger King) A155
Macedo, Alex (Burger King) A155
MacEwan, Pam P261
Macfarlane, C.N. A197
Macfarlane, Gregory J. P130
Macfarlane, Ken A365
MacGibbon, Alan N. (Deloitte) A276
MacGibbon, Alan N. (Deloitte) A276
MacGowan, Bill A631
MacGregor, Catherine A772
MacGregor, J. Scott A324
Machacek, Lisa Piova A539
Machado, A. Ricardo A678
Machado, C. Patrick E238
Machata, Julie P249
Machell, Simon W45
Machenaud, Hervé W136
Macher, Erin K. A437
Macheras, Ann B. P211
Machetti, Claudio W140
Machida, Katsuhiko W361
Machida, Kiyomi W381
Machida, Yukio W373
Machielse, Bernardus N.M. P393
Machin, Stuart W101
Machon, Monika A27
Macht, Michael W438
Macht, Patricia K. (CalPERS) A167
Macht, Patricia K. (CalPERS) A167
Machuzick, John T. A382
Maciag, Sandra J. E290
Macias Gomes, João W80
Macias, Stephen A452
Macias, Yolanda P624
Maciel, Jason P649
Macik, Cheryl (Wakefern Food) A927
Macik, Cheryl (Wakefern Food) A927
Macin, Maelia P637
MacInnes, Dennis P196
MacInnis, Frank T. (EMCOR) A327
MacInnis, Frank T. (Williams
  Companies) A952
MacIntyre, Drew E. W392
MacIntyre, Gregg W296
MacIntyre, Larry P311

MacIntyre, Sandy P50
Maciolek, Jerzy B. E152
Macip, Marcus E218
Mack, Andrew T. E346
Mack, Anne Marie P91
Mack, Carter D. E207
Mack, John J. (Morgan Stanley) A605
Mack, John J. (NewYork-Presbyterian
  Hospital) P439
Mack, Melissa A934
Mack, Michael J. A271
Mack, Peter A351
Mack, Stephen A866
Mackay, A. D. A112
MacKay, Dave P130
Mackay, E.A. G. (MillerCoors) P409
Mackay, E.A. G. (SABMiller) W343
Mackay, Iain J. W190
Mackay, Leo S. A541
Mackay, Martin W40
MacKay, Mike E306
Mackay, Tara E47
Mackay, Tom P624
MacKay, William L. A33
MacKeigan, John P558
Mackenzie, Amanda W45
Mackenzie, Andrew W65
Mackenzie, April (Grant Thornton
  International) A403
Mackenzie, April (Grant Thornton
  International) A403
MacKenzie, George A57
MacKenzie, John W30
MacKenzie, Ken W29
Mackenzie, Robert D. P579
MacKenzie, Stuart J. (The Carlyle
  Group) A847
MacKenzie, Stuart J. (The Carlyle
  Group) A847
MacKerracher, JoAnna W99
Mackey, Chris W254
Mackey, Ed P180
Mackey, John P. A950
Mackey, Rosemary W. (Red Cross) A737
Mackey, Rosemary W. (Red Cross) A737
Mackie, Alison W220
Mackie, Jane W426
Mackie, Peter P135
MacKimm, Nancy P334
Mackin, David L. P223
Mackin, Ginny A304
Mackin, Grainne W125
Mackin, James Patrick A583
MacKinnon, Elinor C. P89
MacKinnon, Gail G. P600
Mackle, Anthony A143
Mackley, Scott E292
Macklin, Roger E130
Mackney, David P266
Mackowski, Christopher P472
MacLean, Brian W. A871
MacLean, Drew P153
MacLean, John R. A63
MacLean, Robert A57
Maclean, Tom P490
MacLeay, Thomas H. P421
MacLellan, Daniel P221
MacLellan, J. Daryl A211
MacLellan, Steve A646
MacLennan, David W. (C.H. Robinson
  Worldwide) A159
MacLennan, David W. (Cargill) A172
MacLennan, David W. (Cargill) A172
MacLeod, Amy A380
MacLeod, John L. P608
MacLeod, Kevin J. W138
MacLeod, Marcia M. A952
MacLeod, Robert W214
MacLeod, Sean (NHL) A637
MacLeod, Sean (NHL) A637
MacLeod, Valerie P313
Maclin, Joan C. P529
Maclin, Samuel Todd A494
MacLiver, Donald H. A65
MacMahon, John P. A247

MacMedan, Julie C. E99
MacMillan, Andy A666
MacMillan, Katherine P332
MacMillan, Michael A866
MacMillan, Richard A. E218
MacMurray, Thomas E. P416
Macnab, Kevin A869
Macnamara, Brian G. A449
MacNamara, Thomas G. E375
Macnee, Walter M. A567
Macnow, Joseph A921
Macomber, Todd E293
MacPhee, James M. (Liberty
  Mutual) A534
MacPhee, James M. (Liberty
  Mutual) A534
Macpherson, David A340
Macpherson, Donald G. A926
Macpherson, Lisa H. (Hallmark) A414
Macpherson, Lisa H. (Hallmark) A414
Macpherson, Nina W145
Macri, Steven (Warner Music) A933
Macri, Steven (Warner Music) A933
Macrie, Mike (Land O'Lakes) A519
Macrie, Mike (Land O'Lakes) A519
Macris, Achilles O. A494
Macsherry, John E111
MacSwain, Claudia N. P211
Macsween, John E388
MacWillson, Alastair W6
Macy, Richard H. (Pension Benefit
  Guaranty) A682
Macy, Richard H. (Pension Benefit
  Guaranty) A682
Madan, Akshay (New York Life) A625
Madan, Akshay (New York Life) A625
Madan, Karan W119
Maday, Gregg (Time Warner) A862
Maday, Gregg (Warner Bros.) P657
Madden, Joe A590
Madden, Joseph M. E255
Madden, Michael J. P487
Madden, Steven E332
Madden, Teresa S. A958
Maddison, Tom A960
Maddock, Ernest E. A518
Maddocks, Mark E. A95
Maddocks, Vance G. A186
Maddox, Elton H. P132
Maddox, Jeff E254
Maddox, Kristy P469
Maddox, Paul W296
Maddox, Peter P137
Maddrey, Nicole M. A934
Maddux, Denver E221
Maddux, Franklin W. P224
Maddux, Randy E178
Mader, David A. A138
Madere, Consuelo E. A603
Madhavan, Ashok A168
Madia, John P133
Madigan, Christine P434
Madigan, Sarah P637
Madigan, Thomas E. A666
Madigan, Trevor W282
Madison, Bill (CalPERS) A167
Madison, Bill (CalPERS) A167
Madison, J. Craig P520
Madison, Kathryn A. P302
Madison, Michelle P624
Madison, Paula P428
Madison, Tanya M. E282
Madlinger, Sukanya R. A514
Madore, Marsha M. A771
Madrid, Annette L. E204
Madrid, James D. P386
Madridejos, Ignacio W91
Madsen, Andrew H. A267
Madsen, Laurence P180
Madzy, Edward P65
Mae, Kouji W229
Maeda, Kazutoshi W207
Maeda, Kiyoshi (Verio) P646
Maeda, Kiyoshi (NTT) W291
Maeda, Koichi W352

Maloney, Bill (Barnes & Noble College Booksellers) P63
Maloney, Bill (Statoil) W378
Maloney, Bob A906
Maloney, Cathleen M. (BJ's Wholesale Club) A129
Maloney, Cathleen M. (BJ's Wholesale Club) A129
Maloney, Daniel J. A662
Maloney, Don P62
Maloney, Greg A491
Maloney, Kevin E116
Maloney, Mary D. A612
Maloney, Patrick (Health Management Associates) A427
Maloney, Patrick (Barnes & Noble College Booksellers) P63
Maloney, Paul P63
Maloney, Sean M. A464
Malony, Patrick W320
Malphrus, Stephen R. P209
Maltas, Ken P581
Maltbie, Christine P253
Maltese, Anthony E. E255
Maltezos, Louis P. E22
Maltsbarger, Richard D. A543
Maltz, Allen P. (Blue Cross and Blue Shield of Massachusetts) A132
Maltz, Allen P. (Blue Cross and Blue Shield of Massachusetts) A132
Malus, Alan J. A855
Malverdi, Fabrizio W245
Malvido, Fernando P520
Malzahn, Dan A655
Mamman, Nancy E97
Mammel, Kevin P492
Mammola, Domenicoluca W180
Man, Edward (The Carlyle Group) A847
Man, Edward (The Carlyle Group) A847
Manary, Michelle P92
Manasco, Shon J. (USAA) A908
Manasco, Shon J. (USAA) A908
Manber, Udi A402
Mance, Craig (Hilton Worldwide) A441
Mance, Craig (Hilton Worldwide) A441
Manchester, Paula A267
Manchisi, James A138
Manchisi, Michael A567
Mancinelli, Louis A224
Mancini, Christopher E292
Mancini, Joseph H. A960
Mancini, Laraine P600
Mancini, Lisa A. A257
Mancini, Louis J. A135
Mancuso, Charlie P214
Mancuso, Michael J. A232
Mancuso, Robert P. P594
Mancuso, Salvatore A44
Mandac, Lorvo W255
Mandala, Steven P428
Mandara, Allison P124
Mandarano, Kelly A312
Mande, Sidharth A271
Mandel, Andrea J. P190
Mandel, Carol A. P449
Mandel, James L. E249
Mandel, Michael W102
Mandelbaum, Jay A494
Mandelid, Glenn W397
Mandell, Brian P590
Mandelstam, Peter A650
Manders, Carrie P558
Manders, Matthew G. A207
Mandersson, Magnus W145
Mandes, Richard J. P20
Mandhana, Om P42
Mandino, Matthew W. A720
Mandl, Michael J. P201
Mandler, Ronald A516
Mandraccia, Crocifissa A11
Mandraffino, Erika W142
Manduzzi, Lee P511
Mandyck, John P114
Manerikar, Nirmal V. P210

Manes, Gianna M. A304
Manfred, Robert D. (Major League Baseball) A551
Manfred, Robert D. (Major League Baseball) A551
Manfredi, Filippo A278
Mangalindan, Mylene A438
Mangan, Pete J. E358
Manganello, Timothy M. (BorgWarner) A140
Manganello, Timothy M. (Federal Reserve Bank of Chicago) P210
Mangano, Joy A451
Mangelsdorf, Paul A823
Mangen, Bill (Cox Communications) A251
Mangen, Bill (Cox Communications) A251
Manger, Richard W129
Manget, Joe (Boston Consulting) A141
Manget, Joe (Boston Consulting) A141
Mangiagalli, Marco W347
Manginelli, Gail P328
Mangione, Gino P48
Mangione, Jacqueline A312
Manglik, Harsh W6
Mango, Jeff P127
Mangone, Ken A478
Mangoni, Andrea W394
Manhard, Kimberly J. E35
Maniar, Paresh (Maxim Integrated Products) E233
Maniar, Paresh (Maxim Integrated Products) E233
Manicardi, Edoardo P670
Manion, Doug A147
Manion, Jane M. (Performance Food) A687
Manion, Jane M. (Performance Food) A687
Manion, Mark D. (Norfolk Southern) A644
Manion, Mark D. (Norfolk Southern Railway) P446
Manis, G. Scott A838
Manis, Jonathan P576
Manista, Raymond J. (Northwestern Mutual) A649
Manista, Raymond J. (Northwestern Mutual) A649
Manke, Richard L. P532
Manley, Carl P533
Manley, Chris P151
Manley, Frederick E. A30
Manley, Jonathan A336
Manley, Lisa A221
Manley, Mark R. (AllianceBernstein) A40
Manley, Mark R. (AllianceBernstein) A40
Manley, Michael (Chrysler) A201
Manley, Michael (Chrysler) A201
Manley, Patrick W452
Manley, Rose Marie A37
Manlowe, David P180
Manly, Marc E. A304
Manly, Robert W. A791
Mann, Alejandro M. A695
Mann, Athena P326
Mann, Bill A160
Mann, Bruce M. W333
Mann, C. Roddy E374
Mann, Cathy G. A413
Mann, Darren E132
Mann, Eric A623
Mann, Jennifer (SAS Institute) A769
Mann, Jennifer (SAS Institute) A769
Mann, Jim W417
Mann, Lindsay W103
Mann, Mary A. A341
Mann, Neil P22
Mann, Peter W296
Mann, R. Tucker A713
Mann, Robert P180
Manna, Joe A538

Mannard, K. Kelly A646
Mannarino, Claudio A. E33
Mannarn, Art W95
Manne, Kenneth W. A516
Mannekens, Henk W80
Mannello, Joseph E158
Manners, Myrna A. P439
Mannheimer, Michael J. (Cox Enterprises) A252
Mannheimer, Michael J. (Cox Enterprises) A252
Mannik, Steven J. (General Re) A385
Mannik, Steven J. (General Re) A385
Manninen, Arto W217
Manning, Andre W307
Manning, Dean P571
Manning, Dennis J. (Guardian Life) A407
Manning, Dennis J. (Guardian Life) A407
Manning, Eileen M. E123
Manning, George T. P334
Manning, Hooker E111
Manning, John F. P644
Manning, Keith D. P679
Manning Magrini, Joyce (Burlington Coat Factory) A156
Manning Magrini, Joyce (Burlington Coat Factory) A156
Manning, Martin F. P15
Manning, Paul B. A688
Manning, Richard P360
Manning, Robert (H-E-B) A412
Manning, Robert (H-E-B) A412
Manning, Robert J. (University of Massachusetts) P631
Manning, Robin E. (TVA) A874
Manning, Robin E. (TVA) A874
Manning, Timothy P. A159
Mannion, Mike P78
Mannion, Sean A. P416
Mannix, Kevin W403
Mano Pinto Simões, Maria J. W141
Manoogian, Richard A. A563
Manor, Moshe W403
Manring, Lewis E. A305
Mans, Gary P627
Mansbach, Hank E238
Mansell, Kevin B. A509
Mansfield, Christopher C. (Liberty Mutual) A534
Mansfield, Christopher C. (Liberty Mutual) A534
Mansfield, John C. (Graybar Electric) A404
Mansfield, John C. (Graybar Electric) A404
Mansfield, John (Hitachi Data Systems) P291
Mansfield, Mari (Quintiles Transnational) A727
Mansfield, Mari (Quintiles Transnational) A727
Mansfield, Robert A74
Mansfield, William L. A913
Mansker, Jimmy D. A136
Manso Neto, João M. W141
Manson, Craig G. P130
Mansukoski, Pentti W285
Mansur, Bernadette (NHL) A637
Mansur, Bernadette (NHL) A637
Mansuri, Muzammil M. A394
Mantanona, Steve A249
Mantega, Guido W304
Mantel, Timothy A. A832
Mantilla, Felix A. P594
Mantle, Janine W92
Manto, Gwendolyn K. (Sports Authority) A804
Manto, Gwendolyn K. (Sports Authority) A804
Mantovani, Massimo W142
Mantua, Joe P81
Manuel, Mark A. P162
Manuel, Penny M. A797

Manville, John A210
Manwani, Harish W426
Many, Moshe W403
Manzano, Wilhelmina P439
Manzi, Jim P. A855
Manzini, Aldo A592
Manzotti, Maurizio W203
Mao, Julin E240
Mao, Matthew A29
Maortua, Jorge W172
Mapes, Michelle S. E164
Maquera, David E74
Maquet, Alain A461
Maquet-Diafouka, Michael (New York Life) A625
Maquet-Diafouka, Michael (New York Life) A625
Maquiera, George A920
Mara, Shaun P. A269
Maranell, Michael L. (Ag Processing Inc.) A23
Maranell, Michael L. (Ag Processing Inc.) A23
Marano, Joe A954
Marantette, Thomas M. P160
Maranto, Tony C. A335
Maratto, Mike P433
Maravall Herrero, Fernando W93
Maravei, Dan E188
Marbach, Alain W69
Marbach, Mary L. E376
Marbaugh, David J. A324
Marberry, Michael P323
Marbert, Larry P632
Marburg, Gerhard E45
Marcarelli, Dean P. P125
Marceau, Philippe P315
Marced, Maria W415
Marcel, Jeff E100
Marcel, Vincent W430
March, Bruce H. W196
March, Kevin P. A843
Marchal, Sylvie P334
Marchant, Ian W358
Marchant, Kandice Kottk P590
Marchant, Paul W38
Marchase, Richard B. P627
Marchesini, Roberto E144
Marchessaux, Philippe W69
Marchetti, Page W. P211
Marchetti, Stefano W203
Marchetto, Peter A. (Tishman Construction) A865
Marchetto, Peter A. (Tishman Construction) A865
Marchi, Michael (Kohler) A510
Marchi, Michael (Kohler) A510
Marchick, David M (The Carlyle Group) A847
Marchick, David M (The Carlyle Group) A847
Marchildon, Christine W392
Marchionne, Sergio (Chrysler) A201
Marchionne, Sergio (Chrysler) A201
Marchionne, Sergio (CNH Global) W97
Marchionne, Sergio (Fiat) W153
Marchiony, Brian J. A494
Marchiori, Dave P655
Marcial, Edwin D. E193
Marciano, Maurice A408
Marciano, Paul A408
Marcin, Robert H. A264
Marcinelli, James A. P300
Marcinelli, Ronald P. A228
Marcinowski, Stefan W56
Marco, Lori J. A447
Marcone, Rock P39
Marcopolus, Ted P237
Marcos, Jorge E134
Marcotte, Gary A87
Marcum, R. Alan A281
Marcus, Bruce D. A576
Marcus, Deborah P123
Marcus, Jeffrey P210
Marcus, Robert D. P600

A = AMERICAN BUSINESS
E = EMERGING COMPANIES
P = PRIVATE COMPANIES
W = WORLD BUSINESS

Marcus, Steven B. A126
Marcus-Wyner, Lynn E76
Marcuse, Paul W. W420
Marcy, Mike A842
Marden, William W. E146
Marder, Dari E181
Mardon, Denis W41
Mardrus, Christian W324
Mareburger, Robert S. A664
Marenco, Patricia P53
Marenghi, Julio P607
Marengo, Ana (New York City Health and Hospitals) A624
Marengo, Ana (New York City Health and Hospitals) A624
Marengère, Michel L. E328
Marenzi, Gary P405
Mares, Eyal E174
Maresca, Bob P93
Maresca, Robert A. P404
Marescotti, Manlio A557
Maresky, Neil W40
Maret, Karine W69
Marfone, Patrick A97
Margala Klein, Hope P676
Margarites, Nicholas G. E327
Margaritis, William G. A349
Margason, Scott P305
Margerum, Suzanne C. E66
Margeson, Jacilyn P92
Margevich, Robert (Akzo Nobel Inc.) P20
Margevich, Robert (Akzo Nobel) W19
Margherio, Scott (BJ's Wholesale Club) A129
Margherio, Scott (BJ's Wholesale Club) A129
Margherita, Michele P97
Margison, Richard L. P627
Margo, Elizabeth A549
Margolin, Eric M. A176
Margolin, Ilene D. P200
Margolis, Karyn A94
Margolis, M. Pauliina E377
Margulies, Ricard P149
Margulis, Heidi S. A452
Marhofer, John A. E75
Mariani, Pierre W124
Mariani, Wally R. W317
Mariano, Robert A. (Roundy's Supermarkets) A753
Mariano, Robert A. (Roundy's Supermarkets) A753
Maridet, Pascal W100
Marie, Brian P212
Marien, Philippe W73
Marilley, Leanne D. (Norfolk Southern) A644
Marilley, Leanne D. (Norfolk Southern Railway) P446
Marin, Gustavo C. P140
Marine, Jay A45
Marineau, Philip A. E319
Marinelli, Steve A30
Marinello, Charles A735
Marinello, Kathryn V. E335
Mariner, Jonathan D. (Major League Baseball) P551
Mariner, Jonathan D. (Major League Baseball) A551
Marinescu, Alexandra A632
Marinet, Pierre W149
Marino, Andrew (The Carlyle Group) A847
Marino, Andrew (The Carlyle Group) A847
Marino D'Arienzo, Annette P89
Marino, John (1st United Bank) E2

Marino, John (FlightSafety) P221
Marino, Joseph A920
Marino, Ken P76
Marino, Philip P. E95
Marino, Rita W142
Marino, Robert A. P294
Marino, Vincent P551
Marino, Wayne A. E364
Marino, William J. P294
Marion-Bouchacourt, Anne W369
Marjoram, Chris A471
Marjoram, Silvia E23
Mark, Joe P563
Mark, Kelly S. A607
Mark, Richard J. A50
Markarian, James E190
Markel, Scott P239
Markell, Eric M. P490
Markell, Peter K. P465
Marken, Michael E287
Markert, Stephen E. E376
Markey, Edward W. A400
Markezich, Ron A595
Markfield, Roger S. A52
Markham, Kathy J. A503
Markheim, Steven E121
Markiewicz, Les W339
Markin, L. Jeffrey E376
Markley, Steve P182
Markley, William C. A483
Markman, Maurie P372
Markman, Russell P63
Markoe, Linda P321
Markopoulos, Jody A376
Markovich, John E279
Markovich, Paul P89
Markowitz, Arnold E33
Markowski, Elizabeth M. A532
Marks, Alan A316
Marks, Amanda P624
Marks, Daniel J. (ServiceMaster) A782
Marks, Daniel J. (ServiceMaster) A782
Marks, David B. (Wells Fargo) A940
Marks, David (CUNA Mutual Group) P165
Marks, David (OrthoSynetics) P456
Marks, Dawn A69
Marks, Elyse E341
Marks, Eugene A590
Marks, Jeffery A518
Marks, John J. P394
Marks, Michael E. A766
Marks, Peter J. (Robert Bosch LLC) P511
Marks, Peter (Co-operative Group) W99
Marks, Peter J. (Robert Bosch) W330
Marks, Richard P261
Marks, Stuart E54
Marks, Terrance M. A853
Marks, Terry E320
Markunas, Glad A267
Markward, Abigail (Bausch & Lomb) A108
Markward, Abigail (Bausch & Lomb) A108
Markwardt, William F. P532
Markwith, Candace A838
Marlborough, Stewart E99
Marler, Peter A. A573
Marley, Bradley W. E143
Marley, Brian T. (Belk) A119
Marley, Brian T. (Belk) A119
Marlin, Richard E283
Marmer, Lynn A514
Marmor, Ben A152
Marmugi, Alain W430
Marnatti, James P228
Marold, Paul P6
Marolda, George P624
Maronati, Manuela E195
Marone, Alfonso P428
Maroone, Michael E. A87
Marotta, Daniel A. A149
Marotta, Dean L. A966
Marotta, Sabrina J. A516

Marquardt, Jeffrey C. P209
Marques Gonçalves, José António W163
Marques, Jose (Western and Southern Life) P665
Marques, Jose (Deutsche Bank) W119
Marques, José D. P664
Marquette, Stephen G. P491
Marquez, Fidel A338
Marquez, Shannon P386
Marr, Ann W. P671
Marrandino, Donald P. (Caesars Entertainment) A165
Marrandino, Donald P. (Caesars Entertainment) A165
Marraro, Francesca (HMS Holdings) E175
Marraro, Francesca (Health Management Systems) P283
Marren, Alexandria P. A887
Marren, Bernard T. E272
Marrett, Phillip E. P32
Marriott, J. W. A557
Marriott, John W. A557
Marriott, Neil P266
Marriott, Peter R. W44
Marriott, Richard E. A449
Marrocco, John E143
Marroquin, Tracine P325
Marrotte, James P. E231
Mars, Frank (Mars, Incorporated) A559
Mars, Frank (Mars, Incorporated) A559
Mars, John F. (Mars, Incorporated) A559
Mars, John F. (Mars, Incorporated) A559
Mars, Thomas A. A928
Mars, Victoria (Mars, Incorporated) A559
Mars, Victoria (Mars, Incorporated) A559
Marsal, Bryan P. A525
Marsalese, Sherri A218
Marschilok, Stephen A420
Marsden, George (E. & J. Gallo) A309
Marsden, George (E. & J. Gallo) A309
Marsden, R. Frederick E114
Marseilles, Bill E146
Marsh, Amy K. P634
Marsh, Andrew A332
Marsh, Anitra C. A711
Marsh, Brad W443
Marsh, Brenda A105
Marsh, Gary P. E244
Marsh, Joseph B. E352
Marsh, K. Russel E114
Marsh, Kevin B. A770
Marsh, Laurie M. A613
Marsh, Michael L. A312
Marsh, Patrick P180
Marsh, Peter P610
Marsh, Steve (Cox Communications) A251
Marsh, Steve (Cox Communications) A251
Marsh, Thomas R. A662
Marsh, Ward P140
Marsh, William D. A97
Marshall, Beth P52
Marshall, Carol W99
Marshall, Chris P78
Marshall, David A. P210
Marshall, Douglas H. A960
Marshall, Edith E175
Marshall, Edwin C. P311
Marshall, Hillary W92
Marshall, Jan A799
Marshall, Laurel P670
Marshall, Lee E352
Marshall, Mariann Wojtk A714
Marshall, McAlister C. A144
Marshall, Pamela J. P92
Marshall, Patrick J. P677
Marshall, Richard N. A798
Marshall, Robbie P188
Marshall, Robert R. A66

Marshall, Ron P466
Marshall, Ryan A720
Marshall, S. Jane W240
Marshall, Scott R. A947
Marshall, Steven W50
Marshall, Thurgood (US Postal Service) A907
Marshall, Thurgood (US Postal Service) A907
Marshall, Todd A832
Marshall, Troy P624
Marshman, Scott A. E279
Marsili, Daniel B. A224
Marsland, John W. A29
Martel, Roland M. A459
Martel, Sébastien W351
Martell, James J. E138
Martello, Wan Ling A928
Marten, Dan E181
Marten, Iván (Boston Consulting) A141
Marten, Iván (Boston Consulting) A141
Marten, Jon P. A678
Martens, Steve A600
Martensen, Robert P443
Marth, William S. W403
Martha, Joseph A138
Martie, John A939
Martikainen, Ahti W398
Martin Anderson, Kristine A138
Martin, Andre (Mars, Incorporated) A559
Martin, Andre (Mars, Incorporated) A559
Martin, Andrew (Goodrich Corp.) A398
Martin, Andrew (Compass Group) W105
Martin, Antonio (New York City Health and Hospitals) A624
Martin, Antonio (New York City Health and Hospitals) A624
Martin, Bill A754
Martin, Brad (Random House) A733
Martin, Brad (Random House) A733
Martin, Brian M. A506
Martin, Carl P668
Martin, Christine (Cox Communications) A251
Martin, Christine (Cox Communications) A251
Martin, Christopher C. A121
Martin, Craig L. A483
Martin, Daniel B. (El Paso Pipeline Partners) E120
Martin, Daniel B. (El Paso Corporation) A321
Martin, Daniel P. (Mutual of Omaha) A609
Martin, Daniel F. (The Cleveland Clinic) P590
Martin, Daniel P. (Mutual of Omaha) A609
Martin, Dave A326
Martin, David L. (Cardiovascular Systems) E62
Martin, David M. (Life Partners Holdings) E219
Martin, David W. (ServiceMaster) A782
Martin, David W. (ServiceMaster) A782
Martin, Denis W306
Martin, Dyrdra (AllianceBernstein) A40
Martin, Dyrdra (AllianceBernstein) A40
Martin, Elaine R. P631
Martin, Fiona W65
Martin Garcia, Felix W114
Martin, Gary P554
Martin, Gemma (Deloitte) A276
Martin, Gemma (Deloitte) A276
Martin, George F. P438
Martin, Gordon G. P20
Martin, Greg P352
Martin, Iain P186
Martin, Jack P286
Martin, Jackie (Vivid Entertainment) P648

Martin, James K. (Dominion Resources) A295
Martin, James D. (Thomas H. Lee Partners) P595
Martin, Jana M. P584
Martin, Jay G. A97
Martin, Jayme (NIKE) A640
Martin, Jeff (Southwest Airlines) A799
Martin, Jeff (Giant Food) P247
Martin, Jeff (Stop & Shop) P570
Martin, Jeffery W. (Sempra Energy) A781
Martin, Jennifer H. P597
Martin, Jim P254
Martin, John (Riverbed Technology) E303
Martin, John C. (Big Lots) A126
Martin, John (Darden) A267
Martin, John C. (Gilead Sciences) A394
Martin, John K. (Time Warner) A862
Martin, John A. (Flintco) P222
Martin, John T. (M. A. Mortenson) P371
Martin, John (Nissan) W281
Martin, John (Wolseley) W443
Martin, Jordi A491
Martin, Jules A. P449
Martin, Kathryn (Memorial Sloan-Kettering) P399
Martin, Kathryn A. (University of Minnesota) P633
Martin, Keith (Associated Wholesale Grocers) A85
Martin, Keith (Associated Wholesale Grocers) A85
Martin, Ken (Cablevision Systems) A161
Martin, Ken (NHL) A637
Martin, Ken (NHL) A637
Martin, Kim A503
Martin, Kirt A820
Martin, Larry E168
Martin, Lauralee E. A491
Martin, Leslie A642
Martin, Lorna A70
Martin, Marcus L. P636
Martin, Mark A66
Martin, Mary A909
Martin, Matthew A. P211
Martin, Melissa A828
Martin, Miguel A44
Martin, Mike (Cargill) A172
Martin, Mike (Winn-Dixie) A955
Martin, Mike (Cargill) A172
Martin, Murray D. A697
Martin, Nigel W85
Martin, Patricia A. A324
Martin, Paul E. (Baxter International) A110
Martin, Paul (University of Miami) P632
Martin, Peggy A. (Catholic Health Initiatives) A183
Martin, Peggy A. (Catholic Health Initiatives) A183
Martin, Philippe W431
Martin, Ray P53
Martin, Rebecca R. A900
Martin, Richard J. (Unified Grocers) A881
Martin, Richard J. (Unified Grocers) A881
Martin, Rick A916
Martin, Robert V. (Epoch) E131
Martin, Robert W. (Thor Industries) A858
Martin, Robert T. (BMO Financial Group) W66
Martin, Robin A. A464
Martin, Roger W. E383
Martin, Roland P163
Martin, Ronald T. A224
Martin, Rosemary W436
Martin, Roy M. A856
Martin, Samuel M. A4

Martin, Scott (ORBIT/FR) E273
Martin, Scott (Guardian Life) A407
Martin, Scott (Guardian Life) A407
Martin, Sean B.W. A73
Martin, Steve (Merge Healthcare) E240
Martin, Steve (Young & Rubicam) P677
Martin, Thomas L. P416
Martin, Tim P358
Martin, Toby E111
Martin, Todd P50
Martin, William A. A66
Martin, Willie C. A305
Martin-Flickinger, Gerri A13
Martin-Löf, Sverker (Ericsson) W145
Martin-Löf, Sverker (Skanska) W367
Martin-Löf, Sverker (Svenska Cellulosa) W387
Martin-Vachon, Anne A642
Martincich, Carl P369
Martindale, Kenneth A. A744
Martindale, Steven L. A459
Martineau, Alexis (The Carlyle Group) A847
Martineau, Alexis (The Carlyle Group) A847
Martineau, Parker E157
Martinelli, Dominic E321
Martinelli, Mark W190
Martinelli, Maurizio W430
Martinelli, Raymond M. E318
Martinet, Mark A529
Martinetto, Joseph R. A194
Martinez, Alba P594
Martinez, Alfonso P445
Martinez, Ana L. P443
Martinez, Angel R. E97
Martinez, Annette A638
Martinez, Arthur C. A451
Martinez, Belinda P178
Martinez, Carlos A. (National Western) E252
Martinez, Carlos (University of Texas System) A899
Martinez, Carlos (University of Texas System) A899
Martinez, Claude W245
Martinez, Frederic A754
Martinez, Gustavo A471
Martinez, Kelsey P563
Martinez, Louis E. A339
Martinez, Maria E310
Martinez, Mark E23
Martinez, Mauricio P219
Martinez, Mel R. A494
Martinez, Monica A228
Martinez, Robert E. P446
Martinez Serna, Javier E. P171
Martinez-Quiroga, Jorge A94
Martini, James P668
Martini, Jeffrey A. E314
Martini, Lisa A334
Martini, Michael E146
Martino, Gary R. A345
Martinovich, Robert F. A664
Martins, Anthony J. P532
Martins da Costa, António W141
Martins, José Carlos W428
Martins, Tito Botel W428
Martinson, Chris P668
Martnez, Belén W354
Martocci, Barbara (TVA) A874
Martocci, Barbara (TVA) A874
Marton, Keith I. P487
Martorana, Clare A. E380
Martorano, Ryan P287
Martore, Gracia C. A375
Martrenchar, Yves W69
Martt, Anne V. P623
Marttin, Berry W318
Martucci, Maximiliano A920
Marty, Jason C. P59
Martyn, Diane W320
Martyr, David R. A265
Martz, Gary R. A405
Martz, Ronald E. A97

Martínez, Amparo Moral W194
Martínez Córcoles, Francisco W194
Martínez, Enrique R. A287
Martínez, Robert E. A644
Martínez San Martín, Miguel W325
Martínez Sibaja, Alejandro W302
Martínez Simancas Sanchez, Julián W194
Marucci, Anthony S. E65
Marukawa, Kiyoshi W209
Marumo, Masato (The Carlyle Group) A847
Marumo, Masato (The Carlyle Group) A847
Marumoto, Akira W252
Marushack, Joseph P. A238
Marusiak, Luke E197
Maruyama, Akira W284
Maruyama, Haruya W116
Maruyama, Kenji W23
Maruyama, Takao W273
Maruyama, Yoshinori W23
Marventano, David A359
Marventano, Jessica P143
Marvin, D. Jane A752
Marvin, David B. A228
Marvin, Jay P552
Marvin, Timothy A449
Marvul, Mike E193
Marx, Erich W281
Marx, Oscar B. E28
Marx, William L. P399
Mary, Bernard W109
Maryland, Patricia A. (Ascension Health) A82
Maryland, Patricia A. (Ascension Health) A82
Marziale, Michael L. P438
Marzilli, Christopher A380
Marzion, Kenneth W. (CalPERS) A167
Marzion, Kenneth W. (CalPERS) A167
Marín, Javier W172
Mas, Jorge (MasTec) E230
Mas, Jorge (MasTec) E230
Mas, José R. (MasTec) E230
Mas, José R. (MasTec) E230
Masaki, Toshio W410
Masaracchia-Roberts, Sue P493
Mascaraque, Cesar P49
Mascarenas, Paul A. A365
Mascaro, Dan A714
Mascelli, Armond (Red Cross) A737
Mascelli, Armond (Red Cross) A737
Mascera, Laurence E158
Mascher, Christof W25
Mascia, Angelo (New York City Health and Hospitals) A624
Mascia, Angelo (New York City Health and Hospitals) A624
Mascitelli, Susan P439
Mascola, Don P336
Mascolo, Lisa M. W6
Mascolo, Pablo A224
Masding, Simon W25
Masegi, Mitsuhiko W116
Masek, Matthew A. P372
Masel, Jonathan E129
Maser, James G. A893
Masetti, Alexander W. A29
Mashouf, Reza E306
Maskatia, Arif W8
Maslak, Peter P399
Maslen, William P92
Maslin, Jon P503
Maslowski, James P279
Mason, Andrew D. E165
Mason, Chance E212
Mason, Daniel R. (CBS Corp) A188
Mason, Daniel R. (CBS Radio) P124
Mason, Erick P267
Mason, Graham W315
Mason, Greg P293
Mason, Heather L. A5
Mason, Jeanne K. A110
Mason, Jonny W208

Mason, Kelvin R. (Gulfstream Aerospace) A409
Mason, Kelvin R. (Gulfstream Aerospace) A409
Mason, Mark A213
Mason, Mike P19
Mason, Phillip J. A318
Mason, Rob P309
Mason, Robert A. (Valassis) A910
Mason, Stephen G. (Chick-fil-A) A198
Mason, Stephen G. (Chick-fil-A) A198
Mason, Thomas E. (Battelle Memorial) A107
Mason, Thomas E. (Battelle Memorial) A107
Mason, Tim J. R. W401
Mason, Tyler A895
Masquelier, Michel P309
Masrani, Bharat B. W392
Massa, George J. (Hilton Worldwide) A441
Massa, George J. (Hilton Worldwide) A441
Massabki, Elie E157
Massad, Lori (AllianceBernstein) A40
Massad, Lori (AllianceBernstein) A40
Massana, Kim A856
Massarany, Hany W331
Massaroni, Kenneth M. W360
Masschelin, Paul J. W196
Masse, Stephen J. (US Postal Service) A907
Masse, Stephen J. (US Postal Service) A907
Massee, Ned W. A580
Massengill, R. Scott A435
Massey, Andrea E298
Massey, Barry P221
Massey, Monica (Dairy Farmers of America) A263
Massey, Monica (Dairy Farmers of America) A263
Massey, Susan P283
Massicotte, Archie (Navistar International) A616
Massicotte, Archie (Navistar) P425
Massie, Perry T. E274
Massie, Thomas H. E274
Massiera, Alain W109
Massimino, Jack D. E85
Massingberd, Geoff A568
Massingill, Teena A761
Massip, Gaultier W287
Masson, David P632
Masson, Florent W124
Masson, Jeff P336
Masson, Stephane C. A557
Mast, Brian E119
Mastella, Larry P249
Masteller, Sheila P487
Master, Rob W426
Masters, Andrew E373
Masters, Blythe S. A494
Masters, Janet (American Family Insurance) A54
Masters, Janet (American Family Insurance) A54
Masters, Jeffrey J. P249
Masters, Joseph A904
Masters, Kyle P386
Masters, Seth J. (AllianceBernstein) A40
Masters, Seth J. (AllianceBernstein) A40
Masters, Trevor W401
Masterson, Margaret W51
Masterson, Melissa E277
Masterson, Michael M. P520
Masterson, Scott E. P226
Masterton, Bill A838
Mastiaux, Frank W130
Mastrandrea, Kristin E81
Mastrangelo, Matthew P663
Mastrangelo, Tony E23
Mastriani, Mark P221

McNeill, David A. E140
McNeill, Edward V. (Turner Corporation) A873
McNeill, Edward V. (Turner Corporation) A873
McNeill, Jennifer E364
McNeill, John H. P97
McNeill, Philip W240
McNellis, John C. A516
McNerney, W. James A135
McNiff, Mike A284
McNitt, Douglas W. E327
McNulty, Jim (Milliken) A598
McNulty, Jim (Milliken) A598
McNulty, John R. A627
McNulty, Stephen E205
McNutt, Robert M. A405
McParlan, Michael P. P39
McPartland, Pete G. P534
McPartlin, Jim A538
McPeak, Blaine E. (Dean Foods) A269
McPeak, Blaine E. (WhiteWave) P667
McPeak, Claire W354
McPhail, Neil A124
McPherson, Amy C. A557
McPherson, Bill W19
McPherson, Coco P663
McPherson, Craig E100
McPherson, John M. A389
McPherson, Julie W29
McPherson, Pauline W13
McPhie, Jeffery P221
McPhillips, Mike P617
McQuade, Daniel P. (Tishman Construction) A865
McQuade, Daniel P. (Tishman Construction) A865
McQuade, Eugene M. A213
McQuade, J. Michael A893
McQuaid, Meredith P633
McQuay, Michael W72
McQueen, Al P10
McQueen, Eric P679
McQueen, Todd P529
McQueeney, Michael G. A221
McQuilkin, Kevin P180
McQuilkin, Scott A. E194
McQuillan, Beth A224
McQuillan, David P340
McQuillen, David W107
McQuivey, Raul S. E338
McRae, Gerry P221
McRae, Lawrence D. A247
McRae, Matthew P649
McRaith, Kevin P. E178
McRee, Sandra K. P306
McRitchie, Alec W72
McRobbie, Michael A. P311
McRobert, Michael P. E234
McRoberts, James S. A164
McRoberts, Mike A369
McRoberts, Terry A877
McSally, Mike P581
McShane, Gerald J. P456
McShane, James (Columbia University) A226
McShane, James (Columbia University) A226
McShane, Michael A152
McShepard, Randell A755
McSlarrow, Kyle E. A227
McStravick, Gregory (SAP America) P521
McStravick, Gregory (SAP) W354
McSween, W. Scott E56
McTaggart, Paul W107
McTague, Dave A640
McTavish, Paul A761
McTernan, Bernita (Catholic Healthcare West) A185
McTernan, Bernita (Catholic Healthcare West) A185
McTernan, Neil (The Carlyle Group) A847

McTernan, Neil (The Carlyle Group) A847
McTier, Karen P657
McVey, Bernard P. A648
McVey, Keshmira P92
McVey, Phil P351
McVey, Richard M. E230
McVicker, Eric P62
McVittie, Kimberly W95
McWane, C. Phillip P390
McWatters, Denise C. A443
McWay, Michael J. P386
McWeeny, Philip A673
McWhinney, Deborah D. A213
McWhinney, Tama A607
McWhirter, Stephen E310
McWhorter, Anthony L. A868
McWilliams, Larry S. A168
McWilson, James B. P485
McWilton, Christopher A. A567
McWright, Julie P214
Meacham, Phil P250
Meachen, Edward A900
Mead, Andy W270
Mead, Bryan P624
Mead, Dana G. (Kleiner Perkins) P343
Mead, Dana G. (MIT) P411
Mead, Daniel S. (Verizon) A914
Mead, Daniel S. (Cellco) P127
Mead, Gareth A916
Mead, Peter W. A663
Mead, Robert E. A19
Meade, Andrea D. A771
Meador, Clifton K. P644
Meador, David E. A303
Meador, Leroy P598
Meadows, A. Stephen A747
Meadows, Donnie P336
Meadows, Karen P92
Meagher, Gary (NHL) A637
Meagher, Gary (NHL) A637
Meakins, Ian K. W443
Meaney, Richard A66
Meaney, Scott A391
Means, Jonathan D. A499
Means, William L. E113
Meares, C. M. W190
Mears, Chuck (Winn-Dixie) A955
Mears, Chuck (TEKsystems) P581
Mears, Julian W92
Mears, Phillip W. (Catholic Health Initiatives) A183
Mears, Phillip W. (Catholic Health Initiatives) A183
Mears, Richard W. A670
Mears, W. Thomas E169
Mecham, Rory P276
Mechler, Hal P. E187
Mechler, Tim P276
Mecke, John E116
Mecke, Stephen C. E331
Meda, Christine E301
Medairy, George P540
Medd, Gary L. A271
Medeiros, Erin E6
Medeiros, Katherine A. (Catholic Healthcare West) A185
Medeiros, Katherine A. (Catholic Healthcare West) A185
Meden, Scott A. A642
Medendorp, Amy A823
Medenica, Gordon A627
Meder, Dietmar W112
Mederos, Ana A838
Medin, Milo S. A402
Medina Carrillo, Germán W139
Medina, Edward R. P676
Medina, Fernando (USAA) A908
Medina, Fernando (USAA) A908
Medina, Joe A955
Medina Restrepo, Luis Felipe W343
Medina-Mora, Manuel A213
Medlin, Edwin (Maxim Integrated Products) E233

Medlin, Edwin (Maxim Integrated Products) E233
Medlin, George L. P416
Medlin, Rick P235
Medlin, Stephen L. A111
Medlock, Ed P662
Meduri, Vijay E282
Medvedev, Alexander I. W165
Mee, David G. A479
Mee, Terence R. A215
Mee, Thomas A. E114
Meehan, Avice A. P299
Meehan, D. Nathan A97
Meehan, John P279
Meehan, Judy A52
Meehan, Kevin (Burton) P102
Meehan, Kevin (Credit Suisse) W107
Meehan, Krissy A903
Meehan, Martin T. P631
Meehan, Michael J. P590
Meehan, Paul P58
Meehan, Robert E. P294
Meehan, Steven W420
Meek, Don P607
Meek, Joseph C. A427
Meek, Pamela (SAS Institute) A769
Meek, Pamela (SAS Institute) A769
Meeker, David P. A389
Meeks, Philip G. (Cox Communications) A251
Meeks, Philip G. (Cox Communications) A251
Meenan, Sean A939
Meers, Lisa A930
Meffert, Ralf (General Re) A385
Meffert, Ralf (General Re) A385
Mega, John S. A516
Megale, Luisa A53
Meggers, Kay A35
Meghdessian, Mira A299
Megia, Diego W321
Megin, James P76
Megli, Steven C. A464
Megna, Ronald J. A748
Mehan, Raj A820
Mehdi, Yusuf A595
Meheut, Bertrand W435
Mehl, Brad P473
Mehl, Bruce F. P456
Mehlman, Guillaume W27
Mehmel, Robert F. P190
Mehnert, Dana A. A420
Mehra, Asit A663
Mehra, Pritha (US Postal Service) A907
Mehra, Pritha (US Postal Service) A907
Mehra, Sanjeev K. P279
Mehrberg, Randall E. A717
Mehrotra, Louise A487
Mehrotra, Sanjay A766
Mehta, Bijal A920
Mehta, Kavan J. P579
Mehta, Nikhil A. E72
Mehta, Salil P428
Mehta, Sonny (Random House) A733
Mehta, Sonny (Random House) A733
Mehta, Tarak W4
Mehula, Guy (Parsons Corporation) A679
Mehula, Guy (Parsons Corporation) A679
Mei, Alex E267
Meichner, Amy P502
Meier, Andre W452
Meier, Andreas (BASF Corporation) P65
Meier, Anke W180
Meier, April A947
Meier, Armin P606
Meier, Christoph G. W420
Meier, James D. E151
Meier, Peter P474
Meier, Robert E158
Meier, Steven A817
Meier, Thomas E360

Meier, Tom (Kaiser Foundation Health Plan) A496
Meier, Tom (Kaiser Foundation Health Plan) A496
Meierhoefer, Cameron E80
Meighan, Robert A473
Meijer, Doug (Meijer) A584
Meijer, Doug (Meijer) A584
Meijer, Fred (Meijer) A584
Meijer, Fred (Meijer) A584
Meijer, Hendrik G. (Meijer) A584
Meijer, Hendrik G. (Meijer) A584
Meijer, Rob (Cargill) A172
Meijer, Rob (Cargill) A172
Meikle, Andrew W80
Meilland, Cyril W69
Meinecke, Chris P520
Meinel, Wulf (The Carlyle Group) A847
Meinel, Wulf (The Carlyle Group) A847
Meinig, Peter C. P154
Meinitz, Sabine A843
Meintjes, Victor A. (Liberty Mutual) A534
Meintjes, Victor A. (Liberty Mutual) A534
Meirás Amusco, Iñigo W152
Meis, Barb P537
Meiseles, Daniel (NBA) A618
Meiseles, Daniel (NBA) A618
Meisenheimer, W. Edward A499
Meisenzahl, Greg P325
Meisenzahl, Paul P215
Meisler, Luiz A666
Meismer, Denise A351
Meisner, Nancy K. A842
Meissner, Christian W284
Meissner, Laurel G. A70
Meissonnier, Julien P116
Meister, Hans-Ulrich W107
Meister, Jutta W400
Meister, Kurt A340
Mejaly, Joseph A589
Mejia, Carols E. A498
Mejia, Maria Ferna A224
Mekawi, Hesham W74
Mekkonen, Jussi W285
Mekrut, William A. P223
Mel, Amiram W282
Mela, Dave W426
Melamed, A. Douglas A464
MeLampy, Patrick J. E6
Meland, Greg R. E95
Melani, Kenneth R. (Highmark) A440
Melani, Kenneth R. (Highmark) A440
Melbourne, Angus A772
Melby, Colton R. E92
Melby, Scott E. A557
Melcher, David F. A476
Melching, Ed A616
Melchione, Rocco P61
Mele, Andrew P604
Mele, Francesco W284
Mele, James P294
Mele, Mark L. A41
Melendez, Augustin A312
Melendez, Lou (Major League Baseball) A551
Melendez, Lou (Major League Baseball) A551
Melendi, Robert J. A230
Meleta, Karen (Wakefern Food) A927
Meleta, Karen (Wakefern Food) A927
Melfi, Andrew C. E160
Melfi, Anthony P98
Melfi, Mitch H. (Catholic Health Initiatives) A183
Melfi, Mitch H. (Catholic Health Initiatives) A183
Melga, Takayoshi W279
Melgaard, Dag W397
Melichar, Larry P293
Melick, Geoffrey P607
Melillo, Matt P131
Melin, Eric G. A613
Meline, David W. A2

A = AMERICAN BUSINESS
E = EMERGING COMPANIES
P = PRIVATE COMPANIES
W = WORLD BUSINESS

Monsalve, Javier (Maxim Integrated Products) E233
Monseau, Marc A487
Monser, Edward L. A328
Monson, Lane P312
Montag, Bernd (Siemens Corp.) P543
Montag, Bernd (Siemens AG) W363
Montag, Heinrich W130
Montag, Thomas K. (Bank of America) A100
Montag, Thomas K. (Merrill Lynch) P403
Montague, Christopher A. W392
Montague, Lisa W245
Montalbano, Alfredo W45
Montalbano, John S. (RBC Wealth Management) P500
Montalbano, John S. (RBC Financial Group) W321
Montalto, Stephen E277
Montalvo, Carlos O. A438
Montalvo, Darrin P563
Montalvo, Mike E30
Montano, Thomas A262
Montanti, Louis A. P416
Monteferrante, Domenic W95
Montegari, John L. A176
Montegon, Véronique Roque W357
Monteiro, Sandy P624
Monteith, Timothy J. A563
Montejo Velilla, Salvador W139
Montelongo, Michael P552
Montemayor, Jaime P234
Monteoliva Díaz, Javier W199
Montera, Ken P67
Montero, Rodolfo W186
Montes, Susan R. P632
Montesano, Jennifer A380
Montesano, Jin A512
Monteágudo, Ivonne W441
Montfort, Richard A. E112
Montgomery, A. Bruce A394
Montgomery, Bob A799
Montgomery, David R. P314
Montgomery, Dirk A. (OSI Restaurant Partners) A669
Montgomery, Dirk A. (OSI Restaurant Partners) A669
Montgomery, George E102
Montgomery, Glenn A. A204
Montgomery, Graciela E97
Montgomery, Keith A81
Montgomery, Marie P53
Montgomery, Ron E290
Montgomery, Tom A801
Montgomery, W. Swope E49
Montgomery, Walter G. P677
Montilus, Pascal A224
Montini, Enio Anthony A744
Montmerle, Bruno W150
Monto, Richard E260
Montouché, Thierry W100
Montoya, Luis A684
Montoya, Pedro W131
Montpas, Courtney E99
Montreuil, Paul H. E182
Montrose, Andy P236
Montross, Franklin (Berkshire Hathaway) A123
Montross, Franklin (General Re) A385
Montross, Franklin (General Re) A385
Monts, Lester P. P632
Monts, Michael A. A893
Montupet, Jean-Paul L. A328
Montville, Phillis D. E17
Monty, Richard L. P412
Mood, Francis P. A770
Moodie, Michael P500
Moodispaw, Leonard E. E211

Moody, Donald R. A652
Moody, Jeff P572
Moody, Joan P638
Moody, Robert L. E252
Moody, Ross R. E252
Moody, Sandi T. (Chick-fil-A) A198
Moody, Sandi T. (Chick-fil-A) A198
Moody, W. Darin A324
Moomjian, Michael P96
Moon, D. C. A328
Moon, David W. A528
Moon, Heechul W383
Moon, Jo W37
Moon, John (Flex-N-Gate) P219
Moon, Mark F. A607
Moon, Randall J. A11
Moon, Regina (Red Cross) A737
Moon, Regina (Red Cross) A737
Mooney, Andrew P. A290
Mooney, Ben A817
Mooney, Beth E. A500
Mooney, Bryan P. E250
Mooney, Chris P98
Mooney, Dee K. A594
Mooney, James F. A916
Mooney, Jeffrey L. A247
Mooney, John W. (DuPont) A305
Mooney, John (Haworth, Inc.) P280
Mooney, John W. (Pioneer Hi-Bred) P480
Mooney, Kay A19
Mooney, Randy (Dairy Farmers of America) A263
Mooney, Randy (Intel) A464
Mooney, Randy (Dairy Farmers of America) A263
Moons, John P105
Moonves, Leslie A188
Moor, Kristian P. A27
Moore, A. Bruce A424
Moore, A. Scott A65
Moore, Adam E104
Moore, Alison Banks P294
Moore, Alyce P352
Moore, Angela P379
Moore, Benjamin E363
Moore, Bill (Energy Future) A330
Moore, Bill (Energy Future) A330
Moore, Brad (APi Group) P39
Moore, Brad (Tribune Company) P607
Moore, Brandon A955
Moore, C. Louis A111
Moore, Carol M. E66
Moore, Charles A591
Moore, Chip P52
Moore, Clint W439
Moore, Colin A814
Moore, Dana P129
Moore, David C. (Universal Corporation) A896
Moore, David J. (24/7 Real Media) P3
Moore, Donald L. A657
Moore, Donna J. E45
Moore, Douglas (AMR) P33
Moore, Douglas T. (Sears) P532
Moore, Dwight P276
Moore, Edward W. A755
Moore, Elaine P546
Moore, Elizabeth D. A234
Moore, Ellen J. A204
Moore, Evelyn A267
Moore, Gary (Boeing) A135
Moore, Gary B. (Cisco Systems) A210
Moore, Gayle P624
Moore, George C. (RBS Global) P500
Moore, George E. (Temple University) P584
Moore, Jack E. (Hallmark) A414
Moore, Jack E. (Hallmark) A414
Moore, James R. (Huntsman International) P304
Moore, James M. (OSF Healthcare System) P456
Moore, Jason A602
Moore, Jeff (AgriBank) P19

Moore, Jeff (Vans) P645
Moore, Jim W. E148
Moore, John A. (Acorn Energy) E8
Moore, John R. (Array BioPharma) E38
Moore, John G. (Leggett & Platt) A524
Moore, John (Tesoro) A842
Moore, John (CPS Energy) P159
Moore, Judy Kay A324
Moore, Julie S. (US Postal Service) A907
Moore, Julie S. (US Postal Service) A907
Moore, Kevin (ADM) A11
Moore, Kevin P. (Rooney Holdings) P513
Moore, Kirk P450
Moore, Martez P82
Moore, Marti A195
Moore, Martin R. (Prudential plc) W315
Moore, Mary Beth A37
Moore, Meredith A650
Moore, Michael S. A928
Moore, Morris L. A743
Moore, Pat E45
Moore, Paul P236
Moore, Peter R. A322
Moore, Randy A. A57
Moore, Renee E23
Moore, Richard (Dillard's) A284
Moore, Richard W. (TVA) A874
Moore, Richard W. (TVA) A874
Moore, Rob P463
Moore, Robert D. (PAETEC) P462
Moore, Scott (Union Pacific) A883
Moore, Scott (Intergraph) P315
Moore, Selwyn A568
Moore, Sharelynn A475
Moore, Simon R. (Air Products) A29
Moore, Simon C. (The Carlyle Group) A847
Moore, Simon C. (The Carlyle Group) A847
Moore, Stephen L. (Catholic Health Initiatives) A183
Moore, Stephen L. (Catholic Health Initiatives) A183
Moore, Steve A121
Moore, Sue A900
Moore, Theodore R. E57
Moore, Tim A699
Moore, Timothy L. (Genentech) P241
Moore, Tommy A. (First Investors Financial Services) E144
Moore, Tommy (Goodwill Industries) P254
Moore, Troy E243
Moore, Vance P546
Moore, Walter K. P241
Moore, William F. (Red Cross) A737
Moore, William T. (Tenet Healthcare) A838
Moore, William F. (Red Cross) A737
Moorefield, John A. A22
Moorer, Glynda M. P408
Moorkamp, Mary P526
Moorman, Charles W. (Norfolk Southern) A644
Moorman, Charles W. (Norfolk Southern Railway) P446
Moorman, Jean A35
Moorman, Lew E293
Moorman, Tom A138
Moorthy, Ganesh E244
Moorthy, Vinay P670
Moosa, Nazo (The Carlyle Group) A847
Moosa, Nazo (The Carlyle Group) A847
Moosmann, Sönke W354
Moosmayer, Klaus W363
Moote, Paul P545
Mooty, Charles W. P208
Mora, Alberto (Mars, Incorporated) A559
Mora, Alberto (Mars, Incorporated) A559

Moraco, Anthony J. A762
Moraga, Christelle A961
Moragas Freixa, Josep W164
Morais, Diane P25
Morales, Christian A464
Morales, Colin E198
Morales Gil, Carlos A. W302
Morales, Juan Carlos A102
Morales, Vince A703
Morali, Philippe A594
Moran, Albert S. P190
Moran, Allison P494
Moran, Charles E. P173
Moran, David C. (Heinz) A431
Moran, David C. (Crown Equipment) P162
Moran, Estrella E47
Moran, Ignacio C. W450
Moran, James M. (Navistar International) A616
Moran, James D. (Crown Equipment) P162
Moran, Jim P425
Moran, John A268
Moran, Matthew W69
Moran, Rich P430
Moran, Robert F. A690
Moran, Shane P266
Moran, Sheila E310
Moran, Thomas E. (Eaton) A314
Moran, Thomas J. (Mutual of America) P416
Moran, Timothy (Catholic Healthcare West) A185
Moran, Timothy (Catholic Healthcare West) A185
Morange, William A. (MTA) A608
Morange, William A. (MTA) A608
Morano, Hernán W367
Morant, Sébastien W432
Morath, Christopher J. E307
Moraw, Eric A. P281
Morbello, Gianpiero W8
Mordenti, Joyce E238
Morder, Tom A. (Chick-fil-A) A198
Morder, Tom A. (Chick-fil-A) A198
Morea, Dom (First Data) A354
Morea, Dom (First Data) A354
Morean, William D. A480
Moreau, Claude P. A842
Moreau, Nicolas W47
Moreau, Steven C. P563
Moreci, Stephen F. A142
Moreira, John M. A651
Morel, Hugo W422
Moreland, Bevann P523
Moreland, Blair P58
Moreland, Darl S. E14
Moreland, Kenneth V. A831
Moreland, Leonard A. E65
Moreland, Mark D. E88
Morell, Paul A906
Morelli, Marco W203
Morelli, Vincenzo P603
Morelon, Luc W233
Moreno, Babette P197
Moreno, Jeanne M. A794
Moreno, Karen R. A375
Moreno, Mark A. P372
Moreno, Rafael A380
Moreno, Rick P366
Moreno, Vasco E211
Moreno, Vicente W6
Moret, Blake A749
Moret, Pamela J. P597
Moretti, August J. E14
Moretti, David (MTA) A608
Moretti, David (MTA) A608
Moretti, Lucia V. A278
Moretti, Marissa A376
Moretto, Riccardo W452
Moretz, Lawrence R. (Salvation Army) A764
Moretz, Lawrence R. (Salvation Army) A764

O'Hare, Patrick P558
O'Hehir, Debra P439
O'Herlihy, Christopher A459
O'Kane, Katie P553
O'Keane, Brian J. P19
O'Keefe, Bob (NFL) A635
O'Keefe, Bob (NFL) A635
O'Keefe, Edward A100
O'Keefe, Kathleen P634
O'Keefe, Mary A. A709
O'Keefe, Paul A255
O'Keefe, Peg (Catholic Health
  Initiatives) A183
O'Keefe, Peg (Catholic Health
  Initiatives) A183
O'Keefe, Sean C. W131
O'Keefe, Thomas G. E287
O'Keeffe, John W445
O'Keeffe, Patrick A63
O'Keeffe, Wendy P663
O'Kelly, Stafford A5
O'Konek, Joseph W399
O'Laughlin, Michael A620
O'Leary, Bernie E77
O'Leary, Christopher D. A382
O'Leary, David C. A817
O'Leary, Joseph D. A690
O'Leary, Patrick (Piper Jaffray) E280
O'Leary, Patrick J. (SPX) A807
O'Leary, Richard A. A468
O'Leary, Ryan E111
O'Leary, William J. E383
O'Looney, Michael W53
O'Loughlin, Brian J. P152
O'Malley, Chris A160
O'Malley, Dan (Gulfstream
  Aerospace) A409
O'Malley, Dan (Gulfstream
  Aerospace) A409
O'Malley, John P. (International Data
  Group) A467
O'Malley, John P. (International Data
  Group) A467
O'Malley, John P. (Westcon) P663
O'Malley, Michael P166
O'Malley, Patrick (Union Pacific) A883
O'Malley, Patrick J. (Seagate
  Technology) W360
O'Malley, Tom P624
O'Mara, Frank A. E40
O'Mara, Thomas K. P54
O'Meara, Christopher M. A525
O'Meara, George A210
O'Meara, John-Paul W12
O'Meara, Patrick P311
O'Meara, Vicki A. A697
O'Melia, Wayne D. A831
O'Muircheartaigh, Colm A. (University
  of Chicago) A898
O'Muircheartaigh, Colm A. (University
  of Chicago) A898
O'Mullane, John A587
O'Neal, Craft P450
O'Neal, Jim A642
O'Neal, Leslie K. A836
O'Neal, Rodney A278
O'Neil, Jack P181
O'Neil, Mark T. A838
O'Neil, Robert J. E45
O'Neil, Scott M. A161
O'Neil, Terry P496
O'Neil, Valerie A814
O'Neil-White, Alphonso P284
O'Neill, Chris A402
O'Neill, Dan A474
O'Neill, Eileen A287
O'Neill, Geoffrey A. (University of
  California) A897
O'Neill, Geoffrey A. (University of
  California) A897
O'Neill, Heidi A640
O'Neill, James P298
O'Neill, Jhn P. A707
O'Neill, Joan P675
O'Neill, Kevin P598

O'Neill, Martin A163
O'Neill, Michael (Mentor
  Corporation) P401
O'Neill, Michael J. (Lenovo) W237
O'Neill, Molly K. P191
O'Neill, Peggy E190
O'Neill, Peter A817
O'Neill, Sean W177
O'Neill, Shane A532
O'Neill, Thomas P. (Tufts Health
  Plan) P611
O'Neill, Thomas (Adecco) W11
O'Neill, Thomas C. (BCE) W61
O'Neill, Tim W51
O'Neill, Timothy J. (Goldman
  Sachs) A397
O'Neill, Todd W204
O'Phelan, Maria H. P532
O'Quinn, Marvin (Catholic Healthcare
  West) A185
O'Quinn, Marvin (Catholic Healthcare
  West) A185
O'Quinn, Michael G. P585
O'Ree, Willie (NHL) A637
O'Ree, Willie (NHL) A637
O'Reilly, Chris E258
O'Reilly, James F. A265
O'Reilly, Peter (NFL) A635
O'Reilly, Peter (NFL) A635
O'Reilly, Richard J. P399
O'Reilly, William M. P534
O'Riordain, Shane W340
O'Rourke, Betsy A754
O'Rourke, Joe W54
O'Rourke, John E220
O'Rourke, Lori A539
O'Rourke, Marina P572
O'Rourke, Michael (Catholic Health
  Initiatives) A183
O'Rourke, Michael (Catholic Health
  Initiatives) A183
O'Rourke, P. Terrence P608
O'Rourke, Steve W65
O'Rourke, Terence W224
O'Rourke, Tiarnán E134
O'Rourke, Timothy C. P584
O'Rourke, William (Essex Rental) E133
O'Rourke, William J. (Alcoa) A35
O'Shaughnessy, Lizbeth S. A820
O'Shaughnessy, Robert T. A720
O'Shea, Amy G. A360
O'Shea, Don E275
O'Shea, John A834
O'Shea, Kate W37
O'Shea, William J. A168
O'Sullivan, Barry A210
O'Sullivan, Eugene M. E15
O'Sullivan, Francis K. W237
O'Sullivan, James J. W252
O'Sullivan, Joe A343
O'Sullivan, John A420
O'Sullivan, Michael (NextEra
  Energy) A634
O'Sullivan, Michael B. (Ross
  Stores) A752
O'Sullivan, Patrick H. W296
O'Sullivan, Paul P398
O'Sullivan, Sharon A287
O'Toole, Audry P579
O'Toole, Brian (GeoEye) E156
O'Toole, Brian (Sisters of Mercy Health
  System) P546
O'Toole, Hugh (MassMutual) A564
O'Toole, Hugh (MassMutual) A564
O'Toole, Matthew H. P505
O'Toole, Peter A376
O'Toole, Tara P181
O'Toole, Thomas F. A887
O'Toole, Timothy T. P219
O. Doughty, Dennis A138
Oades, Charlotte A221
Oakey, Thomas M. E79
Oakland, Steven T. A793
Oakley, Glenn A287
Oakley, Julian E134

Oaks, Robert K. P358
Oates, Doug E132
Oates, Jonathan W343
Oates, Robert P. E373
Oatman, David E138
Oba, Isao W352
Obaid, Thoraya A. P621
Obata, Morinobu W260
Obata, Tooru W279
Obeirn, Carli P626
Obendorf, Steven E. P34
Oberfeld, Steven J. A786
Oberg, Soren L. P595
Oberhausen, Thomas J. P180
Oberhelman, Douglas R.
  (Caterpillar) A181
Oberhelman, Douglas R.
  (Navistar) P425
Obering, Henry A. A138
Oberland, Gregory C. (Northwestern
  Mutual) A649
Oberland, Gregory C. (Northwestern
  Mutual) A649
Oberlander, Michael I. A151
Oberlerchner, Fritz W380
Obermann, René W122
Obermayer, James A261
Obermayer, Matthias A35
Obermeyer, Paul R. A228
Obermiller, John G. P584
Oberosler, Bob A744
Oberrender, Robert W. P461
Oberson, Gilles W258
Oberster, Alan C. A864
Oberton, Willard D. A346
Oblon, Ed A224
Obolsky, Mitchel E244
Obray, Robert P49
Obray, Ronald E. E290
Obregon, Andres (The Carlyle
  Group) A847
Obregon, Andres (The Carlyle
  Group) A847
Obrock, Bill P75
Obstler, David M. E249
Ocampo, Bernadette D. P439
Ocasio-Fant, Diana A471
Occhionero, Mark A. E88
Occi, Anne (Major League
  Baseball) A551
Occi, Anne (Major League
  Baseball) A551
Och, Daniel S. (Och-Ziff Capital
  Management) E265
Och, Daniel S. (NewYork-Presbyterian
  Hospital) P439
Ochi, Hitoshi W259
Ochiai, Hiroyuki W413
Ochiai, Yukio W295
Ochner, Sheila (University of Texas
  System) A899
Ochner, Sheila (University of Texas
  System) A899
Ochoa, Max (Cox Enterprises) A252
Ochoa, Max (Cox Enterprises) A252
Ochs, Mike P170
Ochs, Millard (Time Warner) A862
Ochs, Millard (Warner Bros.) P657
Ochs, Tom P532
Ochsner, Paul (Mutual of Omaha) A609
Ochsner, Paul (Mutual of Omaha) A609
Ochsner, R. John A720
Ockerbloom, John P. A484
Oda, Takeshi W229
Odajima, Masaru W205
Oddis, Joseph M. P91
Oddone, Piermaria J. (University of
  Chicago) A898
Oddone, Piermaria J. (University of
  Chicago) A898
Odeen, Philip A. A18
Odeh, Saleem N. A26
Odell, Stephen T. A365
Odelstam, Jan W367
Odencrantz, George P545

Odenheimer, Daniel J. E178
Odier, Édouard W16
Odone, Toby W74
Odorico, Rick P171
Odqvist, Christer P520
Odum, Marvin E. (Shell Oil) A785
Odum, Marvin E. (Shell Oil) A785
Odum, Marvin E. (Royal Dutch
  Shell) W339
Oe, Kumiko (AllianceBernstein) A40
Oe, Kumiko (AllianceBernstein) A40
Oecking, Christian W363
Oelerich, Frank P180
Oelschlaeger, Tina (International Data
  Group) A467
Oelschlaeger, Tina (International Data
  Group) A467
Oeltjen, Edward P34
Oerter, Werner W219
Oesterle, Stephen N. A583
Oesterreicher, Martin W388
Oetman, Donna W219
Off, George W. P117
Offerman, Michael J. E59
Offir, Ronald A490
Offit, Kenneth P399
Offutt, Caroline E154
Oficialdegui, Rogelio A278
Oftedal, Svein W447
Ogan, Mark A. P493
Ogas, Ray (NFL) A635
Ogas, Ray (NFL) A635
Ogasawara, Takeshi W263
Ogata, Hikaru W369
Ogawa, Daisuke W161
Ogawa, Katsumi W265
Ogawa, Kenshiro W226
Ogawa, Kiyoshi W381
Ogawa, Masaru W373
Ogawa, Yoichiro (Deloitte) A276
Ogawa, Yoichiro (Deloitte) A276
Ogden, Kurt D. P304
Ogden, Stan E. A50
Ogden, Thomas D. A228
Oge, Margo T. P204
Ogg, Larry B. A966
Ogilvie, Scott (Bechtel) A114
Ogilvie, Scott (Bechtel) A114
Ogimura, Michio W381
Ogisu, Naotoshi W117
Ogiwara, Yasuaki W284
Oglesby, Ann M. A238
Oguchi, Toru W143
Oguchi, Yukihiro W117
Ogura, Masamichi W162
Ogura, Satoru W384
Oguri, Akira W110
Oh, Benny A794
Oh, Cecilia E338
Oh, David E378
Oh, Elizabeth P663
Oh Huber, Marie A26
Oh, Irene E115
Oh, M.H. P668
Ohashi, Shigeru W381
Ohashi, Tetsuji W222
Ohashi, Yoji W23
Ohbatake, Masami W361
Ohinata, Masafumi W36
Ohira, Noriyoshi W259
Ohkado, Shingo W409
Ohle, Jörg P70
Ohls, Uwe W219
Ohlsson, Mikael W195
Ohm, John R. A652
Ohm, Seong A928
Ohmichi, Masao W262
Ohmori, Kazuo W381
Ohno, Koji W23
Ohno, Nobuyuki W184
Ohno, Osamu W184
Ohnuki, Hailey P309
Ohringer, Mark J. A491
Ohta, Kenji W361
Ohta, Seiichi W262

Phipps, Bonnie L. (Ascension Health) A82
Phipps, Bonnie L. (Ascension Health) A82
Phipps, P. Cody A892
Phipps, Scott (TPC Group) E355
Phipps, Scott (Tesoro) A842
Phipps, Stefani E146
Phlegar, Charles D. P154
Phlegar, Jeffrey S. (AllianceBernstein) A40
Phlegar, Jeffrey S. (AllianceBernstein) A40
Phongmany, Lulu P320
Phyfer, Cheri M. A786
Piacente, Dean M. A257
Piacentini, Diego A45
Piacenza, Bruno W180
Pianalto, Sandra P209
Pianalto-Cameron, Rosanna P209
Piani, Olivier W25
Pianta, Robert C. P636
Piasecki, Nicole W. A135
Piatt, Rodney L. A610
Piazza, John W320
Piazza, Richard J. E237
Piazza, Steven P492
Picard, Gilles A587
Picard, Jean-Paul (Deloitte) A276
Picard, Jean-Paul (Deloitte) A276
Picard, Leslie (Time Warner) A862
Picard, Leslie (Time Inc.) P600
Picard, Olivier W85
Picard, Raynier (Baker & Taylor) A97
Picard, Raynier (Baker & Taylor) A97
Picardo, Richard (Guardian Life) A407
Picardo, Richard (Guardian Life) A407
Picarelli, Sergio W11
Picarillo, David P. (Topco Associates LLC) A867
Picarillo, David P. (Topco Associates LLC) A867
Picca, Bruno W203
Picca, Vicky (NBA) A618
Picca, Vicky (NBA) A618
Picchi, Michael D. E81
Piccini, Gabriele W423
Piccini, Silvio D. E103
Piccinin, Claudia A278
Piccinini, Robert M. P523
Picciolil, Ernest S. A111
Piccione, Joseph J. P456
Piccirillo, Fred A516
Piccirillo, Jeffrey A. P520
Pichai, Sundar A402
Piche, Joe P189
Pichette, Patrick A402
Pichler, Karl E293
Piciacchio, Sharon A703
Pick, Robert S. A227
Pickard, Ann W339
Pickard, Frank C. A915
Pickard, J. Duncan A387
Pickel, Michael W175
Picken, Matt P499
Picken, Todd G. (MassMutual) A564
Picken, Todd G. (MassMutual) A564
Pickens, David T. A267
Pickering, Anthony B. E379
Pickering, Rick A761
Pickering, Ruth W80
Pickering, Sammy G. A335
Pickett, Christopher E295
Pickett, David P. W392
Pickett, Denise A53
Pickett, Donald E. E313
Pickett, Stephen E. A319
Pickrum, Michael P82
Pickus, Charlene P166
Pickut, David E132
Pico, Les (NFL) A635
Pico, Les (NFL) A635
Picone, Vincenzo A376
Picot, Russell C. W190

Piechoski, Michael J. (Peter Kiewit Sons') A689
Piechoski, Michael J. (Peter Kiewit Sons') A689
Piedmont, Brian P496
Piedra, Miguel (Burger King) A155
Piedra, Miguel (Burger King) A155
Pienknagura, Jose M. P303
Pieper, Jay B. P465
Piepho, Arlan G. A391
Pierallini, Mauro (Chrysler) A201
Pierallini, Mauro (Chrysler) A201
Pierce, Andrew W. E152
Pierce, Charles E. A711
Pierce, Christopher A138
Pierce, David N. E152
Pierce, Don P183
Pierce, Gerald P661
Pierce, James M. W420
Pierce, Jeff A711
Pierce, Joan A224
Pierce, John P266
Pierce, Judith P436
Pierce, Kathleen A336
Pierce, Larry A801
Pierce, Leslie A. A283
Pierce, Lewis P. P521
Pierce, Lori P632
Pierce, Mark P92
Pierce, Matthew P430
Pierce, Nancy P239
Pierce, Paul P4
Pierce, Robert C. A224
Pierce, Sandra E. P286
Pierce, Todd P241
Pierce, W. Norman E253
Piersma, John P496
Pierson, Branden A901
Pierson, François W47
Pierson, George J. W50
Pierson, Jamie G. A964
Pierson, Jennifer A186
Pierson, Timothy A. E66
Pierzga, Ed P352
Piesche, Stefan E83
Piesko, Michael L. P551
Pieters, Marten W436
Pietkiewicz, Steve E222
Pietrantonio, Joseph M. A29
Pietras, Joseph E197
Pietrok, Gary (Peter Kiewit Sons') A689
Pietrok, Gary (Peter Kiewit Sons') A689
Pietrunti, Michael W229
Pietrusko, Robert G. E375
Pietrzak, Tim P39
Piette, Daniel W245
Pigford, James (Army and Air Force Exchange) A79
Pigford, James (Army and Air Force Exchange) A79
Piggott, Julie A. A157
Pigman, Steve P125
Pignone, Marty F. A796
Pigott, Jim P394
Pigott, Julie T. A797
Pigott, Mark C. A674
Pike, Gavin W125
Pike, Thomas H. W6
Pikkarainen, Heikki W427
Piland, Todd (H-E-B) A412
Piland, Todd (H-E-B) A412
Pilarski, Barbara J. (Chrysler) A201
Pilarski, Barbara J. (Chrysler) A201
Pilat, David A950
Pilaud, Eric W357
Pilch, Samuel H. A43
Pilcher, Marni A475
Pilcher, Simon H. W. W315
Pilkington, Edward W125
Pilla, Domenic A577
Pillai, Devadas D. A464
Pillai, Mani W452
Pillay, Navanethem P621
Pillet, Laurent W303
Pilnick, Gary H. A498

Pilnik, Richard D. (Quintiles Transnational) A727
Pilnik, Richard D. (Quintiles Transnational) A727
Pilon, Lawrence J. A926
Pilosof, Richard V. P499
Piltz, Kevin M. E239
Pimental, Marcello P445
Pimentel, Albert A. W360
Pimentel, Armando A634
Pimentel, Dan A287
Pimentel, Lawrence A754
Pina Pereira, Adília W141
Pincemin, Clodine W371
Pinchasi, Irit W403
Pinchev, Alex E300
Pinchuk, Nicholas T. A794
Pinckney, Wendy P308
Pinckney, William S. P26
Pincus, Robert P. E114
Pineci, Roy A657
Pineda, Kimberly A666
Pineda, Richard P337
Ping Choon, Teh W365
Pingel, Spencer A224
Pinger, Markus W90
Pinheiro, Ivete E2
Pini, Luca W133
Pinion, John R. P241
Pink, Charles W103
Pinkasy, Moshe E273
Pinker, Jürgen (The Carlyle Group) A847
Pinker, Jürgen (The Carlyle Group) A847
Pinkerton, Mac S. A159
Pinkes, Andrew J. A852
Pinkett, Kathleen L. P532
Pinkham, Gary W145
Pinkney, Dan P58
Pinkston, Arnold A. A115
Pinkston, Patrick A271
Pinkston, Peggy E315
Pinn, Vivian W. P443
Pinner, Ernest S. E66
Pinney, Alesia L. E191
Pinnington, Timothy P. W392
Pinnix-Ragland, Hilda A713
Pino, Jeffrey P. (United Technologies) A893
Pino, Jeffrey P. (Sikorsky) P545
Pino, Paul (W.L. Gore) A924
Pino, Paul (W.L. Gore) A924
Pinou, Thomas E304
Pinsent, Tony W80
Pinsker, Robin P675
Pinson, C. Wright P644
Pinsonneault, David W392
Pinter, David W. A355
Pinto, Daniel E. A494
Pinto, Dominic (Amtrak) A64
Pinto, Dominic (Amtrak) A64
Pinto, Fernando (The Carlyle Group) A847
Pinto, Fernando (The Carlyle Group) A847
Pinto, Joe A210
Pinto, John J. E261
Pinto, Mark R. A76
Pinto, Tina A487
Pintoff, Craig A. A889
Pinzer, Reinhard W363
Pio, Bart P573
Pion, Jeffrey S. A186
Piotrowski, Kevin P312
Piper, Burkhard G. W331
Piper, Dave P313
Piper, Heather P42
Piper, M. Anderson (Chick-fil-A) A198
Piper, M. Anderson (Chick-fil-A) A198
Piper, Tad W. P107
Pipes, J. David A943
Pipito, Frank A387
Pipkin, Katie E67

Pipoly, Ronald E. E30
Piquemal, Thomas W136
Piraino, Enrico A791
Piraino, Thomas A. A678
Pires, José A. P478
Piret, Claude W124
Pirhonen, Janna W217
Pirovano, Tullio E212
Pirtle, Ronald M. A278
Piry, László W267
Pisana, Brenda A844
Pisani, Assunta S. (Stanford University) A810
Pisani, Assunta S. (Stanford University) A810
Pisani, Ralph E188
Pisano, Wayne F. W351
Pisarczyk, Richard V. A343
Piscatelli, Mark E280
Pisciotta, Matteo R. A668
Piscitelli, Ralph W284
Piscitello, Charles P477
Piscopo, Vince P655
Pisklov, Oleg W220
Pistacchio, Dave A161
Pistell, Anne F. P675
Pistella, Tom P394
Pistilli, Dale A946
Pistole, John S. P181
Pistono, Paul A935
Pistor, Robert L. A880
Pita de Abreu, António M. W141
Pitaro, James A. A290
Pitasky, Scott A595
Pitkin, Steve A213
Pitkänen, Eija W379
Pitner, James P98
Pitt, Denice P16
Pitt, Tim P. A741
Pittaway, David B. P115
Pittelli, Eugene E. P162
Pittenger, John C. (Koch Industries, Inc.) A508
Pittenger, John C. (Koch Industries, Inc.) A508
Pittinger, Robert H. W47
Pittman, Keith P75
Pittman, Myrna J. P20
Pittman, Robert W. P143
Pitts, Floyd W. (Red Cross) A737
Pitts, Floyd W. (Red Cross) A737
Pitts, Gary L. A335
Pitts, James F. A648
Pitts, Jeremy D. P59
Pitts, Lawrence H. (University of California) A897
Pitts, Lawrence H. (University of California) A897
Pitts, Ralph A. (Belk) A119
Pitts, Ralph A. (Belk) A119
Piva, Gary R. P669
Piva, John P650
Pizarro, Pedro J. A319
Pizzi, Mark (Nationwide) A615
Pizzi, Mark (Nationwide) A615
Pizzo, David P84
Pizzuti, Marjory P254
Pič̇ch, Ferdinand K. (MAN) W248
Pič̇ch, Ferdinand K. (Volkswagen) W438
Plaat, Mitchell E. A235
Place, Tristan E212
Placido, José (Dexia) W124
Placido, José (RBC Financial Group) W321
Plack, James E. E22
Plaeger, Frederick J. A335
Plaeger, Susal P443
Plaisance, Melissa C. A761
Plaisance, Morrison R. A282
Plake, Mark A. A443
Plamann, Alfred A. (Unified Grocers) A881
Plamann, Alfred A. (Unified Grocers) A881

Poston, Fred L. P408
Posyagin, Boris S. W165
Poteete, Carl E78
Poterre, Francoise A5
Poteshman, Michael S. A872
Potestá, Alessandro W149
Potharlanka, Ravi E140
Poti, Roberto W133
Potier, Benoît W230
Potka, Veli-Jussi W379
Potrikus, Liona P620
Pott, Jeff W40
Pott, Lindsay P36
Pott, Richard W57
Potter, Alfred K. P249
Potter, Carol E328
Potter, Christopher H. A794
Potter, George W54
Potter, James G. (Del Monte
   Foods) A273
Potter, James G. (Del Monte
   Foods) A273
Potter, Seth E188
Potter, Simon M. P210
Potter, Stephen W. (Osiris
   Therapeutics) E273
Potter, Stephen N. (Northern
   Trust) A646
Pottorff, Gary W. A641
Potts, Christian T. A474
Potts, David (RPX) E306
Potts, David T. (Tesco) W401
Potts, Randy J. E383
Poucher, Nicholas A872
Pouk, John R. A26
Poulakowski, Thomas J. P416

Poulios, Pana P131
Pouliot, David A348
Poulley, Sean P369
Poulliot, Brian (BJ's Wholesale
   Club) A129
Poulliot, Brian (BJ's Wholesale
   Club) A129
Pounds, Greg E. E53
Pounds, Jeff A952
Pouparina, Cuky A489
Poupart-Lafarge, Arnaud W34
Poupart-Lafarge, Henri W27
Poupeau, Jean-Francois A772
Poupet, Guy W369
Poutiainen, Erkki W285
Poux-Guillaume, Grégoire W27
Pouyanné, Patrick W411
Pouyat, Alain W73
Povich, Lon F. (BJ's Wholesale
   Club) A129
Povich, Lon F. (BJ's Wholesale
   Club) A129
Povinelli, Brian A815
Povlivka, Mark A. A748
Powalski, Jennifer E259
Powazek, Derek A438
Powchik, Peter E301
Powder, Scott P15
Powderly, Kevin M. A186
Powe, Dorothy H. A572
Powell, Allen (EBSCO) A317
Powell, Allen (EBSCO) A317
Powell, Andrew K. W. E86
Powell, Bradley S. A340
Powell, Bridget W190
Powell, Chris E296
Powell, Colin P343
Powell, Cynthia B. A111
Powell, David M. (NetJets) P433
Powell, David (BHP Billiton) W65
Powell, Denny (Catholic Healthcare
   West) A185
Powell, Denny (Catholic Healthcare
   West) A185
Powell, Derek P657
Powell, Eleanor F. A336
Powell, Gareth (Baker & Taylor) A97
Powell, Gareth (Baker & Taylor) A97

Powell, Gavin W190
Powell, Ian W314
Powell, James A856
Powell, Karan H. E25
Powell, Kendall J. A382
Powell, Lee A807
Powell, Michael A218
Powell, Nigel A640
Powell, Pat (Golden Horizons) A395
Powell, Pat (Golden Horizons) A395
Powell, Rice (FMCNA) P224
Powell, Rice (Fresenius Medical
   Care) W158
Powell, Richard C. (Bloomberg
   L.P.) A131
Powell, Richard C. (Bloomberg
   L.P.) A131
Powell, Robert J. A944
Powell, Robin D. E114
Powell, Rodney O. A645
Powell, Roger C. J. P594
Powell, Scott E. A494
Powell, Simon N. P399
Powell, Theresa A. P584
Powell, Thomas G. A305
Power, Alison G P154
Power, Joseph M. A50
Power, Marsha A838
Power, Steve P556
Power, Steven (ReachLocal) E296
Power, Terry W320
Powers, Andrew J. A536
Powers, Anita M. A657
Powers, B. Shaun A30
Powers, Brian E73
Powers, Gregg J. A522
Powers, James G. P620
Powers, Joseph B. A58
Powers, Katelind A844
Powers, Kelli A603
Powers, Kenneth F. P416
Powers, Marc D. A444
Powers, Mary Ellen P334
Powers, Meggan A506
Powers, Mike P62
Powers, Robert P. A17
Powers, Scott (ICG Group) E180
Powers, Scott F. (State Street) A817
Powers, Steve A249
Powers, Wayne A963
Powers, William C. (University of Texas
   System) A899
Powers, William C. (University of Texas
   System) A899
Powis, Thierry A587
Poyhonen, John W. E317
Poza-Grise, Maritza J. A305
Pozzi, Karen P114
Pozzi, Steven R. A204
Prabhu, Krish A. A86
Prabhu, Nagi E298
Prabhu, Vasant M. A815
Prache, Olivier E124
Pradeep, Vasundhara W107
Pradeilles, Didier W430
Pradhan, Jaideep E137
Prado Eulate, Borja (Endesa
   S.A.) W139
Prado Eulate, Borja (Enel) W140
Prado, Francisco P152
Prado, Jose Luis A684
Prado, Mike A811
Praedel, Ulrich W85
Pragana da Cruz Morais, Jorge
   M. W141
Prague, Ronald J. E342
Prahl, Bob P227
Prahl, Paula A124
Prakel, Andrew P667
Pramaggiore, Anne R. A338
Pramanik, Bhaskar A595
Pranaitis, Jeff P413
Prandi, Andrea W133
Praskach, Dean C. E15
Prasto, Gary P226

Prater, John P17
Prather, N. King P87
Prati, Richard E158
Pratt, Brian E286
Pratt, David E226
Pratt, Don P250
Pratt, Greg E181
Pratt, Jeanne A866
Pratt, Jennifer L. E321
Pratt, Jill A572
Pratt, John P403
Pratt, Michael J. A124
Pratt, Mitchell W. E73
Pratt, Timothy A. A142
Pratt, Vicki E170
Pray, Trisha P637
Praylo, Paul W. (Tishman
   Construction) A865
Praylo, Paul W. (Tishman
   Construction) A865
Preesman, Pim W307
Preete, Kerry J. A603
Preiser, Douglas W. A500
Preite, Russ P127
Prelipp, Steven H. A303
Prelle, Hermann W420
Prendergast, David A43
Prendergast, Gregg P238
Prendergast, Michael A932
Prendergast, Rick P351
Prendergast, Thomas F. (MTA) A608
Prendergast, Thomas F. (MTA) A608
Prendergast, Thomas F. (New York City
   Transit Authority) P436
Prenni, Mark P81
Prentice, Gregor E208
Prentice, Jim W95
Prescott, Edward S. P211
Present, Randall C. A262
Presley, Greta J. A424
Presley, Steve P432
Pressler, Susan S. P11
Pressley, Donald L. A138
Pressley, W. Michael A868
Pressly, Greg A591
Pressman, Ronald R. A376
Prest, D. W. W214
Prestele, Peter E335
Prestidge, D. Mark A514
Preston, Alex H. M. (The Carlyle
   Group) A847
Preston, Alex H. M. (The Carlyle
   Group) A847
Preston, Amie A535
Preston, Forrest L. P366
Preston, Isaac P355
Preston, John R. P556
Preston, Joseph A434
Preston, Michael P213
Preston, William E. E344
Preti, Robert A. E256
Pretorius, Craig A271
Pretty, Mike A431
Preuss, Dominic P186
Preuss, Michael W57
Prevo, James K. E163
Prevost, Patrick M. A163
Prevost, Scott A316
Prevot, Thierry W231
Prevoznik, Michael E. A726
Prewett, Kevin A461
Prezelj, Irene M. A355
Prezzi, Laura P581
Pribyl, Brian M. E252
Price, Adam E266
Price, Ann H. P644
Price, Barbara J. P530
Price, Ben A287
Price, Brian P81
Price, Charles D. E84
Price, Donald F. E248
Price, Duncan P. A215
Price, Ernest E52
Price, Gary W45

Price, Harold A. (Golden
   Horizons) A395
Price, Harold A. (Golden
   Horizons) A395
Price, James K. (ExamWorks) E135
Price, James D. (UBS) W420
Price John, Sharon P571
Price, Jonathan W45
Price, Keith A400
Price, Kim S. (Citizens South) E71
Price, Kim (Pepco Energy
   Services) P474
Price, Mark W213
Price, Michael E. (Dillard's) A284
Price, Michael (Tauber Oil) P579
Price, Patricia M. A543
Price, Paul A605
Price, Paula A. (Giant Food) P247
Price, Paula A. (Stop & Shop) P570
Price, Robert A260
Price, Sandra J. A806
Price, Scott A928
Price, Steve H. A274
Price, Thomas S. A196
Price, Tracy K. A8
Price, Vince P506
Prichard, David A. (Spectrum
   Brands) A802
Prichard, David (Ingram
   Industries) P313
Prideaux, Michael W79
Prideaux, Nigel W45
Pridgen, Daisy A295
Prieb, Laurel (Major League
   Baseball) A551
Prieb, Laurel (Major League
   Baseball) A551
Priergaard, Henrik W285
Priest, Andrew W. E302
Priest, Marlon L. P91
Priest, William W. E131
Prieur, C. James A219
Prigge, Robert E. P569
Primelles, Oscar (MasTec) E230
Primelles, Oscar (MasTec) E230
Primer, Jonathan P394
Primiano, Deborah P349
Primorac, David W240
Prince, Brian P646
Prince, J. Michael A408
Princen, Caroline E. W5
Principal, Beverley (Stanford
   University) A810
Principal, Beverley (Stanford
   University) A810
Princivalle, Karin V. (Medco
   Health) A582
Princivalle, Karin V. (Medco
   Health) A582
Pring, Mike P670
Pringle, David L. A22
Pringuet, Pierre W303
Printz, Steve P469
Prior, Cornelius B. E40
Prior, David B. (University of Texas
   System) A899
Prior, David B. (University of Texas
   System) A899
Prior, David J. (University of
   Virginia) P636
Prior, Graham E117
Prior, Jim P677
Prior, Michael T. E40
Prior, Stuart P597
Priore, Theresa D. P276
Prioux, Noël W87
Prising, Jonas A555
Prisuta, Ian (Giant Eagle) A392
Prisuta, Ian (Giant Eagle) A392
Pritchard, David E271
Pritchard, Jon P663
Pritchard, Marc S. A711
Pritchard, Mike P303
Pritchard, Peter W37
Pritekel, Ted P287

A = AMERICAN BUSINESS
E = EMERGING COMPANIES
P = PRIVATE COMPANIES
W = WORLD BUSINESS

Pritzker, Nicholas J. P269
Pritzker, Thomas J. A455
Privette, Tara E282
Probert, Timothy J. A413
Probert, Tony W213
Probst, Lawrence F. A322
Probst, Marc P315
Probst, Susan P496
Procell, Adam E220
Prock-Schauer, Wolfgang W242
Procopio, Donald W. P2
Proctor, Christopher W79
Proctor, Deborah A. P563
Proctor, Dominic W445
Proctor, Donald R. A210
Proctor, Georganne C. (TIAA-CREF) A859
Proctor, Georganne C. (TIAA-CREF) A859
Proctor, George (New York City Health and Hospitals) A624
Proctor, George (New York City Health and Hospitals) A624
Proctor, James M. P390
Proctor, Rick P596
Proctor, Timothy D. W125
Prodouz, Stefanie A324
Prody, Tom P39
Proebstl, Siegmar W363
Proeschel, Steven E280
Proffitt, Alan P6
Proffitt, Billy A49
Proffitt, Jackie P513
Proffitt, Josh E218
Proffitt, Michael P575
Profitt, Josh E218
Profumo, Alessandro W424
Proglio, Henri (Electricité de France) W136
Proglio, Henri (Veolia Environnement) W431
Pronsati, Paul E344
Pronschinske, Mike P227
Prophet, Anthony A438
Propst, Beverly L. (Graybar Electric) A404
Propst, Beverly L. (Graybar Electric) A404
Prosceno, Mike W354
Prosinski, Jeffrey P323
Prosise, Robert (EBSCO) A317
Prosise, Robert (EBSCO) A317
Prosperi, David P. A70
Prosser, John W. A483
Prosser, Richard W417
Prost, Jacques A324
Prot, Baudouin W69
Protas, Lucille (New York Life) A625
Protas, Lucille (New York Life) A625
Proto, Nicholas L. P210
Protsch, Eliot G. E60
Protter, Andrew A. E238
Proud, Danya A574
Proud, David N. E74
Proudfit, Elizabeth E262
Proulx, Jim A135
Prout, Gerald R. A360
Prouty, Kevin P312
Prouty, Timothy J. A186
Prouvé, Cedric A336
Provencio, Marla P8
Provoost, Rudy S. W307
Provost, Francois W324
Provost, Hank P667
Provost, Steve A146
Prozzi, Patricia P401
Pruder, Katie P92
Pruellage, William M. P115
Pruett, David M. A111

Pruett, Greg S. A694
Pruitt, Charles A900
Pruitt, David E17
Pruitt, Gary E. P623
Pruitt, Mike P228
Prunetti, Donna E127
Prunty, James O. A940
Prusch, Erik E. E74
Prutton, Simon E315
Pruzan, Jonathan A605
Pryde, Robbie J. W392
Pryor, David B. (Ascension Health) A82
Pryor, David B. (Ascension Health) A82
Pryor, Jay R. A197
Pryor, Juliette (U.S. Foodservice) A879
Pryor, Juliette (U.S. Foodservice) A879
Pryor, Stephen D. A343
Pryor, Vikki L. (Red Cross) A737
Pryor, Vikki L. (Red Cross) A737
Przybus, Brent A961
Przymusinska, Agnieszka A278
Psaras, Diane A267
Ptacek, Erin A926
Ptak, Frank S. P380
Ptaszynski, John E252
Pua, Roger A376
Pucci, Mike W171
Pucci, Paolo E37
Pucci, Roberto W351
Puccio, Krisana E293
Pucel, Kenneth J. A142
Pucher, Louis J. A783
Puckett, Jeff P137
Puckett, Karen A. A191
Puckett, Lance P205
Puckett, M. Susan P219
Pudles, Stephen B. E33
Pudlin, Helen P. A700
Pudlowski, Matt A731
Puebla, Eduardo W107
Puechl, Robert L. A796
Puffer, Dennis P409
Puffer, Terence P622
Pufunt, Dan A491
Pugh, Ben P166
Pugh, Bryan A930
Pugh, Spencer (Battelle Memorial) A107
Pugh, Spencer (Battelle Memorial) A107
Pugh, Stacy L. E339
Pughes, Michael P242
Pugliese, Angela A379
Pugliese, David (Cox Communications) A251
Pugliese, David (Cox Communications) A251
Puig Márquez, Juan A. W302
Pujadas, Juan W314
Pujol, Henry J. A754
Pulatie, David L. A767
Pulcrano, Samuel M. (US Postal Service) A907
Pulcrano, Samuel M. (US Postal Service) A907
Puleo, Paula A. P407
Pulford, Ian W80
Pulick, Michael A. A926
Pulido, Rick P219
Pulis, Brenda J. (Energy Future) A330
Pulis, Brenda J. (Energy Future) A330
Pulkownik, Theodore C. P652
Pullen, David A124
Pullen, Des W38
Pullen, Neil W270
Pulley, Kirk G. A707
Pulliam, Evelyn J. A829
Pulliam, Larry G. A829
Pullin, Dennis W. P395
Pullin, Stephen A271
Pullola, Kristian W282
Pulman, David W171
Puls, Carole A324
Pulse, M. Leste A557
Pulsipher, Gary W. P546

Pulver, Paul A249
Pulvers, Sherry E149
Puma, Grace M. A684
Pumarejo, Mari A714
Punch, Wayne (Milliken) A598
Punch, Wayne (Milliken) A598
Punnett, Valerie P439
Punshi, Sidharth A494
Puntus, Noah J. P548
Puopolo, Michael P657
Puopoly, Scott A210
Purcell, Chris P651
Purcell, Kevin J. E12
Purcell, Marcia (Random House) A733
Purcell, Marcia (Random House) A733
Purcell, Peter J. P209
Purcell, Steve P325
Purcell, Tim P480
Purdy, Brian P124
Purdy, Greg A754
Pures, Robert J. P294
Puri, Ajay K A654
Purificaç̃o Carvalho, Eugénio A. W141
Purnell, Julie A557
Purple, Glenn L. E118
Purpura, Nate E119
Purser, Kenneth W. A524
Purtilar, Mark W. A400
Purvis, Edgar M. A328
Puryear, Kay A711
Pusateri, Robert F. A239
Pusateri, Tony E298
Pusch, Dianne A73
Pusey, James M. A662
Pusey, Stephen C. W436
Pusswald, Sven W298
Putegnat, Scanlon H. P291
Puth, David W. A817
Putnam, Christopher S. E342
Putnam, Michael C. W367
Putnam, Roger L. (MassMutual) A564
Putnam, Roger L. (MassMutual) A564
Putter, Joshua S. A427
Putthoff, Tama S. P85
Putur, Christine A812
Pyatt, Rick A398
Pyden, Thomas J. P309
Pye, Hugh W190
Pye, J. David E360
Pye, Ken N. E244
Pyenson, Eric J. E3
Pyka, Kathy A844
Pyke, Nigel P166
Pyle, Michael R. E279
Pylipow, David E. A825
Pylypyshyn, Michael E279
Pym, Richard A. W288
Pyne, George P309
Pynnonen, Brett A348
Pyott, David E. I. A39
Pyrch, Karen G. P92
Pätsi, Tuomo E178
Pébereau, Michel W69
Pécresse, Jérôme W27
Pénicaud, Muriel W114
Péretié, Michel W369
Pérez Colmenero, Antonio W151
Pérez Fernández, Gonzalo W194
Pérez, Gustavo E3
Pérez, Jorge W91
Pérez, Juan Pérez Luis W9
Pérez Marcote, Jorge W199
Pérez Marcote, Oscar W199
Pérez, Moisés W186
Pérez Renovales, Jaime P. W172
Pérez Rodríguez, Florentino W9
Pérez Tremps, José Maria W152
Périllat-Piratoine, Christophe W430
Pérol, François W271
Pölchen, Astrid W354
Pörschke, Frank W102
Pötsch, Hans D. (Porsche) W310
Pötsch, Hans D. (Volkswagen) W438

Q

Qian, Changgeng E93
Qian, Xiao A245
Qu, Mindy (Dow Corning) A300
Qu, Mindy (Dow Corning) A300
Quade, David C. E46
Quade, William A. (Associated Wholesale Grocers) A85
Quade, William A. (Associated Wholesale Grocers) A85
Quader, Khandker Nazru A766
Quadracci, Betty Ewens A722
Quadracci, J. Joel A722
Quadrino, Umberto W136
Quaglini, Massimo W133
Qualls, Mark P279
Qualters, Christopher J. P54
Quandt, Stefan W67
Quarella, Michael E21
Quarles, David A. E222
Quarles, Randal K. (The Carlyle Group) A847
Quarles, Randal K. (The Carlyle Group) A847
Quarles, W. Gordon E71
Quarrie, Brian (First Data) A354
Quarrie, Brian (First Data) A354
Quart, Barry D. E35
Quartermain, Mark (Shell Oil) A785
Quartermain, Mark (Shell Oil) A785
Quartermain, Mark (Royal Dutch Shell) W339
Quartermaine, Mark W80
Quatela, Laura G. A312
Quatmann, Edmund L. A748
Quattrociocchi, Stephen E85
Quay, Kathy P163
Quazi, Paula W426
Queck, Palle F. W204
Queenan, Daniel P604
Queiroz, Odilon (Anheuser-Busch) P38
Queiroz, Odilon (Anheuser-Busch InBev) W32
Quek, Sean W107
Quellhorst, Timothy S. P162
Query, K. Rex A652
Quesnelle, George M. W171
Quick, Chuck M. E179
Quigley, Brian W. (Altria) A44
Quigley, Brian W. (UST llc) P643
Quigley, Cheri P451
Quigley, John E184
Quigley, Margaret A842
Quigley, Mark P515
Quigley, Patrick E292
Quigley, Peter W. A499
Quilici, François-Xavier W45
Quilici, Vince P18
Quimby, Sean E388
Quinata, John P92
Quincey, James R. A221
Quindlen, Thomas M. A376
Quiniones, Gil C. (New York Power Authority) A626
Quiniones, Gil C. (New York Power Authority) A626
Quinlan, Kevin W. E32
Quinlan, Lorraine E320
Quinlan, Mark J. A664
Quinlan, Paul T. E325
Quinlan, Peter S. E320
Quinlan, Raymond J. A211
Quinlan, Steven J. E255
Quinlan, Thomas J. A728
Quinlan, Tim A616
Quinn, Amy (Cox Communications) A251
Quinn, Amy (Cox Communications) A251
Quinn, Barney A789
Quinn, Beth J. A254
Quinn, Chris P434
Quinn, George W388

COMBINED HOOVER'S HANDBOOK INDEX OF EXECUTIVES

A = AMERICAN BUSINESS
E = EMERGING COMPANIES
P = PRIVATE COMPANIES
W = WORLD BUSINESS

Rentler, Barbara A752
Rentner, Deanna A923
Rentzel, Keith M. P24
Renwick, Glenn M. A714
Renz, Gerhard W34
Renz, Justin A. E386
Renzer, David P624
Renzi, Anthony A369
Repar, Lawrence P. P384
Repetto, Chris A473
Repond, Daniel W350
Reppert, Todd A. E228
Requardt, Hermann (Siemens Corp.) P543
Requardt, Hermann (Siemens AG) W363
Resch, Edward J. A817
Resendez, Edward E123
Resheske, Frances A. A234
Resinger, James E. A443
Resler, Barclay T. A221
Resman, Cindy A583
Resnick, Jed (LeFrak Organization) A521
Resnick, Jed (LeFrak Organization) A521
Resnick, Lynda R. P512
Resnick, Stewart A. P512
Resnik, John A. A858
Resnikoff, Bruce P624
Restall, Hugo P186
Restel, Anthony J. E179
Restivo, Neal R. P131
Restivo, Vince P279
Restrepo, Claudia E. P445
Resweber, Christopher P. A793
Retailleau, Cedric W303
Retallick, Phillip G. E74
Retegno, Giambattista W133
Retelny, Gary E249
Rettig, Bernd W379
Reu, Tanya P502
Reuhl, Catherine P276
Reum, W. Robert P34
Reuschel, Jeff P280
Reuss, Mark L. A384
Reuss, Michele M. (Giant Eagle) A392
Reuss, Michele M. (Giant Eagle) A392
Reusser, Curtis C. A398
Reuter, Bruce A. E94
Reuter, Jenny P227
Reuter, Louis F. P439
Reutersberg, Bernhard W130
Reuther, Michael W102
Revai, Dan P534
Reverse, Charlotte W47
Revesz, Richard L. P449
Revri, Anurag P89
Rex, Paul E122
Rexach, Frank P280
Rexford, John H. A21
Rey, Bernard W324
Rey, Francine P334
Rey-Giraud, Agnes A342
Reyburn, Donald L. A146
Reyda, Vincent A. P223
Reydel, Stephen J. A817
Reyes, Carlos P451
Reyes, Cecilia W452
Reyes, David K. P508
Reyes, G. Wayne E26
Reyes, Gregorio A545
Reyes, J. Christopher P508
Reyes, James (Active Network) E8
Reyes, James (Reyes Holdings) P508
Reyes Lagunes, José O. A221
Reyes, M. Jude P508
Reyes, Pedro (University of Texas System) A899

Reyes, Pedro (University of Texas System) A899
Reyes, Ricardo E350
Reyes, Thomas A. P508
Reyes, Timothy D. A35
Reymondet, Pascal W422
Reyna, Metin W342
Reyna, Stephanie P502
Reynier, Hubert W109
Reynish, Steve D. L. A556
Reynolds, Britt T. A427
Reynolds, Catherine M. A217
Reynolds, Dave A452
Reynolds, David P166
Reynolds, Emily J. (TVA) A874
Reynolds, Emily J. (TVA) A874
Reynolds, Glen P669
Reynolds, Jamie P663
Reynolds, Jim P537
Reynolds, John A673
Reynolds, Jon W80
Reynolds, Kim A. E308
Reynolds, Leslie A. A546
Reynolds, Louis J. (The Carlyle Group) A847
Reynolds, Louis J. (The Carlyle Group) A847
Reynolds, Marc P530
Reynolds, Marie W66
Reynolds, Marshall T. E128
Reynolds, Mary B. A866
Reynolds, Paul L. A351
Reynolds, Peter W320
Reynolds, Ralph P180
Reynolds, Robert A. (Graybar Electric) A404
Reynolds, Robert A. (Graybar Electric) A404
Reynolds, Sharon L. E10
Reynolds, Shelley L. A45
Reynolds, Stanley W. P4
Reynolds, Steve W21
Reynolds, Thomas C. (Seattle Genetics) E315
Reynolds, Thomas A. (University of Chicago) A898
Reynolds, Thomas A. (University of Chicago) A898
Reynolds, Tom (Black Entertainment Television) P82
Reynolds, Tom (Frito-Lay) P234
Reynolds, William L. E264
Reynolds, Yoke San L. P636
Reynoldson, Mike A594
Re ón Tú ez, Ramón W199
Rhea, Robert H. P212
Rheault, Christian E215
Rhee, Stephen P6
Rheel, Robert P680
Rhein, Kevin A. A940
Rhenman, Torkel A305
Rhind, Islay A221
Rhine, Bruce C. E251
Rhinehart, Mary K. P333
Rhoa, Brian (Red Cross) A737
Rhoa, Brian (Red Cross) A737
Rhoades, Alan E100
Rhoades, Charles S. E312
Rhoades, Craig T. A17
Rhoades, Danielle P186
Rhoades, Kelly A50
Rhoades, Richard P45
Rhoads, Barry A471
Rhoads, Michael S. A890
Rhoads, Rebecca B. A735
Rhoda, Michael D. A954
Rhode, Jason P. E70
Rhodes, Blake M. A631
Rhodes, C. Douglas P276
Rhodes, Colin E376
Rhodes, David (Boston Consulting) A141
Rhodes, David (Boston Consulting) A141
Rhodes, Gary L. A695

Rhodes, Glenn E364
Rhodes, Graham M. A29
Rhodes, Howard E. E269
Rhodes, Janice P526
Rhodes, Jimmy P366
Rhodes, Len P505
Rhodes, Lou (Chrysler) A201
Rhodes, Lou (Chrysler) A201
Rhodes, Robert P669
Rhodes, Taylor E293
Rhodes, William C. (AutoZone) A88
Rhodes, William (Becton, Dickinson) A117
Rhodin, Michael D. A456
Rhone, Sylvia P624
Rhoten, Diana A632
Rhydderch, Michael P166
Rhyne, Mary Anne W171
Rhyu, James P186
Riabokobylko, Sergey P166
Rial, Sergio (Cargill) A172
Rial, Sergio (Cargill) A172
Riant, Martin A711
Riban, Agn s (The Carlyle Group) A847
Riban, Agn s (The Carlyle Group) A847
Ribatt, Gregg S. P571
Ribeiro, Americo W41
Ribeiro, Cesar E222
Ribeiro, Ciro P478
Ribeiro Ferreira, Miguel W141
Ribeiro, Jack (Deloitte) A276
Ribeiro, Jack (Deloitte) A276
Riboud, Franck W114
Ribovic-Ell, Sandra A. P107
Ricard, Alexandre W303
Ricard, Patrick W303
Ricchiuti, Franco P18
Ricci, Eddie P577
Ricci, John C. E162
Ricci, Mark (Hilton Worldwide) A441
Ricci, Mark (Hilton Worldwide) A441
Ricci, Rich W53
Ricciardi, Frank A. E86
Ricciardi, Michael F. (Topco Associates LLC) A867
Ricciardi, Michael F. (Topco Associates LLC) A867
Ricciardi, Natale S. A692
Riccio, Janet A663
Riccitiello, John S. A322
Rice, Alan J. A921
Rice, Brian S. (Kellogg) A498
Rice, Brian J. (Royal Caribbean Cruises) A754
Rice, Charles A332
Rice, Cherie C. A935
Rice, Clayton A453
Rice, David A74
Rice, Daymond P650
Rice, Deborah L. (Highmark) A440
Rice, Deborah L. (Highmark) A440
Rice, Derica W. A324
Rice, Jeffrey R. A293
Rice, Jennifer E255
Rice, John D. (ADM) A11
Rice, John G. (GE) A376
Rice, Joseph J. A940
Rice, Melissa A920
Rice, Ronald A. A755
Rice, Susan W119
Rice, Thomas R. A838
Ricetti, Christophe W271
Rich, Bradford R. A790
Rich, Frank P39
Rich, Gary G. A97
Rich, James H. P584
Rich, Jonathan P77
Rich, Melinda R. P510
Rich, Robert R. (University of Alabama at Birmingham) P627
Rich, Robert F. (University of Illinois) P629
Rich, Todd W. P241
Rich, Tracy L. (Guardian Life) A407
Rich, Tracy L. (Guardian Life) A407

Richard, Alfredo P583
Richard, Auguste E280
Richard, Eric W107
Richard, Frances P45
Richard, Henri (Freescale Semiconductor) A371
Richard, Henri (Freescale Semiconductor) A371
Richard, Patrick W432
Richard, Paul (Shaw Industries) A785
Richard, Paul (Shaw Industries) A785
Richard, Philippe W41
Richard, Robert A. A303
Richard, Stephen O. (NBA) A618
Richard, Stephen O. (NBA) A618
Richard, Stéphane W157
Richards, Aileen (Mars, Incorporated) A559
Richards, Aileen (Mars, Incorporated) A559
Richards, Christine P. A349
Richards, Daniel A. E83
Richards, Digby W445
Richards, Douglas J. E337
Richards, Edward A. A30
Richards, Jerry A947
Richards, Joan P229
Richards, Marc P31
Richards, Pat P315
Richards, Peter S. P433
Richards, Roy P557
Richards, Steven W. (TTM Technologies) E361
Richards, Steven (Muzak Holdings) P419
Richards, Thomas E. (CDW) A189
Richards, Thomas E. (CDW) A189
Richards, Tim P498
Richardsen, Ernie A744
Richardson, Bradley C. A283
Richardson, Brent D. E162
Richardson, Bruce M. P312
Richardson, Christopher C. (Grand Canyon Education) E162
Richardson, Christopher W. (KIT digital) E212
Richardson, Corey E111
Richardson, D. Jeffrey A545
Richardson, Debra J. (American Equity Investment Life Holding Company) E25
Richardson, Debra A. (Investors Bancorp) E199
Richardson, Elizabeth W323
Richardson, Hal P463
Richardson, Jamie P667
Richardson, Jane (Red Cross) A737
Richardson, Jane (Red Cross) A737
Richardson, Jeff A351
Richardson, Jim E30
Richardson, Joanna E279
Richardson, John B. E114
Richardson, Jonathan P579
Richardson, Karen P236
Richardson, Kim E88
Richardson, Lindon (OSI Restaurant Partners) A669
Richardson, Lindon (OSI Restaurant Partners) A669
Richardson, Matthew L. (Hilton Worldwide) A441
Richardson, Matthew L. (Hilton Worldwide) A441
Richardson, Michael R. (Casey's General Stores) A179
Richardson, Michael (Nordstrom) A642
Richardson, Paul W. G. W445
Richardson, Rich (Peter Kiewit Sons') A689
Richardson, Rich (Peter Kiewit Sons') A689
Richardson, Robert J. (Worthington Industries) A957
Richardson, Robert (Young's Market) P678

552

HOOVER'S HANDBOOK OF EMERGING COMPANIES 2012

A = AMERICAN BUSINESS
E = EMERGING COMPANIES
P = PRIVATE COMPANIES
W = WORLD BUSINESS

Semmler, Donald J. A557
Semrau, Kelly M. (S.C. Johnson) A759
Semrau, Kelly M. (S.C. Johnson) A759
Sen, Laura J. (BJ's Wholesale Club) A129
Sen, Laura J. (BJ's Wholesale Club) A129
Sen, Michael W363
Sen, Pradipta A328
Sen, Sandip P16
Sena, Kathleen P634
Sena, Peter P. A355
Senackerib, Michael P. A435
Senard, Jean-Dominique W257
Senatore, Sara (AllianceBernstein) A40
Senatore, Sara (AllianceBernstein) A40
Senchak, Andrew M. E211
Sencindiver, Christopher P604
Senecal, Garry W240
Senequier, Dominique W47
Senf, J. Eduardo A629
Seng Lim, Kim A224
Seng, Tee Fong W107
Senge, Jim E117
Senglaub, Keith P214
Sengmuang, Daranee A379
Sengupta, Aparup P16
Senior, David M. A59
Senior, Edgar W107
Senk, Glen T. A903
Senkler, Robert L. P532
Senn, Arthur L. A81
Senn, Martin W452
Senn, Randal M. A770
Sensabaugh, Karen A293
Senser, Jerrold K. (New York Life) A625
Senser, Jerrold K. (New York Life) A625
Sensibaugh, Amanda A557
Senske, Kurt M. P597
Senter, Peter D. E315
Sento, Brian P5
Seo, Kenji W273
Seong, Yu W311
Sepp, Thomas W452
Sepulveda, Carlos M. P317
Sequeira, Frances P91
Sequeira Lacayo, Farley W441
Sera, Gary P585
Serafin, John H. P594
Serafin, Marek W309
Serafini, Francesco A438
Serafini, Hester P180
Seraphine, Michael P565
Serati, Tammy S. A410
Seravalli, Mary Ellen E53
Serbin, Daniel S. A678
Serbousek, Jon C. (Biomet) A127
Serbousek, Jon C. (Biomet) A127
Serdar, Cenk W436
Sereda, Mikhail L. W165
Sereda, Peter L. A835
Seremet, Dennis M. A655
Serff, Jared P. A475
Serfontein, Deward W296
Sergejeff, Carl-Gustaf W217
Sergesketter, Randal A. A271
Serianni, Charles F. A742
Serino, Joe A640
Serino, Joseph A. A327
Serko, Jonathan P166
Serna, Angel W452
Seroka, Todd P309
Serota, Jack P253
Serpa, Liliana E156
Serpe, Michael P197
Serpico, Vincent P354
Serra, Andrea A577
Serra, Eileen M. A494
Serracane, Claudio W133
Serradell, Sheilah E101
Serrano, Luis A. E51
Serrano, Valentin W41
Serrao, Darren A168
Serre, Michel W430
Serri, Andrew M. A50

Serrone, H. James E353
Serruya, Michael E339
Sertori, Peter W354
Servan-Schreiber, Pierre P548
Servant, Pierre W271
Service, James E. E309
Servodidio, Mark J. (Avis Budget) A91
Servodidio, Mark J. (Avis) P56
Servodidio, Mark J. (Budget Rent A Car) P99
Servold, Mike P496
Serwe, Stephan A474
Serwer, Andy P600
Sessa, Carolyn F. P166
Sessa, Daniel M. A528
Sessions, Tripp A943
Sestak, Paul (Golden State Foods) A396
Sestak, Paul (Golden State Foods) A396
Sestak, Ray A627
Seter, Arthur H. (New York Life) A625
Seter, Arthur H. (New York Life) A625
Seth, Munish W21
Seth, Shashi A963
Sethov, Inger W287
Seton, John W80
Setos, Andrew G. P229
Setta, Salli A267
Sette, Mario (Springs Global US) A805
Sette, Mario (Springs Global US) A805
Setzer, Nikolai W106
Seufer-Wasserthal, Peter E76
Sevaldsen, Erik W115
Sevang, Thomas W285
Sevegrand, Isabelle A475
Seveney, Jon (Motiva Enterprises) A606
Seveney, Jon (Motiva Enterprises) A606
Severa, Richard A80
Severin, Bo W350
Severin, Marcus W299
Sevich, Larry (Giant Eagle) A392
Sevich, Larry (Giant Eagle) A392
Sevier, Landers (EBSCO) A317
Sevier, Landers (EBSCO) A317
Sevilla, Brian A367
Sevilla, Daniel J. P565
Sevillano Chaves, Carmen W199
Sevillia, Olivier W85
Seward, Edgar E. E164
Sewell, D. Bruce A74
Sewell, Gina E. A281
Sewell, Michael J. A208
Sewell, Susan P8
Sexauer, Roger N. P190
Sexton, Greg P143
Sexton, James J. P286
Sexton, John E. P449
Sexton, Kevin J. P608
Sexton, Lisa E280
Sexton, Michael W. P593
Sexton, Thomas G. A41
Seyama, Masahiro W300
Seymour, Andrew (Perdue Incorporated) A686
Seymour, Andrew W. (Pilgrim's Pride) A695
Seymour, Andrew (Perdue Incorporated) A686
Seymour, Bill A124
Seymour, Charlotte (Hilton Worldwide) A441
Seymour, Charlotte (Hilton Worldwide) A441
Seymour, David A906
Seymour, Laura P39
Seymour, Peter P8
Seymour, Scott J. (American Family Insurance) A54
Seymour, Scott J. (American Family Insurance) A54
Seymour, Steven D. E86
Seznec, P. W155
Seznec, Reynald W405
Sgarcitu, Bogdan (Bechtel) A114
Sgarcitu, Bogdan (Bechtel) A114
Sgarro, Douglas A. A260

Shaaban, Muhammad P621
Shabaz, Ali P260
Shabley, Les P219
Shabot, M. Michael P398
Shachmut, Kenneth M. A761
Shachtman, Nancy A408
Shack, Timothy G. A700
Shackelford, Donald B. A351
Shadduck, David A. P609
Shadley, Eric A372
Shadowens, Rob (Meijer) A584
Shadowens, Rob (Meijer) A584
Shae, Kate P16
Shafer, James E128
Shafer, Jay E19
Shafer, Walter F. A695
Shaff, Karen E. A709
Shaffer, Bradley A. A387
Shaffer, Carol M. E202
Shaffer, Karen C. A642
Shaffer, Kathleen E163
Shaffer, Kathy P276
Shaffer, Michael A. A721
Shaffer, Penny P84
Shaffer, Reuben A514
Shaffer, Robert A351
Shafir, Robert S. (Credit Suisse (USA)) A255
Shafir, Robert S. (Credit Suisse) W107
Shafter, A. James A11
Shah, Ajay V. P180
Shah, Atish A455
Shah, Gaurang W296
Shah, Jai A563
Shah, Jatin A688
Shah, Jigar W433
Shah, Mahesh A438
Shah, Manish P578
Shah, Neal E134
Shah, Neel A280
Shah, Nirav P292
Shah, Pragnesh P434
Shah, Pranab (US Postal Service) A907
Shah, Pranab (US Postal Service) A907
Shah, Raheel A. A464
Shah, Roshan A186
Shah, Samita W107
Shah, Vik E237
Shahkarami, Amir A338
Shailor, Barbara A. P675
Shainberg, Gary W80
Shak, Steven E155
Shakeel, Bassem A. W246
Shalala, Donna E. P632
Shale, Melanie E193
Shalett, Lisa A. P403
Shalhoub, Lorraine J. (Chrysler) A201
Shalhoub, Lorraine J. (Chrysler) A201
Shallcross, John P. E235
Shallcross, Richard J. A424
Shallow, Bob E305
Shamber, Mark E. A888
Shambrook, Jonathan P554
Shamia, Gadi E296
Shamieh, Charlie A27
Shamion, Vicki A509
Shamlou, Nick N. E184
Shammas, Shukri A322
Shammo, Francis J. A914
Shan, Helen A697
Shanahan, Patrick M. A135
Shanahan, Teri A470
Shanahan, William R. (Arena Pharmaceuticals) E35
Shanahan, William M. (CBRE Group) A186
Shanas, Gary P8
Shand, Eric D. A940
Shank, Jeffrey B. E353
Shank, Richard A777
Shankar, Ramesh (TVA) A874
Shankar, Ramesh (TVA) A874
Shankardass, Amit P547
Shanks, Janet A249
Shanks, Robert L. A365

Shanley, Marlene W51
Shannon, Arthur J. A688
Shannon, Daniel (University of Chicago) A898
Shannon, Daniel (University of Chicago) A898
Shannon, David M. (Carlisle Companies) A174
Shannon, David M. (NVIDIA) A654
Shannon, Holden A280
Shannon, Joe P143
Shannon, John (NHL) A637
Shannon, John (NHL) A637
Shannon, Kathleen E. A27
Shannon, Keith P526
Shannon, Michael P214
Shannon, Patrick J. W202
Shannon, Roger D. P569
Shannon, Scott A. A159
Shannon, Steve P305
Shannon, Tim E181
Shannon, William G. P416
Shantilal, Dhiren A499
Shao, Nicholas (The Carlyle Group) A847
Shao, Nicholas (The Carlyle Group) A847
Shao, Renkun E11
Shaopeng, Chen W237
Shapard, Robert S. (Energy Future) A330
Shapard, Robert S. (Energy Future) A330
Shape, Ronald L. E252
Shaper, Peter A420
Shapira, David S. (Giant Eagle) A392
Shapira, David S. (Giant Eagle) A392
Shapiro, Alan A947
Shapiro, Bill P600
Shapiro, David T. A268
Shapiro, Devra G. E200
Shapiro, Dina A35
Shapiro, Douglas A862
Shapiro, Fred P675
Shapiro, Glenn P519
Shapiro, Harold T. E102
Shapiro, Howard-Yana (Mars, Incorporated) A559
Shapiro, Howard-Yana (Mars, Incorporated) A559
Shapiro, Michael H. (RBS Global) P500
Shapiro, Michael H. (Environmental Protection Agency) P204
Shapiro, Peter M. E121
Shapiro, Robert A. E346
Shapland, Darren W208
Shappell, James R. (Parsons Corporation) A679
Shappell, James R. (Parsons Corporation) A679
Shar, Jonathan A105
Share, Scott (Catholic Health East) A182
Share, Scott (Catholic Health East) A182
Sharer, Kevin W. A60
Shariff, Shuaib W95
Sharifov, Vagit S. W243
Sharkey, Jeffrey P332
Sharkey, Michael E320
Sharko, Rich W314
Sharland, Jill W333
Sharma, C. M. P16
Sharma, Deepak A213
Sharma, Deven A576
Sharma, Devesh A230
Sharma, Kavita (Columbia University) A226
Sharma, Kavita (Columbia University) A226
Sharma, Neelima A812
Sharma, Pankaj P166
Sharma, Paul P186
Sharma, Vibhu R. P680
Sharma, Vivek P595

Singhal, Sita A949
Singletary, Rennie M. P521
Singleton, Alfred R. E71
Singleton, Bob A210
Singleton, David P. P14
Singleton, John A. A7
Singleton, Kenneth P. P166
Singleton, Lisa B. (Energy Future) A330
Singleton, Lisa B. (Energy Future) A330
Singleton, William D. P50
Sinha, Ajay P200
Sinha, Awadhesh K. E332
Sinha, Janmejaya (Boston Consulting) A141
Sinha, Janmejaya (Boston Consulting) A141
Sinha, Vikas E13
Sinicrope, Marty E118
Sinigaglia, Antonello W41
Siniscalchi, Patric (Avis Budget) A91
Siniscalchi, Patric (Avis) P56
Siniscalchi, Patric (Budget Rent A Car) P99
Sinko, Donald A. P590
Sinn, Jerry L. P190
Sinnaeve, Michael R. W246
Sinneck, Michael J. P236
Sinnott, Eamonn A464
Sinnott, John A724
Sinofsky, Steven J. A595
Sinsheimer, Dave (Peter Kiewit Sons') A689
Sinsheimer, Dave (Peter Kiewit Sons') A689
Sipe, Carol P. (Liberty Mutual) A534
Sipe, Carol P. (Liberty Mutual) A534
Siperstein, Allan P590
Sipes, Robert A. A713
Sipia, Joseph A. A205
Sipla, Greg P581
Sipla, Gregory T. (Owens-Illinois) A673
Sippel, Dean R. E334
Sippial, Charles A. P585
Siqing, Chen W51
Siracusa, Paul A. A205
Siracuse, Suzanne P160
Sirany, Jacqueline P. P371
Sirchio, John K. A152
Sire, Antoine W69
Siregar, Emmanuel W33
Sirisena, Mervyn W365
Sirkin, Allen E. A721
Sirlin, Edwin J. E320
Sirois, Charles W95
Sironi, Cesare W394
Sirotkin, Mikhail W165
Sisco, Deanne P58
Sisco, Robby D. A163
Siskind, Arthur M. A632
Sistek, Robert M. E84
Sistino, Lorenzo W153
Sisto, Dennis M. P563
Sistovaris, Violet G. A641
Sita, Veresh P144
Sitohang, Helman W107
Sivakumar, Swaminathan A464
Siverd, Robert J. A379
Sivori, John P. A428
Six, Rob P512
Sixt, Frank J. W192
Sizemore, Carolyn T. A257
Sizemore, Dale H. E353
Sjafril, Irwin W137
Sjoberg, Daniel A529
Sjoerdsma, Mike P394
Sjoreen, Jim A536
Sjulstad, Ole Bjørn W397
Sjöström, Robert W387
Sjöö, Tommy W356
Sjöblom, Tove Stuhr W378
Sjöhelle, Rune K. W285
Skaaden, Geir E111
Skaff, George E321

Skagen, Randy C. A652
Skagerlind, Mike P320
Skaggs, Robert C. A641
Skaggs, Steve A628
Skala, P. Justin A224
Skalak, Thomas C. P636
Skaletsky, Mark B. E345
Skall, Russell (OSI Restaurant Partners) A669
Skall, Russell (OSI Restaurant Partners) A669
Skalli, Jaafar W186
Skalstad, Anne K. E. W285
Skare, Randy P293
Skarie, David P. A731
Skarulis, Patricia C. P399
Skarupa, Andrew A. E297
Skaugen, Kirk B. A464
Skedgell, Misty P612
Skeens, Grant (USAA) A908
Skeens, Grant (USAA) A908
Skeith, Donna (USAA) A908
Skeith, Donna (USAA) A908
Skelley, Sean A124
Skelt, Paul W80
Skelton, Daniel K. E72
Skena, Dave P234
Skene, Richard W186
Skeoch, Keith W377
Skerritt, Susan A102
Skiba, Thomas P. P351
Skidmore, David W. P209
Skidmore, Harley P527
Skidmore, Kent A218
Skiem, Paul P508
Skiff, Sebastian P166
Skilton, Gary C. P14
Skingsley, Geoff W231
Skinner, David (CIGNA) A207
Skinner, David (Costco Wholesale) A249
Skinner, Heather A946
Skinner, Henry M. A111
Skinner, James A. (McDonald's) A574
Skinner, James E. (Neiman Marcus) A622
Skinner, James E. (Neiman Marcus) A622
Skinner, Margaret W. (Guardian Life) A407
Skinner, Margaret W. (Guardian Life) A407
Skinner, Michael J. E78
Skinner, Samuel K. E118
Skinner-Twomey, Karen P108
Skirvin, Michael A866
Skjervem, John D. A646
Sklarsky, Frank S. W419
Skoch, Daniel A. E231
Skoda, Randall (Topco Associates LLC) A867
Skoda, Randall (Topco Associates LLC) A867
Skodol, Ted W426
Skoglund, Cynthia A115
Skoglund, Peter W107
Skogsbergh, James H. P15
Skogstad, Silje W121
Skokan, Mike P305
Skoland, Arne W287
Skold, Lee B. (Cargill) A172
Skold, Lee B. (Cargill) A172
Skolnik, David A228
Skoog, Christopher R. A333
Skorin, Yurii P210
Skornicki, Eliezer A230
Skorton, David J. P154
Skory, John E. A355
Skosky, William E22
Skou, Søren W2
Skoufalos, Yannis A711
Skove, David J. A714
Skovhus, Per Damborg W115
Skrdlant, Joanna E330
Skrzypinski, Peter R. P416

Skröder, Christian E. A872
Skudutis, Tom (Magna Mirrors) P375
Skudutis, Tom (Magna International) W246
Skula, Catherine M. A741
Skurek, John C. A864
Skyler, Edward A213
Slaats, Paul E180
Slaats, Ronald W318
Slacik, Charles P. A115
Slack, Bill P387
Slade, Rick E163
Slager, Chris A168
Slager, Donald W. A742
Slagle, Dennis R. W439
Slagter, Martin E176
Slaoui, Moncef W171
Slark, Martin P. A600
Slaski, Peter P511
Slaski, Rob W37
Slat, William A. P483
Slater, Catherine I. A947
Slater, Gary P506
Slater, Gavin R. W269
Slater, James E.R. A102
Slater, Jeff M. P346
Slater, Steve P556
Slatin, Mike A328
Slatkin, Harry P67
Slaton, Mike (Stater Bros.) A819
Slaton, Mike (Stater Bros.) A819
Slattery, Frank P. P327
Slattery, Michael K. P646
Slattery, William A817
Slaughter, Don A267
Slavin, Peter L. P465
Slavin, Wendy W95
Slavitt, Andrew M. A895
Slavsky, Allan A938
Slavtcheff, Craig P573
Slawin, Kevin R. E140
Sleeper, William D. P245
Sleightholme, Mike A213
Sletmoe, Arnstein W287
Slettebo, John (University of Texas System) A899
Slettebo, John (University of Texas System) A899
Slichenmyer, William J. E42
Slider, Barry L. E147
Slifstein, Barry M. A755
Sliney, David D. E332
Slipsager, Henrik C. A8
Sliva, Christopher A269
Slivken, Ken P31
Sliwka, Frank P618
Sliwkowski, Mary B. P241
Sload, Michael A224
Sloan, Gary A838
Sloan, Gretchen E319
Sloan, J. David W392
Sloan, Maceo K. (TIAA-CREF) A859
Sloan, Maceo K. (TIAA-CREF) A859
Sloan, O. Templ P242
Sloan, O. Temple (General Parts) P242
Sloan, Pat A663
Sloan, Robert D. A332
Sloan, Thomas R. E49
Sloan, Timothy J. A940
Slomsky, Wayne T. E96
Slone, Deck S. A78
Slone, Reuben E. A660
Slonina, Kajetan W320
Slotkin, Doug E387
Slott, David M. P32
Slottow, Timothy P. P632
Sloves, Evan A210
Slow, Ellyn P433
Slubowski, Michael A. P608
Sluijter, Pascal W320
Sluitner, Zsolt W363
Slump, David J. A419
Slusher, Andy A964
Slusher, John F. A640
Sluzewski, James A. A549

Sly, Lynne D. P340
Sly, Patrick J. A328
Sly, Rachel P537
Smale, Alison A628
Smales, Alicia A. A794
Small, Brian P85
Small, David J. P127
Small, Dawn A80
Small, Harold I. A437
Small, Jeffrey P188
Small, Jim (Major League Baseball) A551
Small, Jim (Major League Baseball) A551
Small, Jordan M. (US Postal Service) A907
Small, Jordan M. (US Postal Service) A907
Small, Nicholas M. A211
Small, Peola (New York City Health and Hospitals) A624
Small, Peola (New York City Health and Hospitals) A624
Small, Robert J. P33
Small, Tony E387
Smalley, Diane P546
Smalley, Gary G. A359
Smalley, Janet P585
Smallhouse, Cathy E45
Smallman, Adam P186
Smargon, Carole P65
Smart, George M. A355
Smart, Jill B. W6
Smart, Richard E266
Smart, Steven R. A126
Smashum, Olivia A862
Smati, Zin P238
Smeaton, Gordon (NFL) A635
Smeaton, Gordon (NFL) A635
Smelley, William P325
Smeltser, Jeremy W. A807
Smeltzer, Roger P279
Smeraglinolo, Anthony A516
Smerczynski, Tom P581
Smerklo, Michael A. E318
Smetana, Mark P196
Smette, Darryl G. A281
Smiley, Gary (Gulfstream Aerospace) A409
Smiley, Gary (Gulfstream Aerospace) A409
Smiley, Keith R. A755
Smiley, Norman C. E80
Smirnov, Stephanie A471
Smisek, Jeffery A. A887
Smit, Alan P89
Smit, Jeff P337
Smit, Neil A227
Smit, Stephen A817
Smit, Willie W34
Smith, A. Wade A17
Smith, Aaron E147
Smith, Alan E. (Genzyme) A389
Smith, Alan (Brenntag North America) P97
Smith, Alex (ASDA) W37
Smith, Alex (Royal Mail) W340
Smith, Alfred J. A31
Smith, Allen L. A465
Smith, Alvin P537
Smith, Amelia P161
Smith, Andrea B. A100
Smith, Andrew (Power Integrations) E284
Smith, Andrew (Royal Dutch Shell) W339
Smith, Angela E43
Smith, Anne M. (Peapack-Gladstone Financial) E279
Smith, Anne S. (Sempra Energy) A781
Smith, Anthony H. A855
Smith, Barbara R. A230
Smith, Barry W14
Smith, Brad (Skullcandy) E324
Smith, Brad D. (Intuit) A473

Stevenson, Ewen W107
Stevenson, Jennifer A5
Stevenson, John P600
Stevenson, Kevin P. E282
Stevenson, Kimberly S. A464
Stevenson, Mitchell H. (Army and Air Force Exchange) A79
Stevenson, Mitchell H. (Army and Air Force Exchange) A79
Stevenson, Shannan A711
Stevenson, Steve P130
Stevenson, Tim E. P. W214
Steverlynck, Juan A502
Steverson, Lewis A. A607
Steward, David L. P671
Steward, Jesi E274
Steward, Larry E. A303
Steward, Russ (TVA) A874
Steward, Russ (TVA) A874
Stewardson, Charles A143
Stewart, Alan W249
Stewart, Anne P561
Stewart, Brad A827
Stewart, Brian E. E278
Stewart, Carol A498
Stewart, Carol-Anne (GlaxoSmithKline) W171
Stewart, Caroline W420
Stewart, Cecelia A213
Stewart, Clark D. E57
Stewart, Craig D. E57
Stewart, Dan (University of Texas System) A899
Stewart, Dan (University of Texas System) A899
Stewart, David L. A293
Stewart, Doug P565
Stewart, George E99
Stewart, Gregory C. P249
Stewart, J. Wayne E66
Stewart, Jan P239
Stewart, Jane B. (ABC, Inc.) P8
Stewart, John O. (Hostess Brands) A450
Stewart, John O. (Hostess Brands) A450
Stewart, John D. (Finmeccanica) W155
Stewart, John M. (Legal & General Group) W236
Stewart, Laurie K. A29
Stewart, Marta R. (Norfolk Southern) A644
Stewart, Marta R. (Norfolk Southern Railway) P446
Stewart, Michael K. (Marathon Oil) A556
Stewart, Michael (McKinsey & Company) A579
Stewart, Michael R. (Perrigo) A688
Stewart, Michael D. (The Carlyle Group) A847
Stewart, Michael D. (The Carlyle Group) A847
Stewart, Michael (McKinsey & Company) A579
Stewart, Nathan A322
Stewart, Peter G. E209
Stewart, Randy P92
Stewart, Robert (Buffalo Wild Wings) E55
Stewart, Robert A. (Watson Pharmaceuticals) A938
Stewart, Robert (Winn-Dixie) A955
Stewart, Ron A514
Stewart, Scott D. (Northrop Grumman) A648
Stewart, Scott (FHLB Chicago) P215
Stewart, Shelley W419
Stewart, Tara A305
Stewart, Todd P97
Stewart, William A138
Steyerthal, Jorge A. A703
Steyn, David A. (AllianceBernstein) A40
Steyn, David A. (AllianceBernstein) A40
Stiborek Meyer, Marilyn A961

Stice, J. Michael A196
Stichnoth, Roseann P210
Stickevers, Ken A572
Stickford, Eric (Guardian Life) A407
Stickford, Eric (Guardian Life) A407
Stickler, Peter A. W156
Stickler, Randy G. A453
Stickler, Shannan P487
Stickles, Kevin P661
Stickney, Alexander R. (Cox Enterprises) A252
Stickney, Alexander R. (Cox Enterprises) A252
Stief, Brian J. A489
Stiefel, Charles W. W171
Stiekes, Robert E. A427
Stieler, Frank W185
Stiers, Mark W. A303
Stiff, David A356
Stigers, Thomas M. A747
Stiles, Deborah (Columbia University) A226
Stiles, Deborah (Columbia University) A226
Stiles, Syndee (McLane Foodservice) A579
Stiles, Syndee (McLane Foodservice) A579
Still, David P276
Still, Debra W. A720
Still, Duane A223
Still, Jay P. A696
Stiller, Robert P. E163
Stillig, Martin E264
Stillwell, Jerry B. P664
Stilwell, Jack P191
Stilwell, McDavid E168
Stimpson, Catharine R. P449
Stimpson, Hayley W45
Stimson, Helen A26
Stingle, Robert V. (MassMutual) A564
Stingle, Robert V. (MassMutual) A564
Stinner, Charles G. A29
Stinnes, George W78
Stinnett, Donald W. A424
Stinnett, Wayne D. A190
Stinson, David (TVA) A874
Stinson, David (TVA) A874
Stinson, Kenneth E. (Peter Kiewit Sons') A689
Stinson, Kenneth E. (Peter Kiewit Sons') A689
Stinson, Stacy L. A254
Stipancich, John A629
Stipp, Keith D. A278
Stipp, Maria D. E78
Stirek, John A. P604
Stiritz, William P. A731
Stirling, Alex G. (The Carlyle Group) A847
Stirling, Alex G. (The Carlyle Group) A847
Stiroh, Kevin J. P210
Stirrat, Ian W80
Stites, Suzanne (Mars, Incorporated) A559
Stites, Suzanne (Mars, Incorporated) A559
Stitt, Michael P272
Stitz, Michaela A640
Stitzlein, Jim P534
Stobbart, William L. P472
Stobie, John J. P396
Stobo, John D. (University of California) A897
Stobo, John D. (University of California) A897
Stocchetti, John P215
Stock, Carolyn P337
Stock, Elane B. A502
Stock, Keith (TIAA-CREF) A859
Stock, Keith (TIAA-CREF) A859
Stock, Lawrence A. A480
Stockburger, Michael P413
Stockdale, Caroline A583

Stocker, Michael A. (New York City Health and Hospitals) A624
Stocker, Michael A. (New York City Health and Hospitals) A624
Stockham, Neal P579
Stocking, Richard A827
Stockland, Wayne L. (Ag Processing Inc.) A23
Stockland, Wayne L. (Ag Processing Inc.) A23
Stockman, Gary A663
Stockman, James D. A284
Stocks, Neil R. W420
Stockton, Bryan G. A568
Stockton, Chris A952
Stockton, David J. P209
Stockton, Dmitri L. A376
Stockton, Wayne W. A126
Stockwell, Ashley (Virgin Media) A916
Stockwell, Ashley (Virgin Group) W433
Stoddard, Eric P. A940
Stoddard, Paul P284
Stoddart, Clive A70
Stoddart, Mary A124
Stoddart, Pete (Cargill) A172
Stoddart, Pete (Cargill) A172
Stodder, Mark W. C. E109
Stoe, George P. A957
Stoeckel, Emily Heisl P286
Stoeckel, Frederic E325
Stoeckel, Howard B. P660
Stoeckel, Thomas W112
Stoessl, Michael A. A244
Stoffel, Scott A5
Stoffels, Paul A487
Stoffers, Brian F. A186
Stofko, Larry P563
Stoicheff, Jeffrey P472
Stoken, Marc F. A890
Stoker, Graeme W80
Stokes, Celia E209
Stokes, Charles D. P398
Stokes, Edmund W190
Stokes, Gary L. A838
Stokes, Gemma W270
Stokes, Jack P50
Stokes, Leigh (Cox Communications) A251
Stokes, Leigh (Cox Communications) A251
Stokes, Nick A. P90
Stokes, Tony E357
Stolar, Kathleen S. A476
Stolarczyk, Mark A592
Stolberg, Doug W44
Stolkey, Dennis P300
Stoll, Jérôme W324
Stoll, Michael J. A514
Stoll, Roger G. E87
Stolle, Russ R. P304
Stoller, James K. P590
Stoller, William H. P207
Stollings, Anthony M. E143
Stolper, Edward M. P107
Stolpestad, James A. W25
Stolyar, Nikolai F. W165
Stolz, Philip M. (Hearst Corporation) A430
Stolz, Philip M. (Hearst Corporation) A430
Stolz, Robert W447
Stomberg, Jeff W320
Stone, Aaron J. (AMC Entertainment) A47
Stone, Aaron J. (AMC Entertainment) A47
Stone, Andrew P. E300
Stone, Brian A176
Stone, Carol (BJ's Wholesale Club) A129
Stone, Carol (BJ's Wholesale Club) A129
Stone, Carolyn J. (Dynegy) A307
Stone, Chad P573
Stone, David (AES) A18

Stone, David M. (Columbia University) A226
Stone, David M. (Columbia University) A226
Stone, Evan D. E382
Stone, Greg A365
Stone, Jace (Gulfstream Aerospace) A409
Stone, Jace (Gulfstream Aerospace) A409
Stone, Jeff (Duke Realty) E111
Stone, Jeff (Purple Communications) E290
Stone, Jeffrey M. (Progress Energy) A713
Stone, Jim P75
Stone, John D. A662
Stone, Jon W53
Stone, Kathryn P205
Stone, Randy P523
Stone, Robert E. (Healthways, Inc.) E171
Stone, Robert (Royal Caribbean Cruises) A754
Stone, Rod W131
Stone, Roger W. E210
Stone, Sam (Dairy Farmers of America) A263
Stone, Sam (Dairy Farmers of America) A263
Stone, Spencer H. A868
Stone, Theresa M. P411
Stone, William J. E136
Stoneburner, Charles P. A208
Stonehocker, Tim W13
Stonehouse, Steve A218
Stoneley, Dean A365
Stoneman, Dan E52
Stoneman, Perry W85
Stoner, Jonathan W314
Stopello, Roberto P583
Storch, Gerald L. A869
Storch, Walter E58
Storck, Denise P416
Stordahl, Ann (Neiman Marcus) A622
Stordahl, Ann (Neiman Marcus) A622
Storey, Debbie A86
Storey, Jeffrey K. A529
Storey, Robert P573
Storgaard, Michael C. W2
Storino, Tammy P563
Stormo, Chris I. P162
Stornelli, Sabatino W155
Storp, Adrian W8
Storr, Robert P675
Storto, David E. P465
Story, J. Eric E187
Story, Jack P312
Story, Kendra A. P7
Story, Roger P98
Story, Susan N. A797
Storckers, Anna W285
Stotlar, Douglas W. A235
Stott, Jakob W420
Stott, John P. A11
Stott, Kermit P. E18
Stourm, Hubert W374
Stout, Michael D. (hhgregg) E173
Stout, Michael W. (Thor Industries) A858
Stout, Neil A224
Stout, Rodger A. E228
Stout, Susan (TVA) A874
Stout, Susan (TVA) A874
Stoutamire, Belinda A955
Stoute, Steve A471
Stovall, Jeffrey E111
Stovall, Robert L. E265
Stovall, Ron A53
Stover, Mitchell L. A832
Stovickova, Petra A711
Stowe, Barry L. W315
Stowe, Garnett A735
Stowe, Robert D. A743
Stoyle, Nadia P606

A = AMERICAN BUSINESS
E = EMERGING COMPANIES
P = PRIVATE COMPANIES
W = WORLD BUSINESS

Straarup, Peter W115
Strable, Deanna D. A709
Strachan, John P166
Strader, Frederick M. A845
Strader, H. Gregg E179
Strader, Jerry P610
Strader, Jim P211
Straehle, Joachim H. W318
Straface, Nancy P367
Strafstrom, Steve A811
Strah, Steve A355
Strain, Daniel J. (Chick-fil-A) A198
Strain, Daniel J. (Chick-fil-A) A198
Strain, John A953
Straka, Angeline C. A188
Strambi, Lyell W317
Strampel, William D. P408
Strand, Jani A52
Strandberg, Carolyn P401
Strandmo, Dana P293
Strang, Cameron (Warner Music) A933
Strang, Cameron (Warner Music) A933
Strange, Cathy A950
Strangfeld, John R. A716
Strassberg, Leslie P200
Strassburger, Alexander H. (The Carlyle Group) A847
Strassburger, Alexander H. (The Carlyle Group) A847
Strassell, Greg P124
Strassl, Wolfgang W268
Strassler, Marc A. A744
Stratakos, Anthony E378
Stratman, R. Joseph A652
Stratman, Victoria D. P107
Stratton, Dene B. P405
Stratton, Harold M. E333
Stratton, Jeffrey P. A574
Stratton, John G. P127
Stratton, Kim W289
Straty, Stephen M. A484
Straub, Matthew E173
Straub, Maximiliane P511
Straub, Stefan W248
Straube, David W6
Straubel, Jeffrey B. E350
Strauss, Alan P445
Strauss, Christianne L. A382
Strauss, Julie Alexa P214
Strauss, Mark F. A57
Strauss Sansone, Judith A260
Strauss, Toby W239
Strauß, Thorsten W62
Strayer, Jacqueline F. A489
Streatfield, Douglas W296
Street, Andy W213
Streetman, Rusty P78
Streett, Mary A338
Strege, Kathy A640
Strehle, Don A111
Streicher, Joanie P551
Strein, Klaus W331
Streit, Paula A746
Streit, Steven W. E162
Streitfeld, Victoria A446
Streker, Cathy A. A845
Strelzick, Paul E325
Strenger, Hermann Josef W57
Strenkert, Arthur L. A327
Strenski, Robert A126
Streppel, Joseph B.M. W225
Streubig, Andreas W299
Streule, Roman P524
Streyle, Harry P5
Strianese, Michael T. A516
Strickland, Douglas K. E283
Strickland, Samuel R. A138
Strickland, Stacey A955

Strickland, Steven C. (Rock-Tenn) A747
Strickland, Steven C. (RockTenn CP) A748
Strickler, Kristen P227
Strider, Julie A549
Strietelmeier, Michael A871
Strigini, Bruno A587
Strine, Michael P332
Stringer, Howard W375
Stringer, Joanne C. A646
Stringer, Suzanne M. P675
Stringham, Peter E. P677
Strite, Toby E206
Strizzi, David M. P623
Strobaek, Michael W420
Strobel, Russ M. A638
Strode, Dave P287
Strodtman, Keith P130
Stroedter, Friedrich Karl W119
Strohmaier, Debra A405
Strom, Jon P253
Strom, Steven R. A484
Stromberg, William J. A831
Stromquist, Gary D. A531
Stronach, Frank P375
Strong, Andrew L. P585
Strong, James A. W444
Strong, Michael J. A186
Strong, Scott P590
Strong, Wendi E. (USAA) A908
Strong, Wendi E. (USAA) A908
Strong, Willard P521
Strong, William H. A605
Strongin, Marc A81
Strongin, Steven H. A397
Stroomer, Kees W320
Strop, Garry D. E325
Stropes, David W. A157
Stropp, John P634
Strotbek, Axel W43
Strother, James M. A940
Strothmann, Dirk W430
Stroucken, Albert P. L. A673
Stroud, Dan P432
Stroud, Matthew A267
Stroud, Randy A695
Stroud, Rodney S. A829
Stroud, Steve P260
Stroup, Gary A. A181
Stroupe, T. Richard E253
Strozyk, Randy P33
Strub, Alain W109
Strubbe, Todd B. A945
Strube, Jürgen F. W67
Struble, Julia A. A65
Struckmeyer, Charles S. P209
Struewing, Ben E111
Strum, Debora W354
Strumeyer, Gary A102
Strumph, Peter M. E76
Strumwasser, Ira (Blue Cross Blue Shield of Michigan) A133
Strumwasser, Ira (Blue Cross Blue Shield of Michigan) A133
Strunk, Thomas W. P671
Strup, Richard F. P508
Strupp, Kindra A324
Struth, Werner W330
Struthers, Ian B. W392
Strutz, Eric W102
Strutz, Richard A940
Stryker, David P65
Stryker, Jeffrey L. E56
Strzelec, Barry A30
Stuart, Barkley J. P250
Stuart, R. Neil P327
Stuart, Robert J. A435
Stubblefield, Greg R. A334
Stubblefield, William P192
Stubbs, Bill P78
Stuchenrenberg, Paul P675
Stuckes, Richard W19
Stuckey, Karen A928
Stuckey, Kelly A844

Stuckey, Robert G. (The Carlyle Group) A847
Stuckey, Robert G. (The Carlyle Group) A847
Stuckey, Scott E226
Studenski, Mikhail N. W391
Studer, James D. (University of Texas System) A899
Studer, James D. (University of Texas System) A899
Studer, James (Univision) P637
Studholme, Penny (Cargill) A172
Studholme, Penny (Cargill) A172
Stuenkel, Wayne E. P487
Stuever, A. Lawrence A749
Stuewer, Sherri K. A343
Stuligross, Dennis (Gulfstream Aerospace) A409
Stuligross, Dennis (Gulfstream Aerospace) A409
Stultz, James L. A662
Stultz, Steve A95
Stultz, Timothy J. E251
Stultz, Tom P309
Stumbo, Scott E. A427
Stump, David C. E178
Stump, Denise S. A777
Stump, James M. A443
Stumpf, Heribert W363
Stumpf, John G. A940
Stumpf, Mark W196
Stuono, Robert D. A576
Stup, Steve W934
Stupans, Peteris W217
Sturany, Klaus W175
Sturdivant, Donald P379
Sturdy, Christopher R. A102
Sturgeon, Brian M. A829
Sturgeon, Michael M. A945
Sturgeon, Robert J. E318
Sturges, Robert B. E260
Sturgess, Matthew H. E221
Sturgill, Keith A311
Sturgill, Richard A955
Sturken, Craig C. A801
Sturm, Jacklyn A. A464
Sturm, Jim W445
Sturmey, John W420
Sturtz, Stan P469
Stusdal, Anders W367
Stussi, Doug P369
Stute, Jeff A494
Stutman, Mark P257
Stuttard, Ian W337
Stutts, Michael S. A657
Stutz, Carin L. A146
Stutz, Nan A866
Stuver, Douglas K. A676
Stuyck, Stephen C. P372
Styka, David R. A344
Stynes, James P180
Stärk-Johansen, Anne W285
Ständberg, Kaarina W282
Sténson, Henry W145
Stéphenne, Jean W171
Stüger, Thomas W242
Su, Lisa (Freescale Semiconductor) A371
Su, Lisa (Freescale Semiconductor) A371
Su, Tony H.S. A305
Suardi, Franco A512
Suarez, J. P. A928
Subasic, Stephen M. A668
Subbloie, Albert R. E345
Subbotin, Valery W243
Subotnick, Stuart P404
Subramaniam, Rajesh A349
Subramaniam, Shivan S. P223
Suchecki, Tomek P672
Suchoff, Andrew J. E335
Suchomel, Kimberley L. A249
Suckale, Margret W56
Suckow, John A525
Suckrow, Carsten A66

Sud, James P. A950
Sudac, Irene (Cabot) A163
Sudac, Irene S. (Snap-on) A794
Sudderth, Gregory A. (Blue Cross Blue Shield of Michigan) A133
Sudderth, Gregory A. (Blue Cross Blue Shield of Michigan) A133
Suddes, Adele A845
Sudhoff, Stefan W180
Sudo, Akira W410
Sudo, Noriyuki W222
Suehnholz, Raymond P154
Suematsu, Hiroyuki W83
Suematsu, Kouichi W161
Suen, Samson P672
Suess, Michael W363
Suet, Patrick W369
Suever, Catherine A. A678
Suever, Mike J. P300
Sueyoshi, Harry P668
Suffel, Holger W112
Suffern, Robert C. (CommScope) A231
Suffern, Robert C. (CommScope) A231
Suffin, Stephen A726
Sugano, Karen P523
Sugano, Nobuyuki W361
Suggitt, Melissa W83
Sugi, Hikaru (DENSO America) P179
Sugi, Hikaru (DENSO) W116
Sugihara, Koichi W413
Sugimori, Masato W381
Sugimoto, Akira W117
Sugimoto, Kiwamu W209
Sugimoto, Toyokazu W385
Sugiura, Masayasu W18
Sugiura, Yasuyuki W260
Sugiyama, Nao W294
Sugiyama, Seiji W266
Suh, Chan P18
Suk-Bum, Ko W311
Suk-Ryul, Yoo W349
Suko, Todd A. A419
Sukut, Russell D. A179
Sulat, James R. E247
Sulek, Alan E147
Sulentic, Robert E. (CBRE Group) A186
Sulentic, Robert E. (Trammell Crow Company) P604
Suleski, David P. E40
Sulick, Peter E113
Suliteanu, David W245
Sulkin, Jane (Harvard University) A421
Sulkin, Jane (Harvard University) A421
Sullenbarger, Daniel J. A556
Sullivan, Aline W45
Sullivan, Anne Rollo (Columbia University) A226
Sullivan, Anne M. (New York City Health and Hospitals) A624
Sullivan, Anne Rollo (Columbia University) A226
Sullivan, Anne M. (New York City Health and Hospitals) A624
Sullivan, Barry W. A344
Sullivan, Bo E88
Sullivan, Bob (Springs Global US) A805
Sullivan, Bob (Springs Global US) A805
Sullivan, Brendan E104
Sullivan, Brian (Mutual of America) P416
Sullivan, Brian (BP) W74
Sullivan, Catherine P8
Sullivan, Chip P188
Sullivan, Chris W337
Sullivan, Chuck (Hilton Worldwide) A441
Sullivan, Chuck (Hilton Worldwide) A441
Sullivan, Daniel L. (QUALCOMM) A724
Sullivan, Daniel G. (Federal Reserve Bank of Chicago) P210
Sullivan, Diane M. A151
Sullivan, E. Thomas P633
Sullivan, Eugene E366

Sullivan, Foster P454
Sullivan, Frank C. A755
Sullivan, Gail F. A389
Sullivan, Gary W85
Sullivan, Gene P556
Sullivan, George E. A817
Sullivan, Gregory (Gleacher & Company) E158
Sullivan, Gregory W. (STAG Industrial) E331
Sullivan, James J. (Quality Systems) E292
Sullivan, James P. (Abbott Labs) A5
Sullivan, James (International Data Group) A467
Sullivan, James (International Data Group) A467
Sullivan, John J. (Mesa Laboratories) E242
Sullivan, John (Costco Wholesale) A249
Sullivan, John F. (SRP) P561
Sullivan, Joseph C. (Airgas) A30
Sullivan, Joseph A. (Legg Mason) A522
Sullivan, Karen P534
Sullivan, Katie P465
Sullivan, Kenneth M. A791
Sullivan, L. Jay A30
Sullivan, Linda G. A319
Sullivan, Maria M. (CDW) A189
Sullivan, Maria M. (CDW) A189
Sullivan, Mark R. (MedQuist Holdings) E239
Sullivan, Mark E. (Bose) P93
Sullivan, Mark J. (DHS) P181
Sullivan, Mary Beth P493
Sullivan, Michael J. (AFL-CIO) P17
Sullivan, Michael L. (Source Interlink) P555
Sullivan, Owen J. A555
Sullivan, Pat P182
Sullivan, Patrick (Chubb Corp) A204
Sullivan, Patrick M. (Sigma-Aldrich) A788
Sullivan, Patrick J. (Mutual of America) P416
Sullivan, Paul V. (BJ's Wholesale Club) A129
Sullivan, Paul V. (BJ's Wholesale Club) A129
Sullivan, Reid A188
Sullivan, Robert (CSX) A257
Sullivan, Robert A. (Fifth Third) A351
Sullivan, Scott P. (NVIDIA) A654
Sullivan, Scott P. (Visa Inc) A917
Sullivan, Sharon L. A324
Sullivan, Shauna J. (Cox Enterprises) A252
Sullivan, Shauna J. (Cox Enterprises) A252
Sullivan, Steven R. A50
Sullivan, Suzanne M. A278
Sullivan, Teresa A. (University of Michigan) P632
Sullivan, Teresa A. (University of Virginia) P636
Sullivan, Thomas P. (Ruger) E309
Sullivan, Thomas R. (Progress Energy) A713
Sullivan, Thomas C. (RPM International) A755
Sullivan, Tim P662
Sullivan, Timothy P. (Ancestry.com) E31
Sullivan, Timothy E. (SunTrust) A823
Sullivan, William P. (Agilent Technologies) A26
Sullivan, William D. (L-3 Communications) A516
Sullivan, William (Capgemini) W85
Sully, MJ E279
Sulpizio, Rich A724
Sult, James E280
Sult, John R. (El Paso Pipeline Partners) E120

Sult, John R. (El Paso Corporation) A321
Sultemeier, Ronald A. P173
Sulzberger, Arthur O. A628
Sumi, Shuzo W407
Sumikawa, Masaaki W210
Summe, Gregory L. (The Carlyle Group) A847
Summe, Gregory L. (The Carlyle Group) A847
Summer, Thomas S. (Advance Publications) A16
Summer, Thomas S. (Advance Publications) A16
Summerer, Gerhard W129
Summers, Barbara L. P372
Summers, Kevin A949
Summers, Patricia H. A483
Summers, Scott E. E286
Sumner, Martin W. (The Carlyle Group) A847
Sumner, Martin W. (The Carlyle Group) A847
Sumner, Polly A. E310
Sumner, Robert W. E304
Sumoski, David A. A652
Sump, Dale (University of Texas System) A899
Sump, Dale (University of Texas System) A899
Sun, David (Kingston Technology) A504
Sun, David (Kingston Technology) A504
Sun, David (Ernst & Young Global) W146
Sun, Elizabeth W415
Sun, Eugene A5
Sun, Jack W415
Sun, Jeanne-Mey A829
Sun, Lijun E343
Sun, Michael P647
Sun, Peter E256
Sun-Won, Kim W311
Sunaoshi, Hisashi W250
Sund, Michael W. E235
Sundaresan, Arvind W85
Sunday, Delena M. A642
Sunday, Mark E. A666
Sundby, Eric A387
Sundgren, Jan-Eric W439
Sundheim, Nancy S. A885
Sundman, Peter E. A522
Sundström, Mikael W356
Sung Ji, Nam E158
Sung, Jung Woo (The Carlyle Group) A847
Sung, Jung Woo (The Carlyle Group) A847
Sung-Ho, Park W311
Sung-Hwan, Jang W311
Sung-Kwan, Baek W311
Sungela, Melissa A4
Sunmonu, Mutiu W339
Sunnucks, Stephen A851
Suominen, Arja W282
Suplizio, Vicki E17
Supovitz, Frank (NFL) A635
Supovitz, Frank (NFL) A635
Supowitz, Paul P634
Supron, Pete A777
Surace, Richard E61
Surane, John J. (Ace Hardware) A9
Surane, John J. (Ace Hardware) A9
Surdykowski, Andrew J. E193
Sureddin, Scott P207
Suresh, Subra P411
Surette, Maureen E320
Surface, Carol A. A124
Surges, Jeffrey A. E240
Surgner, W. Hildebrandt A44
Surh, Tina P449
Surhoff, Peter (Major League Baseball) A551

Surhoff, Peter (Major League Baseball) A551
Suri, Anil K. A694
Suri, Rajeev (Siemens Corp.) P543
Suri, Rajeev (Nokia) W282
Surinach, Ignacio Segur W9
Suris, Oscar A940
Surlien, Stein A666
Surma, John P. A890
Surplus, Scott C. (Holly Energy Partners) E175
Surplus, Scott C. (HollyFrontier) A443
Surrette, Deborah P569
Susalla, Therese A473
Suse, Philip F. P59
Susienka, Cindy H. (Golden Horizons) A395
Susienka, Cindy H. (Golden Horizons) A395
Susik, W. Danie A757
Susko, Bryan T. P551
Susman, Sally A692
Susor, Robert J. A387
Sussman, Douglas R. (MTA) A608
Sussman, Douglas R. (MTA) A608
Sussman, Jack P123
Sustana, Mark A526
Sutcliffe, George E290
Sutcliffe, Ian (Motiva Enterprises) A606
Sutcliffe, Ian (Motiva Enterprises) A606
Suter, Ursula A420
Sutherland, Allan C. A459
Sutherland, Andrew A666
Sutherland, Anne A499
Sutherland, Ben E284
Sutherland, Euan A. W220
Sutherland, Graham W80
Sutherland, L. Frederick (ARAMARK) A77
Sutherland, L. Frederick (ARAMARK) A77
Sutherlin, Michael W. A493
Sutphin, Eric N. A453
Sutter, Denise A391
Sutter, Fred A. A174
Suttle, J. Lloyd P675
Suttle, John W48
Suttmeier, Catherine H. P454
Sutton, Brian E111
Sutton, Chris P562
Sutton, Jodi E318
Sutton, Mark (Almost Family) E17
Sutton, Mark S. (International Paper) A470
Sutton, Mark S. (Shorewood Packaging) P543
Sutton, Mel W38
Sutton, Neil W80
Sutton, Richard O. P62
Sutton, Simon A862
Suutarla, Timo W427
Suver, Susan M. A890
Suwa, Kunio W226
Suzuki, Eiichi W276
Suzuki, Hidehiko W162
Suzuki, Hideyo (Cargill) A172
Suzuki, Hideyo (Cargill) A172
Suzuki, Hiroyuki (Nomura Holdings) W284
Suzuki, Hiroyuki (Yamaha Motor) W449
Suzuki, Hisami W263
Suzuki, Joji W373
Suzuki, Kaori W354
Suzuki, Kenji W413
Suzuki, Kunimasa W375
Suzuki, Luciano (Liberty Mutual) A534
Suzuki, Luciano (Liberty Mutual) A534
Suzuki, Masahito W449
Suzuki, Masatoshi W293
Suzuki, Motoyuki A456
Suzuki, Osamu W385
Suzuki, Shigeki W413
Suzuki, Shoichiro W295
Suzuki, Takatoshi W383

Suzuki, Tetsuya W293
Suzuki, Tomoyuki W375
Suzuki, Toshiaki W161
Suzuki, Toshifumi P4
Suzuki, Toshihiro W385
Suzuki, Yasuo W222
Suzuki, Yoshihisa W373
Suzuki, Yuji (Credit Suisse) W107
Suzuki, Yuji (Mitsubishi UFJ Financial Group) W263
Suárez Coppel, Juan J. W302
Suárez de Lezo Mantilla, Luis W325
Svanberg, Carl-Henric W74
Svanholm, Poul J. W2
Svedlund, Per-Olov W356
Svens, Lasse W285
Svensk, Ari W217
Svenson, Eric B. A717
Svoboda, Frank M. A868
Svärd, Jan W19
Swaback, Ray P394
Swackhamer, Merlin L. P523
Swafford, Preston D. (TVA) A874
Swafford, Preston D. (TVA) A874
Swagger, Diane P129
Swain, Carla P7
Swain, Cathy (University of Texas System) A899
Swain, Cathy (University of Texas System) A899
Swain, Don P219
Swain, O. Clay E361
Swain, Paula J. E188
Swales, Tim P333
Swallow, Michael P579
Swan, James E. A770
Swan, Julie O. A829
Swan, Kelly A952
Swan, Mara E. A555
Swan, Meghan (JR Simplot) A496
Swan, Meghan (JR Simplot) A496
Swan, Peter A. P508
Swan, Robert H. A316
Swan, Winifred L. E264
Swanberg, Dale P655
Swaner, Michele A952
Swank, Steve E306
Swanke, Mary-Clare P416
Swann, Paul E193
Swannell, Robert W249
Swanner, R. Ronald E327
Swansen, Russell W. P597
Swanson, Al (PAA Natural Gas Storage) E275
Swanson, Al (Plains All American Pipeline) A699
Swanson, Allan (U.S. Foodservice) A879
Swanson, Allan (U.S. Foodservice) A879
Swanson, David S. P660
Swanson, Dennis D. A135
Swanson, Glen A124
Swanson, Kevin A711
Swanson, Nancy (Procter & Gamble) A711
Swanson, Nancy R. (Securian Financial) P532
Swanson, Pamela M. A30
Swanson, Richard M. E337
Swanson, Robert H. E222
Swanson Sillan, Amy A862
Swanson, Todd E142
Swanson, William H. A735
Swarte, Jiska P18
Swartling, David R. A254
Swartout, Vince E109
Swartz, Brian L. A73
Swartz, Greg E280
Swartz, Michael L. A387
Swartz, Robert S. P556
Swartz, Steven R. (Hearst Corporation) A430
Swartz, Steven R. (Hearst Corporation) A430

Takeuchi, Hideshi W260
Takeuchi, Satoru W439
Takhautdinov, Shafagat F. W391
Takizawa, Masahiro W449
Taks e-Jensen, Peter P621
Tal, Benjamin W95
Talago, Chris P654
Talamini, Lisa P328
Talamo, John A535
Talarico, Richard W. E15
Talaulicar, Anant A258
Talayero, Mauricio A249
Talbert, Marc (Guardian
   Industries) A406
Talbert, Marc (Guardian
   Industries) A406
Talbot, Graham W339
Talbot, Kevin W45
Talbot, Richard E. P499
Talbot, William (American Campus
   Communities) E23
Talbot, William (EVCI Career
   Colleges) E133
Talbott, Julie P143
Talerico, Jan (Giant Eagle) A392
Talerico, Jan (Giant Eagle) A392
Tali, Pietro Franc (Eni) W142
Tali, Pietro Franc (Saipem) W347
Talke, Kurt G. E279
Tallett-Williams, Michael A536
Talley, Cindy E245
Talley, John P487
Tallman, Karen A. E36
Talma, Arja W217
Talotta, Alessandro W394
Talwalkar, Abhijit Y. A545
Talwar, Rohit P472
Talwar, Vikram E137
Talán, Mónica P637
Tamagnini, Andrea W203
Tamai, Kouichi W161
Tamakoshi, Ryosuke W263
Tamamura, Ryuhei W383
Tamanini, William E2
Tamasi, Tony A654
Tamba, Toshihito W207
Tamberlane, John E320
Tamburi, Carlo W140
Tamburro, Mark W282
Tamer, Katherine M. P623
Tamir, Mary E279
Tamlyn, Nigel E161
Tammi, Nancy P156
Tammivuori, Jyrki W379
Tamoney, Thomas H. A684
Tamura, Minoru W385
Tamura, Yoshiaki W36
Tan, Benjamin A703
Tan, Cheryl A923
Tan, Cynara W314
Tan, Ethel M. L. W365
Tan, Georgina E149
Tan, John H. A228
Tan, Kevin (Cox Enterprises) A252
Tan, Kevin (Cox Enterprises) A252
Tan, Michele (Catholic Health
   East) A182
Tan, Michele (Catholic Health
   East) A182
Tan, Millie (Quintiles
   Transnational) A727
Tan, Millie (Quintiles
   Transnational) A727
Tan, Paul W. L. W365
Tan, Peter (Burger King) A155
Tan, Peter (Burger King) A155
Tan, Puay-Chin W426
Tan, Tom A140
Tan, Vait Leong A480
Tan, William S. K. W365
Tanabe, Ann E344
Tanabe, Eiichi W260
Tanabe, Hiroyuki W373
Tanabe, Hitokazu W292
Tanabe, Toshihide W279

Tanabe, Yasuo W184
Tanai, Tsuneo W188
Tanaka, Hiromichi W294
Tanaka, Hiroshi W284
Tanaka, Hisao W410
Tanaka, Kazuaki W250
Tanaka, Koji W184
Tanaka, Lance A842
Tanaka, Masaaki W263
Tanaka, Masakazu W226
Tanaka, Nobuyoshi W83
Tanaka, Seiichi W265
Tanaka, Shigeru W384
Tanaka, Takaaki (NuVasive) E264
Tanaka, Takaaki (Toshiba) W410
Tanaka, Takashi W293
Tanaka, Tatsuo W263
Tanaka, Toshizo W83
Tanbourgi, Gabriel W56
Tanchoux, Pascal A512
Tanck, Marvin A. P254
Tanco, Chris P4
Tanda, Stephan B. W128
Tandoi, Larry (Golden State
   Foods) A396
Tandoi, Larry (Golden State
   Foods) A396
Tandon, Atul W334
Tandy, Bradley J. (Biomet) A127
Tandy, Bradley J. (Biomet) A127
Tandy, Karen P. A607
Taneff, George E228
Tanehashi, Makio W266
Taneja, Rajat A595
Tanemo, Shinichi W375
Taney, Amy A476
Tang, Darin (Unisource) A884
Tang, Darin (Unisource) A884
Tang, David A48
Tang, Edmund E107
Tang, Eugene A491
Tang, Francis E107
Tang, Jackson (Liberty Mutual) A534
Tang, Jackson (Liberty Mutual) A534
Tang, K. P. A92
Tang, Kin F. E330
Tang, Roger C. P127
Tang, Sam A851
Tang, Sharon E11
Tang, Teller A456
Tangeman, Amy J. A340
Tangney, Michael J. A224
Tanguay, Réal C. W413
Tanguy, Olivier W41
Tani, Keizo W410
Tani, Kenji W260
Tani, Makoto W384
Tani, Yasuhiro W83
Tanigaki, Masahide W184
Tanigawa, Kazuo W410
Tanigawa, Yasuo W182
Taniguchi, Nobuyuki W361
Taniguchi, Norihiko W162
Taniguchi, Shinichi (Nippon
   Steel) W279
Taniguchi, Shinichi (Sojitz) W373
Tanna, Catherine W63
Tannahill, Christi R. P279
Tannenbaum, Carl R. P210
Tannenbaum, Leonard M. E141
Tanner, Bruce L. A541
Tanner, David A. P132
Tanner, Glenn E. E202
Tanner, Gregg A. A269
Tanner, Ronald R. P584
Tanner, Teresa A. A351
Tanous, James J. P205
Tanous, Will (Warner Music) A933
Tanous, Will (Warner Music) A933
Tansky, Burton M. (Neiman
   Marcus) A622
Tansky, Burton M. (Neiman
   Marcus) A622
Tanzer, Kim P636
Tanzer, Martin S. A904

Tao, Clarence W69
Tapella, Bryan (Ace Hardware) A9
Tapella, Bryan (Ace Hardware) A9
Tapiero, Jacques A324
Tapper, John W445
Tarangelo, Terry E320
Tarantini, Riccardo W153
Tarantino, Joseph A. A746
Tarapchak, Richard C. (Navistar
   International) A616
Tarapchak, Richard C. (Navistar) P425
Tarapore, Kairus K. P130
Tarasco, Eileen M. P416
Tarasievich, Eric P642
Taratus, Ken P413
Tarbell, Stanley M. A353
Tarbet, Michael P150
Tarbox, Andrea K. E210
Tarbox, Richard C. (SunGard) A821
Tarbox, Richard C. (SunGard) A821
Tarde, Merv P317
Tardif, Christian W19
Targett, Greg W442
Targhetta, Javier A370
Tari, Farzad E188
Taride, Michel A435
Tarino, Gary E. A15
Tarkoff, Janet L. E207
Tarkoff, Robert M. A13
Taron, Florence W303
Tarpey, Kenneth E80
Tarrant, David A616
Tarrant, Kevin R. A914
Tarrant, Thomas E. A484
Tarshis, Andrew E181
Tarsitano, Laura P493
Tarumi, Hiroyuki W260
Tarver, John E279
Tarver, Van A514
Tasaka, Hitoshi W116
Tasca, Nino P473
Taschner, Peter A11
Tashjian, Charles H. A228
Tashjian, Lee C. A359
Tashma, Lauren S. A112
Tassan, Franck W87
Tassinari, Florence P233
Tassler, Nina (CBS Corp) A188
Tassler, Nina (CBS) P123
Tasso, Federico P262
Tassone, Joseph E183
Tassopoulos, Timothy P. (Chick-fil-
   A) A198
Tassopoulos, Timothy P. (Chick-fil-
   A) A198
Tata, Ratan N. W390
Tatapudy, Rao P116
Tatarinov, Kirill A595
Tataseo, Frank A. A216
Tate, Amy (TVA) A874
Tate, Amy (TVA) A874
Tate, Brenda R. A918
Tate, G. Truett W239
Tate, James Donal A780
Tate, John E. P162
Tate, Kevin W254
Tate, Michael T. E258
Tateishi, Hisao W210
Tatelman, Michael A274
Taten, Bruce M. A244
Tateosian, David E146
Tatera, Robert A224
Tates, Jim A777
Tatsuno, Tetsuo W36
Tatsuta, Yasuto W252
Tattersall, Al E77
Tattersfield, John E167
Tatum, Greg A695
Tatum, Jim E142
Tatum, Mark A. (NBA) A618
Tatum, Mark A. (NBA) A618
Tatum, Steve (Koch Industries,
   Inc.) A508
Tatum, Steve (Koch Industries,
   Inc.) A508

Taub, Bruce P123
Taub, Leon P210
Taub, Stephen (MacAndrews &
   Forbes) A547
Taub, Stephen (MacAndrews &
   Forbes) A547
Tauber, David W. P579
Tauber, Richard E. P579
Taubman, Paul J. A605
Tauby, Anne W131
Tauke, Thomas J. A914
Taulbee, Richard K. P664
Taunton, Michael J. A80
Taupin, Vincent W369
Taussig, Timothy T. E131
Tavares, Carlos (Nissan) W281
Tavares, Carlos (Renault) W324
Tavares, Silvio (First Data) A354
Tavares, Silvio (First Data) A354
Tavernier, Jacques W432
Tavill, Gail A237
Tavolini, Giorgio W394
Tavoso, Richard P499
Tawada, Etsuji W221
Taxter, Michael W. A478
Tay, Paul A757
Taylor, Aileen W337
Taylor, Alison L. P543
Taylor, Andrew C. A334
Taylor, Ann T. A221
Taylor, Barbara P221
Taylor, Benjamin P565
Taylor, Bernard E134
Taylor, Bob W19
Taylor, Brad W392
Taylor, Brandon (The Carlyle
   Group) A847
Taylor, Brandon (The Carlyle
   Group) A847
Taylor, Cathy A39
Taylor, Charles A. A197
Taylor, Charlotte (Quintiles
   Transnational) A727
Taylor, Charlotte (Quintiles
   Transnational) A727
Taylor, Christine (MacAndrews &
   Forbes) A547
Taylor, Christine (MacAndrews &
   Forbes) A547
Taylor, Christopher W. (Chick-fil-
   A) A198
Taylor, Christopher W. (Chick-fil-
   A) A198
Taylor, Colin W288
Taylor, Dan (Google) A402
Taylor, Dan (RBC Wealth
   Management) P500
Taylor, Darren C. P85
Taylor, David J. (Air Products) A29
Taylor, David L. (Ball Corp.) A99
Taylor, David S. (Procter &
   Gamble) A711
Taylor, David (Ingram Industries) P313
Taylor, Denny P413
Taylor, Desmond F. P422
Taylor, Dylan P144
Taylor, Ellen E30
Taylor, Emily C. A293
Taylor, Gary J. A332
Taylor, George R. P595
Taylor, Glenn C. (Medco Health) A582
Taylor, Glenn C. (Medco Health) A582
Taylor, Gregory D. (Lubrizol) A546
Taylor, Gregory J. (AgriBank) P19
Taylor, Harold E218
Taylor, James B. (BPZ Resources) E51
Taylor, James (Sodexo USA) P552
Taylor, Jason A711
Taylor, Jean M. P579
Taylor, Jeff P668
Taylor, Jim E131
Taylor, Jodi A237
Taylor, John C. (AMERCO) A49
Taylor, John C. (MeadWestvaco) A580

A = AMERICAN BUSINESS
E = EMERGING COMPANIES
P = PRIVATE COMPANIES
W = WORLD BUSINESS

Taylor, John (Gilbane Building Company) P249
Taylor, Joseph (Emergency Medical Services) P201
Taylor, Joseph M. (Panasonic Corp) W300
Taylor, Julie A. A284
Taylor, K. Jon A355
Taylor, Karen D. A386
Taylor, Keith D. E132
Taylor, Kevan A842
Taylor, Kim P326
Taylor Kindle, Jo Ann A334
Taylor, L. Edward P207
Taylor, Lance B. P8
Taylor, Loren R. P629
Taylor, Lyndon C. A281
Taylor, Maggie W445
Taylor, Mark (Arrow Electronics) A80
Taylor, Mark (Eli Lilly) A324
Taylor, Michael V. P533
Taylor, Mike (Tesla Motors) E350
Taylor, Mike (Guardian Life) A407
Taylor, Mike (Guardian Life) A407
Taylor, Nel P507
Taylor, Paul D. A590
Taylor, Peggy (Biomet) A127
Taylor, Peggy (Biomet) A127
Taylor, Peter J. (University of California) A897
Taylor, Peter J. (University of California) A897
Taylor, Peter (British American Tobacco) W79
Taylor, Quinn P8
Taylor, R. Jeffrey E200
Taylor, R. Keith (The Carlyle Group) A847
Taylor, R. Keith (The Carlyle Group) A847
Taylor, Rhonda M. A293
Taylor, Richard G. A. (Intel) A464
Taylor, Richard (Jones Lang LaSalle) A491
Taylor, Robert L. (Cooper Industries) A244
Taylor, Robert W. (Weyerhaeuser) A947
Taylor, Robert N. (Do it Best) P182
Taylor, Ron A229
Taylor, Ronald P. (Hy-Vee) P305
Taylor, Roxanne W6
Taylor, Ryan A807
Taylor, Scott C. A828
Taylor, Sharon C. A716
Taylor, Simone Himbe P632
Taylor, Stephen M. A613
Taylor, Susan (Pension Benefit Guaranty) A682
Taylor, Susan (Pension Benefit Guaranty) A682
Taylor, Suzanne S. A612
Taylor, Timothy G. P135
Taylor, Trevor A. E260
Taylor, Ty P53
Taylor, Vincent T. A516
Taylor, Wendy A398
Taylor, William E. (ITT Corp.) A476
Taylor, William S. (Stanley Black and Decker) A811
Taylor-Huppert, Sharon (Cox Communications) A251
Taylor-Huppert, Sharon (Cox Communications) A251
Taylor-Laws, Kathy P523
Taziev, Mirgazyan Z. W391
Tazin, Sergei A. W130
Tchernonog, Alain (Electricité de France) W136

Tchernonog, Alain (Veolia Environnement) W431
Teague, A. J. A333
Teague, Monica A949
Teague, R. Keith (Cheniere Energy) E67
Teague, R. Keith (Cheniere Energy Partners) E68
Tear, Kristian W375
Tearte, Curtis H. A456
Teasley, Karla Olson A57
Tecca, Christian M. E3
Techar, Franklin J. W66
Tecotzky, Mark E123
Teddy, R. Wayne (Cargill) A172
Teddy, R. Wayne (Cargill) A172
Tedeschi, Franco A63
Tedesco, Janice A476
Tedesco, Michael A484
Tedesi, Luca W203
Tedjarati, Shane A446
Tedrow, Maureen A332
Tee Hooi, Teoh W365
Teed, Bill A871
Teeken, Josef W299
Teel, James E. P495
Teel, Michael J. P495
Teel-Wolter, Jennifer P495
Teem, Paul L. E71
Teer, Diane A580
Teerlink, Ron W337
Teeter, William D. A876
Tefft, Tom A583
Tegeder, David E. (Ag Processing Inc.) A23
Tegeder, David E. (Ag Processing Inc.) A23
Tegge, Andreas W354
Tegt, Robert A. A447
Teh, Benjamin E287
Tehan, Anna (Deloitte) A276
Tehan, Anna (Deloitte) A276
Tehle, David M. A293
Teichert, Gorm E220
Teichmann, David L. E358
Teirlinck, Didier W202
Teissler, Scott (Time Warner) A862
Teissler, Scott (Turner Broadcasting) P612
Teixeira, Maria Ferna (First Data) A354
Teixeira, Maria Ferna (First Data) A354
Tejada, Jackie A287
Tejada, Vicente Prado W9
Tejima, Masao E271
Tejima, Shunichiro W273
Tejón, José M. W172
Tekolste, Robert R. P520
Tel, Martijn E34
Telesca, John O. A747
Telesz, Scott E. A705
Telfer, Martin P59
Telford, Meaghan W269
Telford, Ric A456
Telg, Kenneth A. A940
Telkamp, Bruce A. E119
Telling, Martin A663
Tellock, Glen E. A553
Temares, M. Lewis P632
Temares, Steven H. A118
Temby, Judith A. A900
Tempany, Gary W254
Temperley, Nick W125
Temple, Gregory E. A90
Temple, Jim P205
Temple, Mike A901
Templet, Bobby P. A741
Templet, Joseph R. A892
Templeton, Richard K. A843
Templeton, Troy D. E98
Templin, Roy W. A949
ten Brinke, Henk Jan W336
Tena, Ignacio (Deloitte) A276
Tena, Ignacio (Deloitte) A276
Tench, Jeff A529
Tendler, Lois P436

Teneza, Gregory J. (AllianceBernstein) A40
Teneza, Gregory J. (AllianceBernstein) A40
Tengowski, Mark W. E376
Tennefoss, Michael E38
Tennison, Lynden L. A883
Tenwick, David A. E10
Tenzer, Judy A53
Teo, Alan P544
Teo, Alfred S. (Sigma Plastics) P544
Teo, Alfred S. (Sigma Plastics) P544
Teo, Andrew P544
Teo, Faith T. W54
Teo, Lay Lim W6
Teo, Mark P544
Teodorani-Fabbri, Pio W149
Teoh, Danny W224
Teper, Jeff A595
Tepman, Avi A76
Teppala, Toni W285
Terada, Tetsuro W260
Terada, Toshifumi W277
Teragawa, Masatsugu W361
Terajima, Yoshinori W277
Teramura, Motonobu W260
Teranishi, Hideki W292
Teranishi, Shinichi W373
Terao, Minoru W273
Teraoka, Kazunori W373
Terasaka, Reiji (The Carlyle Group) A847
Terasaka, Reiji (The Carlyle Group) A847
Terashi, Shigeki W413
Terashima, Fumitoshi W352
Terberger, Eva W219
Tercek, John A754
Terenghi, Barbara W133
Terifay, Robert J. E301
Terkelsen, Franklin L. A915
Termer, Dan L. E244
Terpay, Susan A644
Terracciano, Anthony P. A763
Terracciano, Louis P663
Terracina, Roy D. E368
Terranova, Manuel A376
Terrell, Karenann K. A928
Terrell, Robin W213
Terreri, Keith D. A591
Terrett, Mike J. W334
Terrone, Michael R. E143
Terry, David A284
Terry, Hilliard C. A26
Terry, Jane W334
Terry, Phillip R. A591
Terry, Ronald J. (New York Life) A625
Terry, Ronald J. (New York Life) A625
Terryn, Kristof W452
Tersigni, Anthony R. (Ascension Health) A82
Tersigni, Anthony R. (Ascension Health) A82
Teruya-Feldstein, Julie P399
Terver, Bernard W186
Tervonen, Jyrki W174
Terwilliger, John F. (Houston American Energy) E177
Terwilliger, John (Mutual of America) P416
Teschner, Charles L. A576
Teshima, Hirokazu W352
Tesija, Kathryn A. A832
Teslik, Sarah B. A71
Tesmer, Donna P71
Tesoriero, Joseph S. A291
Tesoriero, Tom P357
Tess, Andrew (EBSCO) A317
Tess, Andrew (EBSCO) A317
Tessier, Drew A883
Tessler, Allan R. E131
Tessler, Hervé A960
Tessler, Michael E53
Tessmer, Jim P294
Testa, Dave (EBSCO) A317

Testa, Dave (EBSCO) A317
Testa, William A. P210
Testi, Andrea W133
Testroet, Dave P389
Testut, Cédric W157
Tetrault, Lynn W40
Tetreault, Edward A339
Tetreault, James P. A365
Teuber, William J. A326
Teuffer, Mario P238
Teulie, Pierre Alexandre W87
Teuscher, Craig E378
Teuwsen, Bjorn W307
Tew, David P546
Tew, Paul P151
Tewell, Patrick J. E79
Tewksbury, Gregory J. P632
Texeira da Silva, Rubens W304
Texter, Leonard R. A379
Textor, Marise E355
Teyssen, Johannes W130
Tezuka, Kazuo W221
Thacher, Carter P. P668
Thacher, John P. P668
Thacker, Bob A660
Thacker, Kimberly A366
Thacker, Michael A438
Thackery, Ron P33
Thackwray, Ian W186
Thadani, Navin E300
Thaelan, Steve P102
Thain, John A. A211
Thakur, Randhir A76
Thalheimer, Gary P655
Thaman, Michael H. A671
Thames, H. Davis E67
Thamm, Michael A178
Thamodaran, Dhamu A791
Than, Ralph A. A528
Thaning, Cathrine W354
Thapar, Charu P166
Tharmaratnam, Anand (Quintiles Transnational) A727
Tharmaratnam, Anand (Quintiles Transnational) A727
Tharp, Jim P463
Tharrington, Jeannie A711
Thatcher, Kevin L. A794
Thatcher, Michele R. P234
Thatcher, Robert J. E62
Thaule, Jørgen W397
Thaus, Kurt B. A835
Thawerbhoy, Nazim G. A483
Thayer, Jonathan W. A243
Thayer, William P367
Thayne, Sarah W80
Thedinga, John W. (American Family Insurance) A54
Thedinga, John W. (American Family Insurance) A54
Thees, Thomas M. A484
Theeuwes, Alfons E286
Theile, Lindsay Linds A376
Theilen, Mary A. (American Family Insurance) A54
Theilen, Mary A. (American Family Insurance) A54
Theiler, Matt P565
Theiler, Richard F. P592
Theilmann, Michael T. A478
Theisen, Darlene P286
Theisen, Henry J. A121
Theiss, Neil G. A829
Thelan, John D. A249
Thelen, Ann A597
Thelen, Brian D. A278
Thelen, Gerhard A. (Norfolk Southern) A644
Thelen, Gerhard A. (Norfolk Southern Railway) P446
Thelin, Anders W350
Themelis, Nicholas E230
Thene, Tony R. A35
Theobald, Malcolm A772
Theobald, Neil D. P311

Weisman, Lorenzo D. W69
Weiss, Andrew P593
Weiss, Brian K. E15
Weiss, Charles F. A657
Weiss, David I. (Interpublic
Group) A471
Weiss, David (Pepco Energy
Services) P474
Weiss, Emily A293
Weiss, Gernot W156
Weiss, Heinrich W112
Weiss, Holly A577
Weiss, Howard P115
Weiss, Janet A. P632
Weiss, Jeffrey A. E103
Weiss, Jerry A369
Weiss, Jonathan A940
Weiss, Jordan P. P512
Weiss, Michael (Robert Half) A746
Weiss, Michael (CBS Radio) P124
Weiss, Peter W. A869
Weiss, Steven H. A164
Weiss, Susan A338
Weissberg, Jed (Kaiser Foundation
Health Plan) A496
Weissberg, Jed (Kaiser Foundation
Health Plan) A496
Weisselberg, Allen P593
Weissenberg, Adam F. P177
Weissman, Dawn C. P416
Weissman, Howard J. E59
Weissman, Neil J. P395
Weissman, William F. E307
Weist, Bob P161
Weisz, Stephen P. A557
Weith, Joachim (FMCNA) P224
Weith, Joachim (Fresenius Medical
Care) W158
Weitman, Gary P607
Weitzel, Benjamin E319
Weker, Bill A831
Welby, Christine A923
Welcer, Tim P281
Welch, Carol L. A640
Welch, Charles M. P609
Welch, Christopher A. E106
Welch, Daniel (Evergreen Solar) E135
Welch, Daniel G. (InterMune) E195
Welch, David (Bechtel) A114
Welch, David (Winn-Dixie) A955
Welch, David (Bechtel) A114
Welch, Dennis E. A17
Welch, Edward P. P548
Welch, Jacqueline M. P612
Welch, James M. (Express-1 Expedited
Solutions) E138
Welch, James S. (Brown-Forman) A152
Welch, James L. (YRC Worldwide) A964
Welch, Jim P7
Welch, John D. E138
Welch, Kristen A287
Welch, Leif (Cox Enterprises) A252
Welch, Leif (Cox Enterprises) A252
Welch, Linda J. (US Postal
Service) A907
Welch, Linda J. (US Postal
Service) A907
Welch, Michael R. E138
Welch, Richard G. A957
Welch, Robert (Computer Sciences
Corp.) A232
Welch, Robert J. (Jefferies Group) A484
Welch, Susan P470
Welch, Thomas H. E139
Welcher, Blake A. E111
Weldon, Kent R. P595
Weldon, Terri P207
Weldon, William C. A487
Welfare, Meghan A955
Welker, Jay S. A940
Wellauer, Thomas W388
Wellborn, W. Christopher A599
Weller, Brad A796
Weller, Brenda P92
Weller, Richard J. W202

Weller, Timothy E129
Wellman, Jason W. P532
Wellman, Karen P675
Wellman, Michael P547
Wells, Antonia E240
Wells, Darren R. A400
Wells, David (Netflix) E257
Wells, David (BCE) W61
Wells, Greg A799
Wells, James M. A823
Wells, Mark W2
Wells, Michael A. W315
Wells, Rob P624
Wells, Robert J. (Sherwin-
Williams) A786
Wells, Steve P604
Wells, Thomas E269
Welman, Jurie P135
Welsch, Frank W438
Welsh, Evan W354
Welsh, Hugh C. W128
Welsh, Jack D. A138
Welsh, James A946
Welsh, John E. A379
Welsh, Kelly R. A646
Welsh, William F. E45
Welters, Anthony (UnitedHealth
Group) A895
Welters, Anthony (NYU) P449
Weltman, Matthew R. E320
Welty, Keith P421
Welyki, Robert J. (CDW) A189
Welyki, Robert J. (CDW) A189
Welz, Edward A. (New York Power
Authority) A626
Welz, Edward A. (New York Power
Authority) A626
Wemmer, Dieter W452
Wenaas, Jeffrey P287
Wendel, Jon S. P305
Wendell, Beth P259
Wendland, Dennis A203
Wendler, chip A831
Wendling, Louise A249
Wendt, Doug (Gulfstream
Aerospace) A409
Wendt, Doug (Gulfstream
Aerospace) A409
Wendt, E. Lisa (Blue Cross Blue Shield
of Michigan) A133
Wendt, E. Lisa (Blue Cross Blue Shield
of Michigan) A133
Wendt, Roderick C. P327
Wenerstrom, Stewart A126
Weng, Mok Kwong W230
Wenger, Derrick A484
Wenger, Howard J. E337
Wenger, Kaspar W186
Wenger, Stefan L. E305
Wenig, Devin N. A856
Wenk, Donna B. P462
Wenker, Kristen S. A382
Wenner, Elisabeth A512
Wenner, Jane P663
Wenner, Jann S. P663
Wenner, Jim P540
Wenners, Douglas J. A939
Wenning, Joachim W268
Wenning, Werner W130
Wennlund, Lloyd A. A646
Wenping, Gao W237
Wente, Heinz-Gerhard W106
Wentworth, Carol P609
Wentworth, Deana P487
Wentworth, Robert J. P483
Wentworth, Steve A335
Wentworth, Timothy C. (Medco
Health) A582
Wentworth, Timothy C. (Medco
Health) A582
Wentz, Kathryn E355
Wentzell, John A. P173
Wenz, Ray P679
Wenzel, Gregory G. A138

Wenzel, Irene (OSI Restaurant
Partners) A669
Wenzel, Irene (OSI Restaurant
Partners) A669
Wenzel, Russ P386
Wenzel, Thomas W451
Wenzl, Sharon P152
Wereb, Stephen A10
Werfelman, William (New York
Life) A625
Werfelman, William (New York
Life) A625
Werkema, Gordon P210
Werlen, Thomas W289
Wermers, Markus A348
Werner, Benny N. E80
Werner, David P75
Werner, Elizabeth A. A27
Werner, Gregory P371
Werner, Hans C. W389
Werner, Kenneth (Time Warner) A862
Werner, Kenneth (Warner Bros.) P657
Werner, Patrick W233
Werner, Roger L. E274
Werner, Thomas H. (SunPower) E337
Werner, Thomas G. (Norfolk
Southern) A644
Werner, Thomas G. (Norfolk Southern
Railway) P446
Werner, Todd S. P62
Werner, Uta A960
Werning, David P. A271
Wernli, Robert E52
Werpy, David G. A2
Werpy, Todd A11
Wertheim, Alison A194
Wertz, Bryon A. A835
Wescoat, Kyle P649
Wesley, Charles R. (Alliance Holdings
GP) E14
Wesley, Charles R. (Alliance
Resource) E15
Wesley, James P3
Wesley, John W. A502
Wesley, Mark A814
Wesley, Rosalyn D. A112
Wesp, Clyde P563
Wessel, Alan D. A922
Wessel, Thomas C. (Acorda
Therapeutics) E7
Wessel, Thomas (Analog Devices) A66
Wessels, Alexander W128
Wessling, Holger W129
Wessling, Joachim W25
Wesslink, Michael W254
Wesson, Bruce F. E236
West, Barry J. E74
West, Celeste M. P14
West, Christopher K. E168
West, David (Arrow Electronics) A80
West, David J. (Del Monte Foods) A273
West, David H. (Omnicare) A662
West, David E. (Rent-A-Center) A741
West, David J. (Del Monte Foods) A273
West, Denmark P82
West, Elena A746
West, Fay E337
West, George E. A674
West, Henry J. P380
West, Kathryn E. P465
West, Linda B. A305
West, Marc P261
West, Mary E. E95
West, Mary Beth (Kraft Foods) A512
West, Peter (Mars, Incorporated) A559
West, Peter (Mars, Incorporated) A559
West, Renee A592
West, Robert L. A335
West, Roderick J. (Dollar
General) A293
West, Roderick K. (Entergy) A332
West, Shannon A249
West, Stephanie P180
West, Teresa L. A843
West, Tony (Catholic Health East) A182

West, Tony (Catholic Health East) A182
West, William Corey A666
Westad, Christopher P. E4
Westbrook, Sandra J. P493
Westbury-Haines, Denise W80
Westcott, Mike W270
Westcott, Thomas W. E173
Westdale, Maggie A70
Westdorp, Jim (Kohler) A510
Westdorp, Jim (Kohler) A510
Westdyk, Tom A211
Westenborg, Jack P250
Westenfield, Denise M. E95
Wester, Harald J. W153
Westerbeek, Roelof W128
Westerbos, Rudolph J. P135
Westerdahl, Joyce A666
Westerfield, Jerry P487
Westergren, Tim E276
Westerlund, Thomas E306
Westerman, Bryan (MasTec) E230
Westerman, Bryan (MasTec) E230
Westerman, Frederick G. A532
Westerman, Matthew A397
Westerman, William J. A387
Westervelt, John L. E65
Westfall, Karen P71
Westfall, Kevin P. A87
Westfall, Lynn D. A842
Westfall, Margo E184
Westhoff, Frank W129
Westin, David P50
Westlake, Blair A595
Westlake, W. James W321
Westlie, Trond □. W2
Westling, John T. A928
Westman, Dean J. A961
Westman, John C. E264
Westman, Timothy G. A328
Westmark, Anders W374
Weston, Chris W92
Weston, David W30
Weston, Galen G. W240
Weston, George G. W38
Weston, Graeme P433
Weston, Graham M. E293
Weston, Ian P186
Weston, Jaime (NFL) A635
Weston, Jaime (NFL) A635
Weston, Peter W339
Weston, Tim (TVA) A874
Weston, Tim (TVA) A874
Weston, W. Galen W169
Weston-Webb, Andy (Mars,
Incorporated) A559
Weston-Webb, Andy (Mars,
Incorporated) A559
Westphal, Mark W. P405
Westpheling, Jane Ann A221
Westra, Marike W307
Westrake, Bill P646
Westrate, William B. (American Family
Insurance) A54
Westrate, William B. (American Family
Insurance) A54
Westwell, Steve W74
Westwood, Gavin W85
Wetekamp, James M. P97
Wetherbee, Robert A37
Wetselaar, Peter E96
Wettberg, Stefanie W56
Wetterau, Jörg W181
Wetterau, Mark S. (Golden State
Foods) A396
Wetterau, Mark S. (Golden State
Foods) A396
Wettstein, Wieland F. E100
Wetzel, Aaron L. A271
Wetzel, Mark L. E112
Wetzel, Robert E. P211
Wexler, Gene L. A81
Wexner, Leslie H. (Limited
Brands) A535
Wexner, Leslie H. (Ohio State
University) A661

COMBINED HOOVER'S HANDBOOK INDEX OF EXECUTIVES

Wyard, Brett G. (The Carlyle
  Group) A847
Wyard, Brett G. (The Carlyle
  Group) A847
Wyatt, E. Lee A112
Wyatt, Frank B. (CommScope) A231
Wyatt, Frank B. (CommScope) A231
Wyatt, Gary E. A543
Wyatt, George E218
Wyatt, John H. A. (Stanley Black and
  Decker) A811
Wyatt, John T. (The Gap) A851
Wyatt, Kenneth A191
Wyatt, Mark A304
Wyatt, Michael P. A720
Wyatt, Natalie A176
Wyatt, Stephanie P375
Wyatt-Tilby, James W30
Wyborn, Matthew W314
Wychulis, Daniel A. E207
Wyckoff, Bill P553
Wyckoff, Richard L. (C&S
  Wholesale) A158
Wyckoff, Richard L. (C&S
  Wholesale) A158
Wyckoff, Sandra S. A713
Wyett, Roger A640
Wygod, Martin J. E380
Wyke, Martin A916
Wylie, John W200
Wylie, Scott E19
Wyllie, Melissa E171
Wyllie, Robert P590
Wyman, Jill L. E143
Wyman, Malcolm I. W343
Wyman, Peter L. W314
Wyman, Todd D. W202
Wymbs, Robert P483
Wynaendts, Alexander R. W13
Wynblatt, Michael A314
Wynes, David P201
Wynn, Jean A102
Wynne Smith, Mark A491
Wynne, Thomas M. (Alliance Holdings
  GP) E14
Wynne, Thomas M. (Alliance
  Resource) E15
Wynne, William R. P148
Wyrick, David A339
Wyrsch, Anne E118
Wyrzykowski, Maciej P153
Wyse, Beverly A135
Wyse, Christopher P234
Wyse, Kenneth L. A721
Wyse, Regina G. A748
Wyshner, David B. (Avis Budget) A91
Wyshner, David B. (Avis) P56
Wyshner, David B. (Budget Rent A
  Car) P99
Wysolmierski, Jill M. A92
Wysong, Jay L. P31
Wyss, Andre W289
Wytiaz, Michael S. P664
Wyzga, Michael S. A389
Wäreby, Jan W145
Wœrsted, Gunn W285
Wölfer, Andreas W424
Wössner, Marc W62
Würth, Bettina W447
Würth, Markus W447
Würth, Reinhold W447

X

Xenakis, Michael E271
Xenos, Jim P369
Xiangdong, Liu W366
Xiao, Feng (The Carlyle Group) A847
Xiao, Feng (The Carlyle Group) A847
Xie, Ken E149
Xie, Michael E149
Xuezheng, Ma (TPG) P603
Xuezheng, Ma (Lenovo) W237
Xun Yi, Dong E322

Y

Yaari, Aharon W403
Yabe, Ryuzou W409
Yablonski, Stephen C. E160
Yabuki, Jeffery W. A356
Yabuta, Kenji W263
Yaccarino, Linda P428
Yadav, Uday A314
Yaeger, Mark E227
Yaffa, Glenn D. (Altria) A44
Yaffa, Glenn D. (UST llc) P643
Yaffe, Kenneth (NHL) A637
Yaffe, Kenneth (NHL) A637
Yager, John E298
Yaggi, W. Timothy A563
Yagi, Kazuo W294
Yagi, Shinsuke W18
Yagi, Takashi W162
Yagi, Toshiro W407
Yagi, Yoko (AllianceBernstein) A40
Yagi, Yoko (AllianceBernstein) A40
Yahalomi, Lior E. A918
Yahata, Shunsaku W373
Yahes, Jarrod E137
Yahia, Laurance H. S. (Liberty
  Mutual) A534
Yahia, Laurance H. S. (Liberty
  Mutual) A534
Yahn-Urlaub, Patty A240
Yajima, Susumu W295
Yajima, Torao W143
Yajnik, Sanjiv A170
Yakich, Wayne P380
Yalow, Elanna S. P346
Yalung, Patrick G. A940
Yamabayashi, Naoyuki W384
Yamabe, Kiyoaki P163
Yamada, Eiji W292
Yamada, Hirohisa W18
Yamada, Kazuhiro (The Carlyle
  Group) A847
Yamada, Kazuhiro (The Carlyle
  Group) A847
Yamada, Masanori W83
Yamada, Masayoshi W110
Yamada, Noriaki W252
Yamada, Ryuji (NTT) W291
Yamada, Ryuji (NTT DoCoMo) W293
Yamada, Shinichi W292
Yamada, Sumito W161
Yamada, Takuji W188
Yamada, Tsutomu W205
Yamada, Yoshihiko W300
Yamagishi, Masaaki W263
Yamaguchi, Chiaki W413
Yamaguchi, Chikara W260
Yamaguchi, Dave P293
Yamaguchi, Eiichi W209
Yamaguchi, Gorou W229
Yamaguchi, Hiroshi W408
Yamaguchi, Kazuchika W259
Yamaguchi, Masanobu W273
Yamaguchi, Masato W110
Yamaguchi, Roy (OSI Restaurant
  Partners) A669
Yamaguchi, Roy (OSI Restaurant
  Partners) A669
Yamaguchi, Tsuyoshi W281
Yamaguchi-Hughes, Marci
  (International Data Group) A467
Yamaguchi-Hughes, Marci
  (International Data Group) A467
Yamaguti, Hiroshi W76
Yamaji, Hajime W449
Yamaji, Hiromi W284
Yamakawa, Yoji W110
Yamaki, Masaharu W252
Yamakita, Atsushi W295
Yamamori, Kazuyoshi W410
Yamamoto, Akimasa W182
Yamamoto, Hiroshi W252
Yamamoto, Hirotoshi W294
Yamamoto, Ikuya W279

Yamamoto, John P178
Yamamoto, Kazumune W383
Yamamoto, Masami W162
Yamamoto, Masato W273
Yamamoto, Mineo W23
Yamamoto, Nobuyoshi W295
Yamamoto, Steve A724
Yamamoto, Takahiko W182
Yamamoto, Tsutomu W250
Yamamoto, Yasuyuki W229
Yamamoto, Yoshiro W143
Yamamura, Shinichiro W18
Yamamura, Tsuyoshi W209
Yamanaka, Akira W162
Yamanaka, Susumu W222
Yamanaka, Yasushi W116
Yamane, Shuji W294
Yamane, Yoshi W188
Yamanouchi, Nobutoshi P334
Yamanouchi, Takashi W252
Yamasaki, Hisao E306
Yamasaki, Steven T. (Maxim Integrated
  Products) E233
Yamasaki, Steven T. (Maxim Integrated
  Products) E233
Yamasaki, Toshi P646
Yamashita, Masaya W188
Yamashita, Mitsuhiko W281
Yamashita, Toru W292
Yamashita, Yoichi W229
Yamashita, Yoshinori W327
Yamauchi, Hiroshi A22
Yamauchi, Junko W23
Yamauchi, Miyoshi W361
Yamauchi, Takashi W265
Yamauchi, Yasuhiro W281
Yamauchi, Yasuhito W18
Yamazaki, Fujio W110
Yamazaki, Hiromasa W284
Yamazaki, Hiroshi W69
Yamazaki, Jun P621
Yamazaki, Kunio W23
Yamazaki, Masao W408
Yamazoe, Shigeru W250
Yammine, Bassam W107
Yamori, Tsutomu W229
Yan, Lu W237
Yanaga, Fumihiro W76
Yanagi, Hiroyuki W449
Yanagi, Jeff E279
Yanagie, Hiroshige W292
Yanagihara, Makoto W277
Yanaginuma, Nobuyuki W273
Yanai, Jun W260
Yanai, Shlomo W403
Yanai, Takahiro W263
Yancey, Carol B. A387
Yancey, George D. E79
Yancey, Shaun P. P468
Yancey, W. Timothy (Chick-fil-A) A198
Yancey, W. Timothy (Chick-fil-A) A198
Yancopoulos, George D. E301
Yancy, Larry F. P537
Yando, Greg (Dairy Farmers of
  America) A263
Yando, Greg (Dairy Farmers of
  America) A263
Yang, Angela P472
Yang, Cathy (Dow Corning) A300
Yang, Cathy (Dow Corning) A300
Yang, Chiang Yuan A464
Yang, David E110
Yang, Eun K. A484
Yang, Gil P403
Yang, Henry (OmniVision
  Technologies) E269
Yang, Henry T.Y. (University of
  California) A897
Yang, Henry T.Y. (University of
  California) A897
Yang, Ian A464
Yang, Jae Hoon W238
Yang, James P186
Yang, Jerry A963
Yang, Julia (The Carlyle Group) A847

Yang, Julia (The Carlyle Group) A847
Yang, Sarah E330
Yang, Silas S.S. W314
Yang, Sung (Cox
  Communications) A251
Yang, Sung (Cox
  Communications) A251
Yang, T. C. W8
Yang, Taiyin A394
Yang, William E244
Yang, Wilson A340
Yang, Woong-Pill W238
Yang, Xiang-Dong (The Carlyle
  Group) A847
Yang, Xiang-Dong (The Carlyle
  Group) A847
Yanito, Tamara M. E330
Yanjun, Wang W366
Yankovich, Steve A316
Yankowski, Daniel H. A705
Yanling, Zhang W51
Yannantuono, Daniel E367
Yannotta, Pat P149
Yano, Atsushi W384
Yano, Kaoru W273
Yano, Masahide W260
Yano, Masatoshi W266
Yanos, Neal A. A839
Yantz, Helen T. P152
Yao, Amy P89
Yao, Mary A340
Yaouanc, J-P.D. A328
Yap Hwee, Jen W125
Yaqub, Amer A934
Yarbrough, Melvin L. E355
Yardemian, Raffi P462
Yardis, Robert P571
Yardley, James C. (El Paso Pipeline
  Partners) E120
Yardley, James C. (El Paso
  Corporation) A321
Yarmuth, William B. E17
Yarrington, Patricia E. A197
Yasuda, Shosuke W260
Yasuda, Shota W263
Yasue, Hideyuki W250
Yasui, Junji W273
Yasui, Mitsuya W162
Yasujima, Arata W209
Yasukawa, Takuji W215
Yasuo, Yongdu W76
Yates, Connie P496
Yates, Erik P663
Yates, Gary R. P533
Yates, John E38
Yates, Lloyd M. A713
Yates, Richard L. A845
Yates, Robert W331
Yates, S. Whit A484
Yates, Scott (Cox
  Communications) A251
Yates, Scott (Cox
  Communications) A251
Yau, Robert E166
Yau Seng, Chin W365
Yavatkar, Raj A464
Yavello, Greg A287
Yayoshi, Masafumi W385
Yazaki, Haruhisa W263
Yazaki, Taeko W277
Yazdi, Mahvash A319
Ybarguengoitia, Xavier W245
Ybarra, Paco A213
Ybarra, Stacy E191
Yeager, J. Michael W65
Yeagley, Albert W. A793
Yeakey, Chris E111
Yeaman, Kevin J. E110
Yearick, Molly A721
Yearwood, Robert E285
Yeast, Sally P498
Yeates, Steven W339
Yeatman, Matthew C. A391
Yeatman, Perry A512
Yeatter, Dick P221